TEXTBOOK OF
CLINICAL
PARASITOLOGY

This book is made in full compliance with Government Directive L 120 limiting the bulk of paper.

TEXTBOOK OF
CLINICAL
PARASITOLOGY

INCLUDING LABORATORY

IDENTIFICATION AND TECHNIC

BY

DAVID L. BELDING, M.D.

PROFESSOR OF BACTERIOLOGY AND EXPERIMENTAL PATHOLOGY, BOSTON
UNIVERSITY SCHOOL OF MEDICINE; MEMBER OF STAFF OF EVANS
MEMORIAL, MASSACHUSETTS MEMORIAL HOSPITALS

D. APPLETON-CENTURY COMPANY
INCORPORATED

NEW YORK   LONDON

PREFACE

The present book is an outgrowth of a planographed *Manual of Human Parasitology,* which has received favorable comment and has been used in several medical schools. At the suggestion of certain teachers this earlier work has been expanded here into a textbook of medical parasitology for medical students, physicians, medical personnel in the armed services, public health officials, laboratory workers and biologists. It describes the protozoan, helminthic and arthropod parasites of man, and the diagnosis, treatment and prevention of the diseases they produce. It differs from the traditional textbook of parasitology in the extensive use of tables and graphic representations that facilitate study and access to information, in the presentation of the immunity of parasitic infections, and in the inclusion of a special section on technical methods for laboratory workers.

The present war focuses attention on the control of parasitic diseases among military forces and civilian populations in the tropical and subtropical countries of the Eastern and Western Hemispheres. Likewise, geographical barriers are being swept away by the intermingling of populations through modern transportation, and tropical as well as cosmopolitan parasites present clinical and public health problems in all parts of the world. Consequently, medical parasitology is receiving increasing consideration in the curriculum of medical schools, in the practice of medicine and in public health administration.

Parasitology covers numerous and varied fields in protozoology, helminthology and entomology. Its scope extends beyond the intimate knowledge of specialized workers in these fields. The writer has approached the subject not as a specialist, but from the broad viewpoint of a biologist with a medical background, who has followed for many years the teaching of parasitology to medical students. Therefore, the arrangement and allotment of subject matter are based upon the practical needs of medical students, physicians and laboratory workers, and the zoology of the parasite has been subordinated to the pathology, diagnosis, treatment and prevention of the disease.

Diagnosis is simplified and ready access to information is provided by arranging the more important parasites in tables and keys, by grouping closely allied parasites so that their morphological and pathological activities may be readily compared, and by following a uniform order of presentation, so that comparable facts for each parasite may be found under the same headings. The modern methods of treatment are given for each parasite and the chemotherapeutic agents are described in a special section. Considerable attention is devoted to life cycles and modes of transmission because of their importance in the application of preventive measures.

The problem of selection and condensation of material has been met by featuring the common cosmopolitan parasites and those of the Western Hemisphere, by relegating the uncommon or minor parasites to small type and space, by grouping closely allied species and, wherever possible, by tabulating data. The writer has endeavored to consider the subject as a whole, to allot space commensurate with the importance of each parasite, and, to the best of his ability, to evaluate divergent views. Each specialist, forgetful of these limitations, may consider that his particular field is inadequately treated, that errors of omission and commission have occurred, and that his contributions have not received due consideration. Since parasitology is replete with references, dates, and nomenclature that are inconsistent both as to use and spelling, it is practically impossible, even with careful preparation, for a book of this type to be free from typographical errors.

The arrangement of the illustrations, largely diagrammatic or semidiagrammatic drawings to scale, is designed to give, independent of the text, a complete picture of the morphology and life cycle of the parasite. The diagrams of life cycles and a few drawings are original, and several unpublished photographs have been used. The other illustrations have been taken or adapted from numerous sources. Except where specific credit is given, group drawings or those labeled schematic representations have been adapted or compiled from so many sources that it is impractical to give citations.

The references are restricted to comparatively recent sources or to such older publications as mark important developments or present diverse opinions. The selected references at the end of the chapters, primarily designed for students and largely limited to publications in English and to available journals, either represent important contributions or contain additional references. Numerous footnotes with authors' names and dates enable interested readers to obtain the complete references in indices to current literature.

The writer wishes to acknowledge the generous help of Dr. Alice T. Marston, Mr. Ferdinand C. Lane, Mr. Francis E. Smith and Mrs. Ruth D. Tolman in the preparation of material, and of Miss Martha Henderson, Miss Beulah Merrill and Mrs. Maura Franceschini in typing and proofreading the manuscript. He is indebted to Mr. C. E. B. Bernard, Miss Laura Ornstedt and Miss Rosina Don Dero for the drawings, to Dr. Horace K. Giffen and Dr. Merrill L. Welcher for original photographs, to Professor C. M. Wenyon for the loan of the beautiful colored drawing of malarial parasites (Plate IV) and to Ballière, Tindall and Cox, publishers of Wenyon's *Protozoology,* for permission to use it; and to various authors for illustrations taken from books and journals. He deeply appreciates the many helpful suggestions of Dr. Donald L. Augustine of the Harvard Medical School, and is obligated to the authors and publishers of Hegner, Root, Augustine and Huff's *Parasitology* for material and illustrations. He is beholden to the many workers in the field of parasitology whose original publications have provided the material for the book and to the publisher, D. Appleton-Century Company, for guidance throughout the throes of publication.

DAVID L. BELDING

CONTENTS

Section I
GENERAL PARASITOLOGY

Chapter I
PARASITES AND PARASITISM

Chapter II
THE PATHOLOGY OF PARASITIC INFECTIONS

Chapter III
THE IMMUNITY OF PARASITIC INFECTIONS

Chapter IV
THE TRANSMISSION OF PARASITIC DISEASES

Chapter V

THE DIAGNOSIS OF PARASITIC DISEASES

Chapter VI

THE TREATMENT AND PREVENTION OF PARASITIC DISEASES

Section II

THE PROTOZOA

Chapter VII

THE BIOLOGY OF THE PROTOZOA

Chapter VIII

THE PARASITIC AMŒBÆ OF MAN

Chapter IX

THE INFUSORIA OF MAN

Chapter X

THE INTESTINAL, ORAL AND VAGINAL FLAGELLATES OF MAN

Chapter XI

THE BLOOD AND TISSUE FLAGELLATES OF MAN

Chapter XII

THE SPOROZOA

Chapter XIII

THE SPOROZOA: THE MALARIAL PARASITES OF MAN

Section III

THE NEMATHELMINTHES OR ROUND WORMS

Chapter XIV

THE NEMATODES

Chapter XV

THE SUPERFAMILIES TRICHINELLOIDEA AND DICTOPHYMOIDEA

Chapter XVI

THE SUPERFAMILY RHABDITOIDEA

Chapter XVII

THE SUPERFAMILIES STRONGYLOIDEA, TRICHOSTRONGYLOIDEA AND METASTRONGYLOIDEA

Chapter XVIII

THE SUPERFAMILY OXYUROIDEA

Chapter XIX

THE SUPERFAMILY ASCAROIDEA

Chapter XX

THE SUPERFAMILY SPIRUROIDEA

Chapter XXI

THE SUPERFAMILY FILARIOIDEA

Chapter XXII

THE SUPERFAMILY DRACUNCULOIDEA

Chapter XXIII

THE ANCANTHOCEPHALA

Section IV

THE CESTOIDEA OR TAPEWORMS

Chapter XXIV

THE CESTOIDEA

Chapter XXV

THE SUPERFAMILY BOTHRIOCEPHALOIDEA

Chapter XXVI

THE SUPERFAMILY TÆNIOIDEA: FAMILIES ANOPLOCEPHALIDÆ, DAVAINEIDÆ, DILEPIDIDÆ AND HYMENOLEPIDIDÆ

Chapter XXVII

THE SUPERFAMILY TÆNIOIDEA. THE GENERA TÆNIA AND MULTICEPS

Chapter XXVIII

THE SUPERFAMILY TÆNIOIDEA: THE GENUS ECHINOCOCCUS

Section V

THE TREMATODA OR FLUKES

Chapter XXIX
THE TREMATODA

Chapter XXX
THE SUPERFAMILY FASCIOLOIDEA

Chapter XXXI
THE SUPERFAMILY OPISTHORCHOIDEA

Chapter XXXII
THE SUPERFAMILY HETEROPHYOIDEA

Chapter XXXIII

THE SUPERFAMILY TROGLOTREMATOIDEA

Chapter XXXIV

THE SUPERFAMILIES DICROCŒLIOIDEA, ECHINOSTOMATOIDEA AND PARAMPHISTOMOIDEA

Chapter XXXV

THE BLOOD FLUKES OF MAN

Section VI
ARTHROPODA

Chapter XXXVI
THE PARASITIC ARTHROPODS OF MAN

Chapter XXXVII
THE CLASSES ONYCHOPHORA, MYRIAPODA AND CRUSTACEA

Chapter XXXVIII
CLASS INSECTA (HEXAPODA)

Chapter XXXIX
THE ORDER DIPTERA (FLIES)

Chapter XL

THE SUBORDER ORTHORRHAPHA: THE FAMILY CULICIDÆ (MOSQUITOES)

Chapter XLI

THE SUBORDER ORTHORRHAPHA: THE FAMILIES CHIRONOMIDÆ, PSYCHODIDÆ, SIMULIIDÆ AND TABANIDÆ

Chapter XLII

THE SUBORDER CYCLORRHAPHA: THE BLOODSUCKING FLIES OF THE FAMILIES MUSCIDÆ AND HIPPOBOSCIDÆ

Chapter XLIII

THE SUBORDER CYCLORRHAPHA: THE NON-BLOODSUCKING FLIES OF THE FAMILIES OSCINIDÆ, ŒSTRIDÆ, SARCOPHAGIDÆ, CALLIPHORIDÆ, MUSCIDÆ AND ANTHOMYIDÆ

Chapter XLIV

THE PARASITIC LICE OF MAN

Chapter XLV

THE SIPHONAPTERA OR FLEAS

Chapter XLVI
ORDER HEMIPTERA: TRUE BUGS

Chapter XLVII
THE CLASS ARACHNIDA

Chapter XLVIII
THE SUPERFAMILY IXODOIDEA (TICKS)

Chapter XLIX
THE PARASITIC MITES

Section VII

TECHNICAL METHODS FOR THE DIAGNOSIS AND TREATMENT OF PARASITIC INFECTIONS

TEXTBOOK OF
CLINICAL PARASITOLOGY

INCLUDING LABORATORY
IDENTIFICATION AND TECHNIC

Section I

GENERAL PARASITOLOGY

Chapter I

PARASITES AND PARASITISM

Parasitology is the science which deals with organisms that take up their abode, temporarily or permanently, on or within other living organisms for the purpose of procuring food. In a broad sense parasitology includes plants such as bacteria and fungi; animals such as Protozoa, helminths and arthropods; and borderline forms such as spirochaetes and ultramicroscopical viruses. In the more restricted sense employed in this textbook the term applies only to animal parasites.

The science of parasitology in relation to disease has been developed by zoologists and medical men. While zoologists have studied the morphology, physiology and life history of the parasite, physicians have concerned themselves with the reaction of the host to the parasite (symptomatology, pathology and immunity) and with the treatment of the infected host. The combined efforts of medicine and zoology are continually intensifying the importance of parasitology, particularly in the broad field of disease prevention. The medical aspect is concerned primarily with the parasites of man, but a knowledge of the parasites of other animals sheds light upon human parasitology. When information concerning the human forms is incomplete, studies of closely related species in animals foretell with considerable accuracy the probable development of similar species in man. Likewise, the knowledge derived from the study of the structure, life cycle and activities of similar free-living forms may provide valuable information concerning the less known parasitic species.

HISTORY

Because of their size the large parasitic worms were among the first agents noticed and studied as probable causes of disease. The famous Ebers papyrus, about 1600 B.C., contains some of the earliest records of the presence of pathogenic worms in man. That the Israelites knew something of the relationship of helminths to human ailments, a knowledge doubtless acquired in Egypt, is shown by the laws of the Mosaic code concerning animal flesh. Persian, Greek and Roman physicians were also familiar with various parasitic worms.

Modern parasitology dates from 1379 when Jehan de Brie discovered the liver luke, *Fasciola hepatica,* in sheep. During the eighteenth century many parasitic worms and arthropods were described, but there was little progress until the advent of the compound microscope made possible the study of the small protozoan parasites and the life cycles and detailed structures of the larger forms.

Following the recognition of *Trichinella spiralis* by Paget in 1835, knowledge concerning the helminthic parasites of man began to accumulate. Many new species were discovered, prominent among which were the hookworm, *Ancylostoma duodenale,* in 1838 by Dubini, and the blood fluke, *Schistosoma hæmatobium,* in 1851 by Bilharz. Between 1850 and 1900 investigators traced the life cycles of *Tænia solium, Echinococcus granulosus, Fasciola hepatica* and *Ancylostoma duodenale,* and between 1900 and 1920 those of *Schistosoma japonicum, Clonorchis sinensis, Diphyllobothrium latum* and *Ascaris lumbricoides.*

The first protozoan parasite of man, *Endamœba gingivalis,* was observed by Gros in 1849. The intestinal flagellates, *Giardia lamblia* and *Trichomonas hominis,* were identified in the early sixties. In 1875 Lösch corroborated the earlier observations of Lambl upon motile amœbæ in patients with diarrhea. In 1880 Laveran observed the malarial plasmodia. In 1900 Leishman discovered *Leishmania donovani,* the cause of kala-azar, and in 1901 Forde found *Trypanosoma gambiense,* the parasite producing African sleeping sickness.

Although certain arthropods had been recognized as parasites since early times, their rôle in spreading disease was not fully established until Smith and Kilborne demonstrated in 1893 that ticks were the transmitting agents of Texas fever in cattle. In 1898 Ross observed the development of the avian malarial parasite in the mosquito and in 1900 Reed and his co-workers proved the transmission of yellow fever by *Aëdes ægypti.* Subsequently, other arthropods were found to be vectors of disease: the tsetse fly in African sleeping sickness in 1903; the tick in African relapsing fever, a spirochaetal disease, in 1905; the rat flea in plague in 1906; the body louse in typhus fever, a rickettsial disease, in 1909; and the reduviid bug, *Triatoma megista,* in South American trypanosomiasis in 1909.

TYPES OF PARASITES

Parasitism includes any reciprocal association in which one species depends upon another. This association may be accidental and temporary or fixed and permanent. In **symbiosis** there is a permanent association of two organisms that cannot exist independently; in **mutualism** both organisms are benefited; and in **commensalism** one partner is benefited and the other is unaffected.

The term parasite, however, is ordinarily applied to a weaker organism that obtains food and shelter from another and derives all the benefit from the association. The harboring species, known as the host, may show no harmful effects or may suffer from a wide range of functional and organic disturbances. There is such a wide range of parasitic types that it is difficult to draw a sharp distinction between a permanent parasite and a temporary resident like a biting insect. Thus, arthropods that produce local and general reactions by the injection of toxic substances may be classed as parasites, although they are often more important as mechanical vectors of disease or as intermediate hosts.

Various descriptive names denote special types or functions of parasites. An **ectoparasite** lives on the outside and an **endoparasite** within the body of the host. Parasites are termed facultative when they are capable of leading both a free and parasitic existence, and obligatory when they take up a permanent residence in and are completely dependent upon the host. An incidental parasite is one that establishes itself in a host in which it does not ordinarily live. An occasional or periodic parasite seeks its host intermittently to obtain nourishment. Temporary parasites are free-living during part of their existence, while permanent parasites remain on or in the body of the host from early life until maturity, sometimes for their entire life. Pseudoparasites are artifacts mistaken for parasites. Coprozoic animals are fecal contaminants that have passed through the alimentary tract without infecting the host.

NOMENCLATURE

Animal parasites are classified according to the International Code of Zoological Nomenclature. Each parasite belongs to a phylum, class, order, family, genus and species. At times the further divisions of suborder, superfamily, subfamily and subspecies are employed. The names are Latinized, and the scientific designation is uninominal for subgenera and higher groups, binominal for species, and trinominal for subspecies.

The law of priority obtains as to the oldest available name, even if only a portion of the parasite or its larva has been described. To be valid a generic name must not have been given already to another genus of animals. The names of genera and species are printed in italics; the generic name begins with a capital, and the specific name with a small letter. The name of the author is written without italics and without punctuation after the name of the parasite. The date of the discovery follows the author's name separated by a comma, e.g., *Dientamœba fragilis* Dobell and Jepps, 1918. When a species is transferred to another genus or when the specific name is combined with another generic name, the name of the original author is placed in parentheses and the name of the author of the new combination follows the parentheses, e.g., *Ancylostoma duodenale* (Dubini, 1843) Creplin, 1845.

The family name ends in "idæ," the superfamily in "oidea," and the subfamily in "inæ." The terminations of certain divisions are indicated by the following examples:

Division	Example
Phylum	Platyhelminthes
Class	Trematoda
Order	Prosostomata
Suborder	Distomata
Superfamily	Fascioloidea
Family	Fasciolidæ
Genus	*Fasciola*
Species	*Fasciola hepatica*

CLASSIFICATION

Animal parasites may be divided into two main groups, protozoa and metazoa. The former are simple unicellular organisms. The latter are multicellular animals, the cells of which are differentiated to perform special functions but are dependent upon one another for their existence. The metazoan cell differs in structure and function from the protozoan cell in the absence of differentiation into ectoplasm and endoplasm, in the absorption of food and excretion of waste products by osmosis, in reproduction by mitotic division only, and in the structure of the nucleus.

Animal parasites are legion. They are represented in practically every division of the animal kingdom and some classes are entirely parasitic, e.g., SPOROZOA, CESTOIDEA and TREMATODA. The distribution of parasites in the animal kingdom is indicated in Table 1.

GEOGRAPHICAL DISTRIBUTION OF PARASITES

Several conditions govern the geographical distribution of parasites. Their endemicity depends upon the presence and habits of a suitable host, upon easy escape from the host, and upon environmental conditions favoring survival outside the host. Consequently, diseases due to parasites are most prevalent in the tropics.

VITAL REQUIREMENTS OF PARASITES

The activities of living organisms are directed toward maintaining the individual and the race. Animals require protection from enemies and a favorable environment in order to carry on unimpeded the bodily functions of digestion, excretion, respiration and reproduction. The requirements of parasites do not differ essentially from those of free-living animals, except for such modifications as are necessary for existence in their hosts.

Parasites often lack the necessary organs for digesting raw food materials and depend upon the host for predigested food. Parasites also require moisture. An adequate supply is assured inside the host, but during the free-living existence of the parasite, inadequate moisture will either prove fatal or prevent larval development. Likewise, temperature exerts an important influence upon parasites, some of which are susceptible to slight variations. High temperatures are detrimental; a temperature of 45° to 47° C. kills many species in from 5 to 10 minutes. Low temperatures arrest the development of larvæ and ova and may even destroy them. Each species has an optimal temperature range for its development.

TABLE I

DISTRIBUTION OF PARASITES IN THE ANIMAL KINGDOM

Phylum	Class	Parasitic species	Human Parasites
PROTOZOA	SARCODINA	Many	+
	INFUSORIA	Many	+
	MASTIGOPHORA	Many	+
	SPOROZOA	All	+
COELENTERATA		Few	−
PORIFERA		Rare	−
ARTHROPODA	INSECTA	Very many	+
	ARACHNIDA	Very many	+
	CRUSTACEA	Many	−
PLATYHELMINTHES	CESTOIDEA	All	+
	TREMATODA	All	+
	TURBELLARIA	Few	−
	NEMERTEA	Few	−
NEMATHELMINTHES	NEMATODA	Very many	+
	ACANTHOCEPHALA	All	+
	NEMATOMORPHA	All (larva)	?
ANNELIDA		Rare	+
MOLLUSCA		Few	−
CHORDATA		Rare	−

HOSTS

The range of a parasite is confined to the habitat of its host. Parasites restricted to a single species of host generally have a more limited range than those that infect several species. Moreover, parasites with alternate or complicated life cycles are more restricted in distribution, since the chances of survival decrease as the complexity of the life cycle increases. Increased egg-production and parthogenetic development tend to counterbalance decreased chances of survival. Parasites with the simplest life cycles are most likely to have a cosmopolitan distribution because of their relative independence of such environmental factors as climate, temperature and humidity. The parasites of man are limited by the range of their

TABLE 2

PRINCIPAL GEOGRAPHICAL DISTRIBUTION OF THE IMPORTANT PROTOZOAN AND HELMINTHIC PARASITES OF MAN

Parasite	Cosmopolitan	North America	South America	Central America and West Indies	Europe	North Africa	Tropical Africa	North Asia	South Asia	Australia	Malaysia	Oceania
PROTOZOA												
Balantidium coli	●											
Endamœba coli	●											
Endamœba histolytica	●											
Giardia lamblia	●											
Leishmania braziliensis		●	●	●								
Leishmania donovani					●	●	●	●	●			
Leishmania tropica					●	●	●		●			
Plasmodium falciparum		●	●	●	●	●	●		●	●	●	●
Plasmodium malariæ		●	●	●	●	●	●		●		●	●
Plasmodium vivax	●											
Trichomonas vaginalis	●											
Trypanosoma cruzi			●	●								
Trypanosoma gambiense							●					
Trypanosoma rhodesiense							●					
NEMATHELMINTHES												
Acanthocheilonema perstans			●			●	●			●		
Ancylostoma braziliense		●	●	●			●		●		●	●
Ancylostoma duodenale			●		●	●		●	●	●	●	●
Ascaris lumbricoides	●											
Dracunculus medinensis			●	●		●	●		●		●	
Enterobius vermicularis	●											
Loa loa							●					
Mansonella ozzardi			●	●								

TABLE 2—Continued

PRINCIPAL GEOGRAPHICAL DISTRIBUTION OF THE IMPORTANT PROTOZOAN AND HELMINTHIC PARASITES OF MAN

Parasite	Cosmopolitan	North America	South America	Central America and West Indies	Europe	North Africa	Tropical Africa	North Asia	South Asia	Australia	Malaysia	Oceania
NEMATHELMINTHES—Continued												
Necator americanus		●	●	●			●		●	●	●	●
Onchocerca volvulus		●	●				●					
Strongyloides stercoralis		●	●	●	●	●	●		●	●	●	●
Trichinella spiralis	●											
Trichuris trichiura	●											
Wuchereria bancrofti			●	●		●	●		●	●	●	●
PLATYHELMINTHES (CESTOIDEA)												
Diphyllobothrium latum		●			●		●	●	●			
Dipylidium caninum	●											
Echinococcus granulosus	●											
Hymenolepis nana	●											
Tænia saginata	●											
Tænia solium	●											
PLATYHELMINTHES (TREMATODA)												
Clonorchis sinensis									●			
Fasciola hepatica	●											
Fasciolopsis buski									●		●	
Heterophyes heterophyes						●			●		●	
Metagonimus yokogawai					●			●	●		●	
Opisthorchis felineus					●			●	●			
Paragonimus westermani			●	●			●	●	●		●	
Schistosoma hæmatobium						●	●		●			
Schistosoma japonicum									●			
Schistosoma mansoni			●	●		●	●					

intermediate hosts; hence, the establishment of new intermediate hosts is one means of widening parasitic distribution.

CLIMATE

Although many important species of parasites have a world-wide distribution, tropical countries where optimal conditions of temperature more often occur are most favorable for their survival. A short summer season prevents the development of many species requiring high temperatures during their larval stages and tends to establish zones of distribution according to latitude. By limiting the range of animal hosts, temperature indirectly affects the distribution of parasites.

Warm temperatures do not always favor the existence of parasites. Intense dry heat or direct sunlight will destroy the larval forms. Dry plateaus in the tropics because of lack of humidity are practically free from parasites except for resistant species or those that are transferred directly from host to host.

Moisture governs the distribution of parasitic species. Not only is it essential for the development of the free-living larvæ, but it is also necessary for the propagation of intermediate hosts such as mosquitoes, flies, snails and fishes. The amount of moisture depends upon temperature, latitude and topography. Regions where these factors produce heavy rainfall for a good part of the year usually have parasites in greatest abundance. Drainage has been used effectively in moist climates to reduce parasitic infection in man.

CUSTOMS AND HABITS OF THE HOST

The distribution of parasites is also governed by economic and social conditions. Customs considered financially profitable may be hygienically unsound. For instance, the irrigation of the Nile Delta and the paddy fields of China favors the spread of schistosomiasis, and the use of night soil in agriculture provides an important source of parasitic infection.

Ignorance of sanitary measures or economic inability to enforce them usually explains the irregular distribution of parasitic diseases in favorable areas. Where individual and community sanitation is lacking and low standards of living are accompanied by overcrowding and absence of hygienic facilities, the promiscuous deposition of excreta favors the spread of parasitic infections. Raw or insufficiently cooked food may be a source of disease if infected by parasites or if contaminated by night soil or polluted water. Parasites may also be transmitted by infected food handlers. Religious rites such as immersion in heavily contaminated water may be responsible for the transmission of parasitic diseases.

MOVEMENTS OF POPULATION

Historical events involving the intermingling of populations have spread bacterial and parasitic diseases. The importation of the Negro to the Western Hemisphere was accompanied by hookworm infection and schistosomiasis. Japanese immigrants introduced the lung fluke to Brazil and Argentina, and immigrants from the Baltic countries brought the fish tapeworm to the Great Lakes region of the United States of America. The study of parasites has also been of value in tracing the movements of animal populations throughout the world.

GEOGRAPHICAL DISTRIBUTION OF IMPORTANT PROTOZOAN AND HELMINTHIC PARASITES OF MAN

The usual geographical distribution of the more important parasites of man is given in Table 2. In designating geographical regions the parallel of latitude dividing North and Tropical Africa is taken arbitrarily as 20°N, and that dividing North and South Asia as 40°N. Australia is separated from Oceania.

THE EVOLUTION OF PARASITES

The present relationship between parasite and host has been gradually evolved throughout the ages. While no instance of a sudden change from a free-living to a parasitic existence has been recorded, evolution has produced so many gradations of parasitic existence that no sharp line can be drawn between occasional parasites and allied free-living species. In the earliest stages of parasitic existence the host acted simply as a vehicle of transportation. Later the parasite became dependent upon the host for food, and finally it reached the degenerate state of consuming the tissues of the host. Naturally, adaptation of a free-living organism to an endoparasitic existence demands more adjustment than is required for an ectoparasitic existence. Whether endoparasitism evolved directly from ectoparasitism or from commensalism and symbiosis is unknown. In any event, the process has produced far-reaching changes in the parasite and in its life history, and has affected the life of its host.

CHANGES IN THE PARASITE

The dependent existence of the parasite has brought about structural changes in both adult and larval forms. Organs no longer necessary have atrophied and others useful for a parasitic existence have developed. The more specialized endoparasites show the greatest changes.

Retrogressive Changes.—The most marked retrogressive changes are found in the organs of locomotion and alimentation. Although in many instances the larval forms retain the power of locomotion, the adults, because of their more sedentary habits, may show partial or complete degeneration of the muscles of locomotion. In adult tapeworms the digestive tract has disappeared, while that of the flukes has undergone marked changes, and digestion is effected by absorption through the integument. In certain species the organs of excretion have been practically eliminated, although as a rule they are little altered. There is general retrogression of the nervous system and sense organs to conform to the altered existence. Such changes in morphology are of value in identifying species.

Development of Useful Organs.—A parasitic existence has produced specialization in the organs concerned with resistance, attachment and reproduction. A thickened integument resists the digestive juices of the host and protects against desiccation and physical injury. The spinous integument of the intestinal flukes

prevents abrasion. The cysts of the Protozoa and the special coverings of the ov
and larvæ of the helminths protect the parasite during the free-living period and
aid in resisting the digestive juices when ingested by the host. Hooks, setæ and
suckers, fortified by a highly developed musculature, anchor parasitic worms in the
body of the host and facilitate migration through the tissues. The shape of the
parasite also becomes adapted for maintaining its hold in the host. In the adult
and larval stages of some worms, secretory glands near the mouth aid in feeding
and penetration.

Parasitism necessitates quantitative and qualitative changes in the reproductive
organs. Sporogeny and parthogenesis supplement sexual development in the
SPOROZOA. The nematodes are bisexual and have specialized sexual organs. In
the tapeworms each segment or proglottis contains a full complement of male and
female reproductive organs, which are capable of producing thousands of ova. With
few exceptions the flukes also are hermaphroditic. Self-fertilization in some species
has become the usual method of reproduction. Propagation in free-living generations or asexual multiplication of larvæ in intermediate hosts has markedly increased the reproductive output.

CHANGES IN RELATION OF PARASITE AND HOST

Since the existence of a parasite depends upon its transfer from host to host, its
life history has been modified by evolution to meet the changing conditions of
environment. An ideal parasitic existence depends upon (1) the presence of an
available host, (2) ability to secure entrance to the host, and (3) adaptability to
residence without endangering the life of the host.

The evolution of a parasite usually extends over a long period before final
adaptation to a particular host is effected. Parasitism involves not only existence in
the host and favorable conditions for reproduction, but also the development of
proper channels of transmission. A casual relationship has changed into one in
which the host is essential for the life of the parasite. Hence, changes in the
environment and habits of the host may produce changes even in the free-living
existence of the parasite.

The ability of a parasite to infect more than one host favors its existence. The
presence of a parasite in a new species is usually the fortuitous result of the habits
of its previous host. Such a transmission may result from (1) changes in the
habits of the previous host that preclude parasitic infection, (2) conditions favoring
a longer or shorter existence outside the body of the host, (3) the coexistence of
the two hosts for a sufficient period, or (4) changes in the habits of the new host
that render it susceptible to invasion.

The influence of the parasite on the evolution of the host ranges from no appreciable effect to local extermination of the species. Throughout the ages this mutual
association has been a significant factor in modifying the biological equilibrium of
animal life. Since the parasite lives at the expense of its host, its ultimate goal is to
adapt its existence so that it will not shorten the life of its host. The well-adapted
parasite that lives in a state of equilibrium with its host is likely to have had a much
longer parasitic existence than the parasite that manifests a poorly adjusted rela-

ionship by injuring its host. As a parasite becomes better adapted it tends to cause less damage and to establish a more harmonious existence.

The host in turn tends to build up a gradually increasing immunity against the parasite. Susceptible hosts perish, leaving the more resistant. Thus natural selection raises the individual and collective immunity of the host-species to such an extent that the parasite may be unable to attain its development. Similarly, the habits of the host undergo changes that tend to raise resistance to parasitic infection.

THE LIFE CYCLES OF PARASITES

Parasites have developed more or less complicated life cycles through adaptation to their hosts and external environment. Most parasites except certain insects attain sexual maturity in their hosts. Some spend their entire lives within the host, one generation following another; others on leaving the host are exposed to the vicissitudes of an external environment. During their extracorporeal life they may remain quiescent in the form of resistant cysts, ova or larvæ, or they may undergo active growth and metamorphosis. Furthermore, the larval parasite may pass through developmental stages in an intermediate host before it reaches a final host.

Hosts.—The **final** or **definitive host** harbors the adult or sexually mature parasite. Every species of carnivorous or omniverous animal at some time has sheltered one or more types of parasite. Indeed parasites may themselves be infested with smaller parasites. Man is not always the final host. He may be the only definitive host, the most important host in the spread of the disease, one of several animal hosts, or merely an incidental host of a parasite prevalent in other animals.

Animals that harbor the same species of parasites as man are known as **reservoir hosts.** Such hosts insure the continuity of the parasite's life cycle and act as potential sources of human infection. Chief among reservoir hosts are domestic animals such as dogs, cats and pigs.

Part or all of the larval stage may be passed in another animal, known as the **intermediate host.** Frequently one host is herbivorous and the other carnivorous. Certain species of trematodes and cestodes have two intermediate hosts. The terms primary and secondary designate the first and second intermediate hosts when more than one is required.

As a rule parasites evince host-specificity: that is, a parasite infects naturally only one or at most a few species of animals. Species-specificity is a manifestation of special adaptation. It is a variable factor, depending on the invasive power of the parasite and the susceptibility of the host. A resistant host may prove impenetrable, may throw off the infection after a short period, or may serve merely for a brief phase of the parasite's life cycle.

The determination of a natural parasite also depends upon ecological factors. The presence of the possible host must coincide not only with the presence of the parasite but also with its infective period. Experimental infections, which cannot be sure of duplicating natural conditions, may not always disclose the true hosts. The ease of transmission depends upon the nature and needs of the parasite and upon the distribution and habits of the host. In man the chances of infection are

TABLE 3

PRINCIPAL HOSTS OF THE IMPORTANT PROTOZOAN AND
HELMINTHIC PARASITES OF MAN

Parasite	Definitive Hosts	Intermediate Hosts
PROTOZOA		
Balantidium coli	Man, hog	
Endamœba coli	Man	
Endamœba histolytica	Man	
Giardia lamblia	Man	
Leishmania braziliensis	Man	*Phlebotomus* (sand-fly) (?)[1]
Leishmania donovani	Man, dog	*Phlebotomus* (sand-fly) (?)[1]
Leishmania tropica	Man	*Phlebotomus* (sand-fly) (?)[1]
Plasmodium falciparum	Mosquito	Man
Plasmodium malariæ	Mosquito	Man
Plasmodium vivax	Mosquito	Man
Trichomonas vaginalis	Man	
Trypanosoma cruzi	Man, armadillo, bat	Reduviid bugs[1]
Trypanosoma gambiense	Man, ruminants	Tsetse fly[1]
Trypanosoma rhodesiense	Man, ruminants	Tsetse fly[1]
NEMATHELMINTHES		
Acanthocheilonema perstans	Man	*Culicoides* (gnat)
Ancylostoma braziliense	Man, cat, dog	
Ancylostoma duodenale	Man	
Ascaris lumbricoides	Man, hog	
Dracunculus medinensis	Man, fur-bearing mammals	*Cyclops*
Enterobius vermicularis	Man	
Loa loa	Man	*Chrysops* (deer fly)
Mansonella ozzardi	Man	*Culicoides* (gnat)
Necator americanus	Man	
Onchocerca volvulus	Man	*Simulium* (black fly)
Strongyloides stercoralis	Man, dog (?)	
Trichinella spiralis	Man, hog, rat	Man, hog, rat
Trichuris trichiura	Man	
Wuchereria bancrofti	Man	Mosquito

[1] In trypanosomal and leishmanian infections, where sexual development is not defined, it is logically impossible to designate the final or intermediate host. For convenience the insect harboring the leptomonad stage is considered here to be the intermediate host.

TABLE 3—Continued

PRINCIPAL HOSTS OF THE IMPORTANT PROTOZOAN AND
HELMINTHIC PARASITES OF MAN

Parasite	Definitive Hosts	Intermediate Hosts
PLATYHELMINTHES (CESTOIDEA)		
Diphyllobothrium latum	Man, dog, cat	*Cyclops* and *Diaptomus*, fresh-water fishes
Dipylidium caninum	Man, dog, cat	Flea
Echinococcus granulosus	Dog and other CANIDÆ	Man, sheep, cattle, hog
Hymenolepis nana	Man, rat, mouse	Man, rat, mouse
Tænia saginata	Man	Cattle
Tænia solium	Man	Hog, man
PLATYHELMINTHES (TREMATODA)		
Clonorchis sinensis	Man, dog, cat	Snails, fresh-water fishes
Fasciola hepatica	Man, herbivora	Snails
Fasciolopsis buski	Man, hog	Snails
Heterophyes heterophyes	Man, dog, cat	Snails, fresh-water fishes
Metagonimus yokogawai	Man, fish-eating mammals	Snails, fresh-water fishes
Opisthorchis felineus	Man, dog, cat	Snails, fresh-water fishes
Paragonimus westermani	Man, carnivora	Snails, fresh-water crabs and crayfishes
Schistosoma hæmatobium	Man	Snails
Schistosoma japonicum	Man, domestic animals	Snails
Schistosoma mansoni	Man	Snails

increased with (1) lack of species-selectivity, (2) density of population, (3) travel, (4) infected food and food handlers, and (5) lack of sanitation.

Life Cycle.—The perpetuation of the life of a parasite depends upon its transmission from host to host. Various stages in the life cycles of the different parasites of man have been worked out, but many details are still unknown. Certain parasites have elaborate life histories involving several hosts, while others have simple cycles. From a medical standpoint knowledge of the life history is important, since it often

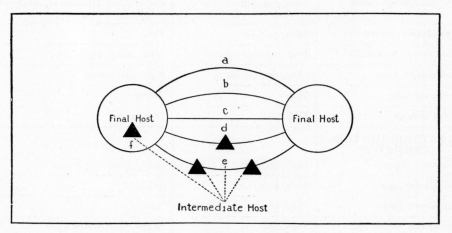

FIG. 1.—LIFE CYCLES OF PARASITES

a, transmission with existence outside host; *b,* transmission with development during free-living existence; *c,* direct transmission from host to host; *d,* transmission through one intermediate host with or without free-living existence; *e,* transmission through more than one intermediate host with or without free-living existence; *f,* final and intermediate host in same animal.

indicates the stages at which preventive measures can be most effectively applied. Figure 1 gives a diagrammatic representation of the various types of life cycles.

The more complicated the life cycle, the fewer are the chances of survival. It seems almost incredible that the life cycles of certain parasites can ever be completed. However, overdeveloped reproductive organs and parthogenetic multiplication tend to offset the increased hazards of a complex life history. Thus, under favorable conditions multiplication may become so rapid that strenuous measures are necessary to prevent infection.

Chapter II

THE PATHOLOGY OF PARASITIC INFECTIONS

Various distinctions have been made between the terms infection and infestation, although they are often used indiscriminately to denote parasitic invasion. In this textbook **infection** is applied to invasion by endoparasites (Protozoa and helminths) and **infestation** to the external parasitism of ectoparasites (Arthropoda) or to the presence of parasites in soil or plants.

Since a parasite lives at the expense of its host regardless of whether or not it produces a serious drain on the host's vitality, a distinction should be made between parasitic infection and parasitic disease. The welfare of the parasite is concerned only with infection, and disease is an incidental result. On the other hand the welfare of the host is dependent upon the severity of the pathological changes and their effect upon its life and habits.

Maladjustment between parasite and host produces characteristic pathological changes and symptoms in the host. The degree of injury depends upon (1) the number, size, shape and activity of the parasite, (2) its location in the host, and (3) its toxicity. Injury is caused chiefly by the toxic products or by the activities of the parasite. Parasites become pathogenic when they cause organic changes sufficient to produce abnormal functioning.

ACTIVITIES OF THE PARASITE

Before an organism can establish a successful parasitic existence, it must be able to pass through its normal life cycle and to provide infective forms for the invasion of new definitive or intermediate hosts. From the standpoint of the parasite, infection falls into three stages: (1) the developmental period from the time of entry to maturity and the production of offspring; (2) the period of multiplication, in which protozoan and a few helminthic parasites increase to an optimal number; and (3) the period of decline in which, although the parasites can no longer be recovered from the host, evidence of their presence still persists (Fig. 2). The existence of a period of latency (Fig. 2) for parasites, comparable to that of bacteria, is debatable.

Distribution in the Host.—The distribution of the parasite in the body of the host is determined by the method of entry, by tissue-selectivity, and by the resistance of the host. Parasites may be classed as coelozoic, inhabiting the body cavities; as histozoic, residing among the tissue cells; and as cytozoic, living within the cells. In most instances there is a principal or primary site of infection for each species, tissue-specificity being one of the most striking characteristics of parasitic infections. For instance, the fluke *Paragonimus westermani* lives in the lungs; the fluke

Clonorchis sinensis in the liver; and the filarial worm *Wuchereria bancrofti* in the lymphatics. The most common localization is in the digestive tract, which harbors over two-thirds of the parasites of man. Under certain conditions some parasites may leave the primary site and take up secondary locations in other organs, thus producing a more generalized infection.

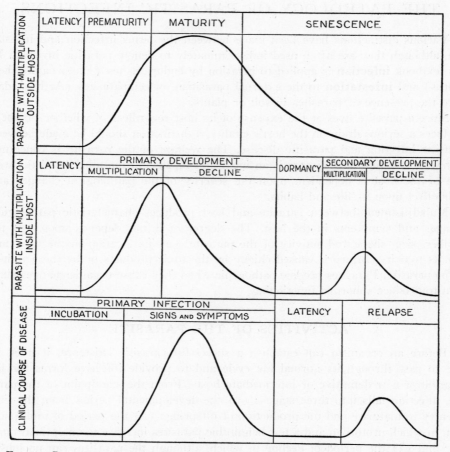

FIG. 2.—SCHEMATIC REPRESENTATION OF DEVELOPMENT OF A PATHOGENIC PARASITE

Migratory Excursions within the Host.—After entering the host the parasite migrates to that part of the body which serves as its permanent residence. The route depends somewhat upon the point of entry. Most of the parasites inhabiting the intestinal tract gain entrance through the mouth and pass either directly to their customary site or first develop to maturity at a higher level and then move downward to their permanent location. A few species follow a more circuitous route. The embryonate ova of *Ascaris lumbricoides* hatch in the upper part of the small intestine. The larvæ pierce the intestinal wall to enter the lymphatics or blood stream; pass to the lungs, where they remain for several days; then pass up the bronchi to the glottis; and after being swallowed reach the small intestine where they become adult worms. Other species migrate from the intestine to various organs of the body, such as the liver, lungs and tissues. When the infective organisms gain access through the skin or blood, they reach their final destination in the tissues by any one of a number of direct or circuitous routes.

Resistance.—Parasites have acquired certain protective properties, which enable them to survive under adverse conditions and to withstand the antagonistic reactions of the host. The development of resistant or "fast" strains of parasites in immune hosts is a subject of academic interest.

Methods of Attack.—Each pathogenic parasite has its own peculiar method of invasion and attack. More than a suitable channel of entry is necessary; the parasite must have certain invasive powers. Its weapons of attack are the power of locomotion, enzymes for dissolving tissue for food or for penetration, and the production of toxic substances. The invasive and pathogenic powers of the parasite seem to diminish with long residence in the host, since there is evidence that parasites from chronic infections produce fewer pathological effects in a new host than those from acute infections.

Mechanical Action.—Mechanical injury is produced by both adult and larval forms. Its severity depends upon the nature of the parasite and the particular organs involved. Prominent among the various methods of injury are: (1) larval migrations through the body (*Trichinella*); (2) movement of the ova in the tissues (*Schistosoma*); (3) obstruction of intestines (*Ascaris*), of capillaries (*Plasmodium*), of biliary passages (*Clonorchis*), and of lymphatics (*Wuchereria*); (4) pressure (*Echinococcus*); and (5) injury at the points of attachment (*Ancylostoma*).

Irritative Action.—Many parasites, without producing toxic substances, act as foreign-body irritants in the tissues of the host and call forth a chronic inflammatory reaction designed to encapsulate them. Encapsulation of the larvæ of *Trichinella spiralis* and of the echinococcal cysts serve as illustrations. The hyperplastic and adenomatous proliferations of the bile ducts of the liver in *Clonorchis sinensis* infections represent another form of tissue response.

Toxic Action.—Certain parasites elaborate toxic substances which, when absorbed, injure the host. These substances may be true diffusible exotoxins, or they may be endotoxins that are liberated after the disintegration of the parasite. Only one parasite, a sarcosporidian, has been found to produce a toxin which fulfils the criteria for true exotoxins such as thermolability, incubational period and neutralization by an antitoxin. It is almost impossible to differentiate between endotoxins and the products of proteic disintegration. The most important toxic substances are the tissue-lysins, hemolysins and anticoagulins. Proteic products, although primarily somewhat toxic, become more so after the host has become sensitized. This phenomenon has been demonstrated experimentally by sensitizing animals with extracts of parasites and observing their exaggerated symptomatic response to subsequent infection. As a rule symptoms of intoxication are more general than specific.

PATHOLOGICAL CHANGES IN THE HOST

The protective reaction of the host to a pathogenic parasite represents the organic and functional response of a living organism to a harmful stimulus. Such a stimulus calls forth overactivity of the protective and reparative processes. Even though the external manifestations may be local, there are always concomitant systemic changes of a cellular or humoral nature involving the chemistry, immunity, metabolism, and the nervous and circulatory systems of the body.

The demonstrable effects of an injury may be immediate (acute) or delayed (chronic). An acute injury may (1) terminate fatally, (2) heal completely, (3) leave a chronic residue, or (4) produce mild or severe secondary manifestations. A chronic injury may progress slowly to a fatal termination or may continue as a low-grade process.

A knowledge of the parasite and of the lesions in the host provides a basis for diagnosis, prognosis and treatment. It is important to know as much as possible about the following: (1) the number and rate of increase of the invading organisms; (2) the primary site of the infection and the tendency to metastatic involvement of other organs; (3) the opportunity for mechanical and obstructive damage; (4) the amount of tissue destruction; (5) the additional complications resulting from ova and larvæ; (6) the loss of blood; and (7) the toxic disturbances, both local and systemic. Such disturbances may be due to the toxic properties of the parasite or to the supersensitiveness of the host.

Stages of Infection.—Infection in the host passes through the following stages: (1) an incubational period from the time of entry of the parasite until the appearance of clinical symptoms, during which there is either multiplication or growth of the parasite; (2) the acute illness, characterized by signs and symptoms that represent the reaction of the host to the injury produced by the larval, immature or adult parasite; (3) the convalescent period, characterized by abatement of symptoms, when the host is beginning to restrict the pathogenic activities of the parasite; and (4) a period of latent infection, during which an equilibrium, broken by occasional relapses, is established between parasite and host (Fig. 2).

Systemic Disturbances.—Metabolic disturbances are less marked than in bacterial diseases, but they may appear in the form of anemia, jaundice or secondary bacterial infections. While a parasite may be the primary cause of a disease, superimposed bacterial infections may be responsible for the clinical entity. The activities of both pathogenic and nonpathogenic parasites may pave the way for such infections. Thus, parasitic infections may produce serious or even fatal systemic disturbances through the destruction of vital organs by the direct action of the parasite or by secondary bacterial infections.

Blood.—Parasitic infections not infrequently produce changes in the blood. Loss of blood, the action of toxins upon the blood cells and the blood-forming system, and secondary bacterial infections often lead to secondary anemia. The blood picture varies with the species of parasite and the stage of the disease. Moderate leukocytosis may be present during the active stages of helminthic infection, but eosinophilia is the most constant leukocytic change.

Signs and Symptoms.—Signs and symptoms are manifestations of deranged function arising from organic changes that either stimulate or suppress the activities of the affected organs. The location of the parasite in a vital organ, its toxic action and the intensity of the infection determine the presence, time of appearance, and the severity of the symptoms. The manifestations may be local or general depending upon the nature of the pathogenic agent and the response of the host. Frequently the host can compensate for the decrease in function of vital organs to such an extent that injury to the tissues may not become evident until considerable damage has been caused.

When the damage caused by a parasite calls forth symptomatic response on the part of the host, a typical clinical case of the disease results. A high percentage of hosts manifest symptoms when the adjustment between host and parasite is poor. When the maladjustment is less marked, the percentage is lower and in many instances mild or atypical cases pass unrecognized. Certain individuals because of unusual resistance maintain an equilibrium between the parasite and the host irrespective of their natural incompatibility. The infected person who shows slight or no clinical evidence of the disease, the "carrier," is an important problem in the prevention of parasitic diseases.

Symptoms of parasitic infection may be induced by supersensitiveness on the part of the host, since an infection which normally calls forth no appreciable clinical response may, in the sensitized host, result in a pronounced reaction. These manifestations may take the form of an exaggerated local reaction, urticaria, edema, gastro-intestinal symptoms, and pulmonary complications covering the entire range of the allergic phenomena associated with foreign proteins.

Special Pathology.—The selective affinity of parasites for special tissues determines to a large extent the distribution of lesions. The damage may be restricted to the infected organs or it may manifest itself indirectly in other organs. As a rule the pathological changes are more or less characteristic of the infecting organism, and certain locations and types of lesions are associated with particular parasites. Table 4 gives the principal tissues affected and the chief characteristic lesions produced by the more important protozoan and helminthic parasites of man.

TABLE 4

PRINCIPAL LESIONS CAUSED BY THE IMPORTANT PROTOZOAN
AND HELMINTHIC PARASITES OF MAN

Parasite	Habitat of Adult and Larval Parasite	Characteristic Pathological Findings
PROTOZOA		
Balantidium coli	Intestine	Ulcers
Endamœba coli	Intestine	None
Endamœba histolytica	Intestine, liver	Ulcers, abscesses
Giardia lamblia	Intestine	Enteritis (?)
Leishmania braziliensis	Skin and mucous membranes	Ulcers
Leishmania donovani	Liver, spleen	Reticulo-endotheliosis
Leishmania tropica	Skin	Ulcers
Plasmodium falciparum		
Plasmodium malariæ	Blood, liver, spleen, brain	Erythroclasis, pigmentation, splenomegaly
Plasmodium vivax		
Trichomonas vaginalis	Vagina	Vaginitis
Trypanosoma cruzi	Blood, heart, brain	Endotheliosis, destruction of tissue cells
Trypanosoma gambiense	Blood, lymphatics, brain	Lymphadenitis, meningo-encephalitis
Trypanosoma rhodesiense	Blood, lymphatics, brain	Lymphadenitis, meningo-encephalitis
NEMATHELMINTHES		
Acanthocheilonema perstans	Body cavities, blood	Local irritation
Ancylostoma braziliense	Intestine, skin	Creeping eruption, enteritis
Ancylostoma duodenale	Intestine	"Ground itch," pneumonitis, enteritis, petechiæ
Ascaris lumbricoides	Intestine	Enteritis, pneumonitis
Dracunculus medinensis	Subcutaneous tissues	Cutaneous ulcers, abscesses
Enterobius vermicularis	Intestine	Mild enteritis
Loa loa	Subcutaneous tissues, blood	"Calabar" swellings (subcutaneous)
Mansonella ozzardi	Body cavities, blood	None
Necator americanus	Intestine	"Ground itch," pneumonitis, enteritis, petechiæ
Onchocerca volvulus	Skin and subcutaneous tissues	Cutaneous nodules
Strongyloides stercoralis	Intestine	Enteritis, pneumonitis
Trichinella spiralis	Intestine, muscles	Enteritis, myositis

TABLE 4—Continued

PRINCIPAL LESIONS CAUSED BY THE IMPORTANT PROTOZOAN
AND HELMINTHIC PARASITES OF MAN

Parasite	Habitat of Adult and Larval Parasite	Characteristic Pathological Findings
Trichuris trichiura	Intestine	Mild enteritis
Wuchereria bancrofti	Lymphatics, blood	Lymphangitis, elephantiasis
PLATYHELMINTHES (CESTOIDEA)		
Diphyllobothrium latum	Intestine	Mild enteritis
Dipylidium caninum	Intestine	Mild enteritis
Echinococcus granulosus	Liver and other viscera	Hydatid cysts
Hymenolepis nana	Intestine	Mild enteritis
Tænia saginata	Intestine	Mild enteritis
Tænia solium	Intestine, tissues	Mild enteritis, cysticerci
PLATYHELMINTHES (TREMATODA)		
Clonorchis sinensis	Liver	Hepatic cirrhosis, biliary fibrosis
Fasciola hepatica	Liver	Hepatitis, hepatic cirrhosis
Fasciolopsis buski	Intestine	Ulcerative and hemorrhagic enteritis
Heterophyes heterophyes	Intestine	Enteritis
Metagonimus yokogawai	Intestine	Enteritis
Opisthorchis felineus	Liver	Biliary fibrosis, occasional hepatic cirrhosis
Paragonimus westermani	Lung	Fibroid ulcerative tubercles
Schistosoma hæmatobium	Vesical and pelvic plexuses	Hyperplasia and fibrosis of bladder
Schistosoma japonicum	Mesenteric veins	Enteric papillomata and fibrosis, splenic fibrosis, hepatic cirrhosis
Schistosoma mansoni	Mesenteric veins	Enteric papillomata and fibrosis

Chapter III

THE IMMUNITY OF PARASITIC INFECTIONS

INFECTION AND RESISTANCE

Resistance to infection by animal parasites resembles resistance to bacterial infections. It differs chiefly in the type of reaction and in the greater importance of environmental factors. The host escapes infection by the resistance of its tissues, which prevents the prolonged existence of the parasite, and by the external barriers to the transmission of the parasite in the form of environment, ecology and habits. The latter, which are not associated with tissue-immunity, apply to the resistance of the individual and more particularly to that of the aggregate or herd. In brief, the resistance of the host depends upon its habits in relation to the life cycle of the parasite as modified by geographical and climatic conditions, upon the barrier which it presents to the invading parasite, and finally upon its humoral and cellular immunity.

Resistance to infection is a relative affair. It varies with the invasiveness of the parasite, number of invading organisms, length of exposure, adverse external conditions, and immunity of the host. Varying degrees of resistance, but rarely absolute immunity, are found. The host may be able to withstand invasion by the parasite, to establish an equilibrium with it, to reduce its numbers, to curtail its activities, or even to destroy it.

Distinction must be made between resistance to parasitic infection and to parasitic disease. The former is concerned with the diverse external factors that govern the access of the parasite to the host and with the various protective barriers inside the host against the establishment or multiplication of the parasite. The latter represents the ability of the host to destroy the parasite or to curtail its pathogenic activities so as to avoid serious damage to the tissues.

SYSTEMIC AND EXTRASYSTEMIC IMMUNITY

Immunity or the power of resistance of the host to a parasite may be due to systemic or to external factors.

Extrasystemic Immunity.—Extrasystemic or external immunity is produced by such extracorporeal factors as habits, occupation, associations and environment. Since external factors alter the general resistance of the host, extrasystemic immunity is not truly specific. This type of resistance is more important in parasitic infections than in bacterial diseases, particularly in relation to herd immunity as distinct from individual immunity.

External factors that alter the resistance of the host include diet, fatigue, anatomical abnormalities, previous or existing disease, climate, habits and customs.

An insufficient or poorly balanced diet lowers resistance and even a diet capable of maintaining health may, because of insufficient vitamins, produce susceptibility to infection. Clinical evidence indicates that chronic fatigue lowers the threshold of susceptibility and that it may transform a latent into an active infection or change a subclinical into a clinical disease. Structural or even functional abnormalities increase the chances of parasitic invasion: for example, stasis favors the development of parasitic infection in the intestinal tract. Abnormalities may permit the prolongation of a parasitic infection which normally would have a brief self-limited existence, and at times may allow secondary infection to transform an apparently harmless ailment into a serious disease. An existing disease or endocrine dysfunction that tends to lower the general level of health increases susceptibility to infection and presents favorable conditions for the development of the parasite. Conversely, the presence of parasites may aggravate coexistent diseases and even prevent their normal healing.

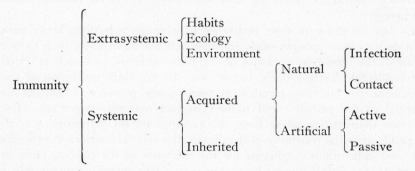

The geographical distribution of parasitic diseases and their seasonal fluctuations indicate the importance of climate. A warm, moist environment favors the rapid development of most parasites and decreases the resistance of the host. Frequency of exposure, which results from segregation, occupation and unhygienic surroundings, tends to overcome resistance. Unhygienic habits and customs among the poor or ignorant classes, especially when augmented by overcrowded living conditions, provide endless opportunities for infection.

Systemic Immunity.—Systemic immunity refers to the protective mechanism developed within the tissues of the host against the invading parasite. It may be cellular or humoral, general or local, and naturally or artificially acquired. The following discussion deals mainly with systemic immunity, although at times it is difficult to differentiate it from extrasystemic immunity.

NATURAL IMMUNITY

Immunity may be a natural heritage of race, species or individual. It may take the form of a resistance against parasites collectively or against a specific parasite. The action of the digestive juices, the impenetrability of the skin, the temperature of the body, the parasiticidal action of the body fluids, the phagocytic activities of the corpuscular elements, and numerous other factors share in the creation of resistance. Immunity manifests itself not only in the actual presence of antibodies and allied substances, but also in the capacity of the individual to form such antibodies in response to stimuli. In some infections the dominant factor in natural immunity appears to be the phagocytic action of the body cells and in others the formation of humoral antibodies.

Inheritance.—The origin of the antibodies in natural immunity has caused much controversy. Aside from the passive transfer of immune bodies from mother to offspring through the placenta or in the colostrum, there is evidence of inheritance according to genetic laws. In man the production of isohemagglutinins, a special group of iso-antibodies (antibodies against materials originating in other individuals of the same species), shows definite evidence of Mendelian inheritance. The antibodies produced against parasites are hetero-antibodies (antibodies against materials originating in another species). The problem of their inheritance is complicated by the possibility of acquiring immunity through exposure and latent infection. Hence, only the capacity for antibody formation can be definitely associated with heredity.

Species.—Species differ in their resistance to parasitic infection. Many parasites of man do not occur spontaneously in other animals. Conversely man harbors relatively few of the numerous parasites of the lower animals, and such infections are usually incidental. Extrasystemic factors may be the chief protection of man against these parasites, but body metabolism, temperature, presence of nutrient materials essential to the parasite, and tissue-resistance are also important. Host-specificity, other than that resulting from opportunities for the transmission of the parasite, depends upon the resistance of the tissues, the various barriers to extension in the host, and unfavorable conditions for the existence of the parasite. For example, a parasite may infect several hosts, but may attain sexual maturity only in one because of tissue-resistance or the lack of some substance essential to its development. Morphologically indistinguishable species, such as the ascarids of man and hog, appear to possess specific physiological properties of adaptation to their specific hosts.

Race.—Differences in immunity to certain parasitic diseases have been observed in the various races of man. While opportunity for infection, exposure of body and an unhygienic environment in part account for racial differences in immunity, the most reasonable explanation appears to be prolonged exposure for generations. For instance, the Negro has been subject to hookworm infection for many centuries, while the white races in the Southern United States have been exposed only during the past two hundred years. The longer association apparently has brought about a greater natural resistance to hookworm disease on the part of the Negro. Likewise, infections with *Ascaris lumbricoides* are reported to produce less clinical disturbance in Chinese than in European children.

Individual.—Individuals vary in their resistance to parasitic infections, particularly in the extent of the pathological changes produced by the parasite. While freedom from infection may be due largely to environment and habits, individual resistance to parasitic disease may be an inherited insusceptibility associated with physical well-being, or it may be a specific immunity against a particular disease that is either inherited or is acquired from prolonged contact and subminimal infections. This variation has been attributed to anatomical, physiological and chemical differences.

Resistance usually increases with age. The more frequent exposure through faulty hygiene and the absence of immunity acquired from previous subclinical infections and contact with parasites in part account for the lower resistance of children. Nevertheless, there is evidence that age itself is a factor in systemic natural immunity. Age-immunity is present in many specific hosts and is particularly noticeable in unusual or incidental hosts, young animals being susceptible, and adults resistant, to infection. Experimental protozoan and helminthic infections are more easily produced in puppies, kittens and chickens than in adult animals. Not only does increased age prevent infection and reduce the number of infecting organisms, but it may also cause retardation in the growth and development of the parasite. Evidently anatomical and physiological differences in the young render them more susceptible than adults.

Herd-Immunity.—The immunity of a herd or group differs from that of its individual members. The term herd-immunity not only denotes the summation of the individual immunity of its members but also includes the resistance offered to the spread of infection when a focus is established. Parasitic infections are particularly dependent upon all the natural conditions that hinder the spread of infection in a herd. The most important of these are: (1) the proportion of individuals resistant because of previous exposure or by natural immunity; (2) the dose, rate of infection, length of exposure and invasive powers of the invading parasite; and (3) the hygienic and ecological habits of the host.

ACQUIRED IMMUNITY

Acquired immunity is developed naturally by previous infection, by low-grade latent infection, or by contact with parasites. It may be produced artificially by either active or passive immunization. Although in many bacterial and viral diseases a single attack may confer immunity for a definite period or for life, protozoan and helminthic infections tend to relapse or become chronic, and a state of immunity is but slowly developed in the host. However, continuous exposure in native populations apparently results in some degree of immunity to infection and produces a tolerance to the toxic effects of certain parasites. In many instances it is impossible to differentiate between a concomitant immunity due to an existing latent infection that prevents superinfection and a residual immunity produced by a past infection.

Active Immunity.—Active immunity is the resistance acquired by an animal through the reaction of its own tissues. It may be the result of natural infection or it may be produced artificially by inoculations with living parasites (*Leishmania tropica*), by a combination of living parasites and parasiticidal drugs, or by dead parasites or their products.

Two general types of immune bodies, demonstrable by serological methods, are produced: antitoxins and antibodies. Antitoxins neutralize the toxins and antibodies destroy the parasite directly or stimulate their destruction by phagocytosis. Since only one parasitic genus, *Sarcocystis,* has been found to produce a true soluble toxin, antitoxins are probably of little importance in parasitic diseases.

Passive Immunity.—Passive immunity is produced by the transfer of serum or whole blood from an immunized animal to another animal. Passive immunization possesses the advantage over active immunization of conferring immediately a highly immune state, but since the antibodies are rapidly eliminated, its effect is of relatively short duration. Passive immunization, though successful in certain bacterial diseases, is of little practical value in parasitic diseases.

THE MECHANISM OF IMMUNITY

Systemic immunity depends upon the production by the body of specific substances in response to the introduction of alien materials, which in the case of parasites are their bodies or their products. The alien substances, which, when parenterally introduced into the body, evoke the production of specific antibodies, are known as **antigens.** The exact mechanism of antibody-formation is unknown, but the skin and reticulo-endothelial system are intimately concerned with its production. Antibodies may remain in the tissue cells or may enter the circulation, where they constitute part of the serum-globulin.

The concept of specificity applies to the formation of antibodies; a particular antigen produces an antibody which reacts only with that antigen. A **hapten** may be defined as a separable chemical grouping that determines the specificity of an antigen, though not antigenic in itself. Varied and distinct antibodies may be produced in response to a molecularly homogeneous antigen, and thus it is not surprising that the complex structure of parasites gives rise to many distinct antibodies. Moreover, the similarity of some of these determinant haptens in different species may explain the apparent lack of specificity of some antisera produced against a single species.

The nature of the several antibody-antigen reactions varies and has given rise to certain descriptive terms. **Agglutination** is the aggregation and precipitation of visible, particulate antigens by their corresponding antibodies. **Precipitation** is the aggregation and precipitation of a soluble antigen (precipitinogen) by its specific antibody (precipitin) to produce a visible precipitate. **Lysis** is the reaction between a visible, particulate antigen (lysinogen) and its corresponding antibody (lysin or sensitizer), resulting in the disruption and dissolution of the antigen. Unlike agglutination and precipitation, lysis requires a third substance (alexin) to effect the solution of the antigen by the lysin. **Alexin** (complement) is a thermolabile substance, present in variable amounts in all fresh sera, and acts only after the lysin has combined with (sensitized) the antigen. Alexin has a nonspecific action and enters equally well into all lytic reactions.

The mechanism of immunity in the host varies with different parasites. The lytic substances apparently play the chief rôle in certain parasitic infections, the phagocytic cells are prominent in others, and the local resistance of skin and tissues predominates in still others. Thus, parasitic immunity according to the predominating type may be classed as humoral or cellular and general or local.

HUMORAL IMMUNITY

The body fluids of immune hosts contain antibodies that destroy parasites, inhibit their development or neutralize their toxic products. The antibodies, present in the blood serum and tissues, include agglutinins, precipitins, antitoxins and lysins of various types. These immune bodies are believed to be produced in the skin and in the reticulo-endothelial system, particularly of the spleen, liver and bone marrow.

Precipitation.—Under this heading may be grouped the phenomena of agglutination, precipitation and toxin-antitoxin neutralization. The precipitation of antigen with antibody is the result of first, a specific combination of the two and second, a nonspecific physicochemical alteration, due to cohesive, electrolytic and electrostatic effects, which eventuates in aggregation and sedimentation of particles. Precipitins and agglutinins may be demonstrated by various *in vitro* precipitative and agglutinative serological tests of diagnostic value, and antitoxins by protective tests in animals. Precipitative tests are more important than agglutinative, since suitable agglutinative antigens cannot be prepared for metazoan parasites. True toxins have been demonstrated in only one genus, *Sarcocystis,* and the evidence of their production in helminthic parasites is unreliable. Consequently antitoxins, antibodies produced against true toxins, are of little importance in parasitic immunity. Practically all the toxic manifestations produced by parasites are attributable to endotoxins or protein-cleavage products.

Lytic Reactions.—Lytic reactions include bacteriolysis, cytolysis and alexin-fixation. They are characterized by the interaction of an indispensable third substance, alexin (complement). The combination of antigens with their respective antibodies (lysins) proceeds in the same manner as in the precipitative reactions and differs only in the dissolution of the antigen upon the addition of nonspecific alexin present in fresh serum. The production of a specific trypanolytic substance is an important factor in trypanosomal immunity. Alexin-fixation tests are of use in the serological diagnosis of certain parasitic diseases.

CELLULAR IMMUNITY

The immune host uses the same cellular mechanism in combating pathogenic parasites that the normal host uses against nonpathogenic parasites: namely, phagocytosis by leukocytes (microphages) and by mobile and sessile cells (macrophages), derived chiefly from the reticulo-endothelial system. Phagocytic activity constitutes an important defense against the parasites and their disintegration products. Phagocytic and lytic reactions are fundamentally similar, since both require the presence of alexin. Immune sera stimulate the phagocytic action of the cells or so alter the parasites that they are susceptible to phagocytosis. This stimulating action is variously ascribed to opsonins, tropins and other immune bodies.

Phagocytic immunity in protozoan infections has received considerable study. When undergoing phagocytosis trypanosomes first become attached to the large mononuclear cells and then are incorporated within them. In malaria both parasites and invaded red blood cells are ingested by leukocytes or reticulo-endothelial cells.

The organs rich in reticulo-endothelial cells have a special attraction for leishmanian parasites, and their invasion may influence antibody production. The decomposition products of helminthic parasites are engulfed by the macrophages in the same manner as foreign bodies.

Eosinophilia is characteristic of helminthic infections. Eosinophils are also increased in conditions arising from protein-supersensitiveness such as anaphylaxis, serum sickness, certain skin diseases and bronchial asthma. In helminthic infections their presence may be a manifestation of supersensitiveness or a special defense against the foreign proteins of the parasites. Eosinophils are produced in the bone marrow, pass into the general circulation and are recruited from the blood in the regions of parasitic localization. Their production is stimulated by eosinophilotactic substances in the worms and is related to previous sensitization of the host. Local and general eosinophilia may be produced by the injection of extracts of parasites. Eosinophilia is of value in the nonspecific diagnosis of helminthic infections.

LOCAL IMMUNITY

Local immunity aids in the resistance of the host to parasitic infections. The reaction of inflammation tends to overcome the parasites by antigen-antibody deposits, by primary infiltration of the site of invasion with microphages (polymorphonuclear and eosinophilic leukocytes), by secondary infiltration with macrophages (mononuclears and histiocytes) and finally by proliferation of fibroblasts. Many parasites, irrespective of their route of entry, have a selective affinity for certain tissues of the host. The resistance of these particular tissues and their capacity to localize the infection determine to some extent the immunity of the host. Such local immunity, probably a phase of general immunity, presents a barrier to the spread of the parasite.

SUPERSENSITIVENESS

Supersensitiveness may be defined as a state of abnormally exaggerated response to the injection of, or other contact with, an antigen. Owing to the peculiar association or localization of the antibody in the body cells a dose of antigen, which in the normal individual may produce no apparent change, will lead to severe or even fatal reactions in the supersensitive individual. Allergy, anaphylaxis, serum sickness, atopy and contact-dermatitis are some of the names used for different manifestations of supersensitiveness to various plant and animal proteins. Thus, the proteins of a parasite may produce no effect in a normal host, but may cause severe reactions in a host previously sensitized by infection or contact with that particular parasite or a closely allied species.

Anaphylaxis may be defined as an artificially produced state of supersensitiveness. The proteins of parasitic worms make efficient anaphylactogens. In demonstrating anaphylaxis experimental animals are given a primary small sensitizing dose of the antigen and after an incubational period of about ten days a larger shocking dose of the same antigen. Antibody-formation takes place in the tissue cells, the site varying in different animals. The union of antibody-antigen after the shocking dose liberates histamine, which may cause a drop in blood pressure, vomiting, cardiac failure, and bronchial constriction. Anaphylaxis may be demonstrated *in vitro* by means of perfusion experiments with smooth muscles. Passive anaphylaxis may be produced by transferring a high antibody-serum from one animal to another and may be demonstrated after a short period by a shocking dose.

The toxic manifestations of parasitic infections in man may be partly the result of supersensitiveness. It is difficult to distinguish between toxicity and supersensitiveness. The usual symptoms associated with supersensitiveness are urticaria, cutaneous eruptions, edema, local manifestations in the neighborhood of the parasite, gastro-intestinal disorders, and in severe cases respiratory and cardiac complications. In man supersensitiveness to a parasite, in spite of the unfavorable symptoms produced, may be interpreted as a protective response associated with immunity. It is evidence of previous infection or contact with the parasite. Its presence may be demonstrated by intracutaneous tests, which are of value in diagnosing parasitic infections (Chapter V and Section VII, X).

IMMUNIZATION AGAINST PARASITIC DISEASES

The artificial production of immunity against parasitic diseases has not been particularly effective. Methods of immunization have proved successful only in a few protozoan infections. Inoculations of unexposed parts of the body with *Leishmania tropica* from lesions produces immunity against subsequent disfiguring attacks of oriental sore. Cattle may be immunized against Texas fever by establishing a low-grade or latent infection. Young adults are injected with blood from convalescent cattle which contains a small number of parasites. Injections of pathogenic trypanosomes attenuated by passage through animals or killed in one of several ways have been used by a number of workers with variable success. Experimental immunization of birds with avian malaria apparently sets up a latent infection which protects against superinfection.

Protection by specific drugs against trypanosomiasis, malaria and other infections has been reported. Specific chemotherapy combined with inoculations of living parasites has proved effective in producing immunity against trypanosomal infections. Some workers believe that immunity to malaria may be produced by the administration of drugs in doses large enough to relieve symptoms but small enough to permit the survival of a few parasites.

Chapter IV

THE TRANSMISSION OF PARASITIC DISEASES

The transmission of parasitic diseases involves three factors: (1) the source of the infection, (2) the mode of transmission, and (3) the presence of a susceptible host. The combined effect of these factors determines the dispersibility and prevalence of the parasite at a given time and place.

Figure 3 gives a diagrammatic representation of the factors in disease transmission. On the left the five lines radiating from the source of focus of infection represent the five avenues through which the infective agent may leave the body.

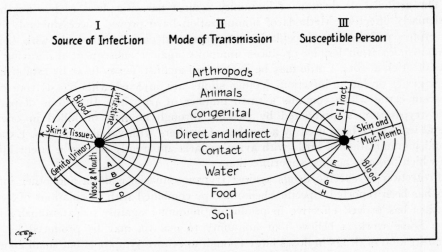

FIG. 3.—THE TRANSMISSION OF PARASITIC DISEASES

A, diagnosis and treatment; *B*, isolation; *C*, blocking outflowing infection; *D*, detection of carriers and missed cases; *E*, immunization; *F*, cleanliness and hygiene; *G*, isolation and screening; and *H*, quarantine.

The four concentric circles, A to D, represent the methods of checking or controlling outflowing infection. On the right a similar series of concentric circles, E to H, surrounds the susceptible contact and represents the measures which protect him against infection. Here the three radiating lines indicate the channels by which the infective agent may enter the body. The lines connecting the source of infection and the susceptible contact show the various modes of transmission.

30

MAN AND OTHER ANIMALS AS SOURCES OF INFECTION

Because of host-specificity, man is the chief source of most human parasitic diseases. The relative importance of human sources in the transmission of certain diseases is at times difficult to determine, since various animals act as reservoir or intermediate hosts and since so many factors enter into the transmission of infection.

Avenues of Exit.—The avenues through which the parasite leaves the primary host vary with the species (Fig. 3). They include: (1) intestinal tract, (2) nose and mouth, (3) skin and tissues, (4) genito-urinary tract, and (5) blood.

The fecal discharges offer the most convenient and common means for the parasite or its ova and larvæ to leave the host, since the majority of parasites inhabit the gastro-intestinal tract. Thus the proper disposal of fecal material becomes the most important method of preventing the spread of parasitic diseases.

Few parasitic diseases, in contrast to the large number of bacterial and viral diseases, are transmitted through the respiratory tract via the nose and mouth. *Trichomonas elongata* and *Endamœba gingivalis* may be transmitted by kissing. The ova of the lung fluke, *Paragonimus westermani,* and rarely those of the blood flukes, *Schistosoma hæmatobium* and *S. mansoni,* may be present in the sputum. The larval forms of *Ascaris lumbricoides* and of the hookworms reach the trachea and glottis in the course of their intracorporeal migrations. Occasionally the adult *Ascaris lumbricoides* is regurgitated. *Leishmania braziliensis,* which causes ulceration of the nasopharynx, may be present in oral and nasal discharges.

A few parasites or their embryonic forms leave the body through the genito-urinary tract. The ova of *Schistosoma hæmatobium* and rarely those of *S. mansoni* are found in the urine. *Trichomonas vaginalis* is present in the vaginal secretions. Microfilariæ of *Wuchereria bancrofti* occur in hydroceles and rarely in the urine.

The skin and subcutaneous tissues provide a means of exit from the body and are readily accessible to insect vectors. Among the parasites of these tissues are the guinea worm, *Dracunculus medinensis,* the leishmaniæ, and filariæ such as *Onchocerca volvulus.* The arthropod parasites are largely ectoparasitic, so most species are capable of leaving one host for another.

Parasites in the tissue without access to the exterior cannot be transmitted unless the infected flesh is eaten by the host. It is possible in this manner for *Trichinella spiralis* and *Echinococcus granulosus* to reach definitive hosts. The consumption by man of animals that act as intermediate hosts is a practical means of spreading infection.

Parasites in the peripheral blood or lymphatics are readily transferred by blood-sucking insects, which act as intermediate hosts or as mechanical vectors. The malarial parasites are transmitted by the mosquito; *Trypanosoma gambiense* and *T. rhodesiense* by tsetse flies; *T. cruzi* by reduviid bugs; *Wuchereria bancrofti* by mosquitoes; *Loa loa* by a tabanid fly; and *Acanthocheilonema perstans* by a midge.

Clinical Case.—In bacterial diseases a distinction may be made between the active case, the atypical or subclinical case, and the carrier. No strict line of demarcation may be drawn, however, since these divisions represent individual variations in the response of the patient. In parasitic diseases still less distinction can be made, since the host often exhibits no clinical symptoms. For instance, in *Endamœba histolytica* infections, scarcely one out of ten infected individuals shows symptoms of dysentery. Likewise, after the disappearance of symptoms the patient may remain an active source of infection as a convalescent carrier. The patient with clinical disease is the most potent source of infection, particularly in rapidly spreading infections or in epidemics. As in bacterial diseases, the species of the infecting organism largely determines whether the clinical or subclinical patient is the more important source of infection.

Carriers.—In the bacterial diseases a carrier is an individual who harbors or transmits pathogenic organisms without showing the usual evidences of infection. Since parasitic diseases, in contrast to bacterial diseases, are usually chronic and may produce few if any symptoms, practically every host eventually becomes a carrier. In other words, the individual in the normal state of infection with an equilibrium between host and parasite is a carrier.

Carriers may be either convalescent or contact. Convalescent carriers have shown symptoms of the disease, but have recovered clinically without eliminating the parasite. Contact or latent carriers harbor the parasite but have never had definite clinical symptoms because of their resistance and adaptability to parasitic infection. There is no clear distinction between these two types. Even in the apparently healthy carrier the parasite lives at the expense of the host and produces more or less injury which may never, or at least not for a long period, give rise to clinical symptoms. The convalescent carrier may be temporary, chronic, or relapsing. A temporary or transient carrier either harbors the parasite for a short time or develops an innocuous state, in which the parasite is incapable of being transmitted to another host. A chronic carrier represents the ordinary type of parasitic infection. A relapsing carrier shows remittent clinical symptoms.

The percentage of human carriers in a community is an index of the endemicity of a parasite. Their incidence may be determined by surveys. The intensity of the infection is also of importance, since the chances of transmission increase proportionately with the number of infective organisms liberated.

The effectiveness of a carrier in transmitting a disease depends upon the stage of infection, upon the presence of an environment favoring the survival and transmission of the parasite, and upon prevailing sanitary customs. Active carriers may be harmless when the environment is unfavorable for the extracorporeal life of the parasite. For instance, a carrier of the hookworm is not a menace in a northern climate except in mines where a favorable temperature and a moist environment are present.

Reservoir Hosts.—Animals that serve as sources of infection are definitive hosts, intermediate hosts or vectors. Animals acting as intermediate hosts or vectors constitute an important means of transmission rather than a primary source of infection, and for that reason are discussed in a later section. When the host-specificity of the parasite is not limited to man, the spread of a disease is enhanced and its control becomes more difficult, since susceptible animals constitute reservoirs of infection difficult to eradicate. Parasites infecting man fall into three classes: (1) man may be the only host; (2) man may be the principal host but other animals may also be infected; or (3) man may be merely an incidental host while another animal is the principal host.

When man is a natural host, the reservoir host may be either a domestic or a wild animal; the dog and cat are reservoir hosts for *Clonorchis sinensis,* while herbivorous animals are hosts of the trypanosomes of African sleeping sickness. Animal hosts may show clinical evidence of disease or they may tolerate the parasite without signs of injury. In either case they serve equally well as sources of infection. It is not always easy to determine whether parasites in mammals, morphologically similar to those in man, are the same species. Likewise, laboratory infections may be established in many animals that are not natural hosts.

MODES OF TRANSMISSION

The methods whereby parasites reach susceptible hosts from their primary sources are varied and at times complex. Some parasites require only direct contact; others with more complicated life histories must pass through various developmental stages either as free-living forms or in intermediate hosts before becoming infective.

Congenital transmission.—Instances of the transmission of parasitic diseases from mother to offspring have been reported, but conclusive evidence is not easy to obtain. Hereditary transmission presupposes the penetration of the placental barrier by the parasite; yet it is difficult to distinguish between such penetration and accidental infection through abrasions at the time of birth. There is satisfactory evidence of the transmission of the malarial parasites through the placenta, but there are no similar records for other protozoan diseases of man, although in animals trypanosomes have been thus transmitted and a few cases in man have been reported. Similarly, although several instances have been recorded for animals, there is no evidence of hereditary transmission of helminthic infection in man.

Contact.—Transmission by contact is less important in parasitic than in bacterial diseases, because the life cycles of parasites more often permit other modes of transmission. Direct contact implies the immediate transmission of infectious material from one host to another. The ectoparasitic arthropods and the protozoan parasites *Leishmania tropica, L. braziliensis, Trichomonas elongata, T. vaginalis* and *Endamœba gingivalis* may be transmitted by direct contact. Indirect contact refers to the transmission of infection by contact with objects soiled by the infectious discharges of the host. Autogenous and heterogenous infections may be caused by hands contaminated by cysts and embryos. Thus, the cysts of *Endamœba histolytica, Balantidium coli,* and most intestinal flagellates, and the ova of *Hymenolepis nana* and of *Tænia solium* may be transmitted from the feces to the mouth. and the ova of *Enterobius vermicularis* may be carried from the perianal skin to the mouth. Hands may be contaminated also with ova of *Echinococcus granulosus* from dogs. with larval *Dipylidium caninum* from dog fleas, and with the embryonate ova of *Ascaris lumbricoides* and *Trichuris trichiura* from the soil.

Food.—Since most parasites inhabit the intestinal tract, food is an important means of transmitting parasitic infections. The infective organism may be present in flesh used as food or it may gain access to food from contaminated water, from night soil, or from the hands of food handlers.

The infective larval stages of certain parasites are present in the flesh of mammals, fishes, crustaceans and mollusks. The cysticerci of *Tænia saginata* may occur in beef, and the cysticerci of *Tænia solium* and the larvæ of *Trichinella spiralis* in pork. Fish may contain the encysted cercariæ of *Clonorchis sinensis* and *Opisthorchis felineus* and the plerocercoid larvæ of *Diphyllobothrium latum*. Certain species of fresh-water crabs and crayfish may carry the encysted cercariæ of *Paragonimus westermani*. *Echinostoma ilocanum* has its metacercarial stage in certain snails which are eaten raw in the Philippines. Man acquires these parasites by eating the insufficiently cooked flesh of infected animals.

Aquatic plants used for food may contain the encysted cercariæ of *Fasciolopsis buski*. More often vegetables are contaminated with soil and water containing the cysts, ova and larvæ of parasites. Thus the consumption of raw vegetables provides a means of infection. Food may also be contaminated by insects, which act as mechanical carriers, and by infected food handlers. The cysts of intestinal Protozoa and the ova of helminths with simple life cycles may be transmitted in food.

Water.—Water serves to transmit parasitic infections in several ways. It acts as a medium for the infection of aquatic intermediate hosts and provides a means of contaminating food. It facilitates infection through the skin by schistosomes; the men and women employed in infested paddy fields and boatmen who are obliged to stand in contaminated waters invariably become infected. Finally, it furnishes a medium for the ingestion of protozoan cysts, helminthic larvæ and *Cyclops* infected with the larvæ of the guinea worm, *Dracunculus medinensis*.

The contamination of water is due to inadequate sanitary measures. There is a lack of sanitation and hygienic knowledge among primitive and ignorant peoples and it is difficult to educate them to use sanitary latrines. For economic reasons there is not sufficient hot water in Chinese homes to maintain bodily cleanliness or to wash utensils. The commodes used by Chinese women for toilets are washed at the common water supply, which may be a well or a river. These polluted waters are used for drinking purposes and for washing rice and other vegetables. In countries where the native population is largely Mohammedan, the requirements of ablution before worship result in promiscuous defecation into drains, ditches, canals and water supplies. Bathing in public pools, as in the sacred rivers of India, or in bathhouses where the water is changed but once a day, is a common practice in many tropical and subtropical countries.

Soil.—Contamination of the soil by feces containing the ova and the larvæ of intestinal parasites enables these forms to complete their free-living development when suitable conditions of moisture and temperature are present. The presence of infective larvæ of the hookworms and *Strongyloides stercoralis* in the soil permits infection through the skin.

Besides promiscuous defecation, the practice most responsible for dispensing parasitic infections, particularly in China, is the pollution of soil and water with night soil (human feces). Because of intensive cultivation with few available animals, night soil is the chief fertilizer. It is usually dumped into vats lined with bricks or stones and allowed to stand until needed. The loosely constructed vats allow constant seepage, and when adjacent to a river the water supply may be contaminated. The semi-liquid mass of night soil, teeming with parasitic ova and larvæ, is diluted with water and applied directly to the growing vegetables, which are frequently eaten raw. The utilization of human excreta as fertilizer in Japan, Korea, Annam, Siam, and Malaysia varies somewhat from the Chinese method but is equally deplorable. Wherever the Chinese truck gardener is found, the same insanitary methods are in vogue, unless prohibited by law.

Animals as Intermediate Hosts.—Animals other than arthropods may spread parasitic diseases as intermediate hosts. More rarely they may act as mechanical vectors. When eaten as food, mammals containing the larval parasites may transmit two important cestodes and one nematode. Fishes similarly transmit one important cestode and at least two trematodes. Gastropod mollusks serve as intermediate hosts for all species of trematodes parasitic in man. When the larval trematodes are liberated in the water from these mollusks, they either infect man directly or invade secondary intermediate hosts.

Arthropods.—Arthropods serve as vectors of parasitic diseases, both as mechanical carriers and intermediate hosts. The many diseases, bacterial, viral, rickettsial and parasitic, which they transmit to man, emphasize the importance of this phylum in preventive medicine, particularly in tropical countries where the eradication of many devastating diseases depends upon the control of insects and arachnids.

Flies and other insects, as mechanical carriers, are responsible for endemic infections, both bacterial and parasitic. The house fly carries the cysts of parasitic Protozoa and the ova of various helminths from feces to food. Not only are its legs and body contaminated, but the cysts and ova pass unchanged through its intestinal tract. Humidity, which preserves cysts, ova and larvæ from desiccation, favors transmission by flies.

Arthropods are more important as intermediate hosts (Table 9). Among the insects mosquitoes serve as intermediate hosts for the malarial plasmodia and the filarial worm, *Wuchereria bancrofti;* the tabanid flies, *Chrysops,* for *Loa loa;* the blackflies, *Simulium,* for *Onchocerca volvulus;* the midges, *Culicoides,* for *Acanthocheilonema perstans;* the tsetse flies, *Glossina,* for the African trypanosomes; the reduviid bugs, *Triatoma,* for *Trypanosoma cruzi;* possibly the sandflies, *Phlebotomus,* for the leishmanian parasites; and the fleas, *Ctenocephalus,* for *Dipylidium caninum.* The crustaceans that serve as intermediate hosts include copepods for the guinea worm and the fish tapeworm, and fresh-water crabs and crayfishes for the lung fluke, *Paragonimus westermani.*

TABLE 5

TRANSMISSION OF THE IMPORTANT PARASITIC DISEASES OF MAN

Parasite	Infective Stage					Mode of Transmission						Avenue of Invasion		
	Cyst	Ovum	Free-living larva	Parasite or larva in host	Larva in or from intermediate host	Water	Soil	Fingers (contact)	Food (contamination)	Flesh of host	Arthropod host	Digestive tract	Skin and mucous membranes	Blood
PROTOZOA														
Balantidium coli	●							●	●			●		
Endamœba coli	●					●			●			●		
Endamœba histolytica	●					●			●			●		
Giardia lamblia	●					●			●			●		
Leishmania braziliensis				●				●			?		●	?
Leishmania donovani				●							●			●
Leishmania tropica				●				●			?		●	?
Plasmodium falciparum				●							●			●
Plasmodium malariæ				●							●			●
Plasmodium vivax				●							●			●
Trichomonas vaginalis				●				●					●	
Trypanosoma cruzi				●							●		●	
Trypanosoma gambiense				●							●			●
Trypanosoma rhodesiense				●							●			●
NEMATHELMINTHES														
Acanthocheilonema perstans					●						●		●	
Ancylostoma braziliense			●				●						●	
Ancylostoma duodenale			●				●						●	
Ascaris lumbricoides		●				●		●	●			●		
Dracunculus medinensis					●						●	●		
Enterobius vermicularis		●						●	●			●		
Loa loa					●						●		●	
Mansonella ozzardi					●						●		●	

TABLE 5—Continued

TRANSMISSION OF THE IMPORTANT PARASITIC DISEASES OF MAN

Parasite	Infective Stage					Mode of Transmission						Avenue of Invasion		
	Cyst	Ovum	Free-living larva	Parasite or larva in host	Larva in or from intermediate host	Water	Soil	Fingers (contact)	Food (contamination)	Flesh of host	Arthropod host	Digestive tract	Skin and mucous membranes	Blood
Necator americanus			●				●						●	
Onchocerca volvulus					●						●		●	
Strongyloides stercoralis			●				●						●	
Trichinella spiralis				●						●		●		
Trichuris trichiura		●					●	●	●			●		
Wuchereria bancrofti					●						●		●	
PLATYHELMINTHES (CESTOIDEA) *Diphyllobothrium latum*					●					●		●		
Dipylidium caninum					●						●	●		
Echinococcus granulosus	●							●	●			●		
Hymenolepis nana	●							●	●			●		
Tænia saginata					●					●		●		
Tænia solium	●				●			●	●	●		●		
PLATYHELMINTHES (TREMATODA) *Clonorchis sinensis*					●					●		●		
Fasciola hepatica					●				●			●		
Fasciolopsis buski					●				●			●		
Heterophyes heterophyes					●					●		●		
Metagonimus yokogawai					●					●		●		
Opisthorchis felineus					●					●		●		
Paragonimus westermani					●					●		●		
Schistosoma hæmatobium					●	●							●	
Schistosoma japonicum					●	●							●	
Schistosoma mansoni					●	●							●	

THE SUSCEPTIBLE HOST

The parasite, after reaching a susceptible host, must gain entrance and set up a favorable residence in order to complete its life cycle. There are three avenues of invasion: (1) the digestive tract, (2) the skin and mucocutaneous surfaces, and (3) the blood through insect-bites. These avenues are represented by the three radiating lines in the right-hand circle in Figure 3, while the concentric circles (E to H) represent the several zones of defense.

Digestive Tract.—The digestive tract is the most common avenue of entrance. Infection usually occurs through the ingestion of food or water containing the infective parasites. The food may be the flesh of an intermediate host; it may be contaminated by night soil or by water and soil bearing larval parasites; or it may be infected by flies and food handlers.

Skin.—The cutaneous surfaces offer convenient access to infective larvæ deposited on the skin by biting or nonbiting insects. Other larvæ, the hookworm for example, enter the skin from contaminated soil; still others, such as the larval blood flukes, penetrate the exposed skin of persons working in contaminated waters.

Blood.—Blood-sucking insects that serve as intermediate hosts may transport the infective forms of the parasite directly or indirectly into the blood or lymph. African trypanosomiasis is transmitted by the tsetse fly, *Glossina,* and malaria by anopheline mosquitoes. Filarial larvæ reach the blood and lymph after the insect host has deposited them at or near the puncture wound.

Races and Customs.—The susceptibility of the host to infection depends upon his individual habits and community associations. Racial and individual immunity in certain diseases may be due to their long endemicity. Hookworm infection in Africa produces serious symptoms in white races but only a mild form of the disease in natives.

Parasitic diseases are more prevalent in densely populated communities, as a result of overcrowding and associated insanitary conditions. Among the poorer classes the lack of effective screening against insect hosts increases the incidence of infection. Inadequate food, which usually means improperly balanced rations, causes undernourishment and susceptibility to infection. Countries denuded of their forests and soil resources suffer from drought and flood with accompanying famine and pestilence, and thus produce a favorable environment for the transmission of parasitic diseases. Lack of clothing, particularly on the extremities, provides entrance through the unprotected skin for such parasites as the hookworms and the blood flukes. The prevailing ignorance of the natives in many tropical and subtropical countries, where ancient customs and habits are intrenched, bars hygienic methods of living. Primitive peoples attribute disease to supernatural causes, and treatment and prevention consist chiefly of charms and offerings to appease the offended spirits. Ignorance, poverty, malnutrition and lack of sanitation create optimal conditions of host-susceptibility in many parts of the world.

Climate.—Climate is an important factor in the prevalence of parasitic diseases. It affects the resistance of the host and determines the survival of the parasite during its free-living existence or during its residence in intermediate hosts. Climate may be defined as the combined effects of the sun, the atmosphere, and the physical features of the earth's surface. A tropical climate is determined by the amount of heat radiating from both land and ocean, but only the lowlands have truly torrid conditions, while the hilly sections have a more varied climate. The effect of a tropical climate is one of general depression and lowered resistance to infection, especially for Caucasians who, as a race, do not become readily acclimated to the tropics and suffer more severely from the effects of heat, light and excessive humidity than the heavily pigmented races.

Chapter V

THE DIAGNOSIS OF PARASITIC DISEASES

The clinical manifestations of parasitic diseases are so general that in most instances diagnosis based upon symptomatology alone is inadequate. Although the experienced clinician may recognize the characteristic signs and symptoms of certain parasitic diseases, final diagnosis and proper methods of treatment require the identification of the parasite. Hence the diagnostician who is proficient in both laboratory and clinical methods has a decided advantage over one who relies solely upon clinical diagnosis.

CLINICAL DIAGNOSIS

A few parasitic diseases, particularly those which involve the multiplication of the parasite or its larvæ in the host, produce characteristic symptoms such as the intermittent regularity of chills, sweating and fever in malaria; the fever, gastro-intestinal symptoms and glandular involvement in early African trypano-somiasis and the mental and physical lethargy in the late stages of the disease; the frequent, bloody, mucoid stools in amœbic dysentery; and the anemia, cachexia and metabolic disturbances in hookworm disease. Nevertheless, in an atypical case the symptoms may be so confusing that no clear clinical picture is presented.

Unfortunately, a larger group of diseases, chiefly of helminthic origin, present few and indefinite symptoms. Parasites may live in the host for years without producing any marked objective or subjective symptoms, and many diseases have such clinical similarity that a definite diagnosis necessitates exhausting all available methods. In spite of these difficulties a careful appraisal of physical signs and symptoms should be made. Even when complete laboratory facilities are available, a clinical estimate saves time and labor by indicating the appropriate line of laboratory approach. When properly evaluated, clinical symptoms may assist in determining the severity of the disease, the prognosis and the treatment.

Certain general symptoms and the more common parasitic diseases with which they are associated are listed below.

ALBUMINURIA	Malaria, bilharziasis.
AMBLYOPIA	Malaria.
ANEMIA	Ascariasis, clonorchiasis, diphyllobothriasis, hookworm disease, paragonimiasis, schistosomiasis, trypanosomiasis, kala-azar, amœbiasis, malaria.
CACHEXIA	Hookworm disease, malaria, trypanosomiasis, kala-azar, schistosomiasis, fasciolopsiasis, clonorchiasis.
CHILLS	Filariasis, leishmaniasis, malaria.

DELIRIUM	Malaria, trypanosomiasis.
DIARRHEA	Ascariasis, trichinosis, hookworm disease, strongyloidiasis, clonorchiasis, fasciolopsiasis, schistosomiasis, paragonimiasis, intestinal flagellate infection.
DYSENTERY	Amœbiasis, balantidiasis.
EDEMA	Hookworm disease, trypanosomiasis, kala-azar, trichinosis, clonorchiasis, fasciolopsiasis.
EOSINOPHILIA	Ascariasis, hydatid cyst, hookworm disease, filariasis, schistosomiasis, trichinosis, fasciolopsiasis, fascioliasis, paragonimiasis.
GAIT-SHUFFLING	Trypanosomiasis.
GLANDULAR ENLARGEMENT	Filariasis, leishmaniasis, trypanosomiasis.
HEMATURIA	Bilharziasis.
HEMORRHAGE	Malaria, kala-azar, hookworm disease, schistosomiasis.
HEMOPTYSIS	Paragonimiasis.
JAUNDICE	Malaria, clonorchiasis.
LEUKOPENIA	Kala-azar, malaria.
MUSCLE PAINS	Trichinosis.
SKIN	Trypanosomiasis, leishmaniasis, trichinosis, filariasis, schistosomiasis, hookworm disease, dracunculiasis, myiasis.
SPLENIC ENLARGEMENT	Kala-azar, trypanosomiasis, malaria, schistosomiasis.

Anemia.—The anemias due to parasitic disease are of the so-called secondary type, but at times are megaloblastic. They are produced by loss of blood and by the action of hemolytic and toxic substances from the parasite and disappear upon the removal of the infection.

Fever.—Fever is an important sign of infection, but except for its periodicity in the malarial infections, is rarely an aid in differential diagnosis. The febrile diseases may have a sudden or a gradual onset and they may terminate by crisis or by lysis. Such diseases as amœbic dysentery, hookworm disease, filariasis, bilharziasis, paragonimiasis and clonorchiasis are characterized by the usual absence of marked fever.

Eosinophilia.—Eosinophilia, a characteristic finding in helminthic infections, is absolute as well as relative and is both local and general. Local tissue eosinophilia may occur with and without general eosinophilia. The mononuclear or polynuclear eosinophilic cells, which constitute from 0.5 to 4.0 per cent of the leukocytes in normal blood, are recognized by the presence of large refractile granules that stain deeply with the so-called acid dyes. The origin of the eosinophil, although still in doubt, is probably in the blood-forming organs, where its stages of development from the primitive blood cell are the myeloblast, the eosinophilic myelocyte and the eosinophil.

Eosinophilia is found in asthma, skin diseases, allergy, muscle degenerations and leukemias as well as in helminthic infections. Its presence appears to be a protective reaction against the invasion of the body by heterogeneous proteins, since the eosinophil functions in the removal or detoxication of foreign material.

Table 6 gives the more important signs and symptoms that may be present in the common parasitic infections of man.

TABLE 6

SYMPTOMATOLOGY OF THE IMPORTANT PROTOZOAN AND HELMINTHIC PARASITIC DISEASES OF MAN

Parasite	Fever	Circulatory						Gastro-intestinal				Skin		Nervous system, disorders of
		Anemia	Eosinophilia	Hemorrhage	Edema	Lymphatic disturbances	Spleen, enlargement of	Dysentery (diarrhea)	Other gastro-intestinal disorders	Liver, enlargement of	Jaundice	Urticaria	Cutaneous and subcutaneous lesions	
PROTOZOA														
Balantidium coli		•						•	•					
Endamœba coli														
Endamœba histolytica	•	•		•				•	•	•				
Giardia lamblia									?					
Leishmania braziliensis	•	•											•	
Leishmania donovani	•	•		•	•	•	•	•	•	•			•	
Leishmania tropica	?												•	
Plasmodium falciparum	•	•					•			•				•
Plasmodium malariæ	•	•					•			•				
Plasmodium vivax	•	•					•			•				
Trichomonas vaginalis													•	
Trypanosoma cruzi	•	•			•	•	•			•				•
Trypanosoma gambiense	•	•			•	•	•						•	•
Trypanosoma rhodesiense	•	•			•	•	•							•
NEMATHELMINTHES														
Acanthocheilonema perstans														
Ancylostoma braziliense			•										•	
Ancylostoma duodenale		•	•	•	•			•	•			•	•	•
Ascaris lumbricoides			•						•			•		•
Dracunculus medinensis			•									•	•	
Enterobius vermicularis			•						•					•
Loa loa			•		•								•	
Mansonella ozzardi														

TABLE 6—Continued

SYMPTOMATOLOGY OF THE IMPORTANT PROTOZOAN AND HELMINTHIC PARASITIC DISEASES OF MAN

Parasite	Fever	Anemia	Eosinophilia	Hemorrhage	Edema	Lymphatic disturbances	Spleen, enlargement of	Dysentery (diarrhea)	Other gastrointestinal disorders	Liver, enlargement of	Jaundice	Urticaria	Cutaneous and subcutaneous lesions	Nervous system, disorders of
						Circulatory			Gastro-intestinal			Skin		
Necator americanus		●	●	●	●			●	●			●	●	●
Onchocerca volvulus			●		●								●	
Strongyloides stercoralis			●	●				●	●			●	●	
Trichinella spiralis	●		●		●				●				●	
Trichuris trichiura									●					
Wuchereria bancrofti	●				●	●							●	
PLATYHELMINTHES (CESTOIDEA)														
Diphyllobothrium latum		●							●					
Dipylidium caninum														
Echinococcus granulosus			●							●				
Hymenolepis nana			●						●					●
Tænia saginata			●						●					
Tænia solium			●						●					●
PLATYHELMINTHES (TREMATODA)														
Clonorchis sinensis			●		●			●	●	●				
Fasciola hepatica	●	●	●					●	●	●		●	●	
Fasciolopsis buski			●		●			●	●	●				
Heterophyes heterophyes			●					●	●					
Metagonimus yokogawai								●	●					
Opisthorchis felineus								●	●	●	●			
Paragonimus westermani			●	●	●			●	●					●
Schistosoma hæmatobium	●	●	●	●	●		●		●			●	●	
Schistosoma japonicum	●	●	●		●	●	●	●	●	●		●	●	
Schistosoma mansoni	●	●	●		●	●	●	●	●	●		●	●	

TABLE 7

PRINCIPAL HABITAT AND SOURCES OF MATERIAL FOR IDENTIFICATION
OF IMPORTANT PROTOZOAN AND HELMINTHIC PARASITES OF MAN

Source	Protozoa	Nemathelminthes	Platyhelminthes
Blood	*Leishmania donovani* *Plasmodium falciparum* *Plasmodium malariæ* *Plasmodium vivax* *Trypanosoma gambiense* *Trypanosoma rhodesiense* *Trypanosoma cruzi*	*Acanthocheilonema perstans* (larva) *Loa loa* (larva) *Mansonella ozzardi* (larva) *Wuchereria bancrofti* (larva)	*Schistosoma hæmatobium* (pelvic veins) *Schistosoma japonicum* (mesenteric veins) *Schistosoma mansoni* (mesenteric veins)
Intestine	*Balantidium coli* *Endamœba coli* *Endamœba histolytica* *Giardia lamblia*	*Ascaris lumbricoides* *Ancylostoma braziliense*, rare *Ancylostoma duodenale* *Enterobius vermicularis* *Necator americanus* *Strongyloides stercoralis* *Trichinella spiralis*, rare *Trichuris trichiura*	*Clonorchis sinensis* (ovum) *Diphyllobothrium latum* *Dipylidium caninum* *Fasciola hepatica* (ovum) *Fasciolopsis buski* *Heterophyes heterophyes* *Hymenolepis nana* *Metagonimus yokogawai* *Opisthorchis felineus* (ovum) *Paragonimus westermani* (ovum) *Schistosoma hæmatobium* (ovum), rare *Schistosoma japonicum* (ovum) *Schistosoma mansoni* (ovum) *Tænia saginata* *Tænia solium*
Skin and mucocutaneous surfaces	*Leishmania braziliensis* *Leishmania donovani* *Leishmania tropica*	*Ancylostoma braziliense* (larva) *Dracunculus medinensis* *Enterobius vermicularis* (ovum) *Onchocerca volvulus* (larva)	

TABLE 7—Continued

PRINCIPAL HABITAT AND SOURCES OF MATERIAL FOR IDENTIFICATION
OF IMPORTANT PROTOZOAN AND HELMINTHIC PARASITES OF MAN

Source	Protozoa	Nemathelminthes	Platyhelminthes
Muscles, subcutaneous tissues, bones, and body cavities	*Trypanosoma cruzi*	*Acanthocheilonema perstans* *Dracunculus medinensis* *Loa loa* *Mansonella ozzardi* *Onchocerca volvulus* *Trichinella spiralis* (larva)	*Echinococcus granulosus* (larva) *Tænia solium* (larva)
Lymphatic glands	*Leishmania donovani* *Trypanosoma gambiense* *Trypanosoma rhodesiense*	*Wuchereria bancrofti*	*Schistosoma hæmatobium* (ovum), pelvic glands *Schistosoma japonicum* (ovum), mesenteric glands *Schistosoma mansoni* (ovum), mesenteric glands
Spleen	*Leishmania donovani* *Plasmodium falciparum* (pigment) *Plasmodium malariæ* (pigment) *plasmodium vivax* (pigment)		*Echinococcus granulosus* (larva) *Schistosoma japonicum* (ovum) *Schistosoma mansoni* (ovum) *Tænia solium* (larva)
Liver	*Endamœba histolytica* *Leishmania donovani* *Plasmodium falciparum* (pigment) *Plasmodium malariæ* (pigment) *Plasmodium vivax* (pigment)		*Clonorchis sinensis* *Echinococcus granulosus* (larva) *Fasciola hepatica* *Opisthorchis felineus* *Schistosoma hæmatobium* (ovum) *Schistosoma japonicum* (ovum) *Schistosoma mansoni* (ovum) *Tænia solium* (larva)

TABLE 7—Continued

PRINCIPAL HABITAT AND SOURCES OF MATERIAL FOR IDENTIFICATION
OF IMPORTANT PROTOZOAN AND HELMINTHIC PARASITES OF MAN

Source	Protozoa	Nemathelminthes	Platyhelminthes
Lung		*Ancylostoma duodenale* (larva) *Ascaris lumbricoides* (larva) *Necator americanus* (larva) *Strongyloides stercoralis* (larva)	*Echinococcus granulosus* (larva) *Paragonimus westermani* *Tænia solium* (larva)
Brain and meninges	*Endamœba histolytica* *Plasmodium falciparum* *Plasmodium malariæ* *Plasmodium vivax* *Trypanosoma cruzi* *Trypanosoma gambiense* *Trypanosoma rhodesiense*		*Tænia solium* (larva)
Genito-urinary system	*Trichomonas vaginalis*	*Wuchereria bancrofti* (larva), rare	*Schistosoma hæmatobium* (ovum) *Schistosoma mansoni* (ovum), rare

LABORATORY DIAGNOSIS

Successful laboratory diagnosis requires a knowledge of certain fundamental laboratory procedures such as microscopic technic, preparation of material for examination, and familiarity with the diagnostic characteristics of the common parasites (Section **VII**). It centers upon the identification of the parasite, ova or larvæ in the feces, blood, lymph, tissues, urine, sputum and secretions of the host. In some diseases diagnosis may be made by specific serological and cutaneous tests. The presence of eosinophilia and anemia is often suggestive of parasitic infection. It is important to remember that a patient may harbor several parasites and that unless a complete study is made the most important species may be overlooked.

SOURCES OF MATERIAL FOR IDENTIFICATION OF IMPORTANT PARASITES OF MAN

Material for the diagnosis of parasitic infections may be obtained from nearly every part of the body. Since intestinal parasites predominate, the feces are most frequently examined. The more important parasites of man are listed in Table 7 according to the sources of material for examination. The arthropod parasites are not included, since, with few exceptions, they are confined to the skin, mucocutaneous surfaces and rarely the subcutaneous tissues.

DIRECT EXAMINATION OF PARASITES

The identification of protozoan and helminthic parasites may be simplified by the use of the following keys. The parasitic arthropods are not included because of the diversity of species. They are classified in the several chapters of Section VI. In identifying parasites morphology is more important than size. Nevertheless, in order to create a proper perspective, the examiner should know the relative size of the different parasites. Since the size of a parasite changes with age and varies with different strains, the range as well as the mean size should be kept in mind. The method of fixation may alter the form and dimensions of a parasite.

KEY FOR IDENTIFICATION OF PARASITIC PROTOZOA OF MAN

Blood
  Outside red blood cells
    Flagellated, active
      Long, slender, 15 to 30 μ, on rat
      Inoculation
        None or few posterior nuclear
        forms.......*Trypanosoma gambiense*
        Posterior nuclear forms
               Trypanosoma rhodesiense
      Short, thick, under 20 μ, rare
             Trypanosoma cruzi
    Nonflagellated
      Oval bodies, 2 to 5 μ, in mononuclear cells and polymorphonuclears............*Leishmania donovani*
  Inside red blood cells
    Red cells enlarged
      Rings, ameboid forms, schizonts, fine pigment, chromatin mass does not project from ring
             Plasmodium vivax
    Red cells not enlarged
      Thick rings, solid band forms, coarse pigment...*Plasmodium malariæ*
      Fine rings, chromatin mass projects from ring. Multiple infections common.
      Crescents......*Plasmodium falciparum*
Feces
  Rhizopoda (with pseudopodia)
    Active movement
      Trophozoite, 20 to 30 μ, red blood cells ingested, fine peripheral chromatin in nucleus. Cyst 7 to 15 μ, 1 to 4 nuclei, glycogen diffuse.............*Endamœba histolytica*
      Vegetative form, 6 to 12 μ, two nuclei, no peripheral chromatin, no cyst...........*Dientomœba fragilis*
    Sluggish movement
      Trophozoite, 20 to 30 μ, coarse peripheral chromatin in nucleus. Spherical cyst 12 to 22 μ, 1 to 8 nuclei, glycogen scanty..*Endamœba coli*
      Trophozoite form, 6 to 10 μ, chromatin in large karyosome, oval cyst 9 μ, 1 to 4 nuclei, none or little glycogen......*Endolimax nana*
      Trophozoite form, 9 to 14 μ, small nucleus with large central compact karyosome, irregular or spheroidal cysts 10 μ, 1 nucleus, glycogen dense....*Iodamœba bütschlii*
  Infusoria (ciliated)
    Ciliated, 30 to 200 μ, large macronucleus, cyst 50 μ, solid kidney-shaped nucleus..........*Balantidium coli*
  Mastigophora (flagellated)
    Pyriform shape
      Bilaterally symmetrical
      Trophozoite, 12 to 15 μ, concave ventral surface, 8 flagella, 2 nuclei, oval ellipsoidal cyst, 9 to 12 μ, 2 to 4 nuclei............*Giardia lamblia*
      Bilaterally unsymmetrical
      Undulant membrane
        Trophozoite pyriform, 10 to 15 μ, axostyle, 3 to 5 free flagella, no cyst. *Trichomonas hominis*
      No undulant membrane

Trophozoite pyriform 10 to 15 μ, 4 flagella, spiral groove, cytostome, oval cyst, 6 to 8 μ, 1 nucleus........*Chilomastix mesnili*
Ovoid shape
  Two flagella
    Trophozoite, 5 to 7 μ, cytostome, pyriform cyst, 4 to 6 μ, 1 nucleus
      Embadomonas intestinalis
  Four flagella
    Trophozoite 7 to 9 μ, oval cyst, 6 to 8 μ, 1 to 4 nuclei
      Enteromonas hominis
Sporozoa
  Flask-shaped oöcysts, with two-layered walls, 25 to 33 μ....*Isospora hominis*
Mouth
  Rhizopoda (with pseudopodia)
    Trophozoite 10 to 20 μ, irregular peripheral chromatin of nucleus, leukocytic inclusions, no cyst
      Endamœba gingivalis
  Mastigophora (flagellated)
    Trophozoite pyriform, with undulant membrane, 8 to 12 μ, 5 flagella
      Trichomonas elongata
Vagina
  Mastigophora (flagellated)
    Trophozoite pyriform, with undulant membrane, 15 to 18 μ, 5 flagella, no cyst............*Trichomonas vaginalis*
Spinal fluid
  Flagellated

Long, slender, 15 to 30 μ, but many shapes and sizes..*Trypanosoma gambiense*
      Trypanosoma rhodesiense
Short, thick, under 20 μ
      Trypanosoma cruzi
Lymphatic glands (puncture)
  Flagellated
  Long, slender, 15 to 30 μ
      Trypanosoma gambiense
      Trypanosoma rhodesiense
Skin and mucocutaneous surfaces
  Ulceration with atrophy of epidermis
  Intracellular oval bodies
      Leishmania tropica
  Granulomatous nodules and ulcers
Skin
  Intracellular oval bodies
      Leishmania donovani
  Nasal and buccal mucosa
  Intracellular oval bodies
      Leishmania braziliensis
Liver and spleen (puncture)
Active body, with pseudopodia, 20 to 30 μ................*Endamœba histolytica*
Oval bodies, 2 to 5 μ, in large endothelial cells..........*Leishmania donovani*
Pigmented cytoplasm, phagocytosed by endothelial cells..*Plasmodium falciparum*
      Plasmodium malariæ
      Plasmodium vivax
Muscles
Elongated tubular mass of small crescentic spores, rare..*Sarcocystic lindemanni*

KEY FOR THE IDENTIFICATION OF CYSTS OF PROTOZOAN PARASITES OF MAN (PLATE 1)

Large, over 30 μ
  Oval, large elongated nucleus, degenerate cilia, 50 to 60 μ.......*Balantidium coli*
Small, under 30 μ
  Spherical or subspherical
    Regular
      4 nuclei in mature cyst, chromatoidal bodies thick rods, glycogen diffuse, 7 to 15 μ..*Endamœba histolytica*
      8 nuclei in mature cyst, chromatoidal bodies splinter-like, glycogen massed, 12 to 22 μ..*Endamœba coli*
    Irregular
      1 nucleus in mature cyst, chromatoidal bodies absent, glycogen large compact mass, 9 to 11 μ
        Iodamœba bütschlii
  Oval or ellipsoidal
    4 nuclei in mature cyst, small spherical chromatoidal bodies,

glycogen diffuse and ill-defined, filamentar inclusions, 8 to 10 μ
      Endolimax nana
    4 nuclei, sometimes 2, at one end, 4 flagella, 2 axostyles, lateral shield, 2 groups curved fibrils, 9 to 12 μ................*Giardia lamblia*
    4 nuclei 2 at each pole in mature cyst, usually 2 nuclei, 1 at each pole. Refractile granules, 6 to 8 μ
      Enteromonas hominis
  Pyriform
    1 nucleus in mature cyst, 4 to 7μ
      Embadomonas intestinalis
  Lemon-shaped
    Cyst wall thickened at narrow end, 1 nucleus, 1 flagellum, refractile granules, 6.5 to 10 μ
      Chilomastix mesnili

PLATE I

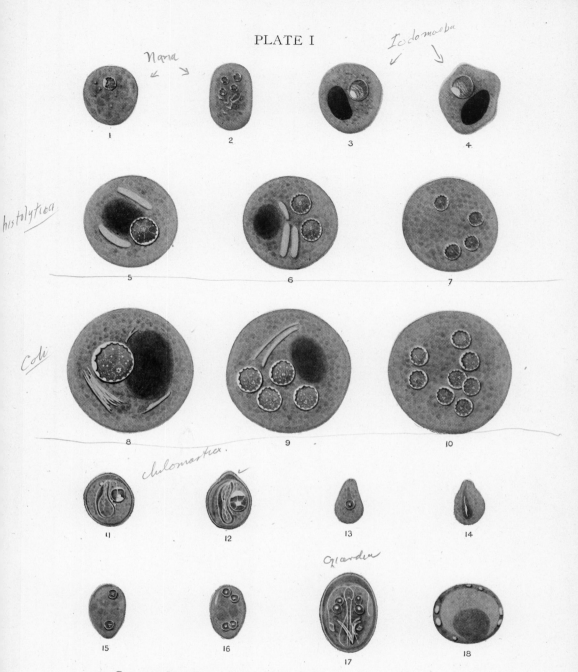

Nana

Iodomœba

histolytica

coli

chilomastix

Giardia

Cysts of Intestinal Protozoa Treated with Iodine (× 2000)

1 and 2, *Endolimax nana;* 3 and 4, *Iodamœba bütschlii;* 5, 6 and 7, *Endamœba histolytica;* 8, 9 and 10, *Endamœba coli;* 11 and 12, *Chilomastix mesnili;* 13 and 14, *Embadomonas intestinalis;* 15 and 16, *Enteromonas hominis;* 17, *Giardia lamblia;* 18, *Blastocystis hominis,* a yeast resembling a protozoan cyst.

KEY FOR IDENTIFICATION OF IMPORTANT ADULT HELMINTHS OF MAN

Segmented
  Intestine (source of material)
    Large, over 1 meter
      Genital pore on lateral margin of proglottis
        Scolex with hooks, uterus, 7 to 12 branches, 2 to 4 meters
                                Tænia solium
        Scolex without hooks, uterus, 15 to 30 branches, 4 to 10 meters...............*Tænia saginata*
      Genital pore on flat surface of proglottis
        Scolex without hooks, 3 to 10 meters.......*Diphyllobothrium latum*
    Small, under 50 cm
      Two lateral pores on proglottis
        Scolex with hooks, 10 to 50 cm.............*Dipylidium caninum*
      One lateral pore on proglottis
        Scolex rhomboidal, with hooks, 2.5 to 4 cm.......*Hymenolepis nana*
Unsegmented
  With suckers
    Intestine (source of material)
      Ceca not branched, no shoulders, 2 to 7.5 cm..........*Fasciolopsis buski*
      Ventral sucker in midline, protrusible gonotyle with 80 cone-shaped spines, 0.10 to 0.17 cm
                Heterophyes heterophyes
      Ventral sucker to right of midline, no spines in genital pore, 0.10 to 0.25 cm.....*Metagonimus yokogawai*
    Bile ducts and liver (source of material)
      Large, shoulders, ceca branched at anterior end, cuticle spinose, maximum 3.5 cm......*Fasciola hepatica*
      Small, 1 to 2 cm, cuticle smooth, slender
        Testes, branched, 1.0 to 2.5 cm
                    Clonorchis sinensis
        Lance-shaped, testes lobed and situated posteriorly, 0.7 to 1.2 cm.............*Opisthorchis felineus*
    Lungs (source of material)
      Genital pore in midline, testes lobed, 0.7 to 1.2 cm.
                Paragonimus westermani
    Blood (portal veins source of material)
      Sexes separate
        Male, 1.0 to 1.5 cm, small tubercles on cuticle. Female 2.0 cm, ovary posterior
                Schistosoma hæmatobium

Male, 0.6 to 1.4 cm, large tubercles on cuticle. Female 1.2 to 1.6 cm, ovary anterior
                Schistosoma mansoni
Male, 0.9 to 2.2 cm, smooth cuticle. Female, 1.2 to 2.6 cm, ovary in middle
                Schistosoma japonicum
Without suckers, cylindrical
  Intestine (source of material)
    Large
      Male 15 to 31 cm, posterior end curved ventrad. Female 20 to 35 cm........*Ascaris lumbricoides*
    Small
      With cervical alae, bulbar esophagus. Male 0.2 to 0.5 cm. Female 0.8 to 1.3 cm
                Enterobius vermicularis
      Without cervical alae
        Anterior extremity bent, males with copulatory bursa
          Mouth armed with equal sized teeth. Male 0.8 to 1.1 cm. Female 1.0 to 1.3 cm
                Ancylostoma duodenale
          Small mouth armed with small inner and large outer teeth. Male 0.8 to 0.85 cm. Female 0.9 to 1.05 cm
                Ancylostoma braziliense
          Mouth armed with plates. Male 0.5 to 0.9 cm. Female 0.9 to 1.1 cm
                Necator americanus
        Anterior extremity not bent, viviparous. Male 0.05 to 0.08 cm. Female 0.18 to 0.22 cm
                Strongyloides stercoralis
        Whip-like. Male 3.0 to 4.5 cm. Female 3.5 to 5.0 cm
                Trichuris trichiura
        Viviparous. Male 0.14 to 0.16 cm. Female 0.3 to 0.4 cm
                Trichinella spiralis
Lymphatics and subcutaneous tissues and body cavities (source of material)
  Cuticle smooth
    Head with cuticular appendage. Male 4.5 cm. Female 7 to 8 cm
                Acanthocheilonema perstans
    Head unarmed. Male 3.8 cm (partial). Female 6.5 to 8 cm
                Mansonella ozzardi
    Head without cuticular appendage. Male 4 cm. Female 8 to 10 cm.............*Wuchereria bancrofti*

Cuticle rough
  Minute warts. Male 3 to 3.5 cm.
  Female 5 to 7 cm..............*Loa loa*
  Annular thickening. Male 2 to 4
  cm. Female 11.5 to 70 cm
            Onchocerca volvulus

Chitinous shield on head. Male 1.2
to 2.9 cm, rare, in deep tissues.
Female 50 to 120 cm
            Dracunculus medinensis

KEY FOR IDENTIFICATION OF OVA OF IMPORTANT HELMINTHIC PARASITES OF MAN

Most helminthic ova are obtained from the feces, a few from the urine and sputum. The majority are unhatched when oviposited. Some ova have well-developed embryos which under favorable conditions soon hatch, while others require a developmental period, which may extend over several weeks. The mean dimensions of the ova in this key represent the size of the shell in all but *Ascaris lumbricoides* where the mammillated albuminous coat is included (Fig. 4).

Operculum
  Large, over 50 μ, ovum does not contain embryo in feces.
    Ellipsoidal, rounded at both poles, thin shell, small indistinct operculum,
      135 x 80 μ..........*Fasciolopsis buski*
      140 x 80 μ...........*Fasciola hepatica*
    Abundant in sputum, less frequent in feces, thick shell, flat distinct operculum, 95 x 55 μ
            Paragonimus westermani
    Oval, small slightly domed operculum, 70 x 45 μ
            Diphyllobothrium latum
  Small, under 50 μ, embryo in ovum
    Asymmetrical lytic glands in embryo
      Ovum widened at nonoperculated pole, giving appearance of electric light bulb, 29 x 16 μ
            Clonorchis sinensis
      No widening at nonoperculated pole, 30 x 11 μ
            Opisthorchis felineus
    Bilaterally symmetrical lytic glands in embryo
      Ovoidal with slight thickening of opercular rim, 29 x 16 μ
            Heterophyes heterophyes
      Ovoidal with slight thickening of opercular rim, short extension at nonoperculated end, 28 x 16 μ
            Metagonimus yokogawai
No operculum
  Wall smooth
    Wall opaque
      Ovum elongated, wall thin, with spines, ciliated embryo
        Terminal spine, present in urine, rare in feces, 140 x 50 μ
            Schistosoma hæmatobium
        Lateral spine, 150 x 65 μ
            Schistosoma mansoni

Minute lateral knob, 85 x 60 μ
            Schistosoma japonicum
Ovum rounded, thickened wall with radial striæ, hexacanth embryo, hooklets
  Ovum spherical
    35 x 35 μ...........*Tænia solium*
    33 x 33 μ..*Echinococcus granulosus*
  Ovum subspherical,
    35 x 25 μ...........*Tænia saginata*
Wall transparent
  Wall thick
    Barrel-shaped, semi-opaque polar plugs, 52 x 23 μ
            Trichuris trichiura
    Hexacanth embryo with hooklets
      Globular, filaments on inner shell, 40 x 35 μ..*Hymenolepis nana*
      Subspherical, several ova often enclosed in membrane,
      40 x 36 μ......*Dipylidium caninum*
  Wall thin
    Incompletely embryonated
      Ovoidal, bluntly rounded ends, 2 to 4 blastomeres
        60 x 40 μ
            Ancylostoma braziliense
            Ancylostoma duodenale
      70 x 38 μ....*Necator americanus*
    Completely embryonated
      Asymmetrical, one side convex, other flattened, usually contains rhabditiform larva,
      55 x 26 μ..*Enterobius vermicularis*
      Unhatched larva (rare), 54 x 32 μ......*Strongyloides stercoralis*
Wall ornamented
  Brown outer mammillated covering, thick outer shell. Fertile ovum, broadly ovoidal, 60 x 45 μ. Infertile ovum, narrow ovoidal, 90 x 41 μ
            Ascaris lumbricoides

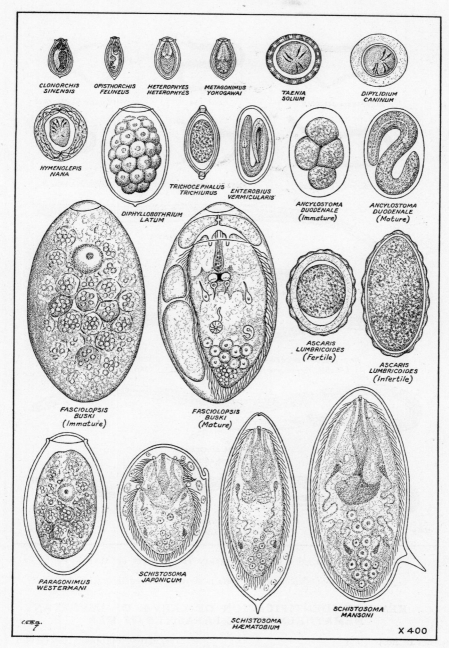

FIG. 4.—OVA OF THE COMMON HELMINTHS OF MAN
(*Trichocephalus trichiurus* above should be *Trichuris trichiura*).

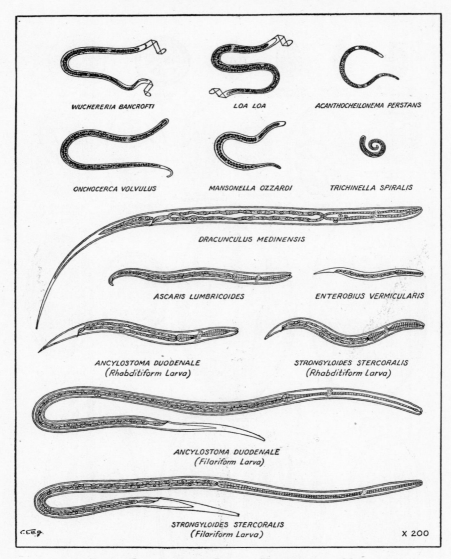

FIG. 5.—LARVÆ OF THE COMMON HELMINTHS OF MAN

(The larva of *Trichinella spiralis* is shown in its earliest stage.)

KEY FOR IDENTIFICATION OF LARVÆ OF IMPORTANT NEMATHELMINTHIC PARASITES OF MAN

In tissues of host
  Blood
    Sheathed
      Regular outline, graceful curves, head same width as body, nuclei of tail not extending to tip, 260 x 8 μ ....*Wuchereria bancrofti*

      Irregular outline, ungraceful curves, head flattened, broad, nuclei of tail extending to tip, 275 x 7 μ..........................*Loa loa*
      Two distinct nuclei at tip of tail, 220 x 5.5 μ.........*Wuchereria malayi*

Unsheathed
  Nuclei extending to tip of tail,
  head blunt, 180 x 5 μ
                Acanthocheilonema perstans
  Nuclei not extending to tip of
  tail, 207 x 5 μ......*Mansonella ozzardi*
Skin and subcutaneous tissues
  Unsheathed
    Head blunt, long tapering tail, 625
    x 20 μ.........*Dracunculus medinensis*
    Nuclei of tail not extending to
    tip, 320 x 8 μ.....*Onchocerca volvulus*
Muscles
  Coiled encysted larva, 950 x 60 μ
                    Trichinella spiralis

Outside tissues of host
  Feces, soil and water
    Rhabditiform larva, short muscular
    esophagus
      Posterior bulbar swelling of
      esophagus
        Short pre-esophageal chamber,
        in fresh feces 225 x 16 μ
                      Strongyloides stercoralis
        Long narrow pre-esophageal
        chamber 275 x 16 μ
                    Ancylostoma braziliense
                    Ancylostoma duodenale
                    Necator americanus

Both median and posterior bulbar
  swellings of esophagus
                Rhabditis (various species)
  Rhabditiform larva, long narrow
  esophagus, coiled, rare in feces 100
  x 6 μ.................*Trichinella spiralis*
  Filariform larva
    Minute fork at tail, 700 x 28 μ
                Strongyloides stercoralis
    Sharply pointed tail, 850 x 35 μ
                    Ancylostoma braziliense
                    Ancylostoma duodenale
                    Necator americanus

In new host
  Intestine
    Rhabditiform larva, posterior bul-
    bar swelling, 250 x 14 μ
                    Ascaris lumbricoides
    Rhabditiform larva, 145 x 10 μ
                    Enterobius vermicularis
  Lungs
    Rhabditiform larva..*Ascaris lumbricoides*
    Filariform larva..*Ancylostoma braziliense*
                    Ancylostoma duodenale
                    Necator americanus
                    Strongyloides stercoralis

SEROLOGICAL METHODS OF DIAGNOSIS

The elaboration of antibodies depends upon the extent of injury to the host, those parasites that invade the tissues provoking the most pronounced immunological response. Ectoparasites or helminths of the intestinal lumen usually do not evoke appreciable concentrations of antibodies. As a rule, intestinal helminths that bring about the formation of antibodies either invade the host during their larval stages or have sufficient contact with its tissues to permit the adsorption of their products or secretions. The resistance of the host may manifest itself by preventing subsequent or superimposed infection or by inhibiting parasitic development in respect to size, length of life and ova-production.

Humoral antibodies such as agglutinins, precipitins and alexin-fixing substances may be demonstrated in the blood serum of the host *in vitro* by means of serological procedures, and supersensitiveness may be shown by intracutaneous tests. Three serological methods are used to detect specific antibodies: (1) agglutination, (2) precipitation, and (3) alexin-fixation. They may be used to reveal the presence of the parasites and to differentiate related species. The same general principles govern the formation of antibodies against parasites as against bacteria.

Classification.—There is some indication that morphologically related groups may also be related antigenically. The evidence is not yet sufficient to influence the taxonomy of parasitic species, but the possibility of supplementing morphological classification by immunological studies presents an attractive problem. Its success

TABLE 8

LABORATORY IDENTIFICATION OF THE IMPORTANT
PROTOZOAN AND HELMINTHIC PARASITES OF MAN

Parasite	Source of Material	Chief Diagnostic Characteristics
PROTOZOA *Balantidium coli*	Feces	Moving ciliate, kidney-shaped nucleus, large cyst
Endamœba coli	Feces	Trophozoite sluggish, no red cells, mature cyst eight nuclei
Endamœba histolytica	Feces	Trophozoite active, with ingested red cells, mature cyst four nuclei
Giardia lamblia	Feces	Ellipsoidal cyst, 2 to 4 nuclei
Leishmania braziliensis	Skin, nasopharyngeal mucosa	Oval nucleated intracellular bodies
Leishmania donovani	Liver, spleen	Oval nucleated bodies in Küpffer's cells
Leishmania tropica	Skin	Oval nucleated intracellular bodies
Plasmodium falciparum	Blood	Red cells distorted, rings and crescents, chromatin projects from ring
Plasmodium malariæ	Blood	Red cells normal size, rings, solid bands, schizonts with 6 to 10 merozoites
Plasmodium vivax	Blood	Red cells enlarged, chromatin in ring form in line with ring, schizonts with 15 to 20 merozoites
Trichomonas vaginalis	Vagina	Active flagellate with undulating membrane
Trypanosoma cruzi	Blood	Short stumpy trypanosome
Trypanosoma gambiense	Blood	Active slender trypanosome
Trypanosoma rhodesiense	Blood	Active slender trypanosome
NEMATHELMINTHES *Acanthocheilonema perstans*	Blood	Unsheathed, nuclei to tip of tail, day and night
Ancylostoma braziliense	Feces	Ovum translucent, segmented
Ancylostoma duodenale	Feces	Ovum translucent, segmented
Ascaris lumbricoides	Feces	Adult size of earthworm, ovum mammillated, unsegmented
Dracunculus medinensis	Skin, subcutaneous tissues	Unsheathed larva, large, long tapering tail
Enterobius vermicularis	Feces	Adult, pointed tail, bulb behind esophagus. Ovum flat on one side
Loa loa	Blood	Sheathed larva, nuclei to tip of tail, usually diurnal
Mansonella ozzardi	Blood	Unsheathed larva, nuclei not to tip of tail, non-periodic
Necator americanus	Feces	Ovum, translucent, segmented

TABLE 8—Continued
LABORATORY IDENTIFICATION OF THE IMPORTANT
PROTOZOAN AND HELMINTHIC PARASITES OF MAN

Parasite	Source of Material	Chief Diagnostic Characteristics
Onchocerca volvulus	Skin, subcutaneous tissues	Unsheathed larva, nuclei not to tip of tail
Strongyloides stercoralis	Feces	Free larva in feces
Trichinella spiralis	Muscle	Coiled larva in ellipsoidal cyst
Trichuris trichiura	Feces	Ovum translucent, plug at each end
Wuchereria bancrofti	Blood	Sheathed larva, nuclei not to tip of tail, usually nocturnal
PLATYHELMINTHES (CESTOIDEA) *Diphyllobothrium latum*	Feces	Proglottid: genital pore on flat surface. Scolex without hooks. Ovum operculated, oval
Dipylidium caninum	Feces	Proglottid small, two lateral genital pores. Ovum transparent, subspherical, hexacanth larva
Echinococcus granulosus	Liver, other organs	Cyst containing larvæ with scolices and hooklets
Hymenolepis nana	Feces	Proglottid small, one lateral genital pore. Ovum transparent, globular, hexacanth embryo
Tænia saginata	Feces	Proglottid: uterus 15 to 30 branches. Scolex without hooks. Ovum, ovoid with radial striæ, hexacanth embryo
Tænia solium	Feces	Proglottid: uterus 7 to 12 branches. Scolex with hooks. Ovum similar to *T. saginata*
PLATYHELMINTHES (TREMATODA) *Clonorchis sinensis*	Feces	Ovum small, operculated, bulb-shaped, embryonated
Fasciola hepatica	Feces	Ovum large, operculated, ellipsoidal, rounded at both ends
Fasciolopsis buski	Feces	Ovum similar to *Fasciola hepatica*
Heterophyes heterophyes	Feces	Ovum small, ovoidal, operculated, embryonated
Metagonimus yokogawai	Feces	Ovum similar to *H. heterophyes*, short extension at nonoperculated end
Opisthorchis felineus	Feces	Ovum small, operculated, embryonated
Paragonimus westermani	Sputum	Ovum, undeveloped embryo, operculated
Schistosoma hæmatobium	Bladder	Ovum nonoperculated, elongated, terminal spine, embryonated
Schistosoma japonicum	Feces	Ovum nonoperculated, ovoidal, minute lateral knob, embryonated
Schistosoma mansoni	Feces	Ovum nonoperculated, elongated, lateral spine, embryonated

will depend upon obtaining antigens (Section **VII**, IX, 1 to 18) capable of eliciting specific immune sera not only for identifying unknown parasites, but also for determining the relationship between allied species. Specific immune sera may be prepared by injecting laboratory animals with gradually increasing doses of antigens (Section **VII**, IX, 22), derived from the whole parasite, its parts or its products.

Diagnosis.—Agglutinative, precipitative and alexin-fixative tests have not been uniformly successful in the diagnosis of parasitic infections, because of unsatisfactory antigens, insufficient antibody-formation, and group or cross reactions in related species. Antibodies may be detected in the serum a few days after infection, but usually are not present in sufficient concentration to give a positive reaction until after the second or third week. Nonspecific flocculation tests have also proved useful in the diagnosis of certain parasitic diseases.

AGGLUTINATION

Agglutinative tests (Section **VII**, IX, 19) are of limited value in the diagnosis of parasitic infections, since the morphology of most parasites is poorly adapted for this type of reaction. Their field of usefulness is restricted to the flagellated Protozoa.

Leishmaniasis.—Immune sera have been used to differentiate the three species parasitic in man and to distinguish between these parasites and similar herpetomonad forms in insects. Agglutinative tests are of no diagnostic value, since the agglutinin titer of patients with kala-azar is but little higher than that of normal individuals.

Trypanosomiasis.—The production of agglutinins against the trypanosomes of animals has been extensively studied. The sera of some normal animals contain agglutinins of low titer, below 1 :100. Titers as high as 1 :12,000 may be produced by artificial immunization. Group-agglutinins render the test of questionable value in differentiating the various species of trypanosomes, but it is useful in detecting dourine in horses. Although group-agglutinins in fairly high concentration have been observed in specific sera prepared against *Trypanosoma congolense, T. brucei* and *T. gambiense,* the test is not used in human trypanosomiasis because other methods of diagnosis are more satisfactory.

PRECIPITATION

The precipitative test (Section **VII**, IX, 20) involves fundamentally the same reaction as the agglutinative. The difference is that the antigen is composed of dissolved material from the parasites and the interaction of the antibody and antigen results in a precipitation of material from a clear solution rather than a clumping of suspended material.

Amœbiasis.—Although precipitins have been demonstrated in low titer in cats infected with *Endamœba histolytica,* the test has not been used in the diagnosis of human amœbiasis.

Leishmaniasis.—Specific precipitins, though present in patients with kala-azar, are of too low a titer to permit diagnosis by this test.

Trypanosomiasis.—A number of investigators have reported successful precipitative tests in horses with dourine. The reaction is group-specific, since it can be elicited equally well with antigens derived from other trypanosomes than *Trypanosoma equiperdum.* The test is not used in the diagnosis of human trypanosomiasis.

Malaria.—Variable results, a high percentage of positive reactions in nonmalarial patients, and lack of a standard antigen preclude the use of precipitative tests in malaria (Chapter XIII).

Nematode Infections.—Specific precipitins have been produced in animals by injecting antigens derived from the various organs and constituents of *Ascaris.* Immune sera against muscle, intestine, cuticle, ova and spermatozoa display a relative specificity for their homologous antigens. A polysaccharide antigen has been isolated which is capable of inducing the formation of precipitins in rabbits and which will react with the sera of animals immunized with extracts of the whole worm or a protein fraction.

The precipitative test has proved of practical diagnostic value in only one nematode infection, trichinosis. High titer precipitins have been demonstrated in rabbits 30 days after infection and have been produced in immunized rabbits as early as five days after the last injections, using antigens prepared from larval *Trichinella spiralis* (Section **VII**, IX, 18). A number of investigators have applied the precipitative test with success to human trichinosis (Chapter XV). The test is usually positive (over 90 per cent) in from four to five weeks after infection. Pseudopositive reactions occasionally occur. The test is of little value in the early stages of the disease, when most needed, but, in combination with the intracutaneous test, is an important means of detecting advanced light or questionable infections.

Trematode Infections.—The precipitative test with antigens prepared from dried flukes yields a high percentage of positive reactions in cattle and sheep infected with *Fasciola hepatica,* but since it does not detect light or recent infections and also gives a fairly high percentage of positive reactions in uninfected animals it is inferior to the detection of ova in the feces. In *F. hepatica* infections in man, cross-reactions are found in schistosomiasis and pseudopositive reactions in syphilis. Antigens extracted from the dried livers of infected snails (Section **VII**, IX, 15) give some 80 per cent of positive tests in men infected with *Schistosoma mansoni* and 4 per cent in noninfected persons, and a larger number in syphilitic patients.

Cestode Infections.—Precipitative tests gave a high percentage of positive reactions in hogs infected with *Cysticercus cellulosæ* and none in uninfected animals. The test has also been helpful in determining cerebral cysticercosis in man. The greatest usefulness of the precipitative test in cestode infections is in the diagnosis of *Echinococcus granulosus.* The test with antigens prepared from hydatid cysts (Section **VII**, IX, 16, 17) in the hands of some investigators has been found not only highly specific but also to yield a high percentage of positive reactions in hydatid disease.

ALEXIN-FIXATION

Alexin-fixative tests have been employed mainly in the diagnosis of hydatid cyst and schistosomiasis, and to a less extent in filariasis and cysticercosis. The reaction is group-specific rather than species-specific.

Amœbiasis.—The test gives over 90 per cent of positive reactions in amœbiasis when antigens prepared from cultures of *Endamœba histolytica* are used (Section **VII**, IX, 2). It is useful in detecting carriers (Chapter VIII).

Leishmania.—Variable results with alexin-fixation have been obtained in leishmaniasis by several workers using antigens prepared from cultures or infected spleens (Section **VII**, IX, 3, 4). Positive results have been found in about 80 per cent of patients, and pseudopositive reactions have been observed in persons with syphilis. The test is not used for diagnosis as it is inferior to the non-specific flocculation tests and other diagnostic methods.

Malaria.—Various percentages of positive results (31 to 73 per cent) with alexin-fixation have been reported in malaria. The reaction is group-specific, antigens from the three species of man and *P. knowlesi* of monkeys being equally efficient (Section **VII**, IX, 8, 9). The maximum titer is obtained one month after the onset of the acute infection, and the antibodies persist for at least one year.

Trypanosomiasis.—Numerous studies have been made on the alexin-fixative test in trypanosomal infections. The reaction is group-specific, since antigens from several species of trypanosomes give equally efficient results (Section **VII**, IX, 5, 6, 7). The test has been particularly successful in the diagnosis of dourine in horses. It is not used in the diagnosis of African sleeping sickness, in which other methods are more effective, but is said to give a high percentage of positive results in Chagas' disease.

Nematode Infections.—Alexin-fixation has been of little practical value in the diagnosis of nematode infections, because of cross-reactions between species. Positive reactions with *Ascaris* antigens have been obtained in both infected and uninfected persons, possibly because of previous infection or contact.

The presence of a group-reaction in filarial infections has been demonstrated by several investigators. Positive reactions in persons infected with *Wuchereria bancrofti* and *Loa loa* have been obtained with an antigen of dried *Dirofilaria immitis* when microfilariæ are present in the blood, but the tests have generally been negative in elephantiasis. Positive results have been reported in *Onchocerca volvulus* infections using antigens made from cysts. The alexin-fixative test has been used for the diagnosis of trichinosis, but the intracutaneous and precipitative reactions are more reliable.

Trematode Infections.—The alexin-fixation in schistosomiasis is a group-reaction for the several species of schistosomes. Cercarial antigens prepared from *Schistosoma spindale,* a sheep and cattle parasite (Section **VII**, IX, 14) give positive reactions in *S. hæmatobium, S. indicum* and *S. spindale* infections. Experimental work with infected goats has shown that the antibodies are detectable within two weeks after infection and may persist up to 18 weeks after the disappearance of the schistosomes. Positive alexin-fixation has been obtained in human schistosomiasis; in *Schistosoma hæmatobium* infections with cercarial antigens, and in *S. japonicum* with antigens from the adult worms. Negative reactions, however, are obtained in an appreciable number of infected persons.

In *Fasciola hepatica* infections in cattle and sheep a high percentage of positive reactions are found in both infected and uninfected animals. Alexin-fixation is less reliable in the diagnosis of clonorchiasis than the detection of the ova in the feces. The test is useful in detecting nonpulmonary paragonimiasis when the worms are lodged in deep foci and the ova are not excreted.

Cestode Infections.—Alexin-fixation has been extensively used since 1906 in the diagnosis of human echinococcal infections using aqueous and alcoholic extracts of hydatid fluid and scolices (Section **VII**, IX, 16, 17). About 85 per cent positive reactions are found in infected persons. The test has some value in detecting the persistence of infection in postoperative cases. It is a group-reaction for somatic cestodes and is not specific for hydatid disease alone, being positive for the cysticercal infections of both *Echinococcus granulosus* and *Tænia solium*. Group-reactions with other tænian worms have been observed and pseudopositive reactions have been reported in patients with kala-azar and syphilis. Only about one-half the persons harboring *Diphyllobothrium latum* give a positive alexin-fixative reaction.

NONSPECIFIC CHEMICAL TESTS

Chemical flocculation tests depend upon changes in the normal protein ratios in the blood serum, particularly an increase in euglobulin.

Malaria.—Henry's melano-flocculation test (Section **VII**, IX, 23) gives a high percentage of positive reactions in malaria. It is effective in the acute stage, but also is sufficiently delicate to detect early and chronic cases. The protein tyrosin test of Proske and Watson (Section **VII**, IX, 24) gives a positive reaction in about 97 per cent of malarial patients. These tests may give false positive reactions in other diseases, especially syphilis, and, therefore, a negative reaction is of particular value in excluding malaria.

Leishmaniasis.—Napier's aldehyde test (Section **VII**, IX, 25) gives about 80 per cent positive reactions in infections with *Leishmania donovani*. It becomes positive about the fourth month of the disease. Chopra's antimony test (Section **VII**, IX, 26) is reported to be more sensitive than Napier's aldehyde test, especially in early kala-azar, but gives more false positives. Sias' precipitation test (Section **VII**, IX, 27) is also useful in detecting kala-azar. Positive reactions are obtained at times in malaria, schistosomiasis, and trypanosomiasis.

Schistosomiasis.—Napier's aldehyde test gives positive reactions in schistosomiasis if there is splenic enlargement. Chopra's and Sias' tests also give positive reactions.

CUTANEOUS TESTS

Cutaneous tests for parasitic infections possess advantages over serological technics in ease of performance and in earlier diagnosis of the disease. The involved mechanism of these tests and their relation to immunology are not thoroughly understood. The test consists of introducing extracts, suspensions or powdered tissue of parasites either intracutaneously or cutaneously (Section **VII,** IX, 1 to 18). The reaction is immediate or delayed (Section **VII,** X). In sensitive individuals an immediate reaction in the form of wheals, which begin to fade within an hour, appears at the site of the inoculation. A delayed reaction in the form of erythema and induration around the site of the inoculation may take place 8 to 24 hours later. The immediate type of sensitivity may be transferred passively to a nonsensitive person, but the delayed type cannot be transferred passively.

Leishmaniasis.—Skin reactions in sensitized rabbits do not differentiate between *Leishmania donovani, L. tropica* and *L. braziliensis.* Phenolized saline emulsions of dead *Leishmania tropica* almost invariably give positive intradermal reactions in oriental sore, and weakly positive reactions in some 10 per cent of uninfected persons.

Trypanosomiasis.—Antigens made by isolating trypanosomes from infected blood have been used for intradermal tests in trypanosomiasis, but have no practical diagnostic value.

Nematode Infections.—Cutaneous supersensitiveness to *Ascaris* in infected and noninfected individuals has been frequently reported. Individuals with no history of infection may give positive reactions and those with a history of infection negative reactions. Lack of correlation between skin sensitivity and *Ascaris* infection is attributed to the toxicity of the *Ascaris* antigen. Skin sensitivity of the delayed type persists in animals for months after removal of the worms. In sensitization with *Ascaris* antigen the delayed reaction appears in 6 or 7 days and the immediate in 7 to 16 days, but only the immediate remains after 20 to 25 days, while passive transfer of sensitivity may be demonstrated after 10 days. While a period of exposure is a necessary precursor of sensitization, continuous exposure does not necessarily produce sensitivity. Reactions are rare in persons under one year and over 40 years of age. The cutaneous reactions to *Ascaris* antigen are group-specific including *Ascaris, Enterobius* and *Trichuris.*

In enterobiasis the immediate type of reaction, though absent in early infections, is found in a high percentage of infected individuals. Antigens, prepared from the adult worms, in low dilutions give cross-reactions with other nematodes, but are fairly specific in high dilutions. Negative are more valuable than positive tests, therefore, in establishing a diagnosis.

Antigens prepared from canine *Dirofilaria immitis* in *Wuchereria bancrofti* infections give a high percentage of positive immediate reactions and also delayed reactions characterized by marked edema resembling Calabar swellings. Similar results have been obtained in loiasis and onchocerciasis with this antigen and with an *Onchocerca volvulus* antigen. The reaction is group-specific for filariæ. Positive cutaneous tests have been reported in dracunculiasis years after the infection has terminated.

Cutaneous tests have not proved satisfactory for the diagnosis of hookworm infections, since the sensitiveness persists indefinitely after the elimination of the parasite and the results are too variable. A conspicuous example of the intracutaneous test as a diagnostic procedure is found in trichinosis. A positive intracutaneous test, confirmed by a precipitative test is almost conclusive evidence of infection, but these tests are of no value in the early stage of the disease when diagnosis is important. Antigens of larval *Trichinella spiralis* (Section **VII**, IX, 18) evoke an immediate positive reaction 11 to 14 days after infection which remains positive for years. Most investigators give this test a high rating but some consider that it is inferior to other diagnostic methods.

Trematode Infections.—The endermal tests in the diagnosis of fascioliasis in cattle are less practical than the detection of ova.

Cercarial antigens from snails infected with *Schistosoma spindale* and *S. bovis* (Section **VII**, IX, 12, 13) gave a high percentage of positive reactions in persons infected with *S. hæmatobium* and a relatively small percentage in noninfected individuals. Similar results with cercarial antigens of *S. mansoni* in Manson's schistosomiasis have also been recorded. Pseudopositive reactions are largely due to sensitiveness against the proteins of the snail. The intracutaneous test with *S. japonicum* antigens has been recommended for field work in endemic areas, since negative reactions occur but rarely in noninfectious individuals. All workers agree that the cutaneous sensitiveness persists long after the apparent cure of the disease.

Cestode Infections.—Intracutaneous tests with antigens derived from the fluid and scolices (Section **VII**, IX, 16, 17) have been used extensively for the diagnosis of hydatid cyst. Intracutaneous tests give a greater number of correct diagnoses than serological tests, from 75 to 100 per cent. The test is useful for preoperative diagnosis. A positive reaction is not absolutely indicative of the disease, since pseudopositive reactions may occur from sensitiveness to sheep protein in the antigen, from trauma and in other cestode infections. A negative reaction is valuable, but not conclusive, evidence for excluding hydatid disease. Failure to react months or years after operation is regarded as evidence of cure, provided rupture of the cyst has not led to desensitization.

The reaction is group-specific for tæniids. Patients with *Tænia solium* and *T. saginata* infections, particularly in the cysticercal stage, give positive reactions with hydatid fluid antigens, and echinococcal infections with tænian antigens. The delayed type of reaction is considered by some workers to be more reliable than the immediate, since there are fewer pseudopositive reactions.

EXAMINATION OF INTERMEDIATE HOSTS

It is often necessary to examine intermediate hosts for the presence of parasites to determine the sources of human infection. The technical methods for such examinations are given in Section **VII**, XI.

VERTEBRATES

Mammals.—The mammals that serve as intermediate hosts for the parasites of man are largely those consumed as food. Many other mammals may be infected, but unless eaten, they are not important in the transmission of disease. The two most important mammalian intermediate hosts are the hog, which may harbor *Tænia solium* and *Trichinella spiralis,* and cattle, which may serve as hosts for *Tænia* *saginata.* The larval stages of various species of DIPHYLLOBOTHRIIDÆ are found in mammals, and also in other vertebrates such as fishes, birds, frogs and snakes.

Fishes.—Many species of fishes serve as secondary intermediate hosts for five rather important trematodes, one cestode, and two unimportant nematodes. These fishes, with the exception of the brackish-water mullets, are all fresh-water species. The CYPRINIDÆ, the most abundant family, containing over 200 genera and 1000 species of small to moderate-sized fishes, has the greatest number of host-species. The following families of fishes contain species that are intermediate hosts of helminths.

SALMONIDÆ: *Diphyllobothrium latum, Clonorchis sinensis, Metagonimus yokogawai.*

CYPRINIDÆ: *Diphyllobothrium latum, Clonorchis sinensis, Opisthorchis felineus, Metagonimus yokogawai, Echinochasmus perfoliatus, Dioctophyme renale(?), Gnathostoma spinigerum.*

ESOCIDÆ: *Diphyllobothrium latum, Echinochasmus perfoliatus.*

GADIDÆ: *Diphyllobothrium latum.*

PERCIDÆ: *Diphyllobothrium latum.*

OSPHROMENIDÆ: *Clonorchis sinensis.*

GOBIIDÆ: *Clonorchis sinensis.*

MUGILIDÆ: *Heterophyes heterophyes.*

INVERTEBRATES

Mollusks.—Gastropod mollusks are the primary intermediate hosts of the trematode parasites of man and are an important factor in their spread. They are discussed with the trematodes in Chapter XXIX.

Arthropoda.—The examination of arthropod intermediate hosts for parasites employs the technical methods of dissection in Section **VII**, XII. The larval stages of many parasites of animals other than man are found in these hosts, and it requires considerable experience to distinguish the species parasitic for humans. In some instances this can be done only by producing the adult parasite through feeding experiments. Table 9 lists the parasites of man that may be found in the different arthropods.

TABLE 9

ARTHROPODA AS INTERMEDIATE HOSTS OF PROTOZOAN AND HELMINTHIC PARASITES

Class	Order	Family	Genus	Host of
CRUS-TACEA	COPEPODA	CYCLOPIDÆ	Cyclops	Diphyllobothrium erinacei Diphyllobothrium latum Drepanidotænia lanceolata Dracunculus medinensis Gnathostoma spinigerum
		DIAPTOMIDÆ	Diaptomus	Diphyllobothrium latum Drepanidotænia lanceolata
	DECOPODA	ASTACIDÆ	Astacus Cambarus	Paragonimus westermani
		GRAPSIDÆ	Eriocheir Sesarma	
		POTAMONIDÆ	Parathelphusa Potamon Pseudothelphusa	
MYRIA-PODA	DIPLOPODA		Julus Fontaria	Hymenolepis diminuta
INSECTA	DIPTERA	CULICIDÆ	Aëdes	Wuchereria bancrofti
			Anopheles	Plasmodium falciparum Plasmodium malariæ Plasmodium ovale Plasmodium vivax Wuchereria malayi Wuchereria bancrofti
			Armigeres	Wuchereria malayi Wuchereria bancrofti
			Culex	Wuchereria bancrofti
			Mansonia	Wuchereria malayi Wuchereria bancrofti
		CHIRONOMIDÆ	Culicoides	Acanthocheilonema perstans Mansonella ozzardi
		PSYCHODIDÆ	Phlebotomus	Leishmania braziliensis (?) Leishmania donovani Leishmania tropica (?)
		SIMULIIDÆ	Simulium	Onchocerca volvulus
		TABANIDÆ	Chrysops	Loa loa
		MUSCIDÆ	Glossina	Trypanosoma gambiense Trypanosoma rhodesiense
	ANOPLURA	TRICHODECT-IDÆ	Trichodectes	Dipylidium caninum
	HEMIPTERA	REDUVIIDÆ	Rhodnius	Trypanosoma cruzi
			Triatoma	

TABLE 9—Continued

ARTHROPODA AS INTERMEDIATE HOSTS OF PROTOZOAN AND
HELMINTHIC PARASITES

Class	Order	Family	Genus	Host of
INSECTA (Cont.)	COLEOPTERA	SCARABÆIDÆ, TENEBRIONI-DÆ and other families	(Various genera)	*Hymenolepis diminuta* *Macracanthorhynchus hirudinaceus* *Moniliformis moniliformis* *Gongylonema pulchrum*
	LEPIDOP-TERA	PYRALIDÆ	*Asopia* *Aglossa* *Aphornia*	*Hymenolepis diminuta*
		TINEIDÆ	*Tinea*	
	ORTHOPTERA	BLATTIDÆ	(Various genera)	*Hymenolepis diminuta* *Gongylonema pulchrum* *Moniliformis moniliformis*
	SIPHONAP-TERA	PULICIDÆ	*Pulex*	*Dipylidium caninum* *Hymenolepis diminuta*
			Xenopsylla	*Hymenolepis diminuta*
		ARCHARO-PSYLLIDÆ	*Ctenocephalides*	*Dipylidium caninum* *Hymenolepis diminuta*
		DOLICHO-PSYLLIDÆ	*Ceratophyllus*	*Hymenolepis diminuta*
			Hoplopsyllus	
		HYSTRICHO-PSYLLIDÆ	*Ctenopsyllus*	*Hymenolepis diminuta*
ARACHNIDA	ACARINA	ARGASIDÆ	*Ornithodorus*	*Trypanosoma cruzi* (exper.)
		IXODIDÆ	*Amblyomma*	*Trypanosoma cruzi* (exper.)
			Rhipicephalus	*Trypanosoma cruzi* (exper.)

Chapter VI

THE TREATMENT AND PREVENTION OF
PARASITIC DISEASES

The prevention of parasitic diseases depends upon the erection of barriers to the spread of parasites through the practical application of biological and epidemiological knowledge. In tropical countries, where preventive measures are imperative, it is often difficult to secure the necessary coöperation; but when control measures have official backing, striking results are obtained. The control of parasitic disease includes the following procedures: (1) reduction of the source of infection in man by therapeutic measures; (2) education in personal prophylaxis to prevent dissemination of infection and to reduce opportunities for exposure; (3) sanitary control of water and food, living and working conditions, and waste disposal; (4) destruction or control of reservoir hosts and vectors; and (5) erection of biological barriers to the transmission of parasites.

TREATMENT OF PARASITIC DISEASES

Prompt and adequate treatment of infected individuals is an essential part of any program for the prevention of parasitic diseases. The elimination of potential sources of infection requires the treatment of both the symptomatic patient and the asymptomatic carrier. Inability to detect carriers is the major problem. Preventive chemotherapy with specific drugs is used in certain diseases (malaria) to safeguard susceptible individuals and also in the form of mass therapy to eliminate unrecognized sources of infection.

The successful treatment of the infected patient includes medical and surgical measures, a hygienic regimen to build up general resistance, and specific drug therapy. Intelligent treatment requires a knowledge of the parasite, its pathogenic action, the intensity of the infection, and the physical condition of the patient. The physician should also be familiar with the degree of infectivity and the patient's ability to coöperate intelligently, the sanitary environment, the epidemiology of the disease, and the best methods for controlling the spread of the infection.

General Medical Treatment.—General medical treatment, largely supportive and symptomatic, is designed to sustain the vitality and to increase the resistance of the patient. In the acute stages absolute rest in bed is necessary. Fevers are treated with sponge-baths of alcohol or ice water. When diarrhea without nausea is present, a mild cathartic is administered. When nausea is present warm enemata of physiological sodium chloride solution or 1 per cent sodium bicarbonate are given. Paregoric and other opiates that serve to prevent loss of fluid are given only

65

TABLE 10

DRUGS COMMONLY USED IN THE TREATMENT OF PARASITIC DISEASES

Parasite	No effective chemotherapy	Arsenic			Antimony				Iodine		Alkaloids						Hydrocarbons								Plant Products		
		Arsphenamines	Carbarsone	Tryparsamide	Fuadin	Pentavalent compounds	Potassium antimony tartrate	Sodium antimony tartrate	Chiniofon	Vioform	Atabrine	Berberine sulphate	Emetine hydrochloride	Quinine	Pelletierin	Plasmochin	Bayer 205	β—naphthol	Carbon tetrachloride	Gentian violet	Hexylresorcinol	Santonin	Tetrachlorethylene	Thymol	Leche de higuerón	Oil of chenopodium	Oleoresin of aspidium
PROTOZOA																											
Balantidium coli	●																										
Endamœba coli			●																								
Endamœba histolytica			●						●	●			●														
Giardia lamblia			●						●		●																
Leishmania braziliensis					●	●	●																				
Leishmania donovani					●	●	●																				
Leishmania tropica					●	●	●					●															
Plasmodium falciparum											●			●		●											
Plasmodium malariæ											●			●		●											
Plasmodium vivax											●			●		●											
Trichomonas vaginalis	●																										
Trypanosoma cruzi	●																										
Trypanosoma gambiense				●													●										
Trypanosoma rhodesiense																	●										
NEMATHELMINTHES																											
Acanthocheilonema perstans	●																										
Ancylostoma braziliense																			●		●		●			●	
Ancylostoma duodenale																			●		●		●			●	
Ascaris lumbricoides																					●	●				●	
Dracunculus medinensis	●																										
Enterobius vermicularis																				●	●		●				
Loa loa	●																										
Mansonella ozzardi	●																										
Necator americanus																			●		●		●			●	

TABLE 10—Continued

DRUGS COMMONLY USED IN THE TREATMENT OF PARASITIC DISEASES

Parasite	No effective chemotherapy	Arsenic			Antimony				Iodine		Alkaloids						Hydrocarbons								Plant Products		
		Arsphenamines	Carbarsone	Tryparsamide	Fuadin	Pentavalent compounds	Potassium antimony tartrate	Sodium antimony tartrate	Chiniofon	Vioform	Atabrine	Berberine sulphate	Emetine hydrochloride	Quinine	Pelletierin	Plasmochin	Bayer 205	β-naphthol	Carbon tetrachloride	Gentian violet	Hexylresorcinol	Santonin	Tetrachlorethylene	Thymol	Leche de higuerón	Oil of chenopodium	Oleoresin of aspidium
Onchocerca volvulus						•										•											
Strongyloides stercoralis																				•							
Trichinella spiralis	•																										
Trichuris trichiura																					•				•		
Wuchereria bancrofti	•																										
PLATYHELMINTHES (CESTODA)																											
Diphyllobothrium latum																			•								•
Dipylidium caninum																							•				•
Echinococcus granulosus	•																										
Hymenolepis nana																				•						•	•
Tænia saginata																		•									•
Taenia solium																		•									•
PLATYHELMINTHES (TREMATODA)																											
Clonorchis sinensis						•													•								
Fasciola hepatica													•				•		•								•
Fasciolopsis buski																	•	•	•	•	•						
Heterophyes heterophyes																		•			•					•	•
Metagonimus yokogawai																		•			•					•	•
Opisthorchis felineus				•															•								
Paragonimus westermani	•																										
Schistosoma hæmatobium					•		•	•																			
Schistosoma japonicum					•		•	•																			
Schistosoma mansoni					•		•																				

after the bowels are emptied. Liquids are forced and if necessary diuretics are given. The oral cavity is kept clean and moist. A bland, high-caloric, nourishing diet in liquid, semisolid or solid form, depending upon the condition of the patient, is indicated. Clinical manifestations that interfere with the comfort of the patient and the complications that arise during the course of the disease are treated symptomatically.

In mild or chronic infections all possible means are employed to maintain the vitality and general resistance of the patient. A nutritive, well-balanced diet of proper vitamin content, the elimination of intercurrent diseases, the removal of environmental conditions undermining the health of the patient, and the establishment of a hygienic regimen accelerate recovery.

Surgical Treatment.—Surgery is indicated when it is possible to remove the parasite, to relieve pathological conditions amenable to mechanical treatment, to employ emergency measures to save the life of the patient, and to afford relief or cure when medical treatment is unsuccessful. In general, chemotherapy should be tried before surgery, but in certain parasitic diseases (guinea worm) surgical measures only are effective.

Chemotherapy.—No efficient antiparasitic drug is entirely nontoxic to man. Successful chemotherapy depends upon the use of a drug that has a minimal toxic effect upon the tissues of the host and a lethal action upon the parasite. For instance, tetrachlorethylene, an efficient chemical for the removal of hookworms, is not readily absorbed from the intestine and does not damage the liver or kidneys; whereas oil of chenopodium, although a powerful anthelmintic, is rapidly absorbed from the intestine, is eliminated slowly, and produces considerable damage to the liver and kidneys. The effective remedies in protozoan infections are largely specific; but in the helminthic infections some drugs are definitely helminthicidal while others act merely as vermifuges. The success of chemotherapy depends not only upon the choice of the drug but also upon the condition and response of the individual patient, the method of administration, the dosage, the auxiliary therapeutic preparation and after care of the patient, and additional procedures to prevent reinfection.

Various types of chemicals are used in the chemotherapy of parasitic disease. New preparations, largely synthetic, are being developed and therapeutic methods are continually undergoing revision. However, many drugs, particularly anthelmintics, have been handed down from ancient times. Antiparasitic drugs fall into several general classes: compounds of arsenic, antimony and iodine, alkaloids, hydrocarbon derivatives, and semirefined or unrefined plant products. They are usually administered orally or intravenously, and occasionally intramuscularly and subcutaneously. The more important antiparasitic drugs recommended by various authorities are listed in Table 10 and described in Section **VII**, XIII.

PREVENTION OF PARASITIC DISEASES
PERSONAL PROPHYLAXIS

Personal prophylaxis includes the maintenance of general resistance through hygienic habits and freedom from debilitating diseases. In moist, warm climates frequent bathing is essential for both comfort and health. Clothing for white races in the tropics should be loosely woven, light and white, and the head should be protected by a wide-brimmed, well-ventilated hat. A balanced diet with proper vitamin content is essential but often is difficult to obtain. Where nutritional disturbances are prevalent, special attention should be paid to dental hygiene.

Questionable drinking water must be boiled or treated chemically to avoid the risk of infection. Food should be thoroughly cooked, and vegetables or fruit from infected regions should not be eaten raw unless washed and scalded. Sleeping quarters should be carefully screened and localities frequented by insect carriers avoided. In a few parasitic diseases the prophylactic use of specific drugs has proved of considerable value in protecting susceptible individuals in endemic areas. There are few satisfactory methods of protective immunization.

Education of the individual in personal prophylaxis is one of the most effective means of combatting parasitic diseases. Knowledge of the way these diseases spread and of the measures needed to escape infection should be widely disseminated among the general population. Unfortunately, in the countries where these diseases are most prevalent the limited education, low standard of living and poor sanitary environment of the inhabitants prove serious obstacles to effective control.

SANITATION

Water.—In many countries the water supplies are unsafe for drinking and bathing because of faulty methods of waste disposal. Since there is almost continuous contamination, natural methods of purification cannot be depended upon in tropical countries. Sand filtration, chlorination and boiling, singly or in combination, are the ordinary methods used to obtain safe drinking water. Containers should be boiled to prevent contamination of the purified supply. In emergencies, suspected water may be treated with a few drops of iodine.

Sewage Disposal.—In most rural districts expensive latrines and septic tanks are economically prohibitive; but inexpensive installations of screened, sanitary latrines of water-tight construction are available to replace open privies, and natives should be trained to use them. Human night soil, wherever economically possible, should not be used for the fertilization of vegetable gardens. If night soil stands long enough in closed vats, the parasitic ova and larvæ are killed, but again economic reasons prevent the execution of such an ideal measure.

Food Handlers.—Many parasitic diseases are spread by human carriers. For this reason any person concerned with the handling of food should receive a thorough physical and laboratory examination. More important still, food handlers should keep their nails trimmed and their hands scrubbed.

Housing.—Houses should provide maximal shade and ventilation with the exclusion of heat, and should be located on soil with a constant level of ground water. If the house is placed to windward of swamp land, mosquitoes will be less of a problem. Vegetation should be removed and grass kept cut for a radius of 200 yards. All openings should be protected by well-fitted, fine-meshed screening.

CONTROL OF VECTORS

The control of many parasitic diseases has been made possible by eliminating or reducing the number of intermediate hosts or vectors.

Insects.—Insect vectors are best controlled by the destruction of their natural habitat and breeding grounds. Mosquito control is dependent upon the destruction of the larval forms and the elimination of breeding places. The breeding of flies may be checked by covering garbage and by treating manure in order to destroy the breeding larvæ. Adult flies may be destroyed by trapping or spraying. Drainage and the cutting of thick underbrush reduce the range of various species of biting flies. Special chemical methods are used for the destruction of insect pests in houses. Bathing, clean clothing, and chemical treatment of the skin will rid the body of lice, fleas and mites.

Other Vectors.—The problem of the reservoir host presents many difficulties. The hosts that harbor the parasites of man are more often domestic and less frequently wild animals. Except in a few instances, the destruction of these animals is economically impractical and reliance must be placed on measures for reducing the incidence of infection in these hosts. If the snails that act as intermediate hosts of trematodes are sufficiently segregated, it may be practical to destroy them by the application of chemical or physical agents. It is usually impractical to destroy such intermediate hosts as fish and mammals.

BARRIERS TO PARASITIC INFECTION

Almost every parasite at some stage in its life cycle is susceptible to special exterminative measures. Thus, barriers may be established against the transmission of parasitic infections by breaking the weak links in the life cycles of the parasites, whether this be at the time of invasion of man, at the departure of the parasite from man, or some time during the period of extrahuman existence. The biological approach to the study of the extrahuman existence of the parasites of man holds perhaps the greatest promise for the prevention of parasitic diseases. More extensive knowledge of the relation of the parasite to its external environment and its intermediate hosts, and of the habits, existence and relation of these hosts to man may pave the way for far-reaching biological methods of prevention. At present this field, because of its apparently unsurmountable difficulties, has offered little incentive to investigators.

The environment of the free-living larval stages may be changed by drainage from a favorable moist habitat to one that is dry and unfavorable. The habits of intermediate hosts may be modified; for instance, insects may be made to feed on other mammals instead of man; they may be removed from the habitat of man; and they may be reduced in number by the destruction of breeding places, by deprivation of food, and by the introduction of predators or parasites. Greater protection for man may be provided by screening, sanitary habitations and elimination of contaminated food.

Section II

THE PROTOZOA

Chapter VII

THE BIOLOGY OF THE PROTOZOA

Protozoa are unicellular animals that occur singly or in colony formation. Their unicellular character differentiates them from the multicellular metazoa. A single-celled animal, however, is not homologous to an individual cell of a many-celled animal. Each protozoon is a complete unit capable of performing the physiological functions which in higher organisms are carried on by specialized cells. Parasitic Protozoa, while retaining the general characteristics of free-living forms, have adapted themselves to their altered existence. They can not only survive sudden changes in temperature, moisture and chemical composition, but also resist adverse conditions in the host.

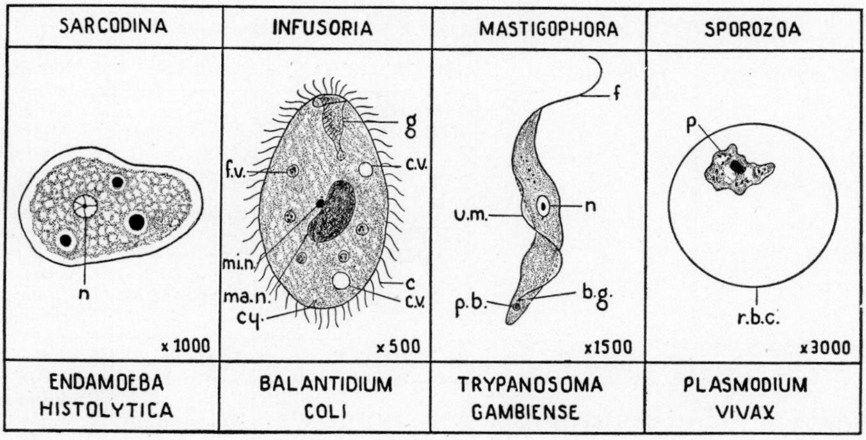

FIG. 6.—CLASSES OF PROTOZOA

b.g., basal granules; *c,* cilia; *c.v.,* contractile vacuole; *cy.,* cytopyge; *f,* flagellum; *f.v.,* food vacuole; *g,* gullet; *ma.n.,* macronucleus; *mi.n.,* micronucleus; *n,* nucleus; *p, Plasmodium; p.b.,* parabasal body; *r.b.c.,* red blood cell; *u.m.,* undulant membrane.

CLASSIFICATION

The parasitic Protozoa of man are included in four classes, each identified by definite characteristics: (1) the SARCODINA or RHIZOPODA, (2) the INFUSORIA, (3) the MASTIGOPHORA, and (4) the SPOROZOA (Fig. 6).

71

Sarcodina.—Pseudopodia form the organs of locomotion and the means of procuring food for these parasites, which are naked and unprotected except in the encysted stage. Reproduction is by fission or by multiplication in a cyst, e.g., *Endamœba histolytica*.

TABLE II

THE PARASITIC PROTOZOA OF MAN

Class	Order	Family	Genus	Species
SARCODINA	AMŒBIDA	ENDAMŒBIDÆ	*Dientamœba*	*D. fragilis*
			Endamœba	*E. coli* *E. gingivalis* *E. histolytica*
			Endolimax	*E. nana*
			Iodamœba	*I. bütschlii*
INFUSORIA	HETEROTRI-CHIDA	BURSARIIDÆ	*Balantidium*	*B. coli*
MASTIGOPHORA	PROTOMON-ADIDA	CERCOMONAD-IDÆ	*Enteromonas*	*E. hominis*
		CHILOMASTI-GIDÆ	*Chilomastix*	*C. mesnili*
		EMBADOMONA-DIDÆ	*Embad-omonas*	*E. intestinalis*
		HEXAMITIDÆ	*Giardia*	*G. lamblia*
		TRICHOMON-ADIDÆ	*Trichomonas*	*T. elongata* *T. hominis* *T. vaginalis*
		TRYPANO-SOMIDÆ	*Leishmania*	*L. braziliensis* *L. donovani* *L. tropica*
			Trypanosoma	*T. cruzi* *T. gambiense* *T. rhodesiense*
SPOROZOA	COCCIDIA	EIMERIDÆ	*Isospora*	*I. hominis*
	HÆMOSPORIDIA	PLASMODIDÆ	*Plasmodium*	*P. falciparum* *P. malariæ* *P. ovale* *P. vivax*
	SARCOSPORIDIA	SARCOCYSTIDÆ	*Sarcocystis*	*S. lindemanni*

Infusoria.—Cilia are the organs of locomotion. These parasites possess a macronucleus and a micronucleus, and divide by transverse fission, e.g., *Balantidium coli*.

Mastigophora.—Flagella serve as organs of locomotion. The body is either naked or enclosed in a membrane. Reproduction is by longitudinal fission, e.g., *Trypanosoma gambiense*.

Sporozoa.—The members of this class are exclusively parasitic and lack definite organs for locomotion or capture of food. Reproductive powers are greatly increased, and life histories are complicated, e.g., *Plasmodium vivax.*

Table 11 gives a tabulation of the parasitic Protozoa of man.

MORPHOLOGY

The vital functions of the Protozoa are carried out by the protoplasm, a coarsely or finely granular viscid substance, differentiated into cytoplasm and nucleoplasm (Fig. 7). Two layers of cytoplasm are recognized, (1) the ectoplasm (thin outer) and (2) the endoplasm (voluminous inner).

Ectoplasm.—The ectoplasm functions in movement, ingestion of food, excretion, respiration and protection. The organs of locomotion are prolongations of ectoplasm known as pseudopodia, flagella or cilia. Food may be taken in at any

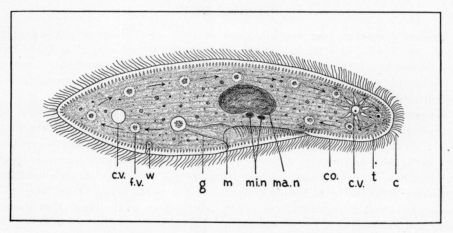

FIG. 7.—DIAGRAM OF A TYPICAL PROTOZOON (*Paramecium*)

c, cilia; *co.*, cortex; *c.v.*, contractile vacuole; *f.v.*, food vacuole; *g*, gullet; *m*, mouth; *ma.n.*, macronucleus; *mi.n.*, micronucleus; *t*, trichocyst; *w*, waste.

point in the cytoplasm or ingested at a particular point. In some species there is a definite area, the **peristome,** through which food passes directly into the **cytostome** and thence through a tube-like **cytopharynx** to the endoplasm. Many species of parasitic Protozoa do not have a definite membrane, the ectoplasm serving as a feeble protective covering; but, under unfavorable conditions or during part of the life cycle, they form cysts with a resistant covering.

Endoplasm.—The coarsely granular endoplasm is concerned with nutrition and, since it contains the nucleus, with reproduction. It may also contain food vacuoles, food reserves, foreign bodies, contractile vacuoles and chromatoidal bodies. **Contractile vacuoles,** which communicate with the cytoplasm by radiating canals, may be observed in some species, intermittently expanding and contracting. They function in the regulation of osmotic pressure and the elimination of waste material.

Nucleus.—The nucleus is essential for maintaining and reproducing life. It is separated from the cytoplasm by a nuclear membrane and consists of a fine reticulum filled with nuclear sap and masses of chromatin. In the vesicular nucleus the chromatin is concentrated in a single mass; in the granular type it is diffusely distributed. More than one nucleus may be present. Near the center of the nucleus is the deeply staining **karyosome**, which plays a part in promitosis. In many Protozoa a **centrosome** is also present. The structure of the nucleus, particularly the arrangement of the chromatin and karyosome, helps to differentiate species. In the MASTIGOPHORA a **kinetoplast** and in the INFUSORIA one or more **micronuclei** may be present. In the former the **kinetoplast** consists of two parts, the larger **parabasal body** and the smaller **blepharoplast** from which the flagellum arises. The **macronucleus** is believed to be concerned with the vegetative activities of the cell and the **micronucleus** with the reproductive functions.

PHYSIOLOGY

Various properties and specializations of their protoplasm, analogous to the systems and organs of Metazoa, enable the Protozoa to perform all essential functions. Movement, respiration, nutrition, excretion, secretion, reproduction and protective functions are carried on either by particular properties of the protoplasm or by structural and functional adaptations known as **organelles.**

Movement.—The power of movement is employed in obtaining food and responding to other stimuli. Motor ability ranges from rapid activity in the flagellated MASTIGOPHORA, to almost negligible movement in the SPOROZOA, encysted forms being inert and vegetative forms active. In general, however, parasitic species are less active than free-living species. Pseudopodia, cilia, flagella, and undulating membranes form the usual means of motility. The pseudopodia of the SARCODINA produce amœboid movements and assist in engulfing food. Their characteristic shapes and movements aid in identification of species. Rhythmic movements of the cilia propel INFUSORIA through their menstruum and draw food particles into the cytostome. The flagella of the MASTIGOPHORA, assisted by the undulating membrane, permit movement in all directions and in some species assist in the capture of food. In the SPOROZOA movement is slight except during certain stages of the life cycle. By using their organs of locomotion as tactile receptors, Protozoa not only respond to physical stimuli but also exhibit positive and negative chemotaxis.

Respiration.—There is no definite organ of respiration. Protozoa respire either directly by taking in oxygen and expelling carbon dioxide or indirectly by utilizing the oxygen liberated from complex substances by the action of enzymes. Because free oxygen is rare in animal tissues, most parasitic Protozoa are anærobic or indirect breathers.

Nutrition.—Nutrition may be effected either by the absorption of liquid food or by the ingestion of solid particles. Occasionally both methods are employed. The solid material is ingested either indiscriminately through the ectoplasm or through the cytostome. Within the protoplasm it is surrounded by a food vacuole, where it is converted by digestive ferments into forms suitable for assimilation.

Movements of the protoplasm carry the food from one part of the body to another, definite paths being followed in some species. The undigested particles are extruded either through the surface of the body or through a specialized opening, the **cytopyge.** Some species store up a reserve food supply.

The various species show selective powers in their choice of food. Parasitic SARCODINA absorb body fluids and ingest portions of the tissues in which they live. The MASTIGOPHORA feed by direct absorption (blood parasites) and by ingestion through the cytostome (intestinal parasites). The INFUSORIA ingest food through the peristome, while the SPOROZOA absorb nourishment directly from the tissues of the host.

Excretion.—Excretion is effected through osmotic pressure, diffusion and precipitation. The liquid and solid waste is probably carried to the surface by protoplasmic movements and discharged into the surrounding medium through the ectoplasm either over the general surface or at definite locations. In some species contractile vacuoles act as excretory organs.

Secretions.—Protozoa secrete digestive ferments, pigments and material for the cyst wall. Pathogenic Protozoa also secrete proteolytic enzymes, hemolysins, cytolysins and various toxic and antigenic substances that are largely responsible for clinical symptoms.

Encystment.—Some Protozoa at times enter an inactive cystic state, in which they secrete a tough resistant membranous wall, undergo nuclear division and store up reserve food material. In parasitic species encystment is usually necessary for survival outside the body and for protection against the digestive juices of the upper gastro-intestinal tract. Thus it is closely associated with the passage from host to host, and constitutes the infectious stage of the parasitic amœbæ, ciliates and intestinal flagellates that are transmitted through contaminated food or water. In some species encystment is a means of reproduction.

Reproduction.—The survival of Protozoa is largely due to their highly developed reproductive powers. In contrast to our rather meager knowledge of reproduction in parasitic Protozoa, considerable study has been given to the reproduction of a free-living infusorian, the Paramecium, which may serve as a type. For long periods the Paramecium reproduces asexually by binary fission. The micronucleus divides by true mitosis, while the macronucleus undergoes simple amitotic division. The body divides transversely, each half receiving a macronucleus and a micronucleus. From time to time conjugation appears essential for the rejuvenation of the protoplasm. It provides a replenishing of the macronucleus and a mixing of the chromatin of two individuals. Two Paramecia unite along their oral surfaces. The macronucleus disintegrates. The micronuclei in each individual divide twice, and all but one of the daughter nuclei disintegrate. The remaining nucleus undergoes a third mitotic division, and one of the two thus formed migrates to fuse with a corresponding nucleus in the other individual. Endomixis, which takes place every 40 to 50 generations, is the process of replenishing the old macronucleus by chromatin from the micronucleus. It appears necessary for continuous reproduction.

Reproduction in the parasitic Protozoa may be sexual or asexual. In the asexual or simple fission type, characteristic of the SARCODINA, MASTIGOPHORA and IN-

FUSORIA, the division of the nucleus may be amitotic, mitotic or so modified that it is not truly characteristic of either type. Certain Protozoa may also reproduce in the encysted state, each cyst giving rise to several new vegetative forms. The **trophozoite** or vegetative protozoon forms a dense resistant cyst wall, within which the nucleus divides to form new cells. Conjugation may precede encystment.

The SPOROZOA reproduce both asexually and sexually and often alternate both generation and host. Asexual development usually takes place in the intermediate host by a process known as **schizogony,** in which the nucleus divides repeatedly without immediately forming new cells. Sexual development, which usually takes place in the definitive host, is known as **sporogony.** Occasionally both methods occur in the same host.

In Protozoa sexual reproduction, the union of two cells, may precede some form of division. Sexual union, **syngamy,** may be permanent or temporary. The permanent form, known as copulation, includes (1) **isogamy,** union between cells of equal size and structure, and (2) **anisogamy,** union between dissimilar cells. In anisogamy sexual differences are evident; the cells are called gametes, the males **microgametes** and the females **macrogametes.** The union of a micro- and a macrogamete produces a **zygote.** Temporary union or conjugation is a rejuvenation process in some species and a reproductive process in others.

Chapter VIII

THE PARASITIC AMŒBÆ OF MAN

The class SARCODINA, comprising unicellular animals that form pseudopodia, includes several orders and many families. Most of the parasitic species in man and other mammals are included in the order AMŒBIDA and the family ENDAMŒBIDÆ. Technical difficulties in the study of these organisms have caused confusion in classification.

FAMILY *ENDAMŒBIDÆ*

At least four genera and six species of amœbæ living in man have been definitely established and many other species of doubtful authenticity have been described. Only one species, *Endamœba histolytica,* is pathogenic to man, and should be differentiated from other parasitic and coprozoic amœbæ.

Genus *Dientamœba* Jepps and Dobell, 1918
  Species *Dientamœba fragilis* Jepps and Dobell, 1918
Genus *Endamœba* Leidy, 1879
  Species *Endamœba coli* (Grassi, 1879) Hickson, 1909
    Endamœba gingivalis (Gros, 1849) Smith and Barrett, 1914
    Endamœba histolytica (Schaudinn, 1903) Hickson, 1909
Genus *Endolimax* Kuenen and Swellengrebel, 1917
  Species *Endolimax nana* (Wenyon and O'Connor, 1917) Brug, 1918
Genus *Iodamœba* Dobell, 1919
  Species *Iodamœba bütschlii* (v. Prowazek, 1912) Dobell, 1919

Genera.—The four genera may be differentiated by their nuclei (Fig. 8). The genus *Endamœba* has a nucleus with a small, more or less central karyosome, a peripheral layer of chromatin granules on the nuclear membrane, and a diffuse, at times radiating linin network. The nucleus of the genus *Endolimax* has a large, often irregular karyosome that consists of several portions connected by strands, and linin fibers radiating to the periphery. The genus *Iodamœba* has a single large karyosome, which is surrounded by a layer of poorly staining granules and is connected with the nuclear membrane by delicate radiating fibrils. The genus *Dientamœba* often has two nuclei. The karyosome consists of four chromatin granules, one often much larger than the others, embedded in a poorly staining matrix. At times linin fibers connect this mass with the nuclear membrane.

Species.—The differential characteristics of the six species of amœba living in man are given in Table 12 and are graphically represented in Figure 9.

Incidence.—Numerous surveys have been made to determine the prevalence of parasitic amœbæ in man in various parts of the world. The incidence of infection varies so widely that it cannot be computed accurately, but it is highest in the

TABLE 12

DIFFERENTIAL CHARACTERISTICS OF AMŒBÆ LIVING IN MAN

	Endamœba histolytica	Endamœba coli	Endamœba gingivalis	Endolimax nana	Iodamœba bütschlii	Dientamœba fragilis
Trophozoite (unstained) **Size (micra)** Average	25	25	15	8	11	8.5
Usual range	20 to 30	20 to 30	10 to 20	6 to 10	9 to 14	8 to 9
Extreme range	10 to 60	10 to 50	5 to 35	6 to 15	5 to 20	3 to 12
Appearance and color	Glassy, faint green	Ground-glass, gray	Greenish refractile bodies in endoplasm	Clear, faint green	Refractile, faint green	Fragile, gray
Visibility of nucleus	Indistinct	Distinct	Indistinct, often obscured by cytoplasmic inclusions	Faintly visible	Indistinct, but sometimes visible	Indistinct
Endoplastic inclusions Red blood cells	Present	Absent	Present occasionally	Absent	Absent	Absent
Bacteria and fungi	Absent in fresh feces	Present, many	Present	Present	Present	Present
Cellular debris	Absent	Present	Present, abundant	Present	Present	Present
Vacuoles	Scanty	Numerous	Very numerous	Numerous	Numerous	Numerous
Pseudopodia	Blade or finger-shaped, formed rapidly, ectoplastic, hyaline	Blunt, formed slowly, endoplastic, granular	Usually blunt and rounded, often formed rapidly, ectoplastic, hyaline	Blunt, formed slowly ectoplastic, hyaline	Blunt or finger-like, formed slowly, ectoplastic, hyaline	Leaf-like, formed rapidly, ectoplastic, hyaline
Motility	Active progression in definite direction	Sluggish, changes in conformation, usually not progressive or directional	Moderately active, progressive	Sluggish, rarely progressive, like E. coli	Sluggish, slightly progressive	Active, progressive

Cultivation	Yes	Yes	Yes	Difficult	Difficult	Yes
Reproduction	Binary fission	Binary fission	Binary fission	Binary fission	Binary fission	Unknown
Trophozoite (stained with iron-hematoxylin) Nuclei Number	1	1	1	1	1	2
Size (micra)	4 to 7	4 to 8	2.5 to 4	1 to 3	2 to 3	1 to 2
Shape	Spherical	Not always spherical	Spherical with deformities	Spherical	Spherical	Spherical
Nuclear membrane	Thin	Thick	Moderately thick	Moderately thick	Thick	Thin
Karyosome	Single, minute, central	Single, large, excentric	Single, fairly large, central or excentric consisting of several granules in a granular halo	One large and several small connected bodies, central or excentric	Single, large, central, surrounded by refractile globules	Large, four chromatin granules in matrix
Chromatin	Thin single peripheral layer of minute dots on inner side of nuclear membrane	Heavy single peripheral layer of coarse dots on inner side of nuclear membrane, Chromatin granules in linin network	Thin irregular single peripheral layer of minute dots on inner side of nuclear membrane	No peripheral chromatin	No peripheral chromatin	No peripheral chromatin
Cyst (stained with iodine) Size (micra) Average	Variable	17	No cysts demonstrated	9	10	No cysts demonstrated
Usual range	7 to 15	13 to 20		8 to 10	9 to 11	
Extreme range	5 to 20	10 to 33		5 to 14	5 to 18	
Shape	Nearly spherical	Usually spherical sometimes oval		Oval or ellipsoidal	Irregular or spheroidal	

TABLE 12—Continued

DIFFERENTIAL CHARACTERISTICS OF AMŒBÆ LIVING IN MAN

	Endamœba histolytica	Endamœba coli	Endamœba gingivalis	Endolimax nana	Iodamœba bütschlii	Dientamœba fragilis
Wall	Thin	Thick		Thin	Thick	
Appearance and color	Greenish-yellow	Yellowish-brown		Pale green, refractile vacuoles	Yellowish-green	
Glycogen	Present in young cysts, diffuse, mahogany brown	Present in young cysts, usually large, dark brown		Sometimes present in young cysts, diffuse, ill-defined brownish	Usually present, large compact, dark brown, diagnostic	
Visibility of nucleus	Indistinct	Distinct		Usually distinct	Indistinct	
Cyst (stained with iron-hematoxylin) Nuclei Number	1 to 4, rarely more	1 to 8, rarely more		1 to 4, rarely more	1, rarely 2	
Number in mature cyst	4	8		4	1	
Size in mature cyst (micra)	1 to 2	2 to 3		1 to 1.3	3 to 4	
Shape	Nearly spherical	Longer than broad, one side less curved than other		Generally oval but often irregular	Usually markedly irregular	
Nuclear structure	Similar to trophozoite	Similar to trophozoite		Similar to trophozoite except karyosome often near membrane	Karyosome and refractile granules at one side	
Chromatoid bodies	Often present, large bars or thick rod-like masses	Sometimes present, splinter-like with square or pointed ends		Occasionally small spherical or elongated granules	Usually absent, small granules	

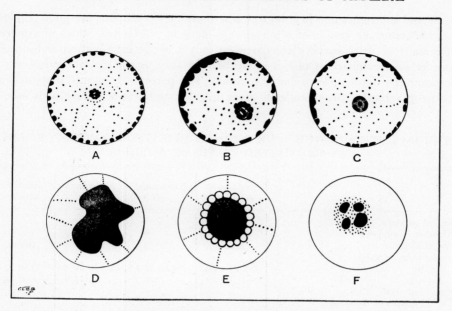

FIG. 8.—DIAGRAMMATIC REPRESENTATION OF THE VARIOUS TYPES OF NUCLEI IN THE AMŒBÆ OF MAN

A, Endamœba histolytica; B, Endamœba coli; C, Endamœba gingivalis; D, Endolimax nana; E, Iodamœba bütschlii; F, Dientamœba fragilis (A, B, D and *F* redrawn from Hegner, Root, Augustine and Huff, *Parasitology,* 1938, D. Appleton-Century Company).

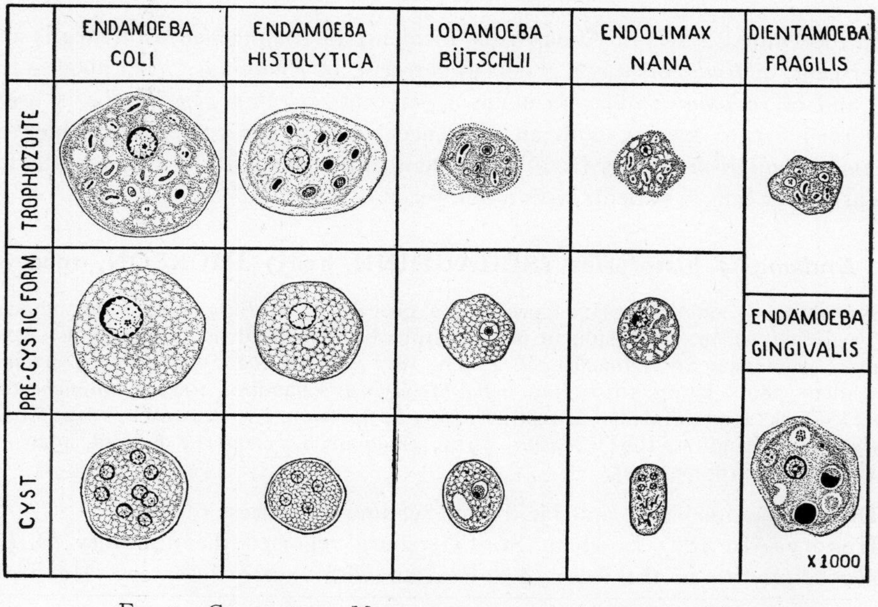

	ENDAMOEBA COLI	ENDAMOEBA HISTOLYTICA	IODAMOEBA BÜTSCHLII	ENDOLIMAX NANA	DIENTAMOEBA FRAGILIS
TROPHOZOITE					
PRE-CYSTIC FORM					ENDAMOEBA GINGIVALIS
CYST					X 1000

FIG. 9.—COMPARATIVE MORPHOLOGY OF THE AMŒBÆ OF MAN

tropics and subtropics and in countries where sanitary conditions are poor. Table 13 gives the composite results of some surveys made in the United States of America. Since many of these surveys are based on only a single examination and since as many as six examinations of feces may be necessary to rule out the possibility of infection,[1] the figures are probably minimal. The percentage of infections depends upon geographical location, endemic areas and thoroughness of the methods used.

TABLE 13

THE INCIDENCE OF THE FOUR COMMON INTESTINAL AMŒBÆ OF MAN IN THE UNITED STATES OF AMERICA

	Endamœba histolytica	Endamœba coli	Endolimax nana	Iodamœba bütschlii
Grouped surveys				
Number of surveys	25	6	5	4
Persons examined	57,561	38,559	34,310	32,903
Percentage infected				
Range	0.2 to 53.0	12.4 to 32.1	11.9 to 26.5	0.9 to 21.0
Average	10.2	29.3	13.6	4.1
Selected surveys				
United States of America[2]				
(8,029 persons)	4.1	19.6	13.2	5.0
Louisiana[3]				
(4,270 persons)	8.3	12.4	19.3	0.9
Tennessee[4]				
(20,237 persons)	11.4	32.1	11.9	4.1

[2] Boeck, W. C. and Stiles, C. W., 1923.
[3] Faust, E. C. and Headlee, W. H., 1936.
[4] Meleney, H. E., Bishop, E. L. and Leathers, W. S., 1932.

In the United States of America the incidence of *Endamœba histolytica* is about 10 per cent, of *Endamœba coli* about 30 per cent, of *Endolimax nana* about 14 per cent, and of *Iodamœba bütschlii* about 4 per cent. *Dientamœba fragilis* is usually considered a rare species, with an incidence below 1 per cent. The incidence of *Endamœba gingivalis* varies from 10 per cent in persons with healthy mouths to as high as 95 per cent in patients with oral disease.

Endamœba histolytica (SCHAUDINN, 1903) HICKSON, 1909

Synonyms.—Some authorities prefer the generic name *Entamœba* rather than the approved *Endamœba*. Confusion in nomenclature has produced many synonyms. Among the more prominent are: *Amœba coli* Lösch, 1875; *Entamœba dysenteriæ* (Councilman and Lafleur, 1891) Craig, 1917; *Entamœba histolytica* Schaudinn, 1903; *Entamœba tetragena* (Viereck, 1907) Hartmann, 1908; *Entamœba hartmanni* v. Prowazek, 1912: *Löschia histolytica* (Schaudinn, 1903) Mathis, 1913; *Endamœba dysenteriæ* Kofoid, 1920; *Entamœba dispar* Brumpt, 1925.

Disease.—Amœbiasis, amœbic dysentery, amœbic abscess of liver.

History.—In 1873 Lösch at St. Petersburg reported the discovery of *Endamœba histolytica* in the feces of a Russian with severe dysentery. He demon-

[1] Dobell, C., 1919.

strated its pathogenicity by infecting a dog, which developed dysentery and intestinal ulcerations. Definite association of the amœba with disease was not established until 1887, when the observations of Koch and Gaffky upon the presence of amœbæ in the intestinal ulcerations of dysenteric patients led to the investigations of Kartulis. Three years later Osler reported its presence in America, and in 1901 Councilman and Lafleur made their important contribution to the pathology of amœbic dysentery and hepatic abscess.

By 1893, Quincke and Roos had dispelled some of the confusion by differentiating the pathogenicity of *Endamœba histolytica* and *E. coli*. Schaudinn in 1903 described their differential characteristics, and Walker in 1911 noted the important difference in the number of nuclei in their cysts. In 1913 Walker and Sellards definitely established the pathogenicity of *Endamœba histolytica* and furnished the basis of our present conception of its host-parasite relation. By feeding the infective cysts to human volunteers, they demonstrated the relation between clinical symptoms and infection. Although Musgrave and Clegg in 1904 first cultured non-pathogenic amœbæ, it was not until 1924 that Boeck and Drbohlav developed a special medium and technic for cultivating *Endamœba histolytica*.

Geographical Distribution.—Cosmopolitan. Its incidence is higher in tropical and subtropical countries and in localities where sanitation is poor.

BIOLOGICAL CHARACTERISTICS

Morphology.—*Endamœba histolytica* may be observed in the feces in three morphological stages: (1) the trophozoic, (2) the precystic, and (3) the cystic (Figs. 9 and 10).

TROPHOZOITE.—The vegetative forms range from 15 to 40 μ in diameter, but the majority are from 20 to 30 μ. Variation in size may be due to fission or to individual races. The trophozoite is distinguished from the other intestinal amœbæ by morphological characteristics of diagnostic importance (Table 12).

In the unstained specimen (Fig. 11) the protoplasm appears homogeneous except for small endoplasmic granules. The wide, clear, refractile ectoplasm constitutes about one-third of the entire animal. Thin, blade-like, ectoplasmic pseudopodia are extended rapidly. The endoplasm may contain up to 10 or more red blood cells in various stages of digestion. The single nucleus may be faintly discerned as a finely granular ring, usually eccentrically placed. Amœbæ from a freshly passed stool do not contain bacteria or intestinal debris.

In specimens stained with hematoxylin after wet fixation (Section **VII**, II, 7, 8), the cytoplasm is granular and the nuclear structure dark (Fig. 10A). There is a clearly-defined nuclear membrane, the inner surface of which is lined with fine granules of chromatin in close contact and usually regularly distributed. At the center of the nucleus is a small, deeply staining karyosome, which may consist of several distinct granules in an achromatic halo-like capsule. A linin network of fine fibrils, at times radiating to the periphery, is discernible between the karyosome and the nuclear membrane. Only freshly passed feces should be examined for trophozoites, since degenerative changes take place rapidly.

PRECYSTIC STAGE.—The precystic amœbæ are colorless, round or ovoid cells, smaller than the trophozoite and larger than the cyst (Fig. 10B). They are devoid of food inclusions. Pseudopodial action is sluggish, and there is no progressive movement. In stained specimens the nucleus resembles that of the trophozoite, but the membrane may be thicker and the karyosome larger. At times vacuoles containing glycogen and forerunners of the dark-staining rod-like chromatoidal bodies of the cysts may be detected. The precystic forms of *Endamœba histolytica* and *E. coli* are similar.

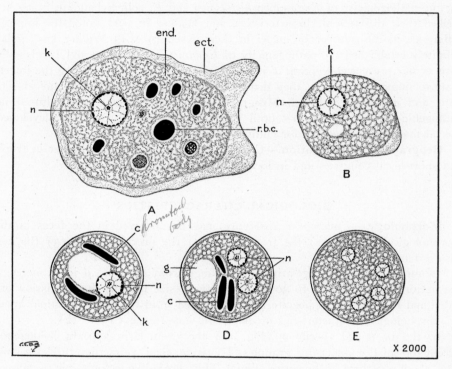

FIG. 10.—SCHEMATIC REPRESENTATION OF *Endamœba histolytica*

A, trophozoite containing red blood cells undergoing digestion; *B,* precystic amœba devoid of cytoplasmic inclusions; *C,* young uninucleate cyst; *D,* binucleate cyst; *E,* mature quadrinucleate cyst.

c, chromatoid bodies; *ect.,* ectoplasm; *end.,* endoplasm; *g,* glycogen vacuole; *k,* karyosome; *n,* nucleus; *r.b.c.,* red blood cells.

CYST.—The cysts (Fig. 10C-E, Plate I, 5-7) are round or ovoid hyaline-appearing bodies, not perfectly symmetrical. They measure from 5 to 20 μ in diameter and have a smooth refractile nonstaining wall about 0.5 μ thick. The great variation in size suggests that individual races produce large or small cysts.[1]

Within the cytoplasm of the young cysts are dark-staining refractive bars or sausage-like bodies with rounded ends that give the reaction of chromatin. There is usually one pair but there may be more. These chromatoid bodies tend to disappear as the cyst matures so that they may be absent in one-half the cysts. Vacuoles containing glycogen are also formed in young cysts. These two types of cytoplasmic inclusions are believed to represent stored food.

The immature cyst has a single nucleus, about one-third its own diameter. As the result of two nuclear divisions the mature cyst contains four nuclei, each one-sixth of its diameter. They resemble the nucleus of the trophozoite except that the peripheral ring of chromatin is thickened at one side. Cysts with one to four nuclei are passed in the feces.

Nutrition.—*Endamœba histolytica* absorbs the tissues dissolved by its cytolytic enzymes and ingests red blood cells and particles of tissue. There is no evidence that it ingests bacteria from the feces or obtains nutritive material from the intestinal content, although bacteria are essential for its cultivation.

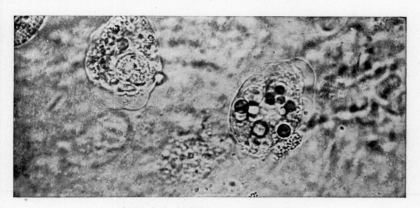

FIG. 11.—*Endamœba histolytica*

Motile forms showing ingested red blood cells and clear ectoplasm (From Army Medical School Collection, Washington, D. C.).

Movement.—The active movements of the trophozoite in warm fresh feces distinguishes *Endamœba histolytica* from other intestinal amœbæ. It moves by wave-like advances of the ectoplasmic pseudopodia and flows in an apparently purposeful manner across the microscopic field. If the trophozoite is not kept at body temperature, movement quickly ceases. The precystic forms are sluggish.

Reproduction.—The amœbæ multiply by binary fission. Nuclear division is a modified form of mitosis.[1] The nucleus enlarges and assumes a spindle shape in which the chromatin is arranged in threads and masses. This spindle form divides without apparent relation to the arrangement of the chromatin. Following nuclear division the cytoplasm splits into two new individuals. Reproduction also takes place through cyst-formation, the mature cyst ultimately producing eight vegetative amœbæ after excystment.

Cultivation.—*Endamœba histolytica* was first cultivated in 1925 on L. E. S. medium (Section **VII**, IV, 1),[5] although Cutler, whose work was not confirmed, reported success in 1918. Other media have proved successful and culturing has be-

---

[5] Boeck, W. C. and Drbohlav, J., 1925.

come an established method of determining the presence of *Endamœba histolytica* in suspected carriers or in stale stools. Except for ingested bacteria the amœbæ in cultures are similar to those in the tissues. In bacteria-free cultures the amœbæ fail to multiply and soon die. Both encystment and excystment take place in cultures.

LIFE CYCLE

The life cycle of *Endamœba histolytica* is comparatively simple. The formation of infective cysts in the large intestine is followed by their passage in the feces, their extracorporeal existence and their ingestion by a new host (Fig. 12).

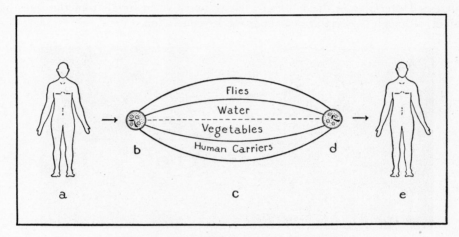

FIG. 12.—TRANSMISSION OF *Endamœba histolytica*

a, man infected with amœba; *b*, cysts in feces; *c*, modes of transmission; *d*, cysts in food; *e*, new host infected.

Hosts.—Man is the principal host of *Endamœba histolytica*. Spontaneous infections, probably caused by cysts from man, have been reported in monkeys, dogs, cats, rats and hogs. Experiental infections have been established in monkeys, dogs, cats, rats, mice, guinea pigs and rabbits. Puppies and kittens are more easily infected than the older animals. Kittens infected by feeding cysts or by rectal injections of trophozoites and cysts succumb in a few days to a fulminating infection with extensive lesions. Puppies react like kittens; but the lesions in older dogs more nearly resemble those in man.[6] No cysts have been recovered from infected cats, rabbits or guinea pigs. Mammals probably play but a minor rôle in the transmission of infection to man, although they are undoubtedly reservoir hosts, since the amœbæ found in spontaneous infections are morphologically identical with *Endamœba histolytica*.

Cyst-formation.—A certain proportion of amœbæ pass from the lesions of the intestinal wall into the lumen of the large intestine. Here they cease ingesting food, decrease in size, become spherical and enter the precystic stage. As a rule cysts are

[6] Faust, E. C., 1932.

not formed in the intestinal wall or in secondary sites of infection. Encystment seems designed primarily for meeting adverse conditions outside the host, although it has been observed in cultures, in the liver, and under experimental conditions of stasis in the colon of kittens.

Transmission.—In acute dysentery the trophic amœbæ are voided in the feces. In chronic patients and carriers the cystic forms predominate. The vegetative forms readily succumb to temperatures above or below 37° C., but the precystic amœbæ and immature cysts are more resistant. It is believed that immature cysts may develop into mature cysts outside the body. The mature cyst is the resistant infective stage. It can survive as long as 30 days in water at 0° C. and 9 days in feces at 22° C. It quickly succumbs to desiccation and is killed in five minutes at 55° C. It is susceptible to phenol, but is more resistant to bichloride of mercury, formalin and chlorine. It can withstand the action of the digestive juices, which probably destroy the trophozoites and immature cysts if they chance to reach a new host. It is doubtful whether immature cysts can infect a new host, although immature uni- and binucleated cysts mature in the small intestine of monkeys.[7]

Man.—When ingested the mature cysts pass unaffected through the stomach. In the lower part of the small intestine the cyst wall disintegrates, liberating a four-nucleated amœba, which divides ultimately into eight small trophozoites.[7] During excystment the quadrinucleate amœba begins to move vigorously, the cyst wall tears, and the organism escapes through the opening. An involved series of nuclear and cytoplasmic divisions results in the formation of eight new amœbæ. These small active amœbæ move downward to the large intestine, where they invade the mucosa, submucosa and muscular tissues of the intestinal wall aided by the action of their cytolytic ferments and by their amœboid movements. Some may remain in the intestinal lumen and eventually become encysted. From the intestinal wall the amœbæ may spread to secondary sites. They may reach the liver via the portal vein, thence by the blood to the lungs, brain and other organs, where they multiply in the tissues.

PATHOGENESIS

PATHOLOGY

The pathological lesions of amœbic infection of the intestinal wall are of three types: (1) early minute nodular flask-like cavities, (2) irregular crateriform ulcers with ragged edges, and (3) communicating sinuses between adjacent ulcers.

Invasion.—The exact mechanism of invasion of the intestinal wall in man is not known. Pathological material from the early stages of the infection has not been available, and the material from the later stages may not be representative, since amœbæ may continue their destructive activities for some time after the death of the host. Our present knowledge of the period of invasion has been derived from experimental work on kittens, monkeys and dogs, in which the pathological lesions are not precisely comparable to those in man.

Apparently the amœbæ first proliferate in the intestinal lumen, while the host

---

[7] Hegner, R., Johnson, C. M. and Stabler, R. M., 1932.

reacts by secreting a protective covering of mucus over the intestinal mucosa.[8] In from 2 to 8 days local invasion occurs in the poorly protected areas. The amœbæ pass through the outer epithelial layer into the mucosa, multiply and produce local dissolution of the tissues with edema. Several theories attempt to explain the formation of the primary ulcer. (1) The amœbæ enter the mucosa intercellularly by their own movements, multiply, and by interference with the circulation produce necrosis in the overlying mucosa.[7] (2) The amœbæ penetrate the mucosa by the action of

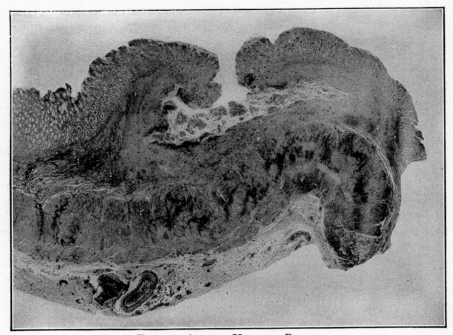

FIG. 13.—AMŒBIC ULCER OF BOWEL

Note that the base of the ulcer extends laterally beneath the mucosa and that the orifice is small in comparison to the basal extent of the ulcer (From Duval and Schattenberg, *Text-book of Pathology*, 1939, D. Appleton-Century Company).

cytolytic enzymes and, increasing this activity through multiplication, form ulcers in the mucosa and submucosa. Cytolytic extracts have been obtained.[9] (3) The entrance of amœbæ provides channels for the bacterial invasion of the mucosa and submucosa. In the solitary follicles the bacteria form abscesses which break through to produce typical ulcers.[10]

Early Ulcer.—The prevailing lesion of amœbic infection is the flask-shaped ulcer (Fig. 13). The early lesion is a tiny area of necrosis in the superficial mucosa or a small nodular elevation with a minute opening. Beneath this opening is a flask-shaped cavity of yellowish-brown necrotic material consisting of cytolyzed cells, mucus and amœbæ. The subsequent development of the lesions depends upon whether the parasite establishes an equilibrium with the host (the asymptomatic

[8] Hiyeda, K. and Suzuki, M., 1932.   [10] Ratcliffe, H. L., 1931.
[9] Craig, C. F., 1927.

patient) or whether it progressively invades the tissues (the patient with acute dysentery).

Superficial Ulcer.—In most infections the early lesions develop into superficial ulcerations. A round or oval ulcer which rarely extends beyond the mucosa is formed by surface erosion or by the discharge of a small abscess. Its base is covered with a gelatinous material in which the amœbæ are imbedded and its edges are thickened but not undermined. At times it may have a crateriform appearance with irregular slightly overhanging edges.

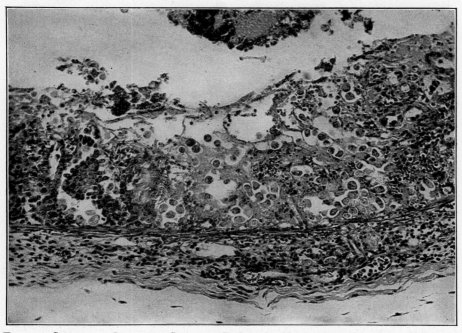

FIG. 14.—SECTION OF INTESTINE SHOWING *Endamœba histolytica* IN MUCOSA (*ca* × 100)

In this case the invasion of the innumerable amœbæ is limited by the muscularis mucosa (From Duval and Schattenberg, *Textbook of Pathology*, 1939, D. Appleton-Century Company).

Normal infection with *Endamœba histolytica*, about 90 per cent of all cases, represents a variable equilibrium between parasite and host, characterized by the absence of noticeable symptoms. The lesions are usually superficial, although severe ulcerations may exist without symptoms, and the process is one of continuous invasion, ulceration and repair. This process differs from the severe ulcerative lesions of acute dysentery in its superficial nature, slow progress, lack of marked lateral extension, absence of extensive secondary bacterial infection, and reparative response of the host.[8]

In this type of infection, in which a balance is struck between parasite and host, new tissue is formed as rapidly as it is destroyed; hence there is often no great change in the mucosa. This quiescent relationship between parasite and host is due to the resistance of the host rather than to the low virulence of the parasite. The number of ingested cysts determines to some extent the course of the infection, as a heavy invasion is more likely to produce acute dysentery. Individual variation in resistance has been demonstrated by the production of both asymptomatic and symptomatic infections with cysts from a convalescent carrier.[11]

Uncomplicated Acute Dysentery.—The 10 per cent of infected individuals who develop acute or chronic dysentery present a different pathological picture.

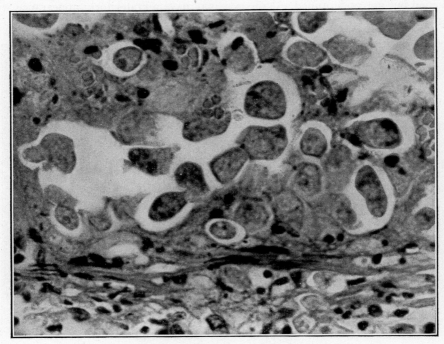

FIG. 15.—*Endamœba histolytica* IN INTESTINAL MUCOSA

Portion of Figure 14 enlarged to show amœbæ, some of which contain red blood cells (From Duval and Schattenberg, *Textbook of Pathology*, 1939, D. Appleton-Century Company).

There is rapid extension of the ulcerative processes and extensive involvement of the superficial and deep layers of the intestine (Fig. 14). The ulcerations range from the early pinpoint superficial lesions to large areas of necrosis, which at times even encircle the bowel (Fig. 16). The small, flask-like, primary ulcer has a crateriform appearance with a wide base and a narrow opening with irregular slightly elevated overhanging edges. It extends downward to invade the submucosa and the muscular layers and laterally along the long axis of the intestine. The subsurface dissolution of tissues is so extensive that ulcers frequently communicate by sinuses and produce honey-combed areas beneath apparently intact mucosa. Sloughing of the overlying mucosa exposes large necrotic areas covered with shreds of cytolyzed tissue. The destruction of the tissues is followed by a regenerative proliferation of connective tissue, which, in cases of extensive damage, may ultimately cause a fibrous thickening of the intestinal wall.

[11] Walker, E. L. and Sellards, A. W., 1913.

The histological changes include histolysis, thrombosis of the capillaries, round-cell infiltration and necrosis (Fig. 15). The usual signs of inflammation other than hyperemia and edema are absent, and unless secondary bacterial infection supervenes, few polymorphonuclear leukocytes are observed. The process is regenerative rather than inflammatory. Red blood cells are abundant because of the destruction

FIG. 16.—ULCERATION OF LARGE INTESTINE IN AMŒBIC DYSENTERY

Note deep crater-like ulcers (From Duval and Schattenberg, *Textbook of Pathology*, 1939, D. Appleton-Century Company).

of small blood vessels. The amœbæ may be found in the base of the ulcers, grouped in cavities, particularly at the base of the intestinal glands, or scattered through the tissues.

Dysentery with Secondary Bacterial Infection.—Extensive ulceration is invariably accompanied by secondary bacterial infection. At times the histological picture is confusing, areas of noninflammatory reaction being interspersed with areas of cellular infiltration, but as a rule the type of ulcer and the tissue-response are characteristic. Bacterial infection may involve the lymph follicles and mesenteric lymph glands and by perforation of the intestine may even cause peritonitis.

Sites of Primary Infection.—The primary lesions, except for about 5 per cent in the lower ileum near the ileocecal valve, are confined to the large intestine. A study of the location of the lesions in 186 patients at autopsy (Fig. 17B) revealed that in 61 per cent the lesions were scattered throughout the colon; in 34 per cent isolated areas were involved in the following order of frequency: cecum, ascending colon, rectum, sigmoid and appendix (Fig. 17A); and in 5 per cent scars alone were found.[12] These figures indicate that intestinal stasis is of importance in deter-

---

[12] Clark, H. G., 1925.

mining the site of invasion, a fact confirmed by the experimental infection of kittens.[13]

Sites of Secondary Infection.—Infection may spread from the intestinal wall to other organs. Amœbæ are more likely to invade secondary sites in patients with clinical dysentery, but not infrequently secondary infections occur in mild or latent disease. Liver abscesses have been found in patients who gave no history of dysen-

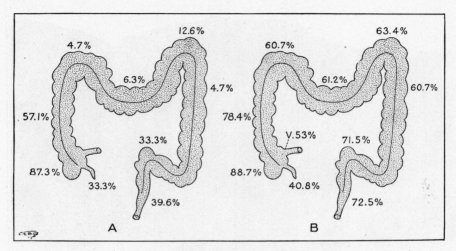

FIG. 17.—DISTRIBUTION OF AMŒBIC LESIONS IN THE INTESTINE

A, regional distribution of lesions in 63 patients examined *post mortem,* where one or few ulcers were present. The percentile figures indicate the frequency of the various sites of primary infection. *B,* regional distribution of lesions in 186 patients examined *post mortem* (Redrawn from Clark, 1925).

tery. Chance determines the establishment of a secondary infection, since in order to reach the liver the amœbæ must enter the blood stream through the eroded capillaries of the portal vein.

In the liver the amœbæ first cause hepatitis and then dissolve the hepatic cells producing single or multiple abscesses usually in the right lobe (Fig. 18). The early abscess is a small oval or rounded mass with a grayish-brown matrix of necrosed hepatic cells. The living amœbæ are continually invading the marginal tissue. As the abscess increases its wall thickens and the contents become a viscid chocolate or reddish mass of hepatic cells, red blood cells, bile, fat and other products of tissue-dissolution, interspersed with strands of connective tissue. There is usually only one abscess, but it may reach a large size and even rupture into the peritoneum or pleura. Secondary bacterial infection produces purulent changes which alter the character of the amœbic abscess.

About one-half of the dysenteric patients who come to autopsy show major or minor involvement of the liver.[12] Evidently the presence of amœbæ in the liver does not invariably cause liver abscess, since only 20 per cent of dysenteric patients are

---

[13] Sellards, A. W. and Theiler, M., 1924.

so affected. Once within the circulation amœbæ may be carried from the liver to any organ of the body. There are authentic records of infections in brain, lung, and spleen, and more questionable instances of the involvement of urinary bladder, testes, epididymis, lymph glands, skin and bone.

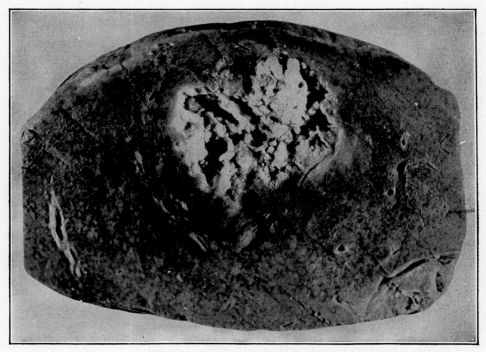

FIG. 18.—AMŒBIC ABSCESS OF LIVER

Note extent of hepatic involvement and the soft macerated central portion (anchovy sauce) (From Duval and Schattenberg, *Textbook of Pathology*, 1939, D. Appleton-Century Company).

SYMPTOMATOLOGY

Walker and Sellards (1913) definitely established the causal relation of *Endoamœba histolytica* to amœbic dysentery. Their experiments proved that frank clinical disease develops in but a small proportion of infected individuals and that most hosts become asymptomatic carriers. Thus the ordinary state of infection is an equilibrium between parasite and host, and the typical infected individual is an asymptomatic carrier. The atypical patient, about one out of ten, develops clinical dysentery. Only 15 per cent of 106 carriers in 1,979 apparently healthy British soldiers in Egypt gave a history of dysentery.[14] Clinical amœbiasis may be considered from the standpoint of (1) incubation, (2) subsymptomatic disease, (3) acute dysentery, (4) chronic dysentery, (5) liver abscess, and (6) carriers.

Incubation.—The time between infection and the appearance of symptoms varies from a few days to months and even years since asymptomatic carriers may develop clinical dysentery at any time. In experimental infections the incubation-

---

[14] Wenyon, C. M. and O'Connor, F. W., 1917.

period averaged 64.5 days and ranged from 20 to 95, but the time between the ingestion of cysts and their appearance in the feces averaged 9 days and varied from 1 to 44.[11] The period of incubation in the severe and highly fatal Chicago epidemic of 1933-34 was under one week in 6.7 per cent of 495 cases, under four weeks in 64.7 per cent (mean 12 days) and under eight weeks in 91 per cent.[15]

Asymptomatic Disease.—The infected individual, who does not manifest typical symptoms, may have a low-grade chronic amœbiasis with slight tissue-invasion. He may show no clinical signs, may be aware of slight discomfort, may have mild toxemia, or may suddenly relapse into typical clinical dysentery. About one-half the nondysenteric harborers of *Endamœba histolytica* exhibit no symptoms. The remainder may show indefinite metabolic disturbances: loss of weight, mental and physical lassitude, vasomotor and nervous disturbances, and vague muscular pains. Minor gastro-intestinal disturbances may also occur: constipation alternating with slight diarrhea, colicky pains with or without abdominal tenderness, flatulence and nausea.

Acute Dysentery.—Acute dysentery varies in severity from the rare fulminating case with marked toxemia to the mild attack with spontaneous recovery. The onset may be sudden with acute abdominal pain, nausea, vomiting, fever (100° to 102° F.) and occasionally chills; more often it is insidious and is preceded by attacks of mild or severe diarrhea. At the height of the attack the patient may have 15 to 20 or more daily movements of blood, mucus and in severe cases bits of necrotic mucosa. Blood morphology is essentially normal; the leukocyte count runs from 7,000 to 11,000 per c.mm. There may be toxemia, prostration, muscular pain and weakness, mental depression, loss of weight, abdominal tenderness, anemia, dehydration, and emaciation. Patients with mild infections as a rule do not have fever.

Chronic Dysentery.—The chronic patient manifests symptoms of dysentery only during exacerbations. At other times he may have normal movements, constipation or minor bowel irregularities. The patient either is recovering from an acute attack or has a continuous low-grade infection. Recurrent attacks may result in extensive scarification of the colon and produce chronic invalidism.

Liver Abscess.—The early symptoms of liver abscess are those of hepatitis: fever, tenderness, liver enlargement and leukocytosis. About two-thirds of the cases give a history of recent dysentery. The symptoms of advanced abscess are: a dull pain often referred to the right shoulder, remittent evening fever, chills, sweating, and a leukocytosis of about 20,000 per c.mm. If the abscess is large and near the surface of the liver, it is often palpable, the area of liver dulness is increased, the respiratory movements are restricted, and the right abdominal muscles are rigid. The patient may be anemic, emaciated and exhausted.

Carriers.—The carrier of *Endamœba histolytica,* unlike the typical bacterial carrier is probably never truly healthy. In nearly every individual excreting cysts there is minor or major injury to the tissues. The only outward distinction between the carrier and the unaffected individual is the presence of cysts in the feces. The contact carrier maintains a low-grade infection, but whenever his resistance is

[15] McCoy, G. W. *et al.,* 1936.

lowered, he may succumb to the disease. The convalescent carrier has recovered from dysentery, but is subject to clinical relapse.

IMMUNITY

The resistance of the host is the chief factor in determining the occurrence of clinical disease in amœbic infections. However, strains of *Endamœba histolytica* vary in virulence.[16] Evidence of racial immunity is inconclusive, although the white races in the tropics seem more susceptible to clinical disease than the natives. Resistance is lowered by an insufficient or ill-balanced diet. Young experimental animals are more susceptible than old. It is possible, though unproved, that an immunity from repeated exposure may develop in persons over 35 years of age. Continued exposure to heavy infections, however, may overcome resistance. Systemic immunity determines the type of infection in the host, but the relation of the carrier state to immunity is not clearly defined. Precipitins [17] and alexin-fixative antibodies [18] have been demonstrated in the blood.

DIAGNOSIS, PROGNOSIS AND TREATMENT

Diagnosis.—The definite diagnosis of amœbiasis depends upon the identification of the parasite in the feces or tissues. At times it is difficult clinically to differentiate amœbic dysentery from bacillary, schistosomal or balantidial dysentery, and from other intestinal diseases such as colitis, chronic gastritis and enteritis, chronic appendicitis, and food allergy. Moreover, mixed infections may cause additional confusion. The character of the stool, though far from constant, is helpful in differentiating amœbic and bacillary dysentery. The typical stool of bacillary dysentery is inoffensive, alkaline, and consists chiefly of bright red blood, pus and mucus with little fecal material. The red blood cells are unaltered. There are numerous polymorphonuclear leukocytes, no eosinophils, a fair number of epithelial and endothelial cells and macrophages, and a moderate number of nonmotile bacilli, but no Charcot-Leyden crystals and pyknotic residues. The amœbic stool is offensive, acid, and consists of adherent blood and mucus with much fecal material. The red blood cells are small, show degenerative changes with altered hemoglobin, and form adhesive masses. Streptococci are the predominating bacteria. The total cellular exudate is scanty; there are few polymorphonuclear leukocytes, some eosinophils, few if any macrophages, and scattered epithelial and endothelial cells. Pyknotic residues and nuclear remnants are numerous and Charcot-Leyden crystals are present.

In chronic relapsing cases with extensive healed lesions the roentgen-ray may prove a diagnostic aid. Intestinal adhesions produce a mottled effect in the films. The roentgen-ray is also valuable in diagnosing liver abscess.

Endamœba histolytica may be detected in the feces, in material obtained by proctoscopic examination, in the aspirated contents of liver abscesses, and in sections of tissue (Section **VII**, II). Ordinarily the examination of the feces is sufficient.

[16] Meleney, H. E. and Frye, W. W., 1933.   [18] Craig, C. F., 1927, 1929, 1933; Tsuchiya,
[17] Wagener, E. H., 1924.   H., 1934; Weiss, E. and Arnold, L., 1934.

Identification is based upon finding the trophozoite in freshly passed feces of dysenteric patients and the cyst in the feces of chronic patients and carriers. It is impossible to differentiate the precystic form from that of *Endamœba coli*.

The trophozoite is distinguished from other vegetative amœbæ by the characteristics given in Table 12. Its important characteristics are: (1) active, progressive and directional motility; (2) ectoplasmic pseudopodia, sharply distinct, hyaline and blade-shaped; and (3) ingested red blood cells partially disintegrated and smaller than normal. The cysts of *Endamœba histolytica* are differentiated in iodine preparations from those of other parasitic amœbæ by: (1) 1 to 4 nuclei, (2) minute central karyosome, (3) diffuse glycogen mass, and (4) large chromatoid bars (Table 12).

When microscopical examination fails to reveal *Endamœba histolytica*, cultural methods and serological tests are indicated. Cultural methods (Section **VII**, IV, 1-3) increase the chances of finding the parasite, particularly in old feces or in chronic cases and carriers. Alexin-fixation (Section **VII**, IX, 2, 21) has proved useful in diagnosing carriers and atypical clinical cases.[18] It is also an aid in controlling treatment, since a negative reaction indicates the probable elimination of the infection. In 1,000 individuals Craig (1933) found 175 positive, of which 157, or 89.7 per cent, had *Endamœba histolytica* in the feces. Of 825 negative individuals 12, or 1.4 per cent, harbored this parasite. The specificity of the test for *Endamœba histolytica* was indicated by the fact that 32.5 per cent of the negative cases harbored other species of intestinal Protozoa.

Prognosis.—Prognosis depends upon the duration and treatment of the disease. Modern therapeusis has improved prognosis. When treatment is started early, the prognosis is good since, except for fulminating cases, patients rarely die during the initial attack. When treatment is delayed and recurrent attacks have occurred prognosis is less favorable, but extensive ulceration, if uncomplicated, usually yields to persistent treatment. Prognosis in liver abscess is less satisfactory and is poor when there is secondary bacterial infection. In brain abscess it is hopeless.

Treatment.—Treatment of amœbiasis may be discussed from the standpoint of (1) the patient with acute amœbic dysentery, (2) the patient with liver abscess, (3) the chronic remittent patient, and (4) the carrier. It is important to cure carriers and chronic patients who act as foci of infection as well as to treat clinical patients in order to prevent relapse and liver abscess. Treatment in amœbic dysentery is designed, first, to relieve acute symptoms and second, to prevent chronic invalidism and the carrier state.

In the acute stage patients will benefit by rest in bed, which should continue for one week after the acute illness. The diet should be bland and consist largely of broths, barley water and milk with lime water. During convalescence a semifluid or soft diet is indicated, and a full diet should be resumed only after the subsidence of symptoms. Strength should be maintained with the smallest necessary amount of high-caloric food. Chilling and overexcitement should be avoided and alcohol absolutely prohibited. In this stage of the disease emetine hydrochloride is the medication of choice (Section **VII**, XIII, 14). Under treatment dysenteric symptoms ordinarily disappear in 8 to 10 days. The treatment is repeated if relapses occur, but since the margin between its toxic and therapeutic doses is small, at least two weeks should intervene between courses. Its administration must be discontinued at once should toxic signs or symptoms appear. Good results have also been reported from the use of emetine bismuth iodide. Massive doses of bismuth carbonate are also recommended.

Hepatic amœbiasis or abscess of the liver is best treated with emetine hydrochloride. Authorities differ on the effectiveness of this drug after the abscess has fully formed, but agree on its beneficial action in the earlier stages. If drug therapy proves ineffective, surgical drainage by aspiration or by laparotomy is indicated. Emetine combined with aspiration appears to be the most satisfactory treatment. Emetine is less effective in pulmonary abscess and is of no value in abscess of the brain.

Emetine hydrochloride, however, is not an efficient amœbicide and its toxicity contraindicates its continuous use. English authorities have found that emetine bismuth iodide is not only effective in controlling acute infections but also has an amœbicidal action. During convalescence the amœbicidal drugs, chiniofon or carbarsone, usually supplant emetine.

In the treatment of carriers and asymptomatic patients the drug of choice is chiniofon, an iodine compound which is believed to destroy the cysts as well as the trophozoites (Section **VII**, XIII, 12). A single course of treatment is usually sufficient but a second course may be required. In carriers resistant to chiniofon, carbarsone, an arsenic compound (Section **VII**, XIII, 5), or vioform, an iodine compound (Section **VII**, XIII, 13) may prove effective. The treatment of the patient with remittent exacerbations depends upon his condition. If he is convalescent, chiniofon is administered, but if diarrhea is present, he is treated as an acute case with rest and emetine hydrochloride.

The progress of treatment may be checked by examining the feces for *Endamœba histolytica*. After each course, stool examinations should be made on three successive days; at least one sample should be obtained by a saline cathartic. Examinations should be repeated at monthly intervals. If no cysts are found over a period of six months, the patient may be regarded as tentatively cured. The alexinfixative test is also useful in determining permanent cure.

PREVENTION

The application of preventive measures in parasitic diseases presupposes a knowledge of the infective stage of the parasite, the mode of transmission and the mechanism of invasion.

Epidemiology.—The incidence of *Endamœba histolytica* in the United States of America appears to be about 10 per cent (Table 13). This figure is probably representative for the temperate zones throughout the world. The parasite is more prevalent in warmer areas and in localities where sanitation is lax. Endemic foci where explosive outbreaks have occurred, as in Chicago, have a higher-than-average incidence. Its distribution appears to be spreading.

The incidence of *Endamœba histolytica* is also influenced by social conditions, age and sex. Poorer classes show a higher incidence probably because of lessened resistance and overcrowding with accompanying insanitary conditions. Children under 5 years show the lowest incidence, because of lack of exposure. The maximal incidence is reached between 25 and 30 years with a sharp decline after 35. Men have a higher incidence than women.

The source of infection is the carrier or asymptomatic contact and the chronic convalescent patient, who are passing infective cysts. In acute dysentery encystment does not occur either because conditions for cyst-formation are unfavorable or be-because the trophozoites are discharged too rapidly to permit encystment. Hence, acute cases are not important sources of infection, since the trophozoites rapidly perish outside the body and are destroyed by the gastric secretions if they reach a new host. The mature cyst is apparently the infective form. The infectivity of immature cysts is still in doubt. The number of cysts discharged per day from carriers varies from 330,000 to 45,000,000 and averages 14,520,000.[19]

The thermal death point of cysts varies from 45° to 68° C. They can survive freezing temperatures, but succumb rapidly to desiccation. The survival periods cited by various investigators are: 16 days in moist feces,[20] 9 days at 22° C., and 35 at 5° C.,[21] 17 days in tap water,[22] and 153 days in distilled water at 12° to 22° C., but 9 days in heavily polluted water.[23] Cysts are killed in 30 minutes by exposure to 1:2,500 mercuric chloride, 1 per cent phenol and 5 per cent formaldehyde. Several investigators report that cysts are resistant to chlorine in many times the strength used to protect drinking water from pathogenic bacteria; however, 4 p.p.m. of chlorine in water free from organic material will kill them in 20 minutes.[24]

In order to produce infection cysts must enter the digestive tract. They reach the oral cavity through: (1) carriers acting as food handlers or as direct contacts, (2) contamination of food by flies and other insects, (3) contamination of vegetables by feces or water carrying infective cysts, and (4) drinking water contaminated by fecal discharges.

The infective carrier is the most potent factor in the transmission of amœbiasis. Carriers among the general population are difficult to discover and constitute a grave problem, but a carrier who is also a food handler theoretically is a serious menace to public health. The danger from this source, however, may be overrated. Investigations have shown that cysts are infrequently found on the hands of carriers,[25] that cysts do not remain viable long on experimentally contaminated hands,[26] and that after washing the hands it is difficult to find cysts even under the fingernails.[27] Animal reservoir hosts are probably of minor importance, but the extent of their responsibility in the transmission of amœbiasis is unknown.

The common house fly is a mechanical vector.[28] It may carry cysts on its feet or pass a large number in its feces. Cysts remain viable in the intestine of flies for 24 to 48 hours. Flies are particularly dangerous in military or civilian camps where

[19] Kofoid, C. A., Kornhauser, S. I. and Plate, J. T., 1919.
[20] Thomson, J. G. and Thomson, D., 1916.
[21] Tsuchiya, H., 1932.
[22] Yorke, W. and Adams, A. R. D., 1926.
[23] Boeck, W., 1921.
[24] Stone, W. S., 1937.

[25] Spector, B. K., Foster, J. W. and Glover, N. G., 1935.
[26] Spector, B. K. and Buky, F., 1934.
[27] Andrews, J., 1934.
[28] Root, F. M., 1921; Frye, W. W. and Meleney, H. E., 1932.

sanitation is inadequate. Viable cysts have been found in the feces of cockroaches.[29] but these and other insects, although possible vectors, are of minor importance.

Where night soil is used as fertilizer, vegetables may be contaminated with cysts. When these vegetables are eaten unwashed or unscalded, they serve as a means of transmitting infection.

The Chicago epidemic of 1933 emphasized the importance of water in the dissemination of amœbic infection.[15] Some 1,409 cases, originating in Chicago during the Century of Progress Exposition, were found in 43 states, 1 territory and 3 Canadian provinces. The majority were traced to two neighboring hotels with a common water supply. The water was polluted by sewage through faulty cross-connections and through a defective plug in an overhead waste pipe that permitted leakage into a water tank. Wells, springs and streams, which in small communities are often exposed to contamination with local sewage, serve to spread the infection.

Prophylaxis.—The prevention of amœbiasis includes the following measures:

1. Detection of potential human sources of infection, especially by surveys of food handlers.
2. Removal of carriers from food-handling occupations.
3. Instruction of carriers in personal hygiene, especially hand-washing, to avoid transmission of cysts.
4. Treatment of infected individuals.
5. Cooking or thorough washing and scalding at 80° C. for one-half minute of raw vegetables from areas where night soil is used as fertilizer.
6. Screening of food from flies and other insects.
7. Sanitary methods of sewage disposal, screening of latrines and possibly disinfection of feces.
8. A properly safeguarded and filtered water supply. Amœbiasis has declined in cities where filtration plants have been established. Chlorination is not as effective as filtration since the cyst is resistant to the concentrations of chlorine that are used to destroy pathogenic bacteria.
9. Sanitary plumbing including precautions against cross-connections.
10. Education of general public concerning amœbiasis.

Endamœba coli (GRASSI, 1879) HICKSON, 1909

Synonyms.—Some important synonyms are: *Entamœba coli* Casagrandi and Barbagallo, 1895; *Entamœba hartmanni* v. Prowazek, 1912 *pro parte; Endamœba hominis* Pestana, 1917; *Löschia coli* Chatton and Lalung-Bonnaire, 1912.

Disease.—*Endamœba coli* is a nonpathogenic commensal of the large intestine of man.

History.—*Endamœba coli* was discovered in India by Lewis in 1870. It was described by Cunningham in 1871 and in more detail from 1879 to 1888 by Grassi, who found the parasite in the feces of healthy as well as diseased individuals. Grassi's description was amplified by Quincke and Roos in 1893, by Casagrandi and Barbagallo in 1895 and

---

[29] Frye, W. W. and Meleney, H. E., 1936.

by Schaudinn in 1903. Quincke and Roos succeeded in differentiating the nonpathogenic *Endamœba coli* from the pathogenic *E. histolytica,* although confusion as to their separate identity continued until Walker in 1911 and Walker and Sellards in 1913 furnished conclusive proof that *Endamœba coli* was a distinct nonpathogenic species.

Geographical Distribution.—Cosmopolitan. Incidence higher in tropics and areas of poor sanitation.

BIOLOGICAL CHARACTERISTICS

Morphology.—The differential morphological characteristics of the trophozoitic, precystic and cystic stages are given in Table 12.

The unstained trophozoite, usually 20 to 30 μ in size, has a coarse granular endoplasm, which is not clearly differentiated from the narrow ectoplasm, and contains bacteria and débris but never erythrocytes or tissue cells. The pseudopodia are blunt and granular. The nucleus is distinctly visible as a ring of refractive granules. In stained specimens (Fig. 19A) the round nucleus has a thick membrane lined with irregularly distributed coarse masses of chromatin, and an eccentric karyosome (Fig. 8B). Chromatin granules may also be present in the linin network.

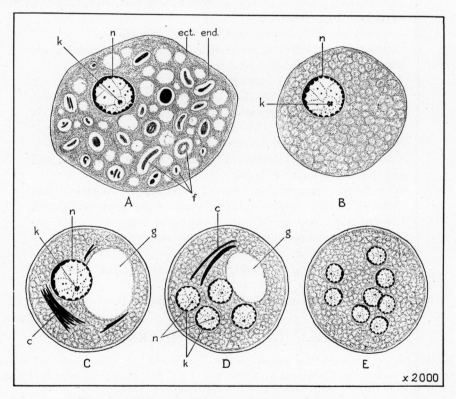

Fig. 19.—Schematic Representation of *Endamœba coli*

A, trophozoite showing inclusions; *B,* precystic stage, no inclusions; *C,* uninucleate cyst with glycogen vacuole and chromatoid bodies; *D,* quadrinucleate cyst with glycogen vacuole and chromatoid bodies; *E,* mature cyst with eight nuclei.

c, chromatoid bodies; *ect.,* ectoplasm; *end.,* endoplasm; *f,* food vacuoles; *g,* glycogen mass; *k,* karyosome; *n,* nucleus.

The spherical precysts (Fig. 19B), 15 to 45 μ, are similar in structure to the trophozoites except for the absence of inclusions. The spherical or slightly ovoid cysts, 12 to 22 μ, are somewhat larger than those of *Endamœba histolytica*. This variation in size suggests the possibility of different races. Immature cysts ordinarily have one, two or four refractive nuclei with eccentric karyosomes resembling the nucleus of the trophozoite (Fig. 19C-D). The mature cysts (Fig. 19E, Plate I, 8-10) have 8 nuclei, though occasionally 16 or even 32 may be present. When the cyst is first formed, a relatively large, sharply-defined glycogen globule may be observed in the cytoplasm, but it usually disappears after the 4-nucleated stage. The dark-staining chromatoid bodies, usually observed only in immature cysts, are slender rods, filaments or sheaves of spicules with sharp, fractured or square ends.

Nutrition.—Nourishment consists of bacteria, vegetable cells and other débris from the intestinal contents.

Movement.—Movement is sluggish and usually not directional. The blunt, broad pseudopodia project slowly.

Reproduction.—The trophozoite reproduces by binary fission. Nuclear division of the mitotic type takes place in the cyst.[30] After excystation each of the nuclei develops into an amœbula.

Cultivation.—*Endamœba coli* may be cultivated on suitable media (Section VII, IV, 1-3), but it has not been possible to maintain a strain beyond a few transfers. Both trophozoites and cysts are found in the cultures.

LIFE CYCLE

The life cycle is similar to that of *Endamœba histolytica*. Cysts form in the large intestine and are passed in the feces, the nucleus dividing to form 8 small nuclei in the mature cyst. The cysts are carried to the small intestine of man in contaminated food or drink. Here they excyst, and the liberated trophozoites pass down to the large intestine and undergo multiplication. Excystation has been observed in cultures but not in the host. Man is the chief host. A similar amœba, probably identical with *Endamœba coli*, has been found in monkeys,[31] and the experimental infection of rats, hogs and monkeys has been reported.[32]

PATHOGENESIS, DIAGNOSIS AND TREATMENT

Endamœba coli inhabits the lumen of the large intestine in man. There is no evidence that it ever produces pathological lesions.

Diagnosis.—*Endamœba coli* is of medical importance only because it may be mistaken for the pathogenic *E. histolytica*. Certain differential characteristics (Table 12) should be emphasized. The trophozoite of *Endamœba coli* has a more granular endoplasm containing ingested bacteria and débris but no red blood cells, often a narrow, less differentiated ectoplasm, broader and blunter pseudopodia, more sluggish indeterminate motility, and a visible nucleus which, when stained, has coarser, more irregular peripheral chromatin and a larger eccentric karyosome. The two species may be confused in the precystic stage in which only nuclear differences are detectable, but the cysts of *Endamœba coli* are larger, have a more granular cytoplasm, when fully developed have eight instead of four nuclei, and contain slender, splinter-like chromatoid bodies.

Treatment.—Treatment is unnecessary from the standpoint of health. The iodine preparations and emetine, efficacious in *Endamœba histolytica* infections, are ineffective in eliminating the parasite, but the arsenical compounds, such as carbarsone, are reported to give good results.

[30] Swezy, O., 1922.   [32] Kessel, J. F., 1923, 1924.
[31] Wenyon, C. M., 1908.

PREVENTION

Epidemiology.—The incidence of *Endamœba coli* in the United States of America is about 30 per cent (10 to 60 per cent), probably a minimal figure. Its distribution and methods of transmission correspond to those of *Endamœba histolytica*. Man readily acquires the infection; 85 per cent positive infections have resulted from feeding cysts to volunteers.[11] Its prevalence in man indicates a high degree of food contamination by fecal discharges and suggests that its incidence may serve as an indicator of potential infection with *Endamœba histolytica*.

Prophylaxis.—Similar to that of *Endamœba histolytica*.

Endamœba gingivalis (GROS, 1849) SMITH AND BARRETT, 1915

Synonyms.—*Amœba gingivalis* Gros, 1849; *Amœba buccalis* Steinberg, 1862; *Amœba kartulis* Doflein, 1901; *Entamœba buccalis* v. Prowazek, 1904; *Entamœba gingivalis* (Gros) Brumpt, 1913; *Endamœba buccalis* Bass and Johns, 1915.

Disease.—Nonpathogenic.

History.—*Endamœba gingivalis*, observed by Gros in 1849 in the tartar of teeth, was the first parasitic amœba discovered. It was reported by Steinberg in 1862 and by Grassi in 1879, and first described in detail by v. Prowazek in 1904. It gained prominence in 1915, when Smith and Barrett, and Bass and Johns incriminated it as the probable cause of pyorrhea alveolaris. Subsequent investigations have not confirmed their conclusions as to its pathogenicity.

Geographical Distribution.—Probably cosmopolitan.

BIOLOGICAL CHARACTERISTICS

Morphology.—The trophozoite (Fig. 20) is the only known form. The usual size is from 10 to 20 μ with a range of from 5 to 35 μ. A clear well-differentiated ectoplasm at times comprises one-half the volume of the actively motile animal, but in the nonmotile forms the ectoplasm is not usually seen. A thin homogeneous surface film, the ectoplastic pellicle, has been described.[33]

The granular endoplasm contains many vacuoles, even when freed of food inclusions. The most striking characteristic of *Endamœba gingivalis* is the large number of food vacuoles, which comprise about one-third its bulk. Within these vacuoles are dark-staining rounded bodies 1 to 5 μ in diameter, rich in chromatin. They are largely derived from the nuclei of degenerated endothelials, lymphocytes and occasionally polymorphonuclear leukocytes. This material may represent ingested degenerated salivary corpuscles.[34] Other vacuoles contain ingested bacteria, which constitute but a small proportion of the food content.

The spherical nucleus, which is usually inconspicuous unless stained, is smaller than that of *Endamœba histolytica* averaging about 3.3 μ and ranging from 2.5 to 4 μ. There are often minor deformities in shape, possibly due to pressure from the food vacuoles. The moderately thick nuclear membrane is lined with a ring of irregularly distributed small masses of chromatin. The large central or eccentric karyosome consists of one or several granules surrounded by a granular halo, from which radiating fibrils extend across a clear zone to the peripheral ring (Fig. 8C).

Nutrition.—*Endamœba gingivalis* is a scavenger of disintegrated cells; bacteria are a minor source of nourishment.

Movement.—Two types of movement have been observed: (1) several small clear pseudopodia may be extruded at once in various directions without producing progress, or (2) one or more large pseudopodia may be extended and the amœba travels in a definite direction.

---

[33] Kofoid, C. A. and Swezy, O., 1924.   [34] Goodey, T. and Wellings, A. W., 1917.

Reproduction.—Reproduction is by binary fission. Binucleated specimens are rarely observed.

Cultivation.—The trophozoites may be cultivated on the usual media (Section **VII,** IV, 1-3) but they do not encyst.

LIFE CYCLE

Little is known of the life cycle of *Endamœba gingivalis* other than the division of the trophozoite. Evidently it has a limited existence outside the host, since the trophozoite is susceptible to adverse external conditions. If the possibility of cyst formation is excluded, transmission must take place by direct contact. Intestinal infection appears impos-

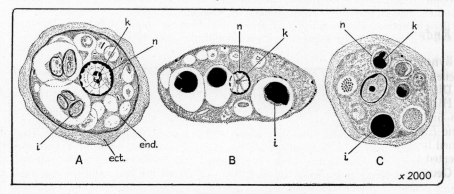

FIG. 20.—*Endamœba gingivalis*

A, trophozoite with a peripheral film of ectoplasm, but no pseudopodia. Food vacuoles with bacteria and with leukocytic nuclei. *B,* trophozoite with three large food vacuoles with leukocytic nuclei, two of which still show traces of adherent cytoplasm. Small vacuoles with remnants of food bodies but no bacteria. *C,* trophozoite showing ingested bodies and character of nucleus.

ect., ectoplasm; *end.,* endoplasm; *i,* inclusion nuclei; *k,* karyosome; *n,* nucleus (*A* and *B* redrawn from Kofoid and Swezy, 1924; *C* redrawn from Goodey and Wellings, 1919).

sible, since the trophozoite is killed by the gastric juice and bile.[35] Man is the principal host, but morphologically similar amœbæ have been found in the mouths of monkeys, dogs, cats and horses. Dogs that had inflamed gingival tissues have been temporarily infected with *Endamœba gingivalis* from man.[36]

PATHOGENESIS

Endamœba gingivalis inhabits the gingival tissues of man. It is found in the tartar of the teeth and in neighboring gingival pockets. While it may be present in healthy mouths, it is especially prevalent in dental caries, pyorrhea, and other suppurative and inflammatory conditions of the mouth and throat. It was once believed to produce pyorrhea, but there is no sound evidence of a causal relationship. The frequent presence of this parasite in pyorrheic lesions is not due to any invasive power but rather to the fact that it is a scavenger of diseased tissues. The occasional ingestion of red blood cells is not in itself evidence of pathogenic activity.

DIAGNOSIS AND TREATMENT

Diagnosis.—Scrapings for examination are taken from the tartar of the teeth or from pockets and rough surfaces near the teeth, where food particles and cellular débris

---

[35] Howitt, B. F., 1926.   [36] Hinshaw, H. C., 1928.

collect. Diagnosis is easy, since this amœba is the only one ordinarily found in the mouth. Its differential characteristics are given in Table 12.

Treatment.—Emetine, once considered an effective remedy, and other amœbicidal drugs have not proved successful. Proper treatment of abnormal oral conditions is the best way to eliminate the parasite.

PREVENTION

Epidemiology.—The general incidence of *Endamœba gingivalis* is estimated to be at least 50 per cent. It runs as high as 95 per cent in persons with pyorrhea alveolaris, carious tartar-covered teeth, and receding spongy gums. It is present in from 10 to 20 per cent of individuals with apparently healthy mouths. The method of transmission is unknown, but is probably direct contact by kissing.

Prophylaxis.—The institution of proper oral hygiene should reduce the incidence of *Endamœba gingivalis* by doing away with conditions that favor its existence.

Endolimax nana (WENYON AND O'CONNOR, 1917) BRUG, 1918

Synonyms.—*Entamœba nana* Wenyon and O'Connor, 1917; *Endolimax intestinalis* Kuenen and Swellengrebel, 1917.

Disease.—Nonpathogenic.

History.—This amœba, although observed by several investigators from 1908 on, was first described as a distinct species by Wenyon and O'Connor in 1917 under the name *Entamœba nana*. In the same year Kuenen and Swellengrebel also described and named it *Endolimax intestinalis*. In 1918 Brug combined the two names and gave it the accepted title of *Endolimax nana*.

Geographical Distribution.—Cosmopolitan.

BIOLOGICAL CHARACTERISTICS

Morphology.—The amœba, frequently confused with free-living species, is found as a trophozoite and in the precystic and cystic stages. The small trophozoite (Fig. 21A) measures from 6 to 15 μ. The granular vacuolated endoplasm contains bacteria, crystals and vegetable cells. The pseudopodia are clear, broad and blunt. The nucleus is indistinct

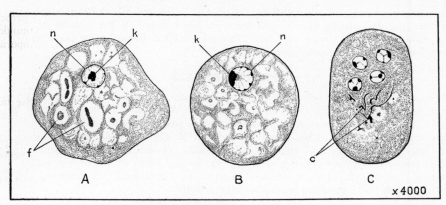

FIG. 21.—*Endolimax nana*

A, trophozoite with ingested bacteria; *B*, uninucleate cyst; *C*, mature quadrinucleate cyst, showing irregular strands of chromatoid substance.

c, chromatoid strands; *f*, food vacuoles; *k*, karyosome; *n*, nucleus (Redrawn from Zinsser and Bayne-Jones, *Textbook of Bacteriology*, 7th ed., 1934, D. Appleton-Century Company).

in the living animal. When stained, it shows a large central or eccentric pleomorphic karyosome sometimes split into several masses connected with slender threads (Fig. 8D). The rather thick nuclear membrane has no attached chromatin.

The precystic amœba is a refractive round or oval body with a finely granular cytoplasm free from ingested material. The oval, often irregular, thin-walled cysts (Fig. 21B and C, Plate I, 1 and 2) measure from 8 to 10 μ, with a range from 5 to 14 μ. Immature cysts have one or two nuclei with a karyosome often in contact with the nuclear membrane. Mature cysts have four nuclei, usually grouped at one end. At times the cysts contain ill-defined masses of glycogen but no definite chromatoid bodies, except short rods or granules (Fig. 21C).

Nutrition.—Similar to *Endamœba coli.*
Movement.—Sluggish movement is effected by broad blunt pseudopodia.
Reproduction.—Binary fission of trophozoites. Nuclear division in cyst.
Cultivation.—It is cultivated with difficulty since it dies after a few generations (Section VII, IV, 1-3).

LIFE CYCLE

Endolimax nana resembles *Endamœba coli* in its life cycle and mode of transmission except that the mature cyst probably produces four new amœbæ after excystation. Amœbæ of the genus *Endolimax* are found in animals, but man appears to be the only host of *Endolimax nana.* Rats and monkeys have been experimentally infected with cysts from man.[32]

PATHOGENESIS, DIAGNOSIS AND TREATMENT

It is a harmless parasite in the large intestine of man.
Diagnosis.—The amœba is identified by its small size, sluggish movement, characteristic nucleus, and its quadrinucleated ellipsoidal cyst (Table 12).
Treatment.—It is resistant to chemotherapy.

PREVENTION

Epidemiology.—Its incidence, about 14 per cent in the United States of America, varies in different localities (Table 13). Its transmission to man is similar to that of *Endamœba histolytica.*
Prophylaxis.—Same as that of *Endamœba histolytica.*

Iodamœba bütschlii (v. PROWAZEK, 1912) DOBELL, 1919

Synonyms.—*Entamœba williamsi* v. Prowazek, 1911; *Entamœba bütschlii* v. Prowazek, 1912; *Endolimax williamsi* Brug, 1919; *Iodamœba williamsi* (v. Prowazek, 1911) Taliaferro and Becker, 1922.
Disease.—Nonpathogenic.
History.—In 1911 and 1912 von Prowazek described two amœbæ, under the names *Entamœba williamsi* and *Entamœba bütschlii.* The confusion over which name applies to this amœba has resulted in the use of both specific names with the generic name of *Iodamœba,* proposed by Dobell in 1919. The deep staining "iodine cysts" recognized by Wenyon and others since 1915 were shown by Dobell in 1919 to belong to this species.
Geographical Distribution.—Cosmopolitan.

BIOLOGICAL CHARACTERISTICS

Morphology.—The trophozoite (Fig. 22A), rarely found in the feces, is usually from 9 to 14 μ in size with a range from 5 to 20 μ. The clear blunt or finger-like pseudopodia form slowly. The endoplasm contains ingested bacteria and débris in vacuoles. In unstained specimens the nucleus, usually indistinct, may sometimes be seen if not obscured by food vacuoles. The stained nucleus is characterized by a centrally-located karyosome one-third to one-half its diameter, surrounded by a layer of granules imbedded in a darker matrix from which fibrils extend to a thick nuclear membrane (Fig. 8E).

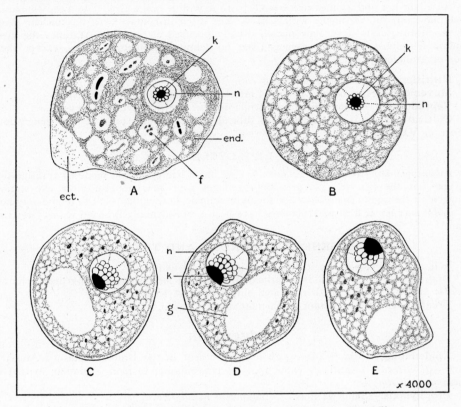

FIG. 22.—SCHEMATIC REPRESENTATION OF *Iodamœba bütschlii*

A, trophozoite with bacteria and organic debris; *B*, precystic amœba; *C*, uninucleate cyst with glycogen vacuole; *D*, irregular uninucleate cyst with glycogen vacuole; *E*, irregular uninucleate cyst with small glycogen vacuole.

ect., ectoplasm; *end.*, endoplasm; *f*, food vacuole; *g*, glycogen vacuole; *k*, karyosome; *n*, nucleus.

The precystic form (Fig. 22B), approximately the same size as the trophozoite, has lost its food granules. It develops into a uninucleated cyst usually from 8 to 10 μ in size but ranging from 5 to 14 μ. The cyst (Fig. 22C-E, Plate I, 3 and 4) is characterized by irregularity of form, a thick cyst wall, and a large compact mass of glycogen that stains deeply with iodine. Small deeply-staining bodies, somewhat like volutin granules, are found in the cytoplasm. Its nucleus differs from that of the trophozoite by its larger size, by an eccentric karyosome often in contact with the nuclear membrane and by the crescent-shaped mass of peripheral granules of the karyosome. Binucleated cysts are rare, 0.1 per cent.[37]

[37] Taliaferro, W. H. and Becker, E. R., 1922.

Nutrition.—Nourishment is obtained by ingesting bacteria and intestinal débris.
Movement.—Sluggish and rarely progressive.
Reproduction.—Binary fission of trophozoite.
Cultivation.—It grows poorly under cultivation, dying out after a few generations.

LIFE CYCLE

The little known life cycle of *Iodamœba bütschlii* probably resembles that of the other intestinal cyst-forming amœbæ. Since most cysts are uninucleate, a single amœba emerges after excystation.[38] Species of *Iodamœba* reported from apes, monkeys, hogs and other mammals may prove to be *Iodamœba bütschlii*. The infection of rats with cysts from man has been reported.[39]

PATHOGENESIS, DIAGNOSIS AND TREATMENT

Iodamœba bütschlii is apparently a harmless parasite of the large intestine of man.
Diagnosis.—*Iodamœba bütschlii* is readily differentiated from other amœbæ by its characteristic nucleus, by the irregular shape of the uninucleated cysts and by the large glycogen body in the cyst (Table 12).
Treatment.—None indicated.

PREVENTION

Epidemiology.—The incidence of infection varies but averages about 4 per cent in the United States of America (Table 13). Transmission is the same as for other cyst-forming intestinal amœbæ. The possibility of animal reservoir hosts requires further investigation.
Prophylaxis.—Similar to that of *Endamœba histolytica*.

Dientamœba fragilis JEPPS AND DOBELL, 1918

Synonyms.—None.
Disease.—Apparently nonpathogenic, although intestinal disturbances have been reported in a few infected individuals.
History.—This species was discovered by Wenyon in 1909, but was first described and named by Jepps and Dobell in 1918.
Geographical Distribution.—Probably cosmopolitan.

BIOLOGICAL CHARACTERISTICS

Morphology.—*Dientamœba fragilis* is known only in the trophozoite form. The trophozoite (Fig. 23) usually is from 6 to 12 μ in diameter but varies from 3 to 20 μ. The ectoplasm is clearly differentiated, the endoplasm is vacuolated and often contains ingested bacteria, and the clear, hyaline pseudopodia are leaf-like. It differs from other intestinal amœbæ in that about three-fifths of the specimens have two identical nuclei. The spherical nuclei, indistinct in unstained specimens, have a delicate membrane and a central karyosome consisting of chromatinic granules imbedded in a matrix of plastin. The granules are usually arranged in a tetrad but more than four may be present in other patterns. One of the granules is larger than the others, and it has been suggested that it is the actual karyosome and that the other bodies are subsidiary masses.[40] Delicate fibrils sometimes connect the granules with the nuclear membrane.
Nutrition.—Nourishment is obtained from the intestinal contents. Bacteria and small vegetable microörganisms are ingested.

---

[38] Smith, S. C., 1927.
[39] Smith, S. C., 1928.

[40] Wenrich, D. H., 1936.

Movement.—The amœba is actively progressive and motile in fresh preparations, and the leaf-shaped pseudopodia are quickly thrust out.

Reproduction.—Simple fission of the mature binucleate amœba produces two uninucleate daughter amœbæ, in each of which the nucleus soon divides to form binucleate amœbæ.[1] Wenrich (1939) has described the details of reproduction.

Cultivation.—It may be cultivated (Section **VII**, IV, 1-3). No cysts are found in cultures.

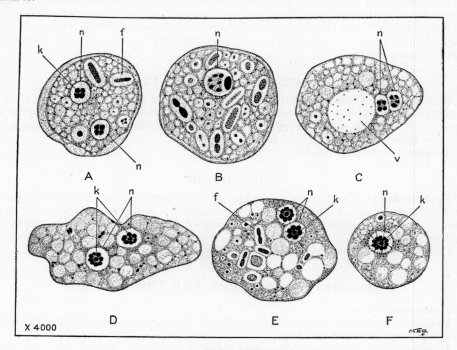

FIG. 23.—*Dientamœba fragilis*

A, fairly typical amœba with compact arrangement of nuclear granules; *B*, large mononucleate amœba with more than four nuclear granules and enlarged single endosome set off by a clear zone; *C*, amœba with two nuclei pressed together (possibly by large central vacuole); *D*, elongate binucleate amœba; *E*, large binucleate amœba; *F*, uninucleate amœba.

f, food vacuole; *k*, karyosome; *n*, nucleus; *v*, vacuole (*A* to *C* redrawn from Wenrich, 1936; *D* to *F* redrawn from Jepps and Dobell, 1918).

LIFE CYCLE

Man is the principal host, but a morphologically similar amœba has been reported in wild monkeys.[41] Since trophozoites usually perish soon after leaving the body and since cysts are unknown, investigators have not adequately explained the transmission of this amœba from host to host without presupposing a resistant form. Trophozoites may survive 24 to 48 hours.[42]

PATHOGENESIS

Dientamœba fragilis is ordinarily considered a nonpathogenic inhabitant of the colon. Reports of intestinal disorders in infected individuals, however, suggest that

[41] Hegner, R. and Chu, H. J., 1930.   [42] Hakansson, E. G., 1936.

this species possibly produces low-grade pathological changes in the large intestine;[43] but such reports must be taken advisedly.

DIAGNOSIS AND TREATMENT

Diagnosis.—The trophozoite is found only in liquid or soft stools. Outside the body it rapidly degenerates into a rounded motionless body, in which the vacuoles coalesce into a large central vacuole, rendering identification difficult. It is identified by its small size and the structure of the two nuclei (Table 12).

Treatment.—Hakansson (1937) reported success with carbarsone.

PREVENTION

Epidemiology.—The incidence of this species has been considered less than 1 per cent. Because of its absence in formed stools, it may be more common, since 4.3 per cent of infections have been found in 1,060 freshman students at the University of Pennsylvania.[44] The method of transmission to man is problematical owing to the absence of cysts. The amœba, however, must gain access to a new host through contaminated food.

Prophylaxis.—The low incidence and probable nonpathogenicity of the parasite render prevention of little moment. Methods of prevention parallel those of *Endamœba histolytica*.

DOUBTFUL SPECIES OF AMŒBA REPORTED FROM MAN

Numerous amœbæ of uncertain or doubtful status have been reported from man, but have not been generally accepted as distinct species. Prominent are *Councilmania lafleuri* Kofoid and Swezy, 1921; *Karyamœbina falcata* Kofoid and Swezy, 1924; *Caudamœba sinensis* Faust, 1923; and *Entamœba dispar* Brumpt, 1925.

COPROZOIC AMŒBÆ

Free-living amœbæ in fecal material may be mistaken for parasitic species. Flies, water or air currents may transfer these free-living species to the feces or their cysts may pass unharmed through the intestine of man. Trophozoites develop when the feces are kept warm and moist for some hours before examination. They may be differentiated from parasitic amœbæ by the ease of cultivation, the presence of a contractile vacuole, and in the cystic stage by the thick cyst wall, one or two nuclei with thick membranes, and a large central karyosome. Among the free-living amœbæ found in the feces are: *Hartmanella hyalina* (Dangeard, 1900) Alexeieff, 1912; *Dimastigamœba grüberi* (Schardinger, 1889) Alexeieff, 1912; *Sappinia diploidea* (Hartmann and Nägler, 1908) Alexeieff, 1912; *Vahlkampfia punctata* (Dangeard, 1910) Chatton and Lalung-Bonnaire, 1912; and *Vahlkampfia lobospinosa* (Craig, 1912) Craig, 1913.

REFERENCES

BOECK, W. C., and DRBOHLAV, J.   The Cultivation of *Endamœba histolytica,* Am. J. Hyg., 1925, 5:371.

CLARK, H. G.   The Distribution and Complications of Amœbic Lesions Found in 185 Postmortem Examinations, Am. J. Trop. Med., 1925, 5:157.

CRAIG, C. F.   Further Observations Upon the Complement-fixation Test for the Diagnosis of Amœbiasis. An Analysis of the Results of the Test in One Thousand Individuals, J. Lab. & Clin. Med., 1933, 18:873.

[43] Wenrich, D. H., 1936, 1937; Hakansson, E. G., 1936.

[44] Wenrich, D. H., Stabler, R. M. and Arnett, J. H., 1935.

CRAIG, C. F.   Amœbiasis and Amœbic Dysentery, Charles G. Thomas Company, Springfield, Ill., 1934.

DOBELL, C.   The Amœbæ Living in Man, John Bale, Sons and Danielsson, Ltd., London, 1919, pp. 150.

FRYE, W. W. and MELENEY, H. E.   *Endamœba histolytica* and Other Intestinal Protozoa in Tennessee. 2, A Study of Flies, Rats, Mice and Some Domestic Animals as Possible Carriers of the Intestinal Protozoa of Man in a Rural Community, Am. J. Hyg., 1932, 16:729.

GOODEY, T. and WELLINGS, A. W.   Observations on *Entamœba gingivalis* from the Human Mouth with a Note on the Trichomonad Flagellate, *Tetratrichomonas buccalis,* n. sp., Parasitology, 1917, 9:537.

HEGNER, R., JOHNSON, C. M. and STABLER, R. M.   Host-parasite Relations in Experimental Amœbiasis in Monkeys in Panama, Am. J. Hyg., 1932, 15:394.

HIYEDA, K., and SUZUKI, M.   Pathological Studies of Human Amœbic Ulcers Especially Those of Carriers, Am. J. Hyg., 1932, 15:809.

JEPPS, M. W. and DOBELL, C.   *Dientamœba fragilis* n.g., n. sp., a New Intestinal Amœba from Man, Parasitology, 1918, 10:352.

KOFOID, C. A. and SWEZY, O.   The Cytology of *Endamœba gingivalis* (Gros) Brumpt Compared with that of *E. dysenteriae* with Special Reference to the Determination of the Amœbas in Bone Marrow in Arthritis Deformans of Ely's Second Type, Univ. California Publ. Zoöl., 1924, 26:165.

McCOY, G. W. et al.   Epidemic Amœbic Dysentery, Nat. Inst. Health. Bull. No. 166, Washington, D. C., 1936.

MELENEY, H. E. and FRYE, W. W.   A Comparison of Five Strains of *Endamœba histolytica* with Reference to their Pathogenicity for Kittens, Am. J. Hyg., 1933, 17:637.

———   The Pathogenicity of *Endamœba histolytica,* Tr. Roy. Soc. Trop. Med. & Hyg., 1936, 29:369.

RATCLIFFE, H. L.   A Comparative Study of Amœbiasis in Man, Monkeys and Cats with Special Reference to the Formation of Early Lesions, Am. J. Hyg., 1931, 14:337.

SPECTOR, B. K., FOSTER, J. W. and GLOVER, N. G.   *Endamœba histolytica* in Washings from Hands and Finger Nails of Infected Persons, U. S. Pub. Health Rep., 1935, 50:163.

SWEZY, O.   Mitosis in the Encysted Stages of *Endamœba coli* (Lösch), Univ. California Publ. Zoöl., 1922, 20:313.

TALIAFERRO, W. H. and BECKER, E. R.   The Human Intestinal Amœba, *Iodamœba williamsi,* and its Cysts (Iodine Cysts), Am. J. Hyg., 1922, 2:188.

WALKER, E. L. and SELLARDS, A. W.   Experimental Entamœbic Dysentery, Philippine J. Sc., 1913 (B), 8:253.

WEISS, E. and ARNOLD, L.   The Specificity of the Complement-fixation Test for Amœbiasis, Am. J. Digest. Dis. & Nutrition, 1934, 1:548.

WENRICH, D. H.   Studies on *Dientamœba fragilis*. I. Observations with Special Reference to Nuclear Structure, J. Parasitol., 1936, 22:76.

WENYON, C. M. and O'CONNOR, F. W.   Human Intestinal Protozoa in the Near East, John Bale, Sons and Danielsson, Ltd., London, 1917, pp. 218.

Chapter IX

THE INFUSORIA OF MAN

The INFUSORIA are characterized by the possession of cilia during part or all of their life cycle and in most instances by the presence of a vegetative macronucleus and a generative micronucleus. Although there are numerous free-living aquatic species and many that are ecto- and endoparasites of vertebrates and invertebrates, few species are parasitic in man and only one, *Balantidium coli,* is of medical interest. The parasites of man belong to the subclass CILIATA and order HETEROTRICHIDA.

MORPHOLOGY AND PHYSIOLOGY

Morphology.—A free-living infusorian of the genus *Paramecium* illustrates the typical morphology and physiology of the INFUSORIA (Fig. 7). It is a slipper-shaped organism with a blunt anterior and a more pointed posterior end. It has an oral groove or peristome, a gullet, a macronucleus and one or several micronuclei, two contractile vacuoles, cilia arranged in striated rows over the surface of the body, a granular endoplasm, and a nongranular ectoplasm containing small spindle-shaped trichocysts, which probably serve as weapons of defense.

Physiology.—Food particles are ingested through the cytostome which leads into the cytopharynx or gullet. At the base of the cytopharynx these particles collect in a droplet and pass directly into the endoplasm enclosed in vacuoles where they are digested by secreted ferments. The indigestible residue is eliminated through a transient anal opening, the cytopyge. Secretion, excretion, and respiration are the same as in the amœba. Forward movement with rotation on the longitudinal axis is accomplished by the action of the cilia, which beat obliquely backward. The timing of the ciliary movements produces a flowing, wave-like effect over the body. In different species the cilia are modified for swimming, crawling and procuring food. The animal reproduces by binary fission. Conjugation takes place every several hundred generations, and endomixis, a replenishing of the macronucleus from the micronucleus, occurs every fortieth or fiftieth generation.

CLASSIFICATION

The INFUSORIA are classified chiefly by the distribution and characteristics of their cilia.

Subclass CILIATA. Cilia throughout life
    Order 1. HOLOTRICHIDA. Cilia of uniform length usually covering entire body.
    Order 2. HETEROTRICHIDA. Cilia large or fused; spiral zone in peristomal groove.
    Order 3. HYPOTRICHIDA. Cilia modified for creeping.

Order 4. PERITRICHIDA. Cilia forming a peristomal disc but usually absent elsewhere.

Subclass ACINETARIA. Cilia present only in young forms; adults have tentacles.

Parasites of Man.—*Balantidium coli* of the order HETEROTRICHIDA is the only species of importance in man. *Nyctotherus faba* has been reported occasionally, but the studies of Witcherman (1938) and Beltrán (1939) show that it should not be considered a parasite of man.

Balantidium.—The members of the genus *Balantidium* are oval ciliates with many oblique longitudinal rows of cilia. They have a kidney-shaped macronucleus, a micronucleus, contractile vacuoles, a peristome, a cytostome, and a cytopyge. About 30 species have been reported from almost as many hosts including primates, sheep, cattle, hogs, opossums, guinea pigs, ostriches, turtles, frogs, toads, fishes, snails, crustaceans, and insects.[1] Many mammalian species of *Balantidium* are morphologically similar, but differ in such physiological processes as nuclear reorganization after conjugation [2] and in their ability to live in other than the specific host.

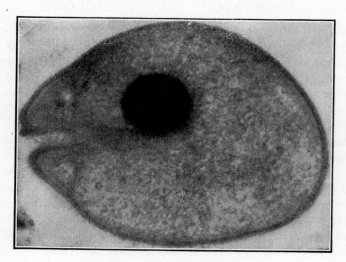

FIG. 24.—*Balantidium coli*

Photograph of a specimen within the intestinal wall of a human host (*ca* × 1250) (From the Army Medical Museum).

Balantidium coli (MALMSTEN, 1857) STEIN, 1862

Synonyms.—*Paramæcium* (?) *coli* Malmsten, 1857; *Plagiotoma coli* Claparede and Lachmann, 1858; *Leucophrya coli* Stein, 1860; *Holophrya coli* Leuckart, 1863.

Disease.—Balantidiasis, balantidiosis, balantidial dysentery, ciliary dysentery.

History.—*Balantidium coli* was first described by Malmsten in 1857 in the feces of dysenteric patients. It was studied in hogs in 1861 by Leuckart and in 1862 by Stein who assigned the parasite to the genus *Balantidium*.

[1] Hegner, R., 1934.   [2] Nelson, E. C., 1934.

Geographical Distribution.—Cosmopolitan. Though common in hogs, it is a comparatively rare parasite of man in most localities.

BIOLOGICAL CHARACTERISTICS

Morphology.—*Balantidium coli* is the largest intestinal protozoon of man. The trophozoite usually measures from 50 to 70 μ in length (range 30 to 150 μ) by 40 to 50 μ (range 25 to 120 μ) in breadth. In one instance the average size of 100 specimens was 86 μ x 66 μ.[3] The grayish-green unstained trophozoite (Fig. 24) is ovoid with a narrow anterior end and is shaped like a sac (balantidium = little bag). The body is enclosed in a delicate protective pellicle (Fig. 25A) beneath which is a

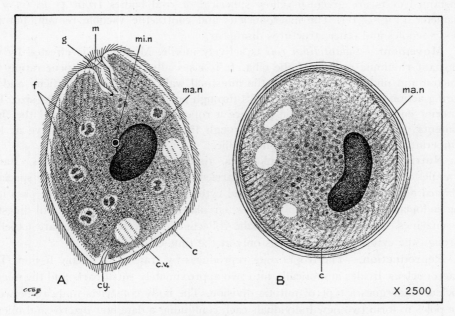

FIG. 25.—SCHEMATIC REPRESENTATION OF *Balantidium coli*

A, trophozoite; *B*, cyst.

c, cilia; *cy.*, cytopyge; *c.v.*, contractile vacuole; *f*, food vacuole; *g*, gullet; *m*, mouth; *ma.n.*, macronucleus; *mi.n.*, micronucleus (Modified from Dobell and O'Connor, 1921).

narrow zone of ectoplasm. The surface is covered by spiral longitudinal rows of cilia, which arise from granules in the ectoplasm and impart a striated appearance to the animal. Between the rows of cilia are ridges in the pellicle caused by the projection of dark granular bands of ectoplasm. At the anterior end, just ventral to the midline, is the narrow triangular peristome, which opens into the cytostome leading to the cytopharynx. Both peristome and cytostome are lined with long cilia adapted for procuring food. At the posterior end is an indistinct excretory opening, the cytopyge.

---

[3] McDonald, J. D., 1922.

Within the granular endoplasm are two contractile vacuoles, one near the anterior end and the other in the posterior third of the organism; a large elongated kidney-shaped macronucleus located obliquely near the middle; a small subspherical micronucleus lying close to the concavity of the macronucleus; and numerous vacuoles containing solid and partly digested food particles. In stained specimens the macronucleus shows dense, deeply-staining masses of chromatin within the nuclear membrane. The micronucleus is composed of closely-packed chromatin.

Cyst-formation appears to be a protective rather than a reproductive function. The trophozoite secretes a double wall with a thick tough outer layer and a thin inner one. The encysted organism at first retains its cilia and revolves slowly within the double wall, but later the cilia degenerate and the animal becomes quiescent. The unstained cysts are greenish-yellow spherical or oval bodies from 45 to 65 μ in diameter (Fig. 25B). The macronucleus and contractile vacuole remain, but the food vacuoles and other structures disappear.

Movement.—*Balantidium coli* is actively motile. Movement is effected by the constant rhythmic motion of the cilia. It is especially adapted for penetrating the mucosa and underlying tissues of the intestinal wall. Its extreme plasticity and its boring action enable the animal to pass through openings even one-half its size. The anterior end elongates, the cilia produce a rotary boring movement, and the fluid contents pass in hour-glass fashion through the opening. It is less active at low temperatures and is negatively heliotrophic.

Nutrition.—Erythrocytes, leukocytes, tissue fragments, oil globules, starch granules and other intestinal débris are carried into the cytopharynx by the specially adapted adoral cilia of the peristome and cytostome. These food particles pass into the endoplasm and, enclosed in vacuoles, circulate in a definite course until digested by enzymes. The solid waste materials, collected in a rectal vacuole, are expelled through the cytopyge, which opens only at the time of discharge.

Reproduction.—The trophozoite reproduces by transverse binary fission. The macronucleus divides amitotically into two approximately equal parts and the micronucleus undergoes a type of mitotic division. The body constricts midway between the poles to form two new individuals each containing a daughter macro- and micronucleus, which after their division retreat toward opposite poles. A new cytostome is formed in the posterior daughter cell. Rapid division may produce nests of balantidia in the tissues.

During the conjugation of *Balantidium coli* in the chimpanzee the micronucleus undergoes two maturation divisions to form four nuclei, of which three degenerate and the fourth divides to produce the stationary and migratory pronuclei.[2] After the exchange of nuclei the conjugants separate; the exchanged nuclei fuse and then divide to form a small and a large nucleus. The smaller undergoes certain modifications to form the micronucleus. The larger divides to form two nuclei, which after a developmental period join to form the macronucleus.

Cultivation.—Barret and Yarbrough in 1922 were the first to cultivate *Balantidium coli* in an artificial medium. Several investigators have been successful with other media or modifications of the original (Section **VII**, IV, 6). Only trophozoites are formed in cultures and cysts have not been observed, although their presence in cultures of *Balantidium caviae* has been reported.[4] Conjugation has also been observed.[5]

LIFE CYCLE

Transmission.—The trophozoite lives in the mucosa and underlying tissues of the large intestine and when passed in the feces probably dies as soon as it meets adverse conditions. Cysts are formed in the large intestine and are found in greatest numbers in the rectum. It is assumed that the cysts are the infective forms, since they may survive outside the hosts for several weeks in a moist environment. When ingested by a new host, the cyst wall dissolves, and the liberated trophozoite invades the intestinal wall and multiplies in the tissues (Fig. 26).

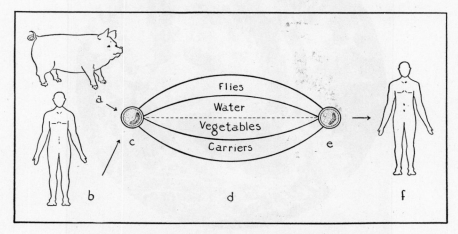

Fig. 26.—Transmission of *Balantidium coli*

a, hog, the principal host; *b,* man, an occasional host; *c,* cyst in feces; *d,* modes of transmission; *e,* cyst in food; *f,* cyst develops into vegetative form in intestine of man.

Hosts.—The varieties of *Balantidium coli* in man and hog are generally considered identical, man being regarded as an incidental host. Morphologically indistinguishable species have been found in the monkey, chimpanzee and guinea pig. Two species, *Balantidium coli* and *B. suis,* have been differentiated morphologically in the hog.[3] Cross-infection experiments by several investigators indicate that *Balantidium coli* of man may be transmitted to monkeys, hogs, cats, guinea pigs and rats; *B. coli* of hogs to monkeys, guinea pigs, rats and rabbits; balantidia of monkeys to hogs; and *B. caviae* of guinea pigs to rats.[6] Attempts to infect man with balantidia of hogs and monkeys have proved unsuccessful. Failure may be attributed to physiological differences in the several strains and to the high resistance of man to infection.

[4] Rees, C. W., 1927.

[5] Jameson, A. P., 1927; Atchley, F., 1935; Nelson, E. C., 1935.

[6] Hegner, R. W., 1926; Rees, C. W., 1927; Schumaker, E., 1930; Andrews, J., 1932; Nelson, E. C., 1935.

PATHOGENESIS

Balantidium coli is found chiefly in the ceca and upper part of the large intestine and rarely in the small intestine more than three feet above the ileocecal valve.

Pathology.—The ciliate invades the mucosa, submucosa and even the muscular layers of the large intestine by means of cytolytic ferments or mechanical penetration (Fig. 27). Injury from the boring of the ciliate may cause hyperemia of the mucosa.[7] All degrees of severity from a simple catarrhal condition to marked ulcera-

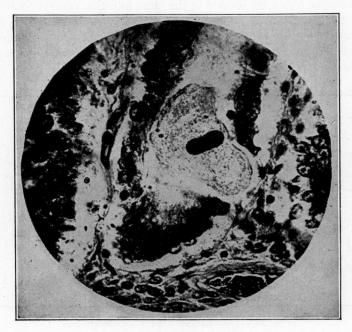

FIG. 27.—*Balantidium coli*

Parasite breaking through the epithelium of a follicle of the colon (After Strong, 1904, from Zinsser and Bayne-Jones, *Textbook of Bacteriology,* 7th ed., 1934, D. Appleton-Century Company).

tion occur. The multiplying parasites form small mucoid abscesses, which break down into round, oval or irregular ulcers like those of *Endamœba histolytica*. The individual ulcers may be discrete with normal or hyperemic intervening mucosa, or they may coalesce or communicate with each other by subsurface sinuses. Sections of the intestinal wall show hemorrhagic areas, round-cell infiltration, abscesses, necrotic ulcers and invading parasites (Fig. 28). Nests of balantidia may be seen in the tissues, capillaries and lymph channels. Secondary sites of infection are seldom found in spite of the local invasion of the blood and lymph.

Symptomatology.—Clinical balantidiasis varies from a mild colitis with diarrhea to an acute or chronic dysentery. The diarrhea may be continuous or intermittent with constipation. The feces contain much mucus and sometimes blood.

---

[7] Walker, E. L., 1913.

Tenesmus, colic and a painful tender colon are the usual symptoms. Nausea, vomiting and other gastro-intestinal disturbances, malaise, and weakness are also observed. Emaciation and secondary anemia are present in patients with long-standing disease.

A carrier state similar to that of *Endamœba histolytica* infections is relatively common. This condition may result from noninvasion of the tissues with multiplication of the parasite and formation of infective cysts in the lumen of the intestine,

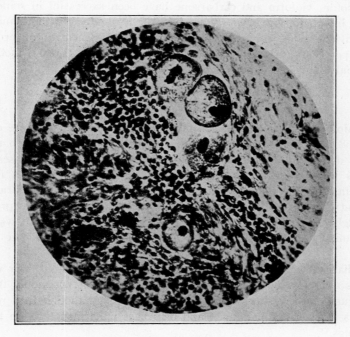

Fig. 28.—*Balantidium coli*

Balantidia deep in tissues of colon with infiltration of lymphocytes (After Strong, 1904, from Zinsser and Bayne-Jones, *Textbook of Bacteriology,* 7th ed., 1934, D. Appleton-Century Company).

but more often is due to an infection with superficial lesions, too mild to produce clinical symptoms.

Immunity.—The low incidence of infection and the failure of experimental infections in man indicate high resistance. The nature of this resistance and the production of the carrier state are not understood.

DIAGNOSIS, PROGNOSIS AND TREATMENT

Diagnosis.—Balantidiasis may be confused clinically with other dysenteries, enteric fevers and cholera. Diagnosis depends upon the identification of the motile trophozoites in diarrheic stools and of the cysts in semiformed or formed stools. The large size of the parasite, the cilia, the large nucleus and the double-walled cyst are the chief identifying features.

Prognosis.—In symptomless individuals the infection undergoes spontaneous cure and usually responds to treatment. Prognosis is less favorable in clinical cases and depends upon the severity of the disease and the patient's response to treatment. Severe infections may prove fatal; a mortality of 29 per cent in patients with severe dysentery has been reported in the Philippines.[8]

Treatment.—No specific chemotherapeutic agent for balantidiasis is known. Therapeutic evaluation of drugs is uncertain, since spontaneous recovery may take place. Chiniofon, vioform and carbarsone have been successful in some cases and have failed in others. Variable results have been obtained with thymol in heavy doses, methylene blue, arsphenamine and stovarsol. Enemata of protargol and argyrol (2 per cent), silver nitrate (1:3,000), quinine (1:1,000), methylene blue 1:3,000), and iodine (1:50,000) have proved useful.

PREVENTION

Epidemiology.—*Balantidium coli* is a common intestinal parasite of hogs; in California 68 per cent of 200 hogs harbored the parasite.[3] Although the parasite has a wide distribution, the incidence in man is low. Only 137 cases of human balantidiasis were recorded previous to 1913 in the literature.[7] An incidence of 1.04 per cent in 3,917 individuals has been reported in southern Brazil[9] and of 0.61 per cent in 3,945 individuals in Cuba.[10] The actual incidence is probably considerably higher since only about one in five infected individuals shows symptoms. Warm, insanitary localities where hogs are abundant apparently have the highest incidence.

Balantidiasis is transmitted mainly by the cysts, which retain their viability for some weeks after leaving the host. Trophozoites are less commonly the infecting agents because of their short extracorporeal viability, although they may survive for ten days at room temperature,[4] and may pass unharmed through the stomach of guinea pigs.[11]

The hog is the chief source of human infections. Man is infected in handling hogs by the hand to mouth transfer of cysts and by ingesting food contaminated through water, soil or flies with infective feces. The low incidence in man rules out human beings as an important source of infection, though carriers among food handlers may be responsible for a small percentage of cases. This low incidence and the failure of experimental infections in man indicate that man is an incidental host.

Prophylaxis.—The prophylaxis of human balantidiasis is based on the prevention of cyst-dissemination through the feces of hogs. Contamination of water supplies may be reduced by confining the animals in sanitary surroundings. The use of hog manure for fertilizing truck gardens should be discouraged. Individuals in contact with hogs should be instructed in methods of personal hygiene and particularly in the need of manual cleanliness. The general prophylactic measures applicable to amœbic dysentery should be employed.

---

[8] Strong, R. P., 1904.
[9] Pinto, C. F., 1919.
[10] Nedergaard, N., 1921.
[11] Hegner, R. W., 1926.

OTHER CILIATES OF MAN

Several ciliates of doubtful status have been described in man, some of them coprozoic free-living species of the genera *Chilodon, Uronema* and *Colpoda,* and others questionable species of *Balantidium* and *Nyctotherus.* Two species, *Balantidium minutum* and *Nyctotherus faba,* have been reported several times in man, but their parasitic status has not been satisfactorily established.

Balantidium minutum.—*Balantidium minutum,* first observed by Schaudinn in 1899, has been reported by several investigators. It differs from *B. coli* in its small size, 20 to 30 μ, and in having a deeper peristome, a spherical macronucleus and a single contractile vacuole.

Nyctotherus faba.—The members of the genus *Nyctotherus* have a convex dorsal and concave ventral surface with a ciliated notch in which the cytostome is situated. *Nyctotherus faba,* first described by Schaudinn in 1899 in Germany, is from 26 to 28 μ in length by 16 to 18 μ in breadth. The peristome extends from the anterior end to the middle of the body. The macronucleus is spherical and contains four or five masses of chromatin, and there is a single contractile vacuole situated posteriorly. Three other specimens have been reported from Italy, Brazil and French Indo-China. It is not certain that this nonpathogenic species is a true parasite of man.

REFERENCES

ANDREWS, J. Host-specificity in *Balantidium coli,* Tr. Cong. Far Eastern Assoc. Trop. Med., 1932, 8:194.

ATCHLEY, F. Effects of Environmental Change on Growth and Multiplication in Populations of *Balantidium,* Am. J. Hyg., 1935, 21:151.

DOBELL, C. and O'CONNOR, F. W. The Intestinal Protozoa of Man, John Bale, Sons and Danielsson, Ltd., London, 1921.

HEGNER, R. Specificity in the Genus *Balantidium,* etc., Am. J. Hyg., 1934, 19:38.

McDONALD, J. D. On *Balantidium coli* (Malmsten) and *Balantidium suis* (*sp. nov.*) with an Account of their Neuromotor Apparatus, Univ. California Publ. Zoöl., 1922, 20:243.

NELSON, E. C. Observations and Experiments on Conjugation of the *Balantidium* from the Chimpanzee, Am. J. Hyg., 1934, 20:106.

——— Cultivation and Cross-infection Experiments with Balantidia from Pig, Chimpanzee, Guinea Pig and *Macacus rhesus,* Am. J. Hyg., 1935, 22:26.

SCHUMAKER, E. *Balantidium coli,* Host-specificity and Relation to the Diet of an Experimental Host, Am. J. Hyg., 1930, 12, 341.

STRONG, R. P. The Clinical and Pathological Significance of *Balantidium coli,* Bureau Govt. Lab. Bull., 1904, No. 26, Manila, P. I.

WALKER, E. L. Experimental Balantidiosis, Philippine J. Sc., (B) 1913, 8:333.

Chapter X

THE INTESTINAL, ORAL AND VAGINAL FLAGELLATES OF MAN

CLASS *MASTIGOPHORA*

The class MASTIGOPHORA comprises Protozoa which, in the adult stage, possess one or more flagella. It includes a diversity of plant-like and animal-like flagellates, and is the largest class of Protozoa. Those parasitic to man are all animal-like flagellates.

The typical species is an elongate unicelluular organism with or without a definite but pliable cell membrane. It has one or more anterior whip-like flagella and a nucleus. Certain species have an undulating membrane and a kinetoplast; e.g. the members of the genus *Trypanosoma*.

Some species obtain their nourishment in the same manner as plants; others as free-living animals, saprophytes or parasites. Various enzymes and pigments are secreted. Locomotion is effected by the flagella and follows a spiral course. Reproduction takes place by longitudinal division, with duplication of the entire morphology and by encystment with the formation of small immature forms. Some parasitic forms require an alternation of hosts to complete their life cycle.

The classification of the numerous and varied species of MASTIGOPHORA is exceedingly difficult. For simplicity the parasitic flagellates of man may be divided into the following six families, which form two groups: (1) those inhabiting the intestine and external atria, where they live free in these cavities or in the crypts and glands, or attach themselves to the surface of the epithelium; and (2) those living in the blood and tissues, the so-called hemoflagellates of the family TRYPANO-SOMIDÆ, which are highly pathogenic.

Order: PROTOMONADIDA
    Family: CERCOMONADIDÆ
        Species: *Enteromonas hominis*
    Family: CHILOMASTIGIDÆ
        Species: *Chilomastix mesnili*
    Family: EMBADOMONADIDÆ
        Species: *Embadomonas intestinalis*
    Family: HEXAMITIDÆ
        Species: *Giardia lambia*
    Family: TRICHOMONADIDÆ
        Species: *Trichomonas elongata*
                Trichomonas hominis
                Trichomonas vaginalis

Family: TRYPANOSOMIDÆ
Species: *Leishmania braziliensis*
Leishmania donovani
Leishmania tropica
Trypanosoma cruzi
Trypanosoma gambiense
Trypanosoma rhodesiense

INTESTINAL AND ATRIAL FLAGELLATES

Almost every species of vertebrate may serve as host to intestinal flagellates, and a single host may harbor several species. At least five species, each belonging to a different genus, have been found in the intestine and two others in the atria of man. Other species have been reported, but in nearly every instance they have proved to be either aberrant or closely related forms of these establishd species or free-living coprozoic flagellates of the genera *Cercomonas* and *Bodo,* which are found in from 0.5 to 1 per cent of all feces.

Animal Hosts.—Because of morphological variation it is difficult to determine whether the species of man and lower animals are identical or whether the same species infect both man and animals. Infection in man has not resulted from the ingestion of cysts of species parasitic in animals, and conversely the infection of animals with the cysts of human species has been uncertain, since experimental animals may be naturally infected with morphologically similar species.

Incidence.—The distribution of the intestinal flagellates of man is cosmopolitan. While infections are most numerous in tropical countries, the incidence is surprisingly high in the temperate zones. Collected surveys give an incidence of 7.4 per cent for *Giardia lamblia,* 3.3 per cent for *Chilomastix mesnili,* and 0.3 per cent for *Trichomonas hominis,* while *Embadomonas intestinalis* and *Enteromonas hominis* are rarely found. The most common intestinal flagellate, *Giardia lamblia,* is nearly three times as prevalent in children as in adults. Since a single examination of the feces fails to detect all cases, these figures probably represent a minimal incidence.

Pathogenicity.—The parasitic flagellates are adapted to exist in darkness at the body temperature of their hosts. Special organs of attachment such as a sucking disk, mouth-attachment, axostyle, and an undulating membrane have been developed to withstand the peristaltic action of the intestine. Their bodies have been altered to resist the action of the intestinal juices and to digest fecal and exudative material. Cyst-formation and rapid multiplication have become necessary to perpetuate their existence.

In spite of a wealth of clinical evidence the pathogenicity of these flagellates is still in dispute. It is difficult to determine whether they produce pathological lesions or whether pathological changes caused by other agents merely favor their existence. With the possible exception of *Trichomonas vaginalis* and *Giardia lamblia* they are probably harmless to man. Intestinal flagellates are found most frequently in the feces of diarrheic patients, because such stools are more often examined and because increased peristalsis favors their appearance in the feces.

Transmission.—The cyst represents the resistant stage of the parasite during its existence outside the host and during its descent through the gastric secretions. Although their thermal death point varies, cysts ordinarily withstand fairly high temperatures. In feces they seldom remain viable more than 10 days, but in clean water they survive much longer. *Trichomonas hominis* is the only one of the five intestinal species in which cysts have not been observed. Its hardy trophozoite may live as long as 79 hours in fecal material. Transmission to a new host evidently occurs through food handlers or through contamination of water and food by sewage and flies.

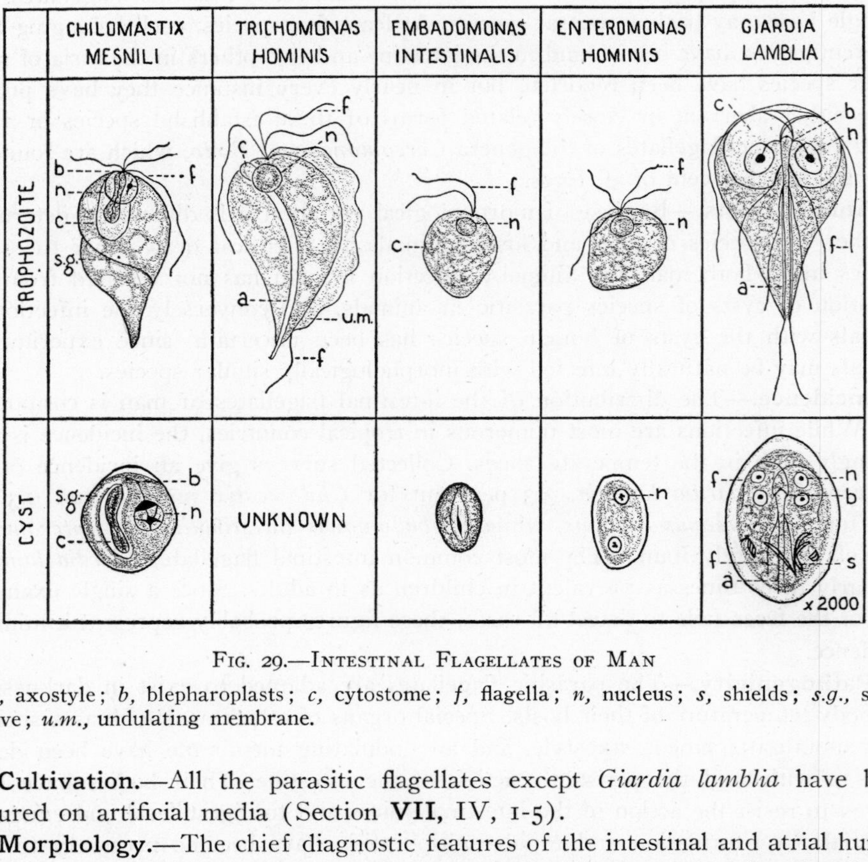

FIG. 29.—INTESTINAL FLAGELLATES OF MAN

a, axostyle; *b,* blepharoplasts; *c,* cytostome; *f,* flagella; *n,* nucleus; *s,* shields; *s.g.,* spiral groove; *u.m.,* undulating membrane.

Cultivation.—All the parasitic flagellates except *Giardia lamblia* have been cultured on artificial media (Section **VII**, IV, 1-5).

Morphology.—The chief diagnostic features of the intestinal and atrial human flagellates are given in Table 14 and are shown in Figure 29. Further details are given under the description of each parasite.

Enteromonas hominis (DA FONSECA, 1915) DOBELL, 1921

Synonyms.—*Octomitus hominis* Chalmers and Pekkola, 1916; *Tricercomonas intestinalis* Wenyon and O'Connor, 1917; *Trichomastix hominis* Chatterjee, 1917; *Diplocercomonas soudanensis* Chalmers and Pekkola, 1919; *Enteromonas bengalensis* Chatterjee, 1919.

TABLE 14

COMPARATIVE MORPHOLOGY OF THE INTESTINAL, ORAL AND VAGINAL
FLAGELLATES OF MAN

	Entero-monas hominis	Chilomas-tix mesnili	Embado-monas intestinalis	Giardia lamblia	Tricho-monas vaginalis	Tricho-monas hominis	Tricho-monas elongata
Trophozoite (unstained) Shape	Ovoid	Pyriform	Ovoid	Pyriform	Pyriform	Pyriform	Pyriform
Length (micra) Mean	8	13	6	14	17	13	10
Usual range	7 to 9	10 to 15	5 to 7	12 to 15	15 to 18	10 to 15	8 to 12
Extreme range	4 to 10	6 to 24	4 to 9	9 to 21	8 to 30	8 to 15	7 to 17
Flagella	4 (3 anterior, 1 posterior)	4 (3 anterior, 1 cytostomal)	2 (1 anterior, 1 posterior)	8 (4 anterior, 2 caudal, 2 ventral)	5 (4 anterior, 1 posterior)	5 (3 to 5 anterior, 1 posterior)	5 (4 anterior, 1 posterior)
Undulating membrane	None	None	None	None	Present	Present	Present
Axostyle	None	None (parastyle)	None	2	1	1	1
Spiral groove	None	Present	None	None	None	None	None
Cytostome	None	Present	Present	None	Present (?)	Present	Present
Trophozoite (stained) Nucleus Number	1	1	1	2	1	1	1
Shape	Oval or cone-shaped	Spheroidal or oval	Spheroidal or oval	Oval	Oval	Oval	Oval
Karyosome	Large	Small	Medium	Large	Not definite	Large	None
Blepharoplasts	2 or more	3	2	2	5	1 to 4	3
Parabasal fibril	None	Present	None	2 present	Present	None	None
Cyst (iodine) Shape	Elongate oval	Lemon-shape with knob at anterior end, occasionally oval	Pyriform	Ellipsoidal	Unknown	Unknown	Unknown

TABLE 14—Continued

COMPARATIVE MORPHOLOGY OF THE INTESTINAL, ORAL AND VAGINAL
FLAGELLATES OF MAN

	Entero-monas hominis	Chilomas-tix mesnili	Embado-monas intestinalis	Giardia lamblia	Tricho-monas vaginalis	Tricho-monas hominis	Tricho-monas elongata
Cyst (iodine) Length (micra)					Unknown	Unknown	Unknown
Mean	7	8	5	11			
Usual range	6 to 8	7 to 9	4 to 6	9 to 12			
Extreme range	[6 to 8	6 to 10	4 to 7	8 to 19			
Flagella	None	1	None	4			
Axostyle	None	None (parastyle)	None	2			
Spiral groove	None	Present	None	None			
Cyto-stome	None	Present	Present	None			
Number of nuclei	1 to 4	1	1	2 to 4			

Disease.—Nonpathogenic.

History.—In 1915 da Fonseca described a species, *Enteromonas hominis*, with two anterior flagella. It has been confused with *Tricercomonas intestinalis* Wenyon and O'Connor, 1917, which has three anterior flagella. Although the latter has been described more frequently, the original name *Enteromonas hominis* is used here to designate both forms. The morphological description, however, is that of the three anterior flagellar type.

Geographical Distribution.—Probably cosmopolitan. It has been reported occasionally from India, Egypt, Samoa, Germany, England, Malaya, Brazil and the United States of America.

BIOLOGICAL CHARACTERISTICS

Morphology.—The trophozoite (Fig. 30A-C) is a small oval flagellate of changeable shape, 4 to 10 μ in length by 3 to 6 μ in width. The cytoplasm contains numerous food vacuoles. At the anterior end is a single vesicular nucleus with a large central karyosome. In front of the nucleus are two or more blepharoplasts from which the three anterior flagella and a posterior flagellum arise. The latter adheres to the flattened side of the body for some distance and then projects free posteriorly or laterally.

The oval cysts (Fig. 30D-F, Plate I, 15 and 16) are from 6 to 8 μ in length by 3 to 4 μ in width. The nucleus divides and the daughter nuclei pass to opposite poles, where they again divide to form the mature quadrinucleate cyst. Most cysts are observed in the binucleate stage. The nuclei have a small central karyosome. Small round refractile bodies, probably of volutin, may be present in the cytoplasm.

Nutrition.—Bacteria and cellular débris.

Movement.—Active jerky progress is produced by the anterior flagella.

Reproduction.—Binary longitudinal division takes place in the trophozoite and nuclear division in the cyst.

Cultivation.—Cultivated on usual media for Protozoa (Section **VII**, IV, 1-5). Cysts form in cultures.

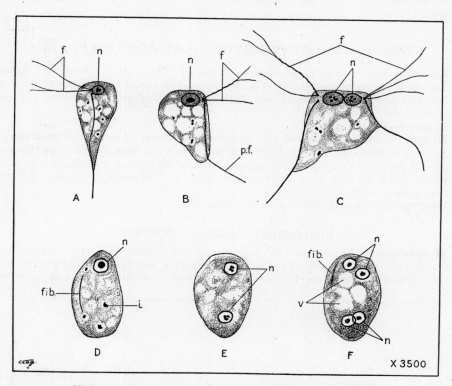

FIG. 30.—*Enteromonas hominis* (*Tricercomonas intestinalis*)

A and *B*, trophozoites showing characteristic caudal protuberance; *C*, dividing trophozoite showing two caudal protuberances and two sets of flagella; *D*, uninucleate cyst; *E*, binucleate cyst; *F*, quadrinucleate cyst.

f, flagella; *fib.*, fibril; *i*, inclusion bodies; *n*, nucleus; *p.f.*, posterior flagellum; *v*, vacuole (Redrawn from Boeck, 1924).

LIFE CYCLE

The life cycle is probably similar to that of the other cyst-forming flagellates. Species of *Tricercomonas* have been described in the rabbit, guinea pig and pig.

PATHOGENESIS, DIAGNOSIS AND TREATMENT

It is a nonpathogenic inhabitant of the intestine of man. Its exact location in the intestine is unknown.

Diagnosis.—By microscopic examination of feces. Its differential characteristics are given in Table 14.

Treatment.—Unnecessary.

PREVENTION

Epidemiology.—Its incidence is low; only about 68 cases have been reported. Its transmission to man is probably through contaminated food and water.

Prophylaxis.—Unimportant. Similar to measures for the prevention of *Endamœba histolytica*.

Chilomastix mesnili (WENYON, 1910) ALEXEIEFF, 1912

Synonyms.—*Cercomonas intestinalis* Marchand, 1875; *Monocercomonas hominis* Grassi, 1881; *Macrostoma mesnili* Wenyon, 1910; *Tetramitus mesnili* Alexeieff, 1910; *Chilomastix hominis* v. Prowazek and Werner, 1914; *Chilomastix davainei* (Moquin-Tandon) Kofoid, 1920.

Disease.—Nonpathogenic.

History.—Davaine discovered this parasite in the feces of patients with cholera in 1854. Prior to Wenyon's careful description in 1910, it had been described and renamed by several workers. Wenyon differentiated it from *Trichomonas* and placed it in a new genus. Alexeieff in 1912 gave it the generic name of *Chilomastix* retaining Wenyon's specific name of *mesnili*.

Geographical Distribution.—Cosmopolitan.

BIOLOGICAL CHARACTERISTICS

Morphology.—The asymmetrical pear-shaped trophozoite (Fig. 31A) varies during life from 13 to 24 μ but when fixed is from 10 to 15 μ in length. It is broadly rounded at the anterior end and tapers to a pointed posterior extremity with a spiral torsion

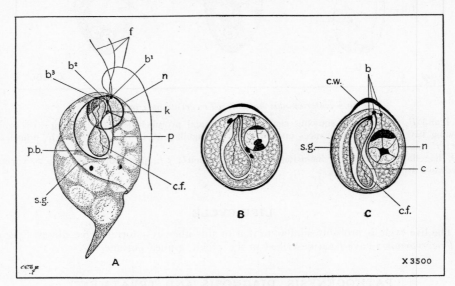

FIG. 31.—*Chilomastix mesnili*

A, trophozoite, ventral view; *B*, cyst, ventral view; *C*, cyst, ventral view, showing thickening of anterior wall.

b, b¹, b², b³, blepharoplasts; *c*, cytostome; *c.f.*, cytostomal flagellum; *c.w.*, cyst wall; *f*, flagella; *k*, karyosome; *n*, nucleus; *p*, parastyle; *p.b.*, parabasal body; *s.g.*, spiral groove (Redrawn from Kofoid and Swezy, 1920).

of the body. The grayish cytoplasm, containing numerous vacuoles and food particles, is enclosed in an elastic membrane, which permits changes in contour. The spiral groove, peculiar to the genus *Chilomastix*, runs obliquely across the ventral surface. The cleft-shaped cytostome with raised unequal lips extends backward for about one-half the length of the body. A short flagellum lies along its floor, while along its sides arising from the blepharoplasts are supporting fibrils. Outside of these are the parabasal body encircling the posterior end of the cytostome and the parastyle. The round or rarely oval nucleus close to the anterior end has a well-defined membrane and a small slightly eccentric karyosome joined to the peripheral chromatin masses by radial linin fibers. At its anterior border is a small centrosome; nearby are chromatin granules, the three[1] or six[2] blepharoplasts. From these arise the three anterior flagella and the cytostomal flagellum, which may correspond to the margin of an undulating membrane.

The lemon-shaped, at times oval cysts (Fig. 31B and C, Plate I, 11 and 12) are bluish green and when stained with iodine become yellowish brown. Their length varies from 6.5 to 10 μ, averaging about 8 μ. The cyst wall is thickened at the narrow anterior end. Stained cysts have a finely granular cytoplasm, a nucleus in general similar to that of the trophozoite, except that the chromatin tends to condense in a peripheral mass, a cytostome with two supporting fibrils, the blepharoplasts, a cytostomal flagellum, a lightly-staining narrow strip corresponding to the spiral groove, and a few refractile, volutin granules.

Nutrition.—The presence of numerous vacuoles and of ingested bacteria and cellular débris indicates that the parasite is a voracious feeder. Food is introduced through the cytostome with the aid of the cytostomal flagellum.

Movement.—*Chilomastix mesnili* is propelled forward by the anterior flagella with a spiral, jerking motion. It is active in fresh feces, but moves less rapidly than *Trichomonas hominis.*

Reproduction.—The trophozoite reproduces by binary fission of the nucleus. Reproduction has been studied in detail by Geiman (1935). Mitotic nuclear division in cysts has been reported,[1] but has not been confirmed by other investigators.

Cultivation.—It is readily cultivated on artificial media (Section **VII**, IV, 1-5).

LIFE CYCLE

The exact habitat of *Chilomastix mesnili* has not been determined. The trophozoite probably lives in the large intestine or cecum, although it has been reported in the small intestine. The lipped cytostome may serve as a means of attachment to the intestinal mucosa. The vegetative flagellate becomes a cyst by freeing the body of inclusions and secreting a cyst wall. In this form it leaves the host in the feces. The resistant cysts have a thermal death point of 72° C. and survive in clean water for 232 days.[3] When ingested by man, excystation takes place in the intestine and probably one trophozoite emerges.

Species resembling *Chilomastix mesnili* have been reported in chimpanzees and monkeys, while other species of the genus have been found in many animals.

PATHOGENESIS, DIAGNOSIS AND TREATMENT

Although *Chilomastix mesnili* is found in diarrheic stools, it is generally considered nonpathogenic.

Diagnosis.—Diagnosis is made by microscopic examination of the feces or by culture. The trophozoites are found in fluid stools and the cysts in formed stools. The trophozoites must be distinguished morphologically from *Trichomonas hominis,* and the cysts, usually abundant, from the small cysts of *Endamœba histolytica* and *Endolimax nana.*

Treatment.—No data.

---

[1] Kofoid, C. A. and Swezy, O., 1920.   [3] Boeck, W. C., 1921.
[2] Dobell, C. and O'Connor, F. W., 1921.

PREVENTION

Epidemiology.—*Chilomastix mesnili* is a fairly common parasite of man. Its incidence varies from 1 to 12 per cent, 23 surveys prior to 1912 giving an average incidence of 3.5 per cent.[4] In the United States of America more recent surveys of 30,534 individuals give an average of 3.3 per cent.

Man acquires the parasite through food or water containing cysts. Food may be contaminated by sewage, flies or infected food handlers. Flies distribute viable cysts in their feces as long as 80 hours after ingestion.[5]

Prophylaxis.—Not important. Preventive measures are similar to those for *Endamœba histolytica*.

Embadomonas intestinalis WENYON AND O'CONNOR, 1917

Synonyms.—*Waskia intestinalis* Wenyon and O'Connor, 1917; *Retortamonas intestinalis* (Grassi, 1879) Wenrich, 1932.

History.—This flagellate was first described in 1917 by Wenyon and O'Connor in Egypt. Grassi in 1879 described similar organisms under the generic name of *Retortamonas*. Some authorities consider that the correct name should be *Retortamonas intestinalis*.

Geographical Distribution.—Probably cosmopolitan. Reported from Egypt, India, England and the United States of America.

BIOLOGICAL CHARACTERISTICS

Morphology.—The ovoid trophozoite (Fig. 32A-C) is from 4 to 9 μ in length and from 3 to 5 μ in width. The nucleus at the anterior end has a delicate membrane and a central karyosome. Anterior to the nucleus are two blepharoplasts from which rise two flagella. The anterior and posterior flagella are usually long and thin, the posterior lying partially in the cytostome. The cytostome, an elongated depression with heavy marginal walls, is situated posterior to the nucleus.

The cysts (Fig. 32D and E, Plate I, 13 and 14) are small pear-shaped bodies 4 to 7 μ long by 3 to 4 μ wide. They contain a single nucleus with a central karyosome and the shadow outline of the cytostome with its supporting fibrils.

Nutrition.—Bacteria and cellular débris are taken in through the cytostome with the aid of the posterior flagellum.

Movement.—The flagella propel the animal in active jerky movements.

Reproduction.—Binary longitudinal fission of trophozoites. Nuclear division has not been observed in cysts.

Cultivation.—Cultivated on usual media (Section **VII**, IV, 1-5). Both trophozoites and cysts are present in cultures.

LIFE CYCLE

The life cycle is little known. The trophozoite inhabits the intestine of man and the cysts are passed in the feces. Apparently a single trophozoite emerges on excystation in the intestine of a new host. Morphologically similar species have been found in rats and guinea pigs. Other species are found in larval and adult insects, amphibians, rabbits, sheep and monkeys.

PATHOGENESIS, DIAGNOSIS AND TREATMENT

Nonpathogenic, although found most often in diarrheic stools.

Diagnosis.—The small size and the characteristic cytostome of the trophozoite and the shape of cyst differentiate it from other intestinal flagellates (Table 14).

Treatment.—No data.

---

[4] Hegner, R. W. and Payne, G. C., 1921.   [5] Root, F. M.. 1921.

PREVENTION

Epidemiology.—The incidence of *Embadomonas intestinalis* is so low that it is rarely encountered in surveys of intestinal Protozoa. Transmission is through food and water contaminated by cysts.

Prophylaxis.—Unnecessary. Similar to the measures used for *Endamœba histolytica*.

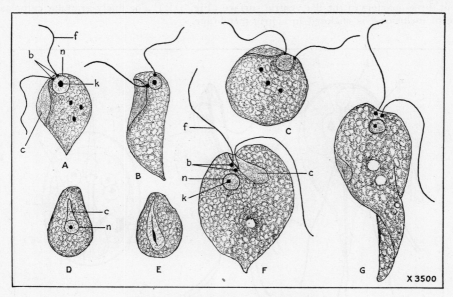

Fig. 32.—*Embadomonas intestinalis*

A to *C, Embadomonas intestinalis,* trophozoites; *D* and *E, E. intestinalis,* cysts; *F* and *G, E. sinensis,* trophozoites.

b, blepharoplasts; *c,* cytostome; *f,* flagellum; *k,* karyosome; *n,* nucleus (*A* to *E* redrawn from Broughton-Alcock and Thomson, 1922; *F* and *G,* redrawn from Faust, 1922).

Embadomonas sinensis FAUST AND WASSELL, 1921

A species closely allied to *Embadomonas intestinalis* has been reported in China. It was first discovered by Faust and Wassell in 1921 and cultured by Watt in 1933. It is characterized by its large size (average length 13.4 μ), relatively small spheroidal nucleus and two free flagella (Fig. 32F and G).

Giardia lamblia STILES, 1915

Synonyms.—*Cercomonas intestinalis* Lambl, 1859; *Lamblia intestinalis* (Lambl, 1859) Blanchard, 1888; *Giardia intestinalis* (Lambl, 1859) Alexeieff, 1914; *Giardia enterica* (Grassi, 1881) Kofoid, 1920.

Disease.—Giardiasis, lambliasis.

History.—*Giardia lamblia* may have been the protozoon described by Leeuwenhoek in his report to the Royal Society of London in 1681. It was first reported by Lambl in 1859 under the name of *Cercomonas intestinalis.* Since that time it has been frequently redescribed and renamed. In 1915 Stiles placed it in the genus *Giardia* under its present name. The first accurate description was published by Simon in 1921.

Geographical Distribution.—Cosmopolitan.

BIOLOGICAL CHARACTERISTICS

Morphology.—The trophozoite (Fig. 33A) is a bilaterally symmetrical, pear-shaped flagellate with a broad, rounded anterior and a tapering posterior extremity. The usual length is from 12 to 15 μ and the breadth is slightly over one-half the length. The dorsal surface is convex. An ovoid concavity with raised margins, the sucking disk, occupies about three-quarters of the flat ventral surface (Fig. 33B). The finely-granular cytoplasm, free of inclusions, is enclosed in a firm membrane.

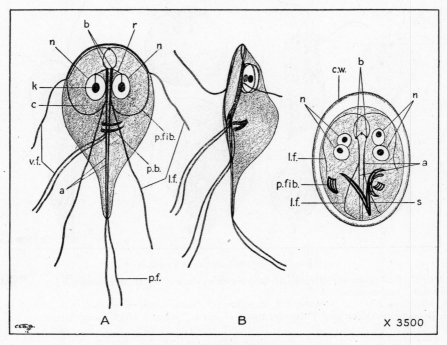

FIG. 33.—*Giardia lamblia*

A, trophozoite viewed from dorsal surface; *B,* oblique lateral view of trophozoite showing the concave sucker-like cytosome on ventral surface; *C,* cyst.

a, axostyles; *b,* blepharoplasts; *c,* sucker; *c.w.,* cyst wall; *k,* karyosome; *l.f.,* lateral flagella; *n,* nuclei; *p.b.,* parabasal body; *p.f.,* posterior flagella; *p.fib.,* parabasal fibers; *r,* rhizoplast; *s,* shield; *v.f.,* ventral flagella (*A* and *B* redrawn from Kofoid and Swezy, 1922; *C* redrawn from Simon, 1921).

There are two nuclei, two axostyles, two blepharoplasts and four pairs of flagella. Two slender rods, the axostyles, extend along the midaxis from the blepharoplasts to the pointed posterior end. The two oval nuclei, connected with the blepharoplasts by rhizoplasts, are in the anterior part of the body dorsal to the sucking disk. Each contains a large central granular karyosome. A centrosome is present at the junction of the rhizoplast with the nuclear membrane.

The two anterior flagella pass forward from the blepharoplasts, cross each other, follow the margin of the body, and emerge on either side. The two posterior lateral flagella pass posteriorly along the lateral shields to emerge in the posterior part of the body. The caudal pair extends out from the ends of the axostyles, and the two ventral flagella pass directly out from the axostyles near the posterior edge of the sucking disk.

A fused pair of deeply-staining curved bars, considered by some to be parabasal bodies, lies diagonally across the axostyles posterior to the sucking disk.

The cysts (Fig. 33C, Plate I, 17) are ellipsoidal bodies with smooth well-defined walls and finely granular cytoplasm. The shrinking of the contents from the wall is a diagnostic feature. The usual length is from 9 to 12 μ and the breadth is slightly more than two-thirds of the length. The spherical nuclei, which usually range from 2 to 4, are as a rule in the anterior end. Many structures of the trophozoite are distinguishable in the cysts: the ridges of lateral shields, the axostyles, the anterior and posterior lateral flagella, and two groups of short curved fibrils.

Nutrition.—Liquid food is absorbed from the surrounding intestinal content, although the parasite may possibly obtain nourishment from the epithelial cells through the sucking disk.

Movement.—The adhesive power of the sucking disk is sufficient to resist ordinary peristalsis; hence trophozoites are rarely found except in fluid stools. When free the trophozoite moves rapidly with a jerky twisting motion propelled by the lashing flagella.

Reproduction.—Although binary longitudinal fission of the trophozoites has been observed, reproduction is mainly by multiplication in the cyst. Encystment, mitotic division, and excystation, followed by separation into new trophozoites, evidently occur in the host.

Cultivation.—Not successful.

LIFE CYCLE

Encystment provides for reproduction and protection. Large numbers of cysts are passed intermittently in the feces, as many as 21,000,000 per gram of feces.[6] Under moist conditions cysts may remain viable for months outside the body.[3] The cysts pass unharmed through the gastric juices of the new host and upon reaching the upper intestine undergo excystation.

Man is the natural host of *Giardia lamblia*. Other species of *Giardia*, differing slightly in morphology, have been found in many animals. Experimental infection of mammals with *Giardia lamblia* has not been particularly successful.

PATHOGENESIS

Clinical evidence, though voluminous, has failed to establish beyond reasonable doubt the pathogenic nature of *Giardia lamblia*. Most clinical evidence is untrustworthy, since pathological changes from other causes may either provide a favorable environment for the harmless existence of the parasite or permit it to act as a secondary invader. However, it is reasonable to assume that the attachment of large numbers of *Giardia lamblia* to the intestinal mucosa may aggravate or prolong an existing condition. Evidence of its association with clinical disease must not be entirely disregarded, since it may possibly produce a low-grade inflammation and functional disturbances, or if not the primary cause, it may be a contributing factor.

The arguments against the pathogenicity of *Giardia lamblia* are: (1) giardial infections in animals produce no lesions; (2) the parasite has no powers of invading the tissues; (3) the incidence of infection is high in apparently healthy individuals; and (4) the associated clinical symptoms are varied and vague. On the other hand there are unquestionable instances of the cure of upper intestinal tract disorders following a reduction in the number of organisms.

Pathology.—*Giardia lamblia* inhabits the small intestine. It is commonly found in the duodenum and occasionally as far down as the ileocecal valve. It has been found in the gallbladder,[7] but no relief of symptoms or reduction of duodenal infection has been

[6] Kofoid, C. A. and Swezy, O., 1922.   [7] Smithies, F., 1928.

observed after cholecystectomy.[8] It does not appear to invade the tissues or produce definite lesions, although it has been reported to cause catarrhal inflammation of the duodenum and even penetrate the epithelium.[9]

Symptomatology.—The symptomatology is unconvincingly vague. Most infected individuals show no symptoms. Those ascribed to giardial infections in adults include anorexia, headache, epigastric pain, irregular bowel movements, alternating diarrhea and constipation, nutritional disturbances, neurasthenia, anemia and fatigability. The symptoms are often those of biliary disease and even approximate the typical syndrome of chronic cholecystitis.[8] Infections in children produce various effects, ranging from no symptoms to those of enteritis. A "giardial syndrome" consisting of protracted diarrhea, gradual distention of the abdomen and retardation in growth have been described[10] and constipation, nervousness, fatigue and loss of appetite have been reported.[11]

DIAGNOSIS AND TREATMENT

Diagnosis.—Giardial infection may be diagnosed by finding the cysts or occasionally the trophozoites in the feces. The latter are more readily obtained by duodenal drainage, which is the most reliable method of diagnosis. The distinctive morphology of both trophozoite and cyst readily distinguishes *Giardia lamblia* from other intestinal flagellates (Table 14).

Treatment.—The elimination of the parasite is difficult. Chemotherapy with iodine and arsenical compounds, dyes and various intestinal antiseptics usually produces only a temporary reduction in number. The duodenal tube offers the most effective method of drug administration. Duodenal flushing with hot magnesium sulphate solution has been advocated.[12] Atabrine, administered orally in doses of 0.1 gm. three times daily for three to five days, has been reported to give a high percentage of at least temporary cures.

PREVENTION

Epidemiology.—The incidence of infection with *Giardia lamblia* is high in both temperate and tropical climates. A compilation of 35 surveys on approximately 20,000 individuals show an average incidence of 12 per cent.[4] The statistics compiled by the Winthrop Chemical Company from 44 surveys on 100,594 individuals throughout the world give an average of 6.9 per cent and a range from 2.4 to 30.0 per cent. In these records the incidence is higher in children, 14.7 per cent, than in adults, 5.3 per cent. The incidence increases from 17 per cent in children from 1 to 5 years to 40 per cent in children from 6 to 12 years.[13]

Cysts are transmitted in food or water contaminated with human feces, through the medium of sewage, flies or food handlers. Among the mammals other than man, rats and monkeys harbor morphologically similar species.

Prophylaxis.—Similar to the measures employed for *Endamœba histolytica*.

GENUS *TRICHOMONAS* DONNÉ, 1836

The genus *Trichomonas* comprises flagellates that have three to five anterior flagella, a posterior flagellum, an undulating membrane, an axostyle, and usually a definite cytostome. Trichomonads are widely distributed among vertebrates and infect nearly every animal associated with man.

Trichomonads of Man.—Five trichomonads have been reported in man, but

[8] MacPhee, L. and Walker, B. S., 1935.
[9] Lyon, B. B. V. and Swalm, W. A., 1925.
[10] Zahorsky, J., 1932.
[11] McClendon, S. J., 1931.
[12] de Rivas, D., 1926.
[13] Maxcy, K. F., 1921.

only three are ordinarily accepted as distinct species: *T. elongata* of the mouth, *T. vaginalis* of the vagina, and *T. hominis* of the intestine. *Pentatrichomonas ardin delteili* and *Tritrichomonas fecalis,* which differ chiefly in the number of flagella, are here considered as varieties of *Trichomonas hominis.* Several investigators even maintain that there is not sufficient basis for separating the morphologically similar trichomonads into three distinct species. The evidence from experimental cross-infections with these species is not conclusive. Temporary vaginal infection in monkeys has been obtained with *T. hominis,*[14] but vaginal infection in monkeys has not been produced by an intestinal simian strain, capable of producing intestinal infection in man.[15] Attempts to establish vaginal infection with *T. hominis* have been successful (three out of eight women) [16] and unsuccessful.[17] Intestinal infection in kittens has been produced with *T. hominis* but not with *T. vaginalis.*[17] *T. vaginalis* appears distinct from the intestinal species, but it needs further differentiation from *T. elongata.*[18] Cultural and morphological studies indicate that the intestinal and vaginal trichomonads are distinct species [19] and that *T. vaginalis* is distinct from the trichomonads of the mouth and intestine.[20]

Morphology.—The principal morphological characteristics of the trichomonads from the mouth, intestine and vagina (Fig. 34) are given in Table 15, adapted from Powell (1936). In unstained preparations they appear as colorless pyriform or oval organisms with three to five anterior flagella and an undulating membrane. Along the outer border of the membrane is a delicate flagellum projecting free posteriorly. The vacuolated cytoplasm is finely granular. An indistinct, hyaline, rod-like structure, the axostyle, extends from the anterior end along the midaxis and projects at the posterior end as a pointed, caudal spine. The organism is enclosed in a delicate plastic membrane which enables it to assume all manner of shapes when burrowing through débris.

Most observers describe an ill-defined, narrow cytostome at the anterior end, but Powell (1936) cannot find it in *Trichomonas vaginalis.* A single oval nucleus in the anterior portion of the body contains a central karyosome or scattered masses of chromatin. Anterior to the nucleus are several dark-staining granules, the blepharoplasts, from which arise the flagella, undulating membrane, and axostyle. From the midposterior granule a rhizoplast runs to the nucleus. The undulating membrane extends backward for one-half to two-thirds the body length. At its outer margin is the posterior flagellum, and near its base a chromatic basal rod. The parabasal fibril, arising from the blepharoplasts, curves around the caudal margin of the nucleus, and ends in the posterior half of the body.

Nutrition.—The presence of a cytostome suggests the ingestion of food at a definite location, but *T. vaginalis* has been observed to ingest particulate substances by local amœboid movements of the cytoplasm.[20]

Movement.—Trichomonads are actively motile. Forward motion is produced by lashing of the anterior flagella. A rotary movement, predominantly clockwise,

---

[14] Hegner, R., 1934.
[15] Dobell, C., 1934.
[16] Karnaky, K. J., 1934.
[17] Kessel, J. F. and Gafford, J. A., 1935.

[18] Bland, P. B., Wenrich, D. H. and Goldstein, L., 1931.
[19] Westphal, A., 1935.
[20] Powell, W. N., 1936.

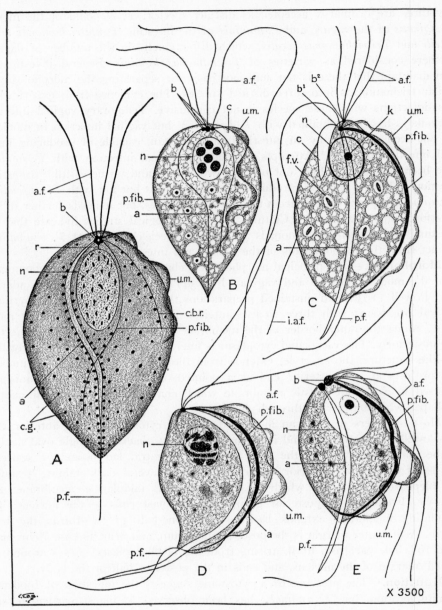

X 3500

FIG. 34.—TRICHOMONADS OF MAN

A, Trichomonas vaginalis; B, Trichomonas elongata (buccalis); C, Pentatrichomonas ardin delteili; D, Trichomonas hominis; E, Tritrichomonas fecalis.

a, axostyle; *a.f.,* anterior flagella; *b, b¹, b²,* blepharoplasts; *c,* cytostome; *c.b.r.,* chromatoid basal rod; *c.g.,* chromatin granules; *f.v.,* food vacuole; *i.a.f.,* inferior anterior flagellum; *k,* karyosome; *n,* nucleus; *p.f.,* posterior flagellum; *p.fib.,* parabasal fiber; *r,* rhizoplast; *u.m.,* undulating membrane (*A* redrawn from Powell, 1936; *B* redrawn from Hinshaw, 1926; *C* redrawn from Kofoid and Swezy, 1923; *D* redrawn from Bishop, 1931; *E* redrawn from Cleveland, 1928).

is effected by the undulating membrane. The larger forms, in which the ratio of the cytoplasmic mass to the motor apparatus is high, move more slowly than the smaller forms.

Reproduction.—Reproduction takes place by binary longitudinal division with mitotic division of the nucleus. The first evidence of division in *Trichomonas hominis* is the appearance of chromatin granules outside the karyosome and the subsequent disappearance of the karyosome.[21] The blepharoplasts divide early. Each daughter trichomonad contains part of the blepharoplasts and two flagella. The parabasal fibril, the chromatic basal rod and the undulating membrane probably pass to one daughter trichomonad and are reproduced in the other, while each new organism develops two additional flagella and an axostyle. The old axostyle probably is absorbed and a new structure grows out of the blepharoplasts,[21] although some observers believe that the axostyle splits. At times the trichomonad constricts in the middle and casts off the posterior mass of cytoplasm. Multiple fission has been reported in *T. elongata*[22] and in *T. hominis*.

Cultivation.—Trichomonads have been cultivated on a variety of media (Section **VII**, IV, 1-5). No cysts have been observed in cultures.

Life Cycle.—Although certain species in animals form cysts, the species in man are known only in the trophozoite stage. Cyst-formation has been reported but is denied by most investigators. In old preparations rounded, moribund or degenerating forms devoid of flagella may be mistaken for cysts. Transmission takes place by the transfer of trophozoites from host to host. The relatively high resistance of the trophozoite enables it to live for a considerable length of time outside the body.

Trichomonas vaginalis (DONNÉ, 1836) EHRENBERG, 1838

Synonyms.—*Tricomonas vaginale* Donné, 1836; *Trichomonas vaginæ* Kölliker and Scanzoni, 1855.

Disease.—Trichomonad vaginitis.

History.—*Trichomonas vaginalis,* the type species of the genus *Trichomonas,* was discovered by Donné in 1836 in vaginal discharges and named *Trichomonas vaginale*. Ehrenberg in 1838 amended the spelling to *Trichomonas vaginalis*. It has been redescribed by at least 20 investigators, most recently by Westphal in 1935, and by Powell in 1936.

Geographical Distribution.—Cosmopolitan.

BIOLOGICAL CHARACTERISTICS

Morphology.—*Trichomonas vaginalis* (Fig. 33A) is a colorless pyriform flagellate, usually from 15 to 18 μ in length by 5 to 15 μ in breadth (Table 15). In fixed preparations it is smaller, averaging 13 μ.[18] Its structure is similar to that of the other human trichomonads except for numerous cytoplasmic granules of

---

[21] Bishop, A., 1931. [22] Ohira, T. and Noguchi, H., 1917.

TABLE 15

PRINCIPAL MORPHOLOGIC CHARACTERISTICS OF TRICHOMONADS FROM THE
HUMAN MOUTH, INTESTINE AND VAGINA

	Trichomonas vaginalis Donné (1836)	*Trichomonas hominis* Davaine (1860)	*Penta-trichomonas ardin delteili* Derrieu and Raynaud (1914)	*Trichomonas elongata* Steinberg (1862)	*Tritrichomonas fecalis* Cleveland (1928)
Size (micra)	8 to 30 by 3 to 17	8 to 15 by 3 to 5	9 to 20 by 7 to 14	7 to 17 by 3 to 8	8 to 15 by 3 to 5
Shape	Variable usually pyriform	Variable usually pyriform	Usually pyriform	Variable usually pyriform	Usually pyriform
Number of free flagella	4	3 or 4 (Bishop) 4 (Lynch)	5 (Kofoid and Swezy)	4	3 (Cleveland)
Number of blepharoplastic granules	5	1 to 3 or 4 (Bishop)	2 (Kofoid and Swezy)	3 (Hinshaw)	1 (Cleveland)
Axostyle	Hyaline but slightly siderophile	Hyaline	Hyaline	Siderophile	Hyaline
Parabasal apparatus	Single fibril	Absent	Absent (Kofoid and Swezy call chromatic basal rod a "parabasal body")	Absent (Hinshaw). Present (Bland and others)	Absent
Undulating membrane	One-third to full length of body but not ending as free, trailing flagellum	Full length of body, ending as free, trailing flagellum	Full length of body, ending as free, trailing flagellum	Two-thirds to three-fourths length of body but not ending as free flagellum	Full length of body, ending as free, trailing flagellum
Chromatic basal rod	Approximately same length as undulating membrane	Full length of body	Full length of body	Approximately same length as undulating membrane	Full length of body
Resting nucleus	Chromatin in rather fine granules. No definite karyosome	Nuclear membrane encloses clear space with conspicuous karyosome	Dark rim of chromatin with prominent central karyosome	Chromatin in very coarse granules. No karyosome	Chromatin in one to several (usually 3 or 4) clumps
Number of chromosomes	4	5 or 6 (Bishop)	?	3 (Hinshaw)	?
Cytoplasm	Coarse chromatic granules present	No chromatic granulation of cytoplasm	No chromatic granulation of cytoplasm	Coarse chromatic granules seldom present	No chromatic granulation of cytoplasm

various sizes. A sausage-shaped parabasal body has been described.[23] Ingested bacteria are seldom present except in specimens from cultures.

Physiology.—It is less active, probably because of its larger size, than the other trichomonads of man. Its reproduction and cultivation are similar to those of other trichomonads.

LIFE CYCLE

Its life cycle is that of a typical trichomonad. Man is the only known natural host.

PATHOGENESIS

Trichomonas vaginalis is an inhabitant of the human vagina. A few instances of its presence in nonspecific purulent urethritis and prostatovesiculitis of males and one instance of upper urinary tract infection in a female have been reported.

Its pathogenicity is still questionable, although it is definitely associated with abnormal conditions of the vaginal mucosa. Clinical evidence tends to support the view that the flagellate is responsible for low-grade inflammatory conditions. However, such conditions may provide a favorable environment and the trichomonad, as a secondary invader, merely aggravates a preëxisting condition. For this reason its frequent association with vaginitis and its disappearance upon cure cannot be accepted as conclusive proof of its pathogenicity.

Pathology.—The usual pathological findings in trichomonad vaginitis are as follows:[17] The vaginal walls are injected and tender, in some instances showing hyperemia and petechial hemorrhages and in advanced cases granular areas. In places the surface is covered with coagulated material containing trichomonads, leukocytes, and red blood cells. In the mucosa are areas of increased vascularity and hemorrhage infiltrated with lymphocytes, a few polymorphonuclears, and occasional plasma cells. At times erosion and necrosis are observed in these areas with invasion of flagellates. The pathological condition appears to be of toxic or bacterial origin and not primarily due to invasion by the flagellates.

Symptomatology.—Clinically patients present signs of vaginal inflammation and complain of itching, burning and discharge. In a fully developed case there is a profuse, annoying, irritating leukorrheic discharge, usually of long duration. The discharge exuding from the introitus is frothy, seropurulent, creamy, yellowish and acid, and contains many vaginal cells, leukocytes, bacteria, and trichomonads. A pool of secretion lies in the posterior fornix. The vaginal and cervical mucosa is highly injected with a bright or dark red punctate mottling. Not infrequently the vulva and surrounding areas are red and chafed. The inflammation ranges from a diffuse redness of the vagina and vestibule to an extensive intertrigo of the vulva and neighboring region.

Only 13 per cent of patients with trichomonad infection complain of symptoms, but the vaginal secretions are invariably altered.[18] The incidence of *T. vaginalis* in women with leukorrhea is more than twice the average rate. At least four investigators claim that trichomonad infection doubles puerperal morbidity.

---

[23] Bland, P. B., Goldstein, L., Wenrich, D. H. and Weiner, E., 1932.

DIAGNOSIS, PROGNOSIS AND TREATMENT

Diagnosis.—Diagnosis is made by microscopic examination of a cover-glass mount of the vaginal discharge diluted with an equal amount of physiological sodium chloride solution. Cultures may also be made on suitable media (Section VII, IV, 1-5). The differential characteristics are given in Tables 14 and 15.

Prognosis.—Favorable.

Treatment.—Trichomonad vaginitis may or may not respond readily to treatment. It is especially important to clear up the condition in pregnant women. The underlying basis for therapy is cleansing with green soap and thorough drying. Swabbing with 1 per cent picric acid, douching with 0.5 per cent lactic acid solution, or insufflating with a powder consisting of 12 parts stovarsol (a pentavalent arsenical), 2 parts salicylic acid, 43 parts kaolin and 43 parts sodium bicarbonate have been recommended. Aldarsone is considered superior to stovarsol.[24]

PREVENTION

Epidemiology.—The incidence of infections is high; the average of four investigations was 23 per cent in 754 nonpregnant women, ranging from 18 to 40 per cent, and the average of five investigations was 25 per cent in 1,353 pregnant women, ranging from 20 to 37 per cent. An incidence of 30.8 per cent in 314 pregnant Negro women and 13.3 per cent in 286 pregnant white women has been reported.[18] The incidence increases when feminine hygiene is deficient. It is even higher in vaginitis; three investigators report an incidence of 53.8 per cent in 365 women with leukorrhea.

Typical symptoms of vaginitis were produced in three normal volunteers by transplanting vaginal exudate from an infected patient.[17] Similar results were obtained in two volunteers by inoculating cultures of *Trichomonas vaginalis* and associated bacteria, although in another volunteer the bacteria alone produced mild symptoms. The method of transmission has not been demonstrated, but contaminated toilet seats may be implicated. Men are presumably infected through coitus.

Prophylaxis.—Attention to personal hygiene should reduce infections.

Trichomonas hominis (DAVAINE, 1860) LEUCKART, 1879

All intestinal trichomonads, irrespective of whether they possess three, four or five anterior flagella, are designated here as *Trichomonas hominis*. At least three have been described as distinct species, *Tritrichomonas fecalis*, *Trichomonas hominis* and *Pentatrichomonas ardin delteili.*

Synonyms.—*Cercomonas hominis* Davaine, 1860; *Monocercomonas hominis* Grassi, 1879; *Trichomonas intestinalis* Leuckart, 1879; *Trichomonas confusa* Stiles, 1902; *Tritrichomonas hominis* Kofoid, 1920; *Pentatrichomonas ardin delteili* (Derrieu and Raynaud, 1914) Kofoid and Swezy, 1923; *Tritrichomonas fecalis* Cleveland, 1928.

Disease.—Intestinal trichomoniasis. Probably nonpathogenic.

History.—This flagellate was first observed and described in 1854 by Davaine who

---

[24] Bland, P. B. and Rakoff, A. E., 1936.

named it *Cercomonas hominis* in 1860. Since that time it has been described by a number of investigators under several names.

Geographical Distribution.—Cosmopolitan. Incidence higher in warmer regions.

BIOLOGICAL CHARACTERISTICS

The characteristics of the *Trichomonas hominis, Tritrichomonas fecalis* and *Pentatrichomonas ardin delteili* are compared in Table 15.

Morphology.—The shape of the trophozoite (Fig. 33C-E) is variable but usually pyriform. The majority of the forms have four anterior flagella. The sharply pointed caudal process, the projection of the axostyle, may be of assistance in maintaining the position of the parasite in the intestine. A cytostome is described by most investigators.

Physiology.—The trichomonad is very active in fresh feces. Bacteria and other food particles are found in the cytoplasm. The ingestion of red blood cells by *Pentatrichomonas ardin delteili* has been considered evidence of pathogenicity,[25] but many trichomonads normally ingest red blood cells in the same manner as other food particles.[26]

Cultivation.—*Trichomonas hominis* has been cultivated by at least ten investigators, *Pentatrichomonas ardin delteili* by three, and *Tritrichomonas fecalis* by one (Section **VII**, IV, 1-5). *Tritrichomonas fecalis* lives indefinitely in feces diluted with tap water but does not grow in the absence of bacteria.[27]

LIFE CYCLE

The parasite rarely leaves the host except during diarrhea. Under favorable conditions large numbers are produced in the intestine. No cysts have been found. The resistance of the trophozoites enables them to reach new hosts and withstand the digestive juices. Man appears to be the only natural host of the three forms of *Trichomonas hominis*. Monkeys [15] and kittens [28] have been experimentally infected with trichomonads from man.

PATHOGENESIS

The parasite inhabits both large and small intestines, but is most numerous in the ileum and large intestine. Conclusive evidence of its pathogenicity has not been established. The ingestion of red blood cells and the frequent presence of the flagellate in diarrheic stools are not proof. Since many infected individuals show no symptoms, this associated diarrhea is probably of bacillary origin, aggravated perhaps by heavy trichomonad infection. However, *Pentatrichomonas ardin delteili* infection is said to be accompanied by a chronic persistent diarrhea with fetid stools [25] and superficial necrosis of the intestinal mucosa in infected kittens has been reported.[28]

DIAGNOSIS, PROGNOSIS AND TREATMENT

Diagnosis.—Diagnosis is established by identifying the trichomonad with its characteristic undulant membrane in the feces or by culture (Table 15 and Fig. 34C-E).

Prognosis.—Since the intestinal trichomonads are resistant to chemotherapy, infections may persist for long periods.

Treatment.—No specific drug is known. Intestinal trichomonads are resistant to emetine hydrochloride, arsenicals, and iodine preparations. Carbarsone has been recommended.[29]

---

[25] Kofoid, C. A. and Swezy, O., 1924.
[26] Hegner, R., 1928.
[27] Cleveland, L. R., 1928.

[28] Kessel, J. F., 1928.
[29] Hegner, R. and Eskridge, L., 1935; Gabaldon, A., 1936.

PREVENTION

Epidemiology.—The incidence of intestinal trichomoniasis is relatively low except in regions where sanitation is poor, 3 per cent in compiled surveys of 20,000 individuals [4] and 0.3 per cent in four surveys of 7,164 individuals in the United States of America. There is a high incidence of 11.9 per cent in the Federated Malay States.

Intestinal trichomonad infections are spread by food and water containing trophozoites. The probable method of infection is the contamination of food by sewage, fingers and flies. Although no cysts are formed, the trophozoite, though susceptible to desiccation, is resistant to external conditions. *Pentatrichomonas ardin delteili* survives in liquid stools for 24 days, in rain, creek and tap water 3 days, and in physiological sodium chloride solution 13 days.[25] *T. hominis* survives for eight days in feces at 5° to 31° C., but remains viable only a few hours in feces diluted with water.[26] Several investigators have observed that trichomonads are able to withstand the gastric juices and pass unharmed through the stomachs of rats, cats, guinea pigs and monkeys.

Prophylaxis.—Unimportant. Preventive measures similar to those for *Endamœba histolytica* may be applied.

Trichomonas elongata (STEINBERG, 1862) WENYON, 1926

Synonyms.—*Tetratrichomonas buccalis* Goodey, 1917; *Tetratrichomonas hominis* Ohira and Noguchi, 1917; *Trichomonas buccalis* (Goodey, 1917) Kofoid, 1920.

Disease.—Nonpathogenic.

History.—This trichomonad probably was observed by Müller in 1773 and by Mandl in 1838-45. Steinberg in 1862 reported three trichomonads from the mouth, naming one *Trichomonas elongata*. Goodey in 1917 first described it in detail under the name *Tetratrichomans buccalis*. Kofoid in 1920 changed this name to *Trichomonas buccalis,* by which it is commonly known. According to the law of priority in nomenclature the correct name is *Trichomonas elongata*.

Geographical Distribution.—Cosmopolitan.

BIOLOGICAL CHARACTERISTICS

Morphology.—The pear-shaped trophozoite has four anterior flagella (Fig. 34B), although forms with three have been reported.[30] Its usual length is from 8 to 12 μ with a range of 7 to 17 μ. Its differential characteristics are given in Table 15.

Physiology.—The animal moves actively by the aid of the flagella and undulating membrane. Nutrition is obtained from the cellular débris in the mouth. It is readily cultivated on appropriate media (Section VII, IV, 1-5).

LIFE CYCLE

The trophozoite evidently is transmitted by direct contact, since no cysts have been observed. Man is the principal host, but a morphologically identical species has been found in the gingival tissues of monkeys.[31]

PATHOGENESIS

Trichomonas elongata is nonpathogenic although it is most frequently found in individuals with oral disease or with poor dental hygiene. Its presence, like that of *Endamœba*

---

[30] Wenyon, C. M. and O'Connor, F. W., 1917.   [31] Hegner, R. and Chu, H. J., 1930.

gingivalis, is due to the favorable environment provided by inflammatory conditions. It has been found in dental caries, pyorrhea, diseased tonsils, and in fusospirochaetal infections of the gums, throat and lungs.

DIAGNOSIS AND TREATMENT

Diagnosis.—*Trichomonas elongata* is the only parasitic flagellate of the mouth. It is difficult to detect in smears but it may be readily demonstrated by cultures.
Treatment.—Unnecessary.

PREVENTION

Epidemiology.—The incidence of *Trichomonas elongata* as determined by three surveys of 550 patients is 22 per cent. It varies widely, being low in clean and high in unclean mouths with diseased teeth and gums.

Infection is usually transmitted through kissing, but it may result from contaminated hands or eating utensils. The organism is quite resistant, remaining alive from 3 to 6 days at room temperature and in distilled water for 10 to 12 hours.[32] The possibility of droplet infection has been suggested.[33]

Prophylaxis.—Attention to dental hygiene will lessen the incidence of infection.

REFERENCES

BEATMAN, L. H. Studies on *Trichomonas buccalis,* J. Dent. Res., 1933, 13:339.

BISHOP, A. The Morphology and Method of Division of *Trichomonas,* Parasitology, 1931, 23: 129.

BLAND, P. B., WENRICH, D. H. and GOLDSTEIN, L. *Trichomonas vaginalis* in Pregnancy; a Clinical and Pathological Entity, Surg. Gynec. & Obst., 1931, 53:759.

BOECK, W. C. Studies on *Tricercomonas intestinalis* (Wenyon and O'Connor, 1917), Am. J. Trop. Med., 1924, 4:519.

BROUGHTON-ALCOCK, W. and THOMSON, J. G. *Embadomonas intestinalis* (Wenyon and O'Connor, 1917). Description of the Cysts and Free Forms Found in a Case in England, Proc. Roy. Soc. Med. (Sect. Trop. Dis.), 1922, 15:8.

CLEVELAND, L. R. *Tritrichomonas fecalis* nov. sp. of Man; its Ability to Grow and Multiply Indefinitely in Feces Diluted with Tap Water and in Frogs and Tadpoles, Am. J. Hyg., 1928, 8:232.

DOBELL, C. and O'CONNOR, F. W. The Intestinal Protozoa of Man. John Bale, Sons and Danielsson, Ltd., London, 1921, pp. 211.

HEGNER, R. Infections of the Vagina of Rhesus Monkeys with *Trichomonas hominis* from Man, J. Parasitol., 1934, 20:247.

HEGNER, R. and ESKRIDGE, L. Elimination and Cross Infection Experiments with Trichomonads from Fowls, Rats and Man, Am. J. Hyg., 1935, 21:135.

HINSHAW, H. C. On the Morphology and Mitosis of *Trichomonas buccalis* (Goodey) Kofoid, Univ. California Publ. Zoöl., 1926, 29:159.

KARNAKY, K. J. *Trichomonas vaginalis* Vaginitis, Urol. & Cutan. Rev., 1934, 38:174.

KESSEL, J. F. and GAFFORD, J. A. Pathology of Vaginitis due to *Trichomonas,* Arch. Path., 1935, 20:951.

KOFOID, C. A. and SWEZY, O. On the Morphology and Mitosis of *Chilomastix mesnili* (Wenyon), a Common Flagellate of the Human Intestine, Univ. California Publ. Zoöl., 1920, 20:117.

—— Mitosis and Fission in the Active and Encysted Phases of *Giardia enterica* (Grassi) of Man, with a Discussion of the Method of Origin of Bilateral Symmetry in Polymastigote Flagellates, Univ. California Publ. Zoöl., 1922, 20:199; also Bull. Johns Hopkins Hosp., 1921, 32:166.

---

[32] Hinshaw, H. C., 1926.   [33] Beatman, L. H., 1933.

KOFOID, C. A. and SWEZY, O. On the Morphology and Behavior of *Pentatrichomonas ardin delteili* (Derrien and Raynaud), Univ. California Publ. Zoöl., 1923, 20:373; also Penta-trichomoniasis in Man, Am. J. Trop. Med., 1924, 4:33.

LYON, B. B. V. and SWALM, W. A. Giardiasis: its Frequency, Recognition, Treatment and Certain Clinical Factors, Am. J. M. Sc., 1925, 170:348.

MACPHEE, L. and WALKER, B. S. Intestinal Giardiasis in New England, with Notes on its Pathogenicity and Symptomatology, Am. J. Digest. Dis. & Nutrition, 1935, 1:768.

POWELL, W. N. *Trichomonas vaginalis* Donné, 1836: its Morphological Characteristics, Mito-sis and Specific Identity, Am. J. Hyg., 1936, 24:145.

SIMON, C. E. *Giardia enterica:* a Parasitic Intestinal Flagellate of Man, Am. J. Hyg., 1921, 1:440.

ZAHORSKY, J. Giardiasis in Young Children, Arch. Pediat., 1932, 49:627.

Chapter XI

THE BLOOD AND TISSUE FLAGELLATES OF MAN

FAMILY *TRYPANOSOMIDÆ* DOFLEIN, 1901

The TRYPANOSOMIDÆ are hemoflagellates and allied forms that live in the tissues of their hosts. The family is divided into six genera, two of which, *Trypanosoma* and *Leishmania,* have species pathogenic to man and other mammals. *Trypanosoma* and *Leishmania* infect vertebrates and invertebrates, *Leptomonas, Crithidia* and *Herpetomonas* invertebrates, and *Phytomonas* invertebrates and plants. The several genera present morphological gradations from *Leishmania* to *Trypanosoma.* Certain stages in the life cycles of these two genera resemble the intermediate forms represented by the genera *Leptomonas, Crithidia* and *Herpetomonas* found in insects and other invertebrates. The relationship of the genera other than *Phytomonas* and the stages of their life cycles in vertebrate and invertebrate hosts are presented in Figure 35.

The flagellates have certain common anatomical structures: (1) a body, slender and elongated in the flagellated stage and round or oval in the nonflagellated stage; (2) a relatively large round or oval nucleus; (3) a spherical or rod-shaped parabasal body with a small, closely associated blepharoplast; (4) a flagellum arising from the blepharoplast and extending forward either to terminate at or project beyond the anterior end of the animal; and (5) an undulating membrane (absent in *Leishmania* and *Leptomonas*) formed by the union of the marginal protoplasm with the flagellum.

Phytomonas.—The species of the genus *Phytomonas* pass through both leishmanian and leptomonad stages. They are placed in a separate genus because they live in plants as well as in invertebrates. Insects are the transmitting agents.

Leptomonas.—Species of the genus *Leptomonas* live only in invertebrate hosts and are transmitted in the cyst-like leishmanian stage. They pass through leishmanian and leptomonad stages in their life cycles. In the leptomonad stage the parasite is elongated and fairly slender. The parabasal body and blepharoplast are situated in the anterior end, and the flagellum projects free anteriorly. There is no undulating membrane and the animal moves by lashing its flagellum.

Leishmania.—The species of the genus *Leishmania* also have both leishmanian and leptomonad stages in their life cycles. They differ from *Leptomonas* in occurring in both vertebrate and invertebrate hosts, the leishmanian stage developing in vertebrates. The methods of transmission from vertebrate to vertebrate have not been fully determined. The leishmanian form is a round or oval body with a postcentral, oval nucleus, anterior to which are the parabasal body and blepharoplast.

Crithidia.—The species of the genus *Crithidia* occur in the leishmanian, leptomonad and crithidial forms, and like *Leptomonas* are transmitted in the cyst-like leishmanian form. They are parasites of invertebrates, especially insects. In the crithidial stage the parasite is long and slender. The parabasal body and the blepharoplast lie immediately in front of the postcentral nucleus. The flagellum passes forward from the blepharoplast, forming a short undulating membrane before it becomes free.

Herpetomonas.—The species of the genus *Herpetomonas* have four stages in their life cycles, occurring as leishmanian, leptomonad, crithidial and trypanosomal forms. They infect only invertebrate hosts and are transmitted in the cyst-like leishmanian stage.

Trypanosoma.—The species of the genus *Trypanosoma* like those of the genus *Her-*

143

petomonas have four stages in their life cycle, appearing as leishmanian, leptomonad, crithidial and trypanosomal forms, but they differ by infecting both vertebrate and invertebrate hosts. They are usually transmitted from vertebrate to vertebrate by insects. In the trypanosomal stage the body is elongated, the nucleus centrally located, and the parabasal body and blepharoplast situated toward the posterior end. The flagellum extends along the outer border of the undulating membrane to project free at the anterior end of the animal.

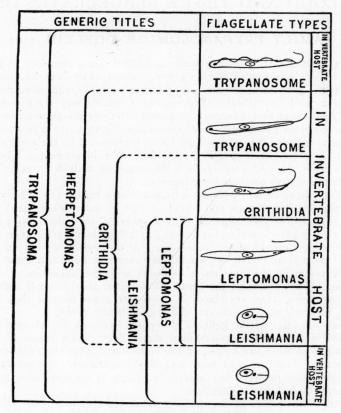

FIG. 35.—THE TRYPANOSOMIDÆ

Diagram illustrating the relationship of five genera of TRYPANOSOMIDÆ and the stages of their life cycles in vertebrate and invertebrate hosts (After Wenyon, from Hegner, Root, Augustine and Huff, *Parasitology*, 1938, D. Appleton-Century Company).

GENUS *TRYPANOSOMA* GRUBY, 1843

The members of the genus *Trypanosoma,* one of the most widely distributed parasitic genera, spend part of their life cycle in the blood and tissues of vertebrates and part in invertebrates. Numerous species are found in the blood and tissues of mammals, birds, reptiles, amphibians and fishes, but in most instances they do not harm the host. Several species, however, are of medical importance, since they produce serious disease in man and domestic animals.

HISTORY

The first hemoflagellate was discovered in 1841 by Valentine in the brown trout. In 1843 Gruby established the genus *Trypanosoma* for a flagellate in the blood of frogs. In 1879 Lewis in India described *Trypanosoma lewisi* of the rat. Evans discovered the first pathogenic species, *T. evansi,* in 1880 in the blood of Indian horses affected with surra. Rouget in 1894 found *T. equiperdum* in Algerian horses affected with dourine. Bruce in 1895 described *T. brucei* in horses and cattle suffering from nagana in Zululand and demonstrated its transmission by the tsetse fly, *Glossina palpalis.* Voges in 1901 obtained *T. equinum* in horses that had mal de caderas.

Forde in 1901 first observed a trypanosome in the blood of man in Africa, and in 1902 Dutton named it *T. gambiense.* Castellani in 1903 found this species in the cerebrospinal fluid of patients with Gambian sleeping sickness. Bruce and Nabarro in 1903 confirmed the relation between the trypanosome and the disease, and with others demonstrated that *Glossina palpalis* was the insect vector. Stephens and Fantham in 1909 discovered *T. rhodesiense* in Rhodesia, and Chagas in 1907 observed *T. cruzi* in Brazil.

BIOLOGICAL CHARACTERISTICS

Morphology.—Trypanosomes are minute, actively motile, fusiform Protozoa, flattened from side to side (Fig. 36). One margin is usually convex and the other concave. The body is long and sinuous with a tapering anterior and a blunt posterior end. Even in the same species the shape varies markedly. There is a large oval nucleus near the middle of the body, and a spherical or rod-shaped parabasal body of variable size near the posterior end. In front of and connected to the parabasal body is a small basal granule, the blepharoplast. The flagellum, arising from the blepharoplast, runs forward along the marginal portion of the undulating membrane, and projects from the anterior end of the body. The undulating membrane extends along the more convex border in a wavy fashion. In the anterior half of the trypanosome minute, deeply staining refractile granules occasionally may be seen. Species differ in shape, size, activity and in the position, arrangement and development of the organs. Measurements of specimens in blood films are used for identifying species and for recording reproductive activity. The latter is determined by the proportion of immature forms that are present in the blood at the time of examination.

Physiology.—The trypanosome travels with a writhing movement produced by the flagellum and the undulating membrane, the degree of motility varying in different species. It obtains nourishment by absorbing the body fluids of its host. Reproduction takes place by longitudinal division.

Cultivation.—Novy and MacNeal in 1903 first cultivated *Trypanosoma lewisi* on agar to which fresh rabbit blood was added after sterilization. The Novy-Mac-Neal-Nicolle (N.N.N.) medium (Section **VII,** IV, 7) is still a popular and satisfactory medium. On cultivation the trypanosomes pass through stages resembling those in the invertebrate host. Crithidial forms develop at low temperatures and trypanosomal forms at high. The cultivation of the species pathogenic for man is comparatively difficult.

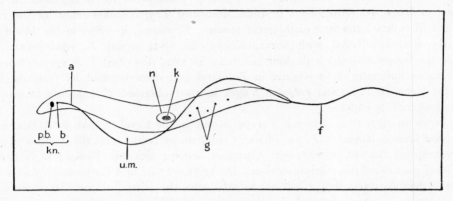

FIG. 36.—DIAGRAM OF A TYPICAL TRYPANOSOME

a, axoneme; *b,* blepharoplast; *f,* flagellum; *g,* chromatic granules; *k,* karyosome; *kn.,* kinetoplast; *n,* nucleus; *p.b.,* parabasal body; *u.m.,* undulating membrane.

LIFE CYCLE

The life cycle of most trypanosomes involves an alternate existence in a vertebrate and invertebrate host, the latter serving as the transmitting agent (Fig. 38). In the vertebrate host, after an incubational period of a few days, there is rapid multiplication of the parasites. As a result numerous small, irregularly sized trypanosomes, some even in stages of division, are present in the blood. In hosts infected with nonpathogenic trypanosomes the period of rapid multiplication is followed by a longer period during which the trypanosomes are of uniform shape and size. Subsequently they decrease in number and finally disappear. In acute infections the number of pathogenic trypanosomes continues to increase until the death of the host or in chronic infections fluctuates with the remissions or exacerbations of the disease.

Within one to two days after ingestion by a blood-sucking insect the trypanosomes multiply intracellularly or extracellularly in the anterior part of the digestive tract. Crithidial and leptomonad forms develop in the hind-gut and rectum or in the proventriculus and salivary glands. Infective forms are produced in one to three weeks after ingestion.

Some trypanosomes display a natural species-selectivity for one vertebrate host; others, less selective, live in several vertebrates. Experimentally it is possible to infect a variety of animals with most species of trypanosomes. The parasites show even greater specificity in the selection of their intermediate hosts; normal cyclic development usually takes place in only a single species. External conditions affecting the habitat and distribution of insect hosts tend to maintain a natural host-specificity.

TRANSMISSION OF INFECTION

Transmission from one vertebrate to another in terrestrial animals is usually by insects and in aquatic animals by leeches. The method of transmission may be direct, indirect or cyclical, or rarely congenital. The direct method is used in the laboratory when blood from an infected animal is inoculated into a healthy one. It occurs in nature when infective material from open lesions is transferred mechanically by contact or by biting and non-biting insects. *Trypanosoma equiperdum,* which produces dourine in horses, is transmitted directly by coitus. *T. hippicum,* which produces murrina in horses and mules, is transferred mechanically by contaminated nonbiting flies; and *T. evansi,* the cause of surra in horses and cattle, and *T. equinum,* the cause of mal de caderas in horses and mules, are also believed to be transmitted in this way. Direct transmission by biting insects involves no cyclic development of the trypanosome. If the biting insect, interrupted during feeding, completes its meal upon a second host, the infective form may be transferred by the contaminated proboscis or by regurgitation. This method of transmission seldom occurs in trypanosomal diseases of man except during epidemics.

In indirect transmission the trypanosome must undergo a cyclic development in a blood-sucking insect before it becomes infective. Trypanosomes with cyclic development in the invertebrate host may be separated into two groups:[1] (1) those that develop in the posterior station, and (2) those that develop in the anterior station. In the first group, which includes parasites of rodents, bats, moles, ant-eaters, carnivora, monkeys and such large herbivora as cattle, sheep and antelopes, the trypanosome passes through an intracellular and extracellular cycle in the hind-gut and rectum and the infective form is extruded in the feces. The new host is infected by the contaminative method or by the ingestion of the trypanosome. In the second group, which includes certain nonpathogenic species and the pathogenic trypanosomes of man, domestic animals and wild game, the trypanosomes develop first in the digestive tract and become infective after reaching the salivary glands. When the insect feeds, the infective forms are injected with the saliva.

Congenital transmission of trypanosomal infections is of little practical importance. In a few instances invertebrate hosts have been reported to pass the trypanosomes to their offspring. Placental transfer has never been proved, but trypanosomes have been transmitted in mother's milk.

PATHOGENESIS

Most species are not injurious to their natural hosts, but some produce marked pathogenic effects and encounter little or no resistance. In most wild animals an equilibrium is soon established, but in man and domestic animals, which apparently are more recent hosts, lack of harmony with the parasite results in disease and often in death. In acute infections death is believed to result from

---

[1] Wenyon, C. M., 1926.

hypoglycemia. In chronic cases death is due to lowered vitality and intercurrent disease. The three species of trypanosomes parasitic in man are pathogenic for man and most laboratory animals but not for wild animal reservoir hosts.

IMMUNITY

The host establishes an immunity against nonpathogenic trypanosomes, but shows little or no resistance to pathogenic species, the organisms increasing in the blood until death intervenes. In rats experimentally infected with the non-pathogenic *Trypanosoma lewisi,* immunity is manifested at first by an inhibition of the reproductive activities of the parasites and later by their partial or complete destruction.[2] On the other hand, no resistance is found in rats and mice infected with the pathogenic *T. brucei* and *T. rhodesiense,* while in dogs and guinea pigs with relapsing infections the rate of reproduction is not lessened and only the adult parasites are destroyed. In man there are apparently periods of increase and decrease in the number of parasites. Resistance to subsequent infection, however, has been reported in mice cured of primary infections with *T. rhodesiense* and *T. brucei.*

Experimental animals that recover from an infection may develop immunity to a specific trypanosome but not to other species. Lytic, agglutinative and alexin-fixing antibodies and protective substances have been demonstrated in varying amounts in the sera of recovered animals.

The normal serum of man destroys the trypanosomes pathogenic for animals *in vitro* and in experimental animals, but does not destroy the three species of man or the common *T. lewisi* of the rat.[3] The blood sera of other animals, except monkeys, have no trypanocidal action. The trypanocidal substance, which is found in the globulin fraction of human serum, is thermolabile at 64° C. for one hour, diminishes rapidly on standing, passes readily through Berkefeld filters and with diminished intensity through collodion ultrafilters, and may be removed from the serum by adsorption with trypanosomes or bacteria (*Eberthella typhosa* and *Proteus vulgaris*). It is probably a nonspecific antibody originating in the liver. It is present in blood and serous exudates but absent in cerebrospinal fluid and urine. It is increased in pregnant women and is found in infants. Trypanocidal activity differs from bactericidal and resembles the virus-neutralizing function in being limited to man and a few primates and in occurring without the presence of alexin. The trypanocidal agent in normal human serum is capable of producing an equivalent antibody or else is closely associated with some antigenic factor.[4] Antiserum prepared against unheated normal serum neutralizes its trypanocidal action *in vitro* and *in vivo,* whereas an antiserum prepared against heated normal serum has no effect.

The serum of patients with trypanosomiasis has the same trypanocidal power as that of normal individuals. Serum-fast strains of animal trypanosomes and the serum-resistant *T. lewisi* are unable to infect man. Consequently, the immunity

[2] Taliaferro, W. H. and Taliaferro, L. G., 1922.

[3] Culbertson, J. T., 1935.
[4] Handler, B. J., 1935.

of man against the pathogenic trypanosomes of animals depends upon other factors than the trypanocidal action of the serum.[3] Reproduction in *T. duttoni* is inhibited by a specific ablastin in immune mouse serum and the trypanosome is destroyed by a specific antibody that acts as a trypanolysin, both substances being similar to those against *T. lewisi* in the rat.[5] Similar antibodies may possibly be produced in man against *T. gambiense*.

CLASSIFICATION

No satisfactory method of classifying trypanosomes has been devised, because of wide variation in morphology, differences in pathogenicity, and incomplete knowledge of life cycles. Classifications have been based on morphology particularly flagellar structure, on natural distribution in various hosts, on methods of transmission and on pathogenicity.

Trypanosomes may be grouped according to hosts: (1) aquatic vertebrates, (2) terrestrial reptiles, (3) birds, and (4) mammals. The trypanosomes of aquatic vertebrates are transmitted by leeches. Among the parasitic species that have been studied are *T. vittatæ* of the tortoise, *T. rotatorium* and *T. inopinatum* of the frog, and *T. giganteum, T. rajæ* and *T. remaki* of fishes. Among the more prominent trypanosomes of terrestrial reptiles are *T. kochi* of the crocodile, *T. chameleonis* of the chameleon, *T. dactyli* of the North American lizard, and *T. najæ* of the cobra. Infections with trypanosomes are common in birds. Of more than a hundred avian species the best known are *T. paddæ* and *T. noctuæ*.

Mammals are hosts for many pathogenic and nonpathogenic trypanosomes. A species nonpathogenic to one mammalian host may be pathogenic for another. Numerous harmless species have been found in bats, moles, shrews, ant-eaters, rodents, primates and in the larger herbivorous and carnivorous animals. Of these species *T. lewisi* of the rat has been thoroughly studied. A number of pathogenic species infect man and domestic animals.

THE TRYPANOSOMES OF MAMMALS

Three species of trypanosomes are pathogenic to man. *T. gambiense* and the closely allied if not identical *T. rhodesiense* produce African sleeping sickness, and *T. cruzi* produce South American trypanosomiasis or Chagas' disease.

The species of pathogenic trypanosomes in mammals other than man are not only of veterinary and economic importance but are also involved in the problem of human trypanosomiasis. They are so closely allied in morphology and habits with the trypanosomes of man that the possibility of interchanges of species makes the problems of reservoir hosts and species-variation most confusing. The group of trypanosomes that closely resemble each other, namely, *T. brucei, T. evansi, T. equiperdum, T. hippicum, T. gambiense* and *T. rhodesiense,* may have descended from a common ancestor. Table 16 gives a résumé of the more important pathogenic trypanosomes of mammals.

---

[5] Taliaferro, W. H., 1938.

TABLE 16
IMPORTANT PATHOGENIC TRYPANOSOMES

	Trypanosoma equiperdum	*Trypanosoma brucei*	*Trypanosoma congolense*
Discoverer	Rouget, 1894	Bruce, 1894	Broden, 1904
Geographical distribution	Asia, North Africa, Europe, America, chiefly Mediterranean countries	Tropical Africa	Tropical Africa
Mammalian hosts Domesticated animals	Horses and donkeys	Equidæ, ruminants and other domesticated animals	Equidæ, ruminants, dogs
Wild animals	None known	Game mammals	Game mammals
Morphology Characteristics	Resembles *T. brucei*	Fairly wide body, relatively short posterior end, wide undulating membrane	Short or no free flagellum, prominent parabasal body
Size (micra)	20 to 30	17 to 28	9 to 18
Pathogenesis Disease	Dourine, mal de coit	Nagana	Unnamed
Site of trypanosome in host	Lesions, rarely in blood	Blood	Blood
Pathology and symptomatology	Edema of genitalia and body wall, cutaneous lesions, anemia and paralysis	Irregular fever, anemia, emaciation, subcutaneous edema. Highly fatal to equines and canines	Chronic wasting disease, with photophobia, edema and weakness
Laboratory animals	Moderately virulent, dogs most susceptible of laboratory animals	Highly virulent for all laboratory animals	Slightly virulent, rats not always infected
Transmission Insect vectors	Usually none, rarely *Stomoxys*, *Tabanus*	*Glossina* (seven species)	*Glossina* (four species)
Method of transmission	Coitus, occasionally mechanical transfer by biting flies	Cyclic development in insect host	Cyclic development in insect host

OF MAMMALS OTHER THAN MAN

Trypanosoma vivax	*Trypanosoma simiæ*	*Trypanosoma evansi*	*Trypanosoma equinum*	*Trypanosoma hippicum*
Zieman, 1905	Bruce *et al*, 1912	Evans, 1880	Voges, 1901	Darling, 1910
Tropical Africa	East Africa (Nyasaland)	Asia, northern Australia, Madagascar	Tropical and subtropical South America	Central America
Equidæ, ruminants	Goats, hogs, sheep	Equidæ, ruminants, dogs	Equidæ, ruminants	Horses, mules. Cattle act as reservoir hosts
Game mammals	Monkeys, wart-hogs	Ruminants, elephants	Water hogs	Vampire bats
Posterior half of body has a bulged appearance	Resembles *T. congolense*, parabasal body some distance from posterior end	Resembles *T. brucei*	Parabasal body said to be absent	Resembles *T. brucei*
18 to 26	14 to 24	18 to 34	22 to 24	16 to 18
Souma	Unnamed	Surra	Mal de caderas	Murrina de caderas, derrengadera de caderas
Lymph glands, less often blood	Blood	Blood	Blood	Blood and lesions
Similar to *T. congolense*	Chronic wasting disease in goats, rapidly fatal in monkeys and hogs without noteworthy symptoms	Irregular fever, anemia, emaciation, ecchymoses. Invariably fatal	Acute infection similar to that produced by *T. evansi*	Weakness, emaciation, anemia, conjunctivitis, ecchymoses, edema, enlarged spleen, paralysis
Slightly virulent, rabbits susceptible	Moderately virulent, rats, mice and guinea pigs refractory	Highly virulent for all laboratory animals	Highly virulent for laboratory animals	Highly virulent for laboratory animals
Glossina (four species)	*Glossina* (two species)	*Tabanus*, *Stomoxys*	*Tabanus*, *Stomoxys*	*Musca* and other nonbiting flies
Cyclic development in insect host. Also mechanical transfer by *Stomoxys*	Cyclic development in insect host	Mechanical transfer by biting flies	Mechanical transfer by biting flies	Mechanical transfer by flies

Trypanosoma gambiense DUTTON, 1902

Synonyms.—*Trypanosoma ugandense* Castellani, 1903; *Trypanosoma hominis* Manson, 1903; *Trypanosoma nigeriense* Macfie, 1913; *Castellanella gambiense* (Dutton, 1912) Chalmers, 1918.

Disease.—Gambian trypanosomiasis, Mid-African sleeping sickness.

History.—African sleeping sickness was first described by Atkins in 1724 and later by Winterbottom in 1803. Almost a century later *Trypanosoma gambiense* was discovered in human blood in West Africa by Forde in 1901 and named by Dutton in the following year. In 1903 Castellani found in the spinal fluid of 20 out of 34 patients with African sleeping sickness a trypanosome, which he called *T. ugandense* but which proved to be *T. gambiense*. In the same year Bruce and Nabarro demonstrated that the tsetse fly, *Glossina palpalis,* was the transmitting agent; and Klein in 1909 accurately described the development of the trypanosome in this insect.

Geographical Distribution.—Tropical West and Central Africa between 15° N. latitude and 15° S. latitude (Fig. 37). It is limited to the range of its vector, *Glossina palpalis.* The eastern limits are Lake Victoria and Lake Tanganyika. On the west coast of Africa it is found between Senegal and Angola.

BIOLOGICAL CHARACTERISTICS

Morphology.—In human blood *Trypanosoma gambiense* is polymorphic, ranging from typical long, slender trypanosomal to short, blunt forms without free flagella or even to bizarre degenerate forms. In the spinal fluid all sizes and shapes occur, including multiple forms and even involuted round or pear-shaped specimens. The length of the trypanosome ranges from 15 to 30 μ and the breadth from 1.5 to 3.5 μ.

In fresh preparations the slender colorless flagellates may be observed moving actively among the blood corpuscles. When stained with the Romanowsky stains the granular cytoplasm is pale blue and sometimes contains dark volutin granules and vacuoles (Plate II, 1). The central nucleus stains red or reddish-purple. At the rounded posterior end is a dark red mass consisting of the almost indistinguishable parabasal body and blepharoplast. From the blepharoplast the attached portion of the flagellum, the axoneme, runs along the edge of the undulating membrane to the anterior pole from which the free flagellum projects. The broad, unstriated undulating membrane, somewhat paler than the corporeal cytoplasm, runs along the margin to the anterior end. When stained with iron hemotoxylin the nucleus shows a distinct membrane and a large central karyosome.

DESCRIPTION OF PLATE II.

BLOOD AND TISSUE FLAGELLATES OF MAN ($\times$ 1500). ROMANOWSKY STAINS

1, *Trypanosoma gambiense* in blood; 2, *Trypanosoma rhodesiense* in blood; 3, *Trypanosoma cruzi* in blood; 4, *Trypanosoma gambiense,* developmental forms in *Glossina palpalis;* 5, *Leishmania donovani* in endothelial cell; 6, *Leishmania tropica* in large mononuclear cell; 7, *Leishmania donovani,* flagellate forms from culture; 8, *Leishmania tropica,* flagellate forms from culture. (Note: In actual stained preparations the colors may be expected to vary from those shown in the plate.)

PLATE II

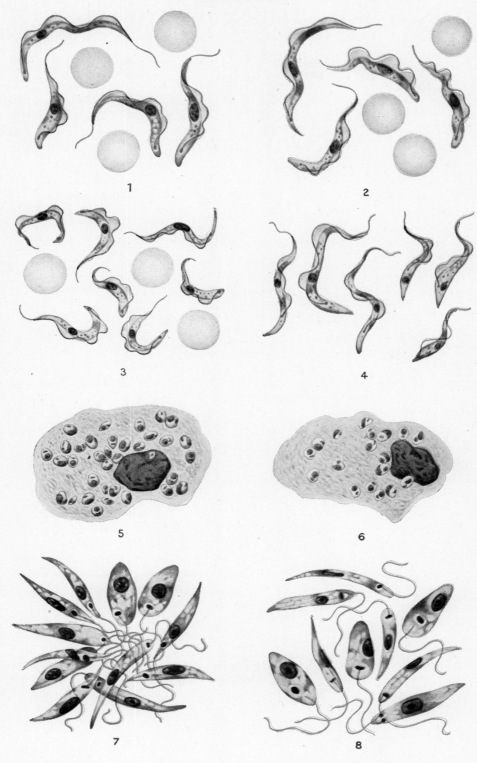

1

2

3

4

5

6

7

8

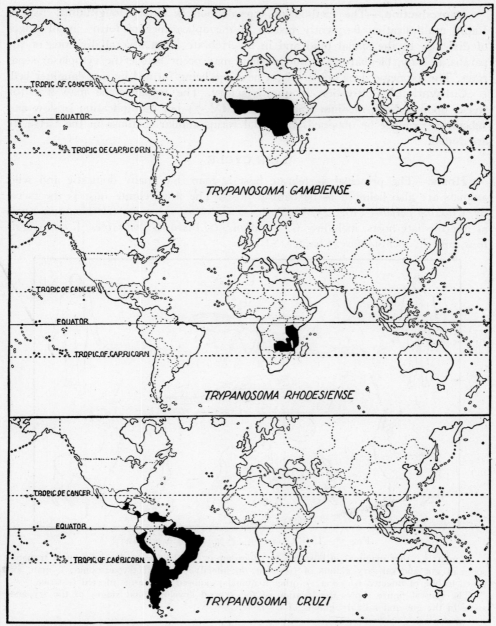

FIG. 37.—GEOGRAPHICAL DISTRIBUTION OF *Trypanosoma gambiense, T. rhodesiense,* and *T. cruzi*

Nutrition.—*T. gambiense* absorbs nourishment from the blood plasma, lymph or cerebrospinal fluid.

Movement.—In fresh preparations the trypanosomes progress with rapid wavy movement among the blood cells.

Reproduction.—The method of reproduction is binary longitudinal fission. Rapid multiplication frequently results in the appearance of forms in all stages of division. In the spinal fluid and in invertebrate hosts several divisions of the parabasal body, blepharoplast, and nucleus may occur before the cytoplasm separates. The axoneme does not divide, a new one being formed by one daughter cell.

Cultivation.—Cultivation is unsatisfactory. The trypanosome may live for weeks upon N.N.N. medium (Section **VII**, IV, 7) but multiplication is slow and subcultures cannot be obtained. Crithidial forms similar to those in the tsetse fly are found.

LIFE CYCLE

Hosts.—The principal vertebrate host is man, but many domestic and wild animals are also believed to be natural hosts. The invertebrate host is the tsetse fly, *Glossina palpalis* (Fig. 237A). At least five other species of *Glossina* may serve as intermediate hosts, including *G. morsitans*, *G. fusca*, *G. pallidipes*, *G. submorsitans*, and *G. tachinoides* (Chapter XLII).

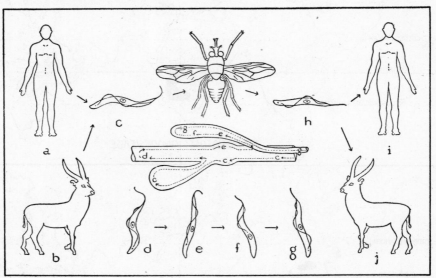

FIG. 38.—LIFE CYCLE OF *Trypanosoma gambiense*

a, man; *b*, other mammalian hosts; *c*, trypanosome in blood; *d* to *g*, development of trypanosome in gut and salivary glands of *Glossina*; *h*, infective form of trypanosome; *i*, man, exposed to bite of infected *Glossina*; *j*, other mammals, exposed to bite of infected *Glossina*.

The central figure shows the location of the several developmental stages of the trypanosome in the gut and salivary glands of *Glossina*.

T. gambiense may be transmitted to wild game, domestic and laboratory animals. It produces an acute or chronic disease, depending upon the species of host and the virulence and animal passage of the particular trypanosomal strain. In cattle, horses, sheep, pigs and dogs the disease runs a chronic course without marked symptoms and may not end fatally. In the smaller laboratory animals and in monkeys death ensues more rapidly.

Metamorphosis.—The rate of development in the tsetse fly depends upon the temperature. Within two days after the fly has sucked infectious blood the trypanosomes begin to multiply in the lumen of the mid- and hind-gut until by the tenth day a large number of broad forms are present (Fig. 38). In 10 to 15 days they develop in the proventriculus into long slender forms (Plate II, 4) that migrate through the esophagus, hypopharynx and salivary ducts to the salivary glands, where in from 16 to 20 days they become crithidial flagellates. Here, after multiplying for 2 to 5 days, they assume the typical infective trypanosomal form. About 21 days after ingestion the infective or metacyclic forms are ready to pass from the salivary glands to a new vertebrate host. In man they increase in the blood stream and enter the lymph channels and connective tissues. Eventually they invade the central nervous system and the cerebrospinal fluid.

PATHOGENESIS

Habitat.—In the early stages of the disease *Trypanosoma gambiense* is found in the blood and lymphatics and in the late stages in the cerebrospinal fluid. It is coelozoic, living in the blood, lymph, and in the intercellular spaces of the lymph nodes, spleen, brain and other organs.

Pathology.—The most important pathological changes occur in the lymphatic and nervous systems. In the early stages of the disease there is a general enlargement of the lymphatic glands, which at first are swollen and soft and later firm and fibrous. The glands usually involved are the postcervical, submaxillary, inguinal and femoral. The spleen and at times the liver are enlarged. In the late stages the central nervous system is involved. There is a chronic leptomeningitis of the brain, characterized by perivascular infiltration of endothelial cells, lymphocytes, plasma cells and proliferated neuroglia cells. Atrophy of the ganglion cells from pressure may occur. The trypanosomes may invade the nervous tissues and the spinal fluid, which increases in volume and shows changes comparable to those of cerebrospinal syphilis. The histopathological findings are those of a meningoencephalitis with perivascular cellular infiltration.

Symptomatology.—The clinical course of the disease progresses from the early or acute stage during the first year to the chronic or sleeping-sickness stage during the second and third years. The incubational period is usually about two weeks, but may be several weeks longer in resistant natives. The first sign of the disease is a fever, which lasts for about a week. A series of febrile attacks then alternate with afebrile periods during which the patient feels comparatively well. The fever may be continuous but is usually remittent with a wide diurnal range. Glandular enlargement, edematous swellings about the eyes and joints, and erythematous skin eruptions are often present. The lymph glands, especially those of the postcervical triangle (Winterbottom's sign), are swollen and tender. There may be headache, cramps and a delayed sensation to pain with deep hyperesthesia (Kérandel's sign).

The chronic stage begins early in the second year. The febrile paroxysms are more pronounced and the headaches more severe. The patient shows signs of physical and mental weakness, such as disinclination to work, avoidance of acquaintances, and a morose, indifferent attitude. At the end of the second year the typical mental lethargy and physical weakness of "sleeping sickness" appear and follow a progressive course. The patient becomes apathetic, dull and drowsy; when roused he can talk intelligently but with lack of interest and with retardation. There may be periods of exaltation followed by deep melancholia. Disturbances of the neuromuscular apparatus appear. The speech is low and tremulous; tremors of the tongue and limbs and even choreiform movements may occur; the gait is slow and shuffling; the patellar reflexes are exaggerated; and there may be a positive Romberg, intention tremor and occasionally nystagmus. *In toto* the condition may simulate multiple sclerosis.

As the disease progresses somnolence increases until the patient falls asleep even in the midst of activity. In the terminal stages, which occur from one to two years after the onset of the "sleeping sickness" stage, the patient passes into an almost continuous sleep, with rapid pulse, low blood pressure, absent knee jerks and marked emaciation. Death may occur from coma, convulsions, asthenia and dehydration, but more often from intercurrent diseases, particularly pneumonia.

DIAGNOSIS, PROGNOSIS AND TREATMENT

Diagnosis.—Clinical diagnosis in the early stages is difficult, since fever and glandular enlargement are also symptoms of other tropical diseases. In differential diagnosis relapsing, enteric and undulant fevers, malaria, ancylostomiasis and syphilis must be considered. Trypanosomiasis should be suspected when a patient from an endemic area shows an irregular fever, palpable lymphatic glands, particularly in the postcervical triangle (Winterbottom's sign), erythematous eruptions of the skin, and delayed response to pain with deep-seated hyperesthesia (Kerandel's sign). The late stages of the disease must be differentiated from cerebrospinal syphilis, encephalitis lethargica and other disorders of the central nervous system.

Final diagnosis depends upon the identification of the trypanosome by laboratory examination of the blood and lymph glands in the early stages and of the spinal fluid in the late stages. The several methods of direct microscopical examination and the inoculation of susceptible laboratory animals with blood, lymphatic juice and spinal fluid should be exhausted before a negative report is rendered. The direct microscopical examination includes cover-glass mounts and thin and thick smears of blood, material aspirated from lymph glands, and concentrated blood and spinal fluid (Section **VII**, III, 6-13, 17, 18, 24). It is difficult to distinguish between *Trypanosoma gambiense* and the closely related *T. rhodesiense* (Table 17).

Prognosis.—The prognosis is favorable only if treatment is instituted before involvement of the nervous system. Untreated cases generally prove fatal, although spontaneous recovery may occur in the early stages.

Treatment.—Treatment is effective when administered in the early stages of the disease. Atoxyl, tartar emetic, Bayer 205 and tryparsamide have proved useful drugs. The last two are the most efficient. Bayer 205 (Section **VII**, XIII, 28) is effective before the involvement of the central nervous system. Tryparsamide (Section **VII**, XIII, 3) is effective not only early in the disease but also in about one-fourth of patients with cerebrospinal symptoms. Because patients tend to develop a treatment-fast condition against a single drug, some authorities favor combined treatment especially in relapsing cases. A satisfactory regimen consists of 3 injections of Bayer 205 at three- to four-day intervals followed after ten days by 6 to 8 injections of tryparsamide at weekly intervals. Proper diet, nursing and freedom from complicating diseases must be maintained to assure full benefit of drug treatment. Hospitalization in the early stages of the disease expedites recovery.

PREVENTION

Epidemiology.—The incidence of Gambian trypanosomiasis in endemic areas varies from 3 to 43 per cent, depending upon the abundance of tsetse flies and the degree of human exposure. At times the infection reaches epidemic proportions. On Buvuma Island 19,049 or about 43 per cent of the natives succumbed to the disease in one year.[6] Two-thirds of the population of Kisantu in the Belgian Congo died of the infection in a single decade.[7] In a period of six years the population of Uganda was reduced from 300,000 to 100,000.

Infection is transmitted to man by the bite of the tsetse fly after the cyclic development of the trypanosome. It is estimated that less than 10 per cent of tsetse flies that bite infected persons develop infective forms. Infection by mechanical transmission, in which the fly carries the trypanosome directly from host to host without cyclic development, is believed to occur during epidemics when infected individuals and tsetse flies are numerous. It is possible that other insects may act as mechanical vectors.

A few instances of infections in the temperate zones among women, whose husbands had contracted the disease in endemic areas, suggest the possibility of transmission through coitus. Rare congenital infections have also been reported, and transmission through mother's milk has been demonstrated in laboratory animals.

It is probable though not proved that game animals are reservoir hosts. Natural and experimental infections have been observed in antelopes, and trypanosomes similar to *T. gambiense* have been found in other wild game. Domesticated animals such as sheep, goats and cattle serve as reservoir hosts and are likely sources of human infection.

Asymptomatic infections in a native population present a difficult problem. Many persons, who may serve as sources of infection, have few if any trypanosomes in the blood and no glandular enlargement, fever or malaise. This type of infection, which is more frequent with *T. gambiense* than with *T. rhodesiense,* is easily overlooked in an ordinary survey.

Prophylaxis.—The most effective prophylactic measures against trypanosomiasis are: (1) infected individuals should be isolated and treated; (2) individuals should be protected from tsetse flies by screens, headnets, leggings and gloves, and all bites should be treated promptly with tincture of iodine; (3) trav-

---

[6] Duke, H. L., 1919.   [7] Blacklock, B. and Yorke, W., 1922.

elers should avoid "fly belts" or travel at night when the tsetse flies do not bite; (4) surveys for detecting carriers and border quarantine of persons leaving infected regions are advisable; (5) tsetse flies may be controlled by destroying their breeding places through clearing brush along streams and by reducing the number of available animal hosts (Chapter XLII); (6) depopulation of severely infected areas may be advisable; and (7) mass prophylactic chemotherapy in endemic areas may prove successful.

A single dose of 2.0 gm. of Bayer 205 protects adults against *T. gambiense* and *T. rhodesiense* for at least three months and probably longer.[8] Workers recommend two doses of 1.0 gm. each one week apart. Some protected individuals may acquire the infection, but it is usually of the cryptic type, which is symptomless for two months or longer, then gradually merges into a typical infection. The possibility of producing active immunity by combining drug therapy and injections of living trypanosomes offers some promise.

Trypanosoma rhodesiense STEPHENS AND FANTHAM, 1910

Synonyms.—None.

Disease.—Rhodesian trypanosomiasis, East African sleeping sickness.

History.—In 1909 Stephens and Fantham observed a trypanosome in the blood of a patient with sleeping sickness in Rhodesia, where *Glossina palpalis,* the intermediate host of *Trypanosoma gambiense,* is not found. Although it was morphologically similar to *T. gambiense,* they designated it as a new species, *T. rhodesiense.* In 1912 Kinghorn and Yorke showed that *Glossina morsitans* was its insect vector.

Geographical Distribution.—Northeastern Rhodesia, South Rhodesia, Nyasaland, Portuguese East Africa and Tanganyika Territory (Fig. 37). Its distribution is distinct from that of *T. gambiense.*

BIOLOGICAL CHARACTERISTICS

Morphology.—Morphologically *Trypanosoma rhodesiense* (Plate II. 2) is indistinguishable from *T. gambiense* except that, when injected into rats, mice and guinea pigs, the nucleus in about 5 per cent of the organisms is situated near the posterior end of the trypanosome, a condition rarely observed in *T. gambiense.*

Physiology.—Nutrition, movement and reproduction are similar to those of *T. gambiense.*

Cultivation.—It is cultivated with some difficulty on N.N.N. medium (Section VII, IV, 7).

LIFE CYCLE

Aside from the fact that *Trypanosoma rhodesiense* spends its metacycle in *Glossina morsitans* and in some regions in *G. swynnertoni,* its life cycle in both vertebrate and invertebrate hosts is identical with that of *T. gambiense.* It is capable

---

[8] Duke, H. L., 1936.

of developing in *Glossina palpalis* and *G. brevipalpis,* but these flies play but a small part in the natural transmission of infection.

PATHOGENESIS

Rhodesian trypanosomiasis runs a more rapid and fatal course in man than the Gambian form and often terminates within one year.

Pathology.—The pathological changes are those of West African sleeping sickness, but lesions in the central nervous system are less common, since death usually intervenes before cerebrospinal invasion.

Symptomatology.—Irregular, febrile paroxysms, more frequent and severe than in Gambian trypanosomiasis, begin after an incubational period of from one to two weeks. There is only slight glandular enlargement. Other symptoms are edema, weakness, emaciation and myocarditis. While mental disturbances may develop, the typical "sleeping sickness" syndrome is usually absent and neurological symptoms are not pronounced.

Immunity.—Spontaneous recovery has never been reported. Age, race, sex and occupation have no effect upon resistance.

DIAGNOSIS, PROGNOSIS AND TREATMENT

Diagnosis.—The blood or better the lymph glands of any person from an endemic area who shows symptoms should be examined for trypanosomes (Section **VII,** III, 6-13, 17, 24). Table 17 gives the differential diagnosis between *Trypanosoma rhodesiense* and *T. gambiense.*

Prognosis.—If treatment is commenced early, the prognosis is favorable; if late, unfavorable. Untreated cases invariably run a fatal course.

Treatment.—Rhodesian trypanosomiasis is apparently more responsive to Bayer 205 (Section **VII,** XIII, 28) than Gambian trypanosomiasis, and if this drug is administered early, the disease may be cured. Treatment is ineffective when trypanosomes are present in the spinal fluid. The disease is resistant to tryparsamide, atoxyl and tartar emetic, which are effective in Gambian trypanosomiasis. However, in relapses of patients under Bayer 205 tryparsamide may be tried.

PREVENTION

Epidemiology.—The incidence of *Trypanosoma rhodesiense* infections is much lower than that of *T. gambiense.* The disease occurs almost exclusively in endemic form; epidemics are rare and of limited extent. The distribution, habits and degree of infectiousness of the intermediate host largely account for its low incidence. Relatively few tsetse flies become infective after feeding upon infected individuals. The principal insect host, *Glossina morsitans,* frequents high bushy areas where wild game abounds and does not breed along water courses. The incidence of infected flies is lower in the cool plateau regions than in the warm valleys. Transmission of the disease to man is similar to that of *T. gambiense* and takes place almost exclusively after cyclic development in the fly.

TABLE 17

DIFFERENTIATION OF *TRYPANOSOMA GAMBIENSE* AND
T. RHODESIENSE INFECTIONS

	T. gambiense	T. rhodesiense
Morphology in infected laboratory animals	Posterior nucleated forms rare	Posterior nucleated forms in about 5 per cent of trypanosomes
Epidemiology Areas of distribution	Central and West Africa	East and South Central Africa
Incidence	High	Relatively low
Principal intermediate host	*Glossina palpalis*	*Glossina morsitans*
Epidemics	Yes	Rare
Pathogenesis Virulence in man and laboratory animals	Less marked	Marked
Disease in man	Acute and chronic, cerebrospinal symptoms pronounced. Duration one to three years.	Acute, cerebrospinal symptoms less pronounced. Duration usually less than one year.
Treatment Tryparsamide	Responsive	Resistant
Bayer 205	Effective	More effective

The major epidemiological problem centers on reservoir hosts among wild and domesticated animals and involves the controversial question of the relationship between *T. rhodesiense* and *T. brucei,* a common nonpathogenic trypanosome of wild game which produces nagana, a disease of domestic animals. The consensus is that *T. rhodesiense* is a strain of *T. brucei* which has become habituated to the human host.

The most convincing evidence that the two trypanosomes, although morphologically identical, are distinct species is found in the experimental inoculation of 131 volunteers with *T. brucei* from infected domestic animals without producing a single case of human disease.[9] The presence of only five cases of trypanosomiasis among large bodies of troops operating in areas infested with *Trypanosoma brucei* and *Glossina morsitans* during the World War tends to substantiate this experimental evidence. In the face of these facts it would be illogical to assert that these two species are absolutely indistinguishable. There is plausible evidence to show that *Trypanosoma rhodesiense* may be a strain of *T. brucei* that has become adjusted to man. Certain strains of *T. rhodesiense* lose their pathogenicity for man after animal passage.[10] Most investigators believe that while man is naturally resistant to animal

---

[9] Taute, M. and Huber, F., 1919.   [10] Duke, H. L., 1935.

strains of *T. brucei,* occasional infections do occur and that after passage through several human and insect hosts the infecting strain becomes virulent to man. The manner in which human infection spreads favors this view.[11] The natural hosts of *Glossina morsitans* are game animals inhabiting the bush away from civilization. When wild land is absorbed by farms, *G. morsitans,* finding no wild hosts available, turns to cattle and man.

The theory has arisen that *T. gambiense* long ago made a permanent change of host from animals to man and thus became distinct from *T. brucei;* while *T. rhodesiense* is a strain of *T. brucei* that is even now in the process of changing hosts and is still capable of reversion. If this theory is correct, then large wild game and domestic animals must be considered potential reservoir hosts.

Prophylaxis.—Prophylactic measures are similar to those employed in Gambian trypanosomiasis. The destruction of game animals, especially near habitations, and the protection of man and domestic animals would reduce the number of tsetse flies by limiting their natural food supply; but these ideal procedures are not practical in many localities.

Trypanosoma cruzi CHAGAS, 1909

Synonyms.—*Schizotrypanum cruzi* Chagas, 1909; *Trypanosoma escomeli* Yorke, 1920; *Trypanosoma triatomæ* Kofoid and McCulloch, 1916.

Disease.—American trypanosomiasis; Chagas' disease.

History.—The causative agent of American trypanosomiasis was discovered in the gut of the reduviid bug, *Triatoma megista,* by Chagas in 1907. At that time its pathogenicity for man was not suspected, although experiments showed that various mammals were susceptible to infection. Later, Chagas found this trypanosome in the blood of a child suffering from a wasting disease prevalent in Brazil.

Geographical Distribution.—South America, including Brazil, Venezuela, Chile, Peru and Argentina, and Central America in Guatemala and Panama (Fig. 37). No cases of the disease in man have been reported in the United States of America and Mexico, but the trypanosome has been found by several investigators in various species of *Triatoma* in Mexico, California and Arizona.

BIOLOGICAL CHARACTERISTICS

Morphology.—In the blood the flagellates appear either as long, thin trypanosomes about 20 μ in length or as short, stumpy forms about 15 μ in length with pointed posterior ends (Plate II, 3). In stained smears the trypanosomes have a characteristic crescent shape. Wright's stain turns the cytoplasm blue and the central nucleus and other structures a deep red or violet. The kinetoplast, consisting of the parabasal body and blepharoplast, is near the posterior pole and is relatively large in the stumpy forms. The free flagellum is about one-third the body length.

In smears or sections of the tissues the round or oval leishmanian forms without flagellum and undulating membrane are more commonly found than the flagellated

---

[11] Kinghorn, A. and Yorke, W., 1912.

forms. They are from 1.5 to 4.0 μ in length and when treated with Wright's stain show a large, central, deep red nucleus and a rod-like or round, dark purple kinetoplast (Fig. 39A).

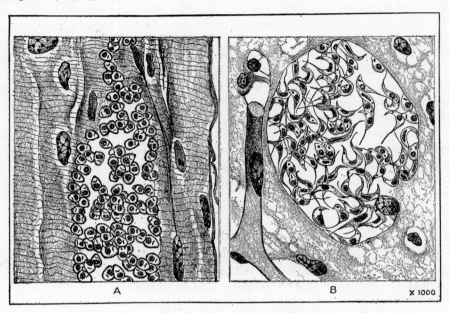

FIG. 39.—*Trypanosoma cruzi* IN TISSUES

A, section of striated muscle of infected guinea pig showing rounded aflagellate *T. cruzi* and destruction of muscle elements; *B,* section of brain, greatly enlarged neuroglia cell distended with flagellate *T. cruzi* (Redrawn from Vianna, 1911).

Physiology.—The trypanosome moves by the action of the flagellum and undulating membrane. It absorbs liquid nutriment from the blood, lymph and products of cellular disintegration. Reproduction, once considered a variety of schizogony, occurs in man by binary longitudinal fission of the leishmanian forms within the tissue cells. The cells distend with the formation of nests of parasites in cyst-like cavities, which on rupture liberate the imprisoned flagellated and nonflagellated forms (Fig. 39 B).

Cultivation.—The parasite has been cultivated upon the N.N.N. medium (Section **VII**, IV, 7).

LIFE CYCLE

Hosts.—The vertebrate hosts are man and various wild animals, including seven species of armadillos, six species of bats (Mexico), dogs, cats, monkeys, opossums and wood rats (California). Experimental infections have been established in rats, mice, lemurs, guinea pigs, dogs and cats. The principal invertebrate host is *Triatoma megista* (Fig. 257). Other arthropods have been found to harbor the trypanosome; at least 15 species of the REDUVIIDÆ (Chapter XLV) are naturally infected, and 4 species of bedbugs and 3 species of ticks that have been infected experimentally.

Reduviid Bug.—When trypanosomes in the peripheral blood of an infected host are ingested by the larva, nymph or adult reduviid bug, *Triatoma megista,* they are transformed into stumpy crithidia that reproduce rapidly in the midgut. By the time the trypanosomes reach the posterior end of the midgut, long crithidial forms appear. After some ten days the crithidial forms change to small trypanosomes and are ready to pass out in the feces as infective, metacyclic forms. During the night *Triatoma megista* bites man painlessly, usually at the junction of cutaneous and mucous surfaces. Since the bug frequently defecates at the same time, the bite is readily contaminated (Fig. 40).

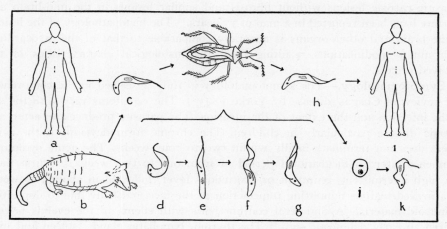

FIG. 40.—LIFE CYCLE OF *Trypanosoma cruzi*

a, man; *b,* armadillo and other mammals; *c, T. cruzi* in blood; *d* to *g,* development of trypanosome in *Triatoma; h,* infective form of trypanosome; *i,* man, exposed to infection; *j,* leishmanian form of *T. cruzi* in man; *k,* trypanosomal form of *T. cruzi* in man.

Man.—Soon after their entrance into man the trypanosomes penetrate the various organs, particularly the endothelial tissues, heart muscles, voluntary muscles and the central nervous system. Within the cells they lose their flagella, assume leishmanian forms, and continue to reproduce until the distended cell ruptures, liberating leishmanian, leptomonad, crithidial and trypanosomal forms. The flagellated forms appear in the blood as trypanosomes and invading new tissues continue the reproductive cycle. It is possible that the leishmanian forms also invade new cells.

PATHOGENESIS

Pathology.—Destruction of tissues by the extensive intracellular invasion of the trypanosome produces disability and finally death. Although any organ may be invaded, the selective sites are the heart and brain. An acute parasitic myocarditis has been described in infants and children with pericardial effusion and cardiac hypertrophy often accompanied by widespread edema and effusion into the pleural and peritoneal cavities.[12] Microscopical examination shows cyst-like collections of

---

[12] Chagas, E., 1935.

leishmanian parasites within the myocardial fibers, degeneration of the muscle fibers with edema, and infiltration of the interstitial tissues by lymphocytes, plasmocytes and endothelial cells. The primary response is an acute inflammatory and degenerative reaction, followed, in the surviving chronic cases, by hyperplasia of the connective tissue and fibrosis of the myocardium with parenchymatous degeneration. Adjacent to these chronic areas are acute lesions with an intensive inflammatory cellular exudate, degenerating muscle fibers, and at times agglomerations of the parasites.

Acute cardiac involvement is not necessarily limited to children, since acute parasitic cardiac lesions without fibrosis and similar lesions in the mid-brain and prostate have been reported in a man of 77 years.[13] The histopathology of the lesions in the brain and other organs is generally comparable to that of the myocardium with minor modifications resulting from the histological characteristics of the involved organs.

Symptomatology.—The symptomatology is fully described in the comprehensive review of Chagas' disease by Yorke (1937). The symptoms vary with the site of the infection and the extent of the invasion. The parasite produces an acute and chronic disease particularly in children. The chronic form develops if the acute illness does not terminate fatally within two to four weeks. The acute symptoms commence after an incubational period of from one to two weeks. At first there is a high intermittent, remittent or continuous fever, followed in about two weeks by a myxedematous nonpitting tumefaction of the face and body due to deposition of mucoid material. A unilateral conjunctivitis with edema of the eyelids is considered an early diagnostic sign.[14] The thyroid, lymphatic glands, spleen and liver are enlarged.

The symptoms of the chronic infection are protean and depend upon the location of the lesions. The disease was originally divided into five clinical classes:[15] (1) a pseudomyxedematous form; (2) a myxedematous form; (3) a nervous form; (4) a cardiac form; and (5) a chronic form with subacute manifestations, particularly febrile paroxysms. Brazilian investigators held the infection accountable for much of the heart disease, infantilism, hypothyroidism and cretinism in Brazil and Argentina. More recent investigators have found that it is not responsible for cretinism and endemic goiter. The chronic cases reported from Panama do not correspond to Chagas' five classes, occur usually in children over 6 years of age, and for the most part are without characteristic symptoms. Evidently the asymptomatic or carrier condition is a definite entity.

Immunity.—Man apparently possesses some degree of resistance to the disease as evidenced by the finding of unsuspected carriers. A relatively high mortality in children is suggested by the low incidence under 15 years and the sharp rise beyond that age in Panama, as determined by the alexin-fixative test.[16] Rats less than 25 days old are susceptible to experimental infection while mature rats are resistant.[17] Sex is apparently not a factor in immunity. Rats that recover from an infection are

---

[13] Lundeberg, K. R., 1938.
[14] Romano, C., 1935.
[15] Chagas, C., 1911.

[16] Johnson, C. M. and Kelser, R. A., 1937.
[17] Kolodny, M. H., 1939.

resistant to subsequent infections and their sera confer partial protection to other rats.[18]

DIAGNOSIS, PROGNOSIS AND TREATMENT

Diagnosis.—The disease should be suspected when the previously mentioned symptoms are present in patients of poor economic status from endemic regions. Clinically it must be differentiated from leishmanian infections, goiter, hypothyroidism, cretinism, chronic malaria and hookworm infection. Final diagnosis depends upon finding the parasite. Methods of direct examination used for the African trypanosomes are applicable, but examination of blood even with concentration methods is usually fruitless except during fever. In suspected chronic cases susceptible laboratory animals may be inoculated with blood or tissues from the patient. *Triatoma,* free from *T. cruzi,* may be allowed to feed on the patient. After ten days their feces are examined for metacyclic forms, which are injected into mice or rats for confirmation. The alexin-fixative test with an antigen made from cultured *T. cruzi* has proved useful in the diagnosis of chronic infections.[19]

Prognosis.—While spontaneous recovery may occur, prognosis in the acute disease is unfavorable. Severe chronic infections often terminate fatally.

Treatment.—There is no specific chemotherapy. The drugs used in African sleeping sickness or leishmaniasis are ineffective. Symptomatic treatment and the improvement of the physical condition of the patient by hygiene, diet and avoidance of concomitant diseases are the only available therapeutic measures.

PREVENTION

Epidemiology.—The incidence of American trypanosomiasis is unknown but is probably higher than generally believed, since the asymptomatic and adult cases are often not recognized. The alexin-fixative test in 1,251 individuals in Panama gave 3.8 per cent positive reactions.[16] The disease is largely limited to children. Sex and race do not influence its course. The rate varies inversely with the standard of living. It is highest in the poorer districts, where cracks in the walls and floors of the thatched adobe huts offer excellent hiding places for the insect vector. The presence of *T. cruzi* in the REDUVIIDÆ and in rodents, but not in man, has been reported in Mexico, Arizona and California, but its incidence in these hosts is probably low.

The insect vector remains hidden during the day and bites at night, usually around the lips and eyes. The infective feces are rubbed or scratched into the wound by the host. The former theory that infection occurs through the salivary secretions has been discredited. Infection is transmitted by contamination of the mucous membranes with the feces of reduviid bugs, by handling (culinary, taxidermic) of infected mammals, and rarely by the uncontaminated bite of the bug.[20] Mice can be infected through the mucous membranes but not through the intact skin and only 5 per cent of uncontaminated bites produce infections.[21] Experimental infections

[18] Culbertson, J. T. and Kolodny, M. H., 1938.

[19] Kelser, R. A., 1936.

[20] Brumpt, E., 1939.

[21] Cardosa, F. A., 1938.

in the absence of fecal contamination are explained by the regurgitation of trypanosomes from the stomach, where they may remain as long as eight days after ingestion.[22] In experimental animals transmission by coitus and through mother's milk
has been recorded but probably rarely if ever occurs in man. Experiments with
human volunteers have demonstrated that the trypanosome can not penetrate unbroken skin but can pass through the conjunctiva.[12]

The reduviid bug becomes infective some 10 days after biting an infected
mammal and may remain so for as long as two years.[23] The tick, *Ornithodorus
moubata,* has been found to harbor infective forms for five years.[24] The chances of
obtaining the infection from reduviid bugs apparently are low. Rarely is more than
one member of a family infected. The trypanosome may have difficulty in gaining
access and establishing itself in man, or the vectors may prefer to feed on dogs and
cats.

Prophylaxis.—Preventive measures call for the destruction of insect vectors
(Chapter XLVI) and the protection of man from their bites. Ideal prophylaxis
would replace insanitary houses with modern dwellings that do not afford hiding
places for the insect hosts; but since this is economically impracticable, protection
of man from reduviid bugs, a difficult procedure among the poorer classes, and the
elimination of these insects by fumigation, whitewashing and the use of insecticides
seem the best available methods of combating the disease.

GENUS *LEISHMANIA* ROSS, 1903

The genus *Leishmania* includes those flagellates that occur as typical leishmanian forms in vertebrate hosts and as leptomonad forms in inveterate hosts and
in cultures. This genus differs from the morphologically similar genus *Leptomonas*
in requiring for the completion of its life cycle a vertebrate as well as an invertebrate host. Ross named the genus after Leishman who in 1903 discovered *Leishmania donovani* in the spleen of a soldier affected with dumdum fever.

BIOLOGICAL CHARACTERISTICS

Morphology.—A typical leishmanian parasite in the vertebrate host is a small
oval protozoon, 2 to 4.5 μ in length by 1 to 2 μ in breadth with no flagellum or
undulating membrane (Fig. 41). In preparations treated with the Romanowsky
stains the cytoplasm, enclosed in an indefinite membrane, is pale blue. Toward the
posterior end is a reddish oval nucleus with a delicate membrane and a large central
karyosome. A deep violet, rod-shaped kinetoplast of variable size is anterior and
tangential to the nucleus. It contains the parabasal body and the dot-like blepharoplast. A delicate axoneme may sometimes be seen arising from the blepharoplast.

In cultures or in invertebrate hosts the parasites become flagellates ranging from
the leishmanian to the typical leptomonad form. The latter varies from a pyriform
to a long, slender spindle shape, 14 to 20 μ in length by 1.5 to 4 μ in breadth. Its
red-staining nucleus has a central karyosome. Anterior to the nucleus is a deep

[22] Dias, E., 1932.
[23] Mayer, M. and da Rocha-Lima, H., 1914.
[24] Mayer, M., 1918.

violet parabasal body and blepharoplast, from which arises a long delicate flagellum that projects from the anterior end.

Physiology.—Only the flagellate form is motile. Food is absorbed from the tissues of the host. Reproduction occurs by binary longitudinal fission. In the flagellate stage the blepharoplast and parabasal body elongate and divide; then the nucleus elongates and divides; a new flagellum is formed by one daughter blepharoplast; and finally the body splits into two new individuals. In the tissues the leishmanian form divides by a similar process.

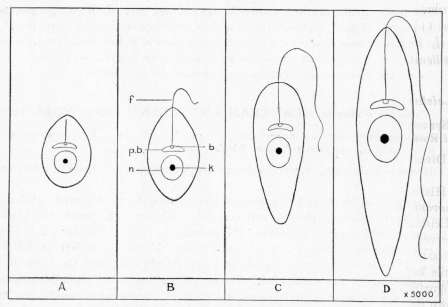

FIG. 41.—SCHEMATIC REPRESENTATION OF *Leishmania*

A, aflagellate parasite in tissues; *B* to *D*, flagellate forms in insects or cultures. *b*, blepharoplast; *f*, flagellum; *k*, karyosome; *n*, nucleus; *p.b.*, parabasal body.

Cultivation.—All three species of the *Leishmania* of man have been cultivated on various media by many workers, but the N.N.N. medium (Section **VII**, IV, 7) is most generally used. *Leishmania donovani* was first cultured by Rogers in 1904 in a sodium citrate solution. The parasite requires a slightly acid medium, aerobic conditions, the presence of blood, and an optimal temperature of 22 to 24° C. All stages between the leishmanian and leptomonad forms develop in cultures.

LIFE CYCLE

The leishmanian parasite may be transmitted from one vertebrate to another by contact. It passes through a developmental cycle in arthropod hosts that feed on infected vertebrates. In the gut numerous leptomonad forms develop and, in some insects, migrate to the pharynx and buccal cavity in 7 to 12 days. Transmission from the insect to a vertebrate host may be by the bite or the contaminative method.

LEISHMANIAN PARASITES OF LOWER ANIMALS

Canine leishmaniasis is due to a species indistinguishable from *Leishmania donovani* of man, and in rare instances similar species have been reported in cats, horses and sheep. Other species occur in lizards and chameleons. Numerous mammals have been experimentally infected.

LEISHMANIAN PARASITES OF MAN

Three leishmanian parasites, similar in morphology but differing in geographical distribution, in clinical manifestations, and in serological reactions are found in man: (1) *Leishmania donovani,* which produces visceral leishmaniasis or kala-azar; (2) *L. tropica,* the cause of cutaneous leishmaniasis or oriental sore; and (3) *L. braziliensis,* the cause of mucocutaneous leishmaniasis or espundia.

Leishmania donovani (LAVERAN AND MESNIL, 1903) ROSS, 1903

Synonyms.—*Piroplasma donovani* Laveran and Mesnil, 1903; *Herpetomonas donovani* Ross, 1904; *Leishmania infantum* Nicolle. 1908.

Disease.—Kala-azar, visceral leishmaniasis, dumdum fever, tropical splenomegaly.

History.—Leishman and Donovan in 1903 independently reported *Leishmania donovani* in the spleen of patients suffering from kala-azar; but precedence is given to Leishman who actually discovered the parasite in 1900. A similar parasite was observed during investigations of a Mediterranean disease of children by Cathoire in 1904, Pianese in 1905 and Nicolle in 1908. Nicolle proposed the name of infantile kala-azar for this disease with its visceral and cutaneous manifestations and designated the parasite as *Leishmania infantum.* More recent investigations have shown that this parasite is identical with *L. donovani.* Nicolle and Compte in 1908 found that canine leishmaniasis was caused by the same parasite.

In 1904 Rogers reported the development of flagellate forms in sodium citrate solution at 22° C., and Patton in 1907 found similar forms in insects that had fed upon infected patients. The problem of the transmission of kala-azar has attracted numerous investigators, and their studies have produced voluminous printed matter and many discredited hypotheses. Its probable transmission by the sandfly, *Phlebotomus argentipes,* is indicated by the studies of the Indian Kala-azar Committee in 1931 to 1934.

Geographical Distribution.—*L. donovani* has a wide distribution (Fig. 42). Kala-azar is endemic in the Mediterranean countries, in Asia Minor, Mesopotamia, southern Russia, India, Turkestan, northern China, the Sudan and Abyssinia. Visceral leishmaniasis occurs in Brazil and Argentina, but the causative organism may be a new species, *L. chagasi.*[25] It appears, however, to be serologically identical with *L. donovani.* Five cases of *L. donovani* infection in children have been reported in the United States of America, but the disease was contracted elsewhere.

[25] Chagas, E., 1936,

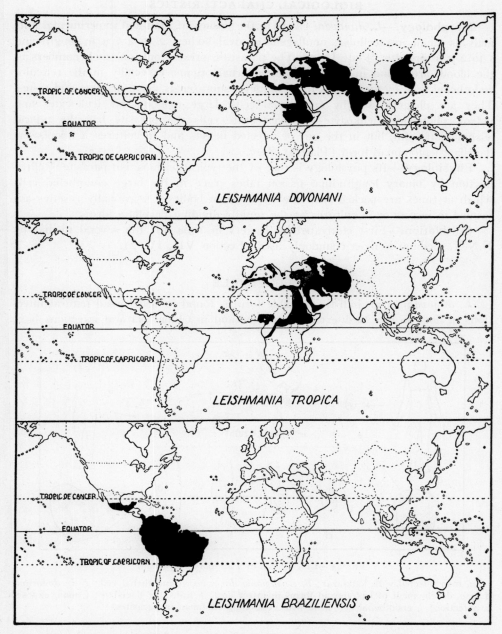

FIG. 42.—GEOGRAPHICAL DISTRIBUTION OF *Leishmania donovani, L. tropica* and *L. braziliensis*

BIOLOGICAL CHARACTERISTICS

Morphology.—*L. donovani* exists in the tissues of man and experimental animals as small intracellular, nonflagellated oval bodies, 2 to 4.5 *μ* in length and 1 to 2 *μ* in breadth (Plate II, 5). The parasites, present only in small numbers in the blood, are found in nearly all the internal organs, especially in the reticulo-endothelial cells of the spleen, liver, kidneys, suprarenals, bone marrow and testes. They are phagocytosed by endothelial cells, large mononuclear leukocytes and polymorphonuclear leukocytes. In vertebrate cells the parasite has the typical leishmanian form, but in the gut of infected insects and in cultures it adopts the flagellate leptomonad form (Plate II, 8).

Physiology.—Its physiology is that of the typical leishmanian parasite. Reproduction by binary longitudinal fission takes place in the large endothelial cells which at times are packed with the leishmanian bodies. Occasionally rosettes are formed in insects or in cultures by the rapidly dividing flagellate forms.

Cultivation.—First cultivated by Rogers in 1904. Of the several media the N.N.N. medium is most commonly used (Section **VII**, IV, 7).

LIFE CYCLE

L. donovani or an indistinguishable form is found in widespread natural infections of dogs in the Mediterranean regions and in China. Natural infections have

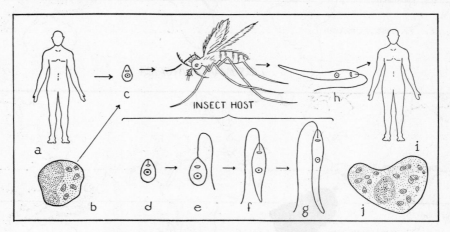

FIG. 43.—LIFE CYCLE OF *Leishmania donovani*

a, man infected with kala-azar; *b, Leishmania donovani* in endothelial cell; *c, L. donovani;* *d* to *g,* development of leptomonad forms in insect host; *h,* infective flagellate; *i,* man, exposed to infection; *j,* endothelial cell from man containing leishmanian parasites.

also been reported in cats, horses, and sheep. Dogs and hamsters are readily susceptible to experimental infections with *L. donovani* of man. Infections have also been produced in mice, rats, guinea pigs, rabbits, jackals, jerboas, gerbils and monkeys. Flagellates similar to *L. donovani* have been found in the sandflies

Phlebotomus argentipes and *P. chinensis* and in the Indian bedbug, *Cimex hemipterus*. *P. perniciosus, P. papatasii* and *P. major* are also believed to harbor the parasite. Sandflies have been artificially infected by feeding upon kala-azar patients. The causative organism of Brazilian visceral leishmaniasis develops in *P. longipalpis* and *P. intermedius*.

The life cycle and transmission of *L. donovani* (Fig. 43) are not yet fully understood. Its invertebrate host is some biting insect, but the method of transmission to man from the insect has not been determined. Infection has been transferred from dog to dog through infected sandflies.[26] When the infective flagellate gains access to man, either directly through the bite or by the contaminative method, it loses its flagellum and assumes the leishmanian form. It multiplies rapidly within the invaded endothelial cells. When the cells rupture, the freed parasites invade other cells or are phagocytosed.

PATHOGENESIS

Pathology.—At autopsy the gross findings are marked emaciation, enlarged liver, large congested spleen with prominent malpighian corpuscles, soft red bone marrow, enlarged lymphatic glands and ulcerations of the colon. Histological examination reveals numerous leishmanian parasites in the endothelial cells of the reticuloendothelial system of the spleen, liver, kidney, bone marrow, intestinal mucosa, mesenteric glands and other organs (Fig. 44). There is fatty infiltration of the liver, and the endothelial cells of the interlobular capillaries are distended with large numbers of parasites. The spleen, which may be fibrosed, shows an increase in reticular endothelium. The lymphatic glands, which are sometimes atrophied, may contain parasites in the lymph spaces. The macrophages and polymorphonuclear leukocytes of the bone marrow are packed with ingested parasites. The heart may show myocardial degeneration; the kidneys may manifest cloudy swelling; and the ulcerated intestinal mucosa may be infiltrated with parasitized macrophages, particularly in the vicinity of Peyer's patches.

Symptomatology.—There are two types of the disease, adult and infantile. Both show visceral and sometimes cutaneous manifestations. In the adult type the incubational period is indefinite, since the onset is insidious and not all infections develop typical manifestations. The first sign is a remittent fever, which may show a double or triple rise in temperature in the first 48 hours. The irregular fever persists for two to six weeks, temporarily subsides, and then recurs. The spleen enlarges early in the disease, and by the sixth month the liver has increased in size. As the disease progresses anemia, cachexia, leukopenia, edema of the skin and emaciation develop. The lymphatic glands are enlarged, and bleeding from the nose and mouth may occur. Intestinal ulceration may cause diarrhea. The pathognomonic symptoms are splenic enlargement, marked leukopenia and severe anemia.

The disease, if untreated, usually ends fatally within two years, but fulminating cases may cause death within a few weeks. The marked leukopenia renders the patient especially susceptible to fatal septic infections and pneumonia.

The symptoms of infantile kala-azar are insidious fever, splenomegaly, gastro-

---

[26] Feng, L. C. and Chung, H. L., 1939.

intestinal disturbances, mental apathy, anemia, emaciation, abdominal distention, cancrum oris, noma, bleeding from nose and gums, and cutaneous hemorrhages (Fig. 46). Secondary infections often cause death in from a few months to three years. The mortality in the untreated disease is somewhat lower than in the adult type.

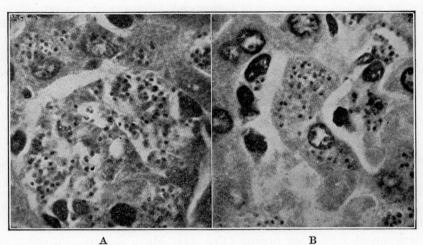

A   B

Fig. 44.—*Leishmania donovani*

In experimentally infected hamster, *Cricetulus griseus. A,* numerous aflagellated forms (Leishman-Donovan bodies) in mass of endothelial cells occluding a capillary, adjacent liver cells also parasitized, *ca* × 650; *B,* parasitized liver cell, *ca* × 1100 (After Meleney, from Zinsser and Bayne-Jones, *Textbook of Bacteriology,* 7th ed., 1934, D. Appleton-Century Company).

A dermal form of kala-azar at times appears as a spontaneous manifestation but more frequently follows insufficient treatment with antimony. This type of infection is characterized by depigmented nodular, granulomatous, nonulcerating lesions of the skin, from which the organisms may be recovered.

Immunity.—Individual susceptibility varies widely. The dermal form of the disease without visceral involvement may be an expression of resistance. Recovery from kala-azar apparently insures a lasting immunity, since second infections are rare.

DIAGNOSIS, PROGNOSIS AND TREATMENT

Diagnosis.—Kala-azar should be suspected in a patient from an endemic area who has chronic irregular fever, leukopenia and splenomegaly. It must be differentiated clinically from enteric fever, malaria and Malta fever. The undulant type of fever with its characteristic double rise, the absence of profound malaise, and a negative Widal reaction distinguish kala-azar from enteric fever. Malaria has a similar cachexia and in children splenic enlargement, but kala-azar does not respond to quinine. Malta fever has comparable febrile manifestations, but rarely shows splenomegaly.

Final diagnosis depends upon finding the parasite in smears or cultures of infected tissues. The following procedures have proved useful:

1. Stained thin films of the peripheral blood (Section **VII**, III, 7). The parasites may be found in the polymorphonuclear and large mononuclear leukocytes in about 10 per cent of patients, but they are so few that at least nine thin films should be examined from each patient.
2. Stained thick films of peripheral blood (Section **VII**, III, 8) in the hands of skilled workers give a much higher percentage of positive results.
3. If the blood is negative, material procured by puncture of the spleen or liver may be stained and examined (Section **VII**, III, 15, 16). Liver puncture, though less certain to yield positive results, is preferred by many workers as a safer procedure.
4. Enlarged cervical lymphatic glands may be excised and examined by smears and sections (Section **VII**, III, 17).
5. Cultures (Section **VII**, IV, 7) may be made from the blood or from aspirated splenic or hepatic tissue. The highest percentage of positive results is obtained from splenic material and the lowest from the blood.
6. Susceptible laboratory animals, especially hamsters, may be injected with blood or tissues.
7. After the fifth month of the disease there is an increase in the globulin of the blood serum. Napier's aldehyde test (formol-gel), Sia's precipitative test for euglobulin, and Chopra's antimony test (Section **VII**, IX, 25-27) are positive in a high percentage of patients.
8. The alexin-fixative test has proved useful in diagnosis, when the parasites cannot be demonstrated.

Prognosis.—The mortality in untreated adults is from 90 to 95 per cent and in children from 75 to 85 per cent. With treatment prognosis is good, as about 90 per cent of the patients apparently recover.

Treatment.—Antimony, although not effective in all cases, is considered a specific remedy for kala-azar. It was formerly administered intravenously in the form of sodium or potassium antimony tartrate (Section **VII**, XIII, 6). In recent years the pentavalent antimony preparations stibosan and neostibosan (Section **VII**, XIII, 8, 9) have been highly recommended for intravenous use; a high percentage of recoveries (97 per cent) in children and a mortality of 1.5 per cent in children without noma and less than 16 per cent in children with noma have been reported.[27] Neostibosan is considered the least toxic and most efficient preparation, especially for dermal leishmaniasis in patients resistant to sodium or potassium antimony tartrate. The trivalent antimony compound, fuadin, has also proved effective. Supportive treatment to maintain general resistance is indicated.

PREVENTION

Epidemiology.—Kala-azar is an endemic disease. Its characteristics vary with its geographical location. It has been regarded as peculiar to Asiatic and Mediterranean countries, but visceral leishmaniasis has been reported in recent years in Brazil and Argentina, although some investigators believe that the Brazilian disease is caused by a new species, *L. chagasi*.[25, 28]

---

[27] Fan, P. L., 1936,

[28] Marques da Cunha, A. and Chagas, E., 1936; Carini, A., 1938.

The transmission of kala-azar still is a controversial problem in spite of the work of numerous investigators. The fact that it is a house-site infection restricted to 300 yards, suggests that the transmitting agent is a blood-sucking insect of limited range. Bedbugs, mosquitoes, lice, mites and ticks have been ruled out by experimental and epidemiological evidence. The *Phlebotomus* flies are the probable vectors, although evidence is still inconclusive (Chapter XLI). There is no question that the parasite develops in the intestinal tract of sandflies which have fed on infected patients or that animals inoculated with the parasites from these flies develop leishmaniasis. Nevertheless, only a small percentage of the many hamsters and the few human volunteers bitten by infected flies has acquired the disease.

The dog is a reservoir host in the Mediterranean countries and in China, where canine leishmaniasis is prevalent. Canine disease, however, is comparatively rare in India.[29] *Phlebotomus chinensis* readily transmits canine leishmaniasis.[26] The cutaneous lesions of dogs in China are an important source of infection for man.[30]

Investigators have considered the possibility of contamination of food and water by the parasites in the urine and feces. No instance of human infection through the digestive tract has been reported, but hamsters may be thus infected. Contact infection in hamsters has also been reported. The possibility of droplet infection must be considered, since *L. donovani* occurs in the nasal discharges.[31]

The environmental factors influencing the distribution of kala-azar appear to be economic conditions, temperature and moisture. The disease is more prevalent in squalid surroundings and more frequent in rural than in urban districts. Several members of a family may be stricken and certain houses appear to be foci of infection. Temperature and moisture favor the probability of insect transmission.

The age, sex and general resistance of the individual apparently affect susceptibility. Malnutrition and debility predispose to infection. Males acquire the disease more frequently than females. In the Mediterranean countries and in China the disease is most prevalent among children and in India among young adults. This difference possibly may be associated with the prevalence of canine leishmaniasis.

Prophylaxis.—Since the exact method of transmission is unknown, only general prophylactic precautions can be applied. Cleanliness and hygienic habits, removal of dense vegetation from the vicinity of dwellings, and soil drainage to prevent the breeding of sandflies are advisable. Protection against sandflies, though difficult because of their small size, is recommended. Infected individuals may be isolated and treated, their feces and urine sterilized, and measures to prevent droplet infection employed.

Leishmania tropica WRIGHT, 1903

Synonyms.—*Helcosoma tropica* Wright, 1903; *Herpetomonas tropica,* Patton, 1912; *Herpetomonas furunculosa* (Wright, 1903) Patton, 1922.

Disease.—Oriental sore, Delhi ulcer, Aleppo, Delhi or Bagdad boil, cutaneous leishmaniasis.

---

[29] Adler, S., 1936.
[30] Feng, L. C., Chung, H. L. and Hoeppli,

R., 1939; Ho, E. A., 1939.
[31] Forkner, C. E. and Zia, L. S., 1935.

History.—The causative agent of oriental sore was observed in 1885 by Cunningham and by Firth in 1891. Since their descriptions were incomplete, credit for its discovery is given to Wright, who described the organism in 1903 in an Armenian immigrant in Boston, Massachusetts.

Geographical Distribution.—*L. tropica* is endemic in the Mediterranean countries of southern Europe and northern Africa, in western and southern Asia, and in central and northeast Africa (Fig. 41). It is considered a disease of the Eastern Hemisphere. It is found in the same countries as kala-azar, but not in the same localities. However, it has been reported in northern South America and in Central America, although the infecting organism may have been *L. braziliensis*.

BIOLOGICAL CHARACTERISTICS

Morphology.—The morphology of *L. tropica* is similar to that of the typical leishmanian parasite (Plate II, 6). It is found in the leishmanian stage in man and in the leptomonad form in insects. The leishmanian form occurs intra- and extracellularly in the margins of cutaneous lesions. The intracellular forms are in large mononuclear leukocytes, polymorphonuclears and epithelial cells. The extracellular forms evidently have been released by rupture of the cells (Fig. 45).

Physiology.—Similar to *L. donovani.*

Cultivation.—Cultivated by numerous workers since the original work of Nicolle in 1908. Leptomonad forms appear in cultures (Plate II, 8).

LIFE CYCLE

The life cycle is probably the same as that of *L. donovani.* The sandflies, *Phlebotomus papatasii* and *P. sergenti,* are believed to be the natural insect hosts. The experimental transmission of the infection to man by the bite of the sandfly so far has been unsuccessful, but the disease has been produced by inoculation with parasites from the fly. Infective forms develop in the fly in from 8 to 21 days. Experimental infections can be produced in mice, rats, guinea pigs, monkeys and dogs.

PATHOGENESIS

Pathology.—In man the disease seems limited to the cutaneous tissues and occasionally the mucous membranes. In experimental animals visceral lesions resembling those of kala-azar may be produced. There is atrophy of the epidermis. In the infected area there is hypertrophy of the corium and its papillæ and infiltration with lymphocytes, plasma cells and large phagocytic cells packed with leishmanian parasites (Fig. 45). Ulceration results from coagulation, necrosis and secondary bacterial infection.

Symptomatology.—The incubational period usually lasts for two months, although it may be as short as one week. Single or multiple sores develop usually on the exposed parts of the body (Fig. 47). A papule the size of a mosquito bite appears, continues to enlarge, and acquires a purple color and a glazed surface. The blind boil becomes covered with brownish scales and by the third or fourth month forms an indurated crusted ulcer, which discharges a thin, offensive pus. At times the coalescence of ulcers and secondary bacterial infection may result in extensive

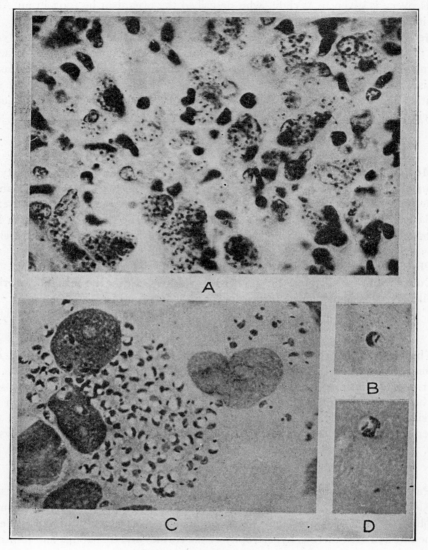

FIG. 45.—*Leishmania tropica*

A, section of cutaneous lesion showing organisms included in large mononuclear cells; *C,* a large mononuclear cell showing cytoplasm filled with organisms, in film stained with Wright's stain; *B* and *D,* dividing forms, Wright's stain (After Wright, 1903, from Zinsser and Bayne-Jones, *Textbook of Bacteriology,* 7th ed., 1934, D. Appleton-Century Company).

ulceration and general infection. The constitutional symptoms of chills and fever have been observed to accompany the appearance of new sores.[32] Uncomplicated

[32] Trow, E. J., 1937.

sores heal within two to ten months but leave depigmented retracted scars which are often disfiguring.

Immunity.—One attack confers lasting immunity. Parents in endemic areas sometimes purposely infect protected parts of the children's bodies in order to prevent disfiguring lesions of the face.

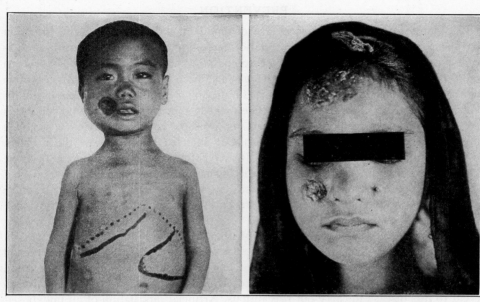

FIG. 46.—KALA-AZAR

Cancrum oris and enlargement of liver and spleen (Photograph from China).

FIG. 47.—DERMAL LEISHMANIASIS

Lesions on forehead, right and left cheek (Courtesy of Dr. H. K. Giffin, American Mission Hospital, Assiut, Egypt).

DIAGNOSIS, PROGNOSIS AND TREATMENT

Diagnosis.—Oriental sore must be distinguished from ulcers due to syphilis, blastomycosis and other infections. The distribution of the lesions and the local presence of the leishmanian parasite establish the diagnosis. Since parasites are not often found in the floor of the ulcer, exudative material is obtained from the indurated margin by puncture (Section **VII**, III, 22). Films of the exudate treated with Giemsa's or Wright's stain are examined for the intra- and extracellular parasites. Cultures may also be made, particularly if microscopical examination is negative. *L. tropica* is differentiated from the other leishmanian parasites by serological tests.

Prognosis.—Favorable.

Treatment.—The antimony preparations, administered as in kala-azar but in smaller quantities, have proved successful for multiple ulcers and generalized infections. Treatment of the individual ulcer by infiltrating its margin with a 1 per cent solution of berberine sulphate (Section **VII**, XIII, 19) for two to four weekly injections is recommended.[33] Other local measures which at times have given good results are emetine hydrochloride injections, carbon dioxide snow, phosphorated oil, roentgen-ray and various ointments. The sores should be protected by dressings to prevent bacterial contamination and auto-inoculation.

PREVENTION

Epidemiology.—Oriental sores are common in endemic areas. The infection may be spread by contact, auto-inoculation is frequent, and insect transmission is believed to occur. The sandflies, *Phlebotomus papatasii* and *P. sergenti,* have been found naturally infected, and the former has also been infected by feeding on human sores. Human infection has been produced by rubbing on the scarified skin of volunteers the macerated intestines of sandflies, which contained the leptomonad forms 8 to 20 days after feeding.[34] However, no workers have been able to establish infections in animals or in man by the bite of infected sandflies, and the problem of insect transmission is still unsolved. It is possible that the sandfly may not be the principal insect vector, because of the small percentage that becomes infected after feeding on lesions and the unsuccessful attempts to produce infections by their bites. The disease has been successfully transmitted to man by the bite of the stable fly, *Stomoxys calcitrans.*[35]

Prophylaxis.—Protective covering of the ulcers will reduce the chances of transmission by contact and by insect vectors. The clothing of an infected person should not be worn by another. Measures to control sandflies and to protect man from their bites may be advisable. It is difficult to induce natives who are indifferent to this disease to carry out precautious. Artificial inoculation of an unexposed portion of the body prevents disfiguring lesions of the face.

Leishmania braziliensis VIANNA, 1911

Synonyms.—*Leishmania tropica,* var. *americana* Laveran and Nattan-Larrier, 1912; *Leishmania peruviana* Velez, 1913.

Disease.—American leishmaniasis, nasopharyngeal or mucocutaneous leishmaniasis, and some 23 local names, among which are: espundia, uta, forest yaws, bubas braziliensis, and pian bois.

History.—In 1909 Carini and Paranhos as well as Lindenberg found leishmanian bodies in ulcerative lesions in patients in Brazil. In 1911 Carini observed these bodies in the nasopharyngeal mucosa, and in the same year Vianna designated the parasite as a new species, *Leishmania braziliensis.* Serological studies by Kligler in 1925 and by Noguchi in 1926 confirmed the specific identity of this parasite.

Geographical Distribution.—Mexico to South America except Chile between 21° north and 25° south latitude, the greatest prevalence being between 5° and 25° south latitude (Fig. 42). A few cases have been reported in Italy and in the Sudan.

---

[33] Rogers, L. and Megaw, J. W. D., 1935.   [35] Berberian, D. A., 1938.
[34] Adler, S. and Theodor, O., 1927.

BIOLOGICAL CHARACTERISTICS

Morphology.—Similar to *L. donovani*.

Physiology.—Similar to *L. donovani*.

Cultivation.—It was first cultivated by Pedrosa and da Silva in 1910. Positive cultures are obtained only from the lesions.

LIFE CYCLE

The development of the parasite in man is similar to that of *L. tropica*. The flagellated forms are sometimes present in the ulcers. It is believed that the parasite spends its leptomonad stage in an insect, probably the sandflies, *Phlebotomus squamiventris, P. intermedius, P. migonei* and others. Baboons, monkeys, cats, dogs and guinea pigs may be infected experimentally. Dogs possibly serve as reservoir hosts.

PATHOGENESIS

American leishmaniasis is characterized by ulcerative granulomatous lesions of the mucocutaneous surfaces, particularly the mucous membranes of the nose, mouth and pharynx, and in Mexico by ulceration of the ears.

Pathology.—The pathology of the cutaneous lesions is similar to that of the oriental sore. Microscopically they show infiltration of large mononuclears, endothelial cells, macrophages and lymphocytes containing the parasites. The lesions of the mucous membranes of the mouth and nasopharynx take the form of fungating, eroding, indurated ulcers, which may develop into extensive necrotic lesions destroying the cartilaginous and overlying tissues of the nasopharynx, pharynx, larynx and mouth. The lesions are invaded by plasma cells, endothelials and macrophages bearing parasites.

Symptomatology.—The length of the incubational period is unknown. The initial lesion appears as a primary papule that ulcerates and ultimately disappears after several months to two years. The secondary mucomembranous lesions of the mouth, nasopharynx and larynx appear before or after the healing of the primary lesion as a thickening of the mucosa that proceeds to nodule formation and ulceration. These lesions are painful and are accompanied by fever, anemia, malaise and, if the larynx is affected, by loss of voice. They frequently cause great deformity. The disease may heal spontaneously or result in death from secondary infection and general debility.

DIAGNOSIS, PROGNOSIS AND TREATMENT

Diagnosis.—American leishmaniasis must be differentiated clinically from yaws and syphilis. The presence of *L. braziliensis* may be ascertained by examining stained smears from the indurated edges of the primary or secondary ulcers (Section **VII**, III, 22). Cultures may also be made (Section **VII**, IV, 7).

Prognosis.—The prognosis is uncertain in untreated cases, but is good when the disease is treated early.

Treatment.—Vianna in 1914 demonstrated in this disease the specificity of antimony for the leishmaniases. Fuadin (Section **VII**, XIII, 11) is the choice of the antimony preparations when lesions of the mucous membranes are present. Two intramuscular injections per week for eight weeks usually cure the patient. Resistant patients may require a second series of fuadin or neostibosan. Local cutaneous lesions may be treated in the same manner as the oriental sore.

PREVENTION

Epidemiology.—American leishmaniasis is endemic in regions below an altitude of 700 meters where heat and moisture are present for the greater part of the year, and is most prevalent during and after the rainy season in the late summer and fall.[36] It is a disease of rural rather than urban districts and is especially common in chicle gum and rubber collectors who work in low, damp forests and jungles. It attacks all ages and both sexes, but adult males are most frequently infected. An incidence of 20 per cent was found in 15,000 individuals examined over a period of six years in Brazil[37] and a 50 per cent incidence in chicle workers in Mexico.[38]

The high incidence among workers in forests where conditions are favorable for shade-requiring insects and the location of the primary cutaneous lesion on the exposed parts of the body suggest the probability of insect transmission. Epidemiological evidence indicates that the disease is transmitted by a winged, biting insect which lives among trees and shrubs, probably a species of *Phlebotomus*.[36] The parasite has been found in *Phlebotomus intermedius;* dogs have been infected by rubbing macerated flies on the scarified skin; and sandflies have been infected by allowing them to feed on human lesions.[39] The disease can be transmitted by direct contact.

Prophylaxis.—Although the natural method of transmission of American leishmaniasis has not been proved, prophylactic measures should be directed toward protection against contact infection and biting insects. Such measures include: isolation and treatment of infected individuals, protection of skin lesions from insects, avoidance of contact with infected individuals, and protection against sandflies.

REFERENCES

ADLER, S. and THEODOR, O. Transmission of *Leishmania tropica* from Artificially Infected Sandflies to Man, Ann. Trop. Med., 1927, 21:89.
BRUMPT, E. Faites experimentaux et cliniques concernant le mode de transmission de la maladie de Chagas ou trypanosome americaine, Compt. rend. Soc. de Biol., 1939, 130:1197.
CARINI, A. Leishmaniose Visceral Americana, Arch. di biol. (São Paulo), 1938, 22 (202):1.
CHAGAS, E. Visceral Leishmaniasis in Brazil, Science, 1936, 84:397.
CULBERTSON, J. T. Trypanocidal Action of Normal Human Serum, Arch. Path., 1935, 20:767.
―――― and KOLODNY, M. H. Acquired Immunity in Rats Against *Trypanosoma cruzi*, J. Parasitol., 1938, 24 (1):83.
DUKE, H. L. Further Studies of Behavior of *Trypanosoma rhodesiense*, Recently Isolated from Man, in Antelope and Other African Game Animals, Parasitology, 1935, 27:68.

[36] Shattuck, G. C., 1936.
[37] de Silveira, R., 1920.

[38] Inchanstegni, A., 1918.
[39] Aragao, H. de B., 1922.

DUKE, H. L. On the Prophylactic Action of "Bayer 205" Against the Trypanosomes of Man, Lancet, 1936, 1:463.

FAN, P. L. Use of a Pentavalent Antimony Compound for Treating Kala-azar in Children, Am. J. Dis. Child., 1936, 52:887.

FENG, L. C. and CHUNG, H. L. Development of *Leishmania* in Chinese Sandflies Fed on Dogs with Canine Leishmaniasis, Chinese M. J., 1939, 56:35.

FORKNER, C. E. and ZIA, L. S. Further Studies on Kala-azar. *Leishmania* in Nasal and Oral Secretions of Patients and the Bearing of this Finding on the Transmission of the Disease, J. Exper. Med., 1935, 61:183.

KELSER, R. A. A Complement-fixation Test for Chagas' Disease Employing an Artificial Culture Antigen, Am. J. Trop. Med., 1936, 16:405.

LUNDEBERG, K. R. A Fatal Case of Chagas' Disease Occurring in a Man 77 Years of Age, Am. J. Trop. Med., 1938, 18:185.

MELENEY, H. E. The Histopathology of Kala-azar in the Hamster, Monkey and Man, Am. J. Path., 1925, 1:147.

SHATTUCK, G. C. The Distribution of American Leishmaniasis in Relation to That of *Phlebotomus*, Am. J. Trop. Med., 1936, 16:187.

TALIAFERRO, W. H. Ablastic and Trypanocidal Antibodies Against *Trypanosoma duttoni*, J. Immunol., 1938, 35:303.

TROW, E. J. Oriental Sore, Arch. Dermat. & Syph., 1937, 35:455.

VIANNA, G. Sobre o Tratamento da Leishmaniose Tegumentar, Ann. paulist. de med. e cirurg., São Paulo, 1914, 2:167.

WENYON, C. M. Protozoology. Baillière, Tindall & Cox, London, 1926. pp. 1563.

WRIGHT, J. H. Protozoa in a case of Tropical Ulcer ("Delhi Sore"), J. M. Res., 1903, 10:472.

YORKE, W. Chagas' Disease, a Critical Review, Trop. Dis. Bull., 1937, 34:275.

Chapter XII

THE SPOROZOA

CLASS *SPOROZOA*

The class SPOROZOA is comprised entirely of parasitic Protozoa that form spores at some stage in their life cycle. A prolonged parasitic existence has produced degenerative changes in the organs of locomotion, digestion and excretion. The numerous genera are widely distributed throughout the animal kingdom, both vertebrates and invertebrates serving as hosts. They live inside and outside the cells of the various organs and in the body cavities of the host. Food is obtained by absorption. Reproduction has become highly specialized.

CLASSIFICATION

The SPOROZOA comprise miscellaneous groups that are difficult to classify. The simple tabulation given below is best suited for the purpose of this textbook. Of the seven orders only one, the HÆMOSPORIDIA, contains important human parasites (malaria) and two others, the SARCOSPORIDIA and the COCCIDIA, rare human parasites.

Subclass 1: CNIDOSPORIDIA
    Reproduction by spore-formation takes place during growth and life of the sporozoon.
    Order 1. MYXOSPORIDIA
    Order 2. MICROSPORIDIA
Subclass 2: ACNIDOSPORIDIA
    Produce simple spores during life of the sporozoon.
    Order 1. SARCOSPORIDIA
    Order 2. HAPLOSPORIDIA
Subclass 3: TELOSPORIDIA
    Reproduction by spore-formation takes place at the completion of growth and ends the life of the sporozoon.
    Order 1. GREGARINIDA
    Order 2. COCCIDIA
    Order 3. HÆMOSPORIDIA

LIFE CYCLE

The SPOROZOA have the most complicated life histories of the several classes of Protozoa. The life cycle often involves two kinds of reproduction, asexual **schizogony** and sexual **sporogony.** The various types of life cycles may involve all or parts of these reproductive stages. The entire cycle may be passed in one host, with or without typical sexual development, or it may involve passage through two hosts, a vertebrate, man, and an invertebrate, the mosquito (malaria). Asexual reproduction, schizogony, takes place in man and sexual reproduction, sporogony, in the mosquito.

The life cycles vary considerably, but the description of a typical one involving two hosts and two methods of reproduction (Fig. 48) will serve to define the confusing terms applied to the developmental forms.

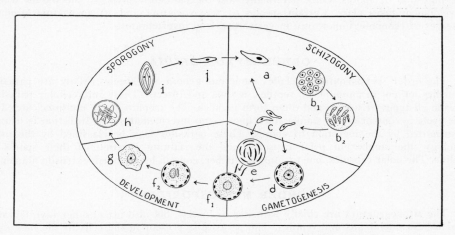

FIG. 48.—LIFE CYCLE OF A TYPICAL SPOROZOON

a, sporozoite; *b₁,* trophozoite in cell; *b₂,* merozoites in cell; *c,* gametocytes; *d,* macrogamete; *e,* microgametocyte containing microgametes; *f₁,* fusion of micro- and macrogametes; *f₂,* zygote; *g,* oökinete; *h,* oöcyst; *i,* spore; *j,* sporozoite.

Schizogony.—The final product of sexual multiplication of this typical parasite is a **sporozoite,** which on entering the tissues of a host, often a vertebrate, forms a **trophozoite.** The trophozoite enlarges to become a **schizont,** within which many new cells develop asexually by schizogony. The small daughter cells of **merozoites** erupt from the schizont and developing into trophozoites repeat the asexual cycle.

Sporogony.—Certain of the merozoites will become male and female **gametocytes,** the female the **macrogametocyte** and the male the **microgametocyte.** Sexual development often takes place in another host, usually an invertebrate. The female gametocyte develops into a **macrogamete,** while the male gametocyte produces numerous **microgametes.** A **microgamete** fuses with the **macrogamete** to form a fertilized **zygote,** which when motile is called the **oökinete** but later when surrounded by a cyst wall is known as the **oöcyst.** Division of the protoplasm in the **oöcyst** results in the formation of **sporoblasts,** which upon developing walls of their own, called **sporocysts,** are the **spores.** From each spore infective sporozoites are liberated and after entry into a new host or within the same host develop into trophozoites and undergo schizogony.

Transmission.—Infection in a new host is usually established by spores. When the mode of transmission is air or water, the spores are protected by a more resistant covering than when they are passed directly from host to host.

SUBCLASS *CNIDOSPORIDIA*

The CNIDOSPORIDIA form spores with one or more polar capsules during their growing period. The active organisms are nonflagellated and amœboid. Infection is acquired by the ingestion of spores. Once within the host the parasites spread to the tissues where development takes place. Certain species of MYXOSPORIDIA and MICROSPORIDIA produce diseases of economic importance in vertebrates and invertebrates.

ORDER *MYXOSPORIDIA*

The order MYXOSPORIDIA includes numerous genera and species. Many are parasitic in fishes, others in amphibians, reptiles, worms and insects. These intercellular parasites invade all types of tissues and often form nodules. The trophozoite is multinucleate. The life cycle is comparatively simple since there is no intermediate host. Infection is usually transmitted by the ingestion of spores. These parasites may be classified by the morphology, the number of polar capsules, and the staining reaction of their spores to iodine. The polar capsules, one to four in number, contain long, coiled, extrusile filaments.

ORDER *MICROSPORIDIA*

The MICROSPORIDIA are chiefly parasites of insects, but also infect other invertebrates and fishes, amphibians and reptiles. The parasite is present in the cells of the host as a small amœboid form, which produces spores by an intricate process. The spores are small and have polar filaments. Of economic importance in this order are *Nosema bombycis* which causes pebrine, a silkworm disease, and *Nosema apis* which causes nosema in bees. The early investigations of Pasteur on pebrine showed that the parasites invade the ovaries of the silkworm and pass with the eggs from one generation to the other.

SUBCLASS *ACNIDOSPORIDIA*

The ACNIDOSPORIDIA occupy a questionable position among the Protozoa. They produce simple spores without polar capsules.

ORDER *HAPLOSPORIDIA*

The HAPLOSPORIDIA, which somewhat resemble the MICROSPORIDIA, are parasites of annelid worms and of fishes and other aquatic vertebrates. The spores have no polar capsule.

ORDER *SARCOSPORIDIA*

The order SARCOSPORIDIA contains only one genus, *Sarcocystis*. Species of this genus are widely distributed parasites of vertebrates. They occur in birds, reptiles, and in several species of mammals including the horse, hog, sheep, cow, mouse, seal, monkey, opossum and antelope. They invade the striated muscles, particularly those of the skeletal body, larynx, diaphragm and tongue. They form long tubular masses of spores called "Miescher's tubes" after their discoverer, Miescher, who observed them in mice in 1843.

Morphology.—Miescher's tubes (Fig. 49A) are elongate cylindrical bodies with rounded ends. Their size varies with the species and stage of development, in cattle

sometimes reaching 5 cm. in length. The mature Miescher's tube has an outer membranous layer, which may be radially striated, and an inner layer from which trabeculæ
pass into the interior. By forming anastomosing partitions the trabeculæ produce variously
sized noncommunicating chambers, filled with sickle-shaped spores in various stages of
development. Miescher's tubes are developed from fusiform sporoblasts, which at first
lie longitudinally and later transversely. Each sporoblast gives rise to a number of spores,
and the limiting membranes of the sporoblasts form the walls of the compartments
containing the spores. The oldest spores (Fig. 49B), 10 to 15 μ in length, are found
in the center. They are surrounded by a thin membrane and contain a nucleated sporozoite
and at one extremity an obliquely striated body. The spores, when liberated, are motile
and travel with a peculiar gliding, slightly rotary movement.

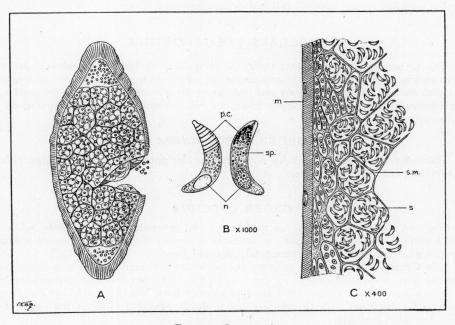

FIG. 49.—*Sarcocystis*

A, Sarcocystis miescheriana, young Miescher's tube; *B*, spores; *C, Sarcocystis blanchardi*,
longitudinal section through Miescher's tube.

m, muscle; *n,* nucleus; *p.c.,* polar capsule; *s,* spore; *s.m.,* sporoblastic membrane; *sp.,* sporozoite (*A* redrawn from Manz, 1867; *B* redrawn from Alexeieff, 1913 and *C* redrawn from van
Eecke, 1892).

Life Cycle.—The life cycle has been studied in *Sarcocystis muris,* a parasite of the
mouse. Infections are produced by feeding mice and guinea pigs with flesh or feces containing spores. How herbivorous animals are infected is unknown. The ingested spores
liberate amœbulæ that penetrate the cells of the intestinal epithelium. After multiplication
they reach the lymphatics and eventually migrate to the muscles where they develop
into sarcocysts. From 40 to 50 days are required before the parasites are found in the
muscles and from 80 to 90 days before spores are produced.

Pathogenesis.—Most species cause no serious damage to their hosts. Fatal infections
have been reported with *Sarcocystis muris* in mice, *S. tenella* in sheep, and *S. miescheriana* in hogs. The parasite apparently produces a true toxin, sarcocystin, which in

small amounts is fatal to rabbits. The tissues surrounding the elongated Miescher's tubes show mononuclear infiltration and some fibrosis.

Sarcocystis lindemanni RIVOLTA, 1878

The parasite in man, designated as *Sarcocystis lindemanni,* may represent one or more of the several species in animals. Human infection is rare and, since it gives rise to no symptoms, is not readily discovered except at autopsy. Some ten instances have been recorded, chiefly in India, Barbados, and the Sudan, since the parasite was first observed by Lindemann in 1868. It has been found in the skeletal muscles and in the muscles of the larynx, heart and tongue. In most instances it causes no appreciable harm to the host, although it has been associated with edema, bone lesions and tuberculosis. Infection probably occurs through infected or contaminated food.

SUBCLASS *TELOSPORIDIA*

The TELOSPORIDIA pass part of their life cycle intracellularly. The subclass includes three orders: (1) GREGARINIDA, many species of which do not reproduce by schizogony; (2) COCCIDIA, in which schizogony and sporogony often occur in a single host; and (3) HÆMOSPORIDIA, in which schizogony takes place in a vertebrate host and sporogony in an invertebrate.

ORDER *GREGARINIDA*

The order GREGARINIDA contains numerous species parasitic in invertebrates, chiefly arthropods, worms and mollusks.

ORDER *COCCIDIA*

COCCIDIA are tissue parasites of vertebrates and invertebrates. Coccidiosis, while of minor clinical importance in man, at times is a serious disease of the lower animals, producing severe lesions of the intestinal tract and liver.

Life Cycle.—The life cycle of a typical coccidium is usually passed in a single host. The resistant oöcysts, after leaving the host in the feces and completing their development, are ingested in contaminated food by another host. The life cycles of the human species have not been fully determined, but probably resemble those of the coccidia of lower animals (Fig. 50).

The sporozoite, a small oval organism, enters an epithelial cell, becomes a trophozoite and finally enlarges to a spherical schizont which nearly fills the cell. The nucleus of the schizont divides repeatedly and each daughter nucleus, surrounded by cytoplasm and ultimately by a cell wall, forms a small merozoite. With the rupture of the epithelial cell the motile merozoites (sporozoites) enter new cells and repeat the asexual cycle.

In the sexual cycle the merozoites develop into male and female gametocytes. In the epithelial cell the male gametocyte after growth divides into a number of microgametes, and when liberated one penetrates a pole of the large oval gamete that has developed from the female gametocyte. The zygote produced by this fusion secretes a cyst wall and becomes an oöcyst. The nucleus of the oöcyst divides into daughter nuclei, which upon the addition of cytoplasm form the sporoblasts. Finally each sporoblast by secreting an enveloping sporocyst becomes a spore, in which sausage-like sporozoites develop. The formation of the spores takes place outside the body, if the oöcyst is passed in the feces. When ingested the spores rupture and the sporozoites infect the new host.

Classification.—Coccidia are classified chiefly by the characteristics of the oöcysts and the number and shape of the sporoblasts and sporozoites. Various species differ in size, shape, color and markings as well as in pathogenicity, host-specificity and tissue-specificity. The important species belong to the family EIMERIDÆ and comprise the genera *Eimeria* and *Isospora*. In the former the mature oöcysts contain four sporocysts, each of which has two sporozoites and in the latter two sporocysts and four sporozoites.

Coccidia of Lower Animals.—Species of *Eimeria* and *Isospora* are found in nearly all classes of vertebrates. Pathogenic species of *Eimeria* occur in rabbits, cattle and birds. Species of *Isospora* are common parasites of dogs and cats.

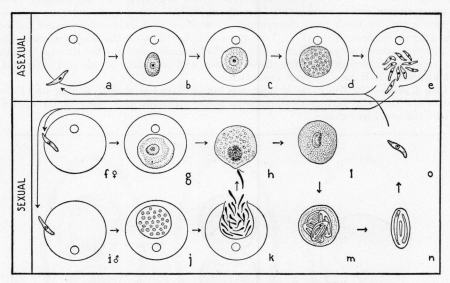

FIG. 50.—LIFE CYCLE OF A TYPICAL COCCIDIUM

a, sporozoite invading cell; *b*, trophozoite developing in cell; *c*, schizont; *d*, mature schizont; *e*, merozoites erupting from cell; *f* to *h*, development of macrogamete in cell; *i* to *k*, development of microgametocyte in cell; *l*, union of macro- and microgametes; *m*, oöcyst with spores; *n*, spore with sporozoites; *o*, sporozoite liberated from spore.

Coccidia of Man.—Man was formerly considered an incidental host, but there is evidence that he is a true host of at least one species, *Isospora hominis*. Four species of *Eimeria* have been reported in man. Three of these species, *Eimeria wenyoni*, *E. oxyspora* and *E. snijdersi*, are probably not parasites of man, but are coprozoic species possibly identical with the *Eimeria* of fishes, since men fed with infected fish may pass similar oöcysts in the feces.[1] Gubler in 1858 found a coccidium in the liver of man resembling *Eimeria stiedæ* of the rabbit. There have been five records of this species, *Eimeria gubleri,* in man, but descriptions other than the size of the oöcyst are not sufficiently detailed to establish it as an accepted species.

Isospora hominis (RIVOLTA, 1878) DOBELL, 1919

Synonyms.—*Cytospermium hominis* Rivolta, 1878; *Isospora belli* Wenyon, 1923.
Disease.—None.
History.—This parasite was first observed by Kjellberg in 1860 and later by Eimer in 1870 in the small intestine of man. Rivolta named it *Cytospermium hominis* in 1878. Wenyon in 1915 described the oöcysts in detail and Dobell in 1919 renamed it *Isospora*

---

[1] Thomson, J. G. and Robertson, A., 1926.

hominis. Wenyon in 1923 proposed a second species, *I. belli,* for the large oöcysts, but this species has not been generally accepted.

Geographical Distribution.—The parasite, though rare, has a wide distribution, having been reported in southern Europe, Africa, Asia, Malaysia, South America and the United States of America.

Morphology.—Only the oöcysts are known. They measure from 25 to 33 µ in length and from 12 to 16 µ in width. Their shape varies, but in general they are elongate ovoids. At the narrower end a micropyle is sometimes visible. The smooth colorless cyst wall has two layers. In fresh feces the granular protoplasm is usually unsegmented and contains a single nucleus (Fig. 51A). Division takes place outside the body and two sporoblasts, which secrete a cyst wall, are formed. Within each spore further division produces four sporozoites, elongate sausage-shaped bodies with a nucleus at one end (Fig. 51C).

Cultivation.—It has not been cultivated.

Life Cycle.—The life cycle is unknown but doubtless is similar to that of *Isospora felis* of the cat. The various developmental stages probably take place in the epithelial cells of the small intestine.

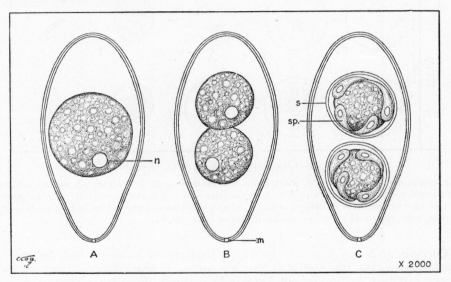

FIG. 51.—*Isospora hominis*

A, unicellular oöcyst; *B,* oöcyst with two sporoblasts; *C,* öocyst with two spores, each containing four sporozoites.

m, micropyle; *n,* nucleus; *s,* spore; *sp.,* sporozoite (Modified from Dobell and O'Connor, 1921).

Pathogenesis.—The oöcysts have been found in apparently healthy individuals and in patients with diarrhea. Pathological lesions have never been observed although some damage to the epithelial cells of the intestinal tract may occur. In most patients with diarrheic symptoms there is a concomitant infection with other intestinal parasites. A few uncomplicated cases have shown a mild diarrhea. A case of accidental human infection has been reported, in which diarrhea with flatulence appeared 6 days after ingestion, and oöcysts, first recovered in the feces in 28 days, continued to be passed for 13 days.[2] However, clear-cut evidence of pathogenicity is not forthcoming.

Diagnosis.—Diagnosis depends upon finding the oöcysts in the feces by microscopic

[2] Connal, A., 1922.

examination of unstained cover-glass preparations. As a rule the oöcysts are present only for a short time, as the infection is limited.

Prognosis.—Favorable.

Treatment.—Unnecessary. Same as for other intestinal Protozoa.

Epidemiology.—The incidence of infection in man is low, slightly over 200 cases having been reported. The incidence is less than 0.1 per cent; only one case has been found in 60,000 patients at the Mayo Clinic.[3] The small number of oöcysts, their appearance after symptoms have subsided, and the brief time that they are present may in part account for the low incidence. No animal hosts have been found, but the low incidence in man suggests that he is only an incidental host. The oöcysts are resistant to sunlight and desiccation and probably remain viable for long periods. They are transmitted to man through food or water contaminated with feces.

Prophylaxis.—Similar to that of *Endamœba histolytica*.

ORDER *HÆMOSPORIDIA*

The order HÆMOSPORIDIA includes those intracellular parasites of the blood of vertebrates that reproduce sexually only in invertebrates. It is composed of three main families, BABESIDÆ, HÆMPROTEIDÆ and PLASMODIDÆ, of which only the last contains species pathogenic to man.

BABESIDÆ.—*Species of* BABESIDÆ (PIROPLASMIDÆ) are found in cattle, sheep, horses, rodents, dogs and monkeys. The small nonpigmented parasites occur in the erythrocytes and in the lymphocytes and endothelial cells of the tissues. Some species, transmitted by ticks, cause serious diseases in cattle and other domestic animals. The discovery of the transmission by ticks of *Babesia bigemina,* which produces Texas fever in cattle, was the starting point for investigations on the relationship of arthropods to disease.

HÆMOPROTEIDÆ.—Among the HÆMOPROTEIDÆ are the following genera: *Hæmoproteus,* found in the red blood cells of birds; *Leukocytozoon,* nonpigmented parasites of leukocytes of birds; and *Hæmocystidium,* parasites of red blood cells of reptiles. Observations on *Hæmoproteus* helped to explain exflagellation in the life cycle of the malarial parasites.

PLASMODIDÆ.—In the PLASMODIDÆ schizogony takes place in the red blood cells of vertebrates and sporogony in mosquitoes. The genus *Plasmodium,* the only one in this family, contains the four species which cause malaria in man, namely *Plasmodium vivax, P. malariæ, P. ovale* and *P. falciparum.* Other species of *Plasmodium* are present in mammals, birds and lizards.

REFERENCES

CONNAL, A. Observations on the Pathogenicity of *Isospora hominis* Rivolta, emend. Dobell, Tr. Roy. Soc. Trop. Med. & Hyg., 1922, 16:223.

DOBELL, C. and O'CONNOR, F. W. The Intestinal Protozoa of Man, John Bale, Sons and Danielsson, Ltd., London, 1921, pp. 211.

MAGATH, T. B. The Coccidia of Man, Am. J. Trop. Med., 1935, 15:91.

THOMSON, J. G. and ROBERTSON, A. Fish as the Source of Certain Coccidia Recently Described as Intestinal Parasites of Man, Brit. M. J., 1926, 1:282.

---

[3] Magath, T. B., 1935.

Chapter XIII

THE SPOROZOA: THE MALARIAL PARASITES OF MAN

THE GENUS *PLASMODIUM*

The members of the genus *Plasmodium* cause malaria in man and other animals, and their morphology and life cycles are closely parallel. They pass through an asexual cycle in vertebrates and a sexual cycle in mosquitoes. In addition to asexual development male and female forms are produced in the vertebrate host. These forms initiate in the mosquito the sexual life cycle, which terminates in the production of infective sporozoites.

Plasmodia of Lower Animals.—In the year 1885 Danilewsky discovered a malarial parasite in birds, the first of some ten avian species that have since been described. Avian malaria is of historic interest. Ross in 1898, using an avian species, worked out the sexual cycle of the malarial parasite in the mosquito. Avian malaria has been used extensively in experimental studies of chemotherapy and of infection and resistance.

Malarial parasites were first observed in monkeys by Koch in 1898. Since that time at least seven species, some resembling those of man, have been found in primates. These species produce asymptomatic, mild or severe infections. Malarial parasites have also been observed in other mammals, including goats, buffaloes, bats, squirrels, flying foxes and jumping rats. Several species occur in lizards in Africa and South America.

Plasmodia of Man.—Four species of *Plasmodium* are parasites of man: *Plasmodium vivax,* the cause of tertian malaria; *P. malariæ,* of quartan malaria; *P. falciparum,* of æstivo-autumnal malaria; and the less-known *P. ovale,* which produces a tertian form of the disease. Several other species of questionable status have been reported.

HISTORY OF MALARIA

The disease malaria is variously known as: paludism, intermittent fever, chills and fever, Roman fever, Chagres fever, marsh fever, tropical fever, coastal fever and ague. In current use are the English term malaria, the French paludisme, and the Spanish paludismo. The term malaria, first used by Torti in 1753, is derived from two Italian words, *mal* (bad) and *aria* (air), because it was believed that the disease was caused by miasmas rising from marshes. Chinese physicians and later Hippocrates divided fever into the continuous, quotidian, tertian and quartan types, the last three being due to malaria. The Roman physician Celsus recognized a benign and severe form of the disease.

In 1638 the Countess del Chinchon, wife of the Viceroy of Peru, was cured of malaria by the bark of certain quinine-producing trees. This incident gave rise to the name cinchona for quinine. Torti in 1753 grouped fevers into those cured and those not cured by quinine. In 1847 Meckel recognized that the dark color of the organs of malarial patients was due to pigment, and a year later Virchow noted this pigment in the cells. In 1875 Kelsch observed pigmented bodies in the blood of malarial patients.

The malarial parasite was discovered in 1880 by Laveran, a French army surgeon in Algeria. Although Richards confirmed Laveran's observations in 1882, they were not generally accepted until 1885, because of the prevailing belief that the disease was of bacterial origin. In 1885 and 1886 Golgi differentiated the types of parasites and described the asexual cycle of the quartan and later of the tertian species. He also discovered that the malarial paroxysm coincides with the period when the sporulating forms reach maturity. In 1885 Marchiafava and Celli named the species producing the quartan form *Plasmodium malariæ*. In 1890 Grassi and Feletti gave the specific name *vivax* to the tertian parasite and in 1897 Welch that of *falciparum* to the æstivo-autumnal parasite.

Gerhardt in 1884 transmitted malaria by the inoculation of blood. Romanowsky in 1891 introduced a new staining technic, which made possible more detailed studies. In 1895 Ross in India observed that exflagellation took place in the stomach of the mosquito and in 1898 published a description of the sporogony of the avian *Plasmodium præcox*. In the same year and the next the Italian investigators, Grassi, Bignami and Bastianelli, reported similar life cycles for the plasmodia of man and produced malaria in volunteers by the bite of infected mosquitoes. The transmission by mosquitoes was proved beyond question by Manson, who working in England in 1890 transmitted the disease to volunteers through the bite of mosquitoes imported from Italy. In 1912 Bass and Johns cultivated the parasites.

GEOGRAPHICAL DISTRIBUTION

Plasmodium vivax has a world-wide distribution extending from 60° N. to 30° S. latitude (Fig. 52). It is especially prevalent in coastal regions and is infrequently found in deserts and mountainous areas. It is the prevailing species in the temperate zones.

P. malariæ, although widespread, has a localized distribution. It is rare in most countries, though it is frequently found in eastern Asia and at times may be the prevailing species in other warm regions. It has been reported in Mediterranean Europe, eastern and southern Asia, Africa, the Philippine Islands, New Guinea, the West Indies, Brazil, Panama, and in the southern part of the United States of America, and in Mexico.

P. falciparum is common in subtropical and tropical regions, but is seldom encountered in the northern portions of the temperate zones. It is the prevailing species in most tropical countries, and is common in southern Europe. It is present only in the extreme southern portion of the United States of America.

The exact distribution of *P. ovale* is unknown. It has been reported in East

Africa, southern Rhodesia, the Belgian Congo, Nigeria, and West Africa, the Philippine Islands, and the west coast of South America.

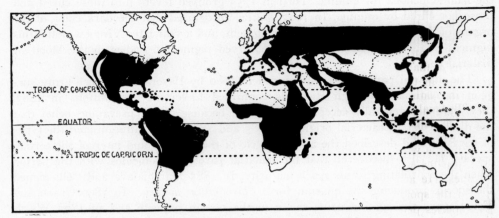

FIG. 52.—GEOGRAPHICAL DISTRIBUTION OF MALARIA

LIFE CYCLE

Plasmodium vivax and the other malarial parasites of man pass their life cycle in two hosts, man and an anopheline mosquito. The cycle in man is known as **schizogony** because of the splitting up of the parasite; that in the mosquito is a phase of sporulation known as **sporogony**. Between schizogony and sporogony there occur the development of sexual forms in the blood of man and the union of male and female forms in the stomach of the mosquito. The malarial parasites are highly host-specific, schizogony taking place in man and sporogony only in one genus of mosquitoes, *Anopheles*.

Man.—When man is infected by the bite of the mosquito, the sporozoites eventually gain access to the red blood cells. They may first invade the reticuloendothelial system and later emerge in the blood stream.[1] However, experiments, in which prompt excision of the skin and subcutaneous tissues at the site of the bite did not prevent infection, suggest direct transmission to the blood.[2]

The **sporozoites** are elongate slender bodies, 10 to 12 μ in length and 1 to 2 μ in width, with a firm cuticle and oval nucleus. They travel with a gliding movement and bore into the red blood cells, although some observers maintain that they are merely attached to the cells. Within the red blood cell the sporozoite develops into a ring-like **trophozoite** and undergoes schizogony, which includes the development of the **schizont** and the division into **merozoites**. Liberated by the rupture of the cell, the merozoites penetrate other red blood cells and repeat the cycle. In addition there is probably a supplementary exo-erythrocytic cycle in the tissue cells, particularly in *P. falciparum* infections, which may explain clinical irregularities and relapses.[3] After several generations of merozoites a new form of the parasite

[1] Raffaele, G., 1937.　　　　　　　　　　　[3] Froes, H. P., 1937; Raffaele, G., 1938.
[2] Boyd, M. F. and Kitchen, S. F., 1937.

appears. Certain trophozoites, instead of passing through schizogony, acquire distinctive characteristics and become sexually differentiated into male and female **gametocytes** in preparation for the sexual cycle in the mosquito.

Mosquito.—When the blood containing mature gametocytes is ingested by an anopheline mosquito, these forms undergo further development in the midgut (Fig. 53). In human blood the macrogametocytes outnumber the microgametocytes three to one. In the midgut of the mosquito the macrogametocyte undergoes maturation into a single macrogamete, while the microgametocyte undergoes exflagellation. In this process it throws off 4 to 6 whip-like nucleated microgametes, each capable of fertilizing a macrogamete.

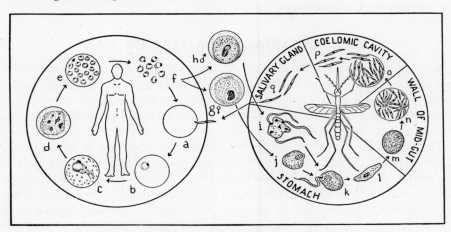

FIG. 53.—LIFE CYCLE OF A MALARIAL PARASITE

a to *f*, asexual cycle in man: *a*, entrance of sporozoite into red blood cell; *b*, early trophozoite; *c*, growing trophozoite; *d*, schizont; *e*, mature schizont with merozoites; *f*, merozoites freed by rupture of cell; *g*, macrogametocyte (female) in blood taken by mosquito; *h*, microgametocyte (male) in blood taken by mosquito; *i* to *q*, sexual cycle in mosquito: *i*, male gametocyte with exflagellating microgametes; *j*, macrogamete from maturation of female gametocyte; *k*, fusion of male and female gametes; *l*, zygote and oökinete; *m*, early oöcyst; *n*, mature oöcyst; *o*, rupture of oöcyst with liberation of sporozoites; *p*, free sporozoites; *q*, infective sporozoites in salivary glands ready for transmission to man by bite of mosquito.

Within a few minutes after maturation the macrogamete is fertilized by one of the actively moving microgametes and the two nuclei fuse. In 12 to 24 hours after the blood meal the **zygote** develops into a worm-like form, the **oökinete**, 18 to 24 μ in length by 3 to 5 μ in breadth. The oökinete penetrates the wall of the midgut with a gliding movement, and about 40 hours after the blood meal develops as a spherical **oöcyst** between the epithelium and muscular layers. Here the oöcyst increases to about four or five times its original size. When many oöcysts are present, the wall of the midgut is dotted with small rounded protuberances. Within the oöcyst hundreds and even thousands of **sporozoites** develop in four to five days through the division of the nucleus and cytoplasm. When the oöcyst ruptures, the sporozoites are liberated into the body cavity and are distributed to all the tissues of the mosquito. Large numbers penetrate the salivary glands and enter the salivary ducts. When the mosquito feeds on man the sporozoites gain access to the blood stream and start their schizogonic cycle in the red blood cells.

The time required for completion of sporogony varies with the species of *Anopheles,* temperature, humidity, and the number and maturity of the sexual forms removed from the peripheral blood. The sexual cycles of the three principal species of malarial parasites are closely similar. They differ in the susceptibility of different species of mosquitoes, in the time required for the development of the infective sporozoite and in the optimal temperature for development. *P. vivax* requires 8 to 9 days at 25° to 30° C. to complete its cycle, *P. malariæ* 18 to 21 days at 22° C., and *P. falciparum* 10 to 12 days at 30° C. Temperatures below the optimum prolong the period of development.

THE MALARIAL PARASITES OF MAN

Species.—The several species of *Plasmodium* vary in their morphology, in their presence in the peripheral blood, in their effect upon the red blood cells, and in their schizogonic cycle (Table 18). They differ in their incubational periods and in the pathological reactions of the host. They also vary in their ability to develop in different species of anopheline mosquitoes.

The term mixed infection refers to the coincidence of two or more species in the same patient. Mixed infections with *P. vivax* and *P. falciparum* are most common, next *P. falciparum* and *P. malariæ,* and least frequent *P. vivax* and *P. malariæ.* All three species have been reported in the same individual. In mixed infections the species appear antagonistic; in patients with general paresis, inoculated with *P. vivax* and *P. falciparum,* one species predominated.[4] Evidently masked mixed infections are more common than malarial surveys indicate. In such cases, although only one parasite may be seen in the blood smear, the other may be transmitted by inoculation.

Strains.—The different strains of a species may show variable characteristics. An Ethiopian strain of *P. falciparum* has been described, which differs from the Italian strain in having larger ring forms, shorter and broader crescents, more rapidly flagellating male gametocytes, and a reduced infection rate for the Italian anopheline mosquitoes.[5]

Number of Parasites.—The number of parasites observed in the peripheral blood varies with the species (*P. falciparum* being most numerous), with the schizogonic cycle, with the time of incubation, and with the initial and recurrent acute or latent clinical forms of the disease. *P. vivax* ordinarily does not exceed 25,000 per milliliter of blood and rarely reaches 50,000.[6] The maximal number is found usually within ten days after the parasites are first detected in the blood.

Multiple Infections.—Infection may so arise that one crop of parasites may mature 24 hours before another, resulting in quotidian or daily febrile attacks. Thus a double tertian infection may result with *P. vivax* and *P. falciparum* and double or even triple infections with *P. malariæ.* The quotidian type of infection

[4] Mayne, B. and Young, M. D., 1938.   [6] Boyd, M. F., 1938.
[5] Raffaele, G. and Lega, G., 1937.

PLATE III

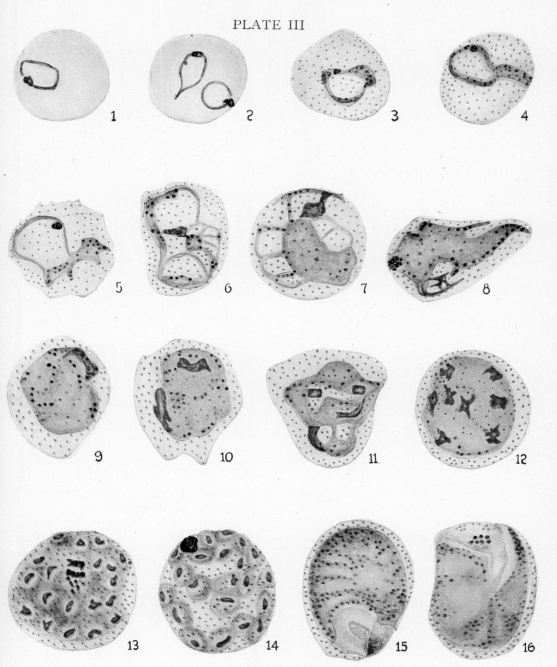

Plasmodium vivax

Sexual and asexual developmental forms of the parasite within the red cells of man from a case of benign tertian malaria. *Plasmodium vivax,* the parasite of benign tertian malaria of man, as seen in dried blood films stained with Romanowsky stain (*ca* × 3200).

1 and 2, young ring forms; 3 to 8, growth of schizont-enlargement of red cell, formation of Schüffner's dots, and development of pigment in cytoplasm of parasite; 9 to 14, nuclear multiplication and schizogony; 15, female gametocyte (macrogametocyte); 16, male gametocyte (microgametocyte) (Modified from Wenyon, *Protozoology,* 1926. Courtesy of Ballière, Tindall & Cox, London).

may be present in the initial attack, but it tends to return to the tertian or quartan form in recurrent attacks through the decline of the supernumerary group of parasites. Multiple infections are very common with *P. falciparum,* common with *P. vivax,* rare with *P. ovale,* and very rare with *P. malariæ.*

Erythrocytes.—The red blood cells vary in their susceptibility and their reaction to the parasites. The reticulocytes (young red blood cells) are more subject to invasion than the mature erythrocytes, and the frequency varies with the species, being extremely high with *P. vivax.*[7] The young red blood cells of birds contain most of the avian plasmodia.[8] The increase in the number of parasites (*P. cathemerium*) in canaries that had an erythroblastosis artificially produced by phenylhydrazine hydrochloride, is probably due to the greater number of selective young red cells available for infection.[9] On the other hand, the predominance of parasites in the young red blood cells is not considered evidence of any selectivity of the plasmodium for reticulocytes.[10] Since infection may take place in the bone marrow and viscera, where reticulocytes predominate, the relative percentage in the blood is not a true criterion.[11]

The infected red blood cells show certain changes. In *P. vivax* and *P. ovale* infections they become pale and enlarged, and with *P. ovale* tend to assume an oval shape with irregular edges. These changes may occur even before the parasites attain their full size. Since the parasites select the large young blood corpuscles, this increase in size may be more apparent than real. In *P. falciparum* infections the cells are of normal size or contracted, and late in the disease somewhat distorted or crenated. They have a darker, brassy and shrunken appearance. In *P. malariæ* infections the cells appear normal, but occasionally may be contracted.

During the development of the parasite fine, round, uniform, pink or reddish-yellow granules (Schüffner's dots) appear in the cells. At first they are distributed evenly over the whole blood corpuscle; later they become slightly larger, more pronounced and fill the whole cell; and finally they often surround the maturing schizont with a narrow stippled margin. These dots are characteristic for infections with *P. vivax* and *P. ovale* but are seldom observed with *P. malariæ* and *P. falciparum.* They are usually well preserved in thick film preparations, thus facilitating diagnosis. Coarse, irregular, red granules known as the "tertian stippling" of Brug (1910) are sometimes observed by the use of special staining methods. Erythrocytes infected with *P. falciparum* sometimes show a bluish basophilic stippling. In *P. malariæ* infections with special staining methods small pink granules (Ziemann's dots) may at times be observed. Cytoplasmic precipitates known as Maurer's dots appear as irregular red spots or clefts in the cytoplasm and occasionally as a deep red band encircling the parasite. This coarse stippling is characteristic of *P. falciparum,* although occasionally found in *P. malariæ* infections.

Among the various theories that have been advanced as to the nature and production of these granules are: (1) they are produced by the amœboid movements of the parasite; (2) they are nuclear particles remaining after the more easily

---

[7] Hegner, R., 1938; Kitchen, S. F., 1938.
[8] Hegner, R. and Eskridge, L., 1938.
[9] Hewitt, R., 1939.
[10] Simons, H., 1939.
[11] Hingst, H. E., 1938.

digestible parts of protoplasm are absorbed; (3) they are due to colloidal disintegration and the formation of precipitates; and (4) they are reticular granules.

Differential Characteristics.—Since the diagnosis of malaria depends upon the identification of the plasmodia in the blood of man, the description of the morphology of the four species is confined to their appearance in human blood. The differential characteristics of these species are given in Table 18.

Plasmodium vivax (GRASSI AND FELETTI, 1890)

The early trophozoite appears in the erythrocyte as a small hyaline disk with the nucleus on one side, giving a "signet ring" appearance (Fig. 54). As the parasite grows it becomes an irregular, finely pigmented organism that shows marked amœboid activity (hence the specific name *vivax*). After 24 hours it fills over half

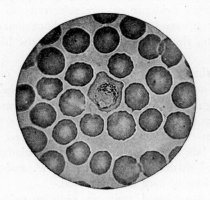
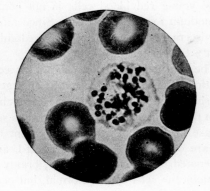

Fig. 54.—*Plasmodium vivax*
Half-grown parasite in signet-ring form (From Army Medical School Collection, Washington, D. C.)

Fig. 55.—*Plasmodium vivax*
Segmenting form (From Army Medical School Collection, Washington, D. C.)

the enlarged red blood cell and is known as a schizont. After 40 hours the schizont has lost its amœboid activity, almost fills the distended cell, and contains accumulations of pigment in a finely granular protoplasm. The pigment, which appears in about eight hours, probably represents a by-product of the hemoglobin. After 48 hours when the schizont has reached its maximal size, 8 to 10 μ, segmentation occurs. The pigment accumulates centrally, the nucleus divides, and with portions of cytoplasm forms round or oval cells, 1.5 to 2 μ in diameter. These merozoites (Fig. 55) are irregularly distributed or arranged in two rows. With the completion of segmentation, the red blood cell ruptures, and the merozoites, 12 to 24 in number, usually 16, are liberated into the blood plasma together with the pigment and cellular residue. Those that escape phagocytosis enter other red blood cells and repeat the schizogonic cycle. The pigment is ingested by phagocytic leukocytes and carried to the internal organs.

In preparations treated with the Romanowsky stains (Plate III, 1 to 14) the cytoplasm of the parasite stains blue and the chromatin of the nucleus red or reddish-violet. The early trophozoite appears as a delicate blue ring with a red chromatin dot. The irregular bluish cytoplasm of the late trophozoite contains small masses of red chromatin and brown pigment, while the enlarged red blood cell may be dotted with pink eosinophilic granules (Schüffner's dots). Within the early oval or rounded schizont are irregularly distributed masses of red chromatin and brown pigment on a blue background. The segmenting schizont contains the merozoites, which appear as rounded bluish bodies, each with a red chromatin dot. The pigment granules tend to collect in a yellowish-brown eccentric mass.

After several generations of merozoites the sexual forms of the parasite appear. The trophozoite that develops into the sexual form apparently has no signet-ring stage, is at first a small oval or rounded body, grows slowly, has slight if any amœboid activity, and acquires little pigment. Eventually it forms a rounded or oval body completely filling the enlarged red blood cell. Two forms may be distinguished, the **macrogametocyte** (female) and the **microgametocyte** (male). The macrogametocyte (Plate III, 15) is a rounded or oval pigmented body, 11 to 15 μ in diameter, with a dark blue, finely granular cytoplasm, which contains brown pigment in small wreathlike peripheral masses and a small, compact, eccentric mass of chromatin. The microgametocyte (Plate III, 16) is a spherical, hyaline, light-blue body containing large and small pigment granules and diffuse chromatin. It stains a less intense blue than the macrogametocyte, is slightly smaller, 9 to 11 μ, and has a greater amount of irregularly distributed pigment and chromatin.

Plasmodium malariæ (LAVERAN, 1881) MARCHIAFAVA AND CELLI, 1885

Plasmodium malariæ is smaller, less active, and is less abundant in the peripheral blood than *P. vivax*. The young asexual forms appear in fresh unstained red blood cells as hyaline ring-like bodies. As the trophozoite grows, it acquires an irregular shape and coarse granules of dark brown or black pigment. Prior to segmentation at 72 hours the schizont almost entirely fills the unenlarged red blood cell.

When treated with the Romanowsky stains the ring forms (Plate IV, 1) resemble those of *P. vivax* but the cytoplasm is a deeper blue, and the parasite is smaller and more compact. The growing trophozoite (Plate IV, 2; Fig. 56) often assumes a band shape across the cell, at first narrow but broadening as growth proceeds. It contains threadlike masses of chromatin, occasionally a vacuole, and marginal accumulations of dark coarse pigment. The schizont (Plate IV, 4 to 6) is smaller than that of *P. vivax*. The mature segmenting schizont (Plate IV, 10, 11; Fig. 57) resembles a daisy or rosette in having a central compact mass of greenish-black pigment surrounded by 6 to 12, usually 9, oval merozoites with a red chromatin mass and blue cytoplasm.

The gametocytes (Plate IV, 14, 15) are similar to those of *P. vivax,* but are smaller and contain less pigment. At times it is difficult to differentiate a wide band form with undivided chromatin from a gametocyte.

Plasmodium falciparum (WELCH, 1897)

Some zoologists consider that the parasite of æstivo-autumnal malaria belongs to a distinct genus *Laverania* because of its crescentic gametocytes. It requires from 36 to 48 hours to complete its schizogonic cycle. It differs from the other plasmodia in that, except in severe or fatal infections, only ring forms and gametocytes are ordinarily seen in the peripheral blood, schizogony taking place in the capillaries of the internal organs and bone marrow. Multiple infection of the red blood cell is common and characteristic.

The early ring forms (Plate IV, 16 to 24; Fig. 58) are small and delicate, often have two red chromatin dots, and may be distorted. They tend to adhere to the periphery of the blood cell and at times the chromatin mass may protrude from the cell. The presence of these characteristic ring forms, even without the gametocytes,

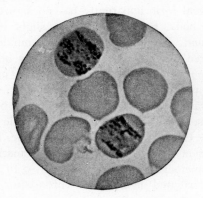
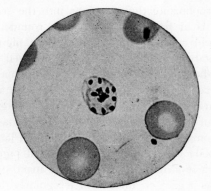

FIG. 56.—*Plasmodium malariæ*

Showing band-like outline (From Army Medical School Collection, Washington, D. C.)

FIG. 57.—*Plasmodium malariæ*

Multinucleate form showing centrally located pigment (From Army Medical School Collection, Washington, D. C.)

is sometimes sufficient to identify *P. falciparum*. As the trophozoite grows, it displays amœboid activity and acquires minute granules of black pigment.

The late trophozoite and schizont may be observed in blood from the spleen or other internal viscera. The oval or round schizonts resemble those of *P. vivax* but

---

DESCRIPTION OF PLATE IV

Plasmodium malariæ (1 to 15) AND *Plasmodium falciparum* (16 to 40) AS SEEN IN DRIED BLOOD FILMS STAINED WITH LEISHMAN STAIN (× 2000)

Plasmodium malariæ: 1, young ring form; 2, young band form; 3, slightly older parasite with granule of pigment; 4 to 6, growth of schizont; 7 to 12, nuclear multiplication and schizogony; 13, older band form of nearly mature gametocyte; 14, female gametocyte (macrogametocyte); 15, male gametocyte (microgametocyte). *Plasmodium falciparum*: 16 to 24, young ring forms; 25 and 26, growth of schizont and development of pigment; these forms usually occur in the internal organs, but are occasionally seen in the peripheral blood; 27 to 30, nuclear multiplication and schizogony; these forms occur rarely in the peripheral blood; 31 and 32, deeply stained cells containing young ring forms and showing Stephens' and Christopher's or Maurer's dots on the surface of the cell; 33 to 35, irregular or amœboid young forms, showing tendency to fusion of one or more parasites ("*Plasmodium tenue*" of Stephens); 36 and 37, developing gametocytes (crescents); 38 and 40, female crescents (macrogametocytes) showing remains of host cell; 39, male crescent (microgametocyte) (From Wenyon, *Protozoology*, 1926, Baillière, Tindall and Cox, London. This plate was made from the original drawing now in the Museum of Medical Science, Wellcome Research Institution, obtained through the courtesy of Professor Wenyon and the Publishers).

PLATE IV

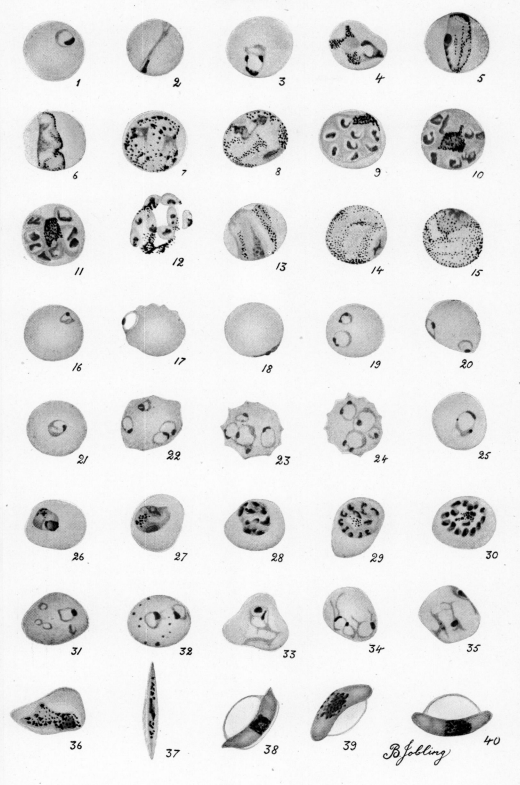

B. Jobling

do not fill the cell. The chromatin is collected in irregular clumps and the granules of pigment are small and irregular. The segmenting schizonts (Plate IV, 28 to 30; Fig. 59) contain from 8 to 36 small merozoites, usually 8, 12 or 24, often arranged in two concentric rings. The infected red blood cells show basophilic stippling and Maurer's dots (Plate IV, 32).

The gametocytes first appear as oval or round blue-staining bodies, about 1.5 μ in size, resembling those of *P. vivax*. They gradually acquire an elliptical shape, stretching the corpuscular covering. When fully developed they are about 10 to 11 μ

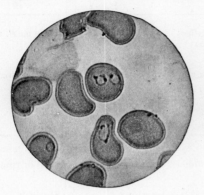
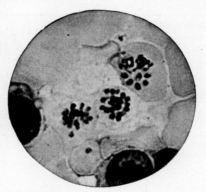

Fig. 58.—*Plasmodium falciparum*

Signet rings, one cell showing double infection (From Army Medical School Collection, Washington, D. C.)

Fig. 59.—*Plasmodium falciparum*

Segmentation (From Army Medical School Collection, Washington, D. C.)

in length by 3 to 4 μ in breadth, have a characteristic crescentic shape, and carry the cytoplasmic remains of the red blood cell within the bowl of the crescent. The gametocytes are found in large numbers in the peripheral blood shortly before death, but usually are more numerous in the internal capillaries.

The mature macrogametocyte (Plate IV, 38, 40) is cylindrical, stains a deep blue, and has a small central red nucleus surrounded by dense brownish-black pigment. At first it appears as a long thin band with a central elongate mass of chromatin stretched across the blood cell. As it grows it distorts the blood cell, becomes elliptical, and finally crescentiform. The mature microgametocyte (Plate IV, 39) has a broad kidney-shape with rounded ends in contrast to the crescentic shape and pointed ends of the macrogametocyte. The cytoplasm stains a lighter blue, and the chromatin and pigment are irregularly scattered throughout the central portion. The microgametocyte at first is a small rounded form with a homogenous protoplasm, a mass of chromatin, and amoeboid prolongations. During its growth the chromatin fragments and spreads either in a central zone or around the periphery.

Plasmodium ovale STEPHENS, 1922

In 1922 Stephens described an East African species which he named *Plasmodium ovale* because of the elongate shape of the infected erythrocytes. Other

TABLE 18

DIFFERENTIAL DIAGNOSIS OF MALARIAL PARASITES OF MAN

	Plasmodium vivax	*Plasmodium malariæ*	*Plasmodium falciparum*	*Plasmodium ovale*
Unstained Preparation				
Developmental stages in peripheral blood				
Trophozoite	+	+	+	+
Schizont	+	+	Rare	+
Gametocytes	+	+	+	+
Young trophozoite				
Size	One-quarter to one-third red blood cell	Slightly smaller than *P. vivax*	One-sixth of red blood cell	Same as *P. vivax*
Form	Hyaline ring	Compact ring	Delicate ring	Hyaline ring
Movement	Active	Sluggish	Active	Sluggish
Pigment	None	Fine, black (occasionally)	None	None
Growing trophozoite				
Form	Amœboid, irregular	Oval or rounded	Rarely seen in peripheral blood	Oval or rounded
Movement	Active	Sluggish	Active	Sluggish
Pigment	Fine, yellow-brown granules	Coarse, black granules or clumps, abundant	Fine, black granules, scanty	Fine, brown granules
Mature schizont				
Size	Fills enlarged red blood cell	Nearly fills red blood cell	Occupies one-half to two-thirds of red blood cell	Occupies three-quarters of enlarged red blood cell
Form	Irregular	Oval or rounded	Seen only in peripheral blood in moribund patients	Oval or rounded
Movement	None	None	None	None
Pigment	Yellow-brown granules	Coarse, black granules or clumps, abundant	Fine, black granules, scanty	Fine, brown granules
Stained Preparations (Romanowsky Stains)				
Infected red blood cell				
Shape	Enlarged	Normal, occasionally contracted	Normal or contracted	Enlarged, oval or irregular
Color	Pale	Normal	Purplish	Pale
Stippling	Eosinophilic granules (Schüffner's dots) Appear late	Usually none. Rarely fine, indistinct dots (Ziemann's dots)	Basophilic granules. Red dots (Maurer's dots)	Eosinophilic granules (Schüffner's dots) Appear early
Multiple infection	Common	Very rare	Very common	Rare

TABLE 18—Continued

DIFFERENTIAL DIAGNOSIS OF MALARIAL PARASITES OF MAN

	Plasmodium vivax	*Plasmodium malariæ*	*Plasmodium falciparum*	*Plasmodium ovale*
Young trophozoite Form	Signet rings, small and large. Single vacuole. Usually one red chromatin dot	Signet rings, small and compact. Usually one large red chromatin dot	Signet rings, small, delicate. Frequently two red chromatin dots. Often adhere to periphery of red blood cell	Signet rings, small and large. One large red chromatin dot
Pigment	None	Fine, black pigment occasionally observed	None	None
Cytoplasm	Light blue	Deep blue	Blue	Deep blue
Growing trophozoite Form	Amœboid, irregular, vacuoles	Oval, band, ribbon-like, compact	Ring, one-quarter diameter of red blood cell	Amœboid
Pigment	Fine, yellow-brown granules	Coarse, black granules or masses, more abundant at periphery	Fine, black granules, scanty	Fine, brown granules
Chromatin	Red dots or threads	Red dots and threads	Often more than one red dot	Red dots and threads
Cytoplasm	Light blue	Deep blue	Blue	Deep blue
Schizont Form	Irregular contour	Oval or round, compact	Rarely seen in peripheral blood, small, oval or round	Round or oval
Pigment	Fine, yellow-brown granules or irregular clumps	Coarse, black granules or masses	Fine, black, irregular granules	Fine, brown granules
Chromatin	2 to 10 granules or clumps	6 to 8 coarse granules, irregular clumps	8 to 12 coarse granules or small clumps	Irregular diffuse masses or filaments
Cytoplasm	Light blue	Deep blue	Blue	Deep blue
Segmenting schizont Merozoites	12 to 24, usually 16 to 18 Two rings or irregular distribution	6 to 12, usually 8 to 10 Symmetrical single ring (rosette)	8 to 36, usually 16 to 24 Two rings or irregular distribution	6 to 12 Usually single ring
Pigment	Eccentric mass, yellowish-brown	Central mass, black	Central or eccentric mass, dark brown	Central or eccentric mass, brown

TABLE 18—Continued
DIFFERENTIAL DIAGNOSIS OF MALARIAL PARASITES OF MAN

	Plasmodium vivax	Plasmodium malariæ	Plasmodium falciparum	Plasmodium ovale
Microgametocyte (male)				
Size	9 to 11 μ	Smaller than P. vivax	7 to 10 μ	Smaller than P. vivax
Form	Spherical	Spherical	Sausage shape, rounded ends	Spherical
Cytoplasm	Pale greenish-blue	Pale greenish-blue	Pale blue	Pale greenish-blue
Chromatin	Abundant, diffuse	Abundant, diffuse	Central, diffuse	Abundant, diffuse
Pigment	Fine, yellowish-brown granules, scattered	Central black masses	Dark brown granules, scattered	Fine brown granules, scattered
Macrogametocyte (female)				
Size	11 to 15 μ	Smaller than P. vivax	10 to 15 μ	Smaller than P. vivax
Form	Spherical	Spherical	Crescentic, pointed ends	Spherical
Chromatin	Compact, eccentric	Compact, eccentric	Compact	Compact, eccentric
Cytoplasm	Deep blue	Deep blue	Deep blue	Deep blue
Pigment	Coarse, yellow-brown granules, abundant	Brownish-black granules, abundant	Coarse, dark brown granules, central	Brown granules
Time gametocytes first appear in blood	At onset of fever	Several months after preliminary attack	One week after onset of fever	——

investigators have confirmed the status of this species. Craig in 1933 considered that it was identical with *P. vivax* var. *minutum,* a species he described in the Philippines in 1900. Infection seems to be confined to the white races, although its presence has been reported in natives of the lower Congo.[12]

Plasmodium ovale is generally considered to resemble *P. vivax,* although it has certain morphological similarities to *P. malariæ,* and has even been regarded as a variety of *P. falciparum.*[13] A high percentage of the infected erythrocytes early show Schüffner's dots, an oval enlargement, and a ragged periphery. Multiple infections of red blood cells are rarely observed. The ring forms stain deep blue except for a large red chromatin dot. The growing trophozoites resemble those of *P. malariæ* in their limited amœboid activity and oval shapes, but they do not form distinct bands. The schizonts are smaller than the red blood cell and when mature usually contain 8 to 10 merozoites. The pigment is scattered throughout the grow-

---

[12] Schwetz, J., 1938.　　　　[13] Ziemann, H., 1938.

ing organism in fine brown granules and is centrally massed in the segmenting schizont. The round gametocytes, that fill about three-quarters of the red blood cell, resemble those of *P. malariæ*.

The fever caused by *P. ovale* is of the tertian type and the schizogonic cycle is completed in 48 hours. The onset is sudden, but the infection is mild and of short duration.

PLASMODIA OF UNCERTAIN STATUS

Other species of plasmodia have been described in man, but their specific status is questionable, and they are generally considered varieties of the accepted species. *P. vivax* var. *minuta* Emin, 1914, found on the Camaran Island in the Red Sea, has certain features resembling *P. ovale,* but evidently is not identical. *P. tenue* Stephens, 1914, *P. falciparum quotidianum* Craig, 1909, and *P. perniciosum* Ziemann, 1915, are probably atypical forms of *P. falciparum*.

CULTIVATION

Bass and Johns (1912) and later workers have cultivated the three common malarial parasites *in vitro* (Section **VII**, IV, 8). Cultures have not been maintained beyond four schizogonic cycles, and subcultures not beyond a few transfers, probably because of phagocytic action by the leukocytes. No sexual forms develop in cultures. Culturing is not a practical diagnostic procedure and is of no particular use except in the production of antigens for serological tests.

PATHOLOGY

Death from acute malaria is confined almost exclusively to infections with *P. falciparum*. There are four important fatal types: (1) **cerebral** (55 per cent) in which the cerebral capillaries are packed with parasites and pigment; (2) **septicemic** (30 per cent) in which there is a massive general invasion of the vascular system; (3) **cardiac** (14 per cent) with coronary embolism and toxic myocarditis; and (4) **renal** (1 per cent) with glomerulotubular nephritis. Occasionally death may result from splenic rupture or from suprarenal and pancreatic involvement.

The pathology of chronic malaria is characterized by pigmentation of the cerebral cortex, spleen, liver and kidneys; anemia; enlargement and fibrosis of the spleen; and enlargement of the liver. Capillary thrombosis, hyperemia, hemorrhage, emboli and pigmentation may be present in the various organs.

Pigmentation.—A characteristic postmortem finding, particularly in *P. falciparum* infections, is the slate gray to black color of the brain, spleen, liver and other viscera. This discoloration is due to the deposition of malarial pigment, which occurs free as well as in the parasites and phagocytic cells. Malarial pigment is believed to be closely related to hematin, although some investigators claim that it resembles melanin. The destruction of erythrocytes also produces small amounts of light-colored hemosiderin.

Blood.—The red blood cells are reduced in number by the destructive action of the parasite and by the hemolytic activity of the reticulo-endothelial cells. The changes in the erythrocytes have already been described. They are abnormally resistant to hypotonic sodium chloride solutions and in severe infections tend to autoagglomerate. The anemia is of the plastic regenerative type. In acute malaria the bone marrow is dark red; in chronic malaria it is light to dark brown. The increase in reticulocytes, which is rapid once regeneration has set in, is correlated with the degree of anemia rather than the severity of symptoms.[14]

Except during febrile attacks the leukocyte count is below normal; the neutrophils are reduced and the lymphocytes and large mononuclears are increased. The

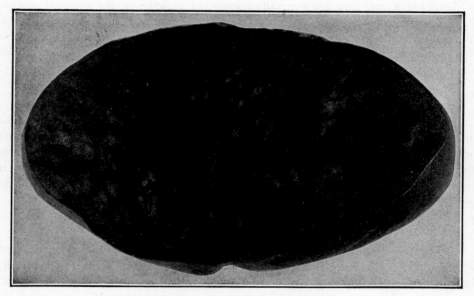

FIG. 60.—SPLEEN IN PERNICIOUS MALARIA

Note the characteristic dark gray slate color (From Duval and Schattenberg, *Textbook of Pathology*, 1939, D. Appleton-Century Company).

presence of pigment and damaged erythrocytes stimulates chiefly the phagocytic monocytes. During afebrile intervals and convalescence lymphocytes predominate. Eosinophils decrease during the febrile attacks and increase in the afebrile intervals, producing a mild eosinophilia during convalescence.

Brain.—In fatal cases the brain shows increased pigmentation of the capillary endothelium and areas of softening resulting from occlusion of the cerebral capillaries by thrombotic masses of free pigment, pigmented plasmodia (usually the sporulating forms of *P. falciparum*), infected erythrocytes, and phagocytes. Numerous small hemorrhages are produced by the rupture of the distended capillaries. In prolonged cases foci of inflammation with proliferation of neuroglia cells, probably of toxic origin, may be present.

Spleen.—In early infections the spleen is soft, moderately enlarged, distended with blood, and susceptible to rupture. In chronic infections the spleen is enlarged,

---

[14] Cicchitto, A. M., 1938.

has a firm consistency from hyperplasia of the connective tissues, and is colored slate-gray to chocolate by pigment in the capillaries and sinusoids (Fig. 60). Hemorrhagic areas are frequent and the parasites, especially schizonts, are abundant.

Liver.—The liver is moderately enlarged and in chronic cases firm in texture. Its color varies from normal to chocolate brown or dark gray. Pigment, parasitized erythrocytes, and phagocytic endothelial cells (Küpffer's cells) containing pigment and parasites may be observed. The pathological picture is that of focal necrosis with the malarial parasites embolic in the capillaries. Cloudy swelling, fatty infiltration, and fatty degeneration may be noted.

Kidneys.—The kidneys may show congestion and hemorrhagic areas due to the rupture of thrombotic capillaries. In fatal cases an acute hemorrhagic glomerulonephritis may result from embolic blocking of the capillaries of the glomerular tufts. In chronic cases there may be a secondary contraction of the kidney with inflammatory and productive lesions. The tubular epithelium may be pigmented. In blackwater fever, a serious complication of malaria characterized by severe hematuria and jaundice, the kidneys are engorged with blood and the tubules are obstructed by deposits of hemoglobin and albumin.

SYMPTOMATOLOGY

Malaria presents such a range of clinical manifestations that no adequate description can be given in a few pages. It tends to progress from an acute to a chronic disease. During the acute stage the disease remains active between the intermittent febrile attacks, which merely denote the sporulating phase of the schizogonic cycle. During the chronic stage the disease is latent except for recurrent attacks. Its severity and persistence depend upon many factors, including the species and strain of the *Plasmodium,* the resistance of the patient, and the environment. The pernicious type is almost always caused by *P. falciparum.* The differential clinical characteristics of infections due to *P. vivax, P. malariæ* and *P. falciparum* are outlined in Table 19.

Period of Incubation.—The usual interval between the bite of the infected mosquito and the onset of acute symptoms is 14 to 17 days for *P. vivax,* 18 to 21 for *P. malariæ,* and 10 to 12 for *P. falciparum.* It may be shortened by multiple exposures and lack of resistance, or it may be prolonged; duration of nearly a year has been observed in experimental infections with *P. vivax.*[15] In the temperate zones tertian infection acquired in the summer or autumn may not result in an acute attack until the following spring. Abortive attacks, however, may be easily overlooked.

Acute Attack.—The first definite manifestation of the disease is an acute fever. Prodromal symptoms of lassitude, lack of appetite, vague pains in bones and limbs, and a slight fever are nearly always present, although frequently unrecognized. Each type of malaria is usually characterized by febrile attacks recurring at definite intervals of from 24 to 72 hours (Fig. 61). In single infections the intervals of the three types of malaria are: (1) 48 hours in tertian infections (*P. vivax* and

---

[15] Boyd, M. F. and Kitchen, S. F., 1938; Mayne, B., 1937; Sack, G., 1938.

P. ovale); (2) 72 hours in quartan (*P. malariæ*); and (3) 24 to 48 hours in malignant tertian (*P. falciparum*). The fever is irregular at first, but it soon follows a regular course except in *P. falciparum* infections. In multiple infections fever may recur at odd intervals; for instance, daily in double tertian infections.

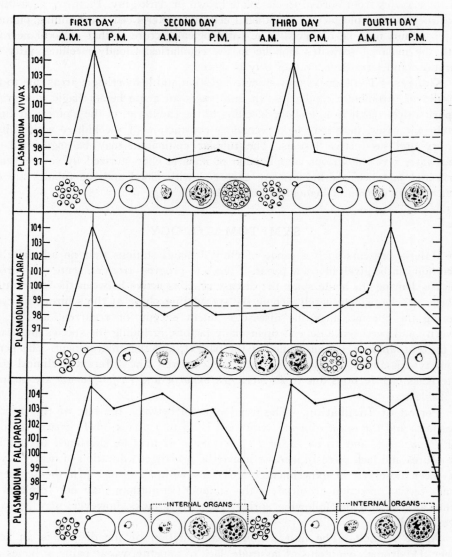

FIG. 61.—Temperature Curves in Malaria Showing Relation to Growth and Schizogony of Malarial Parasites

The febrile attack comprises three stages: shaking chills, fever, and sweating, although the chills may be slight or even absent. At the onset of fever mature schizonts predominate in the peripheral blood in the tertian and quartan types, but are present only in severe infections of the malignant tertian type, in which segmentation takes place almost entirely in the internal organs. At the height of the fever the merozoites predominate in the blood. During the sweating stage most of the parasites have entered the blood cells to complete their development in the subsequent afebrile period.

The fever of the tertian and quartan types consists of a series of high peaks on narrow bases (Fig. 61). Temperatures over 105° F. are not infrequent. The tertian fever lasts for 8 to 12 or even 16 hours, the quartan for 8 to 10 hours, and the malignant tertian, which has a slower rise and is more prolonged, for 16 to 18 or even 36 hours. At its climax the febrile curve of *P. falciparum* shows a plateau with minor oscillations that are often mistaken for an irregular quotidian (daily) infection, and the decline may be interrupted by one or more sharp peaks. In some cases an irregular fever may persist for weeks.

Malarial fever is accompanied by headache, muscular and bone pains, lassitude, malaise, nausea, vomiting, and an increased pulse and respiration rate. These symptoms may be present even with a low-grade fever. The severity of an attack depends not only upon whether it is an initial outbreak or a relapse, but also upon the toxicity of the species, the number of parasites in the blood, and particularly with *P. vivax* upon the number of generations.[16]

Chronic Malaria.—Clinical malaria may simulate almost any disease and some surgical conditions. In the natural course of malaria the acute symptoms gradually subside, latency develops, and eventually most patients become entirely free of the infection. Infections with *P. falciparum* either increase in severity or gradually improve, whereas with *P. vivax* and *P. malariæ* spontaneous remissions only occur after frequent relapses.

Chronic malaria is usually benign, but because of reinfections or relapses may become a serious and debilitating disease. All degrees of clinical manifestations may occur. Persons with no clinical symptoms may harbor the gametocytes in their blood and so constitute important sources of infection. Children, who are more susceptible than adults, may show severe symptoms including fever with or without chills; lethargy and convulsions in the acute stage; and anemia, apathy, debility and splenic enlargement in the chronic stage.

A latent period of about three weeks follows the initial series of intermittent febrile attacks and in turn is followed by characteristic relapses, which may recur over a period of years. The tendency to relapse is most marked in *P. malariæ* infections and least marked in *P. falciparum*. As the disease progresses, the latent periods become longer and the relapses fewer.

Relapses are influenced by seasonal changes and climatic variations. Provocative measures that lower resistance, such as exhaustion, diet, alcohol, muscular exertion, sexual excesses, injuries, exposure to cold, and intercurrent diseases favor recurrent attacks. Clinically a relapse resembles a primary attack and is difficult to differentiate from reinfection.[17] Some of the theories that have been offered to explain remissions and relapses are: the continuous presence of small numbers of

---

[16] Shute, P. G. and Badenski, G., 1937.   [17] Dogra, J. R., 1938.

parasites, the curtailment of asexual development, the production of resistant forms, and the retention of the parasites in the tissue cells.

Pernicious Malaria.—A pernicious and often fatal form of malaria, rarely observed in tertian and quartan infections, is encountered in infections with *P. falciparum*. The cerebral type usually assumes the comatose form with apathy, stupor and coma, but may be meningitic or encephalitic with delirium, psychic disturbances, paralysis and convulsive seizures. Generalized infection may produce hyperpyrexia (above 105° F.) headache, delirium, symptoms of sunstroke, and hemorrhages in the internal organs. When both the circulatory and nervous systems are involved, the disease may assume the fatal algid form with rapid loss of strength, cardiac weakness and collapse. Dysenteric or choleric symptoms may result from necrosis of the intestinal mucosa.

TABLE 19

CLINICAL DIFFERENTIATION OF THE MALARIAS

	Plasmodium vivax	*Plasmodium malariæ*	*Plasmodium falciparum*
Name	Benign tertian	Quartan	Malignant tertian, sub-tertian, æstivo-autumnal
Length of asexual cycle	48 hours	72 hours	24 to 48 hours
Primary attack Onset	Usually sudden	Usually sudden	Insidious or sudden
Febrile cycle	Tertian	Quartan	Irregular, tertian, quotidian or continuous
Duration of febrile paroxysm	8 to 12 hours	8 to 10 hours	16 to 36 hours or longer
Chills	+	+	May be absent
Sweating	+	+	May be absent
Duration of primary attack	2 to 4 weeks	4 to 8 weeks	10 to 14 days
Relapses Tendency	++	+++	+
Period of occurrence	Long	Very long	Short
Splenic enlargement	Early	Early	Late
Incubational period (average)	14 to 17 days	18 to 21 days	10 to 12 days
Cycle in mosquito Length	8 to 9 days	18 to 21 days	10 to 12 days
Optimal temperature	25° C.	22° C.	30° C.

Blackwater Fever.—Complications occur most frequently in malignant tertian infections and include cardiac dilatation, gastero-enteritis, hepatic disorders with jaundice, albuminuria and nephritis, and rupture of the spleen. The most important complication is blackwater fever, which occasionally occurs in patients with chronic relapsing malaria. It has a sudden onset and runs an acute course with severe hemoglobinuria and jaundice. In severe cases impaired renal function may produce uremia. It occurs more frequently in males and is most common in tropical countries, where malignant malaria is prevalent. Its cause is unknown, but it may be due to an inherent or induced hemolytic tendency associated with supersensitiveness to quinine.

IMMUNITY

Resistance to malaria depends upon: (1) the species and strain of *Plasmodium*; (2) environmental conditions such as climate, season and prevalence of anopheline mosquitoes; and (3) the immunity of the host.

Differences in virulence are found in strains of the same species as well as in the several species of *Plasmodium*. Marked variations in the severity of the infection have been observed in syphilitic patients inoculated with different strains of *P. vivax*. The Italian strain of *P. falciparum* causes more severe symptoms, produces a more protracted acute attack and more frequent relapses, and is more resistant to quinine therapy than the Ethiopian strain.[18] It is possible that these strains may have different selective effects on the red blood cells.[10] Individuals in a malarial region are more susceptible to an imported strain, although there is a relative cross-immunity in those infected with the indigenous strain.[19]

The prevalence of malaria may be influenced by factors other than the virulence of the parasite and the individual resistance of the host. Meteorological conditions that affect the transmitting mosquito are reflected in the spread of the disease. Climatic changes also disturb the equilibrium between parasite and host, thus producing clinical symptoms. Mass immigration of susceptible individuals to endemic areas has produced local epidemics involving both immigrants and residents by disturbing the previously balanced conditions of herd immunity. Epidemics have been produced by the influx of imported labor for large-scale construction work (Panama Canal), by troop movements (Macedonia), and by mass movements of population (Greeks from Asia Minor to Greece).

Our knowledge of systemic immunity has been derived chiefly from studies of avian and simian plasmodia, from therapeutic inoculations of syphilitic patients, and from experimental infections in volunteers. Individual resistance to malaria depends upon age, sex, occupation, and the degree of inherent and acquired immunity. Adults are more resistant than children, probably because of acquired immunity from repeated infections. Sex and occupation determine exposure to mosquitoes.

Inherited immunity is so obscured by the active immunity acquired from the disease that little reliable evidence is available concerning its rôle. Apparently a few individuals possess an innate immunity and remain free of the disease even in highly

[18] Mosna, E., 1938.
[19] Ciuca, M., Ballif, L., Chelarescu, M. and Lavrinenko, N., 1937.

endemic areas. Differences in susceptibility have been observed in Negroes and whites; native Africans have milder attacks and require less quinine than Europeans. Negroes are less susceptible to experimental infections with *P. knowlesi* than whites.[20] Caucasians have little natural resistance to *P. ovale*.[21] Racial immunity, however, seems to be confined to localities where malaria has been endemic for generations. Nevertheless, Negro children from non-malarial districts show greater resistance than white children.

After recovering from malaria the patient develops a certain tolerance or resistance to subsequent infection. In endemic areas repeated infections produce some degree of immunity, so that adults are frequently free from clinical disease while young children are severely infected.

Active Immunity.—Active immunity is of two types: (1) **concomitant,** when the infection is present in latent form; and (2) **residual,** after the eradication of the parasite. There is evidence that both forms exist, but in most cases acquired immunity is a concomitant resistance against superinfection rather than a residual immunity from a previous infection. This type of resistance is fairly marked against homologous species, but as a rule does not protect against heterologous species.[22] Immunity to *P. knowlesi* in monkeys depends upon the existence of the parasite in the host, since elimination of the parasite by treatment renders the host susceptible to homologous strains.[23] Induced malaria in syphilitic patients has shown that if the patient is reinoculated with a strain, with which he has been previously injected, infection will succeed only after several weeks and after a number of inoculations, whereas if a different strain is used the first inoculation is regularly successful.

Opinions differ concerning the influence of chemotherapy upon the development of acquired immunity. Some adhere to the idea that it interferes with the development of resistance and should be minimized.[24] Others consider that prompt and thorough treatment does not interfere with the immune reactions of the host.[25]

Experimental studies in the production of active immunity by the injection of living and dead plasmodia have been made in monkeys with *P. knowlesi* and in birds with various avian plasmodia. Observations have also been made upon the immunity produced in syphilitic patients by therapeutic inoculations. Various humoral antibodies have been identified, but protective antibodies have not been as clearly demonstrated. Repeated superinfections apparently produce the greatest immunity in experimental animals. The injection of adrenalin in latent malarial infections has been suggested in order to induce febrile reactions and thus stimulate the production of immunity.[26]

Passive Immunity.—Some degree of success has been obtained in protecting experimental animals with serum from actively immunized or diseased animals. Injections of large amounts of serum from infected birds have inhibited the symp-

[20] Milam, D. F. and Coggeshall, L. T., 1938.
[21] Sinton, J. A., Hutton, E. L. and Shute, P. G., 1939.
[22] Boyd, M. F., Kitchen, S. F. and Matthews, C. B., 1939; Bock, E. and Mohr, W., 1939.
[23] Shortt, H. E., Pandit, S. R., Menon, K. P. and Swaminath, C. S., 1938.
[24] Wilson, D. B., 1939.
[25] Bastianelli, G., 1936.
[26] Pizzillo, G., 1937.

toms but not the multiplication of the parasite in canaries.[8] Prevention of the disease or material reduction in its severity has been effected in susceptible monkeys by injecting large amounts of serum from monkeys with chronic *P. knowlesi* infections.[18] However, passive protection against *P. knowlesi* in monkeys was not produced with antiparasiticidal serum from immunized rabbits.[27]

Mechanism of Immunity.—Systemic immunity in malaria takes the form of a resistance to and a destruction of the parasite or a tolerance to its toxins. The pathogenicity and multiplication of the plasmodia are influenced by both humoral and cellular (phagocytic) defense mechanisms. The humoral factors depend upon: (1) an inherent unsuitability of the tissues for the parasite; (2) the production of antibodies against the parasite; and (3) the production of antitoxins.[28]

Acquired immunity depends primarily upon both an increased rate of phagocytosis and an increase in macrophages proportional to the duration and intensity of the infection. The severity of the primary attack in man is important in determining the degree of the immune response.[29] Experiments with *P. brazilianum* in monkeys indicate that the defensive mechanism involves (1) replacement of the destroyed erythrocytes and lymphocytes and (2) suppression of the parasites mainly through phagocytosis by macrophages chiefly of the spleen and to a less extent of the liver and bone marrow.[30] There is marked phagocytosis of the agglutinated parasites and lymphoid hyperplasia in the spleen at the crisis. Enlargement of the spleen in monkeys usually accompanies acquired resistance and suggests that immunity may be linked to the activity of the reticulo-endothelial tissues.[31] There is a distinct lymphoid reaction in the spleen and activation of the reticulo-endothelial system.[32] The decrease in *P. cathemerium* in canaries at the crisis may be due to increased destruction of the parasites and a temporary lowering of the rate of their multiplication.[33]

Various antibodies have been demonstrated in natural and artificially acquired immunity. Specific agglutinins have been found in monkeys 15 to 45 days after the onset of infection with *P. knowlesi,* the serum of superinfected animals having a titer as high as 1:1,000.[34] Superinfection during the chronic stage of *P. knowlesi* infection in monkeys caused increased production of immune bodies.[35] Alexinfixative antibodies have been produced in monkeys by the injection of dead *P. knowlesi,* but no agglutinative or protective antibodies have been demonstrated.[27]

DIAGNOSIS

Clinical Diagnosis.—The malarial parasites are not always found in the peripheral blood, especially if the patient has been under treatment, and reliance must then be placed on clinical diagnosis. The important diagnostic symptoms are: the

[27] Eaton, M. D. and Coggeshall, L. T., 1939.

[28] Sinton, J. A., 1939.

[29] Young, M. D., 1938.

[30] Taliaferro, W. H. and Cannon, P. R., 1936.

[31] Krishnan, K. V., Smith, R. O. A. and Lal, C., 1934.

[32] Menon, T. B., 1939.

[33] Boyd, G. H., 1939.

[34] Eaton, M. D., 1938.

[35] Coggeshall, L. T. and Kumm, H. W., 1938.

characteristic intermittent fever, relapses, a pale gray or yellowish complexion, anemia, and lassitude. The fever may not be apparent; hence temperature readings should be taken frequently. A fever that does not respond to quinine or atabrine is not of malarial origin. Latent infections may be detected by causing relapses by such provocative stimulants as cold douches, hot baths, strenuous exercise, purging, alcohol, nonspecific foreign-protein injections, and adrenalin. The production of exacerbations and the presence of the parasite in the blood during an induced attack furnish the necessary diagnostic evidence.

Laboratory Diagnosis.—Final proof of malarial infection is the identification of the parasites or their pigment in the blood, but the finding of plasmodia does not rule out the possibility of other superimposed febrile diseases. The blood may be examined by: (1) fresh blood preparations, (2) thin films, (3) thick films, and (4) concentrative methods. Species identification (Table 18) is important. In cover-glass mounts of fresh blood (Section **VII**, III, 6) the parasites may be identified within the red blood cells by their pigment and by their activity (*P. vivax*). The thin film (Section **VII**, III, 7) should always be examined. Even though the parasites, if few, may elude detection, the changes in blood morphology that accompany malarial infection may be noted. When the parasites are few in number the thick film (Section **VII**, III, 8) is a more reliable diagnostic procedure in the hands of experienced workers. Concentrative methods (Section **VII**, III, 9) are seldom more satisfactory than a thorough examination of a thick film. When the thick film fails to reveal the parasite, a positive diagnosis occasionally may be made by culturing the patient's blood (Section **VII**, IV, 8), but this procedure is of so little practical value that it is seldom used.

In chronic infections, especially if the patient is under quinine treatment, the parasites are often rare in the peripheral blood. Repeated thick film examinations, however, will usually reveal the parasites, especially the resistant gametocytes. The blood should be examined on three or four successive days before malaria is ruled out.[16]

The presence of precipitins and alexin-fixative antibodies in malarial patients has been demonstrated by a number of workers. The results indicate a group reaction with the plasmodia rather than a species-specific reaction. This group-specificity is not confined to the human plasmodia, since an antigen obtained from the simian species, *P. knowlesi,* has given positive alexin-fixative reactions in men one to twelve months after the onset of infection with *P. vivax* and *P. falciparum*.[27]

Group-specific reactions, variable results, misleading positive reactions in nonmalarial patients, and lack of a standard antigen (Section **VII**, IX, 8, 9) preclude the practical application of the precipitative test.[36] The alexin-fixative test, with *P. knowlesi* antigen, although not capable of detecting all infections, appears to be specific for human malaria. It is of value in epidemiological surveys and when the parasites are difficult to detect in the blood.[37]

Nonspecific tests based upon increased euglobulin in the blood serum of malarial

---

[36] Taliaferro, W. H., Taliaferro, L. G. and Fisher, A. B., 1927; Taliaferro, W. H. and Taliaferro, L. G., 1928.

[37] Kligler, I. J. and Yoeli, M., 1941; Dulaney, A. D. and Stratman-Thomas, W. K., 1940; Eaton, M. D. and Coggeshall, L. T., 1939.

patients are of diagnostic value; negative reactions are particularly significant. Henry's (1927) melano-flocculation test (Section **VII**, IX, 23), largely used in Europe, gives a high percentage of positive reactions in malarial patients. This test gives from 2 to 3 per cent of positive reactions in nonmalarial and nonsyphilitic patients.[38] False positives are obtained in syphilis, tuberculosis, leptospiroses, leukemia, eclampsia, liver diseases, carcinoma, and diseases causing disturbed equilibrium of the serum proteins.[39] Proske and Watson (1938) have developed a simpler protein-tyrosin test (Section **VII**, IX, 24) for determining changes in the euglobulin, with which they obtained 97.4 per cent positive reactions in malarial patients. They recommend the test for the detection of latent malaria and as a guide to treatment, but it is open to the same objections as Henry's test in respect to pseudopositive reactions in active syphilis and other diseases.

PROGNOSIS

Malaria is a self-limiting disease unless repeated infections occur. *Plasmodium falciparum* infections usually disappear in one to two years and *P. vivax* infections in four to five years; but *P. malariæ* infections persist longer. Observations on 50,000 ex-soldiers in England indicate that the parasites do not remain more than five years in persons who are not exposed to reinfection.[40] Prognosis is favorable in acute *P. vivax* and *P. malariæ* infections, even without treatment. It is grave in *P. falciparum* infections in which a pernicious type often develops; but adequate early treatment is usually sufficient to insure recovery. Chronic malaria in inadequately treated persons, who are poorly nourished or weakened by other diseases, may terminate fatally.

TREATMENT

Specific drugs, developed through pharmacological research and experimental studies of avian and simian malaria, have increased the effectiveness of modern malarial treatment. Three drugs have proved useful: quinine, atabrine and plasmochin. Since their action varies with the species and developmental stages of the parasite, effective chemotherapy depends upon the identification of the infecting species and upon the presence or absence of gametocytes.

Early and intensive treatment of malarial infections is necessary to reduce the number of gametocyte carriers that serve as foci of infection. With proper treatment the patient can be rendered noninfectious. The present practice is to use atabrine or quinine for the acute attacks and plasmochin for gametocyte carriers, although atabrine is effective against the gametocytes of *P. vivax* and *P. malariæ* (Table 20). Ordinarily, atabrine and quinine are administered orally. In pernicious cases with severe symptoms, where rapid action is desired, either may be given intravenously.

There are two general methods of chemotherapy: (1) the noneliminative, and (2) the eliminative. The former only controls the acute symptoms and permits relapses to occur on the assumption that the patient will develop an acquired im-

---

[38] Raynal, J., 1937.   [39] Lippelt, H., 1938.   [40] Broughton-Alcock, W., 1935.

munity. It is only applicable to infections with *P. vivax* and *P. malariæ,* since relapses are dangerous with *P. falciparum.* This method is recommended by the Malaria Commission of the League of Nations, but American authorities consider that its value is more theoretical than real, as attested by the persistence of malaria in regions where this method of quinine administration has been followed for generations. The eliminative method requires more prolonged and intensive treatment for the purpose of destroying the parasite. Relapses may be lessened but cannot be prevented by any method of treatment. They result from inadequate absorption or deficient action of the drug, resistant strains of the parasite, and provocative stimuli. In treating a relapse it is often advisable to use a drug other than that employed in the initial attack.

In addition to drug therapy, measures should be taken to maintain the general

TABLE 20
ACTION OF ANTIMALARIAL DRUGS

	Quinine	Atabrine	Plasmochin
Toxicity	+	++	+++
Cumulative properties	++	+++	+
Effect on malarial parasites Asexual forms			
P. falciparum	+++	++++	±
P. malariæ	+++	++++	+
P. vivax	+++	++++	+
Sexual forms *P. falciparum*	±	±	++++
P. malariæ	+	+++	++++
P. vivax	+	+++	++++

resistance of the patient. During the acute attack the patient should be made as comfortable as possible, the fever reduced and complications alleviated. In the chronic disease special attention should be given to nutrition, digestive disorders, anemia, and general hygienic measures.

Atabrine.—Atabrine (Section **VII, XIII,** 17) is the drug of choice. It is preferable to quinine because of its greater effect upon the asexual forms, its destructive action upon the sexual forms of *P. vivax* and *P. malariæ,* and the shorter time required for its administration (Table 20). It shortens the period of the initial attack, diminishes relapses, and reduces splenic enlargement. Relapses following treatment with atabrine supplemented by plasmochin constitute only a small fraction of those occurring under quinine treatment.[41] The low relapse rate as compared with quinine is probably due to the more effective destruction of the asexual forms and the slow elimination of the drug from the body. Its disadvantages are ineffec-

[41] Calan, J. M. D., 1938; Barbosa, A., 1938.

tiveness against the gametocytes of *P. falciparum,* the advisability of administration under medical supervision, and the yellow color it imparts to the skin.

Quinine.—The same results as with atabrine may be obtained with quinine (Section **VII**, XIII, 16), but a much longer period of treatment is necessary. It has little or no effect upon the sexual forms (Table 20). Its greatest advantage is its safety and its chief disadvantage is that it must be administered in considerable dosage for a long period of time to eliminate the parasites. Certain individuals possess an idiosyncrasy, inherent or acquired by prolonged treatment, which may lead to complications and possibly render the patient resistant to further treatment.

Plasmochin.—Plasmochin (Section **VII**, XIII, 18) has a negligible action upon the asexual forms but destroys the gametocytes of all three plasmodia (Table 20). It is the only drug that is effective against the gametocytes of *P. falciparum.* It is of value in preventing relapses after preliminary treatment with atabrine or quinine, and in rendering gametocyte carriers noninfective. It should be administered after atabrine or quinine treatment if gametocytes are present in the blood, or as a routine if blood examinations are not made. Simultaneous administration of atabrine and plasmochin is not recommended, since it increases the toxicity of each drug. Fewer relapses occur when plasmochin is used after atabrine or quinine than with these drugs alone.[42]

Other Drugs.—Combined treatment with quinine and plasmochin in the form of chinoplasm is effective, particularly if followed by plasmochin. Sulfanilamide and its derivatives have proved unsatisfactory in the hands of most workers because of ineffective action and administrative precautions.

MALARIAL TREATMENT OF SYPHILIS

The treatment of general paresis with induced malaria was first established in 1917. Two methods of inoculation are used: (1) intravenous or subcutaneous injections of malarial blood, and (2) mosquito-borne infection or injections of the sporozoites from mosquitoes. The latter avoids the danger of mixed infections, but because of technical difficulties is less extensively used. Only selected mild strains of *P. vivax* should be used; a mortality of 10 to 14 per cent with the virulent Madagascar strain of *P. vivax* is reported by the Malaria Commission of the League of Nations (1933). The simian parasite, *P. knowlesi,* has also been used. Blood from malarial donors remains potent for about 48 hours if kept cool.

The incubational period after intravenous inoculation varies from 3 to 5 days, depending upon the number of parasites injected and upon the previous exposure of the patient to malaria. With subcutaneous injections the period is usually 8 to 10 days, but may be prolonged to 50 days. Reinfections may require several weeks' incubation unless a different strain is employed. Sometimes infection by mosquitoes is successful after failure of direct inoculation. Patients who have received repeated direct inoculations are still susceptible to natural mosquito-borne infection.

The induced fever may be typical tertian but more often is quotidian. After 8

---

[42] Gentzkow, C. J. and Callender, G. R., 1938.

or 10 paroxysms the malarial parasites are destroyed by a short course of treatment with quinine or atabrine. Induced malaria, other than mosquito-transmitted, differs from natural malaria in the absence of relapses. The clinical symptoms are usually mild, but occasionally a severe attack is induced by a virulent strain of the parasite. Splenomegaly may occur after a second inoculation and rupture of the spleen has been observed. Gametocytes are found in the blood, but in smaller numbers than in natural malaria. Patients undergoing treatment, therefore, should be adequately protected by screening.

EPIDEMIOLOGY

Malaria is the most important parasitic disease of man and its annual toll amounts to millions of lives. It is a serious economic problem, since it lowers the health, vitality and physical development; retards the intellectual, social and national progress of a people; reduces economic efficiency; and renders useless extensive territorial areas. In India malaria is the direct cause of a million deaths annually, 100 million persons are afflicted each year, and its cost is not less than 400 million dollars per year.[43]

The conditions that determine the distribution and prevalence of malaria are: (1) the number of human carriers serving as sources of infection; (2) the presence of susceptible persons; (3) the presence of anopheline mosquitoes capable of transmitting the infection; (4) the environmental factors affecting the prevalence of mosquitoes and the development of the parasite in the mosquito; and (5) the economic condition of the people.

SOURCE OF INFECTION

Man is the only natural host of the four human species of plasmodia. Few attempts to transmit human malaria to primates have succeeded even temporarily.[44] Attempts to transmit *P. knowlesi* and other simian species to man have been more successful.[45]

Carriers.—Not all malarial individuals are sources of infection. The gametocytes in the peripheral blood may be too rare, too immature, or may have an unfavorable ratio of males to females for infecting the mosquito. One male and one female gametocyte to 100 leukocytes is considered the minimum for infecting mosquitoes with *P. vivax* and 11 male and 11 female gametocytes to 100 leukocytes for *P. falciparum*.[46] Carriers may be classified as either active or potential. The active carrier has an infective number of gametocytes in the peripheral blood; the potential carrier has a negligible number, but may suddenly produce a sufficient quantity to become a source of infection. In endemic regions a high percentage of infected individuals are often symptom-free, but if their resistance is temporarily lowered, they may develop clinical symptoms; 45 per cent of infected persons in

[43] Sinton, J. A., 1936.
[44] Taliaferro, W. H. and Cannon, P. R., 1934.
[45] Knowles, R. and Das Gupta, B. M.
1932; Jonesco-Mihaiesti, C., Zotta, G., Radacovici, E. and Badenski, G., 1934.
[46] Boyd, M. F., Stratman-Thomas, W. K. and Kitchen, S. F., 1935.

Mississippi showed no symptoms.[47] The incidence of carriers is greater in the insufficiently treated poorer classes than in those of a higher economic level.

Surveys.—Morbidity statistics give some idea of the prevalence of malaria, but do not reveal the incidence of infection. In East Macedonia the percentile rate was 5.6 for epidemic; 3.5 for high endemic; 2.1 for endemic and 1.0 for low endemic regions.[48] The incidence in a population is determined by (1) the parasite-index and (2) the spleen-index. The former is applicable to both children and adults, the latter principally to children.

The incidence of malaria, as determined by the presence of parasites in the blood, varies widely in endemic areas, depending upon the species of *Plasmodium,* the age-groups examined, the intensity of the infection, the season, and the number of repeated blood-examinations. This method indicates the species and whether multiple infections are present. In Greek Macedonia 44 per cent of positive children were infected with more than one species.[49] The age-group is important since children show a higher parasite-index. Plasmodia were present in the blood of 85 per cent of the Negro children in the Belgian Congo and were rarely found in adults.[50]

Splenic enlargement varies with the species; the largest spleens are found in *P. vivax* infections, next with *P. falciparum,* and smallest with *P. malariæ.*[14] The degree of enlargement is proportional to the duration of the primary attack, and, since the spleen decreases rapidly in size after the cessation of the attack, surveys should be made at the height of the malarial season.[51] The spleen-index usually runs consistently higher than the parasite-index; in western Bengal 48 to 89 per cent *vs.* 17 to 42 per cent,[52] in three villages in Mysore State, India, 21, 15 and 74 per cent *vs.* 17, 16 and 42 per cent,[53] and in the coastal areas of Grenada, B. W. I., 12 *vs.* 5 per cent.[54] The epidemic of 1936 in Calcutta raised the spleen-index from 5 to over 50 per cent.[55]

ANOPHELINE MOSQUITOES

Malaria is transmitted to man by the bite of an anopheline mosquito after the plasmodium has passed through its sporogonic cycle. Mechanical transmission by means of the contaminated proboscis is possible but has not been demonstrated. Infection may be transmitted by inoculation of infected blood and is sometimes produced by the use of contaminated syringes.[56]

A fairly high temperature is necessary to bring about the cyclic development of the plasmodia in the mosquito. At 15° C. *P. vivax* ceases to develop and at 20° C. *P. falciparum* requires about three times as long as at the optimal temperature of 30° C. In cold weather the parasite may remain dormant for at least three months, and there is considerable epidemiological evidence to support the

[47] Bass, C. C., 1919.
[48] Carr, H. P., Mandekos, A. and Barber, M. A., 1935.
[49] Barber, M. A., Mandekos, A. and Rice, J. B., 1937.
[50] Schwetz, J., 1936.
[51] Stratman-Thomas, W. K., 1938.
[52] Timbres, H. G., 1935.
[53] Sweet, W. C., 1937.
[54] Root, F. M. and Andrews, J., 1938.
[55] Sen, P., 1938.
[56] Black, J. B., 1940.

theory of over-winter hibernation. The rate of development is also proportional to the degree of humidity, a saturated atmosphere being most favorable. Likewise, the time required for the production of infective sporozoites varies with the species of mosquito.

Species.—The malarial mosquitoes belong to the genus *Anopheles* of the family CULICIDÆ. Some 19 important species and 24 of minor importance have been identified as intermediate hosts (Chapter XL). Among the important vectors are the several varieties of *Anopheles maculipennis* in Europe, *A. quadrimaculatus* in the United States of America, and *A. culicifacies* in India.

Only certain species of *Anopheles* and particular strains of these species are well suited for the transmission of malaria. A few species because of their prevalence, their domestic habits, and their preference for human rather than animal blood are effective malarial carriers. Other species prefer the open plains and forests and feed largely upon animals. Thus, mosquitoes capable of acting as intermediate hosts may be present in abundance, yet the incidence of malaria may be low. Species that act as important vectors in one region may be negligible in another because of local conditions. The feeding habits and transmitting abilities of mosquitoes may change in a given locality. Thus parts of Europe, in which malaria was once endemic and in which anopheline mosquitoes are still found, are now practically free from the disease.

The natural range of the *Anopheles* is limited to a few miles, usually less than one mile; but winds, ships, railways and airplanes may carry them considerable distances. Malaria thrives best where the population lives primitively in dark, stuffy huts with every opportunity for the mosquitoes to feed on human blood.

Surveys.—Surveys of malarial mosquitoes include: the identification of the prevailing species, both adults and larvæ; their breeding places; their habits in respect to man; their prevalence in relation to the intensity of the disease; the percentage of infected mosquitoes; and climatic and seasonal conditions (Chapter XL). The examination of mosquitoes for malarial parasites involves the dissection of the stomach for oöcysts and of the salivary glands for sporozoites (Section VII, XII, 10, 11).

Experimental Infection.—Various species of *Anopheles* differ in their susceptibility to experimental infection. *A. quadrimaculatus* is a less efficient carrier of *P. falciparum* than of *P. vivax*.[46] The Madagascar strain of *P. vivax* produces more sporozoites in the salivary glands and gives a higher experimental infection rate in mosquitoes than other strains.[57] Some investigators believe that they have detected morphological differences in the pigment and in the size of the oöcysts, oökinetes and sporozoites in the three species of plasmodia in the mosquito, but these dissimilarities are not distinctive enough for clear-cut differentiation between species.

The duration of the infectiousness of mosquitoes is probably limited, although the plasmodia may persist with reduced virulence throughout the life of the insect. Mosquitoes infected with *P. falciparum* produced 84 per cent of infections in human volunteers when the sporozoites were 10 days old or less; 71.8 per cent

[57] Siloi, F.; Kentenich, A. and Boldt, E.,1939.

when 11 to 20 days; 36.3 per cent when 21 to 30 days; and none over 30 days.[58] The maximum number of days after the blood meal when sporozoites are found in the salivary glands is 48 for *P. falciparum* and 34 for *P. vivax*.[59]

FACTORS INFLUENCING EPIDEMIOLOGY

The climate, topography and economic conditions of a country affect the prevalence of malaria.

Temperature.—A temperature of 30° C., optimal for the development of *P. falciparum* in the mosquito, is present only for a brief season in the temperate zones, thus limiting the distribution of this type of malaria to the tropical and subtropical regions. Low temperatures inhibit the sporozonic cycles of all three plasmodia and retard the reproduction of anopheline mosquitoes.

Moisture.—A high humidity generally favors the breeding of mosquitoes and the cyclic development of the parasite. Most malarial mosquitoes breed in stagnant pools. Suitable breeding grounds, depending upon waterways, climate and topography of the country, are provided in some cases during the rainy season, in others during periods of drought, when pools form in the streams, and in still others by improperly operated drainage systems.

Season.—The incidence of clinical malaria shows a seasonable variation; *P. vivax* infections rise in the spring and fall[60] and *P. falciparum* in the autumn. These seasonal outbreaks in part are due to new infections associated with the periodic prevalence of mosquitoes and in part to clinical relapses, which are induced by climatic changes and which under favorable conditions give rise to new infections. When due to relapses alone the seasonal wave lasts about 12 weeks, but when new infections occur the wave lasts 18 weeks.[61] In India the malarial season corresponds to the onset of the monsoon. There is a lesser spring wave in April and May and a fall wave with a November peak that starts in June, one month after the rains.[62]

Topography.—Malaria is a disease of the lowlands. It does not occur over 2000 meters above sea level in Italian East Africa in spite of the fact that suitable anopheline mosquitoes are present.[63] It is sporadic between 1,500 and 2,000 meters, with *P. vivax* prevailing, whereas in the lowlands the index is high for both *P. vivax* and *P. falciparum,* and low for *P. malariae*. An epidemic among Italian laborers in this region occurred mostly in the lowlands, although some cases were found at 2,000 meters above sea level.[64]

The China-Burma Road is a recent illustration of the influence of topography upon malaria as an economic and military problem.[65] This road descends from mountainous regions to traverse the swampy valleys of the Chinese Shan State, notorious for centuries as hotbeds of malaria, from which the inhabitants have been accustomed to migrate to the hills during the rainy summer season. Condi-

---

[58] Boyd, M. F., Stratman-Thomas, W. K. and Kitchen, S. F., 1936.
[59] Kingsbury, A. N., 1935.
[60] Boyd, M. F. and Kitchen, S. F., 1938.
[61] Gill, C. A., 1938.
[62] Mitra, K., 1938.
[63] Lega, G., Raffaele, G. and Canalis, A., 1937.
[64] Pansini, G., 1939.
[65] Robertson, R. C., 1939.

tions attendant upon traffic, such as influx of laborers, overnight depots and the blockage of convoys by freshets in these valleys have resulted in a serious malarial situation. Its solution depends upon the establishment of depots at higher altitudes, protection of laborers and truck drivers by mosquito netting and prophylactic medication, and the application of antimalarial measures.

Economic and Social Conditions.—Malaria is especially prevalent in peoples of primitive culture, where houses are unprotected from mosquitoes, resistance is lowered by malnutrition and disease, treatment is inadequate, and preventive measures are not in force.

PROPHYLAXIS

The prevention of malaria comprises: (1) the reduction of gametocyte carriers, (2) mosquito control, and (3) the protection of susceptible persons.

REDUCTION OF SOURCES OF INFECTION

The first step in the prophylaxis of malaria involves the detection of the cases of malaria, active and latent, in the local population. Surveys by means of blood examinations and spleen-indices, especially in children, will reveal the local extent of infection and the gametocyte carriers. If the incidence is high or the cost of detecting the carriers is excessive, mass treatment of the entire population with atabrine or quinine should be carried out. Otherwise, prompt treatment of persons with clinical malaria and gametocyte carriers is indicated. The administration of plasmochin during the malarial season is usually sufficient to render a carrier incapable of infecting mosquitoes. Chinoplasm, a combination of plasmochin and quinine is also useful for this purpose. Patients with clinical malaria and gametocyte carriers should be isolated from mosquitoes by screening or by removal to noninfectious localities.

MOSQUITO CONTROL

The measures for the control of mosquitoes include: (1) eradication of breeding places, (2) destruction of larvae, and (3) elimination of adults (Chapter XL).

PROTECTION OF THE SUSCEPTIBLE INDIVIDUAL

The nonimmune person may be protected by (1) screening from mosquitoes and by (2) drug prophylaxis. Man may be protected from mosquitoes by mosquito-proofing dwellings, by mosquito bars over beds and by nets, sprays and repellents (Chapter XL). However, it is almost impossible for a susceptible individual in an endemic district to remain free from malaria merely by protection against mosquitoes. Supplementary drug prophylaxis is necessary, especially for armies and large groups of laborers.

Experimental work with syphilitics and volunteers, and investigations on avian and simian malaria indicate that no known drug is capable of destroying the sporozoites before they undergo asexual development. Clinical prophylaxis with the present antimalarial drugs is achieved by destroying the segmenting parasites so that their number is not sufficient to produce symptoms and ultimately they are eliminated. Susceptible soldiers in endemic areas remain free from clinical malaria by the prophylactic use of quinine, yet when treatment is stopped on their transfer to a nonendemic region, a high percentage (47 per cent) develop clinical symptoms.[66]

In individuals thus protected clinical malaria either does not occur or is of a mild character. Consequently, no disastrous epidemic will arise in armies or construction gangs, since the cases will not be severe and will be distributed over a wide period. In some regions medicinal prophylaxis is only necessary at certain seasons. Nevertheless, prophylactic treatment should be continued for some months beyond the danger period. When a prophylactic regimen is once started, it should be carried out faithfully, since irregular prophylaxis tends to produce chronic malaria and gametocyte carriers.

The several drugs used in the treatment of malaria may be used for prophylaxis. Quinine has been commonly employed, but atabrine apparently is more effective.

Quinine.—Two methods of quinine prophylaxis (Section **VII**, XIII, 16) have been employed: (1) the intermittent in which 1 gm. is administered on each of two successive days each week or every fourth day, and (2) the continuous in which 0.4 gm. is given daily. The daily method is more convenient and may be used advantageously with troops, workers and colonists, although some authorities believe that it eventually diminishes the effective action of the drug. Neither method insures absolute protection and may fail in heavily infected districts. If clinical infection occurs, treatment with atabrine is advisable.

Atabrine.—Atabrine (Section **VII**, XIII, 17) is more effective than quinine as a prophylactic; in a three years' study in Sardinia the percentage of infections was 15 per cent when protected by atabrine, 42 per cent with quinine, and 66 per cent unprotected.[67] Its prophylactic value has been demonstrated in Georgia and Alabama.[68] Experimentally its use has delayed malarial attacks as long as 37 weeks. It may be administered preferably in a total weekly dosage of 0.4 gm. on two successive weekdays or at intervals of three days, or 0.05 gm. daily. In highly endemic areas three weekly doses of 0.2 gm. each may be given on alternate days. After leaving endemic areas either the prophylactic dosage should be continued for four weeks or an intensive course of treatment should be followed for one week. Men in Civilian Conservation Corps camps, under atabrine prophylaxis, are enabled to work effectively with a minimum of infections in highly endemic regions of *P. vivax.*[69]

Plasmochin.—Plasmochin (Section **VII**, XIII, 18), has little or no action upon the asexual forms and consequently is not particularly effective as a prophylactic agent. Because of its toxicity it should be used in small doses and with caution. Chinoplasm combines the effects of both quinine and plasmochin, but although gametocidal it does not destroy all the parasites.

[66] McNabb, P. E. and Stewart, T. H. Jr., 1927.

[67] Casini, G., 1939.

[68] Winchester, M. E., 1938; Gill, D. G. and Smith, M., 1938.

[69] Bispham, W. N., 1938.

REFERENCES

BASS, C. C. and JOHNS, F. M. The Cultivation of Malarial Plasmodia (*Plasmodium vivax* and *Plasmodium falciparum*) *in Vitro*, J. Exper. Med., 1912, 16:567.

BOYD, M. F. The Threshold of Parasite Density in Relation to Clinical Activity in Primary Infections with *Plasmodium vivax*, Am. J. Trop. Med., 1938, 18:497.

——— Introduction to Malariology, Harvard Univ. Press, Cambridge, Mass, 1930, pp. 437.

——— and KITCHEN, S. F. An Instance of Protracted Latent Incubation Period in a Patient Infected with a North American Strain of *Plasmodium vivax*, Am. J. Trop. Med., 1938, 18:729.

BOYD, M. F. and KITCHEN, S. F. The Demonstration of Sporozoites in Human Tissues, Am. J. Trop. Med., 1939, 19:27.

KITCHEN, S. F. and MATTHEWS, C. B. Consecutive Inoculations with *Plasmodium vivax* and *Plasmodium falciparum*, Am. J. Trop. Med., 1939, 19:141.

COGGESHALL, L. T. and KUMM, H. W. Effect of Repeated Superinfection upon the Potency of the Immune Serum of Monkeys Harboring Chronic Infections of *Plasmodium knowlesi*, J. Exper. Med., 1938, 68:17.

CRAIG, C. F. Nomenclature of *Plasmodium ovale* Stephens 1922, Am. J. Trop. Med., 1933, 13:539.

EATON, M. D. and COGGESHALL, L. T. Complement Fixation in Human Malaria with an Antigen Prepared from the Monkey Parasite *Plasmodium knowlesi*, J. Exper. Med., 1939, 69:379.

HACKETT, L. W. Malaria in Europe, Oxford Univ. Press, London, 1937.

HEGNER, R. Relative Frequency of Ringstage Plasmodia in Reticulocytes and Mature Erythrocytes in Man and Monkey, Am. J. Hyg., 1938, 27:690.

HINGST, H. E. Erythrocyte Susceptibility to *Plasmodium vivax*, Grassi and Feletti, 1890, Am. J. Trop. Med., 1938, 18:361.

KITCHEN, S. F. The Infection of Reticulocytes by *Plasmodium vivax*, Am. J. Trop. Med., 1938, 18:347.

MALARIA COMMISSION of the League of Nations, Fourth General Report. The Treatment of Malaria, Bull. Health Organ., League of Nations, Geneva, 1937.

MAYNE, B. Protracted Incubation in Malarial Fever. Report of a Case and a Review of the Literature, Pub. Health Rep., 1937, 52:1599.

MILAM, D. F. and COGGESHALL, L. T. Duration of *Plasmodium knowlesi* Infections in Man, Am. J. Trop. Med., 1938, 18:331.

NOCHT, B. and MAYER, M. Malaria: A Handbook of Treatment, Parasitology and Prevention, John Bale Medical Publications, Ltd., London, 1937, pp. 196.

RAFFAELE, G. The Initial Development of Malaria Parasites in the Vertebrate Host, Riv. di malariol., 1937, 16:185.

SINTON, J. A. A Summary of Our Present Knowledge of the Mechanism of Immunity in Malaria, J. Malaria Inst. India, 1939, 2:71.

———, HUTTON, E. L. and SHUTE, P. G. Studies of Infections with *Plasmodium ovale*. I. Natural Resistance to *Ovale* Infections, Tr. Roy. Soc. Trop. Med. and Hyg., 1939, 32:751.

TALIAFERRO, W. H. and CANNON, P. R. Cellular Reactions During Primary Infections and Superinfections of *Plasmodium brazilianum* in Panamaian Monkeys, J. Infect. Dis., 1936, 59:72.

WENYON, C. M. Protozoology, Baillière, Tindall & Cox, London, 1926. pp. 1563.

WILSON, D. B. Implications of Malarial Endemicity in East Africa, Tr. Roy. Soc. Trop. Med. and Hyg., 1939, 32:435.

WINCHESTER, M. E. Atabrine Prophylaxis in Malaria. Report of Third Year's Investigation, Am. J. Trop. Med., 1938, 18 (6):625.

Section III

THE NEMATHELMINTHES OR ROUND WORMS

Chapter XIV

THE NEMATODES

HELMINTHS

The terms "helminths" and "vermes" have been used to designate worm-like animals of three diverse phyla: (1) PLATYHELMINTHES (flatworms); (2) NEMATHELMINTHES (roundworms); and (3) ANNELIDA (segmented worms). In medical parasitology all parasitic worms are collectively referred to as helminths.

Platyhelminthes.—The flatworms have bilaterally symmetrical, leaf-shaped or band-shaped bodies without a body cavity; are mostly hermaphroditic; and have either no digestive tract or a rudimentary one without an anus. The phylum is divided into four classes, of which only the TREMATODA and the CESTOIDEA include important parasites of man.

Class 1. TURBELLARIA Ehrenberg, 1831—mostly free-living.
Class 2. TREMATODA Rudolphi, 1808—parasitic.
Class 3. CESTOIDEA (Rudolphi, 1808) Fuhrman, 1931—parasitic.
Class 4. NEMERTEA Ehrenberg, 1831—almost exclusively free-living.

Nemathelminthes.—The roundworms include many parasitic species as well as numerous free-living forms. Some are obligatory parasites with a free-living phase during their life cycle. They have unsegmented, bilaterally symmetrical, cylindrical or filiform bodies with pointed or rounded ends; vary markedly in size; possess a body cavity; and usually have a complete digestive system. In most species the sexes are separate, the male being the smaller.

Class 1. NEMATODA Rudolphi, 1808, emend. Diesing, 1861—parasitic and free-living.
Class 2. NEMATOMORPHA (Vejdovsky, 1886) Ritchie, 1915—adults free-living, larvæ parasitic.
Class 3. ACANTHOCEPHALA Rudolphi, 1808—parasitic.

NEMATOMORPHA and ACANTHOCEPHALA have been classed here for convenience under the NEMATHELMINTHES, although they have little in common with the NEMATODA. Their systematic position is uncertain. Some authorities place the ACANTHOCEPHALA in a separate phylum.

TABLE 21

CHARACTERISTICS OF HELMINTHS

	NEMATHELMINTHES			PLATYHELMINTHES			NEMERTEA	ANNELIDA
	NEMATODA	NEMATOMORPHA	ACANTHOCEPHALA	TURBELLARIA	TREMATODA	CESTOIDEA		
Free-living species	Many	Adult stage	None	Many	Practically none	Practically none	Almost all	Many
Parasitic species	Many	Larval stage	All	Very few	Almost all	Almost all	Practically none	Few
Parasites of man	Yes	No	Few	No	Yes	Yes	No	Very few
Sexes, separate	Yes	Yes	Yes	No	No	No	Yes	Yes
Shape	Spindle-shape, tapering at both ends	Cylindrical, blunt rounded ends	Tapering posterior end	Cylindrical to spindle shape	Oval or leaf-shape	Ribbon or band-shape	Cylindrical, slightly, flattened	Cylindrical
Segmented	No	No	No	No	No	Yes	No	Mostly
Body cavity	Yes	Yes	No	No	No	No	No	Yes
Digestive tract	Present, usually complete	Atrophied	Absent	Present	Often present, no anus	Absent	Present	Present
Proboscis	No	No	Yes	No	No	No	Yes	Yes

Annelida.—The segmented worms are mostly free-living. The ectoparasitic leeches comprise the parasitic members of this phylum.

The leeches of medical importance belong to the order GNATHOBDELLIDA. These predatory parasites of man and lower animals range up to several inches in length and are either aquatic or terrestrial. They have annulate, muscular bodies, often pigmented; a variable cylindrical or oval shape with a convex dorsal and a flattened ventral surface; a smooth cuticle; anterior and posterior suckers for attachment and locomotion; and a mouth with three hard jaws adapted for blood-sucking. They are hermaphroditic and fertilization takes place by spermatophores. The eggs are usually deposited in hard cases or cocoons on submerged objects or in moist earth.

The chief predators of man and animals are the terrestrial leeches that live in damp tropical forests, where they attach themselves to travelers. Various species have been described in southern Asia, the East Indies, Australia, Oceania and South America. Aquatic species attack bathers and young leeches may be ingested in drinking water.

The bite, usually unnoticed, is detected by the presence of blood or the engorged leech. The wound, though painless, bleeds readily because of the anticoagulative secretions of the leech and heals slowly. Heavy infestations of man and animals may result in serious exsanguination. A number of cases of upper respiratory and digestive tract infestation from drinking water have been reported. Leeches in these locations after narcotization may be removed with forceps. Those attached to the exterior of the body may be removed after application of vinegar or strong salt solution to loosen their hold.

NEMATODA RUDOLPHI, 1808, EMEND. DIESING, 1861

The nematodes are NEMATHELMINTHES that have an intestinal tract, a large body cavity without an epithelial lining and no proboscis. They have elongated, cylindrical, often filiform, smooth, nonsegmented, translucent, flesh-colored bodies that usually taper to a pointed posterior and to a rounded anterior end. The parasitic species of man range in length from less than a millimeter (*Strongyloides stercoralis*) to over a meter (*Dracunculus medinensis*). The sexes are usually separate. The smaller male commonly has a ventrally curved posterior end and, in some species, copulatory spicules and a bursa.

There are numerous free-living and parasitic species. The free-living forms are widely distributed in water and soil. The parasitic species live in plants, mollusks, annelids, arthropods and vertebrates. It is estimated that over 80,000 species [1] and 364 of the 560 known genera [2] are parasites of vertebrates. They closely resemble the free-living forms except for the absence of eye-spots and of special tactile and sensory organs, and for other modifications produced by a parasitic life. Many parasitic species have a free-living phase and some are even able to lead either a parasitic or a free-living existence.

---

[1] Hegner, Root, Augustine and Huff, Parasitology, 1938.

[2] Baylis, H. A. and Daubney, R., 1926.

Table 22

THE NEMATODES OF MAN

Order	Suborder	Superfamily	Family	Genus	Species
ENOPLIDA (Aphasmidia)	DORYLAIMINA	TRICHUROIDEA	TRICHINELLIDÆ	Trichinella	T. spiralis[1]
			TRICHURIDÆ	Trichuris	T. trichiura[1]
				Capillaria	C. hepatica
	DIOCTOPHYMATINA	DIOCTOPHYMOIDEA	DIOCTOPHYMIDÆ	Dioctophyme	D. renale
RHABDITIDA (Phasmidia)	RHABDITINA	RHABDITOIDEA	RHABDITIDÆ	Rhabditis	R. hominis, R. niellyi, R. pellio
				Turbatrix	T. aceti
			STRONGYLOIDIDÆ	Strongyloides	S. stercoralis[1]
		ANGUILLULINOIDEA	ANGUILLULINIDÆ	Heterodera	H. radicicola
	STRONGYLINA	STRONGYLOIDEA	ANCYLOSTOMATIDÆ	Ancylostoma	A. braziliense, A. caninum, A. duodenale[1], A. malayanum
				Necator	N. americanus[1]
			STRONGYLIDÆ	Ternidens	T. deminutus
				Œsophagostomum	Œ. apiostomum, Œ. stephanostomum
			SYNGAMIDÆ	Syngamus	S. laryngeus
		TRICHOSTRONGYLOIDEA	TRICHOSTRONGYLIDÆ	Trichostrongylus	T. colubriformis, T. orientalis, T. probolurus, T. vitrinus
				Haemonchus	H. contortus

Order	Suborder	Superfamily	Family	Genus	Species
RHABDITIDA (Cont.)	ASCARIDINA		METASTRONGYLIDÆ	Metastrongylus	M. elongatus
		OXYUROIDEA	OXYURIDÆ	Enterobius	E. vermicularis[1]
				Syphacia	S. obvelata
		ASCAROIDEA	ASCARIDÆ	Ascaris	A. lumbricoides[1]
				Toxocara	T. canis / T. cati
				Lagochilascaris	L. minor
SPIRURIDA (Phasmidia)	SPIRURINA		GNATHOSTOMATIDÆ	Gnathostoma	G. hispidum / G. spinigerum
		SPIRUROIDEA	PHYSALOPTERIDÆ	Physaloptera	P. caucasica
			SPIRURIDÆ	Gongylonema	G. pulchrum
			THELAZIIDÆ	Thelazia	T. californiensis / T. callipæda
		FILARIOIDEA		Wuchereria	W. bancrofti[1] / W. malayi[1]
				Onchocerca	O. volvulus[1]
				Acanthocheilonema	A. perstans[1]
			DIPETALONEMATIDÆ	Mansonella	M. ozzardi
				Loa	L. loa[1]
				Dirofilaria	D. magalhesi / D. repens
				Filaria (only microfilaria known)	Mf. streptocerca
	CAMALLAMINA	DRACUNCULOIDEA	DRACUNCULIDÆ	Dracunculus	D. medinensis[1]

[1] Important parasites of man.

CLASSIFICATION

Several classifications of the NEMATODA have been made by various authorities including Yorke and Maplestone (1926), Stiles and Hassall (1926), Baylis and Daubney (1926), and Chitwood and Chitwood (1937). The tabulation in Table 22 is intended merely as a convenient arrangement for describing the species parasitic in man. It follows in general the classification of Chitwood and Chitwood (1937), in which the NEMATODA are divided into two main groups: the APHASMIDIA and PHASMIDIA, although it is questionable whether groupings based on the presence or absence of phasmids (caudal chemoreceptors) will ultimately prove practicable.

MORPHOLOGY

The adult nematode is an elongate cylindrical worm, primarily bilaterally symmetrical. It usually has a smooth, finely striated integument, which may bear sensory papillæ, bosses, spines or tuberous processes. The anterior end may be equipped with hooks, teeth, plates, setæ and papillæ for the purpose of abrasion,

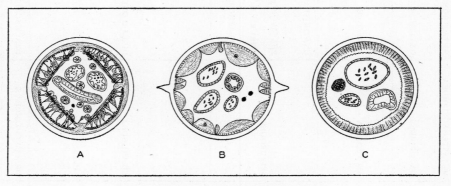

FIG. 62.—MUSCULATURE OF NEMATODES

A, polymyarian type; *B,* meromyarian type; *C,* holomyarian type (Redrawn from Hegner, Root, Augustine and Huff, *Parasitology,* 1938, D. Appleton-Century Company).

attachment and sensory response. The posterior end may possess papillæ, spicules, and a bursa. The supporting body wall surrounds a body cavity, within which lie the digestive, reproductive, and part of the nervous and excretory systems. The body cavity has no epithelial lining, but the parietal and visceral portions are covered by a delicate layer of connective tissue.

Body Wall.—The body wall consists of (1) an outer, hyaline, noncellular cuticle, (2) a subcuticular epithelium, and (3) a layer of muscle cells. The cuticle is usually marked by fine, superficial, regular, transverse striations, often by annulations, and occasionally by longitudinal or oblique striæ. The subcuticular layer consists of a thin syncytial matrix. It is thickened into four longitudinal chords: dorsal, ventral and two lateral, which project into the body cavity and separate the muscle cells into four groups (Fig. 62A). These chords carry longitudinal nerve trunks and often lateral excretory canals.

Beneath the subcuticular layer a single layer of muscle cells lines the body cavity. The outer part of these cells contains contractile fibers and the inner part bordering on the body cavity is undifferentiated. The arrangement of the somatic muscles, as shown in cross-section, is of value in the systematic grouping of nematodes. There are three general types: (1) polymyarian, (2) meromyarian, and (3) holomyarian. In the polymyarian type (Fig. 62A) the cells are numerous and project well into the body cavity (ASCARIDÆ); in the meromyarian type (Fig. 62B) the cells are few in number, two or three to a quarter section (OXYURIDÆ, ANCYLOSTOMATIDÆ); and in the holomyarian type (Fig. 62C) the cells are small and numerous and are closely packed in a narrow zone (TRICHURIDÆ).

Digestive System.—The alimentary tract is a simple tube extending from the mouth to the anus, which opens on the ventral surface a short distance from the posterior extremity (Fig. 63). Its anterior and posterior portions are lined with cuticle. The mouth is usually surrounded by lips or papillæ and in some species is equipped with teeth or plates. It leads into a tubular or funnel-shaped buccal cavity, which in some species is expanded into a pocket or capsule suitable for sucking purposes. The esophagus, lined with an extension of the buccal cuticle, has a muscular wall and a triradiate lumen. The radial direction of the muscle fibers produces a transversely striated appearance. The contraction of the muscle fibers distends the lumen, thereby producing a pump-like suction. The esophagus usually terminates in a bulbar extension, equipped with strong valves. Its size and shape are useful for species identification (Fig. 64). There are usually one dorsal and two ventral esophageal glands.

The intestine or midgut, a more or less flattened tube with a relatively wide lumen, usually follows a fairly straight course from the esophagus to the rectum, and is supported by fibrils from the longitudinal ridges. Its wall consists of a single layer of columnar cells. In the female the intestine leads into a short rectum, lined with cuticle, which anteriorly is provided with a sphincter muscle and posteriorly opens through the anus. In the male the intestine joins with the genital duct to form the common cloaca, which opens through the anus. Around the anal orifice are papillæ, the number and pattern of which aid in the identification of species.

Excretory System.—The excretory system (Fig. 63) consists of two lateral canals that lie in the lateral chords. They start as closed tubes in the posterior part of the worm, pass forward to unite anteriorly in the midventral line and open through an excretory pore in the region of the esophagus. There are no flame-cells. Numerous modifications of the excretory canals are found in the different species; one or even both longitudinal tubes may be lacking and only a lateral or median elongate gland cell without connecting canals may be present. In *Ascaris* the asymmetrical tubular system possibly has a secretory function and excretion may take place through the cuticle.[3]

---

[3] Mueller, J. F., 1929.

Vascular System.—There is no definite circulatory system. The fluid of the body cavity contains oxyhemoglobin and fulfils the functions of blood.

Nervous System.—A ring or commissure of connected ganglia surrounds the esophagus just anterior to the excretory pore (Fig. 63). From this commissure six short nerve trunks pass forward to enervate the head and circumoral region,

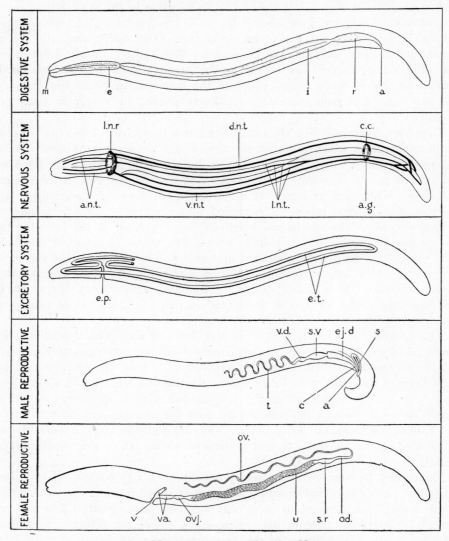

FIG. 63.—MORPHOLOGY OF A TYPICAL NEMATODE

a, anus; *a.g.*, anal ganglion; *a.n.t.*, anterior nerve trunks; *c*, cloaca; *c.c.*, circumcloacal commissure (male); *d.n.t.*, dorsal nerve trunk; *e*, esophagus; *e.p.*, excretory pore; *e.t.*, excretory tubules; *e.j.d.*, ejaculatory duct; *i*, intestine; *l.n.r.*, circumesophageal ring; *l.n.t.*, lateral nerve trunks; *m*, mouth; *ov.*, ovary; *o.d.*, oviduct; *ovj.*, ovejector; *r*, rectum; *s*, spicules; *s.r.*, seminal receptacle; *s.v.*, seminal vesicle; *t*, testis; *u*, uterus; *v*, vulva; *va.*, vagina; *v.d.*, vas deferens; *v.n.t.*, ventral nerve trunk.

and six long nerve trunks extend posteriorly. The large ventral and dorsal trunks run in the ventral and dorsal chords. The smaller lateral trunks, of which the two dorsal arise from the esophageal commissure, and the two ventral from the ven-

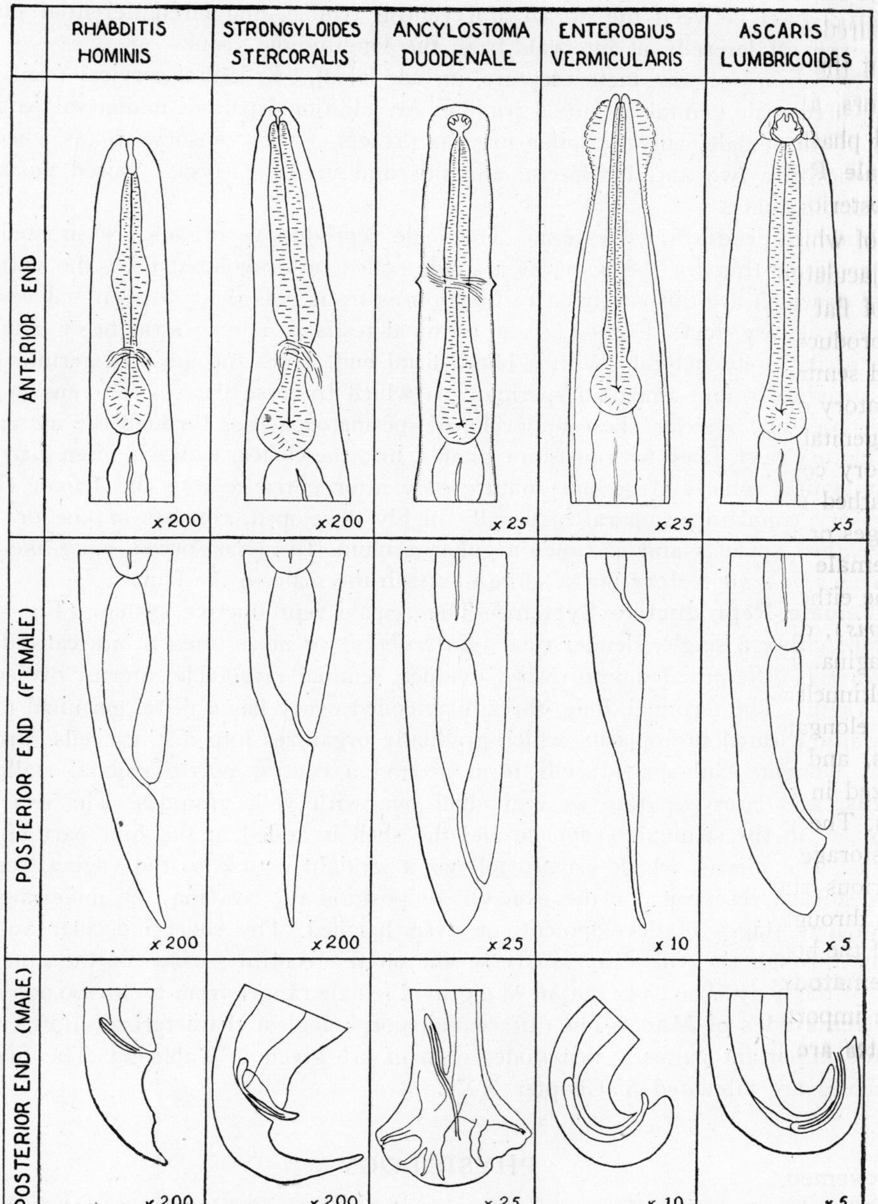

FIG. 64.—DIAGRAMMATIC REPRESENTATION OF DIFFERENTIAL MORPHOLOGY OF
CERTAIN NEMATODES

tral trunk, enter the lateral lines and each lateral pair unites at the level of the anal ganglion. The combined lateral trunks then continue to the caudal region, where they unite after receiving branches from the ventral and dorsal trunks. In the male a circumcloacal commissure arises from the anal ganglion. Lateral commissures pass between the dorsal and ventral trunks, and circumferential fibers are given off laterally at intervals from the longitudinal trunks.

The sensory organs, tactoreceptors, include labial, two lateral cervical (deirids) and paired male genital or bursal papillæ. An additional pair of midlateral papillæ and, in the female, vulval papillæ may be present. Other sensory organs, chemoreceptors, are two anterior lateral amphids and in some species paired postanal lateral phasmids.

Male Reproductive System.—The male reproductive organs are situated in the posterior third of the body, as a single coiled or convoluted tube, the various parts of which are differentiated to function as testis, vas deferens, seminal vesicle and ejaculatory duct (Fig. 63). The terminal testis is a long, straight or sinuous tube of flat epithelial cells with a blind distal end. Here the mass of germinative cells produce round amœboid spermatozoa which traverse the vas deferens to the dilated seminal vesicle. These undeveloped spermatozoa pass through the muscular ejaculatory duct, lined with prostatic glands, into the cloaca, which is often guarded by a genital cone, and become mature only after entrance into the female. The accessory copulatory apparatus, usually highly developed, consists of one or two ensheathed spicules and at times a gubernaculum. In some species wing-like appendages or a copulatory bursa serve to attach the male to the female.

Female Reproductive System.—The female reproductive system (Fig. 63) may be either a single, slender tube (*Enterobius*) or more often a bifurcated tube (*Ascaris*), differentiated into ovary, oviduct, seminal receptacle, uterus, ovejector and vagina. The terminal, long, threadlike, coiled ovary has a distal germinal mass of multinucleated protoplasm, which gradually organizes into distinct cells. Proximally elongate club-shaped cells form around a central nutritive axial stalk or **rachis,** and later separate as individual ova with yolk granules. The ova are fertilized in the seminal receptacle and the shell is added in the first part of the uterus. The uterus, which usually follows a straight course to the vagina, serves as a storage reservoir for the ova. On oviposition the ova may be undeveloped, in various stages of development, or even hatched. The short muscular vagina opens through the vulva, a transverse slit on the ventral surface of the anterior half of the body. The daily output of a gravid female ranges from 20 to 200,000 ova.

Nematodes of Man.—The differential morphological characteristics (Fig. 64) of the important parasitic nematodes of man are given in Table 23. The filarial parasites are tabulated in Chapter XXI.

PHYSIOLOGY

Movement.—Nematodes possess only longitudinal muscles, which produce shortening by their synchronous and bending by their unilateral contractions. Elongation is effected by the elastic properties of the cuticle.

Attachment.—Intestinal nematodes maintain their positions by oral attachment to the mucosa (*Ancylostoma*), by anchorage with their attenuated ends (*Trichuris*), by penetration of the tissues (*Strongyloides*) and by temporary attachment or retention in the folds of the mucosa (*Ascaris*).

Metabolism.—The metabolic processes of parasitic nematodes are essentially anærobic, although ærobic metabolism also may take place.[4] Under anærobic conditions the supply of glycogen in ascarids is appreciably diminished and carbon dioxide and the lower volatile fatty acids (caproic, butyric, and chiefly valeric) are excreted. Glycogen, an energy reserve, is increased in the stages preceding rapid and intense larval development and fat, a food reserve, in those preceding periods of lessened nutrition.[4] The usual end products of protein metabolism, such as urea, uric acid and creatinin, are not found. Intestinal nematodes must possess some form of anærobic metabolism, since the intestinal tract ordinarily contains little or no free oxygen. The size and surface area of these worms determine the type of metabolism; the larger worms obtain their energy from fermentative processes, while the smaller lead a relatively greater, though limited, ærobic existence.[5]

Nematodes survive outside the host under both ærobic and anærobic conditions, although *Ascaris* lives longer in an oxygen-free than in an oxygen-saturated environment.[6] Under ærobic conditions nematodes utilize oxygen at various rates dependent upon the oxygen tension and species, *Necator* having ten times the rate of *Ascaris*.[7] The amount of oxygen consumed is not correlated with the consumption of glycogen, which is the same under both ærobic and anærobic conditions.

Nutrition.—The methods of obtaining food by nematodes may be classed as: (1) biting with tooth-like oral structures (*Ancylostoma*), (2) ingestion of blood (*Ancylostoma*), (3) lysis of tissues (*Trichuris*), (4) feeding on the intestinal contents (*Ascaris*), and (5) absorption of nourishment from the body fluids (filarial worms).

Nematodes of the superfamily STRONGYLOIDEA are bloodsuckers. The hookworm not only ingests blood but also portions of torn intestinal mucosa. It sucks blood by the action of the muscular esophagus which pulsates sometimes at the rate of 120 to 250 movements per minute, ingesting about 0.84 ml. of blood in 24 hours.[8] The blood passes through the worm rapidly, suggesting the utilization of diffusible substances in the plasma as food.

Extra-intestinal digestion has been observed in helminths that are wholly or partially embedded in the tissues of the host. Areas of intestinal mucosa are apparently digested by secretions of some nematodes, and the liquefied tissues serve as nourishment.[9] Immature and adult *Trichinella spiralis* evidently obtain essential nourishment from the intestinal mucosa, since larvæ enclosed in collodion sacs that are permeable to the fluid intestinal contents fail to grow.[10]

---

[4] McCoy, O. R., 1935; Giovannola, A. J., 1936.

[5] von Brand, T., 1938.

[6] Toryu, Y., 1935.

[7] Harwood, P. D. and Brown, H. W., 1933.

[8] Wells, H. S., 1931.

[9] Hoeppli, R., 1933.

[10] Heller, M., 1933.

TABLE 23
MORPHOLOGY OF IMPORTANT NEMATODES OF MAN [1]

	Trichinella spiralis	*Trichuris trichiura*	*Strongyloides stercoralis*	*Ancylostoma duodenale* and *Necator americanus*	*Enterobius vermicularis*	*Ascaris lumbricoides*	*Dracunculus medinensis*
Disease	Trichinosis, trichiniasis, trichinelliasis	Trichuriasis, whip-worm infection	Strongyloidiasis, Cochin-China diarrhea	Ancylostomiasis, uncinariasis, hookworm disease	Enterobiasis, oxyuriasis, pinworm infection	Ascariasis	Dracunculiasis, dracunculosis, dracontiasis
Geographical distribution	Cosmopolitan	Cosmopolitan	Cosmopolitan	Tropical and subtropical 45° N to 30° S latitude	Cosmopolitan	Cosmopolitan	Africa, southern Asia
Location in man	Intestine	Intestine	Intestine	Intestine	Intestine	Intestine	Subcutaneous tissues
Size (mm) Male	1.4-1.5 x 0.04	30-45 x 1.3 (max.)	0.7 x 0.04	(*Ancylostoma*) 8-11 x 0.45 (*Necator*) 5-9 x 0.3	2-5 x 0.15	150-310 x 3	12-29 x 0.4
Female	3-4 0.06	35-50 x 1.7 (max.)	(Parasitic) 2.2 x 0.04 (Free-living) 1.0 x 0.06	(*Ancylostoma*) 10-13 x 0.6 (*Necator*) 9-11 x 0.35	8-13 x 0.4	220-350 x 5	500-1200 x 1.3
Shape (female)	Slender, gradually broadening posteriorly	Cylindrical, attenuate whip-like anterior three-fifths	Filiform (parasitic) Rhabditiform (free-living)	Cylindrical, slightly curved	Cylindrical with attenuate tail	Cylindrical	Cylindrical, elongated
Color	White	Gray or pink	Colorless, translucent	Grayish-white	White	White to reddish-yellow	Milky white

[1] Filarial parasites, see Chapter XXI.

Anterior end Shape	Slender, cylindrical	Attenuate with spear-like projection	Slender, tapering (parasitic) Truncated (free-living)	Blunt, ventral reflex (Ancylostoma), dorsal reflex (Necator)	Blunt, cylindrical with cuticular expansion	Conical	Rounded, with cuticular shield
Mouth	Orbicular, nonpapillate	Small, nonpapillate	4 indistinct nonpapillate lips (parasitic)	Well developed teeth (Ancylostoma) Cutting plates (Necator)	3 retractile lips	3 papillate finely toothed lips	Triangular, papillate
Posterior end Male	Sharp ventrad curvature	Curved ventrad 360°	Short, conical, pointed, ventrad curve	Fan-shaped	Strong ventral curvature, blunt end, papillate	Conical, ventrad curvature, papillate	Coiled ventrad
Female	Bluntly rounded	Bluntly rounded	Short, pointed (parasitic), tapering (free-living)	Bluntly pointed	Tapering, attenuate	Bluntly pointed	Bluntly pointed
Digestive tract Esophagus	Long, narrow	Long, narrow	Slender (parasitic) double bulbed (free-living)	Clavate, posterior bulbus	Prebulbar swelling and posterior bulbus	Short, muscular	Short, narrow, muscular
Anus (female)	Terminal	Terminal	Subterminal	Subterminal	One-third body length from posterior end	Base of tail cone	Subterminal
Male caudal appendages Spicules	0	I	2	2	I	2	2
Alae	Present	Absent	Absent	Present	Present	Absent	Absent
Female reproductive organs System	Single	Single	Paired	Paired	Paired	Paired	Paired
Location of vulva (length of body from anterior end)	I/5	3/5	2/3 (parasitic) 3/5 (free-living)	Postequatorial (Ancylostoma) Preequatorial (Necator)	I/4	I/3	At anterior end

Powdered charcoal, starch granules, semi-digested food, mucus, blood and disintegrated tissue cells may be ingested by nematodes from the intestinal contents. Digestion takes place in the intestine, the esophagus merely serving to force the food to lower levels. Absorption of nutrient material also may take place, since it has been found that *Ascaris* will take up monosaccharids from the surrounding medium.[11] Certain nematodes (filarial worms), although possessing a digestive tract, apparently subsist on readily absorbed substances.

The feeding habits of the free-living larvæ of certain parasitic nematodes have been studied in cultures. Hookworm larvæ feed only during the rhabditiform stage. Larvæ of the dog hookworm utilize bacteria, but show no growth in sterile feces or in suspensions of heat-killed bacteria.[12] In the host the larvæ obtain nourishment by absorption from the body fluids.

Growth.—The growth of free-living nematodes takes place under a wide variety of environmental conditions. Their abundance is correlated with a high organic content of the soil. In general they are able to survive under wide ranges of temperature, moisture, hydrogen-ion concentration and oxygen tension. The free-living larvæ of parasitic species show a similar response to environmental conditions. Desiccation, excessive moisture and extremes of temperature retard growth and may kill the larvæ. Factors governing host-specificity restrict larval development, particularly in immune animals or accidental hosts. The growth of both the larval and adult hookworm follows the typical logistic curve of animal growth and is the same under widely different cultural conditions as in the normal animal.[13]

Longevity.—The life span of nematodes differs with their taxonomic status. The female *Trichinella spiralis* is soon sexually exhausted and may be passed from the intestine in one to two weeks, although it survives in rats from two to three weeks and in guinea pigs five weeks.[14] *Enterobius vermicularis* has a life span of about two months; *Ascaris lumbricoides* may live for about a year; infections with *Strongyloides stercoralis* have persisted for 24 years, though the possibility of autoinfection renders this figure unreliable; and hookworms have been estimated to live from a few months to 20 years, and experimental infections have been observed to persist for at least seven years.[15] Single infections, however, are not typical of repeated natural infections, which bring into play the mechanism of resistance.[16] Microfilariæ have been found in the blood of persons infected with *Loa loa* for 15 years,[17] and *Dirofilaria immitis* has persisted in experimentally infected dogs for at least seven years.[18]

Cultures.—Adult parasites may be maintained for short periods in culture media. Intestinal nematodes in isotonic salt solutions and tissue helmiths in sera do not develop but survive if frequently transferred; *Physaloptera clausa* 10 days and *Thelazia callip'æda* 12 days; the larva of *Ascaris suum* 3 days and the microfilaria of *Dirofilaria immitis* 10 days.[19] Larval forms of RHABDITOIDEA have been grown in various types of culture media containing fecal extracts or other nutrient

[11] Hoffman, R., 1934.
[12] McCoy, O. R., 1929.
[13] Scott, J. A., 1929.
[14] McCoy, O. R., 1932.
[15] Sandground, J. H., 1936.
[16] Chandler, A. C., 1935.
[17] Coutelen, F., 1935.
[18] Fülleborn, F., 1929.
[19] Hoeppli, R., Feng, L. C. and Chu, H. J., 1938.

material and both direct and indirect types of development have been observed.[20] In this way observations have been made as to nutrient requirements and the suitability of environmental conditions for larval growth and development.

Reproduction.—A major portion of the total energy requirements of these worms is expended in the development of elaborate reproductive organs and in the production of large numbers of ova. A female *Ascaris lumbricoides* may contain as many as 27,000,000 ova [21] and may produce 200,000 ova per day.[22] In immune and resistant hosts the number of ova is materially reduced but the nature of the inhibiting mechanism is unknown.[23] The sexes are separate and suitable provision for fertilization must be provided. Males, even in small numbers, are attracted to females. The ingestion of two trichinous larvæ may suffice to establish infection in rats, the single male worm being able to locate the lone female in the intestine.[24]

Resistance.—Existence within the host necessitates the development of protective mechanisms by the parasite. Intestinal forms must resist the action of the digestive juices and tissue invaders that of the body fluids. Protection against digestive action is afforded by the cuticle and by the elaboration of antienzymes such as antipepsin and antitrypsin.[25] Anticoagulins, chiefly formed in the esophageal glands, have been demonstrated in certain bloodsucking species of STRONGYLIDÆ.[26] Hemolysins are found in small quantities in the extracts of nematodes. The migratory activities in the tissues of both larvæ and adults appear to be facilitated by the secretion of histolytic ferments.

Behavior.—Little is known concerning the behavior reactions of adult nematodes, but more information is available regarding those of the larvæ. Adults react to touch, heat, cold and probably to chemical stimuli. The movements of adults and larvæ to selective locations seem to be guided by some chemical stimulus. The penetration of the skin by strongyloid larvæ has been ascribed to various tropisms,[27] though thigmotropism (response to tactile stimuli) is the only proved tropism of the hookworm larva.

LIFE CYCLE

Parasitic nematodes pass through simple or complex life cycles both within and without the definitive host (Table 24 and Fig. 66). Multiplication during the larval stages, so prevalent in trematodes, rarely occurs. In some genera (*Strongyloides, Rhabdias*) it takes place during the free-living phase by the development of sexually-mature free-living individuals that produce a second generation of larvæ. These larvæ either resume their parasitic existence or again develop into mature free-living worms that produce further generations.

The intermingling of a parasitic and nonparasitic existence raises the question of the origin of parasitic nematodes. Most investigators believe that the more

[20] Cordi, J. M. and Otto, G. F., 1934; Chu, H. J., 1936; Beach, T. D., 1936; Augustine, D. L., 1940.
[21] Cram, E. B., 1925.
[22] Brown, H. W. and Cort, W. W., 1927.

[23] McCoy, O. R., 1931; Chandler, A. C., 1932.
[24] Doerr, R. and Menzi, E., 1933.
[25] Harned, B. K. and Nash, T. P., 1932.
[26] Hoeppli, H. R. and Feng, L. C., 1933.
[27] Wakeshima, T., 1933.

primitive free-living and the parasitic worms have developed from a common ancestor and that both have undergone certain modifications, the parasitic worms showing the greatest changes. Many maintain that the parasitic species have developed from the free-living forms and a few even hold that the free-living forms are derived from the parasitic. The intestinal parasite probably is the more primitive form; the more specialized tissue parasites have arisen through the development of selective sites by accidental penetration or in the course of larval migration. Biological races evidently are derived by the selection of genotypical mutants through adaptation to the host.

Hosts.—Most nematodes have only one host, the definitive, the larvæ passing from host to host directly or after a free-living existence. Some species have an intermediate host, rarely more than one, in which the larvæ pass through a cyclic development comparable to that of free-living larvæ. The intermediate host, usually an arthropod, ingests the parasite, which passes from the intestinal tract into the tissues. The same animal is the definitive and intermediate host of *Trichinella spiralis,* the viviparous female depositing in the intestinal wall migratory larvæ that encyst in the muscles. Transmission to a new host depends upon the ingestion of the encysted larvæ. At times the entire life cycle of *Strongyloides* and *Enterobius* may be passed in the definitive host, the normal, extracorporeal, larval development taking place in the intestine.

Larval Development.—The position of the adult parasite in the host to a large extent governs the escape of the ova and the character of the life cycle. When the habitat of the parasite is the intestinal tract, the ova or larvæ leave the host in the feces. When its habitat is elsewhere in the body, there are other avenues of escape: urine (*Dioctophyme renale*), sputum (*Metastrongylus elongatus*), skin (*Dracunculus medinensis*) and blood, lymph or tissue fluids (filarial worms). On oviposition the ova are in various stages of development.

The early development of a typical nematode ovum (*Ancylostoma duodenale*) is shown in Figure 65.[28] The first division is unequal, the larger cell containing the two polar bodies (Fig. 65B). In the four-cell stage (Fig. 65C), the cells lie in the sagittal plane of the egg, the two anterior cells being the forerunners of the ectodermal and the two posterior of the mesodermal, endodermal and stem cells. Subsequent divisions produce a mass of small cells, the morula, at first with an irregular contour (Fig. 65D) and later a more regular outline. The embryo passes through the blastula and gastrula stages to become a tadpole-like creature (Fig. 65F) in which the thick anterior end, occupying the whole diameter of the eggshell, shows a slight depression, the primordium of the mouth, and the alimentary canal appears as a dark strand of cells. As the body grows the narrower posterior portion of the body elongates, bends forward and terminates in a pointed tail (Fig. 65G). Sluggish movements may be observed at this stage. When the glistening embryo attains its full length, over four times that of the eggshell, the anterior end has become more slender and the tail is long and slender (Fig. 65H). The tapering oral extremity with papillate mouth and shallow buccal cavity is set off by an annular constriction and the esophagus, intestine and nerve trunk are recognizable.

---

[28] Looss, A., 1905.

Larval development takes place most frequently in the free-living state and less often within an intermediate host (Fig. 66). In the latter case there may be a brief intervening period of free-living existence (*Dracunculus*), or transition may be directly from definitive host to intermediate host (*Wuchereria*). The unhatched embryo may be fully developed and infective on leaving the host (*Enterobius*) or it may require a definite period of development outside the host before the ova becomes infective (*Ascaris, Trichuris*). The unhatched rhabditiform larva may constitute the infective form (*Ascaris*) and undergo subsequent changes

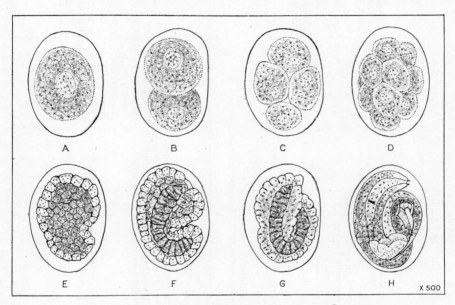

Fig. 65.—Stages in the Development of the Ovum of
Ancylostoma duodenale

A, undivided cell; *B,* two-cell stage; *C,* four-cell stage; *D,* eleven-cell stage; *E,* beginning of flexure of the embryo, the thick end is the anterior; *F,* tadpole stage, the thick anterior end occupies nearly the whole diameter of the eggshell; *G,* the elongation of the body has advanced farther and the tail end is becoming pointed; *H,* embryo has attained about four times the length of the eggshell and the anterior end has decreased in thickness until it is almost uniform with the rest of the body (Redrawn from Looss, 1905).

within the host. The ova may hatch outside the host and the larvæ pursue a free-living existence or hatching may take place within the host (*Strongyloides*). The early rhabditiform larvæ, resembling the adult *Rhabditis,* feed and undergo growth before they become nonfeeding, infective, filariform larvæ. In general the larva resembles the adult except for undeveloped sexual organs and certain larval characteristics that are subsequently lost. *Strongyloides* larvæ may develop into free-living adults and produce one or more generations before resuming their parasitic existence.

The larvæ that undergo a cyclic development in an intermediate host may have a brief free-living existence. The larvæ of the guinea worm, which are deposited

TABLE 24

LIFE CYCLES OF IMPORTANT NEMATODES OF MAN [1]

	Trichinella spiralis	Trichuris trichiura	Strongyloides stercoralis	Ancylostoma duodenale and Necator americanus	Ascaris lumbricoides	Dracunculus medinensis	Enterobius vermicularis
Definitive host	Man and carnivorous mammals	Man, monkey, lemur and hog	Man. Experimentally to dog, cat and ape	Man	Man and hog	Man, dog, cat and fur-bearing wild animals	Man
Intermediate host	Man and carnivorous mammals	None	None	None	None	Cyclops, twelve species	None
Ovum Shape		Barrel-shaped, semiopaque polar plugs	Ovoid with bluntly rounded ends	Ovoid with bluntly rounded ends	Broadly ovoid		Asymmetrical, one side convex, other side flattened
Size (micra) Mean		52 x 23	54 x 32	60 x 40	60 x 45		55 x 26
Range		50-54 x 22	50-58 x 30-34	56-60 x 34-40	45-70 x 35-50		50-60 x 20-32
Shell		Smooth, thick, transparent	Smooth, thin, transparent	Smooth, thin, transparent	Brown outer mammillate covering. Thick, transparent shell		Smooth, thin, transparent
Development on leaving host		Unsegmented	Larva	Incompletely embryonate	Unsegmented	Larva produced viviparously	Completely embryonate
Time of incubation after leaving host		20 to 40 days		Within 24 hours	10 to 15 days		Practically none

Rhabditiform larva Size (micra) at hatching	100 x 6	125 x 8	225 x 16	275 x 16	250 x 14	625 x 20	145 x 10
Characteristic morphology	Long, narrow esophagus, coiled, produced viviparously	Slight posterior bulbar swelling of cylindrical esophagus	Posterior bulbar swelling of esophagus, short preesophageal chamber in both direct and indirect developmental forms	Posterior bulbar swelling of esophagus, long, narrow preesophageal chamber	Posterior bulbar swelling of cylindrical esophagus	Slender; long filiform tail with pointed tip, thin walled esophagus with dilated lumen	Posterior bulbar swelling of esophagus
Free-living filariform larva Size (micra)			700 x 28	850 x 35			
Characteristic morphology			Minute fork at tail	Sharply pointed tail			
Invasion of host Infective stage	Encysted larva	Unhatched ovum containing rhabditiform larva	Filariform larva	Filariform larva	Unhatched ovum containing rhabditiform larva	Larva in Cyclops	Unhatched ovum containing rhabditiform larva
Site of entry	Intestine	Intestine	Skin	Skin	Intestine	Intestine	Intestine
Development	Direct	Direct	Indirect, to intestine via lymph, blood, lungs and glottis	Indirect, to intestine via lymph, blood, lungs and glottis	Indirect, to intestine via intestine, lymph, blood, lungs and glottis	Indirect, via lymph and blood to deep tissues and later to subcutaneous tissues	Direct
Minimal length of life cycle (weeks)	3	9	3	6	8	52	7

[1]Filarial parasites, see Chapter XXI.

in water, are ingested by *Cyclops* and reach man through drinking water. The filarial worms have no free-living existence, since the prerhabditiform microfilariæ are removed by a bloodsucking insect in which they undergo metamorphosis. The final, infective, postrhabditiform larvæ gain entrance into a new definitive host through the wound caused by the bite of the insect.

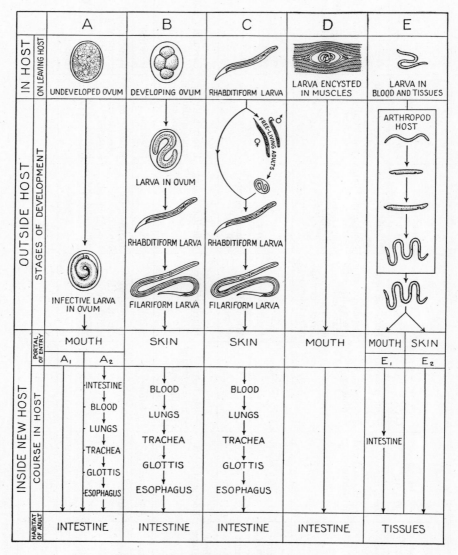

FIG. 66.—TYPICAL LIFE CYCLES OF IMPORTANT NEMATODES

A₁, *Enterobius vermicularis*, *Trichuris trichiura*; *A₂*, *Ascaris lumbricoides*; *B*, *Ancylostoma duodenale*, *Necator americanus*; *C*, *Strongyloides stercoralis*; *D*, *Trichinella spiralis*; *E₁*, *Dracunculus medinensis*; *E₂*, *Wuchereria bancrofti*, *W. malayi*, *Loa loa*, *Acanthocheilonema perstans*, *Onchocerca volvulus*.

Molts.—During larval development nematodes pass through several molts or ecdyses, and with the last molt become immature adults. At each molt a new cuticle is formed and the old is shed. Between molts certain morphological changes occur so that each ecdysis marks a definite transitional period of larval development. The early molts may take place within the eggshell (*Ascaris*), in the free-living larvæ (*Ancylostoma*), or in the intermediate host (filarial worms). The later molts may take place within the definitive host.

Invasion of Host.—The invasion of the host takes place through the intestinal tract and through the skin and mucous membranes (Fig. 66). In most cases the infective larvæ or ova are ingested in food, and become adults by direct and indirect methods of development. The larvæ may develop directly into adults in the intestinal tract (*Trichuris, Enterobius*). They may invade the mucosa, become encapsulated and later emerge as immature adults, which become attached to the intestinal epithelium (*Œsophagostomum*). They may burrow in the walls of the stomach or duodenum and thus migrate to the esophagus and oral cavity (*Gongylonema*). The encysted larvæ of *Trichinella* may be liberated by the digestive juices and develop directly into adult worms. The ingested ova of *Ascaris* hatch into larvæ that penetrate the intestinal wall, pass to the blood, lungs, trachea, and glottis, and after this circuitous route return to the intestinal tract, where they become adults. The infective larvæ of *Ancylostoma* and *Strongyloides* penetrate the skin and also follow an indirect route through the blood, lungs, trachea, and glottis to the intestinal tract. The migration of *Ascaris* larvæ is probably necessitated by the need of oxygen, since the intestine contains little or no free oxygen. However, the European dog hookworm, *Uncinaria stenocephala* and similar nematodes can develop directly in the intestine without preliminary pulmonary migration.[18]

Certain nematodes are parasites of various organs and tissues: *Wuchereria bancrofti* in the lymphatics, *Onchocerca volvulus* and *Dracunculus medinensis* in the subcutaneous tissues, and *Dioctophyme renale* in the kidney. Little is known concerning the route followed by the larvæ and immature worms in reaching these locations. The development of the larval and immature *Dracunculus medinensis* evidently takes place in the deep tissues of the body.

PATHOGENESIS

The effect of parasitic nematodes upon the host depends upon the species, the intensity of the infection and the location of the parasite. Species vary in their ability to produce mechanical or toxic damage and in their selective affinity for vital organs. The number of invading parasites may be sufficient to overcome the resistance of the host. The local reactions, produced by physical and chemical irritation, include inflammation, necrosis, repair and encapsulation as a result of foreign-body response and tissue-sensitization. General reactions occur directly from the absorption of toxic substances or from an allergic response to foreign proteins, and indirectly from nervous reflexes and injury to vital organs. Injury may be produced by both adult and larval parasites.

Nematode infections are believed to interfere with calcium and phosphorous metabolism [29] and to produce changes in blood morphology. In a study of the blood of infected children the erythrocytes were below normal in 18.9 per cent, the hemoglobin was decreased in 58.5 per cent, and leukocytosis was present in 35.9 per cent.[30] The chief alterations in the leukocytes were eosinophilia, neutropenia, and lymphocytosis.

Adult Intestinal Nematodes.—Intestinal parasites in general produce less local and systemic effects than tissue parasites. The local reactions result from irritation (*Ascaris, Enterobius*), invasion of the intestinal wall (*Strongyloides, Trichuris, Trichinella*), and occasionally accidental penetration to extraneous sites. The intestinal mucosa is damaged by biting and blood sucking (*Ancylostoma*), by lytic ferments secreted by the parasite (*Trichuris*), and by mechanical irritation. The general reactions are produced by loss of blood, absorption of toxins, nervous reflexes, and allergy from proteic sensitization.

Adult Tissue Nematodes.—Nematodes that invade the tissues provoke a foreign-body reaction, whereby they are surrounded by cellular and connective tissue infiltration and are either destroyed or encapsulated. The tissues may be injured by the physical and lytic activities of the parasite. Proteic sensitivity and reaction to toxins may produce local eosinophilia. The general effect depends upon the nature and location of the invaded tissues and upon the habits of the parasite: *Wuchereria bancrofti* blocks the lymph channels, *Onchocerca volvulus* produces subcutaneous nodules, *Loa loa* migrates in the subcutaneous tissues, and *Dioctophyme renale* invades the kidney. Dead worms often call forth a more pronounced tissue response than do the living parasites (*Wuchereria bancrofti*).

Larval Nematodes.—The larvæ of certain species during their invasion, migrations and development in the host produce local and general reactions. Penetration of the skin is primarily a mechanical phenomenon assisted by thigmotaxis (*Ancylostoma*) and lymphotaxis (*Wuchereria*). The degree of local reaction and associated general reaction depends upon the sensitiveness of the host to the proteic products of the parasite. The circuitous routes of migration of the larvæ of *Ascaris, Ancylostoma* and *Strongyloides* in the host result in damage to organs not affected by the adult parasite. The local reactions in the liver, lungs and other organs at times may destroy or encapsulate the larvæ. The degree of tissue damage depends upon the intensity of the infection, pneumonitis not infrequently resulting from heavy invasions of *Ascaris*. Likewise, infections may be caused in animals that are not normal hosts, the larvæ passing through their invasive stages with injury to the host but never becoming established as adult parasites (the creeping eruption of *Ancylostoma braziliense* and the dermatitis of *A. caninum*).

The larvæ of *Trichinella spiralis* are responsible for most of the damage caused by this parasite, man acting as the intermediate as well as the final host. The invasion of the muscles and other tissues produces an infiltrative reaction that ultimately results in the encapsulation of the larvæ. Microfilariæ migrate through the blood, lymph and tissues of the host, but except for the involvement of the eye (*Onchocerca volvulus*) cause no apparent injury.

---

[29] Stewart, J. and Shearer, G. D., 1933.　　[30] Gruber, L. I., 1930.

IMMUNITY

Immunity to nematodes may be demonstrated experimentally in a number of ways: (1) reduction in the number of worms that become established, (2) slower growth, (3) smaller size, (4) diminished output of ova, (5) reduction in the number and viability of encysted larvæ (*Trichinella*), (6) incomplete development of larvæ, (7) longer period of incubation, (8) shorter duration of infection, (9) fewer lesions, (10) reduced mortality, (11) evidence of local immunity, and (12) protection through passive immunization. Evidence of present or past infection may be shown by the presence of specific precipitins and other antibodies against the parasite and its products, by active and passive cutaneous supersensitiveness, and by the production of reactions in sensitized uterine strips of guinea pigs.

Resistance depends upon the preëxisting or acquired incompatibility of the host to the parasite and upon the toleration of its effects. Immunity is acquired through the invasion of the tissues by the parasite and its larvæ or through the absorption of its products, but is infrequently evident in purely intestinal species. In rats infected with *Nippostrongylus muris* it is manifest by the formation of detectable antibodies and is primarily humoral with more or less secondary cellular response.[31] The local formation of precipitates immobilizes the worms, retards their development and migration, and sometimes destroys them. These antigen-antibody combinations localize the irritating excretions and secretions of the worm and inhibit its physiological activities. The immobilized worms are surrounded by nodular inflammatory reactions with lymphocytes, monocytes, polymorphonuclears, eosinophils and often edema and hemorrhage. Dead worms are removed by the macrophages and giant cells. Eosinophils which appear late in the immune reaction, are probably associated with the detoxification of foreign proteins and form a barrier to absorption.

It is not clear how immunity acts to stunt growth and retard development. In addition to the localizing precipitates other humoral factors, such as antienzymes and reproduction-inhibiting antibodies, may also function. Local immunity may be considered a phase of general immunity and is basically identical in all organs, even though antibodies may not be demonstrable. Nevertheless, the view has been advanced that immunity to nematodes is of two types: (1) intestinal and (2) parenteral.[32] The former does not produce antibodies, but inhibits growth and reproduction by retarding the nutrition of the parasite through local antienzymes or precipitates.

GENERAL RESISTANCE

Species.—Nematodes differ in host-specificity, although host-distribution is frequently governed by habits and environment. Certain animals, however, exhibit a definite intolerance. Adult *Ascaris lumbricoides* will develop only in man, although its larval cycle may take place in other animals and even the morphologically and serologically similar porcine strain (*Ascaris suum*) will not develop to maturity in man.

---

[31] Taliaferro, W. H. and Sarles, M. P., 1939.   [32] Chandler, A. C., 1937.

Race.—Differences in resistance may be present in the Negro and the white race, but economic, social and hygienic conditions probably explain the higher percentage of nematode infections in Negro children. Negroes, however, show greater clinical toleration of hookworm infection than whites.

Age.—Age apparently increases resistance to nematode infection, but the underlying mechanism, involving nonspecific factors, is obscure. Experiments have demonstrated a greater resistance in old than in young animals: *Trichinella spiralis* in pigeons and dogs and *Capillaria hepatica* in rats (Chapter XV), *Strongyloides ratti* in rats (Chapter XVI), *Ancylostoma caninum* in dogs and *Ancylostoma braziliense* in cats (Chapter XVII), *Nippostrongylus muris* in rats and mice, and *Ascaridia lineata* in chickens (Chapter XIX). Local immunity against the larvæ of *Ancylostoma caninum* has been observed in the skin of old dogs, the reaction being more pronounced than in young animals with the retention or destruction of the larvæ.[33] Age-immunity against *Ascaridia lineata* in chickens and rats has been ascribed to the presence of goblet cells that secrete mucus inhibitory to this parasite and are found only in the older animals.[34] However, the complex factors that govern health, well-being and previous infection, may be sufficient to explain age-immunity.

Diet.—The effect of undernourishment in lowering resistance to nematode infection has been investigated by a number of workers. As a rule, experimental animals must be seriously affected by dietary deficiency before they show a significant lack of resistance. The resistance of man to *Necator americanus* is lowered by a poor diet, and conversely, infected children put on an adequate diet show a decrease in the ascarid and hookworm burden. A diet deficient in calcium and phosphorus diminishes the resistance of chickens to *Heterakis gallinæ* and, though normally resistant to *Syngamus trachealis,* they become susceptible to infection if the diet is deficient in calcium and vitamin A.[35] Loss of blood and iron deficiency render dogs more susceptible to *Ancylostoma caninum.*[36] The consensus is that vitamin A deficiency lowers resistance to *Trichinella spiralis*[37] and to most, but not all, ascarids.

ACQUIRED IMMUNITY

Most experimental studies on acquired immunity have been made with nematodes, the larvæ or adults of which are tissue-invaders. The acquisition of immunity by infection presumes injury to the host sufficient to evoke a reaction. Nematodes that do not invade the tissues or secrete absorbable products produce slight if any immunity. Previous infection with *Heterakis gallinæ,* a nontissue-invader of chickens, does not confer immunity, although resistance is acquired by rats against *H. spumosa,* a closely related species.[38] *Nippostrongylus muris,* a parasite of the rat, has been a favorite subject in studying the production of

[33] Sarles, M. P., 1929.
[34] Ackert, J. E., Edgar, S. A. and Frick, L. P., 1939.
[35] Clapham, P. A., 1934.
[36] Foster, H. O. and Cort, W. W., 1935.
[37] McCoy, O. R., 1934.
[38] Winfield, G. F., 1933; Clapham, P. A., 1934.

immunity by infection and by active and passive immunization.[39] Since the larvæ of this worm invade the skin and lungs and the adults cause inflammation of the intestinal villi, local and general phases of immunity may be followed.

Natural Infection.—In most instances resistance depends upon a preëxisting infection that protects against superinfection rather than on a residual immunity from a past infection. Immunity may completely or partially protect against reinfection; may limit the size, egg-laying capabilities and length of existence of the parasites; and may reduce the number of invading larvæ. Definite residual immunity has been observed in rats against *Strongyloides ratti* (Chapter XVI), but the two types are difficult to differentiate because of the persistence of the parasites. Constant reinfection tends to enhance immunity. Immunity to superinfection has been reported for *Trichinella spiralis* and *Capillaria hepatica* in rats (Chapter XV); *Ancylostoma caninum* in dogs, *Metastrongylus elongatus* in hogs and *Hæmonchus contortus* in sheep (Chapter XVII); *Ascaridia lineata* in chickens, *Toxocara cati* in cats and *Ascaris lumbricoides* in guinea pigs but not in hogs (Chapter XIX).

Active Immunity.—Variable success has attended attempts to immunize animals against nematodes by the injection of antigenic extracts of adult or larval worms. Success has been reported in guinea pigs and mice with *Ascaris lumbricoides* (Chapter XIX), in rats with *Strongyloides ratti* (Chapter XVI), and in rats with *Nippostrongylus muris*. Failure has been reported in mice with *Ancylostoma caninum* (Chapter XVII) and with *Trichinella spiralis* in rats and hogs with extracts, but success with intraäbdominal injections of dead larvæ (Chapter XV).

Passive Immunity.—Evidence for passive immunization is conflicting. Passive immunization of rats against *Nippostrongylus muris* has been interpreted as indicative that protection is dependent in part upon antibodies,[40] although previous investigations indicate that it is not effective.[41] The transfer of immune sera has no effect upon the larvæ of *Trichinella spiralis,* but reduces the number of adult worms and prolongs the life of the host (Chapter XV). It is effective in mice against *Ascaris lumbricoides* (Chapter XIX) but not against *Ancylostoma caninum* (Chapter XVII).

SUPERSENSITIVENESS

Supersensitiveness is a phase of immunity that represents the reaction of the host against the proteic products of the parasitic nematode. Its manifestations are both local and general. It may be a natural attribute of unsuitable hosts or may be acquired by infection or contact. Supersensitiveness may be demonstrated by cutaneous tests with antigens derived from the parasites and their products. In some nematodes such diagnostic tests are specific and in others represent group-reactions for allied species, for example, *Ascaris* (Chapter XIX) and the filarial worms (Chapter XXI).

---

[39] Chandler, A. C., 1932, 1935, 1936, 1937, 1938; Taliaferro, W. H. and Sarles, M. P., 1936, 1937, 1938.

[40] Sarles, M. P. and Taliaferro, W. H., 1936.

[41] Chandler, A. C., 1934, 1935.

REFERENCES

Chitwood, B. G., and Chitwood, M. B. An Introduction to Nematology, Sec. I Part I, 1937, Washington, D. C. Sec. I Parts II and III, Sec. II Part I, 1938, Babylon, N. Y.

Culbertson, J. T. Recent Contributions to the Immunology of Helminthic Infections, Arch. Path., 1938, 25 :85, 256.

———— Immunity Against Animal Parasites, Columbia Univ. Press, New York, 1941, pp. 274.

McCoy, O. R. The Physiology of the Helminth Parasites, Physiol. Rev., 1935, 15 :221.

Taliaferro, W. H. and Sarles, M. P. The Cellular Reactions in the Skin, Lungs and Intestine of Normal and Immune Rats after Infection with *Nippostrongylus muris*, J. Infect. Dis., 1939, 64 :157.

Chapter XV

THE SUPERFAMILIES TRICHINELLOIDEA AND DIOCTOPHYMOIDEA

SUPERFAMILY *TRICHINELLOIDEA* HALL, 1916

The members of the superfamily TRICHINELLOIDEA have a more or less filiform anterior and a broader posterior portion. The posterior part of the esophagus has a thin musculature and is partially surrounded by a column of gland cells. The caudal end of the female is bluntly rounded, while that of the male is curved and bears either a single spicule or none at all. The female has a single ovary and the vulva is situated near the level of the base of the esophagus.

FAMILY *TRICHINELLIDÆ* WARD, 1907

The males possess no spicule or sheath; the females are viviparous. The adults inhabit the intestine and the larvæ the muscles of mammals. One species, *Trichinella spiralis,* is a parasite of man.

Trichinella spiralis (OWEN, 1835) RAILLIET, 1895

Synonyms.—*Trichina spiralis* Owen, 1835; *Trichina spiralis hominis* Kraemer, 1853.

Disease.—Trichinosis, trichiniasis, trichinelliasis.

History.—Trichinosis is probably an ancient disease, although authenic records are lacking. The encysted larval worm in man was first noted in Germany by Tiedemann in 1822 and later in England by Peacock in 1828 and by Hilton in 1833. The larval worm, dissected by Paget, was described in 1835 by Owen who named it *Trichina spiralis.* Other cases of human infection were soon reported in England, Europe and North America. In 1846 Leidy in Philadelphia observed the larval worm in pork. Feeding experiments by Leuckart in 1855 and by Virchow in 1859 established the fact that the viviparous larva reached maturity within a few days in the intestine of experimental animals.

The worm, however, was regarded as merely commensal in man until Zenker in 1860 demonstrated its association with disease following ingestion of infected pork. He described the symptoms, lesions and the adult worms in a young girl who died in Dresden, supposedly of typhoid fever. German investigators from 1881 to 1889 uncovered numerous cases of trichinosis, many occurring in epidemic form. The subsequent exclusion of American pork from the German market resulted in its microscopical examination by the United States government, a practice now discontinued.

Geographical Distribution.—Cosmopolitan, except in the Philippines, Puerto Rico and Australia. Trichinosis is particularly prevalent where pork is eaten raw or insufficiently cooked. It occurs frequently in the Northern Hemisphere and less frequently in the tropics. It is common in Europe and in the United States, but is comparatively rare in Africa and South America.

BIOLOGICAL CHARACTERISTICS

Morphology.—The adult is a small worm with a slender anterior end. The male (Fig. 67B) is from 1.4 to 1.5 mm. long and 0.045 mm. broad. The exit of the cloaca is at the extreme posterior end between two lobular caudal appendages which serve during copulation (Fig. 67E). The female (Fig. 67A) is from 3 to 4 mm. long and 0.06 mm. broad. The vulva (Fig. 67G) is in the anterior fifth of the body, and a single ovary is near the caudal end. The small terminal mouth is orbicular and nonpapillate (Fig. 67C). The larva (Fig. 67F) with a spear-like burrowing tip at its tapering anterior end measures 90 to 100 μ at birth and grows but little until it has entered a muscle fiber where it attains a maximal length of 1 mm. The encapsulated larva has a digestive tract similar to that of the adult, and while the reproductive organs are not fully developed, it is often possible to differentiate the sexes.

Physiology.—The adult worm, attached to or buried in the mucosa of the duodenum or jejunum, feeds on the intestinal contents and possibly derives additional nourishment from the intestinal mucosa. The male dies shortly after copulation. The female is viviparous.

LIFE CYCLE

Trichinella spiralis is found in man, hogs, rats, bears, wild boars, dogs, and cats. The same animal acts as final and intermediate host, harboring the adult parasite temporarily and the larva for long periods. In order to complete the life cycle flesh containing the encysted larvæ must be ingested by another host (Fig. 70). Most animals may be experimentally infected; but although birds and poikilothermal animals may harbor the adult worm, the embryos do not encyst in the muscles.

The larvæ require a minimal development of at least 16 days to become infective.[1] When infected larvæ are ingested by man, they pass to the small intestine where the capsules are dissolved and the larvæ released in a few hours by the action of the digestive juices. The young larvæ attach themselves to or invade the intestinal mucosa.[2] The sexes may be differentiated in 18 to 24 hours.[3] Within two days the worms reach sexual maturity and mate in the small intestine, when the female worm is about half its maximal size. In rats the female worms grow more rapidly than the males and undergo four moults, two before copulation and two after, while the males undergo three ecdyses before copulation.[4] The worms are most numerous in the lower part of the small intestine.[5] After fertilization the male

[1] Trawinski, A. and Maternowska, I., 1934.
[2] Heller, M., 1933.
[3] Geller, M., 1934.
[4] Kreis, H. A., 1937.
[5] Roth, H., 1938.

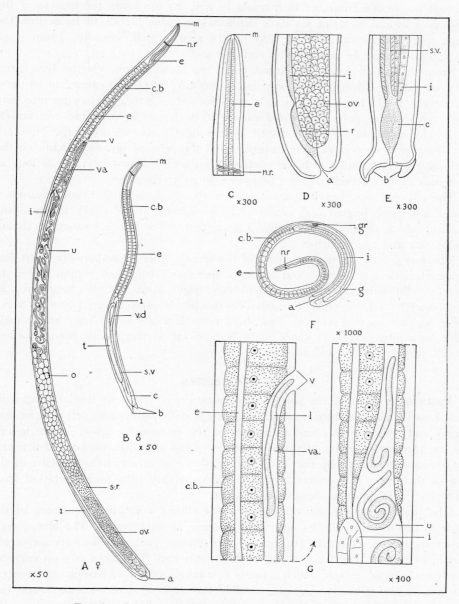

FIG. 67.—SCHEMATIC REPRESENTATION OF *Trichinella spiralis*

A, adult female; *B*, adult male; *C*, anterior end of worm; *D*, posterior end of female; *E*, posterior end of male; *F*, young larval worm; *G*, region of vagina and uterus.

a, anus; *b*, bursa; *c*, cloaca; *c.b.*, cell bodies; *e*, esophagus; *g*, gonads (anlage); *gr.*, granules; *i*, intestine; *l*, larva; *m*, mouth; *n.r.*, nerve ring; *o*, ova; *ov.* ovary; *r*, rectum; *s.r.* seminal receptacle; *s.v.*, seminal vesicle; *t*, testis; *u*, uterus; *v*, vulva; *va.*, vagina; *v.d.*, va deferens (*A* to *E* and *G* compiled from various sources, *F*, adapted from Leuckart, 1868).

dies and the female continues to increase in size, burrows into the mucosa of the intestinal villi and in about six days deposits successive broods of larvæ into the lymph spaces. Occasionally larvæ may be liberated into the intestine. From 1,350 to 1,500 larvæ may be produced by each female.[6]

From the lymph spaces the larvæ enter the blood stream via the lymphatics and after passing through the hepatic and pulmonary filters are carried to all parts of the body. In the blood they are most numerous from 8 to 25 days after infection. They can develop only in striated muscle. The larvæ burrow into the muscle bundles by means of the spear-shaped apparatus at their anterior ends. They are first observed 8 or 9 days after infection, and the peak of invasion occurs on the tenth day. The migration of larvæ continues but with lessened intensity as long as the female worms remain alive, a period of 30 to 37 days.[5]

The muscles most heavily parasitized are the diaphragmatic, masseteric, intercostal, laryngeal, lingual and ocular. Cardiac muscle is relatively immune and invading larvæ develop abnormally. Larvæ that enter the nonmuscular tissues disintegrate and are absorbed.

The larva, lying in the long axis of the muscle fiber grows rapidly, assuming a characteristic spiral shape and attains a maximum length of 1 mm. within 16 days. An ellipsoidal capsule of sarcolemmous origin, about 0.5 mm. long and 0.25 mm. broad with blunt ends, is formed about the coiled worm in 15 to 20 days.[7] The cysts may contain one and sometimes more than one larva. They may remain viable for a long period, 11 years in the hog and 31 in man having been recorded, but ultimately undergo calcification.

PATHOGENESIS

Pathology.—During the period of invasion the activities of the larvæ and the adult females may produce a catarrhal enteritis with congestion, petechial hemorrhages and even necrosis and ulceration of the intestinal mucosa. These lesions and the accompanying symptoms of gastro-intestinal irritation, edema and urticaria are presumably caused by the direct action of the worms and the reaction of the host to their proteic products, although the possibility of a toxic secretion from the cysts or worms has been suggested.

The pathology of trichinosis is concerned chiefly with the encystment of the larvæ in the striated muscles and their presence in vital organs. The larvæ, most numerous in the tendinous portions of the muscle, grow at the expense of the muscle fiber until they reach a size of 0.8 to 1.0 mm. The larva is soon enclosed in a lemon-shaped capsule which consists of a tough mantle of basophilic degenerative muscle and a hyaline capsule, possibly the expression of an antigen-antibody reaction.[8] At first there is an acute inflammatory cellular infiltration about the parasitized muscle fiber with swelling of the adjacent muscle fibers (Figs. 68A and 69). The invaded muscle fiber shows the following degenerative changes: a granular appearance, a swollen spindle shape, an increase in the size and number of nuclei, and the disappearance of striations. The metabolism of the infected

---

6 Roth, H., 1939.   8 Kalwaryjski, B. E., 1939.
7 Topolansky, A., 1930.

muscle is somewhat altered, with a decrease in glycogen and an increase in protein and lactic acid.

As the capsule enlarges, the muscle fibers surrounding the larva are gradually replaced by connective tissue. The mesenchymal cells of young granulation tissue

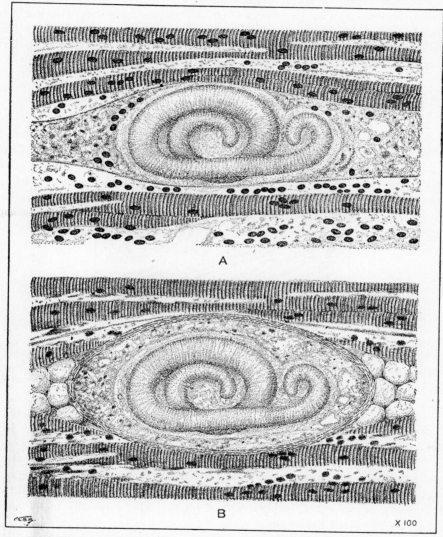

Fig. 68.—Schematic Representation of Encysted Larva of *Trichinella spiralis* in Muscle
A, early stage of encystment; *B*, encysted larva with fat globules at poles of cyst.

at the poles of the capsule become infiltrated with fat and are transformed into fat globules (Fig. 68B). At times there is an infiltration of foreign-body giant cells within the capsule. Calcification, which may begin as early as six months, ordinarily starts at the poles and proceeds toward the center. Usually the capsule calcifies first, but at times there may be primary impregnation of the larvæ which appear as small, rounded, irregularly calcified forms. Newly formed cysts are invisible to the naked eye, but when calcified they appear as fine opaque granules.

During the period of larval migration the myocardium shows focal areas of interstitial infiltration with lymphocytes, eosinophils and polymorphonuclears, and at times fragmentation of the muscle fibers, fatty degeneration and necrosis.[9] These lesions are the result of a residual nonspecific reaction to the migrating larvæ and account for the cardiac symptoms observed in trichinosis.

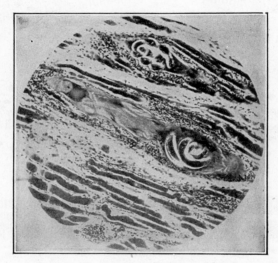

FIG. 69.—LARVAL *Trichinella* IN MUSCLE

Early stage of encystment showing acute inflammatory reaction around parasitized muscle fibers (After Hemmert-Halsweck, from Hegner, Root, Augustine and Huff, *Parasitology*, 1938, D. Appleton-Century Company).

Lesions of the central nervous system are fairly common. There may be an acute nonsuppurative leptomeningitis. The larvæ have been found in the spinal fluid.[10] The changes in the brain are: (1) granulomatous nodules which are apparently reactions around the parasite and are most numerous in the basal ganglia, medulla, and cerebellum; (2) presence of parasites; (3) perivascular infiltration of fibroblasts, granulocytes, leukocytes, and plasma cells, especially in the cortex; and (4) a generalized hyperemia.[11]

The eyes frequently exhibit a characteristic chemosis of the bulbar conjunctiva with round-cell infiltration, necrosis, edema, and accumulations in the periphery of

[9] Zoller, H., 1927; Horlick, S. S. and Bicknell, R. E., 1929; Dunlap, G. L. and Weller, C. V., 1933; Spink, W. W., 1935; Gordon, M. B., Cares, R. and Kaufman, B., 1935.

[10] Horlick, S. S. and Bicknell, R. E., 1929; Blumer, G., 1936.

[11] Hassin, G. B. and Diamond, I. B., 1926; Pund, E. R. and Mosteller, R., 1934; Most, H. and Abeles, M. M., 1937.

the retina, and encapsulated larvæ in the eye muscles.[12] In the choroid there is a marked accumulation of leukocytes and a proliferation of the endothelial cells of the capillary walls, which frequently are thickened, hyalinized and dilated. The larvæ may invade the lungs, pleura, pancreas, gallbladder, kidney, and other organs, producing local inflammation and edema. The heart, kidneys and liver may show fatty degeneration. There may be hyperplasia of the bone marrow with an increase in eosinophils.

Symptomatology.—Because of the involvement of many organs the protean symptoms of trichinosis resemble those of some fifty other diseases.[13] Five factors determine the variability of clinical symptoms: (1) the number of worms; (2) the size and age of the patient; (3) the tissues invaded; (4) the general resistance of the patient; and (5) the presence of concomitant pathological conditions. A distinction should be made between zoological and clinical infection. The number of invading larvæ necessary to produce clinical symptoms can only be approximated, since no data on subclinical infections, other than the surprisingly high incidence of encysted larvæ at autopsies, are available and since the manifestations accompanying these subclinical infections are unknown. It has been estimated that 100 larvæ per gram of muscle will not produce symptoms, but that 1,000 larvæ will.[13] These figures, however, are of doubtful significance, since accurate determinations are impossible and symptoms often are not correlated with the number of larvæ. Some individuals are more resistant than others because of physical vigor and a general immunity to parasitic infections.

The severity of the disease depends upon the number of parasites and the invasion of vital organs or those previously weakened by disease. Death may occur in intense infections or in persons whose resistance is low because of preëxistent weakness in vital organs. In overwhelming infections it may take place in the second or third week but more often it occurs from the fourth to the eighth week from exhaustion, pneumonia or cardiac failure. In epidemics the mortality may be as high as 30 per cent.

Trichinosis follows no typical course, recovery is slow and the predominating symptoms, referable to the organs affected, vary in different individuals. In order of prevalence they include: muscular pains and tenderness, edema of the eyelids, gastro-intestinal symptoms, conjunctival signs, edema, fever, and respiratory manifestations.

The disease is commonly divided into three clinical phases corresponding to the periods of (1) invasion, (2) migration of larvæ, and (3) encystment and repair. During the period of invasion the excysted larvæ and adult worms may produce symptoms of gastro-intestinal irritation and intoxication: nausea, vomiting and a severe watery diarrhea. Fever, profuse sweating, rapid cardiac and respiratory rates, edema of the face, and urticarial manifestations may also occur. At the start of migration, some seven days after infection, the previous symptoms recur from the toxic effect of the larvæ; many embryos and some adults may be found in the stools, and the larvæ are present in the blood. The fever (101 to 105° F.)

---

[12] Key, B. W., 1928; Stoll, H. F., 1929; Carter, L. F., 1930. [13] Hall, M. C., 1937.

is typhoidal in type; there is edema of the face and eyelids, headache, and sometimes delirium. Respiratory, ocular, and cardiac symptoms and more rarely a maculopapular erythema may appear. The second stage usually lasts from 7 to 14 days, but because of the continuous production of larvæ the symptoms of the second and third stages overlap so as to produce a confused clinical picture. Later, when the muscles are invaded, a marked interstitial myositis is established, producing rheumatoid symptoms with muscle tenderness and spasm. The symptoms, which vary with the muscles and organs invaded, include fever, muscle pains and tenderness from the exudative infiltration of the muscle fibers, edema, cachexia, and prostration.

The cardiac symptoms that arise from the pathological changes produced by the larvæ in the myocardium during their migration are usually transient. They are a feeble or dicrotic pulse, muffled heart sounds, an apical systolic murmur, and palpitation. The electrocardiogram shows evidence of myocardial damage by the slurring of the peak of the I.R.S. complex, premature contractions and prolongation of the P-R interval and alterations in the T waves.[14]

Symptoms occasioned by the involvement of the central nervous system are those of encephalitis: drowsiness, headache, nausea and vomiting, fever, mental confusion, disorientation, apathy, stupor, delirium, paralysis, muscular hypertonicity, diminished deep reflexes and coma.[15] The pulmonary symptoms are those of pulmonary edema: blood-stained sputum, dyspnea, persistent cough, hoarseness and chest pains.[16] The characteristic features of ocular involvement, which occur early in over one-third of all patients, are edema of the orbit and conjunctiva, chemosis of the bulbar conjunctiva with photophobia, blurred vision and diplopia, hemorrhage in the sclera and retina, and pain on pressure or on movement of the eyes.[17]

The leukocyte count may range from 4,000 to 34,000 but is usually from 7,000 to 17,000 and is increased during the acute stage of the disease.[18] Eosinophilia, which appears about the fourteenth day, is a characteristic finding. It ordinarily runs from 15 to 50 per cent, but may be as high as 89 per cent. The actual and relative number of eosinophils fluctuates widely in the same patient during the course of the infection and apparently is not correlated with the severity of the disease. The eosinophilia may be low, particularly with concomitant bacterial infections, and it may appear early or late. It persists as long as antibodies are present, a 2 to 7 per cent eosinophilia having been found from four to seven years after the disappearance of clinical symptoms.[19]

Immunity.—Immunity against *Trichinella spiralis* is both natural and acquired. Natural resistance depends upon the species, age and nutrition of the host. Adult

[14] Blumer, G., 1936; Cushing, E. H., 1936; Beecher, C. R. and Amidon, E. L., 1938.

[15] Horlick, S. S. and Bicknell, R. E., 1929; Gordon, M. B., Cares, R. and Kaufman, B., 1935; Spink, W. W., 1935; Blumer, G., 1936; Most, H. and Abeles, M. M., 1937.

[16] Goldwater, L. J., Steinberg, I., Most, H. and Connery, J. E., 1935; Spink, W. W. and Augustine, D. L., 1935.

[17] Key, B. W., 1928; Stoll, H. F., 1929; Carter, L. F., 1930; Spink, W. W. and Augustine, D. L., 1935.

[18] Spink, W. W. and Augustine, D. L., 1935.

[19] Theiler, H., Augustine, D. L. and Spink, W. W., 1935.

worms will develop in both young and old pigeons; but larvæ will only invade the muscles of the young birds, and the number of adult worms resulting from the same test-feeding is greater in young than old dogs.[20] Intensity of infection may break down the natural resistance of experimental animals; in light infections the adult worms remain only 15 days in the intestine and in heavy infections from 4 to 6 weeks.[21] Vitamin A deficiency lowers the resistance of rats so that the adult worms remain longer in the intestine, the encysted larvæ are larger and the animals fail to develop immunity against a second infection.[22]

Natural infection confers an immunity which is dependent upon the presence of the parasite or its products in the host. Humoral immunity is evidenced by the production of precipitative and alexin-fixative antibodies. The resistance of hogs to superinfection is due to local retention of antibodies, supplemented by the action of leukocytes and cells of the reticulo-endothelial system.[23]

Animal experiments indicate that previous infection gives more or less protection against superinfection. Sublethal feedings of larvæ have protected rats against test-feedings lethal for control rats, but variable results have been obtained with monkeys.[24] The previously infected rats had a smaller number of adult worms (1/10) and a noticeably smaller number of encysted larvæ (1/220) than the controls. The duration of acquired immunity and the effect of continuous reinfection is unknown, but it probably persists as long as antibodies are present, positive cutaneous and precipitative tests constituting presumptive evidence of an existing infection.[19]

The artificial production of active immunity has been unsatisfactory. Injections of powdered *Trichinella* failed to immunize hogs and rats.[25] Rats, injected intra-abdominally with dead or living larvæ, developed a slight immunity as evidenced by the smaller number and shorter stay of the adult worms in the intestine.[26] The feeding of metabolic products obtained by treating trichinous meat with gastric juice, induced some immunity in rats, rabbits and guinea pigs.[27]

The transfer of passive immunity has no effect upon the encysted larvæ, but tends to reduce the number of adult worms and to prolong the life of the host. The serum of infected rabbits, when injected into mice, reduced by one-half the number of mature worms that developed in control animals receiving the same test-feeding, but had no effect upon the larvæ of the surviving worms.[28] Immune rabbit serum administered 10 days after rats had fed on lethal doses of infective larvæ prolonged life but had no effect upon the production of larvæ.[29]

DIAGNOSIS, PROGNOSIS AND TREATMENT

Diagnosis.—The clinical differentiation of trichinosis from other diseases is difficult. The symptoms simulate those of many diseases and the typical clinical

[20] Matoff, K., 1936, 1937.

[21] McCoy, O. R., 1932.

[22] McCoy, O. R., 1934.

[23] Bachman, G. W. and Rodríguez-Molina, R., 1933.

[24] McCoy, O. R., 1931, 1932; Bachman, G. W. and Gonzalez, J. O., 1936.

[25] Bachman, G. W. and Rodríguez-Molina, R., 1933; Bachman, G. W. and Gonzalez, J. O., 1936.

[26] McCoy, O. R., 1935.

[27] Spindler, L. A., 1937.

[28] Culbertson, J. T. and Kaplan, S. S., 1937.

[29] Trawinski, A., 1935.

picture of gastro-intestinal disturbances, eosinophilia, suborbital edema, fever, and myositis, either may not be present or may be overshadowed by symptoms referable to cardiac, pulmonary, ocular and meningeal involvement. The elusive gastro-intestinal symptoms may be confused with other intestinal disorders. The temperature curve may suggest enteric fever; the myositis, rheumatic fever; the edema, angioneurotic edema, beri beri or nephritis; and the wide range of tissue-damage, diseases of the heart, lungs, eyes, central nervous system and kidneys. Clinical diagnosis is established by the history of eating pork, the existence usually of more than one case, eosinophilia, myositis and differentiation from the diseases mentioned above.

The several methods of laboratory diagnosis include: (1) examination of the blood for eosinophilia; (2) the detection of adult worms in the feces and larvæ in the blood and spinal fluid; (3) the biopsy of muscles for encysted larvæ; (4) the precipitative test; and (5) the intracutaneous test. Eosinophilia furnishes only presumptive evidence, since it may be present in other helminthic infections and in pulmonary and cutaneous conditions. It tends, however, to be more pronounced in trichinosis. Adult worms are rarely found in the feces. Detection of the migrating larvæ in dehemoglobinized centrifuged blood is seldom successful because of the small number present and the brief migratory period. Larvæ do not invade the spinal fluid often enough to warrant lumbar puncture as a routine.

Biopsy of the deltoid, biceps or gastrocnemius offers the most specific means of diagnosis. The excised muscle is either subjected to direct microscopic examination or is digested with gastric juice in order to concentrate the larvæ. This procedure is useless in the early stages, disclosing the larvæ in only about one-half of the cases, and moreover it is painful for the patient.

The intracutaneous and precipitative tests are the most satisfactory diagnostic procedures, especially in mild or atypical infections and are particularly useful if the reaction is at first negative and later positive. They depend upon the presence of fixed and circulating antibodies which react with antigens prepared by digesting infected muscles (Section **VII**, IX, 18). A positive intracutaneous test confirmed by a precipitative test furnishes fairly conclusive evidence of infection. It is important, however, to remember that these tests are not infallible and that they are of no value in the early stages of the disease when diagnosis is most important. Diagnosis should not be based on a single intracutaneous or precipitative test without taking into consideration the clinical symptoms.[30] The standardization of the antigen and the interpretation of the reaction require further investigation, since the varied results of different workers seem to be due largely to the potency and dilution of the antigen.

The accepted standard for the intracutaneous test is the immediate reaction (Section **VII**, X, 1). It becomes positive 11 to 14 days after infection and persists at least seven years after clinical recovery.[31] Practically all workers agree that it has diagnostic value, especially when supplemented by the precipitative

[30] Bozicevich, J., 1938.
[31] Augustine, D. L. and Theiler, H., 1932; McCoy, O. R., Miller, J. J., Jr. and Fried-lander, R. D., 1933; Spink, W. W. and Augustine, D. L., 1935.

test, but opinions differ as to its specificity. Some have found it inferior to other diagnostic methods.[32] A negative test is of greater diagnostic significance than a positive, since the test is negative in only 10 per cent of trichinous persons and positive reactions are occasionally found in noninfected previously sensitized individuals.[33]

The precipitative test becomes positive during the fourth week of the disease, later than the intracutaneous test, and remains positive for at least a year.[18] Most investigators consider that the test is generally specific: positive reactions are obtained with a 1:100 dilution of the antigen after the fourth week in all trichinous patients;[34] the sera of trichinous patients do not react with *Ascaris* and *Echinococcus* antigens;[1] positive reactions with 1:5,000 and 1:10,000 dilutions of antigen are more specific than those of 1:100 and 1:1,000; nonspecific reactions occur but a positive reaction with a 1:2,500 dilution of the antigen is specific in 90 per cent of trichinous patients.[35] The test is also specific for infected hogs.[36] Pseudo-positive reactions have been observed in malarial patients under quinine treatment.[37] Some investigators question the diagnostic value of the test.[38]

Prognosis.—Prognosis, though unfavorable in severe infections, is normally good. If the patient survives the first month of the acute illness, he will recover slowly and show no residual ill-effects from the encysted larvæ.

Treatment.—Treatment is mechanical (purgation), biological (serum) and chemotherapeutic.[39] On early diagnosis attempts may be made to expel the immature and adult worms by purgation and anthelmintic drugs. Convalescent serum inhibits the development of the parasites but is not parasiticidal and is of value only before the worms have matured. Diagnosis, however, is seldom made until several weeks after infection when the larvæ are already invading the muscles.

Medical treatment is largely palliative, symptomatic and supportive, since treatment directed against the circulating and encysting larvæ and the imbedded females is ineffective. Arsenical and antimony preparations are usually of no value and perhaps dangerous. The effectiveness of sulfanilamide is questionable.[40] Subcutaneous injections of thymol carvasept in olive oil or gum arabic and the oral administration of butolan (carbonic acid ester of p-oxy-diphenyl-methane) are reported to destroy some of the adult worms in experimental animals, thus diminishing the number of encysting larvæ.[39] Attempts have been made to hasten the calcification of encysted larvæ in animals by administering parathormone, calcium gluconate, calcium lactate, viosterol, irradiated ergosterol, and substances containing vitamin D, but the results have been negative or too slight to offset the danger of producing calcification elsewhere in the body.[41]

[32] Kilduffe, D. A., 1933; Heathman, L. S., 1936; Kaljus, W. A., 1936.

[33] McCoy, O. R., Miller, J. J., Jr. and Friedlander, R. D., 1933; Kaljus, W. A., 1936.

[34] Augustine, D. L. and Theiler, H., 1932; Augustine, D. L., 1937.

[35] Bachman, G. W., Rodríguez-Molina, R. and Gonzalez, J. O., 1934.

[36] Augustine, D. L. and Theiler, H., 1935; Trawinski, A., 1934.

[37] Augustine, D. L. and Theiler, H., 1932.

[38] Heathman, L. S., 1936.

[39] van Someren, V. D., 1939.

[40] McCoy, O. R., 1938; McNaught, J. B., Beard, R. R. and Deeds, F., 1939.

[41] Greenwood, D. N., 1935; von Brand, T., Otto, G. F. and Abrams, E., 1938; Wantland, W. W., 1938; van Someren, V. D., 1939.

PREVENTION

Epidemiology.—Trichinous infection in the United States of America is surprisingly high and in recent years has steadily increased. Postmortem examinations of 3,322 individuals revealed an incidence of 12.34 per cent,[42] and 3,000 autopsies in 16 Washington and U. S. naval and marine hospitals, 16.3 per cent.[43] The U. S. Public Health Service reports 4,543 cases from 1842 to 1938.[44] The decrease in the mortality rate from 15.4 per cent in the period from 1842 to 1914 to 4.4 per cent in the ten years from 1926 to 1936 indicates that more atypical cases are being recognized and that more mild cases are being produced, possibly by the dilution of infectious material in the large packing houses. The fact that the presence of one male and two females is always sufficient to infect guinea pigs suggests a possible explanation of the many light infections in man.[5]

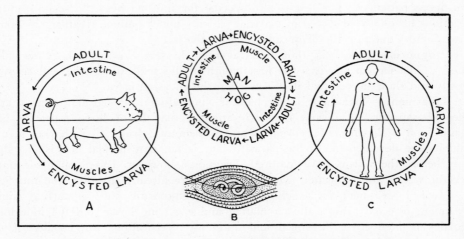

Fig. 70.—Life Cycle and Transmission of *Trichinella spiralis*

A, hog, with trichinosis; *B,* encysted larva in muscles of hog; *C,* man infected by eating trichinous pork.

The incidence is high in the North Atlantic States and is generally low in the southern and midwestern states. Trichinosis shows seasonal fluctuations, reaching its peak during the winter months when there is greater consumption of pork. A high rate is found at autopsy in the older age-groups, and a relatively low rate in the younger age-groups and in Negroes.[42]

The disease is acquired by man from hogs (Fig. 70), the incidence of severe trichinosis in garbage-fed animals being three to five times as great as in grain-fed.[13] In the areas of highest incidence there is a heavy consumption of garbage-fed hogs. Isolated instances of infection from bear meat have been reported. Hogs become infected chiefly from eating uncooked meat scraps in refuse from slaughter houses, markets and private homes. Occasionally they may eat infected rats. Rats

[42] Hall, M. C., 1938.
[43] Kerr, K. B., Jacobs, L. and Cuvillier, E.,
1941.
[44] Sawitz, W., 1938.

acquire the infection by eating garbage and discarded offal from slaughter houses and by eating each other, while the larger carnivora become diseased from feeding on rodents or meat scraps.

Prenatal transmission of trichinosis probably does not occur in man. The transmission of *Trichinella spiralis* from an infected mother to the fetus has not been demonstrated in rats, rabbits, hogs and man,[45] but it has been observed in guinea pigs.[46]

Prophylaxis.—The ultimate eradication of trichinosis in man requires elimination of the infection in hogs. This can be accomplished by abolishing the practice of garbage-feeding, by the sterilization of garbage containing raw meat scraps, and by improving the sanitation of piggeries and slaughter houses to reduce such minor channels of infection as diseased rats. There is sufficient evidence to indicate that universal sterilization of garbage and offal would soon render porcine infection negligible. Until this goal is achieved, the prevention of human trichinosis is dependent upon (1) the inspection of hogs in slaughter and packing houses; (2) proper curing and refrigeration of pork products; (3) thorough cooking of pork; and (4) education of the public.

Federal inspection of slaughter houses in the United States of America deals chiefly with sanitation, rat reduction and disposal of offal, and does not include inspection of the numerous small establishments serving only intrastate markets. The microscopical examination of pork for *Trichinella* larvæ, once considered an important procedure, is no longer included in the federal inspection. Statistics indicate that it is not a safeguard, since one-third of the cases of human trichinosis occurring in Germany between 1881 and 1898 were traced to inspected pork.[47]

The curing of pork products tends to reduce parasites by desiccation, but the ordinary methods of salting and smoking are ineffective. Treatment with salt for 40 days at not lower than 2° C. followed by smoking at 45° C. for 10 days for hams, and holding at 7° C. for 25 days for sausage and bologna is recommended.[48] However, refrigeration at temperatures below −18° C. for several days or 20 days at −15° C. is a more adequate safeguard, since larvæ in pork are destroyed when held from 24 to 48 hours at −18° C.[49]

The chief safeguard for the consumer is thorough cooking of pork. The thermal death point of the larvæ is between 62 and 72° C., but their infectivity is reduced by one hour's exposure at 50° C.[50] Pork products that are eaten raw or semi-raw should be prepared from grain-fed hogs in packing houses under government inspection. The general public should be informed of the danger of trichinosis, its method of transmission, and the necessity for thoroughly cooking pork.

FAMILY *TRICHURIDÆ* RAILLIET, 1915

The males possess a copulatory sheath and usually one spicule. The females are oviparous and the ova are lemon-shaped with polar plugs. The adults are parasites of

[45] Augustine, D. L., 1934.
[46] Roth, H., 1936.
[47] Ransom, B. H., 1915.
[48] Ransom, B. H., 1920.

[49] Augustine, D. L., 1933; Blair, J. B. and Lang, O. W., 1934.
[50] Otto, G. F. and Abrams, E., 1939.

mammals and birds. Two species: *Trichuris trichiura* and *Capillaria hepatica,* are parasites of man.

Trichuris trichiura (LINNÆUS, 1771) STILES, 1901

Synonyms.—*Trichocephalus dispar,* Rudolphi, 1802; *Trichocephalus trichiurus* (Linnæus, 1771) Blanchard, 1895.

Disease.—Trichuriasis, trichocephaliasis, whipworm infection.

History.—The whipworm was described under the genus *Trichuris* in Germany in 1761 by Roederer, who believed that the filiform anterior end was the tail. Goeze in 1782 placed the worm in the genus *Trichocephalus.*

Geographical Distribution.—Cosmopolitan, although most abundant in warm, moist regions.

BIOLOGICAL CHARACTERISTICS

Morphology.—The body of the pinkish-gray adult worm is divided into an attenuate, whip-like anterior three-fifths, and a more robust posterior two-fifths. A spearlike projection (Fig. 71C) at its anterior extremity enables the worm to penetrate and anchor itself to the intestinal mucosa. The mouth leads into a narrow esophagus which resembles a string of beads in its course through the slender portion of the worm. The intestine is a straight tube through the fleshy portion with the anal opening at the extreme posterior end of the worm. The male (Fig. 71B), from 30 to 45 mm. in length, is distinguished from the female by its coiled caudal extremity. At its bulbous posterior end a single spicule, 2.5 mm. in length, protrudes through a retractile sheath set with terminal recurved spines (Fig. 71D). The genitalia comprise a sacculate testis, a vas deferens that curves abruptly to descend to the cloacal region, and an ejaculatory tubule, the cirrus. The female (Fig. 71A), from 35 to 50 mm. in length, has a bluntly rounded posterior extremity. The ovary, a sacculate organ in the posterior fifth of the worm, narrows posteriorly to merge with the coiled oviduct. The latter, near the posterior end of the worm, curves forward to enter the uterus, which in turn forms a narrow serpentine canal as it approaches the vulva. The vulvar opening is at the anterior end of the fleshy portion of the body.

Physiology.—The parasite maintains its position by imbedding the anterior portion in the intestinal tissues of the host, whence it derives its sustenance.

LIFE CYCLE

Man is the principal host of *Trichuris trichiura,* but it has also been reported in monkeys, lemurs and hogs. The closely related species in animals include *T. vulpis* in the dog and wolf, *T. suis* in the hog, *T. ovis* in sheep and cattle, *T. discolor* in the cow, *T. leporis* in the rabbit, *T. campanulus* and *T. serratus* in the cat, and *T. muris* in rats and mice. The species from man and other primates have been considered morphologically indistinguishable from *T. suis* of the hog, the differences in the spines of the spicules being merely minor variations.[51]

---

[51] Schwartz, B., 1926.

The ova (Figs. 72 and 73), from 50 to 54 μ in length by 22 μ in breadth, are barrel-shaped, with an outer and inner shell and transparent polar prominences. The fertilized ova are unsegmented at oviposition. The number produced by a single

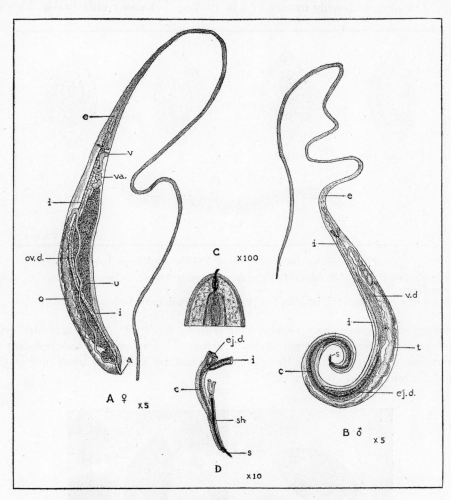

FIG. 71.—*Trichuris trichiura*

A, female; *B*, male; *C*, anterior end showing spear; *D*, cloaca and copulatory organs of male.

a, anus; *c*, cloaca; *e*, esophagus; *ej.d.*, ejaculatory duct; *i*, intestine; *o*, ovary; *ov.d.*, oviduct; *s*, spicule; *sh.*, sheath of spicule; *t*, testis; *u*, uterus; *v*, vulva; *va.*, vagina; *v.d.*, vas deferens (*A*, *B* and *D* adapted from Leuckart, 1876; *C* drawn from photograph by Li, 1933).

female has been variously estimated at from 1,000 to 5,000 per day, but probably averages about 2,000.

Embryonic development takes place outside the host. The time required to produce the unhatched first-stage larva varies from two weeks to several months. Under favorable conditions of temperature and moisture in shady sand, loam or clay, 33 per cent of the ova reach the motile embryo stage in 21 days and 74 per cent in 35 days, but ova in soil exposed to sunlight do not develop.[52] The ova of the dog whipworm, *T. vulpis,* ordinarily mature in 9 to 10 days, but under unfavorable dry sur-

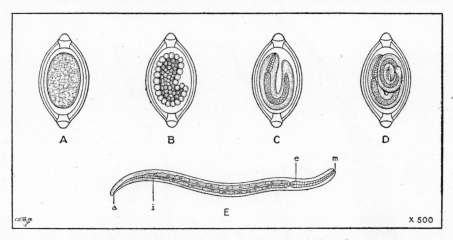

FIG. 72.—THE DEVELOPMENT OF *Trichuris trichiura* LARVA

A, unicellular stage; *B,* multicellular stage; *C,* early larva; *D,* mature larva; *E,* newly hatched larva.

a, anus; *e,* esophagus; *i,* intestine; *m,* mouth (Adapted from Leuckart, 1876).

roundings development may require from 6 to 12 months.[53] A soil saturated with moisture and a shady environment favor viability.[54] The ova are less resistant to desiccation, cold and heat than those of *Ascaris* and are killed in a short time at 52° to 54° C., and at —9° to —12° C.[55]

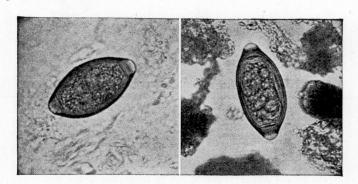

FIG. 73.—OVA OF *Trichuris trichiura* IN FECES (× 500)

(From Todd and Sanford, *Clinical Diagnosis by Laboratory Methods.* Courtesy of W. B. Saunders Company).

[52] Brown, H. W., 1927.
[53] Miller, M. J., 1939.
[54] Spindler, L. A., 1929.
[55] Nolf, L. O., 1932.

Infection is direct, as no second host is required (Fig. 74). When the embryonate egg is ingested by man, the activated larva escapes from the weakened shell. The larval worm (Fig. 72E) penetrates the intestinal villi, especially of the cecum, where it lies from 3 to 10 days near the crypts of Lieberkühn.[56] It then passes into the lumen of the cecum where it develops to the mature adult in approximately 90 days.

PATHOGENESIS

Pathology.—The whipworm is commonly found in the region of the cecum and appendix, but may occur also in the colon, rectum and lower ileum. Although the whip-like anterior portion is imbedded in the mucosa and surrounded by mucus, the parasite usually causes no noticeable pathological reaction. Its secretions may liquefy the neighboring cells of the intestinal mucosa.[57] Contrary to general opinion a few observers believe that the worm may suck blood.[58] Occasionally the anterior portion of the worm may penetrate the submucosa and muscularis and perforate the peritoneum, producing a serious inflammatory reaction. Not infrequently it may be present in the lumen of the appendix and may occlude this organ and even produce appendicitis.

Investigators in tropical countries, where infections are more intense, hold that *Trichuris trichiura* is responsible for various pathological conditions arising directly from the irritative and toxic action of the worm and indirectly from secondary bacterial invasion. Undoubtedly its penetrating habits may facilitate invasion of the intestinal mucosa by bacteria and similarly perforation of the intestinal wall may induce peritonitis, septicemia, perinephritis, pyelitis, and other secondary inflammatory conditions. In tropical America it is considered as a cause of appendicitis and of many infections that are diagnosed as tropical idiopathic peritonitis and amœbic dysentery.[59]

Symptomatology.—Symptoms vary with the numerical intensity of the infection, the extent of intestinal penetration, and secondary bacterial infection. In most instances light infections cause no noticeable symptoms, although pronounced symptoms are not always dependent upon the number of worms.[60] Children and some adults may show nutritional disturbances, digestive disorders, anemia, eosinophilia up to 25 per cent, and nervous manifestations. Pronounced symptoms are rare and are associated with secondary bacterial infection. Usually the first indication of infection is the presence of ova in the feces.

DIAGNOSIS, PROGNOSIS AND TREATMENT

Diagnosis.—Diagnosis is made by finding the characteristic barrel-shaped ova in the feces. Irregular egg-laying renders ova-counts less trustworthy than those of hookworm for calculating the number of worms. Clinically, whipworm infection cannot be differentiated from that of other intestinal nematodes, although eosinophilia is a more constant finding.

---

[56] Hasegawa, T., 1924.
[57] Hoeppli, R. J. C., 1930.
[58] Brown, H. W., 1934; Chitwood, B. G., 1929.
1937.

[59] Fernan-Nuñez, M., 1927.
[60] Caldwell, F. C. and Caldwell, E. L.,

Prognosis.—Prognosis is good as far as the health of the host is concerned, but not so favorable as to the elimination of the worms.

Treatment.—The worm is so firmly and so deeply imbedded that the usual drugs for the removal of other nematodes will remove only a small percentage of whipworms. Repeated treatments with hexylresorcinol (Section **VII**, XIII, 23), the most efficient of these drugs, offer the best chance of removing the parasite.[61] A single treatment of 60 ml. of leche de higuéron (Section **VII**, XIII, 31) has produced 85 per cent ova-reduction and 54 per cent cures,[60] but unfortunately this drug, which is used extensively in South America for whipworm infections, ferments easily and is unpalatable.

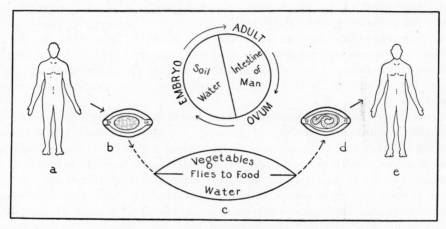

Fig. 74.—Life Cycle of *Trichuris trichiura*

a, man infected with parasite; *b,* ovum; *c,* modes of transmission; *d,* infective unhatched larva; *e,* man infected by ingesting unhatched larva.

PREVENTION

Epidemiology.—*Trichuris trichiura* has a high incidence and is coextensive in distribution with *Ascaris lumbricoides.* In areas of heavy rainfall and high humidity, where shade and moist soil prevail, it is more abundant than *Ascaris,* whereas in dry regions and unshaded areas the situation is reversed.[54] The highest incidence is found in the regions of heaviest rainfall, subtropical climate and highly polluted soil: coastal regions of Puerto Rico, 73 per cent; Mauritius, 91 per cent; Paris, France, 55 per cent in 359 autopsies; and China, where night soil is used as fertilizer, 80 per cent.[62] Surveys in the southern United States totaling over 160,000 white persons give a much lower incidence: Mississippi, 0.04 per cent; Kentucky, 10 per cent; South Carolina, 0.04 per cent; North Carolina, 0.5 per cent; and Florida, 0.4 per cent.[63]

[61] Brown, H. W., 1934.

[62] Cort, W. W. and Stoll, N. R., 1931; Adams, A. R. D. and Webb, L., 1934; Mark, P. K., 1935; Desportes, C., 1938.

[63] Keller, A. E. and Leathers, W. S., 1934, 1936; Leathers, W. S. and Keller, A. E., 1937; Keller, A. E., Leathers, W. S. and Knox, J. C., 1938; Leathers, W. S., Keller, A. E. and McPhaul, W. A., 1939.

Infection results from the ingestion of embryonate ova from hands, food and drink, contaminated directly from infested soil or possibly indirectly through domestic animals, flies, other insects and dust (Fig. 74).

Young children have the highest incidence; [64] those playing in polluted dooryards are most readily infected. The rate of infection is usually higher in females than males, but in the highly endemic regions of China, it is higher in males and there is no appreciable difference between children and adults.[65]

Prophylaxis.—Infection in highly endemic areas may be prevented by: (1) treatment of infected individuals, although lack of specific anthelmintic drugs presents a formidable difficulty; (2) sanitary disposal of human feces, particularly in moist, warm countries; (3) thorough cleanliness of the hands before meals; (4) instruction of children in sanitation and personal cleanliness, with particular attention to keeping the hands from the mouth when playing on the ground; and (5) thorough washing and scalding of uncooked vegetables.

Capillaria hepatica (BANCROFT, 1893) TRAVASSOS, 1915

Synonyms.—*Hepaticola hepatica* (Bancroft, 1893) Hall, 1916.
History.—Discovered by Bancroft in 1893.
Geographical Distribution.—Cosmopolitan in rodents.
Biological Characteristics.—The adult worm resembles *Trichuris trichiura* but has a relatively shorter anterior portion. The elongate ova, 51 to 68 μ by 30 to 35 μ, have an outer shell with radiating pores.
Life Cycle.—*Capillaria hepatica* is a parasite of mice, rats, prairie dogs, beavers, muskrats, hares, peccaries and monkeys. Man is an accidental host. The life cycle is direct. The ova are not excreted but are deposited in the liver where they become fully embryonated within 30 days. When a new host eats infected liver or contaminated food, the ova hatch in the intestine, and the larvæ pierce the intestinal wall. Most of the larvæ migrate to the liver, where in four weeks they become mature worms.
Pathogenesis.—In rodents accumulations of ova in the liver cause an inflammatory reaction with the production of fibrous connective tissue and, in heavy infections, extensive tissue destruction and hepatic cirrhosis. Rats are less susceptible than mice, have a definite age resistance and acquire active immunity by infection.[66] The only reported human infection is that of a soldier in India, who died from septic pneumonia and liver abscess, and had a suppurating liver infiltrated with masses of ova.[67]
Diagnosis.—Diagnosis is possible only by microscopical examination of the liver at postmortem. Numerous observers have reported ova in human feces as a result of eating infected livers, but their presence is not indicative of actual infection.
Prognosis and **Treatment.**—Unknown.
Prevention.—Prophylactic measures are unnecessary.

SUPERFAMILY *DIOCTOPHYMOIDEA* RAILLIET, 1916

The superfamily DIOCTOPHYMOIDEA includes medium to large nematodes parasitic in the digestive tract, kidney and abdominal cavity of mammals and birds. The rudimentary mouth is encircled by one to three rings of papillæ, the cylindrical esophagus is long, and in the female the anus is terminal. The male has a single copulatory spicule and a

---

[64] Klercker, K. O., 1929; Webb, L., 1934; Mark, P. K., 1935.
[65] Cort, W. W. and Stoll, N. R., 1931.
[66] Luttermoser, G. W., 1938.
[67] MacArthur, W. P., 1924.

bell-shaped copulatory bursa unsupported by rays. The female reproductive organs form a single tube. The barrel-shaped ova, except at the poles, are covered with a thick pitted coat. One species, *Dioctophyme renale,* of the family DIOCTOPHYMIDÆ, has been found in man.

Dioctophyme renale (GOEZE, 1782) STILES, 1901

Synonyms.—*Ascaris renalis* Goeze, 1782; *Eustrongulus gigas* (Rudolphi, 1802) Diesing, 1851.

Disease.—Kidney-worm infection.

History.—First observed in 1782 by Goeze in the kidney of a dog.

Geographical Distribution.—Europe, North and South America, and China.

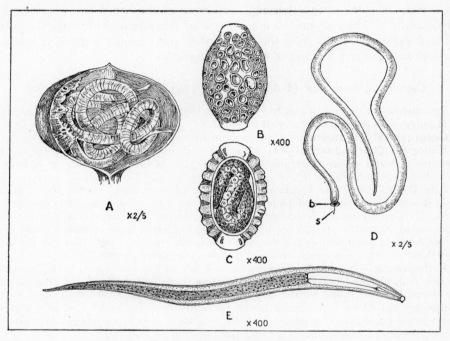

FIG. 75.—*Dioctophyme renale*

A, adult female in kidney of dog; *B,* immature ovum, showing sieve-like sculpturing of shell; *C,* embryonate ovum; *D,* adult male; *E,* larva.

b, bursal cup; *s,* spicule (*A* redrawn from Railliet, 1895; *B, C* and *E* redrawn from Balbiani, 1895; *D* redrawn from Neveu-Lemaire).

Biological Characteristics.—The female (Fig. 75A), 200 to 1,000 mm. by 5 to 12 mm., is a large cylindrical reddish nematode. Two rings of papillæ encircle the hexagonal mouth and other small papillæ mark the lateral lines. The male (Fig. 75D), 140 to 400 mm. by 4 to 6 mm., has a terminal papillate bursal cap with a single copulatory spicule. The brownish-yellow ova (Fig. 75 B and C), 64 to 68 μ by 40 to 44 μ, have a thick pitted shell.

Life Cycle.—The parasite is most frequently found in the dog, but it has been observed in other wild and domestic animals. Some nine cases of human infection have been reported. The ova are highly resistant and may remain viable for long periods, even years. Embryonic development starts at oviposition and is completed within six months in water or moist soil, a fusiform larva (Fig. 75E), about 240 μ in length, being liberated. The life cycle is unknown but probably involves a fresh water fish as intermediate host.

Pathogenesis.—The parasite is usually found in the kidney, less frequently in the intestine, and rarely in the abdominal cavity of mammals. It destroys the kidney substance, leaving an enlarged cystic shell containing the coiled worm and purulent material. All cases of human infection have been of the renal type, and the symptoms have been those of renal disfunction or ureteral obstruction.

Diagnosis.—In renal infection diagnosis is made by finding the characteristic ova in the centrifuged urine.

Prognosis and Treatment.—The prognosis is grave since the only treatment is surgical removal of the kidney.

Prevention.—The epidemiology and method of transmission are unknown, although fresh-water fishes are believed to be the source of mammalian infection. If this belief is true, thorough cooking of fish should provide adequate protection.

REFERENCES

AUGUSTINE, D. L. Trichinosis—Incidence and Diagnostic Tests, New England J. M., 1937, 216:463.

BACHMAN, G. W., RODRÍGUEZ-MOLINA, R., and GONZALEZ, J. O. Anomalous and Non-specific Reactions with *Trichinella spiralis* Antigen in Relation to Other Disease Conditions, Am. J. Hyg., 1934, 20:415.

BLUMER, G. Trichinosis With Special Reference to Changed Conceptions of Pathology and Their Bearing on Symptomatology, New England J. M., 1936, 214:1229.

BROWN, H. W. Studies on Rate of Development and Viability of Eggs of *Ascaris lumbricoides* and *Trichuris trichiura* Under Field Conditions, J. Parasitol., 1927, 14:1.

——— Intestinal Parasitic Worms in the United States; Their Diagnosis and Treatment, Jour. Am. M. Ass., 1934, 103:651.

FERNAN-NUÑEZ, M. Pathogenic Rôle of *Trichocephalus dispar* (*Trichuris trichiura*), Arch. Int. Med., 1927, 40:46.

HALL, M. C. Studies on Trichinosis. III. The Complex Clinical Picture of Trichinosis and the Diagnosis of the Disease, U. S. Pub. Health Rep., 1937, 52:539.

——— IV. The Rôle of Garbage-Fed Hogs in the Production of Human Trichinosis. U. S. Pub. Health Rep., 1937, 52:873.

——— VI. Epidemiological Aspects of Trichinosis in the United States as Indicated by an Examination of 1000 Diaphragms for Trichinæ, U. S. Pub. Health Rep., 1938, 53:1086.

McCOY, O. R., Artificial Immunization of Rats Against *Trichinella spiralis,* Am. J. Hyg., 1935, 21:200.

———, MILLER, J. J., JR., and FRIEDLANDER, R. D. The Use of the Intradermal Test in the Diagnosis of Trichiniasis, J. Immunol., 1933, 24:1.

MOST, H. and ABELES, M. M. Trichiniasis Involving Nervous System; Clinical and Neuropathological Review with Report of Two Cases, Arch. Neurol. & Psychiat., 1937, 37:589.

NOLF, L. O. Experimental Studies on Certain Factors Influencing Development and Viability of the Ova of Human *Trichuris* as Compared with Those of Human *Ascaris,* Am. J. Hyg., 1932, 16:288.

OTTO, G. F. and ABRAMS, E. Quantitative Studies on the Effect of Heat on Trichina (*Trichinella spiralis*) Larvæ, Am. J. Hyg., 1939, 29, Sect. D:115.

ROTH, H. Experimental Studies in the Course of Trichina Infection in Guinea Pigs. I. The Minimum Dose of Trichina Larvæ Required to Produce Infestation of the Muscles, with an Account of the Potential Productiveness of the Female Trichina, Am. J. Hyg., 1938, 28:85.

——— II. Natural Susceptibility of the Guinea Pig to Experimental Trichina Infection, Am. J. Hyg., 1939, 29, Sect. D:89.

SPINDLER, L. A. The Relation of Moisture to the Distribution of Human *Trichuris* and *Ascaris,* Am. J. Hyg., 1929, 10:476.

SPINK, W. W., and AUGUSTINE, D. L. The Diagnosis of Trichinosis with Especial Reference to Skin and Precipitin Tests, J. Am. M. Ass., 1935, 104:1801.

Chapter XVI

THE SUPERFAMILY RHABDITOIDEA

SUPERFAMILY *RHABDITOIDEA* TRAVASSOS, 1920

The superfamily RHABDITOIDEA is composed of relatively simple nematode worms, some of which are entirely free-living while others, depending on environmental conditions, lead an interchangeable free-living and parasitic existence. Species of the genera *Rhabditis, Turbatrix* and *Strongyloides* have been reported as parasites of man, but only one, *Strongyloides stercoralis,* is important.

FAMILY *RHABDITIDÆ* MICOLETZKY, 1922

The family RHABDITIDÆ is composed of small nematodes that have a well-developed, three-sided, prismatic or tubular buccal cavity, usually without teeth; a long cylindrical esophagus with a valved posterior bulb and often a median bulbar swelling; and a smooth cuticle occasionally with a few bristles. The female is oviparous or ovoviviparous, and not infrequently parthogenetic or hermaphroditic. Most species live in decaying material. The parasitic species usually occur in insects, but a few have been found in mammals. Those reported from man include *Rhabditis pellio, R. niellyi, R. hominis* and *Turbatrix aceti,* but they are probably accidental contaminants of lesions.

Rhabditis pellio (SCHNEIDER, 1866) BUETSCHLI, 1873

Rhabditis pellio lives as an adult in decomposing organic matter in the soil, and as a larva probably in the earth worm. The adult measures from 1.0 to 1.9 mm. in length. The larvæ hatch inside the female and feed on her tissues. The adult and larva have been thrice reported from the human vagina, evidently as the result of soil contamination.

Rhabditis niellyi BLANCHARD, 1885

The larvæ of *Rhabditis niellyi* were found by Nielly in 1882 in itching papular cutaneous lesions resembling "craw-craw."

Rhabditis hominis KOYABASHI, 1914

Rhabditis hominis was discovered by Koyabashi in 1914 in the fresh feces of Japanese school children. Attempts to establish infection in man and laboratory animals have been unsuccessful and it is probably a free-living species that contaminates human feces but never attains permanent residence in the intestinal tract.[1] This species may be confused with the free-living stage of *Strongyloides stercoralis,* but is distinguishable by the following characteristics: (1) the male, 0.9 to 1.3 mm. by 0.04 mm., is larger and has a copulatory bursa; (2) the female, 1.4 to 2.0 mm. by 0.12 mm., is larger and much broader; (3) reproduction is ovoviviparous and not usually oviparous; (4) the ova,

---

[1] Sandground, J. H., 1925.

24 to 44 μ, are smaller, more numerous, and are arranged in a double row in the uterus; and (5) the rhabditiform larva, 240 to 300 μ, has a longer buccal cavity.

Turbatrix aceti (MUELLER, 1783) PETERS 1927

The "vinegar eel" is a cylindrical worm free-living in acetic acid and fermenting liquids. The males average 1.5 mm. and the viviparous females 2.4 mm. The rhabditiform larvæ, 222 μ long, develop directly into adults. This worm has been found several times in the human vagina probably from contamination by vinegar douches, and in one instance in the urine of man.

FAMILY *STRONGYLOIDIDÆ* CHITWOOD AND McINTOSH, 1934

Nematodes of the family STRONGYLOIDIDÆ are characterized by rhabditiform free-living and filariform parasitic forms. The former have a short stoma, an esophagus with a valved posterior bulb, a single testis and two spicules in the male, and bifurcate reproductive organs in the female. The parasitic filariform females have a greatly reduced stoma and a long esophagus.

Strongyloides stercoralis is the only species pathogenic for man. The common species infecting mammals are *S. canis* of dogs, *S. simiæ* of monkeys, *S. suis* of hogs, *S. ratti* of rats, and *S. papillosus* of sheep, goats, rabbits and antelopes. Many other species have been reported in mammals and birds. Experimental cross-breeding suggests that the apparently closely allied forms of different hosts constitute distinct species.[2]

Strongyloides stercoralis (BAVAY, 1876) STILES AND HASSALL, 1902

Synonyms.—*Anguillula stercoralis* Bavay 1877; *Strongyloides intestinalis* (Bavay, 1877) Grassi, 1879.

Disease.—Strongyloidiasis. Cochin-China diarrhea.

History.—*Strongyloides stercoralis* was first observed in 1876 by Normand in the diarrheic feces of French soldiers from Cochin-China. The two morphologically different forms, described by Bavay, were considered as coagents of Cochin-China diarrhea until 1884, when Leuckart demonstrated that they were alternate generations of the same species. In 1900 Askanay determined that the female parasite invaded the intestinal mucosa and produced tissue-damage. Between 1902 and 1914 van Durme, Looss, Ransom, and Fülleborn traced the method of invasion via skin, blood, lungs, trachea and pharynx to the intestine. Until a parasitic male was reported in 1932 by Kreis, the development of the ova of the parasitic female was believed to be parthogenetic. Faust, 1933 to 1935, made a detailed study of the development from infective larva to adult.

Geographical Distribution.—Cosmopolitan, paralleling that of the hookworm, but with a lower incidence. It is especially prevalent in tropical and subtropical countries where warmth, moisture and lack of sanitation favor its free-living development.

BIOLOGICAL CHARACTERISTICS

Morphology.—The parasitic female (Fig. 76A), 2.2 mm. by 0.04 mm., is a colorless, semitransparent filariform nematode with a finely striated cuticle. It has a

---

[2] Augustine, D. L., 1940.

slender tapering anterior end and a short conical pointed tail. The short buccal cavity
has four indistinct lips. The long, slender, cylindrical esophagus extends through the
anterior fourth of the body and the intestine continues to the subterminal anus. The
vulva is located one-third the length of the body from the posterior end. The paired
reproductive organs diverge anterior and posterior to the vulva. The uteri contain
a single file of 8 to 12 thin-shelled, transparent, segmented ova (50 to 58 μ by 30
to 34 μ).

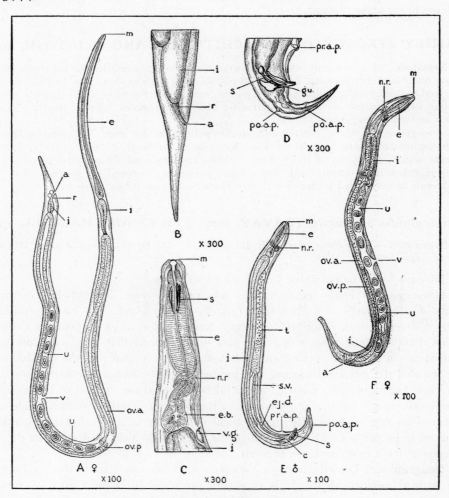

FIG. 76.—*Strongyloides stercoralis*

A, parasitic female; *B*, posterior end of parasitic female; *C*, anterior end of parasitic male (?);
D, posterior end of parasitic male (?); *E*, free-living male; *F*, free-living female.

a, anus; *c*, cloaca; *e*, esophagus; *e.b.*, esophageal bulb; *ej.d.*, ejaculatory duct; *gu.*, gubernaculum; *i*, intestine; *m*, mouth; *n.r.*, nerve ring; *ov.a.*, anterior ovary; *ov.p.*, posterior ovary;
po.a.p., postanal papilla; *pr.a.p.*, preanal papilla; *r*, rectum; *s*, spicules; *s.v.*, seminal vesicle;
t, testis; *u*, uterus; *v*, vulva; *v.g.*, ventral gland (*A, E* and *F* redrawn from Looss, 1911; *B, C*
and *D* redrawn from Kreis, 1932).

The free-living female (Fig. 76F), 1 mm. by 0.06 mm., is smaller than the parasitic female and resembles a typical rhabditoid free-living nematode. The muscular esophagus is double-bulbed and the intestine is a straight cylindrical tube. The reproductive organs are paired, the vulva is located two-fifths the length of the body from the posterior end, and the uteri contain a single column of thin-shelled, transparent, segmented ova (70 by 40 μ).

The description of the parasitic male (?), except for a more distinct buccal capsule, is practically indistinguishable from that of the free-living male.[3] The free-living male (Fig. 76E), 0.7 mm. by 0.04 mm., is smaller than the female and has a ventrad curve to the tail. It has two copulatory spicules and a gubernaculum but no caudal alæ.

Physiology.—The parasitic females penetrate the mucosa of the intestinal villi, where they lie in the stroma between or even within the epithelium of Lieberkühn's glands. Here they secure nourishment and deposit ova. The question of syngenesis or parthenogenesis is still unsettled, although parasitic males have been reported. The successful infection of rats with a single larva of *S. ratti* indicates that males are unnecessary to maintain parasitic fertility. The female worms are eventually encapsulated or destroyed by phagocytosis. Experimental infections in dogs show a primary rapid increase in the yield of larvæ followed by a gradual decrease to non-production.[4]

LIFE CYCLE

Man is the principal host of *Strongyloides stercoralis*. It has been transplanted to dogs and transiently to cats and apes. Similar species are present in many animals, but do not infect man.

Free-living Cycle.—After leaving the host the free-living rhabditiform larvæ may develop into infective filariform larvæ either directly or indirectly through a generation of free-living males and females (Fig. 77). In the direct method the rhabditiform larvæ are immediately transformed into infective filariform larvæ. In the indirect method the larvæ molt and within 24 to 36 hours are differentiated into sexually mature free-living rhabditiform males and females. After fertilization the free-living female produces 60 or more ova that develop into rhabditiform larvæ. These become infective filariform larvæ within a few days or repeat the free-living generations.

The conditions that influence the method of development await further study. Cultural studies suggest that direct development takes place when environmental conditions are unfavorable, and indirect development when the surroundings are favorable.[5] Possibly the indirect method with its marked increase in the number of infective larvæ is associated with tropical climates, while the direct method is more frequently followed in the less favorable colder regions. Nevertheless, both direct and indirect development occur concurrently and even a selected strain does not follow a single method. The mode of development of the progeny of a single homogonically-derived *S. ratti* appears to be determined by conditions in the host rather

[3] Kreis, H. A., 1932.   Beach, T. D., 1934.
[4] Faust, E. C., Wells, J. W., Adams, C. and   [5] Nishigori, M., 1928; Beach, T. D., 1936.

than by the action of the cultural environment upon the larvæ, and shows seasonal fluctuations that possibly are due to the effect of meteorological conditions on the host.[6]

Larva.—The rhabditiform larva (Fig. 78B), 225 by 16 μ, has an elongate esophagus with a pyriform posterior bulb, but lacks the midbulbar swelling of the genus *Rhabditis*. It differs from the rhabditiform larva of the hookworm (Fig. 85) in being slightly smaller and less attenuated posteriorly and in having a shorter buccal vestibule, and a larger genital primordium. The rhabditiform larva of the free-living cycle differs from that of the direct cycle in its larger size and in having three spears on the esophagus. The rhabditiform larva, after a short feeding period,

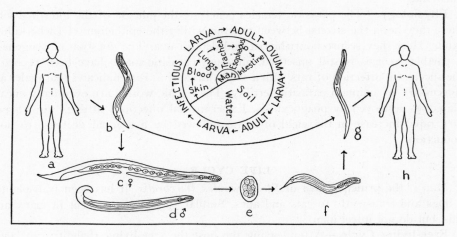

FIG. 77.—LIFE CYCLE OF *Strongyloides stercoralis*

a, man infected with *Strongyloides stercoralis*; *b*, rhabditiform larvæ in feces; *c*, free-living generation, female; *d*, free-living generation, male; *e*, ovum; *f*, rhabditiform larva; *g*, filariform larva; *h*, man infected by filariform larva passing through skin.

molts into a long, slender, nonfeeding, infective, filariform larva (Fig. 78C) about 550 μ in length, similar to that of the hookworm, but usually smaller and with a distinct cleft at the tip of the tail.

Successive free-living generations of mammalian *Strongyloides* have been cultivated in artificial media (Section **VII**, VII, 16, 18) and their nutrient requirements, development and reaction to environmental conditions have been observed.[7] *Strongyloides* larvæ have slight resistance to desiccation, excessive humidity or marked changes in temperature.[3] The larvæ of *S. füllebornis* die at 43° C., and above 37° C. only a few complete their life cycle, while below 8° C. rhabditiform larvæ are killed in 10 hours and filariform larvæ in one week.[8] This inability to withstand low temperatures explains the prevalence of *Strongyloides stercoralis* in tropical and subtropical countries.

[6] Graham, G. L., 1938, 1939.
[7] Schuurmans-Stekhoven, J. H., 1928; Cordi, J. M. and Otto, G. F., 1934; Beach,

T. D., 1936; Augustine, D. L., 1940.
[8] Cordi, J. M. and Otto, G. F., 1934.

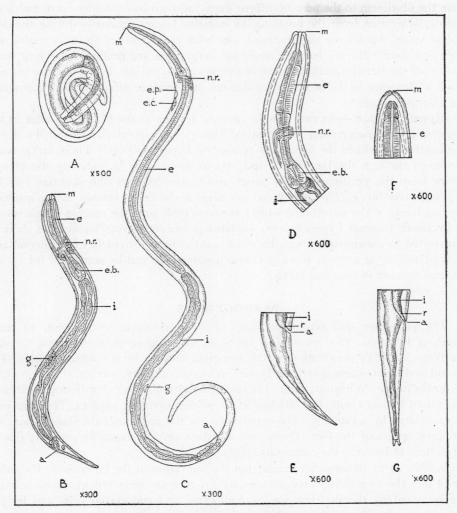

FIG. 78.—LARVÆ OF *Strongyloides stercoralis*.

A, ovum containing mature larva of *S. simiæ*; *B*, rhabditiform larva; *C*, filariform larva; *D*, anterior end of rhabditiform larva; *E*, posterior end of rhabditiform larva; *F*, anterior end of filariform larva; *G*, posterior end of filariform larva.

a, anus; *e*, esophagus; *e.b.*, esophageal bulb; *e.c.*, excretory cell; *e.p.*, excretory pore; *g*, genital rudiment; *i*, intestine; *m*, mouth; *n.r.*, nerve ring; *r*, rectum (*A* adapted and *D*, *E*, *F* and *G* redrawn from Kreis, 1932; *B* and *C* adapted from Looss, 1911).

Course in Host.—The infective filariform larvæ normally penetrate the skin of the mammalian host, eventually enter the venous circulation and pass through the right heart to the lungs, where they penetrate the capillary walls into the alveoli. From the lungs the parasites later ascend to the glottis, are swallowed, and reach the upper part of the intestine where they develop into adults. Occasionally, ingested larvæ may develop directly into adult worms. During their migration the larvæ pass from the filariform to the post-filariform stage and then become adolescent and adult worms. Migration from the lungs to the intestine occurs primarily during the adolescent stage. Adolescent and mature males have been reported in the intestine and the cystic duct.[9] Mature females ready for oviposition are produced in 17 or more days after the initial infection. Some of the larvæ may remain in the alveolar tissues, reach adolescence in the bronchial epithelium and produce offspring that may attain the filariform stage.[9]

Hyperinfection.—At times the larvæ may develop to the filariform stage in the intestine and by penetrating the intestinal mucosa or perianal skin establish a developmental cycle within the host, thus producing hyperinfection.[10] These larvæ reach the lungs through the lymphatics and venous system, or by entering the pleural cavity from the peritoneum. The lungs and cystic duct are the selective foci for hyperinfective larvæ. This condition may arise if the larvæ remain in the intestine over 24 hours, if the intestinal contents are unsuitable or if the mucosa is susceptible to invasion. Internal hyperinfection explains persistent strongyloidiasis in patients transferred to nonendemic areas. Its existence has been proved in experimental animals by finding at autopsy more parasitic females than can be accounted for by the original number of invading larvæ.

PATHOGENESIS

The pathology and symptomatology of strongyloidiasis corresponds to three stages of infection: (1) invasion of the skin, (2) migration of the larvæ through the body, and (3) penetration of the intestinal mucosa by the adult females. The second and third stages, particularly in hyperinfection, may overlap.

Pathology.—Within 24 hours the site of infection shows a profound erythemia and raised blotches with fine, slightly elevated, hemorrhagic papules. The skin may be excoriated by scratching. The usual sites are the ankle and the dorsum and interdigital spaces of the foot. There may also be a delayed reaction, probably due to a residium of larvæ in the cutaneous layers.[11]

Within 24 to 48 hours after infection the migration of the larvæ from the capillaries into the alveoli and bronchioles may produce an acute inflammatory reaction characterized by the proliferation of leukocytes and endothelial cells and by petechial or profuse hemorrhage.[11] Injury to the respiratory epithelium favors bacterial invasion and may culminate in lobular pneumonia. Congestion of the bronchioles, by preventing upward migration, may permit the larvæ to metamorphose into adult worms whose progeny may invade the pulmonary tissues and pleura.

The adult females may be found in the intestinal mucosa from the pylorus to the rectum, but are present in the greatest numbers in the duodenal and upper jejunal regions. In heavy infections the pyloric region of the stomach and the proximal biliary and pancreatic passages may also be involved.[12] The female worms are usually found in the middle and lower depths of the mucosa and, less commonly, at the tips of the villi. They burrow through the mucosa in serpentine channels, depositing

---

[9] Faust, E. C., 1933.

[10] Fülleborn, F.. 1926; Nishigori, M., 1928; Faust. E. C., 1933.

[11] Faust, E. C., 1935.

[12] Faust, E. C., 1932.

their ova as they progress (Fig. 79). The larvæ ordinarily hatch in the mucosa and, leaving the eggshell, bore through the glandular epithelium into the intestinal lumen. At times they invade the submucosa, muscularis, muscular layers, subserosa, lymph spaces, and even reach the peritoneum, kidneys and other organs.

The mechanical and lytic actions of the adult worms, ova and larvæ produce a catarrhal inflammation with round-cell and eosinophilic infiltration. The worms are gradually enclosed in adventitious epithelial sheaths and are eventually phagocytosed. In heavy infections there may be extensive honeycombing and necrosis of the mucosa, followed by fibroblastic tissue-repair. Fatal cases with massive invasion of the intestinal wall by autoinfective larvæ have been reported.[13]

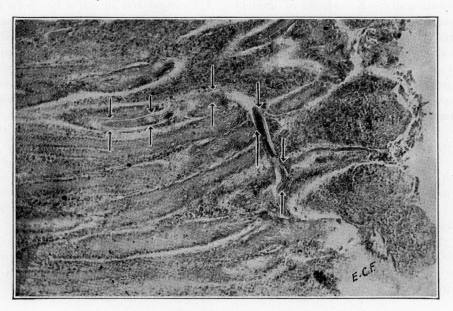

FIG. 79.—*Strongyloides stercoralis* IN DUODENUM, × 100

Section of the duodenum (fifteen-day infection) showing the anterior end of a female worm directed toward the base of the crypt and the middle portion in a transverse tunnel through four or five villi. The tips of the villi show characteristic hyperplasia (From Faust, E. C., *Arch. Path.*, 1935, 10:785).

Symptomatology.—The initial penetration of the skin by the parasites causes intense itching. The patient may have a brief rise of temperature, vague feelings of malaise, a slight headache and at times urticaria. The migration of the larvæ through the lungs may be accompanied by slight febrile attacks, malaise, anorexia, cough and other signs of bronchial irritation, and sometimes symptoms of mild bronchopneumonia.

Light infections frequently cause no intestinal symptoms; moderate give rise to diarrhea alternating with constipation; and heavy produce an intractable, painless, intermittent diarrhea, characterized by numerous, thin, watery, bloody stools. The

[13] Cadman, F. T., 1933; Nolasco, J. O. and Africa, C. M., 1936.

intermittent attacks of diarrhea may be associated with recurrent urticaria and toxic absorption may produce edema. The general condition of the patient is usually not materially affected, but severe, prolonged infection may cause emaciation, intestinal disorders, loss of appetite, anemia, vertigo, rapid pulse on exertion, weakness, and quick fatigue. The anemia is relatively slight in proportion to the weakness and loss of weight, the hemoglobin ranging from 70 to 90 per cent. Leukocytosis may be present during the acute infection, but as the disease becomes chronic only a relative lymphocytosis persists. Eosinophilia is usually from 3 to 13 per cent, but at times may reach 56 per cent. Hyperinfection is believed to be responsible for chronic, recurrent and severe infections.

Immunity.—Knowledge of immunity of *Strongyloides* infection has been derived largely from experimental work with the parasitic species of lower animals. Larvæ are present in the lungs but do not develop to adults in the intestine when an abnormal host, the guinea pig, is infected experimentally with *S. ratti,* a natural parasite of rats and mice.[14] Old rats, when injected subcutaneously with the same number of cultured larvæ, yield from one-third to one-half as many adult *S. ratti* as young rats.[15] Immunity to *S. stercoralis* in older cats and dogs is due to previous infection rather than to age and age-immunity is not exhibited by man.[16] Filariform larvæ of *S. stercoralis* are able to penetrate the skin of boys more readily than that of men.

After repeated infections with *S. ratti* rats acquired a resistance to superinfection that persisted at least 68 days after the infection had disappeared; a similar immunity against *S. ratti* was produced by serial injections of heat-killed larvæ; and its specificity was demonstrated by the failure to immunize rats against this parasite by serial injections of heat-killed *S. stercoralis.*[17]

Supersensitiveness in infected persons is shown by increased cutaneous reactions at the site of entrance of new batches of larvæ or when dried filariform larvæ are injected into the skin. Cutaneous sensitiveness is similar to but appears to be more specific than that produced by *Ascaris.*[18]

DIAGNOSIS, PROGNOSIS AND TREATMENT

Diagnosis.—Certain aspects of strongyloidiasis may obscure the clinical diagnosis; the diarrhea is similar to that of amœbic dysentery and cutaneous supersensitiveness, edema, anemia and emaciation also occur in infections with other nematodes. The presence of characteristic rhabditiform larvæ in fresh feces is diagnostic. They may be passed immediately after hatching or they may grow to two or three times their initial size before leaving the host. Because of the small numbers in chronic infections, concentration methods (Section **VII,** VII) should be employed when direct examination is negative. During purgation or severe dysentery embryonate ova may appear in the feces. Occasionally the ova and larvæ may be found in the sputum. There is little risk of confusion with ancylostomiasis, since the embryonate ova and rhabditiform larvæ of the hookworms are rarely found

---

[14] Sheldon, A. J. and Otto, G. F., 1938.

[15] Sheldon, A. J., 1937.

[16] Sandground, J. H., 1929.

[17] Sheldon, A. J., 1937, 1939.

[18] Fülleborn, F., 1926.

in fresh feces. The rhabditiform larva of *Strongyloides* is distinguished from that of the hookworms by a shorter buccal cavity and a blunter tail, and from the larger coprozoic larva of *Rhabditis hominis* by the absence of the midesophageal bulbus. Cutaneous tests sometimes may be helpful, although usually of little practical value.

Prognosis.—Favorable except in severe cases involving hyperinfection, although eradication of the worms is not always easy.

Treatment.—Numerous anthelmintic drugs have been used without particular success in strongyloidiasis. Favorable results have been reported with the oral administration of gentian violet (Section **VII**, XIII, *27*), one or two courses usually effecting a cure.[19] The drug, thus administered, affects the adult female worms in the intestinal tract but not the larvæ or adults elsewhere in the body. In the latter case the drug may be given intravenously, and in refractory intestinal strongyloidiasis by the duodenal tube. During the rest period of two weeks between courses the stools should be examined to determine the effect of treatment. *S. stercoralis* is more sensitive *in vitro* to nonsymmetrically substituted acridine dyes such as flavicide and rheonin than to gentian violet.[20]

PREVENTION

Epidemiology.—After leaving the host the larvæ metamormophose in the upper layers of moist, shaded soil directly or indirectly into infective filariform larvæ, which, when present in large numbers, form white, polypoid masses. They usually penetrate the feet of persons exposed to contaminated soil. Less often infection may take place through the buccal mucosa from contaminated water or soil.

The irregular incidence of *Strongyloides* infection depends upon suitability of the soil, climatic conditions, and sanitation. Worldwide data, though fragmentary, indicate a low incidence in temperate zones and an uneven frequency in the tropics and subtropics. A considerable number of persons in Louisiana, Mississippi and probably in the other Southern United States are infected.[21] An incidence of 0.9 per cent is reported in New Orleans, with infection most prevalent among white males.[22]

Prophylaxis.—The prevention of *Strongyloides* infection is essentially a question of the sanitary disposal of human wastes. The detection and treatment of carriers, who constitute a large percentage of the infected persons, does not appear practical. Protection of the skin from contact with contaminated soil reduces the chances of infection.

SUPERFAMILY *ANGUILLULINOIDEA* PEREIRA, 1931-1932

The members of the superfamily ANGUILLULINOIDEA are free-living saprophytes or parasites of plants. They differ from the RHABDITOIDEA in having a protrusile oral stylet. The species reported from man belong to the family ANGUILLULINIDÆ Baylis and Daubney, 1926, and are coprozoic inhabitants of the intestine.

---

[19] Sioe, K. J., 1927; de Langen, C. D., 1928; Faust, E. C., 1930, 1932, 1936, 1937; Sensemann, L. A., 1937.

[20] Oesterlin, M. and Krainick, H., 1934.
[21] Levin, A. L., 1930.
[22] Faust, E. C. and Headlee, W. H., 1936.

Heterodera radicicola (GREEF, 1872) MUELLER, 1884

Heterodera radicicola is a parasite of the roots and stems of radishes, celery, turnips and other edible plants. The female is a small, thread-like worm about 1.6 mm. in length, which, when gravid, assumes a pyriform shape, 0.7 mm. in length. The rhabditic male has two testes and two curved copulatory spicules. The ova, 82 to 120 μ in length by 24 to 43 μ in breadth, are ellipsoidal with a slight unilateral flattening (Fig. 80). The larvæ,

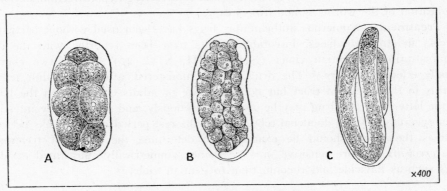

FIG. 80.—OVA OF *Heterodera radicicola*

A, ovum recovered from stool after ingestion of parasitized roots; *B*, ovum from celery roots showing polar globules; *C*, ovum from celery roots showing fully developed embryo (Redrawn from Sandground, 1923).

345 to 370 μ, after hatching either develop rapidly to adults in the same plants or migrate through the soil to the roots of other plants. This nematode once received considerable prominence as a human parasite under the name of *Oxyuris incognito* because the ova were found in the feces of man. Later these ova were identified as those of *Heterodera radicicola* that passed uninjured through the human intestine.[23] The ova may be mistaken for infertile *Ascaris* or hookworm eggs.

REFERENCES

BEACH, T. D. Experimental Studies on Human and Primate Species of *Strongyloides*. V. The Free-Living Phase of the Life Cycle, Am. J. Hyg., 1936, 23:243.

FAUST, E. C. The Symptomatology, Diagnosis and Treatment of *Strongyloides* Infection, J. Am. M. Ass., 1932, 98:2276.

——— Experimental Studies on Human and Primate Species of *Strongyloides*. II. The Development of *Strongyloides* in the Experimental Host, Am. J. Hyg., 1933, 18:114.

——— IV. Pathology of *Strongyloides* Infection, Arch. Path., 1935, 19:769.

———, WELLS, J. W., ADAMS, C., and BEACH, T. D. Experimental Studies on Human and Primate Species of *Strongyloides*. The Fecundity of *Strongyloides* Females of the Parasitic Generation, Arch. Path., 1934, 18:605.

KREIS, H. A. Studies on the genus *Strongyloides* (Nematodes), Am. J. Hyg., 1932, 16:450.

SANDGROUND, J. H. Biological Studies on the Life-History in the Genus *Strongyloides* Grassi, 1879, Am. J. Hyg., 1926, 6:337.

——— Some Studies on Susceptibility, Resistance, and Acquired Immunity to Infection with *Strongyloides stercoralis* (Nematoda) in Dogs and Cats, Am. J. Hyg., 1928, 8,507.

SHELDON, A. J. Studies on Active Acquired Resistance, Natural and Artificial, in the Rat to Infection with *Strongyloides ratti*, Am. J. Hyg., 1937, 25:53.

——— Specificity of Artificial Acquired Immunity to *Strongyloides ratti*, Am. J. Hyg., 1939, 29, Sect. D:47.

[23] Sandground, J. H., 1923.

Chapter XVII

THE SUPERFAMILIES STRONGYLOIDEA, TRICHOSTRONGYLOIDEA AND METASTRONGYLOIDEA

SUPERFAMILY *STRONGYLOIDEA* (WEINLAND, 1858) HALL, 1913

The members of the superfamily STRONGYLOIDEA have a well-developed buccal capsule and a club-shaped esophagus without a distinct valved bulb. The males have a wide conspicuous bursa with radiating rays and usually two copulatory spicules. The females are oviparous and the ova develop into rhabditiform larvæ that may directly infect the definitive host or may require a free-living metamorphosis before becoming infective. The species reported from man belong to three families, ANCYLOSTOMATIDÆ, STRONGYLIDÆ and SYNGAMIDÆ.

FAMILY *ANCYLOSTOMATIDÆ*

The members of this family, commonly known as hookworms, are parasites of the intestinal tract of mammals and at least two species produce serious disease in man. The well-developed buccal capsule is armed and the male has a large bursa with prominent' rays.

Hookworms are characterized by the presence of oral cutting organs in the form of a buccal capsule bearing ventral teeth in the genus *Ancylostoma* and semilunar plates in the genus *Necator*. The species of the genus *Ancylostoma* that affect man are the important *A. duodenale,* Old World hookworm; the South American hookworm, *A. braziliense;* and the dog hookworm, *A. caninum.* Another species, *A. malayanum,* has once been reported in man. Of the genus *Necator,* one species, *N. americanus,* the New World hookworm, is found in man. Infection with *A. duodenale* and *N. americanus* produces the disease variously known as ancylostomiasis, uncinariasis, necatoriasis, and Old World and New World hookworm infection.

HISTORY OF THE HOOKWORMS OF MAN

Hookworm infection probably existed among the ancient Egyptians, and the clinical disease was described in Italy, Arabia and Brazil long before *Ancylostoma duodenale* was discovered by Dubini in 1838. Previous to this discovery species of *Ancylostoma* had been described in animals and had received the name "hookworm" from the appearance of the rayed male bursa. On finding a second infected individual in 1842, Dubini named the worm *Ancylostoma duodenale* and was soon able to discover a number of infected persons. Shortly afterward the presence of the parasite in Egypt was associated with "Egyptian chlorosis." In 1866, Wucherer found the parasite in patients dying with tropical anemia, a severe and widely prevalent disease in Brazil. In 1878, Grassi and Parona discovered that infected individuals could be detected by the presence of ova in the feces. The disease was considered indigenous to tropical and subtropical regions until an epidemic of hookworm anemia broke out among laborers at the St. Gotthard tunnel in Switzerland. Here, from 1877 to 1880 the Italian investigators, Grassi, Maggi, Pavesi and the Parona brothers established the etiopathology and diagnosis of hookworm infection, while from 1879 to 1881 its symptomatology and therapy were defined by Concato, Perroncito, Bozzolo and Graziadei. At the completion of the tunnel the returning laborers spread the infection to the principal mining districts of Hungary, Germany, France, Holland, Belgium, Spain, England, and Sicily.

Perroncito in 1880 first described the metamorphosis of the free-living rhabditiform larva into the infective filariform type. Leichtenstern in 1886 found that the filariform larvæ developed into the adult intestinal worms. During his extensive investigations of hookworm infection in Egypt, Looss in 1896-97 accidentally spilled a culture of hookworm larvæ upon his hand. He noticed that a dermatitis developed at the site, later found hookworm ova in his feces, and thus concluded that he had become infected through the skin. In 1911 by experimental studies with *A. caninum,* the dog hookworm, he was able to work out the route of the migrating larvæ from the skin through the lungs, trachea and glottis to the intestine.

Hookworm disease was recognized in the United States of America as early as 1845 and the parasite was observed in 1893, but it was not differentiated from the Old World variety until 1902, when Stiles described *Necator americanus* as a new species. Much of the anemia prevalent in the Southern United States was subsequently found to be due to this species. In 1909 the Rockefeller Sanitary Commission was established to combat the disease, and since has coöperated with various governments throughout the world in its control. *Ancylostoma braziliense* was first reported from cats and dogs in southern Brazil in 1910, and in the following year was described from a man in Ceylon.

GEOGRAPHICAL DISTRIBUTION OF THE HOOKWORMS OF MAN

The original distribution of *Necator americanus* appears to have been south of the Tropic of Cancer in Africa, southern Asia, the East Indian Archipelago and the islands of the Pacific, and that of *Ancylostoma duodenale* north of the Tropic of Cancer on the shores of the Mediterranean, northern India, North China and Japan. The present distribution of these species has been brought about by the migration of peoples. *N. americanus* was introduced into the Americas by Negro slaves and immigrants, and similarly *A. duodenale* was spread throughout the East by Chinese laborers and colonists.

The present geographical distribution of the hookworm (Fig. 81) extends in the tropical and subtropical zones between 45° N and 30° S latitude, except for the presence of *A. duodenale* in the more northerly mining districts of Europe.

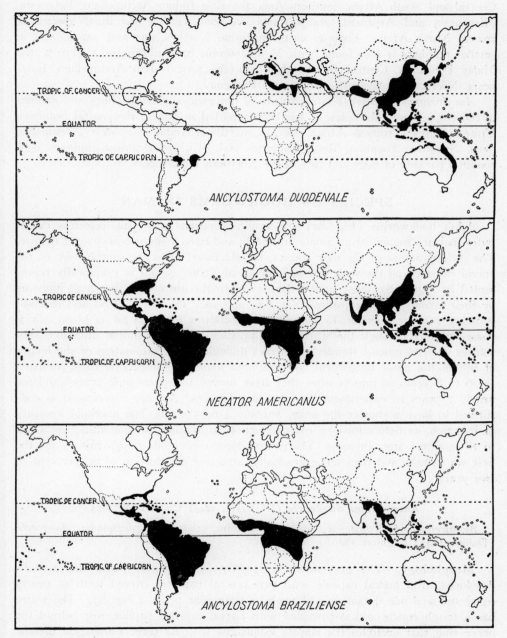

FIG. 81.—GEOGRAPHICAL DISTRIBUTION OF *Ancylostoma duodenale, Necator americanus* AND *Ancylostoma braziliense*

Necator americanus is the prevailing species in the Western Hemisphere and in Central and South Africa, southern Asia, the East Indian Archipelago, Polynesia, Micronesia and Australia. *Ancylostoma duodenale* is the dominant species in coastal North Africa, Europe, northern India, North China and Japan, and in smaller numbers is also found with *N. americanus* in southern India, Burma, the Malay Peninsula, Central and South China, the East Indian Archipelago, Polynesia, Micronesia, Australia, Brazil and Paraguay.

Ancylostoma braziliense is a parasite of domestic and wild felines and canines in the tropics and subtropics. It has been reported in Brazil, the coastal Southern United States, Tropical Africa, Ceylon, northeast India, the Malay Peninsula, Java, Sumatra, Formosa, the Philippines and Fiji. *Ancylostoma caninum* is a common parasite of dogs and cats in the Northern Hemisphere.

SPECIES OF HOOKWORMS IN MAN

Adult hookworms (Fig. 82) are small, cylindrical, fusiform, colorless nematodes that are somewhat attenuate anteriorly and have a slight bow-shaped flexure. The differentiation of the four species, largely based upon the morphology of the buccal capsule and the male bursa, is given in Table 25 and is graphically represented in Figure 83. They attach themselves to the mucosa of the small intestine by their strong buccal capsules (Fig. 87) and suck the host's blood and mucosal substances. Since a single *A. caninum* may withdraw daily 0.8 ml. of blood, which passes rapidly through the worm, it is possible that only simple diffusible substances are consumed.[1] Reinfection makes difficult the determination of the length of life of the adult hookworm. *Ancylostoma duodenale* infections have persisted for 6 to 8 years in miners after they have moved to nonendemic areas[2] and for nearly 7 years in experimentally infected prisoners.[3] *Necator americanus* is considered to have a shorter life span, possibly 4 to 5 years. The maximal intensity of infection, as determined by ova-production, is reached at 6 months[4] or at 12 to 18 months[3] after invasion. Thereafter, the ova-count decreases rapidly for the first six months and then more gradually, attaining a reduction of 80 per cent in two years.

Ancylostoma duodenale (DUBINI, 1843) CREPLIN, 1845

Synonyms.—*Agchylostoma duodenale* Dubini, 1843; *Ankylostomum duodenale* (Dubini, 1843) Bugnion, 1880.

Morphology.—The grayish-white, slightly curved adult worm has a well-developed, oval buccal capsule with two ventral pairs of curved teeth of nearly equal size and one dorsal pair of teeth or triangular plates (Fig. 83). The worm has a tough cuticle and is provided with lateral cervical papillæ just behind the nerve ring that encircles the clavate esophagus with its three esophageal glands. From the valvular, bulbous posterior end of the esophagus a simple straight in-

---

[1] Wells, H. S., 1931.
[2] Lorincz, R., 1935.
[3] Kendrick, J. F., 1934.
[4] Chandler, A. C., 1935.

TABLE 25

DIFFERENTIAL CHARACTERISTICS OF THE HOOKWORMS OF MAN

	Ancylostoma duodenale	*Necator americanus*	*Ancylostoma braziliense*	*Ancylostoma caninum*
Length Male	8 to 11 mm. x 0.45 mm.	5 to 9 mm. x 0.30 mm.	7.8 to 8.5 mm. x 0.35 mm.	10 mm. x 0.4 mm.
Female	10 to 13 mm. x 0.60 mm.	9 to 11 mm. x 0.35 mm.	9 to 10.5 mm. x 0.38 mm.	14 mm. x 0.6 mm.
Shape	Head continues in same direction as curvature of body	Head curved opposite to curvature of body, giving a hooked appearance to anterior end	Similar to *A. duodenale*	Similar to *A. duodenale*
Length of esophagus	1.3 mm. Opening oval, long axis transverse	0.5 to 0.8 mm. Opening small, oval, long axis dorsoventral	Opening very small, long axis dorsoventral	Opening large, oval, long axis dorsoventral
Buccal capsule	Two pairs of curved ventral teeth of nearly the same size, rudimentary inner pair	One pair of ventral semilunar cutting plates	Two pairs of ventral teeth, inner smaller	Three pairs of ventral teeth, inner smallest
Bursa	Broader than long, dorsal ray tripartite	Long, wide and rounded, dorsal ray small, bipartite	Small, almost as broad as long, with short stubby rays	Large and flaring, with long slender rays
Caudal spine in female	Present	Absent	Present	Present
Vulva	Posterior to middle of body	Anterior to middle of body	Posterior to middle of body	Posterior to middle of body
Size of ova (micra)	56 to 60 x 36 to 40	64 to 76 x 36 to 40	55 to 60 x 35 to 40	60 to 75 x 38 to 45

testine extends the length of the body to open into the rectum near the base of the tail cone. A branched excretory vesicle empties at a pore in the midventral line near the head.

The male (Fig. 82A) is identified by a broad, transparent membranous, caudal bursa reinforced by rib-like rays, which are characteristic of the species (Fig. 83). Within the bursa are two bristle-like spicules and the cloaca, into which the rectum and genital canal open (Fig. 82E). A single testis lies in folds along the course of the intestine and opens through the seminal duct into the seminal vesicle which in turn empties into the cloaca through the ejaculatory duct. The vulva is situated at the level of the posterior third of the female (Fig. 82B). The paired female genital organs are situated anterior and posterior to the vulva. Each set comprises a long slender coiled ovary, oviduct, seminal receptacle, uterus, ovejector, and a vagina which fuses with its counterpart near the vulva.

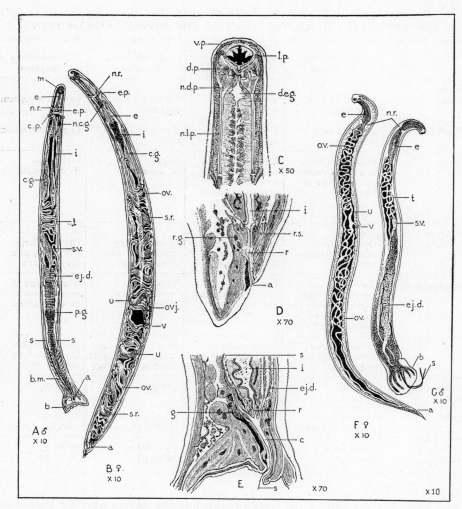

FIG. 82.—IMPORTANT HOOKWORMS OF MAN

A, adult male *Ancylostoma duodenale* from ventral side; *B*, young adult female *A. duodenale* from right side; *C*, anterior end of *A. duodenale* from dorsal side; *D*, longitudinal section through end of female *A. duodenale*, somewhat diagrammatic; *E*, longitudinal section through end of male *A. duodenale*, not quite median; *F*, female *Necator americanus*; *G*, male *N. americanus*.

a, anus; *b*, bursa; *b.m.*, bursal muscles; *c*, cloaca; *c.g.*, cervical gland; *c.p.*, cervical papilla; *d.e.g.*, dorsal esophageal gland; *d.p.*, dorsal papilla; *e*, esophagus; *e.p.*, excretory pore; *ej.d.*, ejaculatory duct; *g*, gubernaculum; *i*, intestine; *l.p.*, lateral papilla; *m*, mouth; *n.c.g.*, nucleus of cephalic gland; *n.d.p.*, nerve of dorsal papilla; *n.l.p.*, nerve of lateral papilla; *n.r.*, nerve ring; *ov.*, ovary; *ovj.*, ovejector; *p.g.*, prostatic glands; *r*, rectum; *r.g.*, rectal ganglion; *r.s.*, rectal sphincter; *s*, spicules; *s.r.*, seminal receptacle; *s.v.*, seminal vesicle; *t*, testis; *u*, uterus; *v*, vulva; *v.p.*, ventral papilla (*A* to *E* redrawn from Looss, 1905; *F* and *G* redrawn after Placencia from Manson-Bahr, 1936).

Necator americanus (STILES, 1902) STILES, 1903

Synonyms.—*Uncinaria americana* Stiles, 1902; *Ankylostomum americanum* (Stiles, 1902) v. Linstow, 1903.

Morphology.—The grayish-yellow adult worm (Fig. 82F and G) is smaller than *A. duodenale* and has a strong dorsal reflex at the anterior end. The various organs are in general similar to those of *A. duodenale*. The small buccal capsule (Fig. 83) is provided with a ventral and a less conspicuous dorsal pair of semi-lunar cutting plates instead of teeth, a concave dorsal median tooth, and a deep

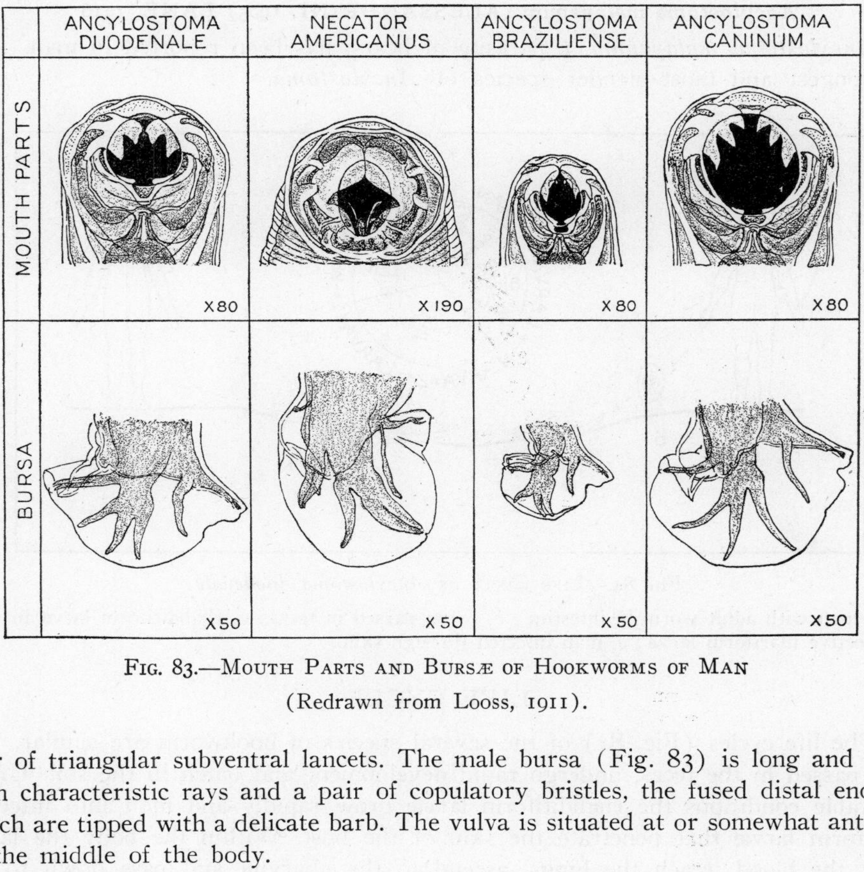

	ANCYLOSTOMA DUODENALE	NECATOR AMERICANUS	ANCYLOSTOMA BRAZILIENSE	ANCYLOSTOMA CANINUM
MOUTH PARTS	X 80	X 190	X 80	X 80
BURSA	X 50	X 50	X 50	X 50

FIG. 83.—MOUTH PARTS AND BURSÆ OF HOOKWORMS OF MAN
(Redrawn from Looss, 1911).

pair of triangular subventral lancets. The male bursa (Fig. 83) is long and wide with characteristic rays and a pair of copulatory bristles, the fused distal ends of which are tipped with a delicate barb. The vulva is situated at or somewhat anterior to the middle of the body.

Ancylostoma braziliense DE FARIA, 1910

Synonyms.—*Ancylostoma ceylanicum* Looss, 1911.

Morphology.—*A. braziliense* is the smallest of the hookworms of man. It is distinguished by a small buccal capsule with a pair of small inner teeth and a pair of large outer teeth (Fig. 83). The male bursa (Fig. 83) is small, almost as broad as long, and is supported by short, stubby rays.

Ancylostoma caninum (ERCOLANI 1859) HALL, 1913

Synonyms.—*Uncinaria canina* (Ercolani, 1859) Railliet, 1900.

Morphology.—The dog hookworm has a large, wide buccal capsule with three pairs of ventral teeth (Fig. 83). The large flaring male bursa, supported by long slender rays, has short, stout copulatory spicules (Fig. 83). This nematode, which may produce a mild dermatitis in man, has proved useful in carrying out experimental work on the life history and the parasite-host relationship of the hookworms. One case of intestinal infection in man has been reported, in the Philippines.

Ancylostoma malayanum (ALESSANDRINI, 1905) LANE, 1916

Ancylostoma malayanum, a parasite of bears, has been reported in man. It is the longest and most slender species of *Ancylostoma.*

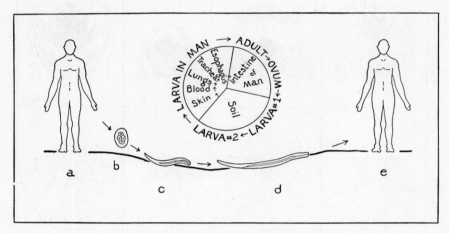

FIG. 84.—LIFE CYCLE OF *Ancylostoma duodenale*

a, man with adult worm in intestine; *b,* ovum passed in feces; *c,* rhabditiform larva in soil; *d,* infective filariform larva; *e,* man infected through skin.

LIFE CYCLE

The life cycles (Fig. 84) of the several species of hookworm are similar. The ova, passed in the feces, undergo rapid development and hatch in the soil. Under favorable conditions the rhabditiform larvæ grow rapidly and molt into infective filariform larvæ that penetrate the skin of the host. Within the body the larvæ enter the blood, reach the lungs, ascend to the pharynx and pass down to the intestine where they become adults.

Hosts.—Man is the principal host of *A. duodenale* and *N. americanus.* Species reported as *A. duodenale* have been found in hogs, dogs, cats, lions, tigers and gorillas, and as *N. americanus* in chimpanzees, gorillas, dogs, hogs and rhinoceri. *A. braziliense* is a parasite of cats and dogs and less frequently of wolves, leopards and man. *A. caninum* is the common hookworm of dogs and cats, and the adult probably does not occur naturally in man.

Ova.—The fertile ovoid ova (Fig. 65) have bluntly rounded ends and a thin shell. Those of the several species are almost indistinguishable, differing only in size. They are unsegmented at oviposition and various stages of division may be observed in the feces. The average daily output of ova by a mature female worm has been estimated as 24,000 to 30,000 for *A. duodenale,* 9,000 and one-half as many as *A. duodenale* for *N. americanus,* 4,000 for *A. braziliense,* and 17,000 for *A. caninum.*[5] Ova-production, as determined by ova-counts, is constant if irregularities of fecal movements are eliminated.[6] Thus the number of worms may be calculated from the ova-count (Section **VII**, VII, 8-11).

Ova hatch into rhabitiform larvæ within 24 hours under favorable conditions of ærated soil, moderate moisture and an optimal temperature. An excess of water, desiccation and exposure to sunlight adversely affect their development. Possibly because of lack of oxygen, they do not develop under water or in concentrated liquid feces. They die in liquid latrine material or night soil in from 4 to 8 weeks depending upon the temperature and, when urine is mixed with night soil, in a considerably shorter time.[7] Temperature also affects survival and development. The ova of *A. duodenale* die in a few hours at 45° C. and within seven days at 0° C., but live indefinitely at 10° C. They hatch in seven to ten days at 7° to 13° C. but develop no further, in two to three days at 13° to 20° C. and in one day at 25° to 33° C.[8]

Larvæ.—The newly hatched rhabditiform larvæ (Fig. 85A), 250 μ x 17 μ, resemble those of *Strongyloides stercoralis* but are somewhat larger, less attenuated posteriorly and have a longer buccal cavity. The rhabditiform larvæ of *A. duodenale* and *N. americanus* are indistinguishable. The rapidly growing larvæ feed actively upon fecal material. At the optimal temperature of 23° to 30° C. they molt usually on the third day when about 400 μ in length (Fig. 85B). They continue to grow until the fifth day when they are between 500 and 700 μ in length, and molt a second time to become slender, nonfeeding, infective filariform larvæ (Fig. 85C). The old skin may either be retained or shed depending upon the environment. In the soil a large proportion of the larvæ become unsheathed.[9]

The large, slender, active filariform larvæ of *A. duodenale* differ from those of *N. americanus* by having a larger and flatter head, less obvious, unequal esophageal spears (Figs. 85E and F), a blunter tail, fainter cuticular striations, a larger and more posterior genital primordium, a narrower esophagus, an intestine without an apparent constriction at the esophageal juncture, and less widely separated granules in the intestinal wall.[10] The larvæ of *A. duodenale, A. braziliense* and *A. caninum* more closely resemble one another but may be distinguished by the very slender tail of *A. braziliense,* the long slender tail of *A. duodenale,* and the short distance from the anus to the tip of the tail, the projectile oral spear, and the faint cuticular striations of *A. caninum.*[10]

[5] Davis, N. C., 1924; Stoll, N. R., 1923; Augustine, D. L., Helmy, M., Nazmi, M. and McGavran, G., 1928; Soper, F. L., 1927; Sarles, M. P., 1929; Herrick, C. A., 1928.

[6] Brown, H. W., 1927.

[7] Oldt, F., 1026; Stoll, N. R., 1926; Maple-stone, P. A., 1926; Dikmans, G., 1929.

[8] Furuyama, T., 1933.

[9] Cort, W. W., Augustine, D. L., Ackert, J. E., Payne, F. K. and Payne, G. C., 1922.

[10] Kobayashi, H., 1928; Schuurmans-Stekhoven, J. H., Jr., 1926.

The filariform larvæ develop certain tropisms, particularly a strong thigmotaxis that facilitates access to a new host. They are also positively phototropic, thermotropic and chemotropic to oxygen and tissue fluids, but negatively baryotropic, hydrotropic and chemotropic to strong chemicals.[11] They frequent the upper half

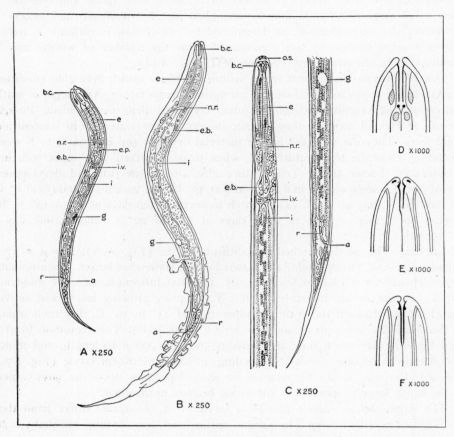

FIG. 85.—LARVÆ OF *Ancylostoma duodenale*

A, recently hatched rhabditiform larva, lateral view; *B*, rhabditiform larva during late stage of first ecdysis; *C*, filariform larva, lateral view; *D*, anterior end rhabditiform larva (schematic); *E*, anterior end filariform larva (schematic); *F*, anterior end filariform larva of *N. americanus* (schematic).

a, anus; *b.c.*, buccal cavity; *e*, esophagus; *e.b.*, esophageal bulb; *e.p.*, excretory pore; *g*, genital primordium; *i*, intestine; *i.v.*, intestinal valve; *n.r.*, nerve ring; *o.s.*, old sheath; *r*, rectum (*A* to *C* redrawn from Looss, 1905).

inch of the soil and, supported by a surface film of water, they project individually or in polyp-like masses from the surface (Fig. 86), thus facilitating transfer to bare feet. Though capable of moving freely over surfaces, larvæ do not change their location unless mechanically transferred, hence a particular area may contain

[11] Wakeshima, T., 1933.

many larvæ while an adjacent area is relatively free. The developmental requirements, resistance and habits of the free-living larvæ have been studied by the aid of various isolation and cultural methods (Section **VII**, VII, 12-15). Larvæ survive and mature best in shaded localities, where they are protected from drying. Heavy clay and compact soils without vegetation are less favorable than loose soils such as light sandy or alluvial deposits and loam or humus covered with vegetation. Droughts, fluctuations in temperature, excessive moisture, natural enemies such as bacteria, fungi and protozoa continually destroy the larvæ. Constant reinfection of the soil, however, tends to maintain the supply in endemic areas. The

FIG. 86.—CHARACTERISTIC POSITIONS OF INFECTIVE HOOKWORM LARVÆ ON MOIST SOIL

(From Hegner, Root, Augustine and Huff, *Parasitology*, 1938, D. Appleton-Century Company).

death rate is greatest in the first 10 days; in heavily infected soils under tropical conditions 90 per cent of the larvæ die in 3 weeks and practically all in 6 weeks.[12] Although larvæ require relatively little moisture, drying is destructive; on dry soil *A. duodenale* dies in 20 days and *N. americanus* in 9 days.[13] Direct sunlight is fatal in 2 hours.[14] Optimal development occurs when the soil is kept constantly moist without alternate drying and excessive wetting.[15] Salt water retards hatching and has 600 times the lethal effect of fresh water.[16] At 0° to 1° C. larvæ survive less than 2 weeks; at −10° to −12° C., less than 24 hours; and at 45° C., less than 50 minutes.[8] Their activity is most marked between 35° and 40° C.; below 15° C. their movements are lethargic and above 40° C. irregular. They develop to the infective stage only between 17° and 37° C.[17] Larvæ cannot develop in undiluted feces; the survival period in fecal receptacles during the summer in Australia is two weeks for *A. duodenale* and one week for *N. americanus*.[14] Larvæ die quickly in urine and the addition of urine to feces increases the death rate.

[12] Cort, W. W., Augustine, D. L. and Payne, G. C., 1921.

[13] Svensson, R. M., 1927.

[14] Heydon, G. M., 1927.

[15] Cort, W. W., 1925.

[16] Caldwell, F. C. and Caldwell, E. L., 1927.

[17] McCoy, O. R., 1930.

Ammonium sulphate, sodium nitrate, gypsum and lime, which are common fecal disinfectants, kill both ova and larvæ.[18]

Infection of Man.—When human skin comes in contact with infested soil, the filariform larvæ enter through the hair follicles or pores, or may bore through the unbroken surface. Damp, clinging soil facilitates infection. From the skin the larvæ enter the lymphatics or venules and are carried in the blood through the heart to the lungs, where they pass from the capillaries into the alveoli. They ascend the bronchi and trachea, are finally swallowed, and pass down the esophagus through the stomach to the intestines, where they undergo the third molt. After a final fourth molt about the thirteenth day they acquire adult characteristics, and mature egg-laying females are produced in from four to seven weeks after infection, averaging 53 days for *A. duodenale*.[3]

Infection may also occur by mouth, the larvæ being taken into the body through drinking water or contaminated food. The larvæ of *A. caninum,* when infection takes place by mouth, develop directly in the gastro-intestinal tract and do not pass through the usual pulmonary cycle, which appears to be an incidental step not vital for development.[19] The larvæ of the dog hookworm, *Uncinaria stenocephala,* develop in the intestinal tract without pulmonary migration, entering the mucosal glands to emerge after some days.[20] In unsuitable hosts, such as rabbits, mice and guinea pigs, only the pulmonary cycle takes place.

PATHOGENESIS

Pathology.—The pathology of hookworm infection is concerned with: (1) the skin at the site of entry; (2) the lungs during the migratory cycle; and (3) the small intestine, the habitat of the adult worm.

Ground itch or hookworm dermatitis, caused by the larvæ in the skin, is most prevalent during the rainy season in the tropics, and in the spring and summer months in the Southern United States. The feet are most frequently affected, particularly between the toes. An itching edematous erythema is followed by a papulovesicular eruption that may become pustular and ulcerative from pyogenic infection and may persist for weeks. Sensitive persons sometimes show urticaria. It is prevalent in infections with *Necator americanus,* but is less frequently observed with *A. duodenale*.[21]

As the migrating larvæ pass into the alveolar spaces from the pulmonary capillaries, they cause petechial hemorrhages and produce a leukocytic and later a fibroblastic infiltration of the alveolar tissues. In heavy infections the inflammatory reaction may be so extensive and severe as to produce lobular consolidation, particularly if accompanied by secondary bacterial infection.

The adult worms adhere to the intestinal mucosa with their powerful buccal capsules sucking blood and tearing off bits of macerated mucosa, thus causing hemorrhage and chronic enteritis (Fig. 87). They secrete an anticoagulant that facilitates their bloodsucking activities, and each time a worm changes its position

---

[18] Oldt, F., 1927.

[19] Foster, A. O. and Cross, S. X., 1934.

[20] Fülleborn, F., 1929.

[21] Fülleborn, F., 1930.

it leaves a minute oozing hemorrhagic area. Secondary bacterial invasion may lead to the formation of small ulcers at these sites. The continuous loss of blood is the chief cause of hookworm anemia. The drain upon the blood-forming organs in even moderate infections produces secondary changes in the hematopoietic system. Myeloid metaplasia may be present in the spleen with advanced evolutional stages in the splenic red blood cells and in some cases infiltration with eosinophilic myelocytes and megakaryocytes.[22]

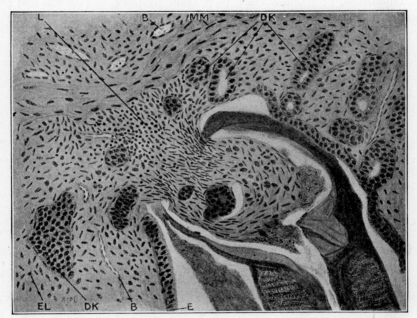

FIG. 87.—SAGITTAL SECTION OF THE HEAD END OF *Ancylostoma duodenale* GRASPING MUCOUS MEMBRANE

B, blood vessels; DK, intestinal glands; E, epithelial cells; EL, eosinophilic leukocytes; L, leukocytic infiltration; MM, muscularis mucosæ (After Oudendal, from Hegner, Root, Augustine and Huff, *Parasitology,* 1938, D. Appleton-Century Company).

Symptomatology.—Hookworm disease is essentially a chronic infection and the infected individual ordinarily shows no acute symptoms. At times, however, massive infections induce acute symptoms consisting of severe abdominal pain, sudden loss of strength, prostration, and circulatory and pulmonary disturbances. Infections with *A. duodenale* are more serious and produce symptoms with fewer worms than infections with *N. americanus.*

Chronic hookworm infection may be grouped into three types according to severity: (1) light infections in which the blood loss is compensated and symptoms are absent, although the infected individual may have a lowered resistance to extraneous disease; (2) infections where the blood loss is not compensated and the patient shows undernourishment, intestinal disorders, anemia, lack of energy,

---

[22] Cruz, W. O., 1934.

and mental and physical retardation; and (3) severe infections with broken compensation, leading to physical exhaustion and cardiac failure.

Complete absence of symptoms is explained by individual resistance, good health, adequate diet or low intensity of infection. Infection without clinical symptoms and anemia has been reported in Hungarian miners.[2] Patients with mild symptoms usually evidence vague dyspepsia and weakness (laziness). In more intense infections there is diarrhea with mucus and blood alternating with constipation, biliousness, profound anemia, palpitation, dyspnea, and mental and physical depression. The patient is listless, with apathetic puffy face (Fig. 88) and flabby

FIG. 88.—TYPICAL FACIAL EXPRESSIONS OF INDIVIDUALS SUFFERING FROM HOOKWORM DISEASE

(After Ashford and Gutierrez, from Hegner, Root, Augustine and Huff, *Parasitology*, 1938, D. Appleton-Century Company).

muscles, and may show paresthesia, mental apathy and sexual dysfunction. In pregnancy hookworm infection predisposes to toxic conditions with albuminuria, edema and lowered renal function.[23] In severe and often fatal infections there is profound anemia, edema often with ascites, diarrhea, mental disturbances and cardiac decompensation.

In highly endemic areas children show physical, mental and sexual retardation, the number of worms in the intestine largely determining the symptomatology. Children with less than 25 worms show no symptoms; with 26 to 100 a slight reduction in hemoglobin and slight mental retardation; and with more than 100 definite injury.[24] In the last instance stunted growth, delayed sexual development, severe anemia and noticeable mental retardation are observed.[25]

[23] King, E. L., 1929; Wickramasuriya, G. A. W., 1935.

[24] Smillie, W. G. and Augustine, D. L., 1926.
[25] Smillie, W. G. and Spencer, C. R., 1926.

Hookworm Anemia.—The most prominent characteristic in hookworm disease is a secondary anemia with diminution in hemoglobin and erythrocytes, which in severe cases gives a light yellowish tinge to the skin. The anemia begins 10 to 20 weeks after infection and is progressive. It is more marked in *A. duodenale* than in *N. americanus* infections. The erythrocytes range from 1 to 3.5 million per cmm. There is a low mean corpuscular volume, a low hemoglobin and a normal or subnormal reticulocyte count.[26] The plasma volume is increased but the total blood volume is diminished.[27] At times the blood picture in severe cases may simulate that of a primary anemia, but this may result from constitutional predisposition or a superimposed primary anemia.[28]

Clinical and experimental evidence indicates that hookworm anemia is due to the loss of blood. The old theory of toxic effects upon the blood-forming organs has never been confirmed, although lytic substances in the worm have been demonstrated.[29] Experiments with dogs infected with *A. caninum* indicate that a comparable microcytic hypochromic anemia that responds to iron-therapy can be produced by intestinal hemorrhage.[30]

Evidently other factors influence its production, since the anemia may be cured by diet and iron-therapy [22] while the patient still harbors the parasites. The degree of anemia is not always correlated with the intensity of the infection.[26] Altered lipid metabolism induced by loss of blood, diet and the condition of the intestinal tract, may play an important part in the production of anemia, although the changes in the blood lipids may be the result of the anemia.[31]

The leukocyte count usually is from 5,200 to 10,000 per cmm.,[26] but in early infections may reach 17,000.[25] Eosinophilia is irregular. The percentage is usually from 2 to 15 per cent [26] but during the early stages it may be as high as 55 per cent.[25] Blood cholesterol, serum protein and serum calcium are low [28] and glucose tolerance is altered.[27]

Creeping Eruption.—The lesions in man produced by *A. braziliense* and *A. caninum* are chiefly local cutaneous reactions at the site of larval penetration. Intestinal infection in man with *A. braziliense* is unknown in the United States of America, but instances have been observed in South America, Africa and the Orient. The adult worms produce eosinophilic infiltration and local tissue destruction in the jejunum.[32]

The so-called creeping eruption which is prevalent in the United States along the Gulf of Mexico is due to the larvæ of *A. braziliense* and develops after contact with moist sand and earth contaminated by the feces of infected dogs and cats.[33] Somewhat similar cutaneous lesions are associated with dipterous larvæ and a nematode, *Gnathostoma spinigerum* (Chapter XX). At the point of invasion a reddish, itchy papule develops and within two or three days narrow linear, slightly elevated, erythematous, serpiginous, intracutaneous tunnels are produced by the

[26] Suarez, R. M., 1933.

[27] Fikri, M. M. and Ghalioungui, P., 1937.

[28] Ashford, B. K., 1931; Fieschi, A., 1932.

[29] van Slyke, W., 1935.

[30] Foster, A. O. and Landsberg, J. W., 1934; Rhoads, C. P., Castle, W. B., Payne, G. C. and Lawson, H. A., 1934.

[31] Donomae, I, 1927; de Langen, C. D., 1934.

[32] Bonne, C., 1937.

[33] Kirby-Smith, J. L., Dove, W. E. and White, G. F., 1926.

migration of the larvæ, which move from a fraction of an inch to several inches each day (Fig. 89). Vesicles form along its course, and the surface becomes dry and crusty. The itching is intense and the resultant scratching may lead to secondary infection. The most common site is on the hands or feet, but the eruption may occur on any part of the body. It persists from several days to weeks. Local eosinophilia and round-cell infiltration may be present. The ethyl chloride spray supplemented by cold, moist, antiseptic dressings is considered the treatment of choice.[34]

Experimental infections in man with *A. braziliense* from a cat have produced cutaneous eruptions persisting for 35 to 54 days but no intestinal infection.[35] The

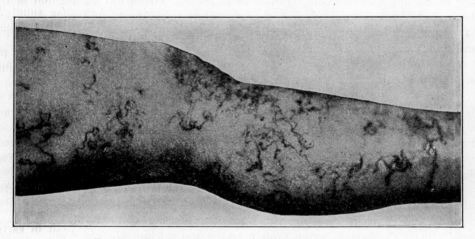

FIG. 89.—CREEPING ERUPTION OF *Ancylostoma braziliense*

Multiple rapidly developing lesions of about two weeks' duration (After Kirby-Smith, Dove and White, 1926).

larvæ do not cause a creeping eruption in the skin of dogs, cats, rats, guinea pigs or monkeys, although nodular lesions are obtained in monkeys.[36] The larvæ of *A. caninum,* as well as the European dog hookworm, *Uncinaria stenocephala,* produce a mild transient dermatitis with vesicular lesions, similar to that of *N. americanus.* The lesions are inconspicuous, disappear within 3 to 14 days, and do not show the conspicuous linear lines of the creeping eruption of *A. braziliense.*[37]

Immunity.—Immunity to hookworm infection has been studied chiefly with *A. caninum* and *A. braziliense.* There is evidence of species-resistance in animals against *A. duodenale* and *N. americanus.* Racial immunity is suggested by the fact that in Mississippi the incidence of hookworm infection in whites is over ten times that in Negroes.[38] Man shows no apparent resistance with age, but experiments indicate age-resistance in dogs and cats to *A. caninum* and *A. braziliense,*

[34] Kirby-Smith, J. L., 1935.
[35] Shelmire, B., 1928.
[36] Dove, W. E., 1932.
[37] White, G. F. and Dove, W. E., 1928;

Heydon, G. M., 1929.
[38] Keller, A. E., Leathers, W. S. and Ricks, H. C., 1934.

as evidenced by the number and growth of adult worms after test-doses of larvæ.[39] Local cutaneous reactions in *A. caninum* infections are more severe and persistent in older dogs. Age-resistance to *A. caninum,* however, may depend upon the general health and hemoglobin level, since hemorrhage and an iron-deficient diet lower resistance.[40]

Previous infection in dogs evidently confers some degree of immunity to *A. caninum* as evidenced by a markedly reduced ova-production[41] and by the development of less than 5 per cent of the number of adult worms obtained in the control dogs.[42] Previous infection enhanced the resistance of dogs to superinfection with *A. caninum* but the immunity disappeared on the removal of the worms by treatment.[43] On the other hand, no immunity from previous infection with *A. caninum* has been reported in dogs.[44] A series of sublethal, oral or cutaneous infections protected mice against five times the lethal dose of *A. caninum,* but the resistance was of short duration.[45] The immunized mice showed a more persistent inflammatory reaction to the larvæ. Attempts to produce artificially active and passive immunity in mice against *A. caninum* were unsuccessful.[46]

DIAGNOSIS, PROGNOSIS AND TREATMENT

Diagnosis.—The clinical picture is usually characteristic but is not sufficiently pathognomonic to permit absolute differentiation from the anemias, debilitating diseases, and other helminthic infections. Final diagnosis depends upon finding the characteristic ova in the feces. They can usually be observed in ordinary cover-glass preparations, but in light infections concentrative methods (Section VII, VII) may be required. The direct cover-glass mount was of value only when there were over 1,200 ova per gram of formed feces and the Stoll dilution ova-counting method was 7.1 per cent more efficient.[47] Cover-glass preparations gave two-thirds as many positive results as dilution ova-counts and missed almost all cases of less than 400 ova per gram of feces.[48] Ova-counting methods (Section VII, VII, 8-11) are useful in surveys since they provide quantitative data for instituting control measures and measuring their results. It is practically impossible to distinguish the ova of *A. duodenale* from those of *N. americanus* except for their slightly smaller size. Hookworm ova are similar but somewhat larger than *Strongyloides* ova, which occasionally may appear in the feces during diarrhea or after purgation. *Trichostrongylus* ova are larger, more elongate and have narrow rounded ends.

Prognosis.—Prognosis is good, except for patients in the terminal stages of the disease or with serious secondary complications. Recovery usually follows improved nutrition, iron-therapy and administration of anthelmintics.

[39] Herrick, C. A., 1928; Scott, J. A., 1928; Sarles, M. P., 1929.

[40] Foster, A. O. and Cort, W. W., 1935; Foster A. O., 1935, 1936.

[41] McCoy, O. R., 1931.

[42] Otto, G. F., Kerr, K. B. and Landsberg, J. W., 1937.

[43] Herrick, C. A., 1928.

[44] Foster, A. O., 1935.

[45] Kerr, K. B., 1935, 1936.

[46] Kerr, K. B., 1938.

[47] Keller, A. E., 1934.

[48] Cort, W. W., Stoll, N. R. and Grant, J. B., 1926.

Treatment.—Treatment consists in building up the general resistance of the patient and anthelmintic therapy. An adequate diet, antianemic iron-therapy, and hygienic measures will materially improve the health of the patient even though he still harbors the worms. A reduction in the number of ova in children under dietary treatment has even been reported.[49] Seriously ill patients should be confined to bed, given a well-balanced diet with ample proteins and iron, and at times receive blood transfusions before the administration of anthelmintic drugs is indicated.

Tetrachlorethylene, carbon tetrachloride and hexylresorcinol have proved the best anthelmintics for hookworms. Oil of chenopodium (Section **VII,** XIII, 30) although effective, is not used because of its toxicity except in combination with carbon tetrachloride and tetrachlorethylene.

Tetrachlorethylene (Section **VII,** XIII, 22) is the drug of choice because of its high efficiency, only slightly less than that of carbon tetrachloride, and its low toxicity.[50] A few instances of tetrachlorethylene intoxication, however, have been reported. A single treatment removes from 77 to 97 per cent of the worms.[51]

Carbon tetrachloride (Section **VII,** XIII, 21) is the most effective drug, a single 3 ml. dose removing from 91 to 98 per cent of the worms and giving a high percentage of cures. Its relatively high toxicity, however, necessitates careful supervision of its administration and thereby lessens its value. Intoxications arising from the irritation or mechanical obstruction of ascarids, chronic or acute alcoholism, undigested food and calcium deficiency may be avoided by preliminary treatment for *Ascaris,* by diet and by the selection of patients.[52]

Hexylresorcinol (Section **VII,** XIII, 23) is moderately effective, a single treatment removing about 70 to 75 per cent of the hookworms. It is especially suited for children and debilitated persons, since it has no untoward or unpleasant effects and treatment may be repeated several times with safety.[53] It is the drug of choice in combined *Ascaris* and hookworm infections, where the action of carbon tetrachloride and possible tetrachlorethylene may be complicated by the activities of the migrating ascarids in causing intestinal obstruction, in producing gastrointestinal disturbances and in permitting excessive absorption of the drugs. A single treatment will remove practically all the ascarids and about 70 per cent of the hookworms and two treatments will eliminate from 85 to 90 per cent of the hookworms and usually all ascarids.[53] It may also be given in mixed infections prior to the administration of more potent antihookworm drugs. A mixture of oil of chenopodium and tetrachlorethylene is also used for the simultaneous removal of ascarids and hookworms.

Mass treatment of large groups reduces the incidence and intensity of infections in endemic regions and is of value in controlling the disease among primitive peoples.[54] Its effectiveness depends upon repetition and upon sanitary measures

[49] Ahmann, C. F. and Bristol, L. M., 1933.
[50] Lambert, S. M., 1933; Brown, H. W., 1934; Fantus, B., 1935.
[51] Soper, F. L., 1926; Schapiro, L. and Stoll, N. R., 1927; Kendrick, J. F., 1929; Pessoa, S. B. and Pascale, H., 1937.
[52] Lamson, P. D., Minot, A. S. and Robbins, R. H., 1928.
[53] Brown, H. W., 1934.
[54] O'Brien, H. R., 1926; Jacocks, W. P., 1929; Lambert, S. M., 1933.

and educational propaganda to prevent reinfection. A combination of oil of cheno-podium and carbon tetrachloride or tetrachlorethylene is often used, since the narcotizing action of the former increases the lethal effect of the latter. This form of treatment removes up to 98 per cent of the hookworms and about 65 per cent of the ascarids.[55]

PREVENTION

Epidemiology.—Our present knowledge of the epidemiology of hookworm infection has been acquired by determining the intensity of infection (infective index) of a population by the ova-count, and by ascertaining the extent and intensity of soil contamination (Section **VII**, VII, 8-15). The prevalence of hookworm infection is determined by: (1) the intensity of infection in a community, which is more important than the number of persons infected; (2) temperature and other environmental conditions favorable for the existence and development of the free-living larvæ; (3) the extent of sanitary sewage disposal and the degree of soil contamination; and (4) the sanitary habits and economic status of the people. Many surveys throughout the world have shown that the incidence and intensity of hookworm infection varies greatly, depending upon the sanitary habits of the peoples and environmental conditions. In practically all countries where hookworm infection is prevalent, the people lack knowledge of and facilities for sanitation. As a result there is habitual pollution of the soil by promiscuous defecation in secluded areas near habitations and places of work. For this reason rural districts usually have a higher rate than urban.

In endemic districts the incidence is spotty since certain areas are heavily infested with larvæ, while others, because of the customs of the people or the nature of the soil, are comparatively free. Thus the incidence for a country or district gives little information other than the geographical distribution of the parasites.

Hookworm larvæ tend to remain where deposited, but they may be carried by floods or transported by animals to other localities. The ova even pass unharmed through the digestive tracts of mammals. Heavy rains tend to reduce soil pollution and the soil will usually clear itself of contamination within a few months if reinfection is prevented. The ova, however, at times show remarkable persistence. They even pass through Imhoff tanks and rubble filter beds, since hookworm dermatitis has been observed in coolies working in three-year-old sludge.[56]

The position of the larvæ on the top soil affords easy transmission to barefooted individuals and to those handling contaminated material. The mature larvæ can move freely over the surfaces of canvas and leather and can even penetrate moist canvas, but cannot pass through leather except through minute holes in the seams.[57]

Prophylaxis.—Before instituting a program of hookworm control it is advisable by means of surveys to determine the average intensity of infection, the extent

[55] O'Brien, H. R., 1926; Ritchie, T. R., 1927; Schapiro, L. and Stoll, N. R., 1927; Daubney, R. and Carman, J. A., 1928; Kendrick, J. F., 1929.

[56] Hirst, L. F., 1932.

[57] Payne, G. C., 1929.

of soil pollution, and the local environmental conditions. Pre- and post-control surveys provide a means of determining the efficacy of prophylactic measures. Hookworm infection may be reduced or even eliminated in a community by: (1) the treatment of infected individuals; (2) the sanitary disposal of fecal wastes; and (3) the protection of susceptible individuals.

Individual treatment checked by laboratory examinations is sufficient, when the incidence and average worm burden are low, or when environmental conditions are not favorable for the survival of the larvæ. Mass treatment is advisable when the incidence is high, the average worm burden over 150, facilities for detecting infected individuals not available, and when sanitation is lacking. Thus soil pollution is diminished and opportunities for acquiring infection are decreased. However, unless mass treatment includes the entire population, is repeated at intervals and is accompanied by improvements in sanitation, its effect is often temporary.[58]

The control of hookworm infection in localities where environmental conditions are favorable for larval development is largely a matter of sanitation. In rural communities, where sewerage systems are impracticable, in order to prevent the pollution of the soil, laws requiring the construction of closed pit or chemical latrines should be enforced and promiscuous defecation discouraged. The use of night soil as fertilizer presents an economic as well as a sanitary problem, which may be solved by chemical disinfection of the feces. In localities where sanitary regulations can be strictly enforced, as on tea, rubber and coffee plantations, striking results in hookworm control have been obtained.

The installation of sanitary measures seems simple, but practically it is surprisingly difficult to overcome the inertia of people toward constructing, maintaining and using sanitary latrines and in revamping their old habits of promiscuous defecation. Education of the public as to the transmission of the disease and the proper use of latrines is as essential as their installation. Attempts to enforce sanitary regulations are less effective than sanitary instruction in the home, publicity campaigns, and training in the schools.

The wearing of shoes in infected areas greatly reduces the chances of infection; the incidence of infection in workers on Brazilian coffee estates has been found to be nine times greater in the unshod,[59] and school children in certain rural districts are heavily infected up to 14 years of age when they begin to wear shoes.[60] Well-made boots and gloves afford some protection for miners.

FAMILY *STRONGYLIDÆ* BAIRD, 1853

The well-developed buccal capsule is without teeth or cutting plates, but bears a crown of chitinous leaf-like processes. The male has two prominent copulatory spicules and the vulva is located in the posterior half of the body. The members of this family are parasites in the digestive tracts of mammals. The species reported from man are *Ternidens deminutus, Œsophagostomum apiostomum* and *Œsophagostomum stephanostomum* var. *thomasi.*

[58] Scott, J. A. and Barlow, C. H., 1938.   [60] Smillie, W. G. and Augustine, D. L.,
[59] Smillie, W. G., 1922.   1925.

Ternidens deminutus (RAILLIET AND HENRY, 1905) RAILLIET AND HENRY, 1909

Ternidens deminutus was discovered in 1865 in the intestine of a Negro of the Comoro Islands off Portuguese East Africa. It is common in natives and monkeys in Southern Rhodesia and has also been reported in man and primates in Nyasaland and Portuguese East Africa. The infective larva is semirhabditoid and not infective through the skin.[61] The worm at times produces cystic nodules in the wall of the colon but gives rise to no particular symptoms.

Œsophagostomum apiostomum (WILLACH, 1891) RAILLIET AND HENRY, 1905

Œsophagostomum apiostomum is a common parasite of monkeys and gorillas and has been reported from man in northern Nigeria. The worm is from 8 to 10.5 cm. in length, the male being slightly smaller than the female. The ova resemble those of the hookworms. Its life cycle is probably similar to that of other strongylids. The larvæ exsheath in the cecum and encyst in the submucosa and muscularis mucosa, where they produce exudative and proliferative nodular tumors. After a period of growth the immature worms erupt from these cystic nodules and complete their growth in the cecum. Rupture of the nodule may produce hemorrhage and mucosal injury, thus paving the way for secondary bacterial infection.

Œsophagostomum brumpti, a parasite of apes, was found by Brumpt in a native of East Africa, and by Joyeux in a Negro in New Guinea. It may be identical with *Œ. apiostomum*.

Œsophagostomum stephanostomum VAR. thomasi RAILLIET AND HENRY, 1909

Œsophagostomum stephanostomum var. *thomasi*, found in man in Brazil, differs only slightly from *Œ. stephanostomum*, a parasite of the gorilla. The immature worms form fibrous nodules in the ileum, cecum and colon.

FAMILY *SYNGAMIDÆ* LEIPER, 1912

The well-developed subglobular buccal capsule is equipped at its base with teeth. The spicules in the male are either absent or short and thick, and the vulva of the female is situated in the anterior part of the body. The members of this family are parasites of the respiratory tract of birds and mammals. The species reported from man is *Syngamus laryngeus*.

Syngamus laryngeus RAILLIET, 1899

Syngamus laryngeus is a parasite of the upper air passages of ruminants. Man is an accidental host. Some six cases of human infection have been reported from Brazil, Puerto Rico, Trinidad, Santa Lucia and the Philippines. The adults, attached to the bronchial and tracheal mucosa, produce coughing and sometimes hemoptysis. Diagnosis is established by finding the adult worm or large ova with membranous polar caps in the sputum.

SUPERFAMILY *TRICHOSTRONGYLOIDEA* CRAM, 1927

The members of the superfamily TRICHOSTRONGYLOIDEA are long thin worms in which the buccal capsule is absent or rudimentary. The male bursa has two large lateral lobes and a small dorsal lobe with well-developed rays. They are intestinal parasites of rumi-

---

[61] Sandground, J. H., 1931.

nants and less frequently of man and other mammals. The species parasitic in man belong to the family TRICHOSTRONGYLIDÆ.

THE GENUS *TRICHOSTRONGYLUS* LOOSS, 1905

The species of the genus *Trichostrongylus* are small nematodes, the males measuring from 4 to 5.5 mm. and the females 5 to 7 mm. They differ chiefly in the structure of the male bursa and of the posterior end of the female (Fig. 90).

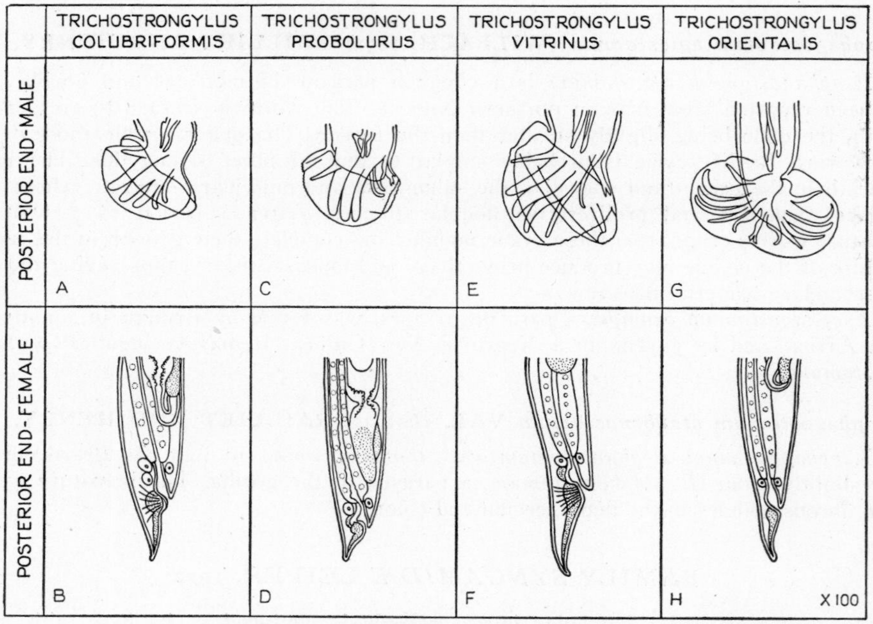

FIG. 90.—GENUS *Trichostrongylus*

Posterior ends of male and female (*A* to *F* redrawn from Looss, 1905; *G* and *H* adapted from Jimbo, 1914).

Diagnosis is based upon finding ellipsoidal ova in the feces, that are longer and have more pointed ends than hookworm ova. These ova range from 73 to 95 μ in length by 40 to 50 μ in breadth and are difficult to distinguish as to species. The embryonate ova, passed into the feces, develop through three larval stages in the soil. The larvæ are resistant to desiccation and can survive for months. Treatment of man is similar to that of hookworm. Prevention lies in avoiding the consumption of raw plants from contaminated soil.

Trichostrongylus colubriformis (GILES, 1892) RANSOM, 1911

T. colubriformis is a parasite of sheep, goats, camels, several wild ruminants, baboons and squirrels. It has been found in isolated cases in man in Egypt, India, Armenia, Australia and the Southern United States.

Trichostrongylus probolurus (RAILLIET, 1896) LOOSS, 1905

T. probolurus is a parasite of the duodenum of sheep, camels and gazelles. Infections in man have been reported from Egypt, Armenia and Siberia.

Trichostrongylus vitrinus LOOSS, 1905

T. vitrinus is a parasite of cattle, sheep, goats and camels. Infections in man have been reported in Egypt, Armenia and Siberia.

Trichostrongylus orientalis JIMBO, 1914

T. orientalis is a not infrequent parasite of man in the farming districts of Japan, Korea, Formosa, South and Central China, and Armenia. It is also found in sheep and camels. The worm has its chief site in the duodenum and is usually found in small numbers. No clinical symptoms are present in mild infections.

OTHER SPECIES OF *Trichostrongylus* FROM MAN

T. instabilis (Railliet, 1893) Looss, 1905, has been reported in man in Armenia and Siberia; *T. axei* (Cobbold, 1879) Mönnig, 1934, in Armenia, Siberia and Mauritius; and *T. skrjabini* Kalantarian, 1928, in Armenia.

Hæmonchus contortus (RUDOLPHI, 1803) COBB, 1898

The sheep wireworm was first described by Rudolphi in 1803 under the name of *Strongylus contortus*. It is a common parasite in the fourth stomach and duodenum of sheep and cattle throughout the world, and has been found in deer, wild sheep, caribou, bison, moose, antelope and other ruminants. It is of considerable economic importance. It has been reported from man in Brazil and in northern Australia.

The parasite is a cream to reddish nematode with an attenuated anterior end equipped with a pharyngeal lancet. The male measures from 10 to 20 mm. in length and the female from 18 to 80 mm. The copulatory bursa of the male has two long lateral lobes and an asymmetrical dorsal lobe. The two spicules of the male are barbed. The vulva is situated about one-fourth of the body length from the posterior end and is covered by a tongue-like fold. The posterior end of the female is pointed. The oval, elongated ova, 75 to 95 μ by 40 to 50 μ, are already segmented when deposited.

Development is direct, with a single host and a free-living stage. The infective, sheathed, third-stage larva, produced about four days after the ovum reaches the soil, is resistant to desiccation and cold. It crawls up moist grasses and is ingested by grazing animals, in which it reaches maturity in 18 to 21 days.

The blood-sucking worm damages the mucosa. When present in appreciable numbers, it produces anemia, edema, emaciation and digestive irregularities in sheep and causes a particularly high mortality in lambs. In man it causes an anemia resembling that of hookworm infection. Diagnosis can be made only by finding the adults or by rearing the larvæ in cultures, since the ova closely resemble those of other strongylids. The parasite is resistant to the usual anthelmintics unless administered in large amounts. Infection in man is accidental. Workers in contaminated fields should refrain from chewing grass and should wash their hands before eating. The spread of the infection in sheep is controlled by using the contaminated grazing fields for crops. The resistance of lambs and of markedly undernourished sheep is lower than that of normal sheep.[62]

SUPERFAMILY *METASTRONGYLOIDEA* CRAM, 1927

In members of the superfamily METASTRONGYLOIDEA, the buccal cavity is absent or rudimentary, and the male bursa is usually small with atypically developed rays. All species belong to the family METASTRONGYLIDÆ, and are parasites of the respiratory and circulatory systems of mammals. One species, *Metastrongylus elongatus*, has been reported from man.

[62] Ross, I. C., 1932; Fraser, A. H. D. and Robertson, D., 1933.

Metastrongylus elongatus (DUJARDIN, 1845) RAILLIET AND HENRY, 1911

Metastrongylus elongatus, the porcine lung worm, is a common parasite of hogs, and at times of deer, sheep and cattle. Three cases of human infection have been reported: two pulmonary and one gastro-intestinal. The parasite is a filiform flesh-colored nematode, the males measuring 12 to 25 mm. in length and the females 20 to 50 mm. The males have a trilobed copulatory bursa and two long spicules.

The thick-shelled ellipsoidal ova, 57 to 100 μ by 39 to 72 μ, are evacuated in the sputum or swallowed and passed in the feces. The larvæ, after hatching in the soil, are ingested by earthworms, in which they develop first in the esophageal wall and finally progress to the infective form in the circulatory system. The definitive host is usually infected by the ingestion of infected earthworms or, less frequently, contaminated soil. In young pigs the worms may produce a fatal bronchitis or pneumonia. Previous infection confers some degree of immunity to superinfection.[63] Man accidentally acquires the infection from ground contaminated by hogs. Diagnosis is made by finding the ova in the sputum or feces.

REFERENCES

BROWN, H. W.   Intestinal Parasitic Worms in the United States; Their Diagnosis and Treatment, J. Am. M. Ass., 1934, 103:651.

CHANDLER, A. C.   Hookworm Disease, 1929, Macmillan Company, New York, 477 pp.

CORT, W. W., *et al.*   Investigations on the Control of Hookworm Disease. I-XXXIV. Am. J. Hyg., 1921-25, Vol. 1-5. Am. J. Hyg. Monographic Series 7, 1926.

DOVE, W. E.   Further Studies on *Ancylostoma braziliense* and the Etiology of Creeping Eruption, Am. J. Hyg., 1932, 15:664.

FIKRI, M. M. and GHALIOUNGUI, P.   *Ancylostoma* Anæmia, Lancet, 1937, 1:800.

FOSTER, A. O. and CORT, W. W.   Further Studies on the Effect of a Generally Deficient Diet upon the Resistance of Dogs to Hookworm Infestation, Am. J. Hyg., 1935, 21:302.

FOSTER, A. O. and LANDSBERG, J. W.   The Nature and Cause of Hookworm Anemia, Am. J. Hyg., 1934, 20:259.

KIRBY-SMITH, J. L.   The Treatment of Creeping Eruption, South. M. J., 1935, 28:999.

LAMSON, P. D., BROWN, H. W. and WARD, C. B.   Anthelmintics; Some Therapeutic and Practical Considerations on Their Use, J. Am. M. Ass., 1932, 99:292.

LOOSS, A.   The Anatomy and Life History of *Agchylostoma duodenale* Dub. A Monograph, Records Egyptian Govt. School of Med. Vol. I-IV, 1905-1911.

OTTO, G. F., KERR, K. B. and LANDSBERG, J. W.   The Immunity to the Hookworm, *Ancylostoma caninum,* Acquired by Dogs as a Result of Previous Infection, J. Parasitol., 1937, 23:560.

RHOADS, C. P., CASTLE, W. B., PAYNE, G. C. and LAWSON, H. A.   Hookworm Anemia: Etiology and Treatment with Especial Reference to Iron, Am. J. Hyg., 1934, 20:291.

SCOTT, J. A. and BARLOW, C. H.   Limitations to the Control of Helminth Parasites in Egypt by Means of Treatment and Sanitation, Am. J. Hyg., 1938, 27:619.

SMILLIE, W. G., and AUGUSTINE, D. L.   Intensity of Hookworm Infestation in Alabama; Its Relationship to Residence, Occupation, Age, Sex and Race, J. Am. M. Ass., 1925, 85:1958.

SUAREZ, R. M.   Clinical Aspects of Uncinariasis, Puerto Rico J. Pub. Health & Trop. Med., 1933, 8:299.

---

[63] Schwartz, B. and Lucker, J. T., 1935.

Chapter XVIII

THE SUPERFAMILY OXYUROIDEA

SUPERFAMILY *OXYUROIDEA* RAILLIET, 1916

The members of the superfamily OXYUROIDEA are small, pin-shaped, mero-myarian nematodes parasitic in the large intestines of vertebrates. The males have a caudal projection and one or two copulatory spicules, and either a poorly developed bursa or none at all. The females are oviparous. The two species occurring in man, *Enterobius vermicularis* and *Syphacia obvelata,* belong to the family OXYURI-DÆ.

FAMILY *OXYURIDÆ* COBBOLD, 1864

The species of the family OXYURIDÆ have a simple mouth surrounded by inconspicu-ous lips, and no buccal capsule. The esophagus has a posterior trivalved bulbus clearly separated from the anterior part of the intestine. The larger female has a pointed elongate caudal extremity, a double germarium and a vulva that is usually situated pre-equatorially. The ova are ellipsoidal and asymmetrical. The smaller male has preänal suckers in only one genus. None of the species requires intermediate hosts.

Enterobius vermicularis (LINNÆUS, 1758) LEACH, 1853

Synonyms.—*Oxyuris vermicularis* (Linnæus, 1758) Lamarck, 1816; *Oxyurias vermicularis* (Linnæus, 1758) Stiles, 1905.

Disease.—Enterobiasis; oxyuriasis; pinworm infection.

History.—The pinworm, *Enterobius vermicularis,* has been known since ancient times. It was first described by Linnæus in 1758.

Geographical Distribution.—Cosmopolitan.

BIOLOGICAL CHARACTERISTICS

Morphology.—*Enterobius vermicularis* is a small, round worm inhabiting the cecum and adjacent portions of the large and small intestines of man. The head is attached to the mucosa of the intestinal wall. The anterior extremity is surrounded by a cuticular expansion (Fig. 91B). Narrow lateral alæ are present. The mouth, provided with three fairly distinct retractile lips, leads into the esophagus which has a prominent posterior bulbus and a prebulbar swelling.

The male worm, 2 to 5 mm. by 0.1 to 0.2 mm., is smaller than the female and is rarely seen. The posterior third of the body is sharply curved (Fig. 91A). The blunt tail bears six pairs of papillæ and a single, terminally-curved spicule, 70 μ in length, but no gubernaculum (Fig. 91C). The caudal alæ are supported by an anterior and a posterior pair of large papillæ.

The female worm, 8 to 13 mm. by 0.3 to 0.5 mm., has a long pointed tail and a rigid body (Fig. 91E). The anus is situated at the junction of the middle and posterior thirds of the body. There is an anterior and a posterior set of reproductive organs, each consisting of a coiled tubular ovary, an oviduct, and a uterus, opening into a common vagina near the vulva. The vulva is one-quarter of the body length

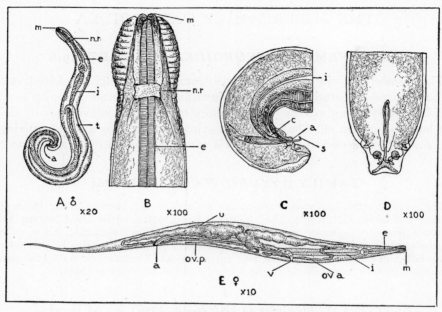

FIG. 91.—*Enterobius vermicularis*

A, male; *B*, anterior end of worm; *C*, posterior end of male, lateral view; *D*, posterior end of male, ventral view; *E*, female.

a, anus; *c*, cloaca; *e*, esophagus; *i*, intestine; *m*, mouth; *n.r.*, nerve ring; *ov.a.*, anterior ovary; *ov. p.*, posterior ovary; *s*, spicule; *t*, testis; *u*, uterus; *v*, vulva (Redrawn from Leuckart, 1876).

from the anterior end. In gravid females the uteri are so distended with ova that they appear to fill the entire body. The ova deposited in the perianal region have usually developed to tadpole-like embryos (Fig. 92). They are asymmetrical with one side flattened and range from 50 to 60 μ in length and from 20 to 32 μ in breadth, averaging 55 by 26 μ. The translucent shell consists of an outer, triple, albuminous covering for mechanical protection and an inner, embryonic, lipoidal membrane for chemical protection.[1] A gravid female worm contains an average of 11,105 ova.[2]

Physiology.—The mature female worms are fairly active and move irregularly in the intestine, but mainly downward toward the rectum. The pressure of the gravid uterus on the esophagus possibly forces the female to release her hold on the intestinal mucosa.[3] The worms are either passed in the feces or the females migrate

---

[1] Zawadowsky, M. M. and Schalimov, L. G., 1929.

[2] Reardon, L., 1938.

[3] Koch, E. W., 1925.

at night from the anus and crawl actively in the perianal and perineal regions, even entering the vagina or more rarely the bladder. The length of life of the individual worm is relatively short, probably less than two months. The male worm dies soon after copulation.

The embryonate ova are deposited in the perianal and genitocrural folds. Since oviposition does not occur until the female worm is stimulated by contact with air, the ova are not commonly laid in the intestine. The ova, expelled in masses by the contractions of the uterus and vagina, are left behind as the worm advances, or if the worm dries it explodes with showers of ova.[4]

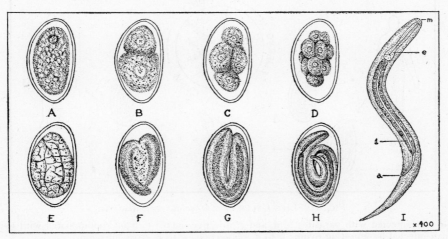

FIG. 92.—STAGES IN THE DEVELOPMENT OF THE LARVA OF *Enterobius vermicularis*
(Adapted from Leuckart, 1876).

LIFE CYCLE

Man is the only known natural host of *Enterobius vermicularis*. Several species of the family OXYURIDÆ, however, are found in mammals. Among these are *Oxyuris equi* of horses, asses and mules, *Aspiculuris tetraptera* of rats and mice, and *Passalurus ambiguus* of the rabbit.

Outside the host an infective larva develops within the shell in a few hours. Ova deposited within the intestine are often immature and those removed from worms in the appendix are not infective. No intermediate host or long period of incubation outside the body is necessary to complete the life cycle. The hands, particularly beneath the fingernails, become contaminated with adherent ova through scratching the perianal regions to alleviate the itching caused by the female worms. Thus, infective ova are readily transferred to the same or another host either directly by hand to mouth or indirectly through food and drink (Fig. 93). The ova that adhere to night clothes and bed linens may also be transmitted by the hands.

Upon ingestion the embryos are liberated in the duodenum. Fully developed ova of *O. equi* will hatch when placed in acid pepsin, pancreatic juice, or 0.1 to 0.2 per

[4] Nevzat, B. A., 1930.

cent hydrochloric acid followed by alkaline sodium carbonate.[5] Hatching occurs *in vitro* between 20° and 40° C. but only when the embryo has become a first-stage larva.[1] The liberated rhabditiform larva (Fig. 92I), 140 to 150 μ by 10 μ, molts twice before reaching adolescence in the jejunum and upper ileum. After mating, the females proceed to the cecum, where they attach themselves to the mucosa and develop to maturity. The duration of the cycle from the time the ovum is deposited to the production of a mature worm is about seven weeks.

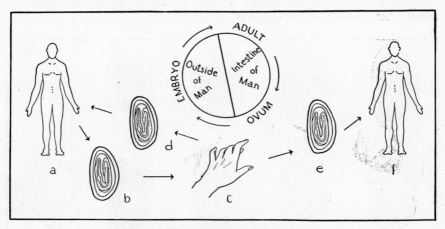

FIG. 93.—LIFE CYCLE OF *Enterobius vermicularis*

a, man infected with parasite; *b, d,* and *e*, infective ovum; *c*, hand contaminated with ovum; *f*, man infected by ingesting ovum; *a* to *d*, reinfection; *a* to *e*, cross-infection.

The presence of embryonate ova, eggshells and adults simultaneously in the intestine suggests that the ova may hatch in the intestine and that hyperinfection may take place within the host.[6] The observations on the oxyurids of rabbits in the intestinal mucosa lends credence to the idea of an intestinal cycle.[7] Likewise, if the worms migrate to the upper ileum, the ova, subjected to the action of the intestinal juices, may hatch.[8] The theory of hyperinfection, however, is open to question, since development of the infective stage depends upon a supply of free oxygen.

PATHOGENESIS

Pathology.—The worms are usually found in the cecum and nearby appendix, colon and lower ileum. At times they may travel up the small intestine and have even been observed in the stomach, esophagus and nose. Mild catarrhal inflammation of the intestinal mucosa may result from their attachment and mechanical irritation, and secondary bacterial invasion may lead to inflammation of the deeper layers of the intestine. A heavy infection has even caused an intestinal obstruction of the colon at the splenic flexure.[9]

[5] Macfie, J. W. S., 1924.
[6] Penso, G., 1935.
[7] Penso, G., 1932; Wetzel, R., 1931.
[8] Lentze, F. A., 1935.
[9] Stokes, A. C., 1929.

Pinworms have been frequently observed in appendices removed for subacute or chronic appendicitis (Fig. 94). The incidence of appendiceal invasion as reported by several investigators ranges from 1.2 to 18.2 per cent, the lowest percentage being in a series of 26,051 appendices. Opinions vary as to the etiological rôle of *Enterobius vermicularis* in appendicitis. It is not considered a significant factor by investigators who find a low percentage,[10] and is credited with some importance by others.[11] The incidence is three times as great in females as in males and is highest under 20 years of age. In most instances the worms are present only in the lumen and do not invade the mucosa. Lymphoid hyperplasia and irritative catarrhal exudation may be present but only a small percentage of *Enterobius* appendices show hemorrhage, ulceration, necrosis, or secondary bacterial invasion.

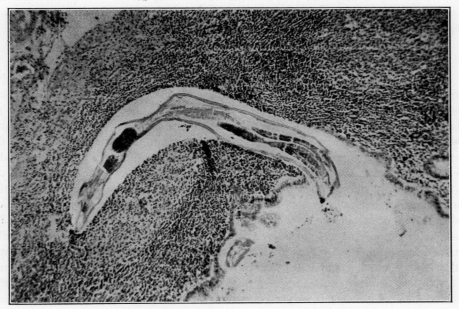

FIG. 94.—*Enterobius vermicularis* IN APPENDIX
(From Sandground, *Physician's Bulletin,* March-April, 1941, Eli Lilly and Company).

The penetration of the intestinal wall and the encystment of the worms in the peritoneum have been reported.[12] The worms invade the peritoneum by way of the female genital tract, causing pseudotuberculous inflammation of the Fallopian tubes.[13]

The migration of the egg-laying female from the anus causes congestion and irritation of the perianal and perineal regions. Scratching, occasioned by the intense

[10] Gordon, H., 1933; Beck, R. C., 1934.
[11] Harris, W. H. and Brown, D. C., 1925; Goodale, R. H., 1934; Ujiie, N., 1935; Bell, M. A., 1936; Botsford, T. W., Hudson, H. W., Jr. and Chamberlain, J. W., 1939.

[12] Alfeeva S. P., 1927; Susman, M. P., 1929; Goodale, R. H. and Krischner, H., 1930.
[13] Smith, W. S. and Denton, J., 1928; Wu, L. C., 1935.

itching, leads to excoriation, eczema and pyogenic infection. An ischio-anal abscess containing adult worms and ova has been observed.[14]

The blood cells show little change. There is a moderate eosinophilia ranging from 4 to 12 per cent and a slight reduction in the number of red blood cells.

Symptomatology.—Intestinal irritation, particularly in children, produces reflex nervous symptoms such as restlessness, disturbances in sleep, picking nose, incoördination, and possibly convulsive seizures. The intense, nocturnal anal pruritis may cause loss of sleep and expenditure of nervous energy, and the by-products of the worm may cause a toxemia in sensitive individuals. The patient may become anemic, nervous and emaciated from loss of appetite and malnutrition, but in most cases there are no demonstrable symptoms. In children the irritation of the perineal region may lead to masturbation. The migrations of the parasite occasionally may produce chronic appendicitis, low-grade peritonitis and chronic salpingitis.

DIAGNOSIS, PROGNOSIS AND TREATMENT

Diagnosis.—The presence of the parasite is suspected clinically in children who show intense nocturnal perianal itching, reflex symptoms and a mild eosinophilia. Diagnosis is made by finding the adult worms or ova. Often the first evidence of infection is the discovery of the adult worms in the feces, particularly after enemata, or in the perianal regions. In the feces the worms must be differentiated from fly larvæ. The ova are seldom found in the feces even with concentrative methods. Swabbing the perianal region with the N I H cellophane swab (Section **VII**, V, 2) gives a high percentage of positive results. The irregularity in the migrations of the gravid females requires repeated examinations to detect ova in the perianal regions and at least four swabbings in the early morning on nonconsecutive days should be made before the patient is considered free from infection. Ova are also frequently obtained from fingernail scrapings. They are identified by their asymmetrical shape and well-developed embryo. Intracutaneous tests, using an extract of the worms as an antigen, appear promising.[15] A negative reaction is useful in eliminating the possibility of infection, but as yet these tests have not been established as routine diagnostic procedures.

Prognosis.—Prognosis, except in secondary complications, is good and there are usually no serious effects, but ease of reinfection makes the elimination of the worms difficult.

Treatment.—Many anthelmintics and numerous types of enemata have been used with more or less success. The most efficient drugs are hexylresorcinol, tetrachlorethylene and gentian violet, but permanent cure depends upon persistent treatment and upon eliminating reinfection by the patient. Oral treatment with hexylresorcinol (Section **VII**, XIII, 23) combined with enemata has given satisfactory results.[16] Treatment is repeated weekly until the pinworms are eliminated, usually within five weeks. A single treatment with tetrachlorethylene (Section **VII**, XIII,

---

[14] Marshall, R. G. and Wood, Q. L., 1938.
[15] Wright, W. H. and Bozicevich, J., 1937; Tsuchiya, H. and Bauerlein, T. C., 1939.
[16] Brown, H. W., 1934; Faust, E. C., Dwyer, H. L. and Casparis, H. 1937.

22) is advocated for children with light infections.[17] Gentian violet (Section **VII**, XIII, 27) is recommended as a quick, cheap specific for oxyuriasis, a single course of treatment giving as high as 91.8 per cent of cures.[18] Enterobicidal and soothing ointments may be applied to the perianal region to reduce reinfection by destroying the female worms and to alleviate itching. Most ointments are of little or no aid in controlling the infection, although some are of value in relieving pruritus. Their enterobicidal properties are questionable, *e.g.*, hexylresorcinol salves do not kill the gravid females,[19] and even if successful these measures would not eliminate the immature females in the intestine. Treatment of one member of a family is futile, if other members are infected.

PREVENTION

Epidemiology.—Pinworm infection is relatively common, particularly among children. Surveys have revealed an incidence of 35 to 41 per cent in the general population and 37 to 57 per cent in children in the United States of America, and in Germany and Russia 66 to 80 per cent in children. The incidence is lowest in nurslings, rises in creeping children, is still higher in those from 2 to 6 years, and reaches its maximum in school children from 6 to 18 years. In Washington, D. C., the incidence was 35 per cent in preschool children, 51 per cent in school children and 22 per cent in adults, with a higher incidence in whites than in Negroes, 45 vs. 15 per cent.[20] There is a slightly higher incidence, about 5 per cent, in boys than in girls.[21] The infection is more prevalent in congested city districts, institutional groups, and among members of the same family. Enterobiasis is primarily a familial or institutional disease and is not restricted to any social class, since its peculiar mode of transmission evades the barriers that hygiene usually creates.

The absence of an appreciable extracorporeal developmental stage favors transmission from child to child. Transmission is effected by the direct transfer of ova from the perianal regions to the hands and thence to the mouth or to food. Since the life of the worm is relatively short, long-standing infections are due to reinfection. The possibility of oral and food infection by dust, first suggested by Oleinikoff in 1929, appears to be substantiated. Pinworm ova, many viable, have been recovered in 90 per cent of all samples of dust collected at various levels in the rooms of seven houses inhabited by one or more infected persons.[22] The presence of viable ova over the mouldings of doorways and windows indicates the ease of transportation by air currents. Ova probably can resist desiccation as long as ten days.

Prophylaxis.—Prevention is concerned with safeguarding the patient against reinfecting himself and infecting others, particularly members of the same family. Personal cleanliness is essential; the fingernails should be cut short, the hands

---

[17] Wright, W. H. and Cram, E. B., 1937; Wright, W. H., Bozicevich, J. and Gordon, L. S., 1937, 1938.

[18] Wright, W. H., Brady F. J. and Bozicevich, J., 1938; Wright, W. H. and Brady, F. J., 1940; Miller, M. J., Choquette, L., Audet, W., Kelso, R. F., and Guenetti, J. A., 1940.

[19] Wright, W. H., Brady, F. J. and Bozicevich, J., 1939.

[20] Cram, E. B. and Reardon, L., 1939.

[21] Levine, Z. S., 1933; Cram, E. B., Jones, M. F., Reardon, L. and Nolan, M. O., 1937.

[22] Nolan, M. O. and Reardon, L., 1939.

thoroughly cleansed after using the toilet and before meals, and the anal region washed and disinfected after defecation. Infected children should be kept from touching the perianal regions during sleep by protective sleeping garments. Since intestinal hyperinfection may take place anthelmintics should be systematically administered. In order to protect others the infected individual should sleep alone; underwear, night clothes and bedding should be carefully handled and laundered; and toilet seats should be scrubbed frequently with cresol. Food should be protected from dust and the hands of infected individuals. Strict hygienic measures alone often fail to reduce the incidence of enterobiasis.[23]

Syphacia obvelata (RUDOLPHI, 1802) SEURAT, 1916

Syphacia obvelata, a common cosmopolitan parasite of the cecum and large intestine of mice and rats, has been reported once in man, an American-Bohemian child in the Philippines. The parasite is characterized by three broad lips and an esophagus with a markedly constricted bulbus. Both sexes have long attenuated caudal extremities. The male, 1 to 1.6 mm. by 0.1 mm., has a deep ventrally curved posterior end, that bears a single, long, slightly-curved, copulatory spicule. The female, 3.5 to 5.7 mm. by 0.4 mm., has a single uterus and a preëquatorial vulva. The ova resemble those of *Enterobius vermicularis,* but are much larger, 125 by 35 μ, and more fusiform. They require no appreciable extracorporeal development and infection is transmitted directly from rodent to rodent. Human infection is accidentally acquired from material contaminated with feces of rodents.

REFERENCES

BELL, M. A. *Oxyuris vermicularis* and Appendicitis, Arch. Pediat., 1936, 53:649.

BROWN, H. W. Intestinal Parasitic Worms in the United States; Their Diagnosis and Treatment, J. Am. M. Ass., 1934, 103:651.

CRAM, E. B. and REARDON, L. Studies on Oxyuriasis. XII. Epidemiological Findings in Washington, D. C., Am. J. Hyg., 1939, 29, Sect. D:17.

FAUST, E. C., DWYER, H. L. and CASPARIS, H. Intestinal Parasitic Infections in Children, J. Pediat., 1937, 10:542.

GOODALE, R. H. and KRISCHNER, H. *Oxyuris vermicularis* in the Peritoneum, Arch. Path., 1930, 9:631.

GORDON, H. Appendical Oxyuriasis and Appendicitis Based on a Study of 26,051 Appendices, Arch. Path., 1933, 16:177.

NOLAN, M. O. and REARDON, L. Studies on Oxyuriasis; Distribution of Ova of *Enterobius vermicularis* in Household Dust, J. Parasitol., 1939, 25:173.

TSUCHIYA, H. and BAUERLEIN, T. C. Intradermal Test as an Aid in the Diagnosis of Enterobiasis, J. Lab. & Clin. Med., 1939, 24:627.

WRIGHT, W. H., BRADY, F. J., and BOZICEVICH, J. Studies on Oxyuriasis. XIV. Controlled Tests with Various Methods of Therapy, U. S. Pub. Health Rep., 1939, 54:2005.

——— and CRAM, E. B. Studies on Oxyuriasis. IV. Some Aspects of the Problem of Therapy, Am. J. Dis. Child., 1937, 54:1276.

[23] Sawitz, W., d'Antoni, J. S., Rhude, K. and Lob, S., 1940.

Chapter XIX

THE SUPERFAMILY ASCAROIDEA

SUPERFAMILY *ASCAROIDEA*

The superfamily ASCAROIDEA contains both free-living and parasitic nematodes. The mouth ordinarily has three conspicuous lips, one dorsal and two subventral, and no buccal capsule. The male usually has one or two copulatory spicules and no caudal alæ. The female has two ovaries and is oviparous. The life cycle requires no intermediate host. The species parasitic in man, *Ascaris lumbricoides, Toxocara canis, Toxocara cati* and *Lagochilascaris minor,* belong to the family ASCARIDÆ.

FAMILY *ASCARIDÆ* BAIRD, 1853

The ASCARIDÆ are parasitic polymyarian nematodes with three well-developed papillate lips sometimes supplemented with three secondary interlabia. There is no posterior esophageal bulb. The female has an abrupt conical tail and usually a preëquatorial vulva. The male has two spicules and in some species a gubernaculum. The ova are usually unsegmented at oviposition.

Ascaris lumbricoides LINNÆUS, 1758

Synonyms.—*Ascaris suum* Goeze, 1782 (probably a physiological variety).

History.—The large intestinal nematode, *Ascaris lumbricoides,* owes its specific name to its resemblance to the common earthworm. Since ancient times it has been recognized and described by zoologists. Davaine in 1863 observed that ingested ova hatched in the human intestine. In 1916 Stewart discovered in mice and rats the indirect cycle of the larvæ through the lungs. Ransom and Foster in 1917, and later Ransom and Cram in 1921, showed that after the preliminary pulmonary cycle the larvæ of *Ascaris suum* developed to adult worms in the intestine of the hog, and Koino and Koino in 1922 traced a similar migration in man.

Disease.—Ascariasis; roundworm infection.

Geographical Distribution.—Cosmopolitan, most abundant in tropical countries where sanitation is lax.

BIOLOGICAL CHARACTERISTICS

Morphology.—The white or reddish-yellow adult worms are elongate nematodes, tapering anteriorly and posteriorly to conical extremities (Fig. 99). On each side is a faint longitudinal line. The smooth cuticle is finely striated. The head (Fig. 95D) has a terminal mouth, surrounded by a broad dorsal and two subventral oval lips. The lips (Fig. 95F) bear sensory papillæ on their lateral margins, two on the dorsal and one on each ventral, and are finely denticulated. A small buccal vestibule leads to a cylindrical muscular esophagus about one-twenty-fifth of the body length (Fig. 95E). There are one dorsal and two subventral unicellular esophageal glands. The cylindrical esophagus leads into a straight, simple intestine that opens into a short rectum at the base of the tail cone. In the female the rectum passes directly to the anus; in the male, indirectly through the cloaca.

The male (Fig. 95K), 150 to 310 mm. by 2 to 4 mm., is distinguished from the female by its smaller size and the ventrad curvature of its papillate posterior extremity (Fig. 95H). The male reproductive organs form a long tortuous tubule in the posterior part of the body with an ejaculatory duct opening into the cloaca. Two equal spicules are recessed on the dorsal side of the terminal part of the ejaculatory duct (Fig. 95G).

The female (Fig. 95L), measures from 200 to 350 mm. in length and 4 to 6 mm. in breadth, although specimens sometimes reach a considerably larger size. The small vulva is located ventrally, about one-third the length of the body from the anterior end. It leads into the vagina which branches to form paired tubules, each comprising a uterus, seminal receptacle, oviduct and ovary. These tubules run in a tortuous course through the posterior two-thirds of the body.

Physiology.—The adult worms normally live in the lumen of the small intestine. Their attachment to the mucosa is temporary since they are capable of moving, and, when freshly evacuated, move with a slow writhing motion. They obtain their nourishment from the semidigested food of the host and possibly from the epithelial cells of the intestinal mucosa. They absorb monosaccharids from the surrounding medium.[1] The worms will survive outside the body for nearly a month in nonnutritive media and survival is longer in an oxygen-free than in an oxygen-saturated environment. Their length of life in the host is about one year.

Both male and female worms are usually present, but not always, male worms having been found alone in 3.3 per cent of 1,820 children.[2] The transfer of spermatozoa seems to be accomplished by the simple apposition of the male and female orifices, the spicules of the male, withdrawn in their sheaths, apparently playing no part in copulation. Spermatozoa are present in large numbers in the posterior gut, cloacal cavity, distal ends of the spicule sheaths and ejaculatory duct of the male, and within the vulva and terminal portion of the vagina.[3] A female worm has a productive capacity of 26 to 27 million eggs[4] and has an average daily output of 200,000.[5] Ova-production is a fairly constant phenomenon and the ova-count usually gives a reliable index of the number of worms.[6]

LIFE CYCLE

The ova are usually unsegmented when they leave the host. Under favorable conditions in water and soil, fully-developed infective embryos are formed in about two weeks. When ingested by the definitive host they hatch in the small intestine

[1] Hoffman, R., 1934.   [4] Cram, E. B., 1925.
[2] Yokogawa, S. and Wakeshima, T., 1932.   [5] Brown, H. W. and Cort, W. W., 1927.
[3] Mueller, J. F., 1930.   [6] Brown, H. W., 1927.

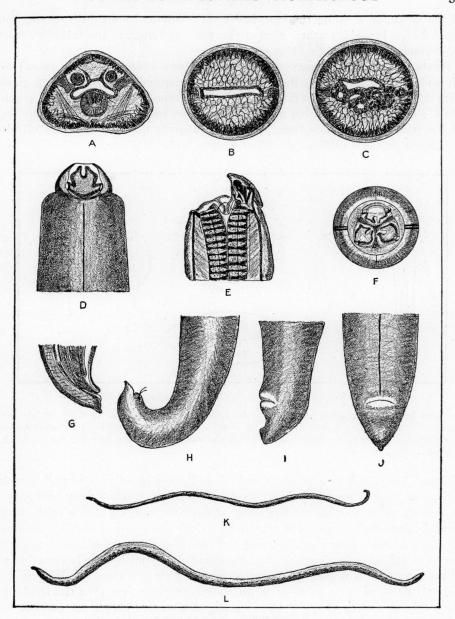

FIG. 95.—*Ascaris lumbricoides*

A, cross section through posterior portion of male showing intestine, ejaculatory ducts and spicules; *B* and *C,* cross sections showing longitudinal lines, musculature and intestine; *D,* anterior end showing lips, dorsal view; *E,* longitudinal section of anterior end; *F,* papillate lips, front view; *G,* longitudinal section of posterior end of male, showing cloaca, gut, ejaculatory duct and spicular sheath; *H,* posterior end of male with extended spicules, lateral view; *I,* posterior end of female, lateral view; *J,* posterior end of female, ventral view; *K,* male worm (× ⅓); *L,* female worm (× ⅓) (Redrawn from Leuckart, 1876).

and the larvæ, penetrating the intestinal wall, follow a definite path of migration (blood, lungs, bronchi, trachea, glottis, pharynx) to return to the intestine, where they become mature worms (Fig. 96).

Hosts.—The natural hosts of the *Ascaris lumbricoides* (*Ascaris suum*) are man and the hog. Although these ascarids are morphologically and serologically identical, there is evidence of a physiological difference in the human and porcine strains, since infective ova from man do not produce mature worms in healthy hogs and the reverse is probably true.[7] The larvæ migrate through the lungs of mice, rats, guinea pigs and rabbits but do not mature in the intestine.

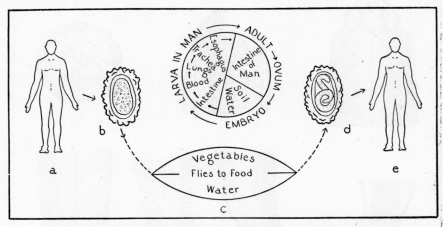

FIG. 96.—LIFE CYCLE OF *Ascaris lumbricoides*

a, man infected with adult worm; *b,* ovum passed in feces, embryo develops outside host; *c,* modes of transmission; *d,* infective larva in shell; *e,* man ingests infective larva which hatches in the intestine, passes to the lungs via the blood and again reaches the intestine via the trachea and glottis.

Ova.—The fertile ova (Figs. 4 and 97 A-E) are broadly ovoid and measure from 45 to 70 μ in length by 35 to 50 μ in breadth, averaging about 60 by 45 μ. There is an outer coarsely-mammillated, albuminous covering and a thick, transparent, hyaline shell composed of several layers, the innermost of fibrillar structure.[8] The easily-broken albuminous covering at times is absent, and is not essential for protection during embryonation.[9] At oviposition the ovum is usually unsegmented and the cytoplasm is densely impregnated with lecithin granules. The infertile eggs (Fig. 4), 88 to 94 μ by 39 to 44 μ, are longer and narrower than the fertile and have a thinner shell with an irregular coating of albumin. They are found not only in the absence of males, but also in about two-fifths of all infections. About 16 per cent of the eggs are infertile, the percentage being greater when the worms are few,

[7] Koino, S., 1922; Payne, F. K., Ackert, J. E. and Hartman, E., 1925; Caldwell, F. C., and Caldwell, E. L., 1926.

[8] Zawadowsky, M. M., 1928; Moretti, G., 1929.

[9] Essed, W. F. R. and van Thiel, P. H., 1934; Ramon, L., Charles, E. E. and Astarloa, E., 1927.

and females from time to time may produce infertile eggs, since repeated copulations are necessary.[10]

Development of Ova.—The development of the ova outside the host is influenced by many factors, but chiefly by temperature, moisture and oxygen. Under favorable conditions the ovum becomes fully embryonated in 10 to 15 days,[11] but does not become infective until the enclosed larva has undergone its first molt.[12] The optimal temperature for development is about 25° C., ranging from 21° to 30° C., although at 30° C. the rate is two and one-half times that at 21° C.[13] Lower temperatures retard development but favor survival of the ova. Dryness and excessive moisture both inhibit normal development. Since ova require oxygen, their development in putrefactive material is retarded.

Resistance of Ova.—Ova survive for long periods and remain viable on the soil or in manure heaps throughout the winter months, when subjected to freezing temperatures.[14] In dry sandy soil or cinders they usually die before reaching the infective stage. A moist, loose soil with moderate shade is favorable for survival. They may even remain viable for five or six years.[15] The embryonate ova cannot withstand drying for prolonged periods, but are more resistant to desiccation than *Trichuris* ova.[16] Exposure to ultraviolet light is fatal,[17] and direct sunlight kills the ova in 3½ to 15 hours at 36.7° C., unless in a moist environment, when they may live as long as 30 days.[18]

Exposure to —9° to —12° C. has no effect upon *Ascaris* ova, although such temperatures are fatal to *Trichuris* ova.[16] Moist heat at 80° C. is rapidly fatal.[15] Immersion in boiling water kills the ova and their infectivity is destroyed in one second at 70° C. and in 45 minutes at 50° C.[19] *Ascaris* ova are more resistant to chemical disinfectants than hookworm ova and are able to withstand temporary immersion in strong chemicals. The inner fibrous membrane of the shell is impermeable, while the outer covering acts as a protection against physical disturbances.[20]

Development in the Host.—The development of the larvæ after ingestion by the host has been studied both in a natural host (hog), and in abnormal hosts (mice, rats, guinea pigs and rabbits), in which the larvæ pass through their developmental cycle but fail to become adult worms. In abnormal hosts the postcyclic larvæ are destroyed by leukocytes, histiocytes and lymphatic cells.[21] The pulmonary cycle has been explained on the basis that the larvæ lack sufficient glycogen to enable them to develop in the oxygen-free intestine.[22]

To be infective the ovum must contain a motile second-stage larva. The first molt takes place outside the host about one week after the production of the first-

[10] Otto, G. F., 1932.
[11] Brown, H. W., 1927; Caldwell, F. C. and Caldwell, E. L., 1928.
[12] Alicata, J. E., 1934.
[13] Brown, H. W.. 1928; Stewart, F. H., 1934.
[14] Brown, H. W., 1928; Yoshida, S., 1920; Otto, G. F., 1929; Ishikawa, S., 1929.
[15] Roman. E., 1939.
[16] Nolf, L. O., 1932.

[17] Zawadowsky, M. M. and Vorob, E., 1935.
[18] Caldwell, F. C. and Caldwell, E. L., 1928.
[19] Ogata, S., 1925.
[20] Zawadowsky, M. M., 1927.
[21] Stewart, F. H., 1929.
[22] Stepanow-Grigoriew, J. and Hoeppli, R., 1926.

stage larva.[23] In the duodenum prior to hatching the activated larva pushes out the thin elastic shell with its head. Stretching finally produces a weak place through which the head erupts and the ensheathed larva is liberated.[24] This rhabditiform larva (Fig. 97F), 200 to 300 μ by 14 μ, has a cylindrical esophagus with a posterior bulb, an elongate intestine and a short rectum.

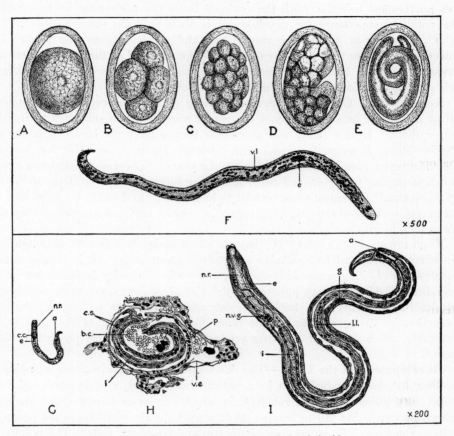

FIG. 97.—LARVAL FORMS OF *Ascaris lumbricoides*

A to *E*, embryonic development of ovum; *F*, larva liberated from eggshell; *G*, larva from liver of mouse; *H*, section of lung of rat showing larva in air vesicle; *I*, fully developed larva from lung of rat.

a, anus; *b.c.*, red blood cells; *c.c.*, circumesophageal collar; *c.s.*, cuticular surface; *e*, esophagus; *g*, gonads; *i*, intestine; *l.l.*, lateral line; *n.r.*, nerve ring; *n.v.g.*, nucleus ventral gland; *p*, pigment; *v.e.*, epithelium of air vesicle; *v.l.*, ventral line (*A* to *E*, adapted from Leuckart, 1876; *F* to *I*, redrawn from Stewart, 1917).

The larvæ traverse the intestinal wall until they reach the lymphatic vessels or the venules. In the portal circulation the larvæ pass to the liver, thence by the hepatic veins to the heart and ultimately to the lungs. In the lymphatics they are

[23] Ransom, B. H. and Foster, W. D., 1921;   1935.
Ransom, B. H., 1922; Alicata, J. E., 1934,   [24] Ortlepp, R. J., 1922.

carried to the mesenteric lymph nodes, whence they may follow three possible routes: (1) to the peritoneal cavity by penetration; (2) to the liver by the portal vessels; or (3) to the right heart by the lymphatic vessels.[25] Larvæ from the peritoneum pierce the liver where, if they remain, they attain a length of 0.6 mm. 4 to 6 days after infection (Fig. 97G), or pass through the diaphragm to the pleural cavities and lungs. The larvæ may reach the heart as early as 17 hours or as late as 6 to 7 days after infection.

In the lungs the larvæ penetrate the capillaries to enter the alveoli (Fig. 97H). Occasionally some return to the left heart through the pulmonary veins and are distributed as emboli in various parts of the body. In the lungs the growing larvæ molt twice, on the fifth to sixth day and on the tenth day. They migrate to the bronchi, ascend the trachea to the glottis, and pass down the esophagus eventually reaching the intestine. During the pulmonary cycle the larvæ have increased in size to 1 to 2 mm. (Fig. 97I). In the early stages of migration they obtain nourishment from the blood plasma but later possibly feed on erythrocytes.[26] After they arrive at the intestine they undergo a fourth molt, from 25 to 29 days after infection, before developing into adults. Egg-laying females are produced in hogs two months after infection.[27]

PATHOGENESIS

Pathology.—The varied pathology of *Ascaris* infection includes the reaction of the tissues to the invading larvæ, the irritation of the intestine by the mechanical and toxic action of the adult, and the complications arising from its extra-intestinal migrations. The pathological reaction to the invading larvæ depends upon their number and upon the histological nature of the organ involved, the compact liver reacting weakly and the less dense lung more severely (Fig. 98). In the latter the larvæ set up an inflammatory process with numerous petechial hemorrhages at the site of entrance into the alveoli. In severe infections there may be an extensive serocellular exudation in the alveoli of red blood cells, leukocytes, eosinophils, fibrin and desquamated epithelium, producing a lobular pneumonia. In advanced cases an entire lobe may be edematous and ecchymotic. In the liver and other organs, in addition to congestion, small inflammatory and necrotic lesions form about the larvæ that fail to reënter the circulation, and eventually these larvæ are encapsulated and destroyed. Serious lesions at times result in the kidneys and brain.

The normal habitat of the adult worm is the small intestine. The worms may migrate into the stomach and by regurgitation escape from the mouth or nose. The death of a two-year-old child following anthelmintic treatment occurred from laryngeal obstruction.[28] The ascarids may descend to the rectum and be passed in the feces.

In heavy infections the worms may produce enough toxic and mechanical irritation to cause enterocolitis in children. Intestinal obstruction with gangrene and intussusception has resulted from masses of worms. A few worms may cause little or no pathological change, but may induce intestinal spasm and temporary occlu-

25 Ransom, B. H. and Cram, E. B., 1921.   27 de Boer, E., 1936.
26 Smirnow, G. G., 1935.   28 Caldwell, F. C., 1922.

sion, thus explaining the colicky pains and nervous symptoms accompanying *Ascaris* infection.[29] The worms may aggravate intestinal diseases and complicate surgical procedures. They may induce appendicitis by invading the appendix and even cause peritonitis by perforating the intestine. They have been observed escaping through appendiceal, umbilical, herniotomy fistulas, and surgical drainage tubes, and have been found in infections of the Fallopian tubes.

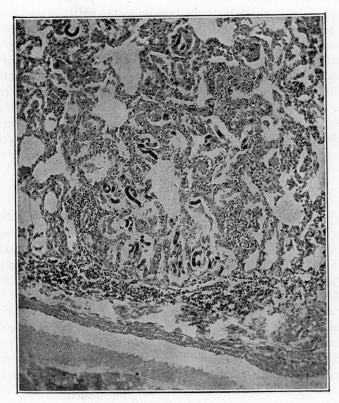

FIG. 98.—LARVÆ OF *Ascaris lumbricoides* IN ALVEOLI OF LUNG OF EXPERIMENTALLY INFECTED MAMMAL (× 100)

Note leukocytic infiltration around parasitized air spaces (From Faust, *Human Helminthology*, 1939. Courtesy of Lea and Febiger, Philadelphia).

Over 90 cases of the invasion of adult ascarids into the gallbladder and biliary tracts (Fig. 99) have been reported in the literature. The principal findings have been chronic irritation and inflammation of the gallbladder and obstruction of the common duct, with jaundice, pain and other symptoms of gallbladder disease. In some instances the gallbladder, common duct, cystic duct and hepatic duct have been filled with worms, as high as 70 having been reported.[30] Preoperative anthelmintic treatment to prevent complications has been advised in suspected cases. Hepatic

---

[29] Harris, H. E., 1923.   [30] Eberle, D., 1920.

abscess [31] and hematoma [32] have been caused by living and dead ascarids, and obstruction of the ampulla of Vater and the common bile duct has produced several cases of acute hemorrhagic pancreatitis with necrosis.[33]

Aberrant ascarids at times are responsible for pathological conditions outside the intestinal tract. Over 207 cases of extopic infections have been collected in the Japanese literature.[34] Obstruction and rupture of the small intestine with embryonate ova forming tubercular lesions in the mesentery,[35] iritis from intraocular invasion of the larvæ,[36] and even two ascarids in the right ventricle of the heart have been reported.[37]

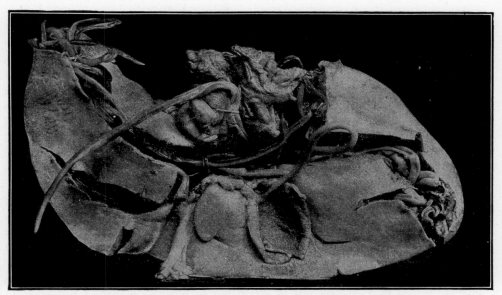

FIG. 99.—LIVER WITH *Ascaris lumbricoides* IN DILATED INTRAHEPATIC BILE DUCTS
(From Smith and Gault, *Essentials of Pathology*, 1938, D. Appleton-Century Company).

Symptomatology.—Clinical ascariasis may be divided into two stages: (1) larval invasion; and (2) adult ascarid infection.

Larval migration is characterized by fever, eosinophilia, urticarial rashes, and changes in the liver and lungs. Bronchial irritation causes spasmodic coughing. Experimental infection in man has produced headache, fever, muscular pains, coughs, dyspnea, hemoptysis and hepatic enlargement.[38] Bronchopneumonia, often fatal, occurs frequently in children in highly endemic regions. Repeated infections tend to maintain a chronic type of pulmonary infection.[39]

The varied symptoms of adult *Ascaris* infection depend upon the location and

[31] de Azevedo, A., 1935.
[32] Ch'in, K. Y., 1936.
[33] Rigby, H. M., 1923; Ch'in, K. Y., 1933; Harrower, G., 1933.
[34] Ujiie, N., 1935.
[35] Africa, C. M. and Garcia, E. Y., 1936.
[36] Calhoun, F. P., 1937.
[37] Boettiger, C. and Werne, J., 1929.
[38] Koino, S., 1922.
[39] Girges, R., 1934.

to a lesser extent upon the number of the worms. The most common complaint is general abdominal discomfort with nausea, colicky pains, abnormal digestive disturbances and loss of appetite. The blood shows an eosinophilia of 7 to 10 per cent and at times a mild anemia. Reflex nervous symptoms, common in young children, include irritability, colicky abdominal pains, disturbed sleep, picking at nose, grinding of teeth, and occasionally convulsions. Symptoms simulating epilepsy and meningitis [40] have disappeared and night blindness has been cured after the removal of the worms.

Supersensitive persons may develop anaphylactic symptoms with nasal, pulmonary, skin, gastro-intestinal and nervous manifestations. The migrations of the worms may give rise to symptoms of appendicitis, cholecystitis, pancreatitis, peritonitis, salpingitis, and nephritis.

Immunity.—The immunity of ascarid infections has received considerable attention particularly as regards allergic phenomena. Natural resistance depends upon host-species, age and physical condition. Only the larval cycle of *A. lumbricoides* from man and hog is present in other animals. The difference between the morphologically and serologically similar human and porcine strains in respect to cross-infection suggests a physiological basis for host-resistance. In experimental human infections pulmonary symptoms have been produced with both human and porcine strains, but mature worms developed only with the former.[38] Age-resistance against *Ascaridia lineata* is manifest by the smaller size and slower growth of the parasite in old chickens.[41]

Resistance in chickens is lowered by loss of blood and inadequate diet. The effect of vitamin A deficiency upon the resistance of chickens, dogs, rats and hogs against ascarids has been studied by a number of workers. Conflicting results have been obtained with *A. lumbricoides* in hogs, but it is the general consensus that vitamin A deficiency lowers resistance to infection with ascarids.

Acquired immunity by previous infection to *Ascaridia lineata* has been shown in chickens [42] and to *Toxocara cati* in cats,[43] but in hogs no increased resistance to superinfection with *A. lumbricoides* has been demonstrated.[44] Immunization of guinea pigs by sublethal infections of porcine *A. lumbricoides* produced resistance of short duration against twice the lethal dose. In these guinea pigs the larvæ grew less rapidly and a greater number were destroyed by cellular activity in the liver and lungs.[45] Likewise, immunization of guinea pigs with antigens of dried *A. lumbricoides* protected one-half the animals against the lethal test-dose and some evidence of the passive transfer of immunity against *A. lumbricoides* was obtained in mice with the sera of immune guinea pigs.

The production of definite toxic substances by ascarids is still unsettled. Saline, aqueous, glycerolic and etheric extracts have been prepared from the whole worm or special tissues. These extracts are hemolytic,[46] have an antipeptic and antitryptic

[40] Raudkepp, F., 1926; Abdulla, M., 1930; Zaw, F. D., 1935.

[41] Herrick, C. A., 1926; Graham, G. L., Ackert, J. E. and Jones, B. W., 1932; Ackert, J. E., Porter, D. A. and Beach, T. D., 1935.

[42] Graham, G. L., Ackert, J. E. and Jones, B. W., 1932.

[43] Sarles, M. P. and Stoll, N. R., 1935.

[44] Morgan, D. O., 1931; de Boer, E., 1936.

[45] Kerr, K. B., 1938.

[46] Fishback, H. R., 1930; Herrick, C. A. and Emery, F. E., 1929.

action [47] and affect unfavorably the growth of fibroblasts *in vitro*.[48] Like histamine they increase the peristaltic action of the intestine, lower the blood pressure, deepen the respirations, decrease the volume of the spleen and liver, and irritate the skin and respiratory passages.[49] Intravenous inoculations produce a fatal histamine type of anaphylactic shock in guinea pigs.[50] Immune serum neutralizes these toxic properties.

Specific antibodies, such as precipitins and anaphylactins, may be demonstrated in infected animals and in those receiving injections of antigens. Various alcoholic and aqueous extracts of the whole or parts of the worm have been used as antigens, and a polysaccharide antigen, which is claimed to produce specific antibodies, has been prepared.[51] The specificity of isolated tissues has been demonstrated by precipitative tests.[52] Specificity of these antigens may also be tested with uterine strips of sensitized guinea pigs. The titer of the precipitins does not necessarily parallel the intracutaneous reaction. A positive skin reaction may persist for months after the removal of the worms. Group-reactions may occur with allied parasites but by proper desensitization it is possible to demonstrate specificity.[53]

Supersensitiveness to *Ascaris* is not uncommon and manifests itself by the usual allergic symptoms of asthma, hay fever, urticaria and eosinophilia. Recurring attacks of urticaria in a mother when her son suffered from *Ascaris* infection have been reported.[54] Supersensitiveness is acquired by contact and does not necessarily predicate previous infection. Anaphylaxis can be produced in guinea pigs sensitized by injections of antigens and passive anaphylaxis can be demonstrated. The production of the Schwartzman phenomenon in rabbits has been reported.[55]

DIAGNOSIS, PROGNOSIS AND TREATMENT

Diagnosis.—The clinical symptoms of intestinal irritation and associated nervous disorders in ascariasis are not distinguishable from those produced by other intestinal helminths. In heavy infections during the migratory larval cycle a tentative diagnosis of *Ascaris* pneumonia may be made. Occasionally the adult worms are passed in the feces or regurgitated. Otherwise definite diagnosis can be established only by finding the ova in the feces. The feces may be examined first in a cover-glass mount, and if direct examination is negative, by any one of several methods of concentration (Section **VII,** VII). The fertile ova (Fig. 4) are readily identified by their mammillated covering, but when this is absent reliance must be placed on other characteristics. Only infertile ova (Fig. 4) may be found in about one-quarter of light infections and both fertile and infertile ova in about two-fifths of all cases.[56] At times only male worms are present, hence no ova can be demonstrated. In such cases diagnosis must be based on clinical symptoms, therapeutic tests, and finding the adult worms. Intracutaneous and precipitative diagnostic tests are not practical. However, highly specific precipitative reactions, even between

[47] Sang, J. H., 1938.
[48] Hoeppli, R., 1935.
[49] Emery, F. E. and Herrick, C. A., 1929.
[50] Macheboeuf, M. and Mandoul, R., 1939.
[51] Campbell, D. H., 1936.
[52] Canning, G. A., 1929.

[53] Turner, A. W., 1926; Fishback, H. R., 1930.
[54] von Fellenberg, R., 1932.
[55] Mu, J. W., 1935.
[56] Leathers, W. S., and Keller, A. E., 1937.

the closely allied human and porcine strains, have been obtained with a polysaccharide antigen.[57] Intracutaneous tests are of little value because (1) there is no significant correlation between infection and positive reactions or between absence of infection and negative reactions;[58] and (2) with *Ascaris* antigen group-reactions are reported for *Ascaris, Enterobius, Trichuris, Trichinella* and *Necator*.[59]

Prognosis.—As a rule, prognosis is favorable, and the infection responds readily to treatment. It is serious only when there is mechanical obstruction of the intestine or when the parasite has invaded vital organs. In highly endemic areas, however, *Ascaris* pneumonia may be a serious problem in children.

Treatment.—Chemotherapy eliminates the adult worms from the intestine, but has no effect upon the migrating larvæ or extra-intestinal adults. Treatment of *Ascaris* pneumonia is wholly symptomatic and supportive. Santonin and oil of chenopodium have been used for years, but the former is only moderately effective in safe therapeutic doses. Oil of chenopodium (Section **VII**, XIII, 30) though effective is dangerously toxic. Various workers report that from 70 to 99 per cent of the worms are removed and that from 35 to 96 per cent of cures are effected by a single treatment.[60] The combined treatment of oil of chenopodium and tetrachlorethylene is recommended for double infections with *Ascaris* and hookworm, but carbon tetrachloride and tetrachlorethylene should not be used alone. Crystalline hexylresorcinol (Section **VII**, XIII, 23) is the drug of choice because it is highly efficient and safe. A single treatment removes from 90 to 100 per cent of the ascarids, and from 70 to 80 per cent of the patients are freed of the parasites in one treatment and 93 to 98 per cent in two.[61]

Surgical interference may be required in acute intestinal obstruction or in pancreatic, biliary and peritoneal invasions. Nutrition is an important factor. When conditions are unsuited for reinfection and a well-balanced diet is maintained, the ascarids disappear in some children within 15 months without the use of anthelmintic drugs.[62]

PREVENTION

Epidemiology.—*Ascaris lumbricoides* is a prominent parasite in both temperate and tropical zones, but is more common in warm countries. It is most prevalent where sanitation is poor. Some countries have a low and others a high incidence; as the Philippines, 74 to 84 per cent; Armenia, 70 per cent; Korea, 53 per cent; and Haiti, 50 per cent. The spotty distribution of endemic areas, however, renders general statistics unreliable. The incidence of human *Ascaris* infection shows no correlation with that of porcine *Ascaris,* and suggests that the two strains are not identical.[18]

Ascaris infection, though present in all parts of the United States of America, has a relatively low incidence in the western and northern states. The extensive

---

[57] Campbell, D. H., 1937.

[58] Rackemann, F. M., and Stevens, A. H., Jr., 1927; Khaw, O. K., 1929; Jones, T. L., and Kingscote, A. A., 1935.

[59] Brunner, M. J., 1928; Maternowska, I., 1934; Schonfeld, W., 1937.

[60] Brown, H. W., 1934.

[61] Lamson, P. D., Brown, H. W., Robbins, B. H. and Ward, C. B., 1931; Brown, H. W., 1932.

[62] Keller, A. E., 1931; Ahmann, C. F. and Bristol, L. M., 1933.

surveys of Leathers and his associates, totaling over 160,000 examinations in the southern states, reveal the following incidence: Kentucky, 34 per cent; North Carolina, 9.5 per cent; South Carolina, 4.0 per cent; Florida, 1.9 per cent; and Mississippi, 1.1 per cent. The incidence in 10,990 patients from the hospital clinics of New Orleans is 6.6 per cent,[63] and in 2,000 persons in southeastern Virginia 30 per cent in adults and 60 per cent in children.[64] The high endemic regions are the Appalachian Mountains and the adjacent regions to the east, south and west with additional centers in south central Louisiana, southwestern North Carolina and in Tampa, Florida.[65] In North Carolina the coastal plains have a low incidence, 6.5 per cent, in spite of the prevalence of hookworm infection, while the mountainous sections show 30.7 per cent.[66]

Ascaris infection occurs at all ages, but it is most prevalent in the 5 to 9 year group of preschool and young school children, who are more frequently exposed to contaminated soil than adults.[67] The incidence in children under 14 years in the Southern United States ranges from 1.4 to 60 per cent.[68] In Shantung, China, it is 44 per cent in primary school children and 23 per cent in older children.[69] The incidence in Negroes in the southeastern United States is over three times that of whites and the intensity of individual infection is over 1.5 times greater.[70]

Economic, educational and sanitary factors affect the occurrence of ascariasis. The lower urban and rural classes, because of heavy soil pollution and unsatisfactory hygiene, are the ones most afflicted. Infection is a household affair, the family being the unit of dissemination. The intensity of infection increases with the number of infected persons per family; when five or more are infected the average ova-count is over seven times that when only one member is infected.[56] Crowding, poor nutrition and lack of medical care promote the spread and intensity of infection.

Ova are most abundant near dwellings, especially in dooryards, where the soil is polluted through lack of sanitary fecal disposal.[71] They are resistant to drying and cold, remain viable on hard clay soil, and require less moisture than those of the whipworm and hookworm. They may be distributed by heavy rains, winds, insects, rodents and larger mammals in which they may pass unharmed through the digestive tract.[72] The parasite is chiefly transmitted by hands that have come in contact with contaminated soil. Ova have been found on vegetables but, if present, only in small numbers,[73] and the danger of infection from this source seems slight. Drinking water is rarely affected.

Prophylaxis.—Since ascariasis is essentially a household and dooryard infection of young children, and is intimately associated with family hygiene, prophylaxis depends upon the sanitary disposal of feces and hygienic education. It seems un-

[63] Headlee, W. H., 1936.
[64] Cort, W. W., Otto, G. F. and Spindler, L. A., 1930.
[65] Otto, G. F. and Cort, W. W., 1934.
[66] Keller, A. E., Leathers, W. S. and Knox, J. C., 1938.
[67] Keller, A. E. and Leathers, W. S., 1936.
[68] Otto, G. F., 1932; Keller, A. E. and Leathers, W. S., 1934.
[69] Winfield, G. F. and Chin, T. H., 1938.

[70] Leathers, W. S. and Keller, A. E., 1937; Keller, A. E., Leathers, W. S. and Knox, J. C., 1938; Leathers, W. S., Keller, A. E. and McPhaul, W. A., 1939.
[71] Brown, H. W., 1927; Cort, W. W., 1931; Headlee, W. H., 1936.
[72] Nakata, K., 1936.
[73] Yosesato, M. and Sumi, I., 1932; Winfield, G. F. and Yao, T. N., 1937.

necessary to devote attention to minor sources of infection, such as vegetables and drinking water, or to possible cross-infection from the *Ascaris* of hogs. Mass anthelmintic treatment is ineffective because of reinfection. Control is difficult not only because of the large number and high resistance of the ova distributed by an infected person, but also because of ignorance, poverty and inertia among the people afflicted. The installation of sanitary latrines is ineffective unless accompanied by an educational campaign designed to improve household sanitation and personal hygiene, with emphasis upon child habits. This educational program calls for the concerted efforts of schools, civic organizations, home economic educators, and public health officers and nurses.

Toxocara canis (WERNER, 1782) JOHNSTON, 1916

Toxocara canis, a common, cosmopolitan, intestinal ascarid of the dog and fox, has been reported once from man in Egypt. It has an arrow-shaped head due to two lateral cephalic alæ. The male, 50 to 100 mm., has a curved posterior extremity that bears two caudal alæ and two long, curved spicules. The female, 90 to 180 mm., has its vulva in the anterior third of the body. The light-brown, globular ovum, 80 by 70 μ, has a pitted shell. The life cycle is similar to that of *Ascaris lumbricoides.* Puppies are particularly susceptible to infection, and prenatal infection may occur.[74] Dogs are immune to reinfection.

Toxocara cati (SCHRANK, 1788) BRUMPT, 1927

Toxocara cati, a common intestinal ascarid of the cat and wild felines, has been reported nine times in man in Europe and North America. It is characterized by broad cervical alæ. The caudal end of the male somewhat resembles that of *T. canis.* The male is 40 to 60 mm. in length and the female 40 to 120 mm. The subglobose ova, 70 by 65 μ, are slightly pitted. Its life cycle is similar to that of *Ascaris lumbricoides.*

Lagochilascaris minor LEIPER, 1909

Lagochilascaris minor, a natural intestinal parasite of the cloudy leopard of the Orient, has been found five times in subcutaneous abscesses in man in the West Indies and Dutch Guiana. It has three large vertically cleft lips that are covered with a heavy cuticle and are separated from the body by a deep groove. The length of the male is about 9 mm. and that of the female 14 mm. The ova, 65 μ in diameter, are globose with thick pitted shells.

REFERENCES

AHMANN, C. F. and BRISTOL, L. M. The Effect of Diet on the Worm Burden of Children Infected with *Necator americanus* and *Ascaris lumbricoides,* South. M. J., 1933, 26:959.
BROWN, H. W. Intestinal Parasitic Worms in the United States; Their Diagnosis and Treatment, J. Am. M. Ass., 1934, 103:651.
CAMPBELL, D. H. An Antigenic Polysaccharide Fraction of *Ascaris lumbricoides* (from Hog), J. Infect. Dis., 1936, 59:266.
CORT, W. W. Recent Investigations on the Epidemiology of Human Ascariasis, J. Parasitol., 1931, 17:121.
GIRGES, R. Pathogenic Factors in Ascariasis, J. Trop. Med., 1934, 37:209.
HEADLEE, W. H. The Epidemiology of Human Ascariasis in the Metropolitan Area of New Orleans, Louisiana, Am. J. Hyg., 1936, 24:479.

[74] Augustine, D. L., 1927.

JONES, T. L. and KINGSCOTE, A. A. Observations on *Ascaris* Sensitivity in Man, Am. J. Hyg., 1935, 22:406.

KELLER, A. E. *Ascaris lumbricoides;* Loss of Infestation Without Treatment, J. Am. M. Ass., 1931, 97:1299.

KERR, K. B. The Cellular Response in Acquired Resistance in Guinea Pigs to an Infection with Pig *Ascaris,* Am. J. Hyg., 1938, 27:28.

NOLF, L. O. Experimental Studies on Certain Factors Influencing the Development and Viability of the Ova of Human *Trichuris* as Compared with Those of Human *Ascaris,* Am. J. Hyg., 1932, 16:288.

OTTO, G. F. The Appearance and Significance of Unfertilized Eggs of *Ascaris lumbricoides* (Linn.), J. Parasitol., 1932, 18:269.

—— and CORT, W. W. The Distribution and Epidemiology of Human Ascariasis in the United States, Am. J. Hyg., 1934, 19:657.

RANSOM, B. H. and CRAM, E. B. The Course of Migration of *Ascaris* Larvae from the Intestine to the Lung, Am. J. Hyg., 1921, 1:129.

STEWART, F. H. On the Life History of *Ascaris lumbricoides,* Parasitology, 1929, 13:37.

WINFIELD, G. F. and CHIN, T. H. Studies on the Control of Fecal-borne Diseases in North China. VI. The Epidemiology of *Ascaris lumbricoides* in an Urban Population, Chinese M. J., 1938, 54:233.

Chapter XX

THE SUPERFAMILY SPIRUROIDEA

SUPERFAMILY *SPIRUROIDEA* RAILLIET AND HENRY, 1915

The members of the superfamily SPIRUROIDEA have two lateral lips and usually a buccal capsule. The esophagus has a short anterior and a long, glandular posterior portion without a cardiac bulb. The male has two unequal copulatory spicules and generally caudal alæ. The vulva is usually equatorial. The ova, except in the GNATHOSTOMATIDÆ, are embryonate at oviposition. The adults are parasites of the digestive tract, respiratory system and of the orbital, nasal and oral cavities of vertebrates. Species parasitic in man belong to the families GNATHOSTOMATIDÆ, PHYSALOPTERIDÆ, SPIRURIDÆ and THELAZIIDÆ.

FAMILY *GNATHOSTOMATIDÆ* BLANCHARD, 1895

The species of the family GNATHOSTOMATIDÆ have two large trilobed lips, with the cuticle of their inner surfaces thickened and usually folded into interlocking, longitudinal, tooth-like ridges. Minute spines cover the whole or anterior part of the body. The male has caudal alæ supported by four or more broad pedunculate papillæ and two unequal copulatory spicules. The oviparous female has a uterus with two to four branches and a postequatorial vulva. The ova have thin finely-sculptured shells. The worms are parasites of the stomach and intestine of fishes, reptiles and mammals. Two species have been found in man, *Gnathostoma spinigerum* and *G. hispidum*.

Gnathostoma spinigerum OWEN, 1836

Gnathostoma spinigerum was discovered by Owen in 1836 in a tiger. It was first observed in man by Levinsen in 1890, as an immature worm from an abscess in a Siamese. Previous to 1933 twelve cases of human gnathostomiasis, all with immature worms, had been reported.

Geographical Distribution.—Siam, India, Malay States, China and Japan, in domestic and wild felines and dogs.

Morphology.—The adult worm is a heavy reddish nematode with a globular cephalic dome (Fig. 100A), covered with 8 to 11 transverse rows of minute hooklets, and a ventrally curved posterior end. The anterior portion of the body below the constricted cervical region bears leaf-like spines, while the posterior portion is smooth. The mouth, guarded by two fleshy lips, opens into a muscular esophagus, surrounded by four cervical secretory glands. The broad intestine enters a short conical rectum that leads to a subterminal anus.

The male, 11 to 25 mm. in length, has a cuticular expansion at the posterior end which bears four pairs of pedunculate papillæ and two unequal chitinous spicules (Fig. 100B). The female, 25 to 54 mm. in length, has two uteri that enter an anteriorly directed vagina and a vulva that is situated in a slightly postequatorial position. The elongate oval ova, 69 μ by 37 μ, have a clear, greenish-tinged, irregularly sculptured shell with a transparent knob at one end, and are usually unsegmented at oviposition.

Life Cycle.—The natural hosts are domestic and wild felines, dogs, hogs and mink. Man appears to be an unnatural host, in whom the parasites do not develop normally.

The ovum hatches within two weeks, liberating, usually through the terminal knob, an actively motile, cylindrical, ensheathed, rhabditiform larva, averaging 265 by 16 μ in size.[1] The rounded anterior end is armed with a heavy spine, while the posterior portion of the body gradually tapers to a rounded tail. It has a rudimentary alimentary canal and cervical glands.

The life cycle involves two intermediate hosts, a *Cyclops* and a fish or an amphibian. When the first-stage larvæ are ingested by one of several species of *Cyclops,* they penetrate the body cavity, undergo metamorphosis, and attain a size of about 400 by 62 μ in about two weeks.[1] In order to become infective to the definitive host the larvæ require

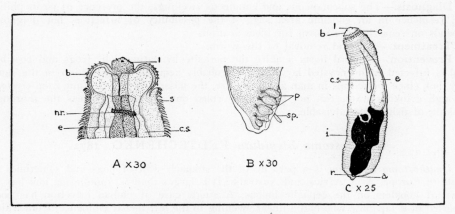

FIG. 100.—*Gnathostoma spinigerum*

A, anterior end of adult worm, lateral view; *B,* posterior end of male, lateral view; *C,* immature worm, lateral view.

a, anus; *b,* ballonet; *c,* cuticular collar; *c.s.,* cervical sac; *e,* esophagus; *l,* lip; *n.r.,* nerve ring; *p,* papillae; *r,* rectum; *s,* spine; *sp.,* spicule (*A* and *B* redrawn from Baylis and Lane, 1920; *C* redrawn from Morishita and Faust, 1925).

further development in a second intermediate host. Encysted larvæ have been found in the fresh-water fishes, *Ophiocephalus striatus, Glossobius giurus* and *Therapon argenteus* in the Philippines;[2] in the fishes, *Clarias batrachus* and *Ophiocephalus striatus,* in the eel, *Monopterus albus,* and in the frog, *Rana rugulosa* in Siam.[3] In the tissues of these hosts the larvæ, lying in round cysts, 1.2 mm. in diameter, measure from 4 to 4.5 mm. in length by 0.31 mm. in breadth, nearly 12 times their size in the crustacean host. In general appearance they resemble the adult worm, but have only four rows of spines on the cephalic bulb and primitive genitalia. When cats are fed infected fish, the adult parasites develop in the stomach wall in about seven months,[4] but cats can not be infected by eating *Cyclops* containing the younger larvæ.[5]

Pathogenesis.—In natural hosts the adult worms form indurated nodules in the wall of the stomach and at times in the intestinal wall. These tumors, containing one or more worms in a purulent fluid, frequently communicate with the intestinal lumen by an opening through which the ova are discharged. In man the immature worms (Fig. 100C)

---

[1] Prommas, C. and Daengsvang, S., 1933.
[2] Africa, C. M., Refuerzo, P. G. and Garcia, E. Y., 1936.
[3] Daengsvang, S. and Tansurat, P., 1938.
[4] Prommas, C. and Daengsvang, S., 1937.
[5] Prommas, C. and Daengsvang, S., 1936.

may locate in the internal organs or near the surface of the body, but do not develop to adults in the wall of the digestive tract. When peripheral, they produce local transitory or persistent swellings with inflammatory exudation and infiltration of eosinophils and plasma cells. The parasites are able to migrate fairly rapidly through the tissues of the host.[6] Abscesses of the breast, mastoid region and subcutaneous tissues have been reported. If the worm tunnels horizontally through the dermal tissues, it produces a type of creeping eruption, which may require differentiation from the lesions produced by dipterous larvæ or *Ancylostoma braziliense.*

The symptoms arise from the local inflammatory reaction and edema. Hemoptysis, hematuria, edema of the pharynx with dyspnea, angioneurotic edema and abscesses have been observed. Eosinophilia is usually present. If the worm does not reach the body surface and escape or is not removed, the infection may last for months.

Diagnosis.—The subcutaneous and cutaneous swellings, the presence of eosinophilia, and residence in an endemic area suggest the possibility of infection, but diagnosis depends on removing the worm for identification.

Treatment.—Surgical removal of the worm.

Prevention.—Natural hosts acquire the parasite by eating fish, frogs and possibly snakes infected with encysted larvæ. Man probably acquires the infection in the same way, but, since the worms in man are immature, the possibility of infection from *Cyclops* through drinking water can not be entirely ruled out. In endemic areas the thorough cooking of fish seems advisable.

Gnathostoma hispidum FEDTSCHENKO, 1872

Gnathostoma hispidum is a parasite of the stomach wall of hogs and sometimes of cattle in Europe, Asia, Africa and Australia. It is larger than *G. spinigerum* and has 12 rows of hooklets on the cephalic bulbus. A single case of human infection has been reported in a Japanese who had a linear swelling in the left thenar eminence, from which an immature female worm was removed.[7]

FAMILY *PHYSALOPTERIDÆ* LEIPER, 1908

The PHYSALOPTERIDÆ have two large triangular lips armed with teeth on their inner surface. The cuticle extends forward to form a cephalic collar. There is no buccal capsule. The caudal end of the male has pedunculate papillæ and large caudal alæ that join ventrally. The oviparous female has a preëquatorial vulva. The transparent thick-shelled ova are embryonate at oviposition. The life cycles probably involve intermediate arthropod hosts. Various species are parasitic in the digestive tracts of birds, reptiles and mammals. *Physaloptera caucasica* is the only species parasitic in man.

Physaloptera caucasica v. LINSTOW, 1902

Physaloptera caucasica, discovered by Ménétriés in the Caucasus, and *P. mordens,* obtained by Leiper in Africa in 1907, are believed to be the same species. It is a natural parasite of monkeys, but is also found among the natives of Tropical Africa. It is a large nematode resembling *Ascaris lumbricoides;* males are from 14 to 50 mm. and females from 24 to 100 mm. in length. It is characterized by its cuticular collar; two fleshy, denticulate, papillate lips, asymmetrical caudal alæ; and four uterine tubules. The embryonate, ovoid ova have a smooth, thick, transparent shell. The life cycle has not been determined. The worm inhabits the esophagus, stomach and small intestine.

---

[6] Maplestone, P. A. and Bhaduri, N. V., 1937.   [7] Morishita, K., 1924.

FAMILY *SPIRURIDÆ* OERLEY, 1885

The SPIRURIDÆ have trilobed, inconspicuous lips without cuticular shields. The buccal capsule has annular or spiral thickenings of its chitinous wall. The caudal alæ of the male are prominent, asymmetrical, and are supported by pedunculate papillæ. The copulatory spicules are unequal and a gubernaculum is present. The vulva of the oviparous female is usually subequatorial. The life cycle involves an arthropod as intermediate host. The various species are parasites of the mouth, esophagus, stomach, intestine, and aorta of birds and mammals.

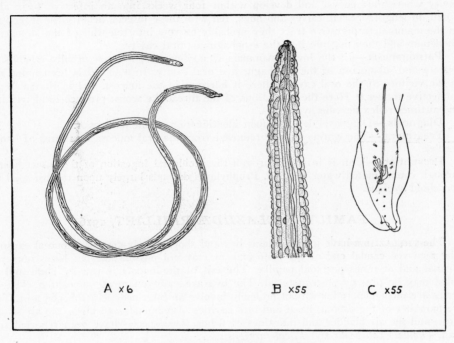

A x6   B x55   C x55

FIG. 101.—*Gongylonema pulchrum*

A, adult worm from man; *B,* anterior end; *C,* posterior end of male (*A* and *B* redrawn from Ward, 1916; *C* redrawn from Baylis, 1925).

Gongylonema pulchrum MOLIN, 1857

Gongylonema pulchrum is a parasite of the upper digestive tract of sheep, cattle, goats, other ruminants, horses, and hogs. It was discovered in man by Pane in Italy in 1864. Some 10 cases of human infection have been reported, 6 in the United States of America, 2 in Italy, 1 in Russia, and 1 in Yugoslavia. Because of inadequate descriptions and immature specimens the variously-named species have been grouped under the single species, *G. pulchrum.*[8]

Morphology.—The long yellowish-white nematode (Fig. 101A) is studded at its anterior extremity with irregular longitudinal rows of bosses (Fig. 101B). The males attain a maximal length of 62 mm. and the females 145 mm. The worms are slender as the maximal breadth is 0.3 mm. for the male and 0.5 mm. for the female. The cuticle

[8] Faust, E. C., Human Parasitology, 1938.

has fine transverse striations. There is a small funnel-shaped mouth and a subterminal anus. The caudal end of the male is curved and bears two asymmetrical, lateral alæ and two unequal spicules (Fig. 101C). The posterior end of the female is bluntly conical. The female genitalia comprise capillary ovaries, divergent uteri, a long vagina and a postequatorial vulva. The ovoid, embryonate ova, 60 by 30 μ, have thick, transparent shells.

Life Cycle.—If the embryonate ova, passed in the feces, are ingested by one of several species of dung beetles or the cockroach, *Blatella germanica* (Chapter XXXVIII), the liberated larvæ, about 250 μ in length, pass through the intestinal wall into the body cavity where they encyst and develop within four weeks into an infective form about 2 mm. in length.[9] Sheep, calves and hogs, fed with these insects, acquire the infection.[10] In the mammalian digestive tract they probably burrow into the wall of the stomach or duodenum and then migrate into the esophagus or oral cavity.

Pathogenesis.—In the lower mammals *Gongylonema pulchrum* usually inhabits the mucosa and submucosa of the esophagus and oral cavity. In man it has been found only in the vicinity of the oral cavity where it burrows in the mucosa and in the subdermal connective tissues.[11] Here the migrations of the threadlike worm produce local irritation and at times reflex nervous symptoms.

Diagnosis.—Diagnosis depends upon identification of the adult worm.

Treatment.—The worms may be removed from the oral mucosa by means of hooked needles.

Prevention.—Man is infected through the accidental ingestion of the insect host or through contaminated water or food. Prophylaxis depends largely upon the personal and household hygiene.

FAMILY *THELAZIIDÆ* RAILLIET, 1916

The THELAZIIDÆ have inconspicuous lips and short, poorly-developed buccal capsules. The recurved caudal end of the male may or may not possess alæ but bears numerous preanal and at times postanal papillæ. The tail of the female is usually blunt and the vulva may be pre- or postequatorial. The ova are embryonate at oviposition. The life cycles are incompletely known but probably involve an intermediate arthropod host. They are parasites of the orbital, nasal and oral cavities of mammals and birds, the air sacs of birds, and the air bladder and intestines of fishes. Two species have been reported from man, *Thelazia callipæda* and *T. californiensis*.

Thelazia callipæda RAILLIET AND HENRY, 1910

Thelazia callipæda was discovered in India in 1910 by Railliet and Henry in the eye of a dog, its natural host. Four instances of ocular infection in man have been reported in China.[12]

Morphology.—The creamy-white adult worm has well-defined, transverse, cuticular striations and a mouth without lips. The male, 5 to 13 mm. by 0.5 mm. has a markedly recurved, papillate posterior end with two unequal copulatory spicules and lateral alæ. The female, 6 to 17 mm. by 0.6 mm., has a postequatorial vulva and paired coiled ovaries and uteri, located in the posterior part of the body. The ova, 57 by 35 μ, are embryonate at oviposition.

Life Cycle.—The life cycle has not been determined but probably involves an arthropod as intermediate host.

[9] Ransom, B. H. and Hall, M. C., 1915.

[10] Baylis, H. A., Sheather, A. L. and Andrews, W. H., 1926.

[11] Ward, H. B., 1916; Stiles, C. W., 1921; Waite, C. H. and Gorrie, R., 1935.

[12] Stuckey, E. J., 1917; Trimble, C. G., 1917; Howard, H. J., 1927; Hsü, H. F., 1933.

Pathogenesis.—The adult worms inhabit the conjunctival sac and frequently crawl over the surface of the eyeball, causing lacrimation and severe pain, and at times giving rise to nervous manifestations and paralysis of the ocular muscles.

Diagnosis.—Diagnosis depends upon the removal and identification of the worm.

Treatment.—Introduction of 2 per cent cocaine into the conjunctival sac will cause the worms to emerge at the canthus where they may be removed with forceps.[8]

Prevention.—Since the life cycle of the parasite has not been determined, the method of transmission is unknown. Contact with infected dogs should be avoided.

Thelazia californiensis KOFOID AND WILLIAMS, 1933

Thelazia californiensis is a parasite of the eyes of dogs and cats. A single case of human infection has been reported in California.[13]

REFERENCES

AFRICA, C. M., REFUERZO, P. G. and GARCIA, E. Y. The Life Cycle of *Gnathostoma spin-igerum,* Philippine J. Sc., 1936, 59:513.

BAYLIS, H. A. and LANE, C. A Revision of the Nematode Family, GNATHOSTOMIDÆ, Proc. Zool. Soc. London, 1920, 2:245.

——, SHEATHER, A. L. and ANDREWS, W. H. Further Experiments with *Gongylonema* of Cattle, J. Trop. Med., 1926, 29:194; 29:346.

DAENGSVANG, S. and TANSURAT, P. Contributions to the Knowledge of the Second Inter-mediate Hosts of *Gnathostoma spinigerum* Owen, 1836. Ann. Trop. Med., 1938, 32:137.

KOFOID, C. A., WILLIAMS, O. L. and VEALE, N. C. *Thelazia californiensis* a Nematode Eye Worm of Dog and Man, with a Review of the Thelazias of Domestic Animals, Univ. California Publ. Zoöl., 1937, 41:225.

MAPLESTONE, P. A. and BHADURI, N. V. Gnathostomiasis in Human Beings, Indian M. Gaz., 1937, 72:713.

MORISHITA, K. and FAUST, E. C. Two New Cases of Human Creeping Disease (Gnathostomia-sis) in China, with a Note on the Infection in Reservoir Hosts in the China Area, J. Parasitol., 1925, 11:158.

PROMMAS, C. and DAENGSVANG, S. Preliminary Report of a Study on the Life-cycle of *Gnathostoma spinigerum,* J. Parasitol., 1933, 19:287.

—— Feeding Experiments on Cats with *Gnathostoma spinigerum* Larvae Obtained from the Second Intermediate Host, J. Parasitol., 1937, 23:115.

RANSOM, B. H. and HALL, M. C. The Life History of *Gongylonema scutatum,* J. Parasitol., 1915, 2:80.

WARD, H. B. *Gongylonema* in the Rôle of a Human Parasite, J. Parasitol., 1916, 2:119.

---

[13] Kofoid, C. A. and Williams, O. L., 1935.

Chapter XXI

THE SUPERFAMILY FILARIOIDEA

SUPERFAMILY *FILARIOIDEA* (WEINLAND, 1858) STILES, 1907

The filarial worms are slender nematodes parasitic in the circulatory and lymphatic systems, muscles, connective tissues or serous cavities of vertebrates. Many species are found in mammals and birds. Filariæ are common in birds in the United States of America, particularly in crows and English sparrows. A simple oval or circular mouth without prominent lips is surmounted by one or two circlets of papillæ; the buccal cavity is absent or rudimentary; the cylindrical esophagus has no bulb; and the intestine is simple. The male usually has two unequal, dissimilar copulatory spicules and infrequently caudal alæ. The females, often three or four times the length of the male, produce embryonated ova that either hatch *in utero* or shortly after deposition. The microfilariæ (prelarval forms) are found in the blood, lymphatics or tissues of the host. The completion of the life cycles of these worms requires intermediate hosts such as mosquitoes and biting flies in which the microfilariæ undergo metamorphosis before becoming infective.

FILARIÆ PARASITIC IN MAN

The principal species parasitic in man are: *Wuchereria bancrofti, Wuchereria malayi, Onchocerca volvulus, Acanthocheilonema perstans, Mansonella ozzardi,* and *Loa loa.* One other species, *Microfilaria streptocerca,* is known only in the larval stage. Single infections with *Dirofilaria magalhæsi* and *D. repens,* and ten or more rare or poorly described species also have been reported. The general characteristics of the common species are given in Table 26.

ADULT FILARIÆ

Morphology.—The creamy white adult worms (Figs. 102 and 103) are filiform nematodes, ranging from 20 to 700 mm. in length, the female usually not more than two times as long as the male. The cuticle is usually smooth, but may be characterized by transverse striations, annular thickenings or bosses. The head ordinarily bears two lateral and four submedian papillæ. The mouth is simple and usually is without definite lips. The buccal cavity is inconspicuous; the esophagus is cylindrical, has no cardiac bulbus and is usually divided into an anterior muscular and a posterior glandular portion; and the simple midintestine may be atrophied posteriorly although an anal opening is present. The vulva of the female is preëquatorial, usually in the esophageal region. In some species the males possess caudal alæ; in others they are absent. The two copulatory spicules are

TABLE 26

PARASITIC FILARIÆ OF MAN

	Wuchereria bancrofti	*Onchocerca volvulus*	*Acanthocheilonema perstans*	*Wuchereria malayi*	*Mansonella ozzardi*	*Loa loa*	*Microfilaria streptocerca*
Disease	Bancroft's filariasis	Onchocerciasis	Acanthocheilonemiasis	Malayan filariasis	Ozzard's filariasis	Loasis	
Geographical distribution	World-wide tropical and subtropical countries	Africa, Central America	Africa, South America	East Indies, southern Asia	South and Central America	Africa	Africa
Definitive host	Man	Man	Man, gorilla, chimpanzee	Man	Man	Man, baboon	Man
Intermediate host (principal)	Mosquitoes: *Culex fatigans, Aëdes variegatus*	Black flies: *Simulium damnosum* and other species of *Simulium*	Midges: *Culicoides austeni* and *C. grahami*	Mosquitoes: *Mansonia* sp.	Midges: *Culicoides furens*	Tabanid flies: *Chrysops dimidiata* and *C. silacea*	Unknown
Location in man Adult	Lymphatics	Subcutaneous tissues	Mesentery, perirenal and retroperitoneal tissues	Lymphatics	Mesentery, body cavities	Subcutaneous tissues	Unknown
Microfilaria	Blood	Skin, subcutaneous nodules	Blood	Blood	Blood	Blood	Skin

usually unequal and dissimilar. The morphological differentiation of the several species is presented in Table 27.

Physiology.—The adult worms inhabit the lymphatics and are found in lymph varices, subcutaneous nodules and internal viscera. Nourishment is obtained from the lymph and tissue fluids. Fertilization is dependent upon the proximity of the males and females and may not always occur.

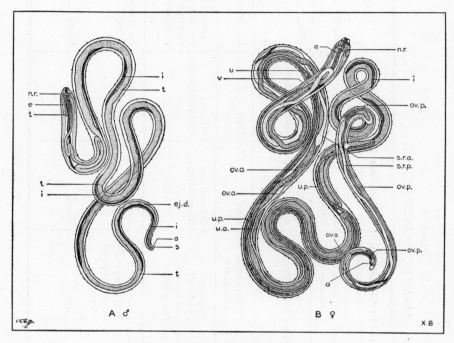

Fig. 102.—Morphology of *Loa loa*

A, male; *B*, female.

a, anus; *e*, esophagus; *ej.d.*, ejaculatory duct; *i*, intestine; *ov.a.*, ovary anterior; *ov.p.*, ovary posterior; *n.r.*, nerve ring; *s*, spicules; *s.r.a.*, seminal receptacle anterior; *s.r.p.*, seminal receptacle posterior; *t*, testis; *u*, uterus; *u.a.*, uterus anterior; *u.p.*, uterus posterior; *v*, vulva (Redrawn from Looss, 1904).

MICROFILARIÆ

The viviparous female gives birth to prelarval microfilariæ (Fig. 104) that have certain morphological characteristics of value in the differentiation of species (Table 28).

Sheath.—The presence or absence of a sheath is a distinguishing feature in fixed and stained specimens. The sheath, present in *Wuchereria bancrofti, W. malayi* and *Loa loa,* is a delicate membrane, which is so close-fitting that it is only detectable as it projects beyond the head or tail. It is not observed when the microfilaria is in the blood stream. Its significance is unknown. It may be the result of an incomplete ecdysis.

TABLE 27
MORPHOLOGY OF ADULT FILARIÆ

	Wuchereria bancrofti	Onchocerca volvulus	Acantho-cheilonema perstans	Mansonella ozzardi	Loa loa	Dirofilaria magalhæsi
Mean size (mm.)						
Male						
Length	40	30	45	38 (partial)	32	83
Width	0.10	0.16	0.07	0.20	0.35	0.41
Female						
Length	83	410	75	70	60	155
Width	0.24	0.35	0.13	0.23	0.50	0.72
Color	Creamy white	Opalescent white	Creamy white	Creamy white	White	White
Cuticle	Smooth	Transverse striations, annular thickenings	Smooth	Smooth	Embossed	Fine, transverse striations
Anterior end						
Shape	Tapering to bluntly rounded, slightly swollen head	Bluntly rounded head	Bluntly rounded, club-shaped head	Rounded swollen head	Slightly tapering with abruptly narrowed head	Slightly tapering, rounded head
Papillæ (pairs)	2 rings of small papillæ	1 lateral 4 submedian	1 lateral 2 sub-median		1 lateral 2 sub-median	Inconspic-uous
Appendages	None	None	Short lateral shield	None	None	None
Posterior end						
Female	Ventral curve, bluntly rounded	Ventral curve	Ventral curve, bifurcated	Rounded with pair of fleshy laplets	Ventral curve, broadly rounded, embossed	
Male	Sharp, ventrad curve	Marked ventrad curve, slightly bulbous end	Strong ventrad curve, bi-furcated	Marked ventrad curve, slightly bulbous end	Slight ventrad curve, broadly rounded	Sharp ventrad curve
Papillæ (pairs)	12 perianal 3 caudal	Variable number of perianal and caudal papillæ	4 preanal 1 postanal		8 perianal 5 preanal 3 postanal	4 perianal 4 postanal
Spicules	Unequal	Unequal	Very unequal		Unequal	Unequal
Alæ	Inconspic-uous	Absent	Absent	Fleshy laplets	Narrow	

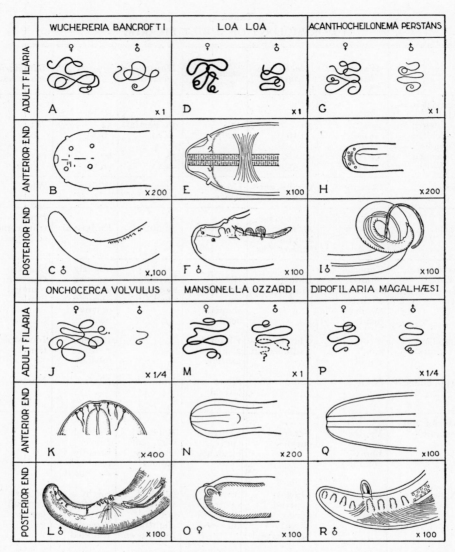

FIG. 103.—ADULT FILARIÆ, SHOWING RELATIVE SIZES AND ANTERIOR AND POSTERIOR ENDS
OF WORMS

(*B, C, F, H, I* and *O* redrawn from Leiper, 1913; *E* adapted from Looss and from Blanchard; *K* and *L* redrawn from Strong *et al*, 1934; *N* adapted from photograph by Daniels, 1899; *Q* drawn from description; *R* redrawn from v.Linstow, 1900).

Column of Nuclei.—The arrangement of the column of cells with deeply staining nuclei, which represents the rudiments of the intestine and perhaps other organs, differs in the several species. These nuclei extend nearly the full length and occupy almost the entire width of the body. Their absence or presence at the

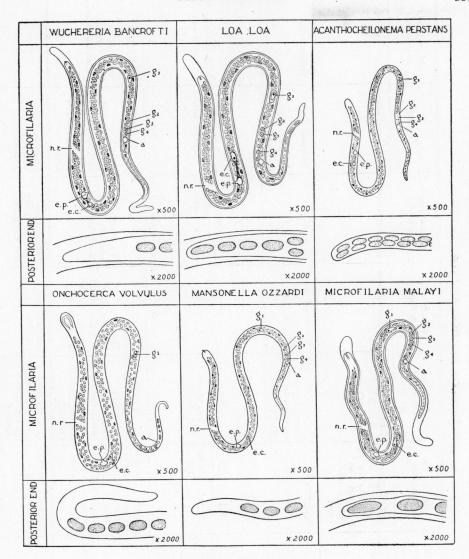

FIG. 104.—MICROFILARIÆ

a, anal pore (tail-spot) ; *e.c.*, excretory cell ; *e.p.*, excretory pore (V-spot) ; g_1, g_2, g_3, and g_4, first, second, third and fourth genital cells. (*Microfilaria malayi* is now *Wuchereria malayi*).

tip of the tail is useful in distinguishing species. In the posterior middle third of the body is an irregular aggregation of granules, the "Innen Korper."

Size.—The size of the microfilariæ varies so greatly that it cannot be used for species-differentiation.

Shape.—Certain species have graceful flowing curves while others are irregular. The caudal extremities of *O. volvulus* and *Mf. streptocerca* are curved, while those

TABLE 28

MORPHOLOGY OF MICROFILARIÆ

	Wuchereria bancrofti	Onchocerca volvulus (Small form)	Onchocerca volvulus (Large form)	Acanthocheilonema perstans	Wuchereria malayi	Mansonella ozzardi	Loa loa	Microfilaria streptocerca
Habitat	Peripheral blood, hydrocele fluid	Lymph spaces of skin, subcutaneous nodules, hydrocele fluid, peripheral blood (rare)		Blood, principally in large arteries	Peripheral blood	Peripheral blood	Peripheral blood	Skin
Periodicity	Nocturnal, usually	Nonperiodic		Nonperiodic, but microfilariæ more numerous nocturnally	Nocturnal, less absolute than W. bancrofti	Nonperiodic	Diurnal	Nonperiodic
Size (micra) Length Mean	260	254	332	195	220	200	275	210
Range	230 to 296	221 to 287	295 to 358	190 to 200	177 to 260	173 to 240	250 to 300	180 to 240
Width Mean	8	6	7	4.5	5.5	4.7	7.3	3
Range	7.5 to 10	5-7	6-9	4 to 5	5 to 6	4 to 5	6 to 8.5	2.5 to 3.5
Appearance	Sheath. Cylindrical, uniform girth; graceful sweeping curves	No sheath. Uniform girth except near caudal end; sweeping curves		No sheath. Slender, delicately curved with deeply staining mass in middle	Sheath. Varying girth, kinky irregular curves, crinkled appearance	No sheath. Slender, delicately curved	Sheath. Noncylindrical, varying girth; ungraceful, stiff, with secondary kinks	No sheath. Transversely striated cuticle
Movement	Lashing, non-progressive	Sluggish, coiling and twisting		Actively progressive, elongating and contracting	Lashing, progressive	Active, constantly coiling and recoiling	Lashing, undulatory, progressive	

Anterior end	Bluntly rounded, not tapering One stylet	Bluntly rounded, enlarged No stylets	Bluntly rounded No stylets	Bluntly rounded Two stylets	Bluntly rounded One stylet	Broad, flat, not tapering One stylet	Bluntly rounded, tapering No stylets
Posterior end	Posterior third of body tapers to delicate point	Abruptly narrowed and sharply curved caudal extremity	Posterior half of body tapers to a bluntly truncate, knob-like end	Tapers from level of anal pore to an acuminate tip. Swollen at two terminal nuclei	Posterior third of body tapers to a bluntly rounded end	Tapers gradually to a relatively thick, caudal extremity, often with sharp flexures	Tapers to blunt caudal extremity bent in a shepherd's crook
Nuclei	Not terminal Discrete, round, uniform-sized, evenly spaced, 2 or 3 abreast	Not terminal	Terminal	Terminal Nuclei crowded together; terminal nucleus elongate	Not terminal	Terminal Central nuclei irregularly crowded, large, oval	Terminal
Anatomical landmarks (percentage of body length)							
Nerve ring	20	26	20	21	22	22	27
Excretory pore	29 (small)	35	30	30 (large)	32	32 (large)	34
Excretory cell	31 (small)	36	36	37 (large)	35	37 (large)	
Anal pore	83 (indistinct)	90	84	82 (distinct)	79	82	86
Genital cell G_1	70	72	71	68	69	69	69
Genital cells	Small, uniform size, G_{2-4} widely separated from G_1		Difficult to demonstrate	Large, relatively near together, G_1 larger than G_{2-4}		Large, relatively near together, G_1 larger than G_{2-4}	
Staining reaction	Weak	Strong	Strong			Strong	Weak

of the others are straight. Some species are characterized by having more pointed tails than others.

Location.—The location, such as blood, skin or tissues, and type of periodicity are also differential aids in distinguishing species.

Anatomical Landmarks.—The percentile location of certain anatomical structures differs in the several species. These structures are (1) the nerve ring; (2) the excretory pore; (3) the excretory cell and its relation to the excretory pore; (4) the anal pore; and (5) the four genital cells, particularly the location and size of the large G_1 and its relative position in respect to G_{2-4}.

Periodicity.—The periodicity of microfilariæ in the peripheral blood varies with the species, although it is relative rather than actual. Ordinarily appreciable numbers of microfilariæ of *Wuchereria bancrofti* are found in the peripheral blood at night, beginning about 9.00 P.M., increasing to a maximum about midnight, and then decreasing to a low point in the late morning. However, a few microfilariæ are found in the blood during the day, and in certain parts of the world such as the Philippines, Fiji and Samoa they are present both day and night, although 43 per cent are found between 10.00 P.M. and 2.00 A.M. and practically none between 10.00 A.M. and 2.00 P.M., indicating a modified periodicity.[1] Various theories to explain the periodicity of the microfilariæ, none of which are wholly satisfactory, have been advanced; including metabolic activity, habits of insect host, cyclic parturition, and location of parasite in the host. Periodicity is associated to some extent with daytime activity and nocturnal rest. If the hours of activity and sleep are reversed, after several days the microfilariæ are present in maximal numbers in the blood during daytime or the peak of the curve is shifted.[2] If the intermediate insect host is nocturnal in its biting habits (*Culex fatigans*) the microfilariæ have a nocturnal periodicity. If diurnal in its biting habits (*Aëdes variegatus*) the microfilariæ may be either diurnal or present both day and night. Periodicity may be due to periodic parturition and simultaneous development of fresh broods of larvæ by the gravid female, all previous batches of larvæ having been destroyed within 24 hours by the mobile cells of the reticulo-endothelial system.[3] In favor of this view is the finding that all female worms when removed from the tissues contain embryos in the same stage of development.[4] Against this view is the probability that the life of a microfilaria far exceeds 24 hours, and that the death of an enormous number of larvæ would produce serious symptoms. Also there is no evidence of cyclic parturition in *Dirofilaria immitis*.[5] It is also possible that the location of the adult parasite in the host may influence microfilarial periodicity.

Existence in Host.—The microfilariæ of *W. bancrofti* reach the blood by migration through the walls of the lmphatics to the neighboring small blood vessels,[6] or more commonly by way of the thoracic duct. The microfilariæ of *Dirofilaria immitis* pass through the lymph nodes of experimental dogs without phagocytic destruction and when artificially imprisoned within a lymph node live at least

[1] Africa, C. M., Garcia, E. Y. and Layco, J., 1935.
[2] Low, G. C.; Manson-Bahr, P. and Walters, A. H., 1933; Hinman, E. H., 1936.
[3] Lane, C., 1929.
[4] O'Connor, F. W. and Hulse, C. R., 1932.
[5] Hinman, E. H., 1935.
[6] O'Connor, F. W., 1931.

five days.[7] By analogy, the microfilariæ of man should not be impeded by lymph nodes. Both "sheathed" and "unsheathed" microfilariæ migrate actively through the arterioles, both with and against the blood stream. The "sheathed" microfilariæ of the frog and ground dove are filtered out of the circulation by the liver and spleen and eventually destroyed by the reticulo-endothelial cells.[8] When microfilariæ are transferred from man to man they disappear from the blood of the recipient within three hours.[9] The microfilariæ of *Dirofilaria immitis* live for ten days at 39° C. *in vitro* and up to eight weeks in the icebox,[5] and those of *W. bancrofti* for five days in tissue cultures [10] and four to six weeks at 4° C.[11]

Key to Microfilariæ.—The microfilariæ may be identified by the following key. The more detailed differential characteristics are given in Table 28.

Peripheral Blood
    Sheathed
        Smooth curves, nuclei not to tip of tail, nocturnal periodicity
                                      W. bancrofti
        Irregular outline, stiff, with secondary kinks
            Diurnal periodicity ....*Loa loa*
            Nocturnal periodicity ....*W. malayi*
    Unsheathed
        Nuclei to tip of tail.....................................*A. perstans*
        Nuclei not to tip of tail................................*M. ozzardi*
Skin and subcutaneous tissues
    Nuclei to tip of tail, tail curved.......................*Mf. streptocerca*
    Nuclei not to tip of tail, head enlarged.....................*O. volvulus*

LIFE CYCLE

The completion of the life cycle requires an intermediate host. The microfilariæ are removed from the blood or tissues by a bloodsucking insect, in which they undergo metamorphosis into mature larvæ. These infective forms are transferred from the proboscis of the biting insect to the skin of man.

Hosts.—The filarial parasites of man are highly host-specific. Only two have been reported in other primates, *Acanthocheilonema perstans* in the gorilla and chimpanzee and *Loa loa* in the baboon. The intermediate hosts are various species of the mosquitoes, tabanid flies, black flies and midges (Table 29). Within these groups there are various degrees of species-specificity. In certain species the larvæ develop normally; in others they show partial or no development. Good experimental hosts are not always important natural vectors, since the transmission of the infection depends upon such factors as their prevalence, habits and contact with man.

Development.—The salivary secretions of the insect possibly exert a chemotactic influence that causes a concentration of microfilariæ near the site of the bite

---

[7] Drinker, C. K., Augustine, D. L. and Leigh, O. C., 1935.

[8] Augustine, D. L., 1937; O'Connor, F. W. and Beatty, H. A., 1938.

[9] Murgatroyd, F., 1933.

[10] Natarayan, C. V., 1932.

[11] Rao, S. S., 1933.

TABLE 29

METAMORPHOSIS OF FILARIAL LARVÆ IN INSECT HOST

	Wuchereria bancrofti	*Onchocerca volvulus*	*Acanthocheilonema perstans*	*Wuchereria malayi*	*Loa loa*
Insect host	*Culex fatigans, Aëdes variegatus.* Complete metamorphosis in 41 species of mosquitoes (*Aëdes*, 8; *Anopheles*, 22; *Culex*, 5; *Mansonia*, 6)	*Simulium damnosum, S. ochraceum, S. callidum* and *S. metallicum*	*Culicoides austeni* and *C. grahami*	Mosquitoes: species of *Mansonia*, 6; *Anopheles*, 2; *Armigeres*, 1	*Chrysops silacea,, C. dimidiata* and possibly *C. longicornis, C. distinctipennis, .C. centurionis*
Duration of cycle (days)	14 to 15	8 to 9	7 to 9	6 to 7	10 to 12
Time of ecdyses Shedding sheath	2 to 6 hours	Within a few hours	Within a few hours	Within 3 hours	Within 1 hour
First	Eighth day	Fourth (?) day	Fifth (?) day	Fourth day	?
Second	Twelfth day	Seventh day	Seventh day	Sixth day	Sixth day
Location in host Gut	0 to 6 hours	0 to few hours (not over 24)	0 to 6 hours	0 to 3 hours	0 to 6 hours
Abdominal cavity	6 to 12 hours	Few hours to seventh day (malpighian tubules)	6 to 24 hours	3 to 10 hours	6 to 48 hours or longer
Thorax	12 hours to thirteenth day	First to seventh day	First to sixth day	10 hours to fifth day	Second to eighth day
Proboscis and head	Fourteenth to fifteenth day	Eighth to ninth day	Seventh to ninth day	Sixth to seventh day	Ninth to twelfth day

	Culex pipiens var. pallens	Simulium damnosum	Culicoides austeni	Anopheles hyrcanus var. sinensis	Chrysops silacea
Morphology First stage	By fourth day short sausage-shaped larva with short pointed caudal end, 147 x 23.6 µ (about one-half length of microfilaria)	By second day thick sausage-shaped, with short pointed tail, 250 x 23 µ	By third day thick, cigar-shaped with sharply pointed posterior end, shortened to 42 per cent of length of microfilaria	By second day sausage-shaped with slender club-shaped tail containing terminal nuclei, length about 150 µ	On second and third day short, stumpy sausage-shaped, coiled in almost complete circle; posterior end tapers to sickle-shaped point; 290 x 32 µ on third day.
	Elongates after fifth day to 315 x 33 µ on eighth day	Elongates on third (?) day	Elongates on fourth day	Elongates on second day, reaching 490 µ on third day	Elongates on third day, assuming a corkscrew appearance; 900 x 37 µ on fifth day
Second stage	After eighth day increases rapidly in length to 1100 x 37 µ on twelfth day. Conical caudal papilla.	Increased length and diminished breadth, filarial appearance	Increased length and diminished breadth, wormlike appearance	Fifth day about 900 x 26.5 µ, conical posterior end	?
Third stage	After twelfth day elongate narrow larva with three subterminal caudal papillæ, about 1700 x 24 µ on thirteenth day	Seventh day elongated larva, about 600 µ, with papillated posterior end. Ninth day elongated slender larva over 760 µ with 2 small caudal and 2 conspicuous perianal papillæ	Seventh day 800 µ, tail blunt with 4 papillæ, resembling a bishop's mitre	Sixth day 1300 x 20 µ, trilobed posterior end	On the sixth day the coils become gentle curves and the tail is rounded and trilobed; cylindrical body tapers toward each end; 1000 x 40 µ. Increases to 2000 x 25 µ on tenth day
Movement	Sluggish, slight bending after seventh day, but after twelfth day active progressive movements	Slow bending and active gliding movements	On fourth and fifth days slow, jerky, doubling-up movements; on sixth day elongates and contracts; on seventh day active progressive movements	Active progressive movements on sixth day	Early stationary bending, twisting and looping; after seventh day rapid darting, coiling and uncoiling
Investigator	Yamada, S., 1927	Blacklock, D. B., 1926	Sharp, N. A. D, 1928	Feng, L, 1936	Connal, A. and Connal, S. L. M, 1922
Fly	*Culex pipiens var. pallens*	*Simulium damnosum*	*Culicoides austeni*	*Anopheles hyrcanus var. sinensis*	*Chrysops silacea*

far in excess of the normal number.[12] After ingestion by a suitable insect the microfilaria casts off its sheath, within a few hours penetrates the wall of the gut, and makes its way to the thoracic muscles. Here it undergoes metamorphosis

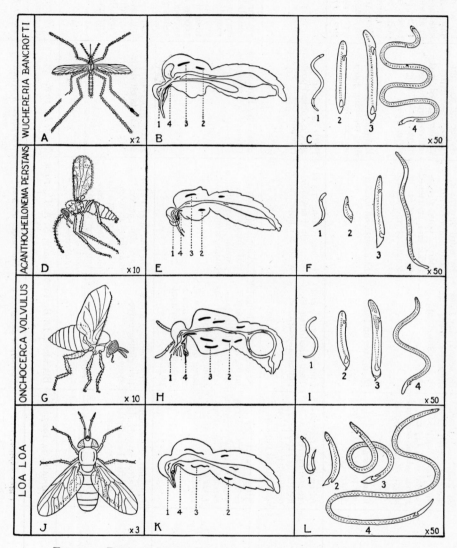

FIG. 105.—DEVELOPMENT OF FILARIAL LARVÆ IN INTERMEDIATE HOSTS

A to *C*, *Wuchereria bancrofti* in *Culex fatigans*; *D* to *F*, *Acanthocheilonema perstans* in *Culicoides austeni*; *G* to *I*, *Onchocerca volvulus* in *Simulium damnosum*; *J* to *L*, *Loa loa* in *Chrysops silacea*.

1, microfilaria entering digestive tract of insect; *2*, early stage in tissues; *3*, late stage in tissues; *4*, mature larva in region of head (*D* and *F* adapted from Sharp, 1928; *G* to *I* adapted from Blacklock, 1926 and 1927; *L* adapted from Connal and Connal, 1921).

with at least two molts before reaching the mature infective stage in 6 to 15 days.
The infective larva migrates to the proboscis from which it passes to a new definitive host. The several filarial species vary as to insect-hosts, time of development,
rate of growth, morphology, and location in the host (Table 29 and Fig. 105).
The length of the cycle varies with the temperature and may be prolonged several
weeks beyond the approximate time given in Table 29. The time of molting and rate

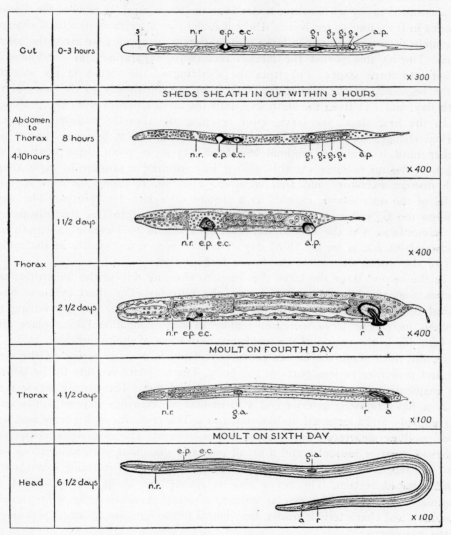

Fig. 106.—Development of Larva of *Wuchereria malayi* in the Mosquito *Anopheles hyrcanus*
var. *sinensis*

    a, anus; *a.p.*, anal pore; *e.c.*, excretory cell; *e.p.*, excretory pore; g_1, g_2, g_3, and g_4, so-called
genital cells; *g.a.*, genital anlage; *n.r.*, nerve ring; *r*, rectum; *s*, sheath (Larval forms redrawn
from Feng, 1936).

of development correspondingly vary. Likewise, an accurate comparison of the several parasites is impossible, since the data represent the observations of different investigators.

Larval Metamorphosis.—The metamorphosis of *Wuchereria malayi* in *Anopheles hyrcanus* var. *sinensis* at 29° to 32° C. shows the typical morphological changes that take place in the cyclic development of filarial larvæ (Fig. 106).[13] The microfilaria casts off its sheath in the gut of the mosquito and penetrates into the abdominal cavity within three hours after the blood meal. It reaches the thoracic muscles in from four to ten hours, where it undergoes a series of structural changes, ultimately producing a mature larva quite different in appearance from the microfilaria. During this period the larva molts twice, separating the developmental period into three stages: (1) from the shedding of the sheath in the intestine to the beginning of the fourth day, (2) from the fourth day to the start of the sixth day, and (3) from the sixth day until the larva emerges from the proboscis.

In the first stage, the larva, after reaching the thoracic muscles, undergoes marked changes in structure. During the first 36 hours it becomes shorter and thicker until it attains a minimal length of 153 μ or about three quarters the length of the microfilaria. At this time it has acquired a sausage or cigar shape, with distinct excretory and anal vacuoles. The tail, retaining the two terminal nuclei of the microfilaria, extends as a slender club-shaped projection. The space between the G_1 cell and the anal vacuole is about two-thirds of that distance in the microfilaria. On the second day the larva begins to increase in length and reaches about 490 μ on the third day. The increase occurs mostly in the middle part of the worm, the site of the future midintestine.

In the second stage the larva continues to elongate during the fourth day and reaches a maximal breadth of 26.5 μ on the fifth day. The short tail now has a conical tip, the nucleated tail of the first stage having been cast off during the previous molt. The larva increases rapidly in size, elongation taking place after the fifth day in the region of the esophagus as well as of the midintestine.

In the third stage the larvæ, previously sluggish, become active on the sixth day and penetrate various parts of the body. The majority migrate to the labium, but frequently return to the head, thorax and abdomen. The mature larva, 1,300 by 20 μ, has a tapering anterior end with two concentric rings of four papillæ each, two amphids, and four small lip-like structures. The posterior end is truncated with three papillate structures, two ventral and one dorsal. The esophagus, comprising a narrow anterior muscular and a broad posterior glandular portion, is about one-third the length of the larva. From it a straight cylindrical intestine extends to a spindle-shaped rectum. The nerve ring is situated at about the middle of the muscular esophagus. The genital anlage, a mass of seven cells with compact cytoplasm and characteristic nuclei, lies ventral to the intestine about 95 μ posterior to the esophagus.

The different organs develop at various times. By the third day the buccal cavity is formed from the cephalic space of the microfilaria, the esophagus from the anterior part of the nuclear column, the midintestine from the posterior part,

[13] Feng, L., 1936.

and the rectum and anus probably from the G cells and the anal vacuole. On the second day the rectum contains a nail-like plug, which is cast off at the fourth day molt. By the fourth day the esophagus communicates with the intestine and the posterior end of the intestine is connected with the rectum, although the two do not communicate until after the final molt. The excretory vacuole increases in size until the fourth day, and then becomes gradually smaller until it is scarcely visible in the mature larva. The genital anlage, possibly derived from the nuclear column rather than from the G cells, is differentiated by the third day.

Development in Man.—When the insect bites man, the larvæ, possibly attracted by warmth, escape from the tip of the proboscis. In the mosquito the larvæ of *Wuchereria malayi* pass out between the outer and inner walls of the labella and not through Dutton's membrane, as described for *W. bancrofti*.[13] The larvæ of *Onchocerca volvulus* glide out of the proboscis of *Simulium,* usually on one side of the terminal end, until about one-tenth of the larva remains in the proboscis. The last part is suddenly delivered as if expelled by muscular contraction.[14] When deposited, the larvæ of *Wuchereria bancrofti* are incapable of penetrating unbroken skin and are susceptible to drying. They are lymphotactic and enter the body through the wound made by the mosquito only when there is an excessive outpouring of lymph.[15] After penetrating the skin they pass through the peripheral lymphatics to the lymph glands where they mature, mate and produce microfilariæ in about a year.

IMMUNITY

There are little available data concerning natural immunity to filarial infections. The high percentage of asymptomatic cases in wuchereriasis suggests host-resistance. The question of susceptibility, however, is complicated by the possibility that lymphangitis and elephantiasis may result from superimposed streptococcal infections rather than from the direct action of the parasite.

Alexin-fixative antibodies have been demonstrated in the blood and serous fluids of patients with wuchereriasis, loasis and onchocerciasis, using as antigens aqueous or alcoholic extracts of fresh or dried *Dirofilaria immitis* (dog) and *Onchocerca volvulus* (Section **VII,** IX, 10, 11).[16] The response appears to be a group reaction for all filarial worms. The blood of rabbits six weeks after a series of injections of aqueous extract of *Dirofilaria immitis* exerts a lethal effect upon the microfilariæ.[17]

Supersensitiveness has been demonstrated by cutaneous and intracutaneous tests in wuchereriasis, loasis and onchocerciasis. The group nature of these reactions has been noted by practically all workers, patients with the various filarial diseases reacting equally well to *Dirofilaria immitis* and *Onchocerca volvulus* antigens. The delayed type of reaction develops rapidly and manifests itself in the

[14] Blacklock, D. B., 1926.
[15] Yokogawa, S., 1939.
[16] Fairley, N. H., 1931, 1932; Gutierrez, V. L., 1931; Lloyd, R. B. and Chandra, S. N..
1933; Connal, A., 1934; van Hoof, L., 1934.
[17] Arnold, J. G., Jr. and Duggan, T. L., 1937.

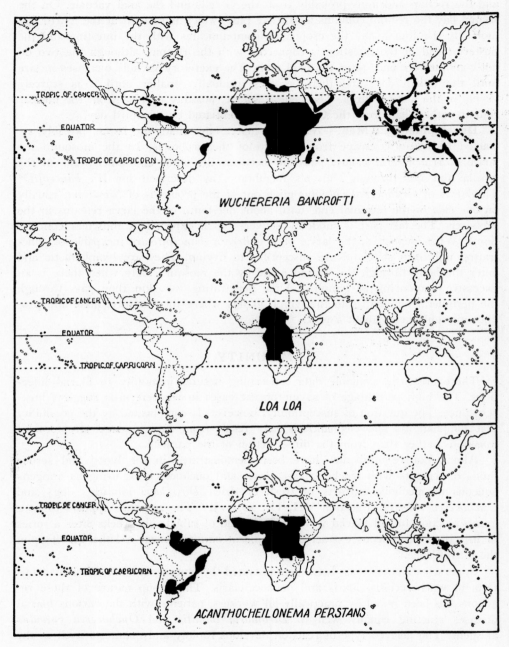

FIG. 107.—GEOGRAPHICAL DISTRIBUTION OF *Wuchereria bancrofti, Loa loa* AND
Acanthocheilonema perstans

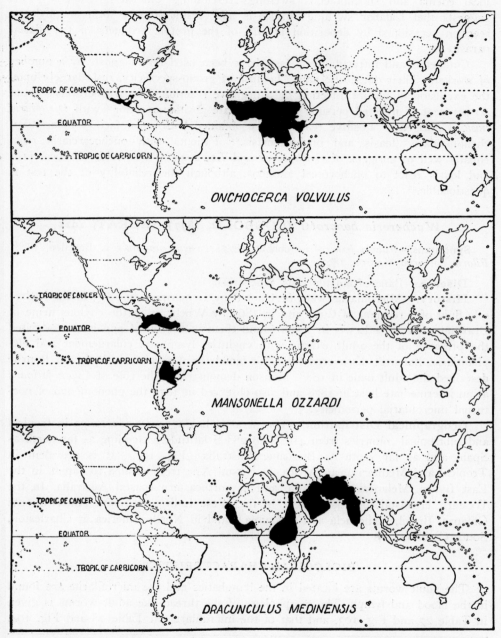

Fig. 108.—Geographical Distribution of *Onchocerca volvulus, Mansonella ozzardi* and *Dracunculus medinensis*

local edema and subcutaneous swellings resembling Calabar swellings.[18] This suggests that Calabar swellings in loasis may result from a local anaphylactic reaction occasioned by deposition *in situ* of the proteic products of the filarial parasite.

Cutaneous and intracutaneous tests have been used for diagnosis by a number of workers. Their diagnostic value, because of group-specificity, rests largely upon the exclusion of filarial infection by a negative reaction.[19] In wuchereriasis about 90 per cent of infected persons give immediate positive reactions with *Dirofilaria immitis* antigens.[20] Positive reactions are obtained with equal facility in acanthocheilonemiasis, loasis and onchocerciasis.[21] Patients with onchocerciasis react equally well to antigens of *Onchocerca* and *Loa loa*.[22] Those with onchocerciasis and loasis react to onchocercal antigens, although the reliability of the test is questionable.[23]

Wuchereria bancrofti (COBBOLD, 1877) SEURAT, 1921

Synonyms.—*Filaria bancrofti* Cobbold, 1877; *Filaria sanguinis* v. Beneden, 1878; *Filaria nocturna* Manson, 1891.

Disease.—Bancroftian filariasis, wuchereriasis.

History.—Microfilariæ were first noted by Demarquay in 1863 in the hydrocele fluid of a resident of Cuba and in 1866 by Wucherer in the chylous urine of Brazilians. In 1872 Lewis in India found them in the blood and later associated the presence of the adult worms with chyluria, lymphatic enlargement and elephantiasis. Bancroft discovered the adult female in Australia in 1876, and Bourne described the adult male in 1888. Manson demonstrated the rôle of *Culex fatigans* as an intermediate host in 1878 and also observed in 1879 the phenomenon of nocturnal microfilarial periodicity.

Geographical Distribution.—The parasite has a worldwide range in tropical and subtropical countries from 41° N to 28° S latitude, extending as far north as Spain and as far south as Brisbane, Australia (Fig. 107). It is prevalent in Tropical and Mediterranean Africa, in coastal Asia from Arabia to Japan, in the East Indies, Melanesia, Polynesia, and in northeastern coastal Australia. In the Western Hemisphere it is present in the West Indies, in South America (the Guianas, Brazil, Venezuela and Colombia), and in North America at Charleston, South Carolina.

BIOLOGICAL CHARACTERISTICS

The adult worms are located in the lymphatics and the microfilariæ are found in the blood and lymph. The morphology of the thread-like adult worms is given in Table 27 and Fig. 103, and that of the microfilariæ in Table 28 and Fig. 104.

---

[18] Fairley, N. H., 1931; Connal, A., 1934; Chandler, A. C., Milliken, G. and Schuhardt, V. T., 1930.
[19] Sayers, E. G., 1934.
[20] Taliaferro, W. H. and Hoffman, W. A., 1930.
[21] Rodhain, J. and Dubois, A., 1932.
[22] Rodenwaldt, E. R. K., 1934.
[23] d'Hooghe, M., 1935.

LIFE CYCLE

Hosts.—Man is the only known definitive host. The intermediate host is a mosquito. Complete larval development to the infective stage has been experimentally demonstrated in some 41 or more species (*Aëdes,* 8; *Anopheles,* 22; *Culex,* 5; and *Mansonia,* 6), and partial development in many others (Chapter XL). Many of these are not important vectors, since either they are not natural hosts or their habits do not bring them in contact with man. The species most commonly associated with wuchereriasis are *Culex fatigans,* a cosmopolitan night-biting mosquito, and *Aëdes variegatus,* a day-biting mosquito in the islands of the Pacific.

Development in Mosquito.—In order to transmit the infection the microfilaria must undergo metamorphosis to an infective stage in the mosquito (Table 29) and must be deposited on the skin of a new host (Fig. 109). This requires

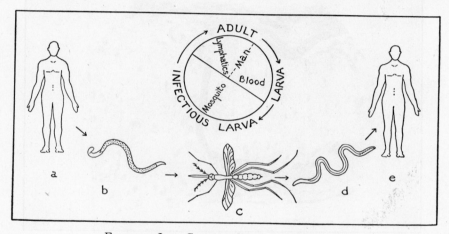

FIG. 109.—LIFE CYCLE OF *Wuchereria bancrofti*

a, man with adult worm in lymphatics; *b*, microfilaria from blood; *c*, microfilaria ingested by mosquito in which larva after metamorphosis reaches the proboscis; *d*, infectious larva deposited on skin of man by biting mosquito; *e*, man infected by larva which penetrates the punctured skin and migrates to the lymph spaces, where it ultimately becomes an adult.

a suitable species of mosquito, conditions favorable for larval development and survival, and access to man before the death of the infected mosquito. The larval cycle ranges from 6 to 20 days, depending upon the species of mosquito, temperature and humidity.

The number of larvæ that develop to maturity depends upon the abundance of microfilariæ in the peripheral blood of the infected individual, the species of mosquito, and the temperature and humidity. Observers have found that 3 microfilariæ per cubic millimeter of blood will produce optimal infections, that 0.5 will fail to infect, and that 10 will kill the mosquito. A concentration of 1.75 microfilariæ per cubic millimeter of blood produced an average of 4 larvæ in *Culex fatigans,* 84 per cent of 565 mosquitoes being infected after the blood meal.[24] Over 100 larvæ were

---

[24] Bachman, G. W. in Gay's Agents of Disease, 1935.

found in 9 of 2,600 *Culex fatigans* after feeding on infected individuals and a higher incidence but a smaller number of larvæ, 4 to 6, in *Aëdes ægypti*.[25] Evidently there is a heavy mortality of both microfilariæ and mosquitoes and the percentage of mosquitoes that actually transmit the disease to man is small.

Temperature and humidity affect the percentage of infected mosquitoes, the intensity of their infection and the rate of development of the larvæ. These factors also determine the abundance and distribution of mosquitoes. The rate and intensity of infection in India in the monsoon months are higher than in the winter and during the hot season.[26] The developmental cycle during the monsoon months requires 10 to 11 days and during the winter 18 to 20 days. If conditions of tem-

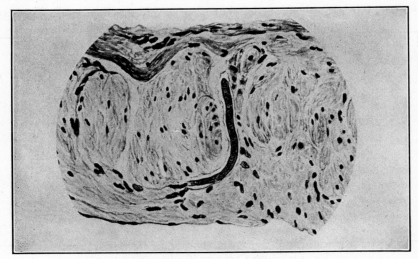

FIG. 110.—MICROFILARIA IN WALL OF LYMPHATIC VESSEL
(After O'Connor, 1931).

perature and humidity are favorable, rapid development of the larvæ will take place even during adverse periods. The few larvæ that penetrate into the celomic cavity of *Culex pipiens* var. *pallens* in winter fail to develop, but those that develop in November are able to survive to the middle of March, a temperature of 54.4° F. giving the longest survival period.[27]

Development in Man.—After penetrating the skin the larvæ pass to the lymphatic glands where they grow to maturity. Reproduction requires the presence of both sexes in these foci and depends upon the intensity of the infection, since relatively few larvæ are present in a mosquito. The microfilariæ migrate from the vicinity of the parent worm through the wall of the lymphatics to the neighboring small blood vessels or are carried in the lymphatic circulation to the blood stream (Fig. 110).[6]

---

[25] O'Connor, F. W. and Beatty, H. A., 1937.   [27] Hu, S. M. K., 1939.
[26] Rao, S. S. and Iyengar, M. O. T., 1930.

PATHOGENESIS

Pathology.—Dead and living adult worms are found tightly coiled in nodular dilatations of the lymphatics, lymph nodes and lymphatic trunks. The living worms apparently cause little damage other than mechanical blockage of the lymphatics, and the living microfilariæ produce no injury. The pathological changes are largely caused by the dead adult worms and microfilariæ which act as foreign-body irritants.

Histological studies indicate that most of the adult worms are found in the afferent approaches or cortical sinuses of the lymph glands.[4] The two sexes may be coiled together in the periglandular tissues, lymphatic vessels of the capsule, cortical sinuses and in heavy infections in the medulla. The most noticeable changes around

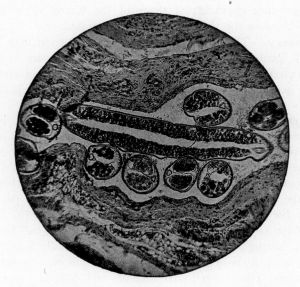

Fig. 111.—Section Showing Adult *Wuchereria bancrofti* within Lymphatics (ca. × 50)

Note perilymphatic fibrosis (From Smith and Gault, *Essentials of Pathology*, 1938, D. Appleton-Century Company).

the living worms are hypertrophy and dilatation, with comparatively little cellular infiltration of the walls of the lymphatic vessels (Fig. 111). There is partial but not complete obstruction of the lumen. Severe inflammatory reaction and massive fibrosis are most marked in the environment of dead and dying worms. There is marked swelling of the endothelium with exudation into the lumen of the vessels and the eventual production of a caseating tuberculoid focus with giant cells, lymphocytes, epithelioid cells and eosinophils. Some investigators consider that the toxic products of the degenerating worms produce an allergic type of inflammation. Eventually the parasite is absorbed, encapsulated or calcified with fibrous occlusion of the lymphatics.

Lymphatic obstruction is brought about by the proliferation of the reticulo-endothelial cells which finally become fibroblasts.[28] Obstruction causes edema and lymph stasis, leading ultimately to lymphangitis and elephantiasis of various parts of the body. Elephantiasis is characterized by a chronic fibromyositis or hypertrophy of the hypodermal and dermal connective tissues with proliferation of collagenous connective tissue.[29] The affected parts first show a firm springiness, then a hardness, and finally become rough, fissured and susceptible to various pyogenic infections.[30]

The location of the obstruction and the site of the inflammation determine the parts of the body affected. Obstruction of the thoracic duct or the median abdominal lymph vessels may affect the scrotum and penis of the male and the external genitalia of the female, and infection of the inguinal glands may involve the lower extremities or external genitalia. Rupture of the lymphatics of the bladder or kidney may produce chyluria; of those of the tunica vaginalis hydrocele or chylocele, and of those of the peritoneum chylous ascites.

Symptomatology.—The course of *Wuchereria* infection may be divided into four stages: (1) incubational; (2) asymptomatic; (3) acute symptomatic; and (4) chronic symptomatic. The high incidence of infections in endemic areas indicates that only a small percentage of infected individuals reach the symptomatic stage.

The incubational period, about one year from the time of infection to the appearance of the microfilariæ in the blood, corresponds to the time required for the growth and sexual development of the worms. The majority of infected individuals remain in the asymptomatic stage for years or throughout life; yet marked pathological changes may occur without symptoms. The extent of the infection, the location of the adult worms, and the sensitiveness of the patient to a large extent determine the appearance of clinical symptoms.

The acute stage is characterized by recurring attacks of lymphangitis and fever. The attack, lasting from two to eight days, is usually ushered in by chills, fever, severe headache, malaise and vomiting, and is followed by febrile remissions and profuse sweating. The affected part becomes red, painful, swollen, and has an erysipeloid rash with a sharply defined line of demarcation. The lymph nodes are enlarged and painful. After an acute attack the skin and subcutaneous tissues tend to remain swollen. The attacks often recur periodically, in some individuals every few weeks and in others at longer intervals.

The chronic stage of the disease is characterized by enlarged glands (chiefly inguinal), lymphoceles, obstructive lymphatic involvement of the genitalia, and elephantiasis of various parts of the body. Elephantiasis commonly affects the lower legs and genitalia and may result in extensive deformity (Fig. 112). Chyluria is a suggestive symptom. The red blood cells and hemoglobin show no noticeable changes and the leukocyte count may be normal or slightly subnormal.[31] The leukocytes rarely number more than 10,000 even during acute attacks of lymphangitis.

Two opinions are held regarding the relationship of filarial infection to lym-

---

[28] Lane, C., 1937.
[29] Suarez, J., 1930.
[30] Knott, J., 1938.
[31] Das, K. K., 1931.

phangitis and elephantiasis: (1) the clinical conditions are entirely due to the action of the filarial worms, and (2) they are the result of bacterial infection, chiefly streptococcic. Investigators who favor the first view point out that lymphangitis and elephantiasis are produced in uncomplicated filarial infections, that the presence of pyogenic bacteria merely indicates secondary infection, and that extensive changes result from the aseptic degeneration and absorption of dead filariæ.[32]

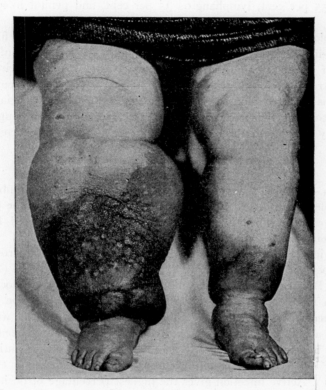

FIG. 112.—ELEPHANTIASIS FROM LYMPHATIC OBSTRUCTION IN PATIENT INFECTED WITH
Wuchereria bancrofti

(From Smith and Gault, *Essentials of Pathology,* 1938, D. Appleton-Century Company).

With the exception of McKinley (1931), who failed to obtain evidence of streptococcal etiology in lymphangitis, investigators have repeatedly isolated streptococci, and more particularly beta streptococci, from patients with lymphangitis and elephantiasis.[33] These workers consider that histological, clinical and bacteriological evidence indicates that the recurrent lymphangitis and resultant elephantiasis are due to streptococcal invasion, especially in supersensitive individuals, and that filarial infections have no direct relationship to these conditions. Likewise, they point out that there is little correlation between filarial infection and elephan-

---

[32] O'Connor, F. W., and Hulse, C. R., 1932;   Grace, F. V., 1931; Grace, F. V. and Warren, Giglioli, G., 1933.   S., 1932.

[33] Suarez, J., 1930, 1933; Grace, A. W. and

tiasis, since patients with elephantiasis often do not show microfilariæ in the blood. In general, statistics throughout the world show that the incidence of microfilariæ in these conditions is no greater than in nonsymptomatic persons. Recent investigations in India, however, indicate that there is a statistically-significant correlation between the disease and infection rate in certain localities, the coefficient in Travancore being + 0.7644.[34] The clinical types of filariasis in Travancore were: elephantiasis 55 per cent, lymphangitis 35 per cent, and genital infections 10 per cent.

The pathological changes in the lymphatics produced by the filariæ furnish a suitable medium for hemolytic streptococci, and superimposed infection favors the growth of fibroblasts.[35] Interference with normal lymphatic circulation predisposes to streptococcal infection.[36] It seems reasonable that recurrent attacks of lymphangitis by superimposed streptococcal infection upon a filarial background would best account for chronic lymphangitis and elephantiasis, although this condition apparently may be produced independently by filarial or by bacterial infection.

DIAGNOSIS, PROGNOSIS AND TREATMENT

Diagnosis.—Clinical diagnosis is based on lymphangitis, lymphatic enlargement, hydrocele, chyluria and elephantiasis. Calcified worms may be demonstrated by the roentgen-ray, which is of assistance in locating associated living worms for surgical removal.

Diagnosis in asymptomatic persons is made by finding the microfilariæ in the peripheral blood or chylous exudates by the thick-film method (Section **VII**, VI, 1, 2, 4). Because of nocturnal periodicity, the blood in most localities should be taken from 10 P.M. to 2 A.M., except where the nonperiodic type prevails. The microfilariæ require differentiation from those of other filarial worms (Table 28). Positive alexin-fixative and intracutaneous reactions have been obtained in wuchereriasis by several workers using aqueous and alcoholic antigens derived from fresh or dried *Dirofilaria immitis* and *Onchocerca volvulus* (Section **VII**, IX, 10 and 11). Active infection gives the highest percentage of positive reactions. The response represents a group reaction for filarial worms. These tests are not of diagnostic importance, although a negative reaction suggests the absence of filarial infection.

Prognosis.—In asymptomatic infections the prognosis is good, although some individuals may later develop symptoms. When severe lymphangitis and elephantiasis are present, the chances of recovery are poor, although afflicted persons may live for years.

Treatment.—No treatment is necessary in nonsymptomatic filariasis. The worms eventually die and are absorbed or calcified. There is no satisfactory chemotherapy for destroying the adult worms or microfilariæ, although recession of symptoms and reduction of microfilariæ have been reported with tryparsamide, sulpharsphenamine, gentian violet, fuadin, and gold salts. The treatment of lymphan-

[34] Iyengar, M. O. T., 1938.
[35] Anderson, J., 1924; Acton, H. W. and

Rao, S. S., 1931; Lane, C., 1937.
[36] Drinker, C. K., 1936.

gitis comprises hygienic measures, elevation of affected parts, elimination of the primary and secondary foci of infection, and use of streptococcal vaccines.[37] Chyluria is treated by rest, general supportive measures, restriction of fluids and mild purgation. Chyloceles are treated as ordinary hydroceles by incision or injections. The excision of varicosed loin glands is not always satisfactory and may accentuate symptoms elsewhere. The lymph scrotum should be kept scrupulously clean, suspended and protected. Surgery, if indicated at all, should entail complete removal of infected foci. Remission of chyluria and slight improvement in elephantiasis have been reported under X-ray treatment.[38] A change to cooler climates is often beneficial.

Surgical treatment of elephantiasis has for its objective the establishment of free communication between the deep and superficial lymphatics, the removal of the adult worms and diseased tissues, and the correction of deformities. It affords temporary rather than permanent relief. Bandaging gives symptomatic relief by gradually reducing the lymphedema and softening the skin, and permits control of the site of the infection before and after surgical operations.[30] None of the operative measures for elephantiasis are entirely satisfactory. Kondoleon's operation endeavors to establish an anastomosis between the superficial and deep lymphatics. Lanz's operation requires stripping of the periosteum of the bone. Auchincloss' operation endeavors to restore the elephantoid legs to normal shape and by removing the diseased fibrotic tissue and calcified worms, establish better drainage for the remaining subcutaneous tissues. Gillies and Frasier's operation consists in the temporary anastomosis of the forearms and thigh so that the stagnated lymph can be carried off by the lymphatics of the arm.

PREVENTION

Epidemiology.—Filarial endemicity is determined by the filarial disease rate (clinical symptoms) and the filarial infection rate (microfilariæ). The incidence of clinical filariasis is usually considerably lower than the microfilarial rate and most investigators, except in certain localities, find little correlation between the presence of microfilariæ in the blood and the occurrence of elephantiasis, lymphangitis and genital involvement. The microfilarial rate in persons with clinical filariasis has variously been reported as higher or lower than in persons without symptoms. In India, where extensive surveys have been made, it is higher in asymptomatic individuals. The microfilariæ evidently tend to disappear in old infections, whereas the clinical symptoms often do not appear until long after the initial infection. Also, the late symptoms may be associated with the death of the worms, thus explaining the absence of microfilariæ in the blood. However, the worm has been found to live as long as 17 years.

Owing to the irregular distribution of low and high endemic centers, which depends upon climatic and topographical conditions, statistics rarely give the actual prevalence of the infection in a country. The filarial disease rate in endemic areas has been variously reported from 3.5 to 14.3 per cent and the microfilarial rate

[37] Suarez, J., 1933. [38] Golden, R. and O'Connor, F. W., 1934.

from 3.3 to 32 per cent (China 4 to 16, India 3.3 to 22, East Indies 20, Fiji 27, and the West Indies and South America 19 to 32). The mosquito infection rate varies from 0.5 to 9 per cent, is dependent upon the species and habits of the mosquitoes and does not always correspond to the infection rate in man. The incidence of infection is influenced by topography, climate, and economic and social conditions. It depends upon the relation of these factors to the abundance and distribution of suitable mosquito-hosts, their contact with man and the development of the parasite in the mosquito. The incidence is high in coastal areas and river estuaries, and is low in mountainous regions, although local conditions cause an irregular distribution of endemic centers. In India the incidence is highest at the sea coast and lowest in the submontane arable regions and plateaus. Infection is most extensive in paddy cultivation areas.[39] The incidence in areas of low endemicity in Travancore, India, is 1 to 5 per cent, moderate 6 to 20 per cent, high 21 to 30 per cent, and hyper over 30 per cent.[34] Temperature and humidity determine the abundance and distribution of the mosquitoes and the growth of the parasite in the insect. Mosquito-hosts may be present, but the temperature may be too low for the development of the larvæ. *W. bancrofti* infections are correlated with density of population and poor sanitation, since its principal vector, *C. fatigans,* breeds mainly in water contaminated with sewage and decaying organic matter.

The incidence of infection varies with race, age and sex, but these variations appear to be due to environmental factors rather than to individual immunity. It is generally lower in Europeans, who are better protected against mosquitoes, than in natives. In India clinical filariasis, particularly elephantiasis, increases with age, but filarial infection is independent of age.[40] The disease rate rises progressively with increasing age, but, except in the first decade of life, the infection rate does not show a similar rise and decreases in the late decades.[34] In Formosa the infection rate in persons over 20 years is about twice that in persons below that age.[15] In British Guiana the infection is rarely found in children under 13 years, but thereafter rises rapidly to a maximum, which remains more or less constant until senescence.[41] In the West Indies the highest incidence occurs in the second decade of life.[42] Females show a lower microfilarial rate than males.[15, 34] Clinical symptoms, however, may be overlooked in females and after the age of 40 the incidence is the same in both sexes.[43]

Prophylaxis.—The prevention of wuchereriasis in endemic areas includes the control of mosquitoes and human sources of infection. Mosquito-control measures are important and may be employed for *Culex fatigans* and and other domestic species (Chapter XL), but are difficult to apply to nondomestic varieties. The human carrier problem is still unsolved because of therapeutic inability to render the blood free of microfilariae and economic barriers to the removal of patients to nonendemic regions. Protection of the susceptible individual is also an educational and economic problem.

[39] Korke, V. T., 1930.

[40] Cruickshank, J. A., Cunningham, J. and Iyer, T. S., 1923.

[41] Romiti, C., 1935.

[42] O'Connor, F. W. and Hulse, C. R., 1935; Hughens, H. V., 1927.

[43] King, H. H., Pandit, C. G., Menon, K. P. and Iyer, P. V. S., 1929.

Onchocerca volvulus (LEUCKART, 1893) RAILLIET AND HENRY, 1910

Synonyms.—*Filaria volvulus* Leuckart, 1893; *Microfilaria nuda* Rodenwaldt, 1914; *Onchocerca cæcutiens* Brumpt, 1919.

Disease.—Onchocerciasis.

History.—*Onchocerca volvulus,* discovered by a German medical missionary in West African natives, was described by Leuckart in 1893. Blanchard in 1899 noted that it occurred in the lymphatic spaces of small tumors. In 1926 Blacklock observed its larval metamorphosis in the vector *Simulium damnosum*. In 1916 Robles reported its presence in Guatemala. His observations were confirmed between 1917 and 1920 by Luna and by Calderon, and in 1921 the occurrence and clinical manifestations of American onchocerciasis were described by at least seven other investigators. Brumpt in 1919 considered the American parasite a new species, *Onchocerca cæcutiens,* because it differed from the African form in geographical distribution, in the arrangement of papillæ and size of male spicules, and in the distribution of the nodular lesions. Subsequent investigations by Fülleborn, Sandground, Cameron and others indicate that these differences are not consistent and that the two forms are the same species. The etiology, transmission and pathology of the disease in Mexico since 1926 have been described by a number of workers and have been extensively studied in Guatemala in 1934 by Strong, Sandground, Bequaert and Ochoa.

Geographical Distribution (Fig. 108).—In Africa onchocerciasis is found on the West Coast from Sierra Leone to the Congo Basin, and extends eastward across Africa through the Congo and the French and British Sudan to Uganda, Nyasaland, and possibly Kenya. American onchocerciasis occurs on the Pacific slope of the volcanic region of Guatemala at an elevation between 2,000 and 4,500 feet in a strip of territory 150 miles long, 40 miles wide at the western end, and 15 miles wide at the eastern, centering at Yepocapa. In Mexico it is present in the states of Oaxaca, Chiapas and Guerrero. The American form of the disease is chiefly confined to the mountainous villages of the large coffee plantations in these countries.

BIOLOGICAL CHARACTERISTICS

The American and African parasites are morphologically indistinguishable. The adult worms (Table 27 and Fig. 103) are found in the subcutaneous tissue, usually encapsulated in fibrous tumors within which the worms are intricately coiled. From these tumors the smaller male worm, 19 to 45 mm. by 0.13 to 0.21 mm., may be readily dissected, but the longer female worm, 115 to 700 mm. by 0.27 to 0.45 mm., is removed with difficulty. The tumors contain a variable number of male and female worms, and microfilariæ. If only one sex is present no microfilariæ are found. The female is viviparous. In the uterus the larvæ, 264 to 290 μ, are coiled in a thin oval membrane, 46 to 61 μ by 33 to 51 μ. There are two types of microfilariæ, large and small (Table 28 and Figure 104).

LIFE CYCLE

Man is the only definite host, although closely allied species of *Onchocerca* occur in other animals. The intermediate hosts are *Simulium damnosum* and *S. neavei* in Africa, and *S. ochraceum, S. callidum* and *S. metallicum* in Guatemala and Mexico.[44] The metamorphosis in *Simulium damnosum* (Table 29 and Fig. 105) requires six to ten days or more. The microfilariæ are ingested by the fly when it bites the skin in the vicinity of the lesions. Before emergence from the proboscis the infective larvæ are coiled in the base of the labrum. Infection of man takes place through contamination of the bite.

PATHOGENESIS

Pathology.—Onchocerciasis, a chronic infection of the skin and subcutaneous tissues, is characterized by the formation of nodules from 0.5 to 2.5 cm. in diameter but occasionally reaching 5.0 cm. (Figs. 113 and 114). They may appear on all parts of the body but are most commonly seen in Africa on the trunk, thighs and arms, and in Central America on the scalp and head. In Guatemala 98 per cent of the nodules are found in the region of the head.[12] In Africa the percentage of individuals thus infected is: o per cent in Nyasaland, 24 per cent in Sierra Leone, and from 30 to 60 per cent in the Belgian Congo. The more general distribution of the nodules appears to be associated with greater body exposure of unclad African natives. The former view that the location of these tumors is dependent upon the site of the bite, does not appear to be justified, since the parasites evidently migrate before their inclusion in subcutaneous fibromata. Exposure to air and sunlight probably attracts the positively phototactic parasite to uncovered parts of the body. It has been suggested that pressure may arrest their progress and that construction of the lymph vessels by hats or headbands may account for the frequency of the American form on the scalp.[12]

The histological appearance of the tumors varies according to age and size. The early nodules show a granulomatous inflammatory reaction with polymorphonuclears, endothelials, small round cells, and occasionally plasma cells and lymphocytes.[44] The late nodules contain fibroblasts, endothelials and often giant cells. They are enclosed in a fibrous capsule, are not richly vascularized and do not show the typical structure of a granuloma. They have a firm, grayish-white peripheral portion, consisting of wavy bundles of collagenous fibers and a soft, orange or yellowish, grumous center. Within the central portion are one or more worms, often both males and females and numerous microfilariæ, which are also found in the neighboring tissues. The tumors are confined to the superficial tissues and do not invade the deeper organs. They rarely break down, although occasionally abscess formation results from secondary pyogenic infection. The histological picture in the tunnel walls varies, since the whole worm does not encyst at the same time. Each segment stimulates a cellular reaction that terminates in fibrous tissue formation, the process continuing until the whole worm is encysted.[45] Four types of

---

[44] Strong, R. P., Hissette, J., Sandground, J. H. and Bequaert, J. C., 1938.

[45] Mohammed, A. S., 1931.

tunnel walls have been described: [46] (1) fibrous with abundant fibroblasts and collagenous fibers; (2) polyblastic with fibroblasts mingled with histiocytes; (3) inflammatory with lymphocytes, plasmacytes and polymorphonuclears; and (4) symplasmatic with the formation of large histiocytes and giant cells from the fusion of histiocytes. The tissues around the tumors may be normal, may contain fibrous connective tissue or may be infiltrated with various types of cells. The scattered

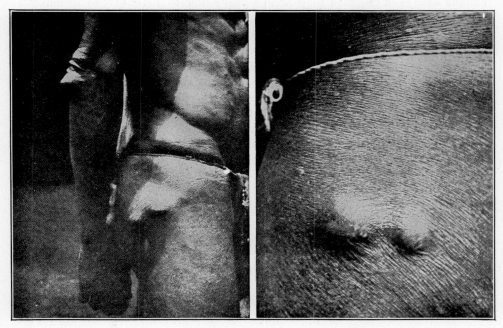

FIGURE 113   FIGURE 114

FIG. 113.—*Onchocerca volvulus*

Nodules on elbow and hip (After Blacklock, 1926).

FIG. 114.—*Onchocerca volvulus*

Nodules and wrinkled skin in gluteal region (After Blacklock, 1926).

microfilariæ sometimes are surrounded by leukocytes and giant cells. In some cases the tumors of the head are lentil-shaped and lie in shallow depressions of the skull adherent to or absorbing the periosteum.[12]

The number of nodules in a patient is usually 3 to 6; there may be only one or as many as 150. A large number of nodules appears to be associated with multiple infections and a high percentage of infected flies.[44] In Mexico the number on the head and shoulders is ordinarily from 3 to 14.[47] The tumors are not adherent to the skin, and vary from small, soft, smooth, barely palpable nodules to large, hard, irregular masses the size of a walnut. In African onchocerciasis they are often found in the region of the great trochanter, scapula, ribs, scalp and joints, particu-

[46] Guzman, G. I., 1934.   [47] Ochoterna, I., 1927.

larly elbow and knee (Fig. 113) but may be present elsewhere on the body. In some cases, the skin over the nodule is thickened, partly adherent and polished from pressure. They usually require about a year to develop, although they have been reported several times in children under one year of age. Their occurrence appears to be a protective reaction against the parasite. Their formation and rate of growth probably depend upon the degree of sensitiveness of the infected person. Tumors have been observed to grow in a year's time to a size of 3 to 10 mm.[12]

The disease may involve the skin without the formation of nodules; in western Kenya subcutaneous nodules are uncommon.[48] The African disease first manifests itself as a skin infection, a common form in children, which may disappear or persist through life. The typical tumors are late manifestations of the disease. The microfilariæ are found in the superficial layers of the skin, subcutaneous tissues and in the tumors, and the unencapsulated adults may also be present in the subcutaneous tissues. In the French Sudan the chronic cutaneous manifestations take the form of xeroderma, lichenification, achromia, atrophy and a pseudoichthyosis with thick, wrinkled skin. The thickening of the skin and localized eosinophilia in the African disease have been attributed to the action of toxins.[45] The final result is fibrosis, destruction of structure and obliteration of the lymphatic network of the skin. The number of microfilariæ in the cutaneous lesions varies from day to day. Their presence causes cellular and perivascular infiltration. Superimposed on this condition may be a pruriginous dermo-epidermitis, the so-called "filarial itch." [49] In the American disease there is sometimes a myxedematous thickening of the skin over the facial bones with a bluish pigmentation known as "erisipela de la costa". It may start as an acute febrile erysipelas or as a slowly progressive myxedema and thickening of the skin, at times accompanied by keratitis and iritis. These attacks are possibly the result of superimposed streptococcal infection or an allergic condition.[12] The symptoms may entirely disappear after removal of the tumors.

Onchocerca volvulus has been reported to cause chyluria, orchitis, elephantiasis, or through the invasion of the blood stream even a fatal pseudosepticemia.[50] The causative rôle of the parasite in these conditions is questionable.

Ocular involvement is frequently observed when nodules are present on the head. The onset is usually slow, rarely acute. An iridocyclitis with perikeratic injections and a contracted, sometimes irregular pupil develops. The iris is thickened, altered in color and is sometimes covered with a dirty exudate. It finally becomes adherent by a ring of synechiæ to the anterior surface of the lens capsule and undergoes radiate atrophy. There is a variable punctate keratitis, corneal infiltration with small nests of leukocytes and monocytes, and superficial and deep vascularization of the cornea. The microfilariæ invade the lymph spaces of the conjunctiva, cornea and iris (Fig. 115). Involvement of the choroid may spread to the choroidoretinal apparatus, the retinal pigment accumulating in thick plaques. Finally, there are atrophy of the eyeball and entrance of the microfilariæ into the sheath of the optic nerve. The eye acts as a trap for the microfilariæ that penetrate deep into the choroid and retina. The reaction is variously attributed to toxins,

[48] Hawking, F., 1939.   [49] Laigret, J., 1929.   [50] Sharp, N. A. D., 1926.

the mechanical action of the living microfilariæ, their secretory products, the dead microfilariæ, and allergy. The reaction against the dead microfilariæ and individual supersensitiveness seem the most reasonable theories.

Symptomatology.—As a rule the patient suffers little discomfort, although at times the nodules are extremely painful and the skin conditions, especially with superimposed infections, cause intense itching.

Patients with American onchocerciasis show an eosinophilia from 20 to 50 per cent. The ocular manifestations, which usually occur some years after the initial infection, are photophobia, iritis and keratitis. The variable early manifestations are conjunctival hyperemia, iritis, and small areas of corneal opacity. Blindness results in over one-eighth of the ocular infections. Ocular complications occur in 10 to 20 per cent of infected persons in Mexico,[51] in 5 per cent in Guatemala,[12] in 43 to 85 per cent in the northwest African Congo.[52] The parasite is believed to be responsible for an endemic blindness in the Anglo-Egyptian Sudan. Other causes, however, account for some of these cases.

Immunity.—The serum of rabbits, injected with onchocercal antigens,

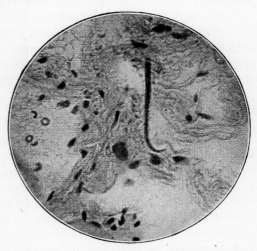

Fig. 115.—Microfilariæ of *Onchocerca volvulus* and Cellular Infiltration at Edge of the Cornea

(From Strong, Sandground, Bequaert and Ochoa, *Onchocerciasis*. Copyright by the President and Fellows of Harvard College, courtesy Harvard University Press).

contains precipitins, but possesses no microfilaricidal properties. The sera of patients give few positive precipitative and variable alexin-fixative reactions. Intracutaneous tests, representative of a filarial group reaction, are less consistent than in other filarial infections.

DIAGNOSIS, PROGNOSIS AND TREATMENT

Diagnosis.—The presence of nodules, eosinophilia and ocular lesions is suggestive of onchocerciasis in endemic areas. It is impossible to differentiate the subcutaneous tumors, except by microscopical examination, from dermoid cysts, lipoma, fibromata and juxta-articular nodules. Diagnosis is made by finding the adult worms in the nodules and the microfilariæ in the skin and nodules. Examination of the skin in the vicinity of the nodules or cutaneous lesions for microfilariæ is the most practical method. The skin may be teased out with needles in a drop of water to liberate the active larvæ or thin slices may be examined directly. Precipitative, complement-fixative, and intracutaneous tests have been less satisfactory than in other filarial infections.

---

[51] Mühlens, P., 1932. [52] Hissette, J., 1932.

Prognosis.—Except in serious ocular involvement prognosis is favorable.

Treatment.—Surgical removal of the encysted parasites, although not always successful, is the most satisfactory method of treatment.[53] Injection of the nodules with gentian violet and other filaricidal drugs is a less certain procedure, but has been used extensively in Guatemala. It is doubtful if the adult parasites can be destroyed by chemotherapy, but antimony preparations or plasmochin kill the microfilariæ and possibly temporarily interfere with their production. It is useful in destroying microfilariæ that persist after surgical removal of the nodules. The injection of plasmochin 1 :1,000 with novocain into the eye destroys the microfilariæ, tends to arrest ocular symptoms and prevents blindness.[54] Improvement of ocular conditions following removal of the tumors from the head has been reported.

PREVENTION

Epidemiology.—The disease is confined to the highlands, usually from 2,000 to 5,000 feet above sea level, where black flies are abundant. In these regions a high percentage of infections is reported among the natives. In Africa the incidence is 45 per cent in Sierra Leone, and 50 to 73 per cent in various parts of the Belgian Congo. In the Santa Emilia district of Guatemala it is 44 per cent; in the Moca district 40 per cent, and in the Santa Adelaida district 58.6 per cent.[12] In Mexico 15,000 cases have been reported in Chiapas and 5,000 cases in Oaxaca.[55] In Mexico and Guatemala the infections are very high on the coffee plantations, where nearly all the workers are infected.

In Africa the disease is uncommon in children under 10 years of age, but in America it is frequently observed in children. The disease is more prevalent in men who are more exposed than women to the bites of black flies. In Africa the disease is comparatively rare in Europeans, probably because of the better protection by clothing against the flies, but in America it is not uncommon in whites.

The endemic areas coincide with the distribution of certain species of *Simulium*, small slender day-biting flies, which breed in clear, swift, upland streams and frequent the wooded ridges (Chapter XLI). In Africa *Simulium damnosum* and probably *S. neavei* are the vectors of onchocerciasis and in Guatemala and Mexico *S. ochraceum, S. callidum* and *S. metallicum,* of which *S. ochraceum* is the most abundant and widely distributed, *S. callidum* prefers shade and *S. metallicum* is comparatively rare. These flies are plentiful the year round in Guatemala, although particularly abundant from February to June, and in Mexico are most abundant from September to February. In Africa 1 to 33 per cent and in Guatemala 11 per cent of wild flies have been found to be infected.

These flies bite outdoor workers or persons who frequent moderately shady places. In Africa they congregate near water or grass-covered banks,—wet rice farms are favorite spots. In grass or low shrubs 80 per cent of the bites are below the level of the knee.[14] On the American coffee plantations the greatest number of infections appear during the gathering of the coffee bean, when the workers are

[53] Strong, R. P., 1937.   [55] de la Torre, I., 1931.
[54] Silva, R., 1932.

most exposed to these flies. The prevalence of the disease, however, seems to depend upon the establishment of endemic foci by the migrations of infected individuals rather than upon the distribution of the insect vector.

Prophylaxis.—Prevention of the disease consists in isolating the sources of infection, controlling the insect vector and protecting susceptible persons. Isolation and treatment of the infected persons appear to be the most practical measures; they should not be allowed to migrate to uninfected territory where black flies are abundant. The destruction of *Simulium* breeding grounds is costly and in most instances impractical. On coffee plantations, where considerable expense is justified, the level of the streams may be regulated by dams and heavy oils applied to the water (Chapter XLI). The individual may be protected to some extent by fly-proof clothing, head nets, repellents and smudges.

Acanthocheilonema perstans (MANSON, 1891) RAILLIET, HENRY AND LANGERON, 1912

Synonyms.—*Filaria sanguinis hominis minor* Manson 1891; *Filaria sanguinis hominis perstans* Manson 1892; *Filaria ozzardi* var. *truncata* Manson 1897; *Dipetalonema perstans* (Manson 1891) Yorke and Maplestone 1926.

Disease.—Acanthocheilonemiasis.

History.—In 1890 Manson found the microfilaria of *A. perstans* in African Negroes at a London hospital. The adult worm, obtained from the mesentery of a native Indian of British Guiana, was first described by Daniels in 1898. Fülleborn in 1908 succeeded in securing partial development of the larva in the mosquito, *Anopheles maculipennis,* and Sharp in 1928 recorded its complete metamorphosis in the midge, *Culicoides austeni.*

Geographical Distribution (Fig. 107).—*A. perstans* is found mainly in Tropical Africa, although it has been reported in Algeria and Tunis. The principal endemic area is the Congo Basin, but it is found in a belt across Africa extending from Senegal to Angola on the West Coast to British East Africa south to the Zambesi Valley on the East Coast. In the Western Hemisphere it is present in western Venezuela, Trinidad, the British and Dutch Guianas, the lower Amazon Valley in Brazil and north-central Argentine. It is also reported in Dutch New Guinea.

BIOLOGICAL CHARACTERISTICS

The adult worms are long cylindrical filiform nematodes with a smooth cuticle (Table 27 and Fig. 103). They are found principally at the root of the mesentery, in the perirenal and retroperitoneal tissues, and in the pleural cavity and pericardium.

The microfilariæ (Table 28 and Fig. 104) are found in peripheral blood, although they tend to concentrate in the larger blood vessels and lungs. Their presence in the peripheral blood is essentially nonperiodic, but they exhibit a diurnal or nocturnal periodicity, which varies with individuals and regions, the nocturnal being perhaps more common.[56] They are more active in the blood than the microfilariæ of *W. bancrofti.* A short form 100 by 4 µ and a long form 200 by 4.5 µ have been observed.

LIFE CYCLE

In addition to man the chimpanzee and the gorilla have been reported as definitive hosts. The intermediate hosts are the midges, *Culicoides austeni* and *C. grahami* (Chapter XLI). Partial development has been observed in mosquitoes.

[56] Bouilliz, M., 1916.

The microfilaria is ingested from the peripheral blood by the bloodsucking midge, in which it undergoes metamorphosis (Fig. 105). The successive stages of development in *Culicoides austeni* have been described (Table 29).[57] After seven to ten days, when the midge bites a definitive host, the mature infective larva, 600 to 1000 μ, wriggles down the proboscis, ruptures the membranous portion of the labium and with a final jerky motion emerges upon the skin.

PATHOGENESIS

The incubational period is unknown. The encysted worms usually occur singly and cause little tissue reaction. The majority of infected persons show no ill effects and most English and French authorities consider that the pathogenic action of the parasite is slight. German authorities, however, have associated its presence with edema, Calabar swellings and abscesses. It may produce lymphatic varices of the groin.[57] The microfilariæ have been found in necrotic foci in the liver.[58] Fever, malaise and headache are among the symptoms noted in East African natives.[59] Febrile pulmonary involvement and, in massive infections, a condition similar to trypanosomiasis have been reported.

DIAGNOSIS, PROGNOSIS AND TREATMENT

Diagnosis.—Diagnosis is made by finding the characteristic microfilariæ in the blood.
Prognosis.—Good.
Treatment.—Intravenous injections of methylene blue are reported to cause the disappearance of the microfilariæ in the blood and the abatement of fever, malaise and headache.[59]

PREVENTION

Epidemiology.—Human infection is extremely common in endemic areas where intermediate hosts are abundant and exposure is frequent. In the highlands and open grassland of the Manife division of the Cameroons 77 per cent of the population are infected, and in the heavily forested regions the incidence is from 92 to 100 per cent.[57] Surveys by Christy in 1903 among 5,708 natives in 157 localities in Africa showed an average incidence of 47 per cent and a range from 0 to 76 per cent, the highest incidence being in areas most frequented by *Culicoides*. Europeans are less subject to infection than natives, and in West Africa the parasite is relatively rare in whites, probably because of better protection from the night-biting *Culicoides*.

Natural infections have been found in 7 per cent of *C. austeni* and in 3 per cent of *C. grahami*. The females are night-biters and rarely attack man before 10:00 P.M. A full moon, a quarter candle-power light or wind will protect man from their bites. These flies breed in forest, jungle and swamp land and are most abundant from June to October, the period of greatest rainfall.

Prophylaxis.—Since moisture is essential for the development of *Culicoides*, drainage operations reduce its breeding grounds. Individuals in endemic areas may be protected by sleeping under finely-meshed mosquito nets and in illuminated rooms.

Wuchereria malayi (BRUG, 1927) RAO AND MAPLESTONE, 1940

Synonyms.—*Filaria malayi* Brug, 1927; *Microfilaria malayi* (Brug, 1927) Faust, 1929.
Disease.—Malayan filariasis.
History.—The microfilaria was obtained from natives of the Celebes by Lichtenstein and studied by Brug in 1927.
Geographical Distribution.—Java, Sumatra, Borneo, Celebes, Flores, Sumba, Ceram, Ceylon, India, the Federated Malay States, Indo-China, and South China.

---

[57] Sharp, N. A. D., 1928.
[58] Bourguignon, G. C., 1937.

[59] Mosler, H., 1939.

Biological Characteristics.—The fine, white, thread-like adult worm, as described by Rao and Maplestone (1940), closely resembles *Wuchereria bancrofti*. The female, 55 mm. by 0.16 mm., is indistinguishable from the latter; but the male, 23 mm. by 0.09 mm., differs in such minor details as the number of papillæ on its spirally curved tail and the structure of the spicules. There are two pairs of large papillæ, one immediately in front of and the other just behind the cloaca, and in close apposition to them two pairs of small papillæ, whereas *W. bancrofti* possesses a larger, variable number of papillæ. The spicules are dissimilar and unequal. The longer has a stout basal and a fine lash-like distal portion. They are more delicate and lack the distinct transverse corrugations that are present on the stout portion of the spicules of *W. bancrofti*.

The validity of this species does not rest upon the morphology of the adult, but upon the structure of the microfilaria, pathology, geographical distribution and selectivity of insect-host. If these criteria are valid, it is possible that the nonperiodic *W. bancrofti* of the Pacific may be entitled to specific rank. Manson-Bahr (1941) has proposed the name, *Wuchereria pacifica* for this variety on the basis of its nonperiodicity, geographical distribution, pathology and insect-host, *Aëdes variegatus*.

The sheathed microfilaria, 177 to 260 μ by 5 to 6 μ, is morphologically distinct from that of *W. bancrofti*. It has a delicate cuticle, a double stylet at the anterior end, and two nuclei at the caudal extremity (Table 28 and Fig. 104). It differs from the microfilaria of *Wuchereria bancrofti* in the larger size of the excretory cell and pore, the larger anal pore, the nucleated tail and the variable size of the G cells.[60] Its nocturnal periodicity is less absolute than that of *Wuchereria bancrofti*, the day to night numerical ratio being 1:20 as compared with 1:100 for the latter. The diurnal curve shows two apices, at 8:00 P.M. and 4:00 A.M., with a depression at midnight.[61]

Life Cycle.—Man is the only definitive host. The intermediate hosts are *Mansonia* (subgenus *Mansonioides*) *annulipes, M. annulatus, M. annulifera, M. indiana, M. longipalpis* and *M. uniformis; Anopheles hyrcanus* var. *sinensis* and var. *nigerrimus, A. barbirostris;* and *Armigeres obturbans*. The microfilaria undergoes two molts in the mosquito and develops into an infective larva at 29° and 32° C. in 6 days (Table 29 and Fig. 106) [13] or 6 to 12 days.[61]

Pathogenesis.—The parasite, like *Wuchereria bancrofti*, produces lymphangitis and elephantiasis, but genital infections are less common.[34, 62] It also differs from *W. bancrofti* in that persons with clinical filariasis show a much higher microfilarial rate than those without symptoms, 78 vs. 27 per cent.[61]

Diagnosis.—Identification of microfilaria in peripheral blood (Table 28).

Prognosis.—Similar to *Wuchereria bancrofti*.

Treatment.—Similar to *W. bancrofti*.

Epidemiology.—It is extensively distributed throughout the East Indies and South Asia; in some areas it is present with *Wuchereria bancrofti*, and in others it is the only filarial parasite. In the Federated Malay States it is endemic in certain riverine areas and the infection is increasing among children, whereas, *W. bancrofti* infections are due to immigrants from India and China.[63] It is the predominating infection in Southern Province, Ceylon. Its incidence, 7.8 per cent, is higher than that of *W. bancrofti* in Travancore, India, where it is distributed in flat, alluvial areas along the seacoast. Its distribution corresponds to that of its principal hosts, *Mansonia* mosquitoes, being highest in low regions with numerous ponds infested with water plants of the genus *Pistia,* which are essential for the breeding of these mosquitoes. Its distribution is essentially rural, while that of *W. bancrofti* is more often urban.

The various mosquito-vectors when allowed to feed on infected persons show from 67 to 99 per cent of infections. In the Dutch East Indies the natural infection rate was 1.9 per cent for *Mansonia annulatus* and 1.2 per cent for *M. annulipes;* [61] in the

---

[60] Feng, L. C., 1933.
[61] Brug, S. L., 1930.

[62] Dassanayake, W. P. L., 1939.
[63] Poynton, J. O. and Hodgkin, E. P., 1938.

Celebes 8.1 per cent for *Anopheles barbirostris;* [64] and in Travancore, India, 26.9 per cent for *M. annulifera.* [34]

Prevention.—The control of *Mansonia* mosquitoes by curtailing their breeding grounds through the removal of the water plant *Pistia stratiotes* is the principal method of prophylaxis (Chapter XL).

Mansonella ozzardi (MANSON, 1897) FAUST, 1929

Synonyms.—*Filaria ozzardi,* Manson 1897; *Filaria demarquayi,* Manson 1897; *Filaria tucumana,* Bigheri and Araoz 1917.

Disease.—Mansonelliasis ozzardi, Ozzard's filariasis.

History.—Manson in 1897 described the microfilaria, in blood collected by Ozzard, in Indians in British Guiana. It was later found to be identical with *Microfilaria demarquayi* reported by Manson from St. Vincent in 1897. The adult parasite was first described by Daniels in 1899 in British Guiana.

Geographical Distribution (Fig. 108).—Yucatan, Panama, Colombia, northern Argentina, British and Dutch Guiana, and the islands of St. Vincent and Dominica.

Biological Characteristics.—The adult worm inhabits body cavities, mesentery, and visceral fat. Its morphology is given in Table 27 and Figure 103. The sharp-tailed microfilaria is unsheathed and nonperiodic (Table 28 and Fig. 104). *Microfilaria tucumana* of Argentina is considered identical with *M. ozzardi.* [65]

Life Cycle.—Man is the only known definitive host. *Culicoides furens* Poey is the vector in St. Vincent, B.W.I. [66] About 5 per cent of wild flies are naturally infected, and 27.5 per cent of those fed experimentally on infected persons. *Culicoides parænsis* is also a potential vector. The larvæ leave the intestinal tract of the midge within 24 hours after the blood meal and develop in the abdomen and thorax of the fly. Infective larvæ are formed by the sixth day after passing through two ecdyses, and by the eighth day migrate to the head and proboscis.

Pathogenesis.—The adult worms apparently cause little damage in the connective tissues of the peritoneum and infected individuals manifest no particular symptoms. Occasionally a hydrocele or enlarged lymph gland is formed. [41]

Diagnosis.—Diagnosis is made by finding the unsheathed nonperiodic microfilariæ in the peripheral blood (Table 28).

Prognosis.—Good.

Treatment.—Unknown.

Epidemiology.—In the Tuira River basin, Darien Province, Panama, 44.5 per cent of the Indians and 10 per cent of the natives are infected. [67] The incidence is from 25 to 30 per cent in northern Argentina and 38 per cent in St. Vincent. In British Guiana the disease is limited to inhabitants of the upper reaches of the rivers.

Prevention.—No established methods. Prophylaxis depends upon control of the insect vectors and protection from their bites.

Loa loa (COBBOLD, 1864) CASTELLANI AND CHALMERS, 1913

Synonyms.—*Strongylus loa* Guyot, 1778; *Filaria oculi humani* Dujardin, 1845; *Filaria lacrymalis* Dubini, 1850 *nec* Gurlt, 1833; *Filaria oculi* Gervais and van Beneden, 1859; *Dracunculus loa* Cobbold, 1864; *Filaria subconjunctivalis* Guyon, 1864.

Disease.—Loasis, eye worm, fugitive swellings, Calabar swellings.

History.—Loasis was first noted by Pigafetta in 1589 in the African Congo, and later, about 1777, by Guyot along the West Coast of Africa, where the parasite was commonly known as "loa" among the natives. Mongin removed the worm in 1770 from

---

[64] Brug, S. L., 1937.
[65] Vogel, H., 1927.

[66] Buckley, J. J. C., 1934.
[67] McCoy, O. R., 1933.

the eye of a Negress in Haiti, and subsequently several instances of eye worm infections were observed among slaves from West Africa. Manson in 1891 found the microfilaria which he named *Microfilaria diurna* in the blood of West African Negroes. He suggested in 1895 that *Chrysops dimidiata* was the probable intermediate host of *Loa loa*. In 1913 Leiper recorded its larval development in *Chrysops dimidiata* and *C. silacea*. In 1905 Stiles placed the worm in the genus *Loa*.

Geographical Distribution (Fig. 107).—The worm is indigenous to tropical West Africa. It frequents the coastal plains from Sierra Leone to Angola and the watershed of the Congo River.

Biological Characteristics.—The adult worms inhabit the subcutaneous tissues. They are thread-like whitish, cylindrical worms from 30 to 70 mm. in length by 0.3 to 0.5 mm. in breadth (Table 27 and Fig. 102). The sheathed microfilariæ have a diurnal periodicity in the peripheral blood (Table 28 and Fig. 104). The length of life of the worm in man has been variously reported as from 4 to 17 years.[68]

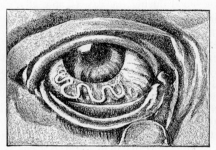

FIGURE 116 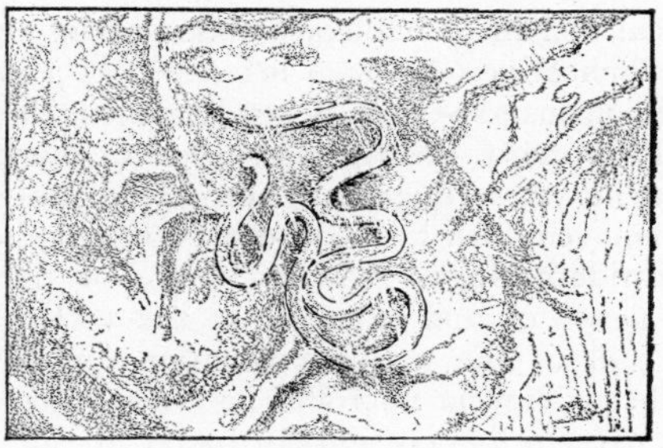   FIGURE 117

Fig. 116.—*Loa loa* in Eye (Redrawn from Fülleborn).

Fig. 117.—*Loa loa* in Subcutaneous Tissues (Redrawn from Fülleborn).

Life Cycle.—Man is the only definitive host. The intermediate hosts are *Chrysops silacea* and *C. dimidiata,* more rarely *C. longicornis* and *C. distincti* and possibly *C. centurionis* (Fig. 235b). In order to become infective for man the larva must pass through a cyclic development of from 10 to 12 days in these flies (Table 29 and Fig. 105).[69] It differs from the larval metamorphosis of *Wuchereria bancrofti* in the mosquito in the location, power of movement, attitude and size of the developing larvæ. Man is infected by the escape of the infective larvæ from the proboscis to the skin, when bitten by *Chrysops*. The larva apparently requires several years to attain maturity in man.

Pathogenesis.—Loasis is a chronic disease; the symptoms do not ordinarily appear until three to four years after the initial infection and the parasites have been found to persist as long as 17 years. The adult worms migrate through the subcutaneous tissues (Fig. 117), the maximal recorded rate being one inch in two minutes. They have been removed from the back, sternum, axilla, groin, breast, penis, scalp, lingual frenum, eyelids, conjunctiva, and anterior chamber of the eye. Occasionally the worms are encapsulated.

The parasite usually causes no serious damage to the host, its common manifestations being itching, irritation and Calabar swellings. There may be an urticarial dermatitis, soreness from induration of the fascia and connective tissue in the vicinity of the tendon sheaths, and abscesses from secondary pyogenic infection. Aggregations of

[68] Ziemann, H., 1926; Coutelen, F., 1935.   [69] Connal, A. and Connal, S. L. M., 1922.

microfilariæ may produce an inflammatory reaction, fibrosis and eosinophilia in the spleen.[70]

Temporary inflammatory reactions, known as fugitive or Calabar swellings, are characteristic of the disease. These painless, nonpitting, subcutaneous swellings, that reach the size of a hen's egg, are most frequently observed on the hands, forearms and in the vicinity of the orbit. They appear spontaneously at irregular intervals, disappear in about three days, and are probably a manifestation of supersensitiveness to the parasite or its products.

The worms are particularly troublesome when passing in front of the eyeball or across the bridge of the nose. Involvement of the eye (Fig. 116) causes irritation, congestion, pain, tumefaction of the eyelids and impaired vision. In one case the patient had pricking sensations and the feeling that a flea was in the eye; the eye was red and lacrimating, the cornea edemic, the aqueous humor slightly bloody, the pupil occluded and the iris congested.[71]

Diagnosis.—Diagnosis is made by recovering the adult worms and more frequently by finding the characteristic microfilariæ in the blood during the day (Table 28). Serological and intracutaneous tests may be employed in suspected cases, but these tests are only indicative of filarial infections as a group.

Prognosis.—Good, depending upon the successful removal of the worms.

Treatment.—Surgical removal of worms is the accepted treatment. A favorable time is during their migration across the nose or through the conjunctiva, where they may be removed with hooked needles. Chemotherapy is unsatisfactory.

Epidemiology.—The incidence of the disease varies greatly; it depends upon the prevalence of and exposure to the vector *Chrysops*. In parts of the Belgian Congo 75 per cent of the native population are infected and in some villages 90 per cent. In northern Nigeria microfilariæ were found in the blood of 7.8 per cent of 1,026 males.[72] The parasite is occasionally found in Europeans who have lived in West Africa. White men are usually protected against the bites of *Chrysops*. The incidence of natural infection in *Chrysops* has been reported as 1 to 35 per cent in Nigeria and 5.3 per cent in the Cameroons. The length of time that the fly remains infective is unknown, but it is at least five days; experimentally infected flies in captivity rarely live beyond the period of larval metamorphosis of the parasite.[69] As many as several hundred larvæ have been observed to leave a single fly. Man is bitten during day time. The fly shuns bright sunlight and frequents woodland, particularly forest swamp land. It prefers dark surfaces and bites Negroes more readily than whites, attacking the ankles, back of the leg and outer side of the hand.

Prophylaxis.—Preventive measures include the control of *Chrysops* (Chapter XLI), which is rarely practical, and protection from its bites.

Loa inquirenda MAPLESTONE, 1938

Two adult infertile females, resembling *Loa loa,* but from two to three times as long have been found once in man.

Dirofilaria magalhæsi (BLANCHARD, 1895) RAILLIET AND HENRY, 1911

In 1887 de Magalhæs described two worms, a male and a female, which were obtained from the left ventricle of a native of Brazil, the only reported case of human infection. The morphology of the adult worm is given in Table 27.[73] The egg-membrane containing the coiled embryo *in utero* measures 38 by 14 μ and the liberated microfilariæ 300 to

---

[70] Klotz, O., 1930.   [72] Sharp, N. A. D., 1923.
[71] Sabrielides, C. A., 1938.   [73] v Linstow, O., 1900.

350 μ by 6 μ. Its life cycle and pathogenesis are unknown, but the intermediate host may be a mosquito as in the case of *Dirofilaria immitis* of the dog.

Dirofilaria repens RAILLIET AND HENRY, 1911

The worm is a natural parasite of dogs in Europe and Asia. One instance of human infection has been reported, in which the worm was removed from a subcutaneous nodule of the eyelid.[74] The intermediate host is a mosquito.

Microfilaria streptocerca (MACFIE AND CORSON, 1922) STILES AND HASSALL, 1926

The adult is unknown. The microfilaria, known also as *Agamofilaria streptocerca,* was discovered by Macfie and Corson in natives of the Gold Coast of Africa, where it was present in 44 per cent of the persons examined.[75] The unsheathed microfilaria (Table 28), 215 μ in length, owing to the curvature of the tail, has the appearance of a walking stick with a crooked handle.[76] The arrangement of the nuclei in the head and the four rounded nuclei in the tail are distinctive. It is found in the skin. The parasite causes no apparent injury. Its life cycle, insect vector and prevention are unknown.

REFERENCES

BLACKLOCK, D. B. The Development of *Onchocerca volvulus* in *Simulium damnosum,* Ann. Trop. Med., 1926, 20:1.

—— The Further Development of *Onchocerca volvulus* Leuckart in *Simulium damnosum,* ibid., 1926, 20:203.

—— The Insect Transmission of *Onchocerca volvulus* (Leuckart, 1893). The Cause of Worm Nodules in Man in Africa, Lancet, 1927, 1:129.

BRUG, S. L. Filariasis in the Dutch East Indies, Proc. Roy. Soc. Med., 1931, 24:664.

BUCKLEY, J. J. C. On the Development, in *Culicoides furens* Poey, of *Filaria* (*Mansonella*) *ozzardi* Manson, 1897, J. Helminthol., 1934, 12:99.

CONNAL, A. and CONNAL, S. L. M. The Development of *Loa loa* (Guyot) in *Chrysops silacea* (Austen) and *Chrysops dimidiata* (van der Wulp), Tr. Roy. Soc. Trop. Med. & Hyg., 1922, 16:64.

FENG, L. The Development of *Microfilaria malayi* in *A. hyrcanus* var. *sinensis* Wied., Chinese M. J., 1936, Suppl. 1:345.

FÜLLEBORN, F. Filariosen des Menschen, Handbuch der path. Mikroorganismen, 1929, 6:1043, Jena.

IYENGAR, M. O. T. Studies on the Epidemiology of Filariasis in Travancore, Indian M. Res. Mem., 1938, 30:1.

—— Filariasis in Travancore, J. Trop. Med., 1939, 42:39.

LANE, C. The Mechanism of Filarial Periodicity, Lancet, 1929, 1:291.

—— The Mechanical Basis of Periodicity in *Wuchereria bancrofti* Infection, ibid., 1929, 2:399.

—— The Mechanism of Microfilarial Periodicity, ibid., 1932, 1:1100.

McCOY, O. R. The Occurrence of *Microfilaria ozzardi* in Panama, Am. J. Trop. Med., 1933, 13:297.

O'CONNOR, F. W. Filarial Periodicity with Observations on the Mechanism of the Migration of the Microfilariæ from the Parent Worm to the Blood Stream, Puerto Rico J. Pub. Health & Trop. Med., 1931, 6:263.

—— The Etiology of the Disease Syndrome in *Wuchereria bancrofti,* Tr. Roy. Soc. Trop. Med. & Hyg., 1932, 26:13.

[74] Skrjabin, K. I., Algansen, A, J, and Schoulmann, E. S., 1930.

[75] Macfie, J. W. S. and Corson, J. F., 1922.

[76] Sharp, N. A. D., 1927.

O'Connor, F. W. and Hulse, C. R. Some Pathological Changes Associated with *Wuchereria* (*Filaria*) *bancrofti* Infection, Tr. Roy. Soc. Trop. Med. & Hyg., 1932, 25:445.

—— and Hulse, C. R. Studies in Filariasis, I. In Puerto Rico, Puerto Rico J. Pub. Health & Trop. Med., 1935, 11:167.

Rao, S. S. and Maplestone, P. A. The Adult of *Microfilaria malayi* Brug, 1927, Indian M. Gaz., 1940, 75:159.

Sharp, N. A. D. *Filaria bancrofti* and *Loa loa*. A Note on Some Methods of Differentiation of Their Embryos, Tr. Roy. Soc. Trop. Med. & Hyg., 1923, 17:177.

—— A Contribution to the Study of *Onchocerca volvulus* Leuckart, with Some Observations on Its Prevalence in Nigeria, Tr. Roy. Soc. Trop. Med. & Hyg., 1926, 19:373.

—— *Filaria perstans;* Its Development in *Culicoides austeni,* Tr. Roy. Soc. Trop. Med. & Hyg., 1928, 21:371.

Strong, R. P., Sandground, J. H., Bequaert, J. C. and Ochoa, M. M. Onchocerciasis with Special Reference to the Central American Form of the Disease, Harvard Univ. Dept. Trop. Med. and Inst. Trop. Biol. & Med. Com. No. VI, 1934, Cambridge, Mass., 234 pp.

——, Hissette, J., Sandground, J. H. and Bequaert, J. C. Onchocerciasis in Africa and Central America, Am. J. Trop. Med., Suppl., 1938, 18:136.

Suarez, J. A Preliminary Report on the Clinical and Pathological Findings in 60 Cases of Lymphangitis Associated with Elephantoid Fever in Porto Rico, Am. J. Trop. Med., 1930, 10:183.

—— Elephantiasis Tropicum, Puerto Rico J. Pub. Health & Trop. Med., 1933, 8:287.

Yamada, S. An Experimental Study on Twenty-four Species of Japanese Mosquitoes Regarding Their Susceptibility as Intermediate Hosts for *Filaria bancrofti* Cobbold, Sc. Rep. Gov. Inst. Inf. Dis. Tokyo Imp. Univ., 1927, 6:559.

Yokogawa, S. Studies on the Mode of Transmission of *Wuchereria bancrofti,* Tr. Roy. Soc. Trop. Med. & Hyg., 1939, 32:653.

Chapter XXII

THE SUPERFAMILY DRACUNCULOIDEA

FAMILY *DRACUNCULIDÆ* LEIPER, 1912

The DRACUNCULIDÆ are long slender worms, the male being much smaller than the female. The anterior end is rounded and sometimes bears a cuticular shield. The simple unlipped mouth is surrounded by papillæ and perianal papillæ are present. The esophagus and intestine are rudimentary and the anus may not function. The male has two sub-equal, finely-pointed spicules and an accessory gubernaculum. The female is viviparous. The vulva is inconspicuous, atrophying before maturity. The vagina is rudimentary or absent in the gravid female. The uterus branches into two divergent tubes and the ovaries are situated at opposite ends of the body. The worms inhabit the body cavity, serous membranes or connective tissues of vertebrates. The species parasitic in man is *Dracunculus medinensis*.

Dracunculus medinensis (LINNÆUS, 1758) GALLANDANT, 1773

Synonyms.—*Filaria medinensis* (Linnæus, 1758) Gmelin, 1790; *Füllebornius medinensis* (Linnæus, 1758) Leiper, 1926. Popularly known as Guinea worm, Medina worm, serpent worm and dragon worm.

Disease.—Dracontiasis, dracunculosis, dracunculiasis.

History.—The Guinea worm has been known since ancient times. It is probably the "fiery serpent" that beset the Israelites. Dracontiasis, named by Galen, was known to Greek and Roman physicians. The morphology of the parasite was first described by Bastian in 1863, and its larval existence in *Cyclops* was observed by Fedtschenko about 1870.

Geographical Distribution (Fig. 108).—In Africa the parasite inhabits the Nile valley, Central Equatorial Africa, and the Northwest and West Coasts. In Asia it is present in Arabia, Persia, Afghanistan, Turkestan and India. Isolated cases have been reported in the Dutch East Indies, though apparently imported,[1] and in the southeastern part of the Soviet Republic. It has been introduced into the West Indies, the Guianas and the Bahia district of Brazil. The ten human cases reported in the United States of America are either of foreign origin or erroneous diagnoses, although the parasite is apparently present in fur-bearing animals.[2]

BIOLOGICAL CHARACTERISTICS

Morphology.—The gravid females measure 500 to 1,200 mm. in length and 0.9 to 1.7 mm. in diameter, averaging about 600 mm. The anterior end bears a cuticular shield and is bluntly rounded. The cuticle is smooth and the oval mouth

---

[1] Marjituo, M. and Essed, W. F. R., 1938.   [2] Chitwood, B. G., 1933.

is surrounded by several pairs of papillæ. The vulva is situated just behind the cephalic shield. The ovarian tubules, oviducts and uteri are paired. In the gravid female the alimentary tract below the esophagus is atrophied and the coiled uteri, distended with larvæ, fill the greater part of the body.

The rarely-observed male, 12 to 29 mm. by 0.4 mm., has a cephalic prominence and a small oral opening (Fig. 118C) surrounded by an inner circle of four to six well-developed papillæ and an outer circle of four double papillæ.[3] The esophagus, slightly over one-third the length of the worm, consists of a short anterior muscular part and a wide posterior glandular part, and is constricted at the level of the nerve ring. A pair of lateral cervical deirids are present below the level of the nerve ring. The caudal end of the male is coiled upon itself. The subterminal

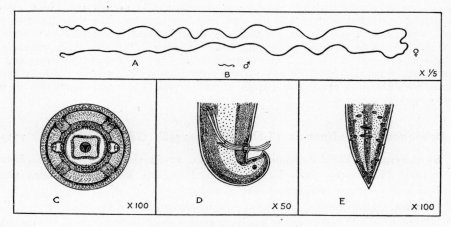

FIG. 118.—*Dracunculus medinensis*

A and *B*, relative sizes of adult male and female; *C*, anterior extremity of male, frontal view, showing mouth surrounded by six inner and eight outer papillæ; *D*, tail of male, lateral view, showing spicules and papillæ; *E*, tail of male, ventral view, showing anus and preanal and postanal papillæ (*C* to *E* redrawn from Moorthy, 1937).

anal opening, 0.25 mm. from the posterior extremity, is surmounted by six postanal and four preanal pairs of papillæ (Fig. 118E). The subequal spicules are from 0.49 to 0.73 mm. in length and the gubernaculum 0.20 mm. (Fig. 118D).

Physiology.—Fertilization probably takes place at an early age in the deeper tissues of the host. Sexually-mature worms, 12 to 24 mm. in length have been found in the deep connective tissues of experimental dogs 67 days after infection. The fate of the males is unknown. Evidently they are absorbed, not calcified. When sexually mature the female migrates from the body cavities or deeper tissues to the subcutaneous tissues of the leg, arm, shoulders or trunk, parts most likely to come in contact with water (Fig. 122). The body of the gravid female is almost completely filled by the uterus distended with active larvæ. When ready to discharge the larvæ, the cephalic end of the worm approaches the skin, producing an indurated papule, which soon vesiculates and eventually forms an ulcer. The

[3] Moorthy, V. N., 1937.

anterior end of the worm protrudes through a small opening at the base of the ulcer. When the surface of the ulcer comes in contact with water a loop of the uterus, which has prolapsed through a rupture in the anterior end of the worm, discharges the motile larvæ into the water. Each contact with water stimulates successive floods of larvæ until the supply is exhausted.

LIFE CYCLE

The larvæ, liberated in water, are ingested by suitable species of *Cyclops,* in which they mature into infective forms in about three weeks. Susceptible definitive hosts are infected through drinking water containing infected *Cyclops* (Fig. 119).

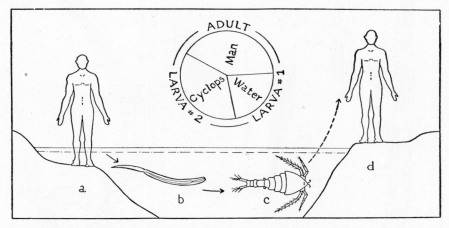

FIG. 119.—LIFE CYCLE OF *Dracunculus medinensis*

a, man infected with *D. medinensis; b,* larva in water; *c, Cyclops* infected after ingesting larva; *d,* man infected by ingesting *Cyclops.*

Hosts.—The definitive hosts, other than man, are domestic and wild fur-bearing animals such as dogs, cats, skunks, wolves, raccoons, minks and foxes. The parasite has also been reported in horses, cattle, monkeys, baboons and leopards. In North America it has been found in the fox, raccoon and mink. The dog is not a natural host; only about one-fifth of experimental animals acquires the infection.[4] The intermediate hosts are at least 12 species of *Cyclops* (Chapter XXXVII and Fig. 212C).

Metamorphosis in Cyclops.—In from one to six hours after ingestion the larvæ reach the body cavity of the *Cyclops,* where metamorphosis takes place.[5] Ordinarily under natural conditions only one larva is found per *Cyclops.* When more than five are present, development is retarded or incomplete. The young crustaceans are more readily infected than old. Infection retards their growth and heavily-infected specimens do not live more than a month. The larva undergoes two molts: (1) fifth to seventh day at 90° to 101°F. or eighth to tenth at 50° to 70°F., and (2) eighth to twelfth day at 90° to 101°F. or thirteenth to sixteenth

---

[4] Moorthy, V. N. and Sweet, W. C., 1938.   [5] Moorthy, V. N., 1938.

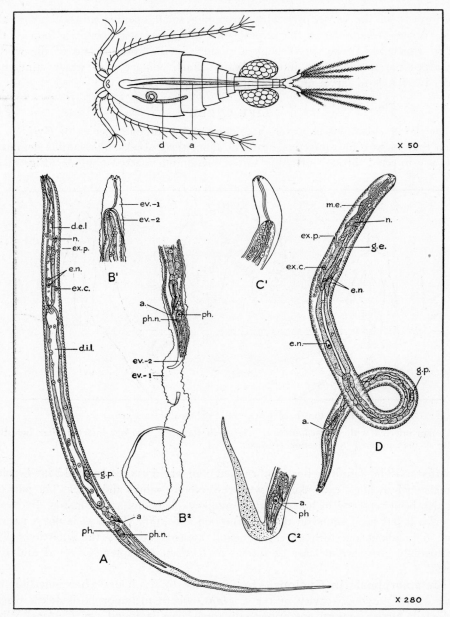

FIG. 120.—METAMORPHOSIS OF LARVA OF *Dracunculus medinensis* IN *Cyclops*

A, first stage larva; B_1 and B_2, cephalic and caudal portions of first stage larva during first molt; C_1 and C_2, cephalic and caudal portions of second stage larva during second molt; *D,* third stage infective larva.

a, anus; *d.e.l.,* dilated esophageal lumen; *d.i.l.,* dilated intestinal lumen; *e.n.,* esophageal *nucleus; ev.1.,* and *ev.2.,* exuviæ of first and second molts; *ex.c.,* excretory cell; *ex.p.,* excretory pore; *g.e.,* glandular esophagus; *g.p.,* genital primordium; *m.e.,* muscular esophagus; *n,* nerve ring; *ph.,* phasmid; *ph.n.,* phasmid nucleus (*A* to *D* redrawn from Moorthy, 1938).

at 50° to 70°F. The larva starts the second molt before it has cast off the exuvia of the first. Thus larval existence is divided into three stages: (1) previous to the first molt, (2) between the first and second molts and (3) after the second molt.

Larva.—The free-swimming larva (Fig. 120A) on liberation from the female worm has a slender rhabditiform shape with a long, filiform tail tapering to a sharply pointed tip. At the time of the first molt (Fig. 120B) it is shorter, thicker and shows changes in the anatomical landmarks. At the end of the second stage (Fig. 120C) its size is approximately the same, but further modifications have occurred in the various organs. The infective third-stage larva (Fig. 120D) reaches its maximal development after 21 days and no further growth takes place for at least 107 days. The larva is actively motile in the body cavity during the first four or five weeks; then becomes inactive and tightly coiled.

Definitive Host.—When the infected cyclops is ingested in drinking water the larvæ penetrate the wall of the digestive tract and migrate to the loose connective tissues. In experimentally infected dogs the worms are most commonly found in the subscapular and retro-esophageal regions and in decreasing order of frequency in the region of the groin, vertebral column, extremities, chest wall, abdominal wall, heart, pericardium, occipital meninges and orbit. The worms may migrate through the circulatory and lymphatic systems to reach their final site. The female worm requires about one year before it seeks the surface of the body for the purpose of discharging larvæ, as evidenced by experimental infections in dogs [4] and monkeys.[6]

PATHOGENESIS

Pathology.—In the deep tissues the dead worms are absorbed without calcification and without marked reaction on the part of the host. Occasionally abscesses may form in the retroperitoneal tissues. When the female worm reaches the surface of the body, it liberates a toxic substance into the subdermal tissues, producing a local inflammatory reaction in the form of a subacute sterile abscess with serous exudation and blister formation.[7] The local cutaneous lesion appears at first as a reddish papule with a vesicular center and indurated margin. The blister contains a clear, yellow fluid with mononuclear cells, eosinophils and polymorphonuclears. The worm lies in a subcutaneous tunnel with its anterior end beneath the blister (Fig. 121). Its course may be marked by induration and edema. Contamination of the ruptured blister by pyogenic bacteria may produce abscesses, cellulitis, and ulcers. At times the worm may become calcified and remain for years as a hard, twisted cord beneath the skin.

Symptomatology.—The incubational period is symptomless and the onset of symptoms occurs just previous to the local eruption. The early manifestations of urticaria, erythema, dyspnea, vomiting, diarrhea, pruritus, and giddiness are caused by the absorption of allergenic (toxic ?) substances from the worm. An eosinophilia of 11 to 35 per cent is produced in dogs. If the worm is broken during extraction and the larvæ escape into the subcutaneous tissues, a severe inflammatory reaction with fever ensues and, if secondary bacterial infection occurs, abscess formation, sloughing of the tissues and even fatal septicemia may result.

[6] Brug, S. L., 1930.   [7] Fairley, N. H. and Liston, W. G., 1924.

Immunity.—Evidence of resistance to superinfection has been observed in dogs and man.[4] The susceptibility of experimental dogs varies inversely with age, but age-resistance has not been noted in man. More females are infected than males, both in man and in experimental dogs. Alexin-fixative antibodies have not been demonstrated with antigens derived from blister fluid, adult worms or embryos.[7] Positive intracutaneous reactions have been obtained with extracts of the worm in 35 of 41 infected persons.[8] This reaction may remain positive for years.

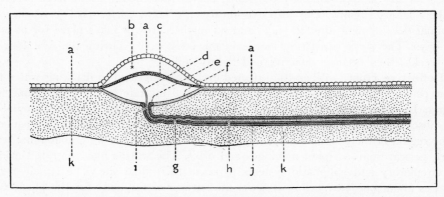

Fig. 121.—Diagram Illustrating Relationship of *Dracunculus medinensis* to Blister and Sheath

a, skin; *b,* blister fluid; *c,* fibrogelatinous layer; *d,* filamentous coil of uterus; *e,* central eschar; *f,* granulomatous base; *g,* convoluted portion of worm; *h,* straight portion of worm; *i,* anterior end of worm; *j,* connective tissue sheath; *k,* subcutaneous tissues (Adapted from Fairley and Liston, 1924).

DIAGNOSIS, PROGNOSIS AND TREATMENT

Prognosis.—The prognosis is usually good, unless extensive secondary infection ensues.

Diagnosis.—Diagnosis is made from the local lesion, worm, and larvæ. Dead or calcified worms may be located by roentgen-ray examination.

Treatment.—Treatment involves the extirpation or destruction of the worm. The ancient method of gradually rolling the worm on a stick so as to remove a few centimeters per day is still employed by natives in Asia and Africa. It is somewhat dangerous, since, if the worm breaks, severe inflammation and sloughing of the tissues may result. Surgical removal by multiple incisions, after localization by roentgen-ray and collargol injections, is preferable. Previous to extraction the worm may be killed by injections of 1:1,000 bichloride of mercury, chloroform or acriflavine. After expulsion of the larvæ the worm may be removed with less difficulty. Ichthyol compresses have been used to reduce inflammation.

PREVENTION

Epidemiology.—In certain localities the incidence is high. Of the 15,000 inhabitants of Shorapur, India, 95 per cent were infected by drinking from contami-

---

[8] Ramsay, G. W. St. C., 1935.

nated springs.[9] The native religious practice of ablution favors the infection of *Cyclops* and the transmission of the disease.

Prophylaxis.—Lack of education makes it difficult to institute prophylactic measures in many localities. In order to protect the sources of drinking water, wells, springs and pools should be surrounded by cement curbings and bathing or washing in these waters should be prevented. Suspected water should be boiled and when-

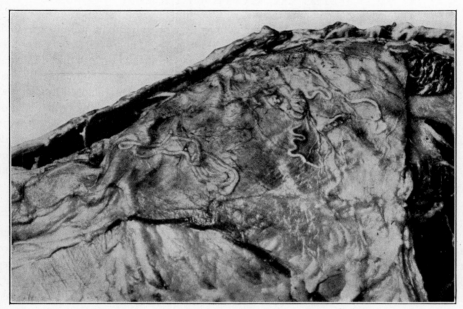

FIG. 122.—GUINEA WORM IN SUBCUTANEOUS THORACIC TISSUES OF EXPERIMENTAL DOG
(After Moorthy and Sweet, 1938).

ever possible supplies should be taken from running water, a source relatively free from *Cyclops*. The destruction of *Cyclops* may be achieved during the season when these crustaceans are abundant by liming wells,[10] by adding three pounds of perchloron and one-half pound of copper sulphate to each 100,000 gallons of water,[11] or by planting fishes of the genus *Barbus* which are destructive to *Cyclops*.

REFERENCES

FAIRLEY, N. H. and LISTON, W. G.   Studies in the Pathology of Dracontiasis, Indian J. M. Res., 1924, 11:922.
MOORTHY, V. N.   A Redescription of *Dracunculus medinensis*, J. Parasitol., 1937, 23:220.
——— Observations on the Development of *Dracunculus medinensis* Larvæ in *Cyclops*, Am. J. Hyg., 1938, 27:437.
——— and SWEET, W. C.   Further Notes on the Experimental Infection of Dogs with Dracontiasis, Am. J. Hyg., 1938, 27:301.

[9] Mirza, M. B., 1938.   [11] Moorthy, V. N., 1932.
[10] Pradhan, Y. M., 1930.

Chapter XXIII

THE ACANTHOCEPHALA

The ACANTHOCEPHALA or proboscidal round worms form a unique group by reason of their structure and extreme parasitic habits. These worms are common parasites of fishes and birds and less frequently of other vertebrates. Although superficially resembling the round worms, they differ in several fundamental characteristics from the NEMATODA and perhaps more nearly resemble the CESTOIDEA. These distinctive features are absence of body cavity and digestive tract, a more or less flattened body, a spinous retractile proboscis, a protonephridial excretory system, and embryonic hooklets. Also they are more closely related serologically to the PLATYHELMINTHES than to the NEMATHELMINTHES.[1] It is more convenient at present to retain their traditional grouping as a class of the phylum NEMATHELMINTHES.

MORPHOLOGY

The worms are mostly small, but range from a few millimeters to over 60 cm. in length. The elongate body is roughly cylindrical or spindle-shaped and more or less flattened when living, but cylindrical when preserved. The surface is irregularly roughened by transverse ridges. There is a retractile proboscis of variable form armed with transverse and longitudinal rows of recurved hooks, a short neck and a body proper (Fig. 123). The form, size and position of the proboscis and the number, shape and arrangement of the hooks are useful in species-differentiation. The closed muscular proboscis sheath, in which the proboscis is inverted, is usually attached to the base of that organ.

The body wall has a thin cuticula and a nucleated subjacent hypoderm. Within the body wall is an anastomosing system of lacunæ with two longitudinal vessels. Paired elongations of the hypoderm, the **lemnisci,** project posteriorly into the body cavity from the junction of the neck and body. The function of the lemnisci, which vary in size and form in the different species, is unknown. The nerve mass lies within the proboscis sheath. A pair of nerve chords, **retinacula,** extend obliquely from it to the body wall. There is no digestive tract, nourishment being absorbed through the body wall.

The sexes are separate, the male being distinguished by its smaller size and muscular copulatory bursa, which, except during coition, is held within the body. The genital pore in both sexes is at the posterior end. The male organs comprise two oval testes, a suspensory ligament, cement glands and cement receptacle. In the female a central ligament extends the length of the body. The ovary, present only during early life, forms egg masses, which, after fertilization, break up into numerous ova

---

[1] Eisenbrandt, L. L., 1938.

with three embryonic membranes. Those with well-developed embryos are discharged from the body cavity by a complicated selective apparatus known as the **uterine bell**.

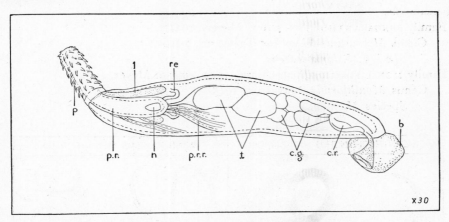

FIG. 123.—MORPHOLOGY OF *Acanthocephalus ranæ* (MALE)

b, bursa; *c.g.*, cement glands; *c.r.*, cement receptacle; *l*, lemniscus; *n*, nerve ganglion; *p*, proboscis; *p.r.*, proboscis receptacle; *p.r.r.*, retractors of proboscis receptacle; *re*, retinaculum; *t*, testes (Redrawn from Van Cleave, 1915).

LIFE CYCLE

The life cycle of the ACANTHOCEPHALA is incompletely known, but involves alternation of hosts. The parasites of aquatic animals probably have crustaceans or larval insects as intermediate hosts and those of terrestrial animals various insects. The well-developed ova, passed in the feces, if necessary complete their embryonation outside the body. When ingested by intermediate arthropod hosts they hatch and undergo metamorphosis into infective larvæ. The arthropod-borne larvæ are ingested by the definitive hosts and develop into adults, which are attached to the intestinal wall by the proboscis (Fig. 125).

CLASSIFICATION

Three orders of ACANTHOCEPHALA are recognized; [2] the PALÆACANTHOCEPHALA (Meyer, 1931) *emend*. Van Cleave, 1936; the EOACANTHOCEPHALA Van Cleave, 1936 and the ARCHIACANTHOCEPHALA (Meyer, 1931) *emend*. Van Cleave, 1936. The two species parasitic in man belong to the last order.

ORDER *ARCHIACANTHOCEPHALA* (MEYER, 1931) EMEND. VAN CLEAVE, 1936

Longitudinal vessels in hypoderm median; giant nuclei of hypoderm few; proboscidal hooks small, infrequently branched and in spiral rows; cement glands

---

[2] Van Cleave, H. J., 1936.

typically eight follicles; uterine bell with both openings united with the two ligamentous sacs; ova ellipsoidal with compact granular middle layer of embryonic
membrane; intermediate hosts terrestrial insects and definitive hosts mostly birds
and mammals.

Family OLIGACANTHORHYNCHIDÆ Meyer, 1931
    Genus *Macracanthorhynchus* Travassos, 1916
        Species *M. hirudinaceus*
Family MONILIFORMIDÆ Van Cleave, 1924, *emend.* Meyer, 1932.
    Genus *Moniliformis* Travassos, 1915
        Species *M. moniliformis*

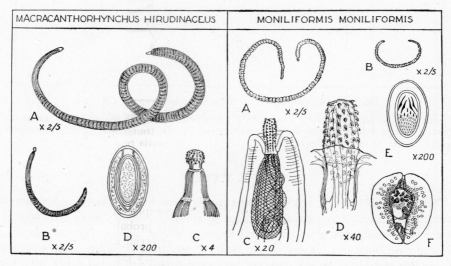

FIG. 124.—*Macracanthorhynchus hirudinaceus* AND *Moniliformis moniliformis*

Macracanthorhynchus hirudinaceus: A, adult female; *B,* adult male; *C,* anterior end of
worm; *D,* ovum. *Moniliformis moniliformis: A,* adult female; *B,* adult male; *C,* anterior end
of worm; *D,* proboscis; *E,* ovum; *F,* larva (*Macracanthorhynchus hirudinaceus: A* to *C*
adapted from Railliet, 1886; *Moniliformis moniliformis: A* and *B* adapted and *C* and *F* redrawn
from Travassos, 1917; *D* redrawn from Van Cleave, 1924; *E* redrawn from Grassi and
Calandruccio, 1888).

Macracanthorhynchus hirudinaceus (PALLAS, 1781) TRAVASSOS, 1917

Synonyms.—*Tænia hirudinaceus* Pallas, 1781; *Echinorhynchus gigas* Bloch, 1782;
Gigantorhynchus hirudinaceus (Pallas, 1781) Railliet, 1893.

Disease.—Unnamed.

Geographical Distribution.—Cosmopolitan.

Morphology.—The milky-white worm, slightly flattened dorsoventrally, has a rugose
appearance with pseudosegmentation. The female (Fig. 124A) is 200 to 650 mm. in
length by 4 to 10 mm. in breadth and the male (Fig. 124B) 50 to 100 mm. by 3 to
5 mm. The retractile proboscis (Fig. 124C) has five or six spiral rows of spines. The
fertilized ovocytes start to divide after their emergence from the ovarian packets into the
ligamentous cavity. Segmentation is characterized by lack of furrows and asynchronism

of division. Development continues until a shelled syncytial ovum with hooks at the anterior end and a spiny cuticular covering is formed in the female worm.[3] The ellipsoidal ova (Fig. 124D), 80 to 100 μ in length, are fully embryonated at oviposition and are encased in three embryonic envelopes.

Life Cycle.—The natural definitive hosts are hogs, wild boars, peccaries, and less frequently dogs and cats. Man is an accidental host. The intermediate hosts are species of coleopterous larvæ (beetles) of the families SCARABÆIDÆ, ALLECULIDÆ and HYDRO-PHILIDÆ (Chapter XXXVIII). The mammalian host is infected by ingesting the infested beetles (Fig. 125). The ova retain their viability after passing through the digestive tract of pigeons and thus may be disseminated widely in the feces and on the soiled feet of birds that forage on land occupied by hogs.[4]

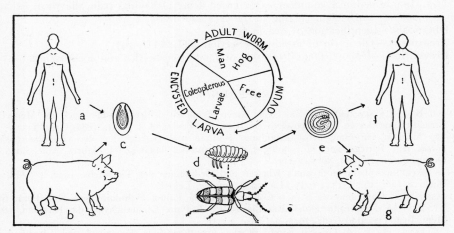

FIG. 125.—LIFE CYCLE OF *Macracanthorhynchus hirudinaceus*

a, man with adult worm; *b,* hog with adult worm; *c,* ovum in feces; *d,* coleopterous larva as intermediate host; *e,* mature larva; *f,* man infected by ingesting larva; *g,* hog infected by ingesting larva.

Pathogenesis.—In hogs the site of attachment shows localized inflammation, eosinophilic infiltration and at times necrosis, which may lead to intestinal perforation. Two instances of human infection, in Bohemia and southern Russia, have been reported.

Diagnosis.—Identification of ova in feces.

Treatment.—Unknown.

Prevention.—Prophylactic measures are unnecessary, since the worm is a rare and doubtful parasite of man.

Moniliformis moniliformis (BREMSER, 1811) TRAVASSOS, 1915

Synonyms.—*Echinorhynchus moniliformis* Bremser, 1811; *Gigantorhynchus moniliformis* (Bremser, 1811) Railliet, 1893; *Hormorhynchus moniliformis* (Bremser, 1811) Ward, 1917; *Moniliformis cestodiformis* (v.Linstow, 1904) Travassos, 1917.

Disease.—Unnamed.

Geographical Distribution.—Cosmopolitan.

Morphology.—The creamy-white adult worm resembles a confluent beaded chain of pseudosegments. The females (Fig. 124A) measure 100 to 270 mm. in length and the

---

[3] Meyer, A., 1928.   [4] Glasgow, R. D. and Deporte, E., 1939.

males (Fig. 124B) 40 to 50 mm. The cylindrical proboscis (Fig. 124D) has 12 to 15 rows of recurved hooks. The ellipsoidal ova (Fig. 124E), 85 to 118 μ x 40 to 52 μ, have three envelopes and four hooklets.

Life Cycle.—The definitive hosts are rats, mice, hamsters, dogs and cats. Man is an accidental host. The intermediate hosts are beetles and the American cockroach (Chapter XXXVIII). In these insects the embryos develop into encapsulated, infective larvæ (Fig. 124F), which, when ingested, become adult worms in the mammalian hosts in about five weeks.

Pathogenesis.—Three cases of natural human infection have been reported from Italy, the Sudan and British Honduras. Experimental infection in man indicates that the parasite, when present in considerable numbers, may produce severe symptoms.[5] In 19 days after infection a volunteer experienced acute abdominal pain, diarrhea, exhaustion, somnolence and violent ringing in the ears and head.

Diagnosis.—Identification of ova in feces.

Treatment.—Oleoresin of aspidium (Section **VII**, XIII, 29).

Prevention.—Unimportant. Protection of food from beetles and cockroaches.

REFERENCES

GRASSI, B. and CALANDRUCCIO, S. Ueber einen *Echinorhynchus,* welcher auch im Menschen parasitirt und dessen Zwischenwirth ein Blaps ist, Zentralbl. f. Bakt., 1888, Orig. 3:521.

MEYER, A. Die Furchung nebst Eibildung, Reifung und Befruchtung des *Gigantorhynchus gigas.* Ein Beitrag zur Morphologie der Acanthocephalen, Zool. Jahrb. Abt. Anat. u. Ontog. d. Tiere, 1928, 50 (2):117.

——— Acanthocephala, in Braun's Klassen und Ordnungen des Tierreichs, 1932, 4 (Abt. II, Buch. 2, Lief. 1): 1-332; 1933 (Lief. 2): 333-582, Leipzig.

TRAVASSOS, L. Contribuccoes para o Conhecimento da Fauna Helminiologica Braziliera. Sec. VI. Revisão dos Acantocefalos Brazilieros. Pt. I. Fam. Gigantorhynchidæ Hamann, 1892, Mem. Inst. Oswaldo Cruz, 1917, 9 (Fasc. 1):18.

VAN CLEAVE, H. J. A Critical Study of the Acanthocephala Described and Identified by Joseph Leidy, Proc. Acad. Nat. Sci. Philadelphia, 1924, 76:279.

WARD, H. B. Acanthocephala, pp. 542-545 in Ward and Whipple's 'Freshwater Biology, 1918, John Wiley and Sons, Inc., New York.

---

[5] Grassi, B. and Calandruccio, S., 1888.

Section IV

THE CESTOIDEA OR TAPEWORMS

Chapter XXIV

THE CESTOIDEA

CLASS *CESTOIDEA* (RUDOLPHI, 1808) FUHRMANN, 1931

The CESTOIDEA are endoparasitic flatworms popularly known as tapeworms. The adults, mostly hermaphroditic, inhabit the intestinal tract of vertebrates, and the larval worms the tissues of vertebrates and invertebrates. These elongate, ribbon-like worms, generally flattened dorsoventrally, have no alimentary tract, and are usually divided into segments or proglottides. The anterior end is modified into an organ of attachment, the scolex, armed with suckers and often with hooks. The subclass CESTODARIA includes a few small, primitive, unsegmented forms that resemble the trematodes. Most species, including those parasitic in man, belong to the subclass CESTODA.

CLASSIFICATION

Numerous classifications have been proposed, the most recent being those of Southwell (1930), Fuhrmann (1931), and Pearse (1936).

SUBCLASS *CESTODARIA* MONTICELLI, 1892

The CESTODARIA are simple, unsegmented worms with a single set of reproductive organs, no alimentary tract, and no definite scolex. The oncosphere has ten hooks. The members of this subclass are chiefly parasites of fishes.

SUBCLASS *CESTODA* VAN BENEDEN, 1849

The CESTODA are segmented worms, each proglottis usually having one or more sets of reproductive organs. There is a definite scolex and the oncosphere has six hooks. The CESTODA include three orders PSEUDOPHYLLIDEA, CYCLOPHYLLIDEA and TETRAPHYLLIDEA, the first two containing species parasitic in man.

ORDER *PSEUDOPHYLLIDEA* CARUS, 1863

The scolex has usually two, rarely one, grooves or bothria and sometimes four proboscides armed with hooks. The uterine pore is on the flat surface of the proglottis, the uterus has a saccular or rosette-like coiled appearance, and the vitellaria are scattered. The ova are operculated and the oncospheres are usually ciliated.

387

ORDER *CYCLOPHYLLIDEA* BRAUN, 1900

The scolex has four cup-shaped suckers and may possess a rostellum. There is no uterine pore, the ova are liberated by the disintegration of the gravid proglottis, and the vitellaria are concentrated. The ova are nonoperculate and the oncospheres are not ciliated.

TABLE 30

THE CESTODES OF MAN

ORDER	SUPERFAMILY	FAMILY	GENUS	SPECIES
PSEUDO-PHYLLIDEA	BOTHRIOCEPH-ALOIDEA	DIPHYLLO-BOTHRIIDÆ	Diphylloboth-rium	D. cordatum D. erinacei D. latum
			Diplogonoporus	D. grandis
			Digramma	D. brauni
			Ligula	L. intestinalis
			Sparganum	S. mansonoides S. proliferum
CYCLO-PHYLLIDEA	TÆNIOIDEA	ANOPLOCEPH-ALIDÆ	Bertiella	B. mucronata B. studeri
		DAVAINEIDÆ	Raillietina	R. celebensis R. madagascariensis R. quitensis
		DILEPIDIDÆ	Dipylidium	D. caninum
		HYMENO-LEPIDIDÆ	Hymenolepis	H. diminuta H. nana
			Drepanidotænia	D. lanceolata
		TÆNIIDÆ	Tænia	T. africana T. confusa T. hydatigena T. saginata T. solium
			Multiceps	M. glomeratus M. multiceps M. serialis
			Echinococcus	E. granulosus

ORDER *TETRAPHYLLIDEA* BRAUN, 1900

The scolex has four bothria, four suckers or four proboscides, sometimes armed with hooks. A uterine pore is rarely present and the vitellaria are diffusely located in lateral margins of the proglottides. The ova are nonoperculated and the onco-spheres are not ciliated. Species are parasites of fishes, amphibians and reptiles.

A simple tabulation of the species parasitic in man, for convenience in presentation, is given in Table 30.

MORPHOLOGY

The adult tapeworm consists of (1) a **scolex** equipped for attachment, (2) a **neck,** the posterior portion of which is the region of growth, and (3) the **strobila,** a chain of progressively developing segments or **proglottides.** The entire worm is sometimes referred to as the strobila, although the term more properly applies to the segmented body. The length of the different species varies from 3 mm. to 10 meters and the number of segments from 3 to 4,000. Morphological variations and

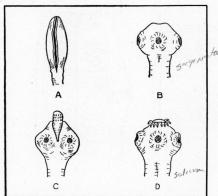

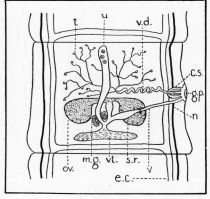

FIGURE 126   FIGURE 127

Fig. 126.—Typical Cestoid Scolices

A, Diphyllobothrium latum; B, Tænia saginata; C, Dipylidium caninum; D, Tænia solium.

Fig. 127.—Schematic Representation of Mature Proglottis of a Tænian Cestode

c.s., cirral sac; *e.c.,* lateral excretory canal; *g.p.,* genital pore; *m.g.,* Mehlis' gland; *ov.,* ovary; *n,* lateral nerve trunk; *s.r.,* seminal receptacle; *t,* testes; *u,* uterus; *v,* vagina; *v.d.,* vas deferens; *vt.,* vitellarium.

malformations, such as bifurcation of the strobila, fusion and fenestration of the proglottides, and supernumerary scolices, are common and have led to confusion of species.

Scolex.—The globular or pyriform scolex (Fig. 126) has three types of organs for attaching the worm to the intestinal wall of the host: (1) elongated suctorial grooves or **bothria** (*Diphyllobothrium latum*), (2) cup-like sucking disks (*Tænia saginata*), and (3) in addition to suckers a proboscis armed with chitinous hooks (*Tænia solium*).

Proglottides.—The proglottides originate in the posterior part of the neck and develop progressively, so that the anterior, immature, undifferentiated segments gradually merge into larger mature proglottides with completely formed sexual organs and these in turn into gravid proglottides, which consist essentially of a uterus distended with ova (Fig. 128). The proglottides vary greatly in number, size and shape according to the species and the stage of development. The small *Echinococcus granulosus* has one immature, one mature and one gravid proglottis, in contrast to the thousands of proglottides in the large *Tænia saginata*. During the life of the worm new segments are continually added, those already formed become sexually mature, and the gravid proglottides either break off from the strobila or disintegrate while still attached.

The mature proglottis (Figs. 127 and 129) contains reproductive organs of both sexes and is actually a functioning individual, a member of a colonial chain or

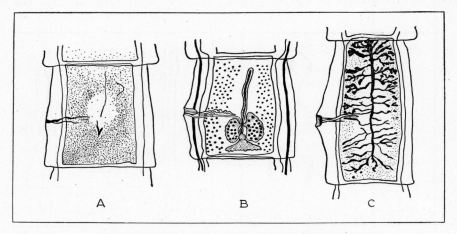

FIG. 128.—PROGLOTTIDES OF A TÆNIAN CESTODE
A, immature; *B,* mature; *C,* gravid.

strobila. The shape and internal structure of the proglottis is useful for species-differentiation. The PSEUDOPHYLLIDEA have a uterine pore through which the ova are liberated from the ripe proglottis, the uterus has no lateral branches distended with ova, and the ripe segments are not cast off as in the CYCLOPHYLLIDEA. The ventral surface is determined by the position of the uterine pore and when this is absent it is the side nearer the ovary. The smaller number of uterine branches in the gravid proglottis distinguishes the pork tapeworm, *Tænia solium,* from the beef tapeworm, *T. saginata* (Fig. 133).

Body Wall.—The body is covered with a homogeneous, elastic, resistant cuticle, like that of the trematodes, but spines or hooklets, if present, are confined to the scolex. The cuticle is continuous from one segment to another. Beneath the cuticle is a single layer of circular muscles and a thin inner layer of longitudinal muscles. Two layers of transverse fibers extend from side to side, enclosing a medullary portion that contains most of the organs. Dorsoventral fibers also pass from one surface to the other. The parenchyma fills the spaces between the organs and the muscular layers. The so-called calcareous corpuscles, refractile bodies of calcium carbonate, 5 to 35 μ in diameter, are present in the parenchyma, particularly in the cortical portion.

Excretory System.—A dorsal and a ventral longitudinal excretory canal extend along the lateral margins of the segments from the scolex to the last proglottis. These collecting trunks anastomose anteriorly in the scolex and open at the posterior border of the terminal proglottis. The adults of many species have but one lateral trunk on each side. A transverse canal connects the longitudinal trunks in the posterior part of each proglottis. The main canals receive branches formed by the collecting tubules of the terminal flame cells distributed throughout the parenchyma.

Nervous System.—A complicated arrangement of ganglia and commissures is located in the scolex. In addition to the cephalic ganglia and its commissures several anterior ganglia are connected by commissures to form a rostellar ring. The sensory and motor peripheral nerves of the anterior end of the worm arise from these ganglia. A main lateral and two accessory longitudinal nerve trunks extend on each side from the cephalic ganglia through the entire series of proglottides. In each proglottis the ganglia of these six lateral nerves are connected by transverse commissures.

Reproductive System.—The cestodes with few exceptions are hermaphroditic. Each mature proglottis contains a complete set of male and female reproductive organs. The male genitalia mature earlier than those of the female, so that the anterior part of the strobila apparently contains only male genitalia.

The male genital pore is the external opening of the vas deferens and the female genital pore that of the vagina. In the superfamily BOTHRIOCEPHALOIDEA the two pores have a common opening on the ventral surface of the proglottis. In the superfamily TÆNIOIDEA the vagina and vas deferens lead into a genital atrium with a single external aperture on the lateral margin of the proglottis. The genital pore may be unilateral, on the same side of each segment (*Hymenolepis*); irregularly alternate, sometimes on the left and sometimes on the right (*Tænia*); or there may be a genital pore on each side when two sets of reproductive organs are present (*Dipylidium*).

The male reproductive organs (Figs. 127 and 129) comprise from 3 (*Hymenolepis*) to 500 or more (*Tænia*) small testes situated in the dorsal part of the proglottis. Minute ducts, **vasa efferentia,** from the testes join to form the **vas deferens,** which follows a convoluted course to the **cirrus,** a protrusile muscular organ enclosed in a thick-walled cirral pouch. The lower part of the vas deferens is often dilated to form the **seminal vesicle.** The cirrus opens anterior to the vagina into a common cup-shaped **genital atrium,** which forms a noticeable papillary projection on the lateral margin of the proglottis, except in the superfamily BOTHRIOCEPHALOIDEA where it opens on the ventral surface.

The female reproductive organs (Figs. 127 and 129) lie toward the ventral surface of the proglottis. The **vagina,** a thin straight tube, extends inward and downward from its opening into the genital atrium, often expanding to form the **seminal receptacle.** The tubular, follicular **ovary,** usually bilobed, is situated in the posterior part of the proglottis. The eggs are discharged into the **oviduct,** which joins with the **spermatic duct** from the seminal receptacle to form a common passage leading to the **oötype,** where fertilization takes place. The **vitellaria** are concentrated in a single or a bilobed mass or diffusely distributed as discrete follicles throughout the proglottis. Their contents enters the oötype through the vitelline duct. Surrounding the oötype is a cluster of unicellular glands, **Mehlis' glands,** which open separately into the oötype. In some species these glands are absent.

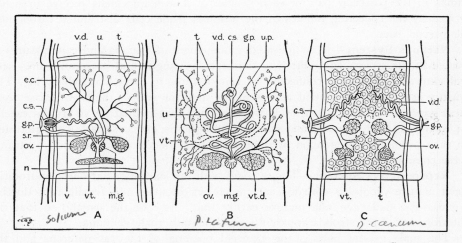

FIG. 129.—SCHEMATIC REPRESENTATION OF MATURE PROGLOTTIDES OF CESTODES

A, Tænia solium; B, Diphyllobothrium latum; C, Dipylidium caninum.

c.s., cirral sac; *e.c.,* lateral excretory canal; *g.p.,* genital pore; *m.g.,* Mehlis' gland; *n,* lateral nerve trunk; *ov.,* ovary; *s.r.,* seminal receptacle; *t,* testes; *u,* uterus; *u.p.,* uterine pore; *v,* vagina; *v.d.,* vas deferens; *vt.,* vitellaria; *vt.d.,* vitelline duct.

The **uterus** extends from the anterior surface of the oötype as a central blind tube of variable form. When a uterine pore is present (*Diphyllobothrium*) (Fig. 129B), it develops into an elongated coil to accommodate the ova from the oötype. Otherwise, it expands in a lobulate transverse sac (*Hymenolepis*), in a reticulate pattern (*Dipylidium*), or by lateral branches (*Tænia*) (Fig. 128C), until it fills the gravid proglottis. The other sexual organs gradually atrophy. The shape and number of branches of the gravid uterus are useful in differentiating species (Fig. 133).

PHYSIOLOGY

Nutrition.—Tapeworms lie in the intestine of the host with the scolex above and the gravid proglottides below. Since they have no digestive tract, they obtain their nourishment by absorbing the semidigested food of the host. The living worms resist the action of the digestive juices probably by forming neutralizing substances. Larval cestodes absorb nourishment from the tissues.

Metabolism.—Cestodes must possess some form of anærobic metabolism to enable them to live in a relatively oxygen-free intestinal tract. Under anærobic conditions *in vitro* they show no reduction in fat, a diminution in glycogen, and the production of carbon dioxide and lactic, succinic and higher acids. Under ærobic conditions oxygen is consumed, but the quantitative formation of acids is the same in both ærobic and anærobic environments.[1] The hypothesis has been advanced that oxygen consumption may result from an oxygen-deficiency arising from the accumulated oxidizable substances that have been produced under anærobic metabolism.[2]

Reproduction.—The reproductive organs attain an excessive development to enhance the chances of completing the life cycle. Hermaphroditism and self-fertilization insure fertility. Asexual reproduction in the intermediate host in *Echinococcus granulosus* and in certain species of *Sparganum* further increases the progeny. The spermatozoa are transferred to the vagina by the protrusile cirrus. Self-fertilization is common, although cross-fertilization between segments of the same or other worms may take place. The ova are fertilized in the oötype, then receive the secretions of the vitelline glands and acquire shells before they are finally stored in the uterus.

Longevity.—Adult tapeworms such as *Tænia solium, T. saginata* and *Diphyllobothrium latum* survive for years in man, while other species are short-lived. Records of infection of 20 to 35 years have been reported, although the possibility of reinfection must be considered, even if the host is in a nonendemic region. *In vitro* cestodes survive for some days, if the serum-medium is frequently changed.

LIFE CYCLE

Hosts.—With the exception of *Hymenolepis nana* all the common tapeworms of man require one or more intermediate hosts. The larval worm develops in the intermediate host following ingestion of the ovum, and the adult worm in the definitive host after the ingestion of flesh containing the encysted larva. In the case of *Hymenolepis nana* a single host suffices for both larva and adult; when man swallows the ovum the larva and later the adult develop. The ovum of *Tænia solium* is also infective for man, but when ingested develops only into the larval form, *Cysticercus cellulosæ*. Man is the intermediate host of *Echinococcus granulosus*, dogs and other animals being the definitive hosts. In most cestodes there is a fairly high degree of species-selectivity in both intermediate and definitive hosts; for instance the final host for *Tænia solium* is man and the intermediate host the hog, and for *T. saginata* man and cattle respectively, complete development usually failing to take place in other species.

Ova.—Two types of ova are produced. When a uterine pore is present (BOTHRIOCEPHALOIDEA) the oval ovum (Fig. 130D) has an operculum, yolk material is abundant, development of the embryo takes place after leaving the host, and

---

[1] Alt, H. L., and Tischer, O. A., 1931;   [2] Harnisch, O., 1933.
Brand, T., 1933.

the fully developed embryo is ciliated. When no uterine pore is present the thin-shelled ovum has no operculum, yolk material is scanty, and embryonal development takes place *in utero*. The ovum of this type (Fig. 130A-C) on leaving the proglottis

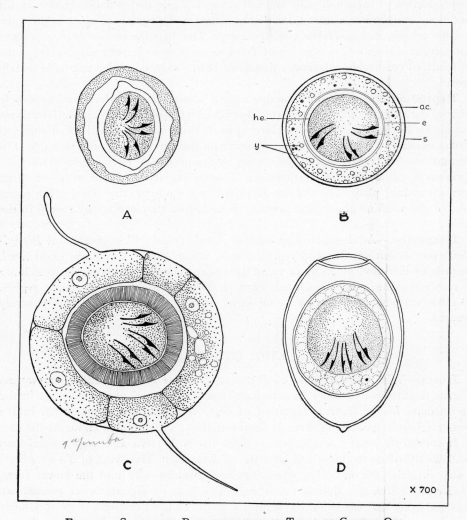

FIG. 130.—SCHEMATIC REPRESENTATION OF TYPES OF CESTOID OVA

A, *Hymenolepis diminuta*; B, *Dipylidium caninum*; C, *Tænia saginata*; D, *Diphyllobothrium latum*.

a.c., albuminous coat; e, embryophore or embryonal shell; h.e., hexacanth embryo; s, outer shell; y, yolk.

consists of an **oncosphere** or hexacanth embryo with six hooklets which is enclosed in one or more envelopes. The outer covering is a delicate structure, which is usually lost before the ovum is passed in the feces. The inner covering is known as the **embryophore.** A third membrane at times is present between these two and the intervening space is filled with fluid or semifluid material containing yolk granules. In the TÆNIIDÆ, where the outer covering is lost, the brownish embryophore is thick and radially striated. In the HYMENOLEPIDIDÆ the embryophore is thin and the eggshell is retained. In *Dipylidium caninum* several ova are enveloped in a single embryonic membrane.

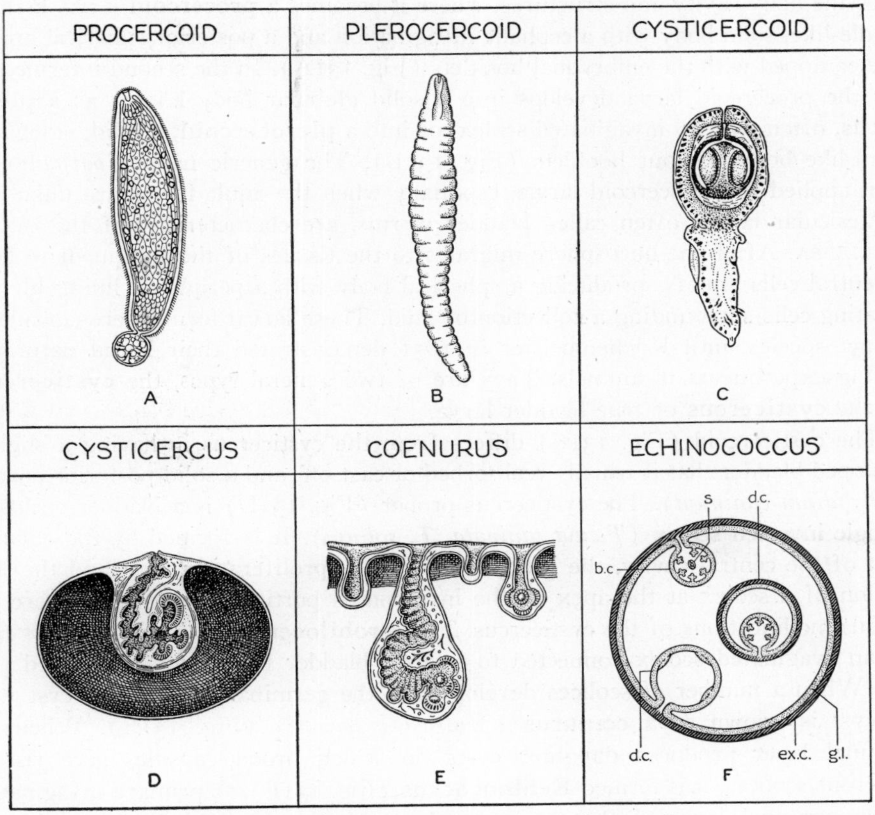

PROCERCOID	PLEROCERCOID	CYSTICERCOID
A	B	C
CYSTICERCUS	COENURUS	ECHINOCOCCUS
D	E	F

FIG. 131.—LARVAL FORMS OF TAPEWORMS

b.c., brood capsule; *d.c.*, daughter cyst; *ex.c.*, external laminated cuticula; *g.l.*, germinal or inner nucleated layer; *s*, scolex (*A* redrawn from Rosen in Braun and Seifert, 1925; *C* redrawn from Hegner, Root, Augustine and Huff, 1938; *D* redrawn from Leuckart, 1863; *E* adapted from Fantham, Stephens and Theobald, 1920).

Larval Development.—The thick-walled ova are quite resistant to heat and desiccation and can survive for long periods on soil or vegetation contaminated with feces. Upon ingestion in a suitable intermediate host, the oncosphere escapes from the embryophore through its own exertions under the stimulation of the digestive juices, or through the rupture of this covering by mechanical action or osmosis. The active oncosphere, aided by its hooklets, penetrates the intestinal wall, enters the lymphatic and vascular systems, where, by active or passive migration, it gains access to selective tissues for its larval development.

The development of the larval stage varies with the species but comprises two main classes: (1) solid larvæ and (2) bladder larvæ. The solid forms are characteristic of the PSEUDOPHYLLIDEA. A ciliated larva, the **coracidium,** liberated in the water, is ingested by a fresh-water crustacean, the first intermediate host. It penetrates the body cavity and structures, where it becomes a **procercoid** larva, a small, spindle-like, solid body with a cephalic invagination and a posterior spherical appendage equipped with the embryonal hooklets (Fig. 131A). In the second intermediate host the procercoid larva develops into a solid globular body known as a **plerocercus,** often with an invaginated scolex, or into a **plerocercoid,** a solid, elongated, worm-like body without hooklets (Fig. 131B). The generic name *Sparganum* is often applied to plerocercoid larvæ, especially when the adult forms are unknown.

Vesicular larvæ, often called bladder worms, are characteristic of the CYCLOPHYLLIDEA. After the oncosphere migrates to the tissues of the intermediate host, its central cells liquefy, producing a spherical body with a peripheral lining of proliferating cells surrounding a collection of fluid. These larval forms were considered distinct species until Küchenmeister in 1851 demonstrated their larval nature by feeding experiments in animals. They are of two general types, the **cysticercoid** and the **cysticercus** or true bladder larva.

The cysticercoid (Fig. 131C) differs from the cysticercus in having a slightly developed bladder that is usually reabsorbed or cast off, and a solid posterior portion (*Dipylidium caninum*). The cysticercus proper (Fig. 131D) is a bladder enclosing a single inverted scolex (*Tænia saginata, T. solium*). It is formed by the enlargement of the central cavity, the invagination of the proliferating wall, and the production of a scolex at the apex of the invaginated portion (Fig. 132). There are various modifications of the cysticercus. The **strobilocercus** (*Tænia tæniæformis*) has an evaginated scolex connected to a small bladder by a long, segmented portion. When a number of scolices develop from the germinal layer of the cyst wall, the cyst is known as a **cœnurus** (*Multiceps serialis*) (Fig. 131E). When the germinal layer produces daughter cysts, in which brood capsules give rise to numerous scolices, it is termed **Echinococcus** (Fig. 131F). A primary invagination of the germinal layer of the echinococcal cyst becomes studded with secondary invaginations, each of which develops a scolex, so that a minute brood capsule containing many scolices is formed and eventually is separated from the wall of the primary cyst. Upon disintegration of the capsule the scolices lie free in the cystic fluid. The daughter cysts, that are formed from broken bits of germinal tissue, brood capsules or scolices, repeat the process of producing brood capsules. In the cœnural and echinococcal forms a single worm through asexual development may give rise to numerous progeny, each capable of producing an adult worm. Hence the chances of completing the life cycle are greatly increased.

The life cycle is completed when the cysticercus is ingested by the definitive host. The encysted larva is liberated by the digestive juices and after the eversion of the scolex attaches itself to the intestinal wall where it proceeds to grow by the proliferation posteriorly of successive segments.

PATHOGENESIS

The injury produced by the adult worm varies with the species. The size and number of the tapeworms determine the general effect upon the host and the extent of intestinal irritation. The attachment of the scolices provides an avenue for bacterial invasion and the presence of the strobila may induce temporary intestinal obstruction. All manner of vague gastro-intestinal and nervous symptoms have been elicited. Lowered vitality and anemia have been associated with tapeworm infection, but usually no definite symptoms are manifest.

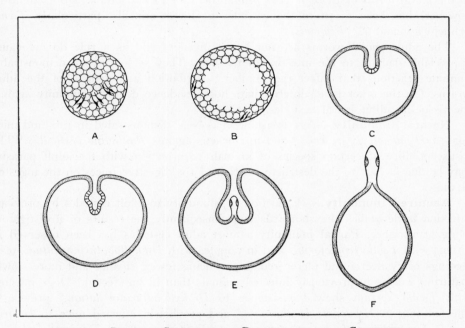

FIG. 132.—DIAGRAM SHOWING THE DEVELOPMENT OF A CYSTICERCUS

A, oncosphere with hooklets; *B,* cavity formed by liquefaction of central cells of oncosphere; *C,* early invagination of bladder wall; *D,* formation of scolex at base of invagination; *E,* beginning evagination of fully developed scolex; *F,* scolex completely evaginated.

The larval stages, however, may produce serious conditions. Cysticerci of *Tænia solium,* in the brain and other organs where removal is difficult, may cause marked symptoms. Echinococcal cysts of the liver and other organs produce symptoms of tumors and because of the difficulty of removal *in toto* may prove fatal.

TREATMENT

The anthelmintic drug most commonly used for the adult worms is oleoresin of aspidium. Carbon tetrachloride is also effective, while numerous other remedies have been tried throughout medical history. Persistent treatment is required, since the scolex must be expelled or else the worm will grow again. Thus it is important to check the results of treatment by careful search for the scolex in the feces. Before subjecting a debilitated patient to such rigorous treatment, his general health should be improved. The more serious larval infections require surgery, and success is dependent upon the location and accessibility of the parasites.

IMMUNITY

Studies on the immunity of cestoid infections in man have been chiefly confined to the larval forms of *Echinococcus granulosus* and *Tænia solium*. More attention, however, has been given to the cestodes of lower animals, particularly *Tænia tæniæformis* and *T. pisiformis*.

The adult tænial worms are not tissue invaders and as a rule do not cause appreciable damage to the intestine of the host. They seldom evoke demonstrable immune reactions that affect the number, distribution and growth of the adult worms. On the other hand, intermediate hosts evidence definite immunity against the tissue-invading larval cestodes.

Natural Immunity.—Age resistance has been demonstrated in rats and mice against *Hymenolepis fraterna*[3] and in chickens against *Raillietina cesticillus*.[4] The insusceptibility of certain species of animals to infection with the adult parasite may be due in part to the destructive action of the digestive juices on the ingested larva.

Acquired Immunity.—Production of immunity to adult cestodes by previous infection is debatable, the standards and consequently the results of investigators being at variance. Partial immunity against adult cestodes has been observed in kittens with *Tænia tæniæformis* and in puppies with *Diphyllobothrium latum,* test-feedings of cysticerci and plerocercoids producing fewer, smaller and more slowly maturing worms in previously infected animals than in uninfected.[5] Dogs infected with *Tænia serrata* showed resistance to *Diphyllobothrium latum,*[6] previously infected rats to *Hymenolepis diminuta,*[7] and previously infected mice to *H. fraterna*.[3] No evidence of protection by previous infection against *Tænia tæniæformis* was found in cats.[8] Inhibition of growth, however, is not satisfactory evidence of immunity in superimposed infections. Crowding, rather than the immunity of the host, is responsible for the small size and slow growth of *Hymenolepis diminuta* in superimposed infections.[9] The size and rate of growth are proportional to the number of worms in the primary infection and, if these worms are first removed by a vermifuge, the growth of the secondary worms is not inhibited.

Evidence of acquired immunity to larval cestodes is fairly conclusive. The presence of a few cysts of *T. tæniæformis* (*Cysticercus fasciolaris*) in the liver of experimentally infected rats prevents subsequent development of cysticerci,[10] and

[3] Shorb, D. A., 1933; Hunninen, A. V., 1935.
[4] Ackert, J. E. and Reid, W. M., 1937.
[5] Ohira, T., 1935.
[6] Wigand, R., 1935.
[7] Palais, M., 1934.
[8] Miller, H. M., Jr., 1932.
[9] Chandler, A. C., 1939.
[10] Miller, H. M., Jr., 1931.

this immunity persists for 60 days after the removal of the cysts.[11] Similar results
have been obtained with the larvæ of *T. pisiformis* in rabbits.[12] Infection with the
cysticerci of *T. pisiformis* partially protects rats against subsequent infection with
larval *T. tæniæformis*.[13] Infected sheep develop some immunity to the larval
Echinococcus.[14]

Active Immunization.—A series of intraäbdominal injections of dried powdered adult *T. tæniæformis* at 2- to 3-day intervals for five weeks protected rats
over a period of five months against test feedings, the cysts soon dying or attaining
only a small size.[15] This immunity seemed to be specific since rats immunized
similarly with *T. pisiformis* had little immunity against infection with *T. tæniæformis*. Similar results were obtained with *T. tæniæformis* in rats [16] and *T. pisiformis* in rabbits.[12] Rats immunized intraäbdominally with powdered suspensions
of adult *Diphyllobothrium latum, Dipylidium* sp. and *T. saginata* showed some
immunity to the larvæ of *T. tæniæformis,* but not as marked as those immunized
with *T. tæniæformis*.[13] Rats and mice were not immunized against *T. tæniæformis*
by injections of fresh or dried cysticerci.[17] Sheep, however, were partially protected
against echinococcal infection by the injection of antigens prepared from the scolices
and membranes of hydatid cysts (Chapter XXVIII).

Partial immunity has been produced in kittens and puppies against adult
Tænia tæniæformis and *Diphyllobothrium latum* respectively by subcutaneous
injections of extracts of these worms.[5] Dogs have been partially immunized against
Echinococcus granulosus by the injection of scolices and membranes of hydatid
cysts (Chapter XXVIII).

Passive Immunization.—The transfer of the serum of immune rats (infected
or artificially immunized with powdered *Tænia tæniæformis*) inhibited the development of cysticerci in normal rats if given within nine days after the time of
feeding the oncospheres.[18] The serum of infected rats was more potent than that
of the immunized.[19] Humoral protective antibodies were present in the serum of
infected rats as early as seven days after infection, and several weeks after infection
were sufficiently potent to destroy the parasites both before and after encystment.
Likewise, the serum of rabbits infected or artificially immunized against *T. pisiformis* conferred passive immunity on normal rabbits.[12]

Antibodies and Intracutaneous Allergy.—Precipitins, alexin-fixing antibodies and cutaneous supersensitiveness have been detected in infected and immunized animals using antigens of various tænial worms. The responses are not
specific but represent a group-reaction for all *Tæniæ*. In some instances immunization with these antigens apparently affords some protection against heterologous
species, although it is more effective against homologous species. A polysaccharid
antigen derived from the cysticerci of *Tænia tæniæformis* is reported to induce

---

[11] Miller, H. M., Jr., and Massie, E., 1932.

[12] Kerr, K. B., 1934, 1935.

[13] Miller, H. M., Jr., 1935.

[14] Turner, E. L., Dennis, E. W. and Berberian, D. A., 1935.

[15] Miller, H. M., Jr., 1930, 1931.

[16] Campbell, D. H., 1936.

[17] Feng, L. C. and Hoeppli, R., 1939.

[18] Miller, H. M., Jr., 1932, 1934.

[19] Miller, H. M., Jr., and Gardner, M. L.,
1932.

the formation of specific antibodies in rabbits and also sensitized guinea pigs, but these antibodies play no apparent rôle in protecting rats against infection.[20] Several instances of group-reactions in alexin-fixative and intracutaneous tests in hydatid disease have been reported (Chapter XXVIII).

DIAGNOSIS

The diagnosis of intestinal tæniasis depends upon identifying the parasite by the characteristics of the proglottides, ova and occasionally the scolex. The

TABLE 31

DIFFERENTIAL CHARACTERISTICS OF THE TAPEWORMS OF MAN

	Diphyllo-bothrium latum	Dipylidium caninum	Hymenolepis nana	Tænia solium	Tænia saginata	Echinococcus granulosus
Length of adult worm	3-10 meters	15-70 cm.	0.5-4.5 cm.	2-4 meters	4-8 meters	0.3-0.8 cm.
Scolex Suckers	2	4	4	4	4	4
Hooks	None	Present	Present	Present	None	Present
Rostellum	None	Present	Present	Present	None	Present
Number of proglottides	3000-4000	60-175	up to 200	800-1000	1000-2000	3
Mature proglottis	Broader than long	Longer than broad	Broader than long	Broader than long	Broader than long	Longer than broad
Uterus of gravid proglottis	Central, coiled	Reticulated capsules	Irregular, sac-like	7-12 lateral branches	15-30 lateral branches	Loose coil in terminal proglottis
Genital pore	Middle	Lateral, on each side	Lateral, on one side	Lateral, alternate	Lateral, alternate	Lateral, alternate
Ovum (size in micra)	70 x 45 operculate	40 x 36 globular	47 x 37 globular, two membranes	35 x 35 radially striated embryo-phore	35 x 25 radially striated embryo-phore	33 x 33 radially striated embryo-phore
Infective larval form	Plerocercoid	Cysticercoid	Cysticercoid (Cercocystis)	Cysticercus	Cysticercus	Echino-coccus
Intermedi-ate host	Copepod and fish	Flea, dog, louse	Man, mice, rats	Hog, man	Cattle	Man, her-bivorous animals
Stage in man	Adult	Adult	Adult, larval	Adult, larval	Adult	Larval

[20] Campbell, D. H., 1939.

differentiation of the important tapeworms of man is given in Table 31 and Figure 133.

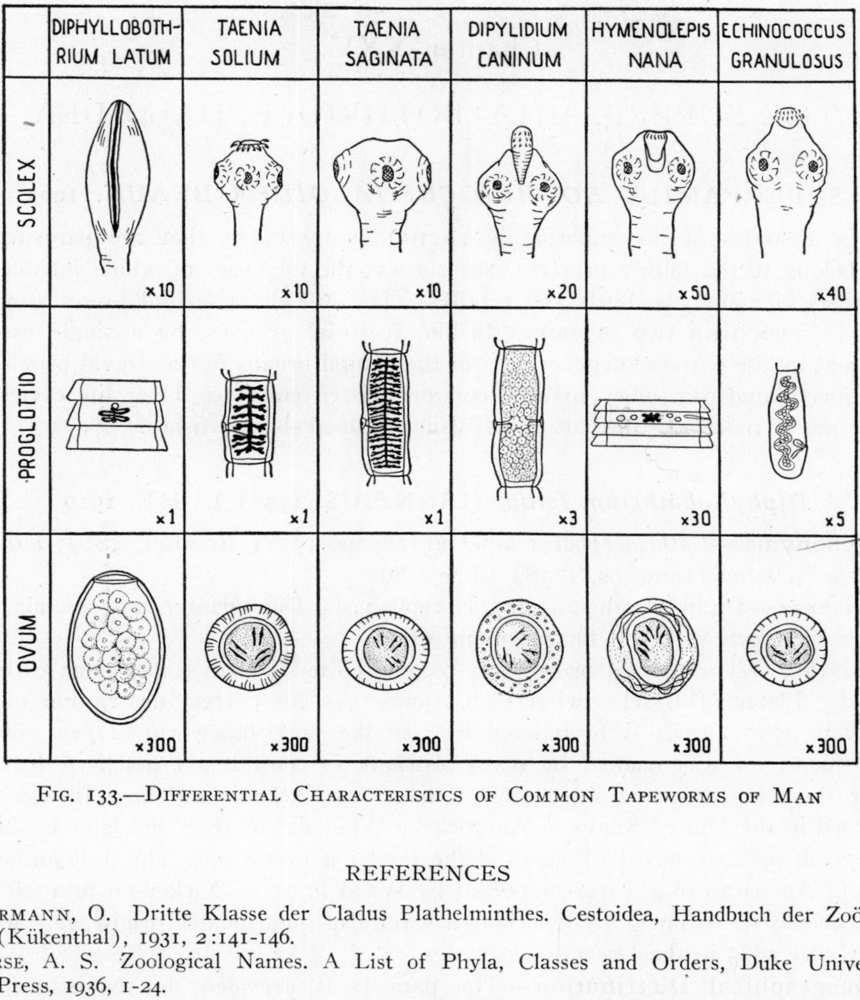

	DIPHYLLOBOTH-RIUM LATUM	TAENIA SOLIUM	TAENIA SAGINATA	DIPYLIDIUM CANINUM	HYMENOLEPIS NANA	ECHINOCOCCUS GRANULOSUS
SCOLEX	×10	×10	×10	×20	×50	×40
PROGLOTTID	×1	×1	×1	×3	×30	×5
OVUM	×300	×300	×300	×300	×300	×300

Fig. 133.—Differential Characteristics of Common Tapeworms of Man

REFERENCES

Fuhrmann, O. Dritte Klasse der Cladus Plathelminthes. Cestoidea, Handbuch der Zoölogie (Kükenthal), 1931, 2:141-146.

Pearse, A. S. Zoological Names. A List of Phyla, Classes and Orders, Duke University Press, 1936, 1-24.

Southwell, T. Cestoda. The Fauna of British India, Including Ceylon and Burma, 1930, 2:1-262.

Stiles, C. W. and Hassall, A. Key-Catalogue of the Worms Reported from Man, Hyg. Lab. Bull. No. 142, 1926, Washington.

Chapter XXV

THE SUPERFAMILY BOTHRIOCEPHALOIDEA

SUPERFAMILY *BOTHRIOCEPHALOIDEA* BRAUN, 1903

The cestodes of the superfamily BOTHRIOCEPHALOIDEA that are parasites of man belong to the family DIPHYLLOBOTHRIIDÆ, the members of which inhabit the intestines of mammals, birds and reptiles. They are characterized by an almond-shaped scolex with two opposing slit-like suctorial grooves, by a single uterine pore and by the extreme degeneration of the genital organs in the gravid proglottis. The operculated ova, when mature, contain ciliated embryos. Their life cycles involve one or more intermediate hosts, usually copepods and fishes.

Diphyllobothrium latum (LINNÆUS, 1758) LÜHE, 1910

Synonyms.—*Bothriocephalus latus* (Linnæus, 1758) Bremser, 1819; *Dibothriocephalus latus* (Linnæus, 1758) Lühe, 1899.

Disease.—Diphyllobothriasis, bothriocephaliasis, *Dibothriocephalus* anemia, fish tapeworm infection, broad tapeworm infection.

History.—The fish tapeworm was recognized as a distinct species as early as 1602 by Plater of Basel, Switzerland. Bonnet by his correct description of the scolex in 1777 clearly differentiated it from the pork tapeworm, *Tænia solium*. Subsequently it was studied by many workers in central and northern Europe, where the adult worm is a parasite of man, dog, cat, fox and hog. It was first observed in the United States of America by Weinland in 1858 and later by Leidy in 1879 in patients who had acquired the infection in Europe. The first authentic cases of American origin were reported by Ward in 1906, Nickerson in 1906 and 1911, and by Warthin in 1911, although several of questionable origin were found as early as 1895 in the Great Lakes states.

Geographical Distribution.—The parasite is prevalent in regions of the northern temperate zones, where fishes from fresh-water lakes form an integral part of the diet. In Europe there are three principal endemic foci: (1) the countries bordering the Baltic Sea; (2) the lake region of Switzerland, extending into France, Bavaria and Italy; and (3) Rumania and the Danube basin. In Asia it is found in Russian Turkestan; in Palestine in the region around Lake Tiberias; in northern Manchuria; in Japan, and in the Philippines (one case). In Africa it is present in the vicinity of Lake Ngami, British Bechuanaland and Uganda, and also in Madagascar. Four apparently autochthonous cases have been found in Ireland. In North America it has been introduced in the Great Lakes region by immigrants from the Baltic countries. There are three principal endemic areas: (1) the northern Michigan peninsula; (2) northern Minnesota; and (3) the vicinity of Winnipeg, Canada.

BIOLOGICAL CHARACTERISTICS

Morphology.—The ivory or grayish-yellow adult tapeworm (Fig. 134) ranges from 3 to 10 meters in length and may have over 4,000 proglottides. Its movements are even more sluggish than those of *Tænia saginata*. The almond-shaped scolex (Fig. 126A), from 2 to 3 mm. in length by 1 mm. in breadth, has two deep suctorial grooves or bothria, which, due to torsion of the neck, appear lateral but actually are dorsal and ventral. An attenuated neck, several times the length of the scolex, is followed by a series of immature segments, which become progressively more fully developed until the last four-fifths of the worm is composed of mature and gravid proglottides.

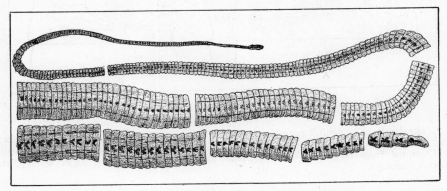

Fig. 134.—Adult *Diphyllobothrium latum*
(Redrawn from Leuckart, 1863).

The mature proglottis, 2 to 4 mm. in length by 10 to 12 mm. in breadth, contains both male and female reproductive organs. The male organs (Fig. 135B) consist of minute spherical testes situated in the dorsolateral part of the proglottis. From these the vasa efferentia converge to form the vas deferens. This convoluted tubule passes forward in the mid-plane of the proglottis and enlarges to form a seminal vesicle before terminating in a muscular cirral organ that opens on the anterior side of the common genital pore. The appearance of the dark rosette-like coiled uterus (Fig. 133) in the mid-part of the gravid proglottis is of diagnostic value. The uterus (Fig. 135A) opens through the uterine pore in the mid-ventral line a short distance behind the common genital pore. The ovary is a symmetrical bilobed structure situated near the ventral surface in the posterior third of the proglottis above Mehlis' gland. The vitellaria, situated laterally, converge in ducts which fuse into a common vitelline duct. The oviduct and vitelline duct join the posterior end of the vagina, which extends from the common genital pore.

Physiology.—Self-fertilization is accomplished by the spermatozoa entering the vagina from the common genital atrium, although cross-fertilization is also possible. The spermatozoa migrate posteriorly and are stored in the seminal receptacle. After fertilization the ova receive a vitelline covering and a shell before passing into the uterus. As the uterus becomes distended it elongates in coils, the birth pore becomes relaxed, and there is a more or less continuous discharge of ova from the proglottis. Unlike the tænial cestodes the gravid segments normally do not separate from the parent worm but disintegrate after completing their reproductive function.

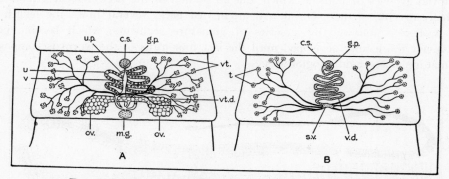

FIG. 135.—REPRODUCTIVE ORGANS OF *Diphyllobothrium latum*

A, female; *B*, male.

c.s., cirral sac; *g.p.*, genital pore; *m.g.*, Mehlis' gland; *ov.*, ovary; *s.v.*, seminal vesicle; *t*, testes; *u*, uterus; *u.p.*, uterine pore; *v*, vagina; *v.d.*, vas deferens; *vt.*, vitellaria; *vt.d.*, vitelline duct (Adapted from Hegner, Root, Augustine and Huff, *Parasitology*, 1938, D. Appleton-Century Company).

The fish tapeworm is apparently long-lived. Cases of prolonged infection in man, some clear-cut and others complicated by the possibility of reinfection, are on record. Infections of over twenty years' duration have been reported.[1] A dog, experimentally infected with *D. mansoni,* was kept under observation for eight years.[2] However, the accuracy of many reported cases of long-time infection is questionable because of the possibility of reinfection.[3]

LIFE CYCLE

The life cycle of *Diphyllobothrium latum* (Fig. 136) involves two intermediate hosts, copepods and fresh-water fishes. The ciliated embryo is liberated from the shell in water and is ingested by a copepod. The latter with the encysted larva in turn is ingested by a fish, in which the larva undergoes further development. Man and other animals are infected by eating raw fish.

Hosts.—The definitive hosts are man, dog, cat and infrequently at least 22 other mammals including mongoose, walrus, seal, sea lion, bear, fox, mink and hog.[4]

[1] Riley, W. A., 1919; Grönberg, A., 1925; Ronka, E. K. F., 1934.
[2] Leiper, R. T., 1936.
[3] Ward, H. B., 1930, 1935.
[4] Lyon, M. W., Jr., 1930.

The first intermediate hosts are fresh-water copepods of the genera *Cyclops* and *Diaptomus*. In Europe the principal host-species are *Cyclops strenuus* and *Diaptomus gracilis*, in North America *C. brevispinosus, C. prasinus* and *D. oregonensis* (Chapter XXXVII).[5] Various fresh-water fishes serve as secondary intermediate hosts. In Europe 17, in Japan 6 (SALMONIDÆ) and in North America 4 species of fishes have been found to harbor the parasite. The species in North America are *Esox lucius* (pike), *Stizostedeon vitreum* (wall-eyed pike), *S. canadense-griseum* (sand pike), and *Lota maculosa* (burbot).[6] In Long Lake, Ely, Minnesota, the

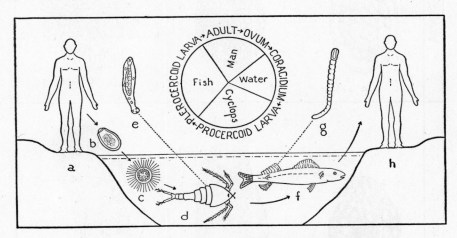

FIG. 136.—LIFE CYCLE OF *Diphyllobothrium latum*

a, man infected with adult tapeworm; *b*, ovum passed in feces; *c*, coracidium or ciliated free-swimming larva; *d*, copepod ingests larva; *e*, procercoid larva in copepod; *f*, fish infected by ingesting copepod; *g*, plerocercoid larva in fish; *h*, man infected by eating raw fish.

wall-eyed pike average 6 and the pickerel 15 larvæ.[7] These fish also harbor the larvæ of other species of *Diphyllobothrium* that may be mistaken for *D. latum*.

Larva.—The yellowish-brown ova, usually found in large numbers in the feces, have a single shell with an inconspicuous operculum at one end and a small knob-like thickening at the other (Figs. 130D and 137A and B). Their mean size is 70 by 45 μ but they range from 55 to 76 μ in length and from 41 to 56 μ in breadth. The ova are destroyed by desiccation and freezing. At a favorable temperature they hatch in 9 to 12 days after reaching water, the embryo, surrounded by its ciliated embryophore, escaping through the opercular opening. Hatching takes place near the surface. The ciliated coracidium (Fig. 137C) swims with an alternating right and left rotation for several days until it is ingested by a suitable species of *Cyclops* or *Diaptomus*. In the intestine of the copepod the coracidium loses its cilia, penetrates the intestinal wall aided by its hooklets, and gains access to the body cavity. Here it increases in size from 55 to 550 μ to form an elongated procercoid larva (Fig. 137F) with a cup-shaped cephalic invagination, many calcareous bodies, a

---

[5] Essex, H. E., 1927.
[6] Vergeer, T., 1928.

[7] Essex, H. E., 1938.

cuticle with bristle-like processes, and a circular caudal appendage with embryonal hooklets.[8] Usually only one or two larvæ develop in a single copepod.

When the infected copepod is ingested by a suitable species of fresh-water fish,

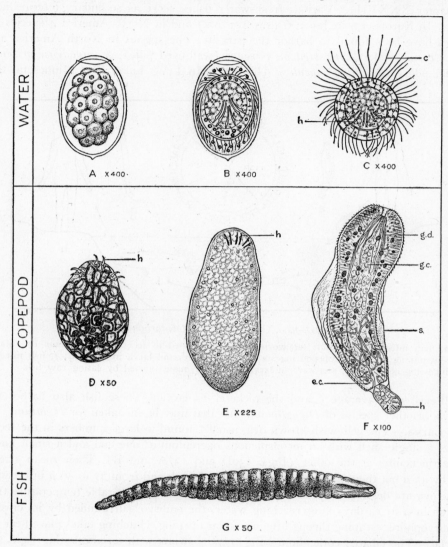

FIG. 137.—LARVAL FORMS OF *Diphyllobothrium latum*

A, undeveloped ovum; *B*, hexacanth embryo in eggshell; *C*, ciliated coracidium; *D*, larva, seven days after infection of copepod; *E*, larva, 20 days; *F*, procercoid larva; *G*, plerocercoid larva.

c, cilia; *e.c.*, excretory cell; *g.c.*, gland cells; *g.d.*, ducts of glands; *h*, hooklets; *s*, old membrane of oncosphere (*C*, *D* and *F* redrawn from Vogel, 1929, 1930; *E* redrawn from Janicki and Rosen, 1916-1917).

---

[8] Vogel, H., 1930.

the procercoid larva penetrates the intestinal wall in a few days and enters the muscles, viscera and connective tissues. The large carnivorous species may obtain the larvæ directly from the copepods or indirectly by ingesting small infected fishes. Here in from 7 to 30 days it is transformed into an encysted plerocercoid larva (Fig. 137G). This larva, known as a sparganum, is an elongate, chalky, spindle-shaped organism from 10 to 20 mm. in length and from 2 to 3 mm. in breadth. The anterior end is evaginated and the contractions of the body give it a pseudosegmented appearance. When raw or insufficiently cooked fish is eaten by a susceptible host the plerocercoid larva adheres to the intestinal wall and grows at an estimated rate of about 30 proglottides a day to reach maturity in about three weeks.

PATHOGENESIS

Pathology.—The adult worm may produce a catarrhal condition of the intestinal mucosa. Usually infection is limited to a single worm, although more have been reported, and the unusual instance is on record in which a man harbored 143 worms.[9] Symptoms are presumed to be due to the absorption of toxic secretions or by-products of degenerating proglottides, but no evidence of a hematoxin has been found.

Symptomatology.—Most persons suffer no ill effects from the fish tapeworm. Some, however, present a variety of clinical manifestations such as functional and organic nervous disturbances, disorders of the digestive tract, malnutrition, stomatitis, anemia, cramp-like abdominal pains, and symptoms of peptic ulcer. An experimentally infected man suffered abdominal pain, lost 18 pounds in weight, and became so weak that he required hospitalization.[10]

A small percentage of infected persons develop a severe *Bothriocephalus* anemia that often is clinically, hematologically and pathologically indistinguishable from cryptogenic pernicious anemia. The erythrocyte count runs from 500,000 to 2,000,000; the hemoglobin may be as low as 25 to 30 per cent, although the color index remains above unity; and the red blood cells show changes comparable to those of pernicious anemia. There is a leukopenia and usually, but not invariably, a more or less pronounced eosinophilia. Achlorhydria is present in four-fifths of these patients and paræsthesia is not uncommon. Over 70 per cent of all the cases of bothriocephalid anemia have been reported from Finland. At Helsingfors from 1898 to 1927, 31 per cent of 744 cases of pernicious anemia were due to fish tapeworm infection.[11] Tapeworm anemia is more prevalent in females than in males and is most frequently observed in the spring and summer. In North America there have been no reported instances of severe anemia in autochthonous cases.

The dramatic improvement in clinical symptoms and hematologic picture, with reticulocyte response and ultimate cure following the expulsion of the worm, are strong evidence of a causal relationship between the parasite and the anemia. Nevertheless factors other than the presence of the worm must be involved. Patients may harbor the parasite for years and suddenly develop a profound anemia that is cured

---

[9] Tarassov, V., 1934.
[10] Tarassov, V., 1937.

[11] Lindstrom, E., 1930.

by the removal of the worm.[12] Bothriocephaliasis ordinarily is a disease of earlier life than is cryptogenic pernicious anemia.[11] Various ideas regarding its origin have been advanced: that the tapeworm is the direct cause of the anemia; that it is a precipitating factor for an existing constitutional predisposition; and that a true pernicious anemia simultaneously occurs in infected individuals.[13] In a review of the literature on bothriocephalid anemia Birkeland concludes that no convincing evidence of a specific hematoxin has been produced, and that patients thus affected are suffering from abortive forms of pernicious anemia.[14] He found that a gradual transition could be traced from a normal state to a definite anemia and that other intestinal worms were also capable of producing a similar condition.

Immunity.—Infected dogs show a partial immunity to superinfection.[15] Alexin-fixative antibodies and precipitins, group-specific for cestodes, have been demonstrated in man. Immunity in man is temporary; within three years after the removal of the parasite from 60 persons in an endemic area 40 became reinfected.[10]

DIAGNOSIS, PROGNOSIS AND TREATMENT

Diagnosis.—Diagnosis usually cannot be made from clinical symptoms, although residence in an endemic locality, a raw fish diet, and the presence in Europeans of a pernicious type of anemia are suggestive. Laboratory diagnosis is based on finding the characteristic operculate ova or the evacuated proglottides in the feces. Serological methods of diagnosis are impractical because of cross-reactions with other cestodes; a high percentage of positive alexin-fixative reactions has been obtained with both *Diphyllobothrium* and *Tænia* antigens.[16]

Prognosis.—Favorable; even the severe anemia clears up after expulsion of the worm.

Treatment.—The two most efficient anthelmintic drugs are oleoresin of aspidium (Section **VII**, XIII, 29) and carbon tetrachloride (Section **VII**, XIII, 21). The former is the drug of choice and the latter is less frequently employed because of its toxicity.

PREVENTION

Epidemiology.—The incidence of fish tapeworm infection is extremely high in the Baltic countries; in the region northward from Lake Ladoga, Finland, 50 per cent of the population are infected [17] and 30 to 50 per cent at Karelia, Finland, and around Leningrad, Russia.[18] It is also high in the lake regions of Switzerland and in the Danube basin. On the Bay of Courland, Germany, where raw fish livers are eaten, 36 per cent of the children are infected.[19]

The development of endemic foci in North America illustrates the transplantation of an Old World parasite to a new environment. Immigrants from the Baltic countries were the original source of infection. Inadequate sewage disposal, the

[12] Grönberg, A., 1925; Haden, R. L., 1923; Hunnicutt, T. N., 1935.

[13] Magath, T. B., 1930; Moschowitz, E., 1931.

[14] Birkeland, I. W., 1932.

[15] Ohira, T., 1935.

[16] Jerlov, E., 1919.

[17] Ehrstrom, R., 1926.

[18] Petruschewsky, G. K. and Tarassov, V., 1933.

[19] Vogel, H., 1929.

presence of suitable fresh-water intermediate hosts, ignorance of the mode of transmission of the infection, and the custom of eating raw or semi-raw fish are responsible for the establishment of these endemic areas. The practice of allowing untreated sewage to enter fresh-water lakes is the most important contributing factor.

The epidemiological studies of Essex, Vergeer and Magath have shown that these North American areas are becoming increasingly infested. Infected fish are found in practically every watershed in Minnesota; [20] about 20 per cent of the pickerel and pike from Lake Winnipeg and Lake Manitoba are infected; [21] and the fishes of the Tahoe region and Lassen National Park, California, are also reported to harbor the parasite.[22] The fishes of the small lakes in Minnesota, Michigan and Canada are more potent sources of infection than the infrequently infected fishes of the Great Lakes, where depth and a low temperature are restrictive factors, since the coracidia do not hatch in cold, deep water.

Infection in man may occur wherever infected fishes from endemic areas are marketed; *e.g.,* 21 cases in New York City.[23] It is estimated that 85 per cent of the pike caught in infested Canadian Lakes are shipped to the United States of America.[24]

Because of the custom of eating raw or insufficiently cooked fish, infection is most prevalent in Jews, Russians, Finns and Scandinavians. Women are more frequently infected than men, possibly through nibbling raw fish when preparing meals. Children are either more susceptible than adults or their feeding habits are more conducive to infection, since 21 of the 26 cases of infection acquired in North America previous to 1931 were in children from 3 to 15 years of age.[25]

Man is the principal source of infection. In endemic regions dogs are heavily infected, while cats, bears, foxes and other fish-eating mammals may also spread the disease to uninhabited regions. The dog may not be an important factor in the spread of the infection, since only a small percentage of the ova develop and its feces are deposited in localities subjected to destructive freezing and drying.[26]

Prophylaxis.—The prevention of bothriocephaliasis in an endemic region depends upon establishing a break in the life cycle of the parasite. The endemic areas should be defined by surveys of the extent and intensity of infestation in fresh-water fishes, at times a difficult procedure because of the presence of nonhuman diphyllobothriid larvæ. The human sources of infection should be detected through surveys and placed under treatment. The presence of dogs and other carnivorous animals as reservoir hosts to some extent complicates the problem, although man is probably the potent source of infection. The disposal of raw sewage into bodies of fresh water should be prohibited or the sewage should be treated with chlorine. Since the ova are killed in 2 per cent formalin, this chemical may be used to disinfect the feces of patients.[5] In spite of administrative difficulties the sale of fish from heavily infested lakes should be prohibited and fish from local markets should

[20] Magath, T. B., and Essex, H. E., 1931.
[21] Nicholson, D., 1928.
[22] Hobmeier, M., 1938.
[23] Waters, H. S., and O'Connor, F. W.,
1932; Plotz, M., 1932.
[24] Vergeer, T., 1929.
[25] Pilot, J., and Levin, I. M., 1931.
[26] Magath, T. B., 1933.

be examined and, if infected, condemned. Freezing at — 10° C. for 24 hours, thorough cooking for at least 10 minutes at 50° C., and proper drying and pickling of the fish will kill the larvæ. The public should be educated as to the danger of eating raw or imperfectly cooked fish. Such information may be broadcast through newspapers, circulars and placards in fish markets.

Diphyllobothrium erinacei (RUDOLPHI, 1819) FAUST, CAMPBELL AND KELLOGG, 1929

The plerocercoid larva, discovered by Manson in 1882 in a Chinese, was the only form known for many years. The adult worm is found in dogs, cats and their wild relatives and only the larval stage in man. Although opinions differ, evidence seems to indicate that the following reported species may be placed under a single species or are closely allied forms that differ in intermediate host selectivity as to homothermal or poikilothermal animals: [27] *D. erinacei* (Rudolphi, 1819) Faust, Campbell and Kellogg, 1929; *D. mansoni* (Cobbold, 1882) Joyeux, 1928; *D. reptans* (Diesing) Meggitt, 1925; *D. okumurai* Faust, Campbell and Kellogg, 1929; *D. ranarum* (Gastaldi, 1854) Meggitt, 1925; *D. decipiens* (Diesing, 1850) Gedoelst, 1911; and possibly *D. houghtoni* Faust, Campbell and Kellogg, 1929.

Geographical Distribution.—The parasite or closely allied species has been reported in China, Japan, French Indo-China, Annam, the Malay Archipelago, Africa, Australia, British Guiana and Puerto Rico.

Morphology.—The adult worm resembles *Diphyllobothrium latum,* but is smaller and has a smaller quadrangular scolex with well-developed free bothrial margins. The mature proglottides are mostly broader than long, but at the distal end of the strobila they are nearly square.

Life Cycle.—The ova, about 65 by 39 μ, though variable in size, are spindle-shaped with pointed ends. They hatch in less than three weeks after reaching water. The ciliated embryo, when ingested by any one of some nine or more species of *Cyclops* such as *C. leuckarti,* passes into the body cavity where it develops into a procercoid larva. When the infected *Cyclops* is swallowed by a frog, snake, bird or mammal, the larva penetrates the wall of the gastro-intestinal tract, migrates to the muscular tissues, and develops into a long, white, ribbon-shaped plerocercoid larva. It has a transversely-wrinkled, flattened body with a longitudinal medial groove on the ventral surface and a broad anterior end. The larva, 30 mm. by 0.7 mm., shows but slight movement. At times budding may occur.

Man, monkeys, cats, pigs, weasels, hedgehogs, rats, chickens, snakes and frogs are intermediate hosts. Man may be infected by drinking water containing larva-bearing *Cyclops.* Infection may also occur by the larvæ penetrating cutaneous lesions. A common method of infection in the Far East is through the application to injured surfaces of poultices of fresh frog flesh, whereby the spargana migrate to human tissues. [28] The larvæ may be found in any part of the body, especially in and about the eyes, in the subcutaneous and muscular tissues of the thorax, abdomen and thighs, and in inguinal regions and thoracic viscera. When the plerocercoid larvæ are eaten by suitable definitive hosts, such as cats, dogs and wild carnivora, the worm attains maturity in the intestine in 16 to 20 days.

Pathogenesis.—The stage of migration is practically symptomless. As the sparganum increases in size the surrounding tissues become edematous and painful to the touch.

[27] Iwata, S., 1933; Joyeux, C., Houdemer, E., and Baer, J., 1934.
[28] Faust, E. C., 1928; Joyeux, C. and Houdemer, E., 1928; Faust, E. C., Campbell, H. B. and Kellogg, C. R., 1929.

Small inflammatory swellings with a slimy matrix and at times a chylous exudate surround the elongating and contracting larvæ. Degenerated larvæ cause an intense local inflammatory reaction. There is an eosinophilic and leukocytic infiltration but no fibrous tissue formation around the parasite. Ocular infection, of relatively frequent occurrence in China, produces painful edematous conjunctivitis with lacrimation and ptosis. Retro-bulbar inflammation may lead to corneal ulceration.

Diagnosis.—Diagnosis is made by finding the characteristic larval forms in the lesions. They should be differentiated from *Sparganum proliferum* which is irregularly shaped and branched.

Prognosis.—Prognosis depends upon the location of the parasite and its removal without serious injury to the host.

Treatment.—Surgical removal of the larvæ is the only satisfactory treatment, although alcoholic injections are sometimes used to kill the worms.

Prevention.—Man so far as is known is infected only with the larval or sparganum stage of the parasite. Drinking water in endemic areas should be boiled or filtered, and the native practice of applying the flesh of frogs and other vertebrates to ulcers or inflamed mucocutaneous areas should be discouraged.

OTHER DIPHYLLOBOTHRIIDS OF MAN

Diphyllobothrium houghtoni **Faust, Campbell and Kellogg, 1929.**—The adult worm has been found in the intestines of man, dog and cat in China. It is smaller than *D. latum,* and has poorly developed bothria and a compactly coiled uterus. The ova, 62 to 35 μ, resemble those of *D. erinacei.* The life cycle is unknown, but the intermediate hosts are probably a copepod and a vertebrate. It may belong in the *D. erinacei* group and its sparganum may infect man.

Diphyllobothrium parvum **Stephens, 1908.**—Because of its smaller size, *D. parvum,* although similar to *D. latum,* has been described as a separate species. It has been reported in Tasmania, Rumania, Japan, Persia and Minnesota in the United States of America. It is a small tapeworm, the largest segments measuring only 5 mm. by 3 mm., and possibly is a dwarf *D. latum.*[29]

Diphyllobothrium cordatum **Leuckart, 1863.**—The adult tapeworm, which attains a length of from 1 to 1.3 meters, is a natural parasite of dogs, seals and walruses in Greenland and Iceland, of dogs in Japan, and probably bears in North America. Infections in man have been reported in Greenland and Japan. Its differential characteristics are the compressed cordate scolex, the almost complete absence of neck, and the transversely compressed proglottides. The broadly oval, operculate ova, 75 by 50 μ, are indistinguishable from those of *D. latum.* Its life history and pathogenicity are unknown, but probably parallel those of *D. latum.*

Diplogonoporus grandis **(R. Blanchard, 1894) Lühe, 1899.**—The double-pored giant tapeworm differs from species of the genus *Diphyllobothrium* in having a double set of genital organs in each mature proglottid. Six instances of human infection have been recorded in Japan. The normal hosts are believed to be whales and seals, and man is probably infected by salt-water fishes, the secondary intermediate hosts. The reported symptoms are colicky abdominal pains, progressive secondary anemia, and alternate diarrhea and constipation. The adult worm, at times reaching a length of 6 meters, is identified by the characteristic short, broad proglottides, which show a median, two uterine and two lateral fields. The short broad scolex is provided with two strong grooved suckers. The brown operculate ova, 65 by 50 μ, are broadly oval.

---

[29] Magath, T. B., 1929.

Digramma brauni (Leon, 1907) Joyeux and Baer, 1929.—*D. brauni,* which has been found twice in man in Rumania, is a small worm about 12 cm. in length with small operculate ova. It is possibly an immature avian tapeworm accidentally acquired by man.[30]

Ligula intestinalis (Goeze, 1782) Gmelin, 1790.—*L. intestinalis* has been obtained twice from man in Rumania and once in France. It is a fleshy, ribbon-shaped tapeworm from 18 to 20 cm. in length and 0.8 to 1.2 cm. in breadth. The worm, a natural parasite of fish-eating birds, is an accidental parasite(?) of man.

GENUS *SPARGANUM* DIESING, 1854

The larvæ of several species of diphyllobothriid tapeworms, the adult forms of which are unknown, have been found in man. They are known as spargana and the disease as sparganosis. The principal species is *Sparganum proliferum,* but *Sparganum baxteri, S. mansonoides,* and other incompletely described species have also been reported.

Sparganum proliferum Ijima, 1905.—The larval worm, discovered by Ijima in 1905, has been reported several times in man in Japan and once by Stiles in 1908 in the United States of America. The adult worm and its life cycle are unknown, since feeding experiments in animals have never produced the adult.

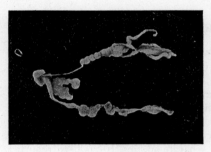

FIG. 138.—*Sparganum proliferum* SHOWING BUDS AND SUPERNUMERARY HEADS (× 10)

(After Stiles from Hegner, Root, Augustine and Huff, *Parasitology,* 1938, D. Appleton-Century Company).

The larval form, 3 to 12 mm. in length by 2.5 mm. in breadth, has a narrow motile anterior end capable of evagination and invagination. It is characterized by irregular, lateral, supernumerary processes which may bud off as new larvæ (Fig. 138). This method of asexual multiplication produces large numbers of spargana in infected persons, over 10,000 having been found in the left thigh of one individual.[31]

The larvæ migrate into the wall of the alimentary tract, mesenteries, kidneys, lungs, heart and brain, where they evoke nodular formation in the tissues. When opened these nodules contain one or more worms in a watery or chylous fluid. In the skin and subcutaneous tissues the wandering larvæ cause acne-like lesions, but the deeper lesions, though producing few symptoms, are more dangerous. Involvement of the lymph channels may produce elephantiasis. The larvæ proliferate if injected into the subcutaneous tissues or abdominal cavity.

Diagnosis is made by finding the characteristic larvæ in the lesions. In severe infection prognosis is grave since treatment is of no avail. No methods of prophylaxis are known.

Sparganum mansonoides Mueller, 1935.—The adult worm is found in cats, wild cats and, occasionally dogs in the United States of America. The first intermediate host is *Cyclops leuckarti, C. viridis* or *C. bicuspidatus,* and the procercoid larva becomes infective in from 18 to 21 days. The natural second intermediate hosts are water snakes and field mice. Experimental infections have been produced orally in mice and monkeys, and by inoculation in mice, rats, guinea pigs, rabbits and monkeys. In these hosts the migrations of the spargana cause extensive tissue-damage and proliferation of fibrous connective tissue. In monkeys blockage of the lymphatics results in elephantiasis and edema. Infected animals develop an eosinophilia of 15 to 35 per cent. Sparganosis in man is probably more frequent than ordinarily supposed, and *S. mansonoides* may be responsible for reported cases of sparganosis in the United States of America.[32]

[30] Joyeux, C. and Baer, J. G., 1929.   [31] Ijima, I., 1905.   [32] Mueller, J. F., 1938,

REFERENCES

BIRKELAND, I. W. *"Bothriocephalus* Anemia." *Diphyllobothrium latum* and Pernicious Anemia, Medicine, 1932, 11:1.

ESSEX, H. E. Early Development of *Diphyllobothrium latum* in Northern Minnesota, J. Parasitol., 1927, 14:106.

FAUST, E. C., CAMPBELL, H. B. and KELLOGG, C. R. Morphological and Biological Studies on the Species of *Diphyllobothrium* in China, Am. J. Hyg., 1929, 9:560.

IWATA, S. Some Experimental and Morphological Studies on the Post-embryonal Development of Manson's Tapeworm, *Diphyllobothrium erinacei* (Rudolphi), Japanese J. Zool., 1933, 5:210.

MAGATH, T. B. and ESSEX, H. E. Concerning the Distribution of *Diphyllobothrium latum* in North America, J. Prev. Med., 1931, 5:227.

MUELLER, J. F. The Life History of *Diphyllobothrium mansonoides* Mueller, 1935, and Some Considerations with Regard to Sparganosis in the United States, Am. J. Trop. Med., 1938, 18:41.

―――― Studies on *Sparganum mansonoides* and *Sparganum proliferum,* Am. J. Trop. Med., 1938, 18:303.

VERGEER, T. *Diphyllobothrium latum* (Linn. 1758). The Broad Tapeworm of Man. Experimental Studies, J. Am. M. Ass., 1928, 90:673.

―――― The Broad Tapeworm in America with Suggestions for Its Control, J. Infect. Dis., 1929, 44:1.

VOGEL, H. Studien über die Entwicklung von *Diphyllobothrium.* II Teil: Die Entwicklung des Procercoids von *Diphyllobothrium latum,* Ztschr. Wiss. Biol. Abt. f. Parasitenk., 1930, 2:629.

WARD, H. B. The Introduction and Spread of the Fish Tapeworm (*Diphyllobothrium latum*) in the United States, De Lamar Lectures, 1929-1930, the Williams and Wilkins Company, Baltimore, 1930.

WARDLE, R. A. Fish Tapeworm. Bull. Biol. Board of Canada, 1935, No. 45, pp. 25, Ottawa.

Chapter XXVI

THE SUPERFAMILY TÆNIOIDEA: FAMILIES ANOPLOCEPHALIDÆ, DAVAINEIDÆ, DILEPIDIDÆ AND HYMENOLEPIDIDÆ

SUPERFAMILY *TÆNIOIDEA* ZWICKE, 1841

The cyclophyllidean tapeworms of man belong to the superfamily TÆNIOIDEA. They are characterized by a scolex with four suckers, the absence of a uterine pore, a lateral genital pore, and in the gravid proglottides nonoperculate ova with a non-ciliated fully-developed oncosphere enclosed in one or more shell layers. The adult worm inhabits the intestines of vertebrates, and the larva the tissues of vertebrates and invertebrates. Five families are of economic and medical importance: ANOPLO-CEPHALIDÆ, DAVAINEIDÆ, DILEPIDIDÆ, HYMENOLEPIDIDÆ and TÆNIIDÆ, the last two including important parasites of man.

FAMILY *ANOPLOCEPHALIDÆ* CHOLODKOWSKY, 1902

The ANOPLOCEPHALIDÆ have a large, globular scolex without rostellum or hooks, no noticeable neck and a relatively large strobila. The proglottides contain a single or double set of reproductive organs, and the marginal genital pores are bilateral, unilateral or irregularly alternate. An elongated saccular uterus with pouch-like branches occupies a transverse position in the proglottis. The embryophore usually has a bicornuate process. The life cycle is unknown, but probably the intermediate hosts are arthropods. Many species are parasites of ruminants, primates and birds, while two, *Bertiella studeri* and *B. mucronata* have been reported in man.

Bertiella studeri (Blanchard, 1891) Stiles and Hassall, 1902, a natural parasite of primates, has been reported several times in man in Mauritius, India, the East Indies, the Philippines and the West Indies. The adult worm, about 29 cm. in length by 6 mm. in breadth, has a spheroidal head with four large oval suckers. The mature flat proglottides are roughly eight times broader than long. The ova, 50 by 46 μ, are irregularly oval and have a pyriform inner shell with a bicornuate extremity.

Bertiella mucronata (Meyner, 1895) Beddard, 1911, a closely related species, has been twice reported in man, in Cuba and in Brazil.

FAMILY *DAVAINEIDÆ* FUHRMANN, 1907

The DAVAINEIDÆ have a cushion-shaped rostellum, armed with a double row of small hammer-shaped hooks, and four suckers usually equipped with minute hooklets. The mature proglottides contain a single or double set of reproductive organs and have irregularly-alternating unilateral or bilateral marginal genital pores. The sac-like tubular uterus may contain ova in capsules or may be entirely replaced by egg-capsules. The oncosphere is surrounded by two thin, transparent membranes. The definitive hosts are mammals and birds. Four species of the genus *Raillietina* have been reported from man: *R. madagascariensis, R. celebensis, R. asiatica,* and *R. quitensis.*

Raillietina madagascariensis (Davaine, 1869) Joyeux and Baer, 1929, the Madagascar tapeworm, has been reported 13 times in man in Mauritius, Madagascar, Nossi-Bé, Siam, the Philippines, Cuba and British Guiana. The long narrow adult worm, from 24 to 39 cm. in length by 0.26 cm. in width, has from 500 to 700 segments. The mature proglottis contains a single set of reproductive organs. The coiled uterine tubules of the gravid proglottis are distended with numerous capsules each containing from one to three elongate, elliptical ova, 57 by 21 μ in size. The life history is unknown, but the cockroach is under suspicion as a possible intermediate host. Rats are believed to be the natural definitive host. Asthenia, anemia, asthmatic bronchitis and functional cardiac symptoms have been observed in an infected child.

Raillietina celebensis Janicki, 1902, the Celebes tapeworm, has been found twice in man, in Japan and in Formosa. It is somewhat longer than *R. madagascariensis,* the gravid proglottides have more egg-capsules, and the ova are larger.

Raillietina asiatica (v. Linstow, 1901) Stiles and Hassall, 1926, a tapeworm of doubtful authenticity, has been reported once in man, in Persia.

Raillietina quitensis Léon, 1935 has been responsible for nine cases of human infection in Ecuador. The long narrow adult worm, from 10 to 12 meters in length by 3 mm. in width, has about 5,000 proglottides. Infected individuals show symptoms of intestinal irritation and discomfort.

FAMILY *DILEPIDIDÆ* FUHRMANN, 1907 EMEND. LINCICOME, 1939

The DILEPIDIDÆ are double-pored tapeworms of moderate size with unarmed suckers, a rostellum usually provided with hooks, single or double reproductive organs in each proglottis, and a sacculated uterus that breaks up into egg-sacs that contain one or more ova. The adults are parasites of mammals and birds. *Dipylidium caninum,* a common parasite of dogs and cats, is the only species found in man. Of the 15 reported and 5 other inadequately described or erroneously classified species of *Dipylidium,* only 3 appear valid.[1] Only two of all these species has been found in the United States of America previous to 1926, when five new species were reported in cats and dogs.[2] However, these five species are probably forms of *D. caninum,* since their classification is based on variable characteristics.[3]

Dipylidium caninum (LINNÆUS, 1758) RAILLIET, 1892

Synonyms.—*Tænia canina* Linnæus, 1758, *pro parte; Tænia cucumerina* Bloch, 1782; *Tænia elliptica* Batsch, 1786; *Dipylidium cucumerinum* (Bloch, 1782) Leuckart, 1863.

Disease.—Dipylidiasis, dog tapeworm infection.

History.—*Dipylidium caninum* was first described by Linnæus in 1758. Melnikov in 1869 demonstrated the larval stage in the dog louse, while in 1880 Grassi found that the dog flea and the human flea were also intermediate hosts.

Geographical Distribution.—Cosmopolitan.

BIOLOGICAL CHARACTERISTICS

Morphology.—The adult worm (Fig. 139A), is 20 to 40 cm. in length with a range of from 15 to 70 cm. It consists of a scolex, a slender neck and 60 to 175 proglottides, the largest having a breadth of from 2.5 to 3 mm. The rhomboidal

---

[1] Venard, C. E., 1938.
[2] Millzner, T. M., 1926.
[3] Schwartz, B., 1927.

scolex (Fig. 139C), 0.37 mm. in length and 0.35 mm. in breadth, has four prominent oval suckers and is capped by a conical or ovoid rostellum armed with 30 to
150 rose-thorn-shaped hooks arranged in one to seven transverse rows. The mus-

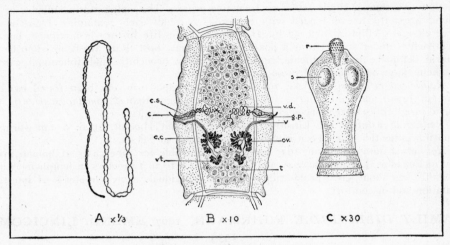

FIG. 139.—*Dipylidium caninum*

A, adult worm; *B*, mature proglottis; *C*, scolex.

c, cirrus; *c.s.*, cirral sac; *e.c.*, excretory canal; *g.p.*, genital pore; *ov.*, ovary; *r*, rostellum;
s, sucker; *t*, testes; *v*, vagina; *v.d.*, vas deferens; *vt.*, vitellarium (*A* redrawn from Brumpt;
B and *C* adapted from Railliet).

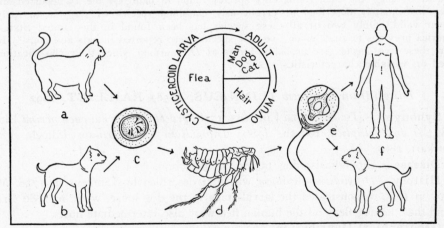

FIG. 140.—LIFE CYCLE OF *Dipylidium caninum*

a, feline host of adult tapeworm; *b*, canine host of adult tapeworm; *c*, ovum passed in feces;
d, larval flea ingests ovum; *e*, cysticercoid larva in flea; *f*, man infected by ingesting flea; *g*, dog
(or cat) infected by ingesting flea.

cular rostellum may be retracted for almost its entire length into a depression at
the anterior margin of the scolex.

The immature segments vary in shape from horizontally rectangular to nearly square. The genital primordia are first discernible between the tenth and fiftieth segments. The mature proglottides (Fig. 139B) are longer than broad and vase-shaped. They have a double set of reproductive organs and a genital pore on each lateral margin. Seminal receptacles are lacking and the irregularly-lobate vitellaria are posterior to the bilobed, lobulate ovaries. The 200 spherical testes occupy most of the available space mediad to the excretory canals. The gravid proglottis, 12 mm. by 2.7 mm., except at the anterior end is packed with membranous egg-capsules. The gravid segments separate from the strobila singly or in groups of two or three.

Physiology.—The free proglottides are capable of moving several inches per hour and either creep out of the anus or are passed in the feces.[1] Upon desiccation they adhere to the anal hairs of the dog. Shedding of the ova is effected by desiccation and the contractions of the proglottis.

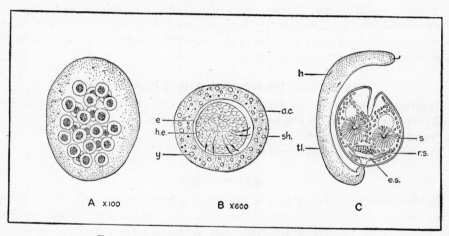

FIG. 141.—LARVAL FORMS OF *Dipylidium caninum*

A, cluster of ova in embryonic membrane; *B,* ovum; *C,* cysticercoid larva.

a.c., albuminous coat; *e,* embryophore; *e.s.,* excretory system; *h,* embryonal hooklets; *h.e.,* hexacanth embryo; *r.s.,* rostellar spines; *s,* sucker; *sh,* shell; *tl.,* tail; *y,* yolk (*C* redrawn from Grassi and Ravelli, 1889).

LIFE CYCLE

The definitive hosts are dogs, cats, hyenas, jackals, dingoes, foxes and wild felines. Man is an occasional host. The intermediate hosts are the dog flea, *Ctenocephalides canis,* the cat flea, *C. felis,* the human flea *Pulex irritans,* which become infected during the larval stage, and the dog louse, *Trichodectes canis* (Chapter XLV). When the gravid segments disintegrate, some of the ova become imbedded in the host's fur, especially the perianal hairs. Here they are ingested by larval fleas, which feed upon the débris in the hairs and skin. In the insect the larva develops into an infective cysticercoid, which, when the flea is ingested by a definitive host through biting or licking its fur, attaches itself to the intestinal wall and in about 20 days becomes a mature adult worm. The ova, from 35 to 60 μ in diameter, are enclosed, usually in groups of 15 to 25, in an embryonic membrane (Fig. 141A).

They have a globular shape, a thick transparent albuminous covering with two membranes and an oncosphere, 25 to 30 μ, with six hooklets (Fig. 141 B). The ova are seldom seen in the feces, since the proglottis rarely disintegrates within the host. They perish on drying in 24 to 48 hours and live only a few minutes in water.

The oncosphere does not escape from its covering until ingested by the larval flea. The embryo hatches in the intestine, penetrates the wall of the gut within 24 hours and reaches the abdominal cavity where it ultimately develops into a pear-shaped infective cysticercoid larva (Fig. 141 C) in the adult flea some 18 days after the pupal stage.[1] There is extensive destruction of the young larval worms by the phagocytic cells of the flea and a high mortality in infected fleas.[4]

PATHOGENESIS

Dogs and cats seldom show appreciable ill effects from this parasite, but in severe infections they may become weak, emaciated, and subject to nervous and digestive troubles. Man, who rarely harbors more than a single parasite, seldom shows symptoms, although children may experience slight intestinal discomfort, epigastric pain, anal pruritus, and reflex symptoms.

DIAGNOSIS, PROGNOSIS AND TREATMENT

Diagnosis.—Diagnosis is made by finding the characteristic, ivory-colored proglottides or infrequently clusters of ova in the feces.

Prognosis.—Favorable.

Treatment.—Oleoresin of aspidium (Section **VII**, XIV, 29).

PREVENTION

Epidemiology.—The parasite is present in a high percentage of dogs; at least 50 per cent in the United States of America. Over 90 cases of human infection, mostly European, have been reported,[5] but such cases are extremely rare in the United States of America. Most infections occur in children under eight years of age and about one-third of the cases are found in infants under six months.[6] Transmission results from the accidental swallowing of infected fleas or lice from dogs and cats, either through contamination of food or by close association with household pets.

Prophylaxis.—Small children should not be allowed to fondle dogs or cats infested with fleas or lice. Dogs and cats that are household pets should be given anthelmintic treatment.

FAMILY *HYMENOLEPIDIDÆ* RAILLIET AND HENRY, 1909

The HYMENOLEPIDIDÆ are small tapeworms of birds and mammals. The scolex may be armed or unarmed and the neck is short. The proglottides, broader than long, ordinarily have a single set of reproductive organs, a unilateral marginal genital pore, a sac-like uterus, and from one to four testes. The ova have thin, transparent shells. Most species require an insect as intermediate host, but some complete their entire life cycle

---

[4] Chen, H. T., 1934.   [6] Blanchard, R., 1914.
[5] Bearup, A. J. and Morgan, E. L., 1939.

in a single vertebrate. The species found in man are *Hymenolepis nana, H. diminuta* and *Drepanidotænia lanceolata.*

Hymenolepis nana (v. SIEBOLD, 1852) BLANCHARD, 1891

Synonyms.—*Tænia murina* Dujardin, 1845 (*nec* Gmelin, 1790); *Tænia nana* v. Siebold, 1852; *Tænia ægyptiaca* Bilharz, 1852; *Hymenolepis murina,* Blanchard, 1891; *Hymenolepis fraterna,* Stiles, 1906.

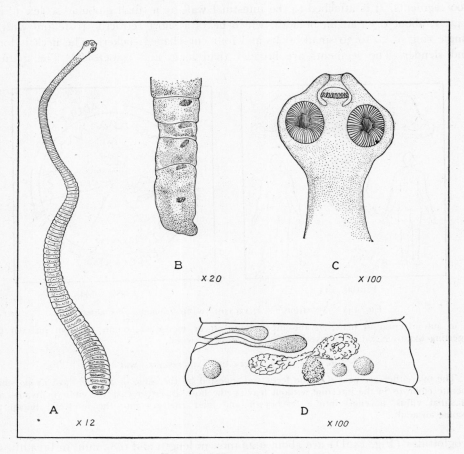

FIG. 142.—*Hymenolepis nana*

A, adult worm; *B,* posterior end of worm with sterile proglottis (third from top); *C,* scolex; *D,* mature proglottis showing reproductive organs (*A* redrawn from Leuckart, 1863; *B* redrawn from Miura and Yamazaki, 1897; *C* redrawn from Blanchard, 1886; *D* redrawn from Leuckart, 1886).

Disease.—Dwarf tapeworm infection.

History.—*Hymenolepis nana* was first described in rats and mice by Dujardin in 1845. It was discovered by Bilharz in an Egyptian boy in 1851 and named *Tænia nana* by von Siebold.

Geographical Distribution.—Cosmopolitan. The dwarf tapeworm is the most common tapeworm of man in the Southern United States. It is more common in warm than in cold climates.

BIOLOGICAL CHARACTERISTICS

Morphology.—The adult worm (Fig. 142A), from 5 to 45 mm. in length (average about 20 mm.) and from 0.5 to 0.9 mm. in breadth, may have as many as 200 segments. It is attached to the intestinal wall by a small globular scolex (Fig. 142C), about 0.3 mm. in breadth, which bears a short retractile rostellum with a single ring of 20 to 30 small hooks and four cup-shaped suckers. The neck is long and slender. The segments are broader than long, and trapezoidal. The mature

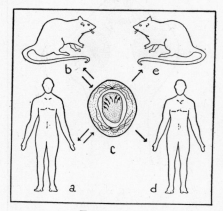

FIGURE 143

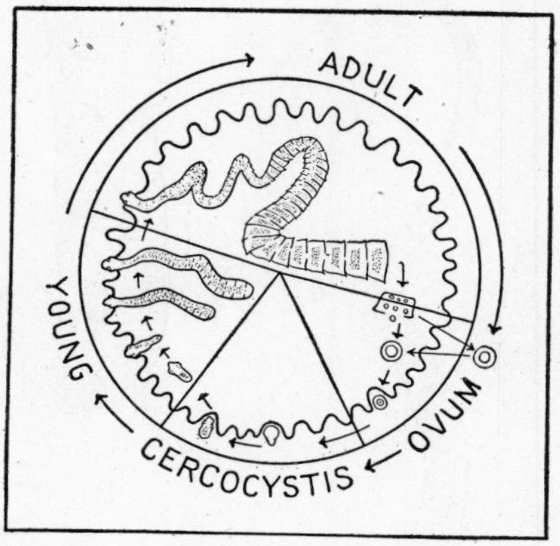

FIGURE 144

FIG. 143.—METHODS OF INFECTION WITH *Hymenolepis nana*

a, autoinfection in man; *b,* autoinfection in rat or mouse; *c,* ovum; *d,* man infected by ingesting ovum; *e,* rat or mouse infected by ingesting ovum.

FIG. 144.—LIFE CYCLE OF *Hymenolepis nana*

The ova either are passed in the feces and ingested by the same or another host or possibly liberate embryos in the intestine without leaving the host. In either case the embryo invades an intestinal villus, develops into a cercocystis and later emerges into the intestinal lumen to become an adult.

proglottides (Fig. 142D) are about 0.22 mm. in length and 0.85 mm. in breadth. A single genital pore is situated laterally toward the anterior border on the left side of each segment. Each proglottis contains three dorsally located testes, vasa efferentia, vas deferens, cirral pouch, ovary, Mehlis' gland, uterus, and a vagina with an enlarged seminal receptacle. After maturity all the organs except the cirral pouch, seminal receptacle and uterus disappear, so that in the gravid proglottis the sacculate uterus becomes a mere egg sac, holding from 80 to 180 ova.

The oval or globular ova (Fig. 145A) are enclosed in two membranes, the inner having two polar thickenings from each of which arise 4 to 8 slender filaments. The space between the two membranes is filled with transparent semisolid material. There is considerable variation in the size of the ovum as reported by different investigators; the outer envelope varies in length from 30 to 60 μ and the enclosed hexacanth embryo, with three pairs of lancet-shaped hooklets, from 16 to 34 μ. The average size is about 47 by 37 μ.

Physiology.—The morphologically indistinguishable murine species, *H. fraterna,* in rats has a short egg-laying period of 1 to 11 days and a short life; the worms begin to disappear rapidly 13 days after maturity.

LIFE CYCLE

The dwarf tapeworm is a common parasite of man, mice and rats. No intermediate host is required for its life cycle (Figs. 143 and 144). The gravid proglottides often rupture within the intestine setting free the ova, which are immediately

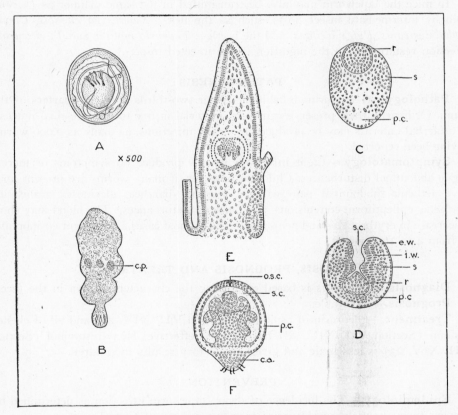

FIG. 145.—LARVAL FORMS OF *Hymenolepis nana*

A, ovum; *B,* hexacanth embryo without cavity; *C,* longitudinal section of embryo after appearance of primordia of rostellum and suckers; *D,* longitudinal section of embryo after invagination of anterior portion; *E,* longitudinal section of intestinal villus containing cercocystis; *F,* longitudinal section of cercocystis with protracted rostellum.

c.a., caudal appendage; *c.p.,* calcareous corpuscles; *e.w.,* external wall; *i.w.,* internal wall; *o.s.c.,* orifice of secondary cavity; *p.c.,* primary cavity; *r,* rostellum; *s,* sucker; *s.c.,* secondary cavity (*A* redrawn from Stiles, 1903; *B* to *F* redrawn from Grassi and Rovelli, 1892).

infective when passed in the feces. When ingested by a new host the oncosphere is liberated in the small intestine and penetrates a villus where it loses its hooklets and in about 90 hours becomes a cercocystis (Figs. 145E and F). The larva then breaks out of the villus into the intestinal lumen, where it attaches itself to the epithelium and becomes a strobilate worm in from 10 to 12 days. It requires about 30 days from the time of infection before ova appear in the feces of experimental rats.

It is possible that hyperinfection may take place in the host. In this event the ovum, liberated in the small intestine, instead of passing from the host in the feces may penetrate a villus, form a cercocystis and repeat its cyclic development. Internal hyperinfection has not been demonstrated in normal mice but has been observed in mice weakened by bacterial disease.[7]

In mice the tapeworm may also be transmitted in the same manner as *D. caninum* by intermediate insect hosts, such as the fleas: *Xenopsylla cheopis, Ctenocephalides canis, Pulex irritans,* and the beetles: *Tenebrio molitor* and *T. obscurus;* infection resulting from the ingestion of the infected insects.[8]

PATHOGENESIS

Pathology.—The worms inhabit the upper two-thirds or three-quarters of the ileum. Ordinarily their presence causes no material injury to the intestinal mucosa. A catarrhal enteritis may be produced by heavy infections, as many as 2,000 worms having been reported.

Symptomatology.—Light infections usually produce no symptoms or merely vague abdominal disturbances. Children, however, if many worms are present, may have asthenia, abdominal pain with or without diarrhea, dizziness, strabismus, headache, epileptiform convulsions, and nervous disturbances.[9] The blood may show a decrease in erythrocytes and hemoglobin and in most cases a consistent eosinophilia of from 4 to 16 per cent.

DIAGNOSIS, PROGNOSIS AND TREATMENT

Diagnosis.—Diagnosis is based on finding the characteristic ova in the feces.
Prognosis.—Favorable.
Treatment.—Oleoresin of aspidium (Section **VII**, XIV, 29) and oil of chenopodium (Section **VII**, XIV, 28) have proved effective. Hexylresorcinol (Section **VII,** XIV, 23) is less toxic and gives satisfactory results in children.

PREVENTION

Epidemiology.—The incidence of dwarf tapeworm infection as determined by surveys throughout the world varies from 0.2 per cent (Australia) to 3.7 per cent (India), although in certain localities it is as high as 28 per cent. In the United States of America the extensive surveys of Leathers *et al* have disclosed an incidence of 0.3 per cent (Florida), 0.4 per cent (Mississippi), 0.6 per cent (South Carolina), 0.7 per cent (North Carolina), 2.7 per cent (Kentucky), and 2.9 per

---

[7] Hunninen, A. V., 1936.
[8] Bacigalupo, J., 1931.
[9] Ransom, B. H., 1904.

cent (Tennessee). The infection is largely confined to children under 15 years of age. The highest incidence is found in the 4- to 9-year group.[10] The incidence rises after the age of 2 years, declines after 8 years, and is slightly higher in boys than in girls.[11] The incidence in Negroes in the United States of America is about one-half that in the white race.[12]

There has been much confusion regarding the relationship of *Hymenolepis* of rodents and man. The murine species, *H. fraterna,* is morphologically identical with *H. nana*. Mice and rats have been experimentally infected with *H. nana* [13] and children have been infected with the murine species.[14] Although these species are interchangeable, certain differences in the facility of development in the reciprocal host have been noted. Similar differences have been observed in rodent strains, one from wild rats being equally infective for laboratory rats and mice and another from white mice being more infective for mice.[15] *H. fraterna* also has a greater tendency than *H. nana* to use insects as intermediate hosts.[16] Apparently the two are not distinct species but physiological strains of a presumptive murine species that has become adapted to man and rodents.

The infection is transmitted directly from hand to mouth and indirectly by contamination of food and water. The unhygienic habits of. children explain the prevalence of the parasite in the younger age groups. Since the ova have feeble resistance and cannot long survive in the soil, transmission is dependent upon immediate contact. Hence, it is not surprising that the geographical incidence of infection does not correspond to that of *Ascaris* or *Trichuris*. Epidemiological evidence indicates that the incidence is highest in insanitary districts where the houses are overrun with rats.[17] The presence of closely allied or identical strains in mice and rats may provide greater opportunity for the infection of children playing in contaminated dirt, although the chief source apparently is man.

Prophylaxis.—Since the life cycle of the parasite involves but a single host and transmission is direct, prevention is difficult. In crowded living quarters the infection is most frequently transmitted by direct contact from one individual to another. Hence, special attention should be paid to personal hygiene. Proper nutrition and a hygienic home environment reduce the chances of infection. Children should be treated to prevent autoinfection and the infection of others. Food should be safeguarded from rats and mice and these pests destroyed.

Hymenolepis diminuta (RUDOLPHI, 1819) BLANCHARD, 1891

Synonyms.—*Tænia diminuta* Rudolphi, 1819; *Tænia leptocephala* Creplin, 1825; *Tænia flavopunctata* Weinland, 1858; *Tænia minima* Grassi, 1886.

---

[10] Shneerson, A. A., 1930; Keller, A. E., Leathers, W. S. and Bishop, E. L., 1932.

[11] Shneerson, A. A., 1930; Keller, A. E. and Leathers, W. S., 1934.

[12] Keller, A. E. and Leathers, W. S., 1934; Otto, G. F., 1936; Keller, A. E., Leathers, W. S. and Knox, J. C., 1938; Keller, A. E., Leathers, W. S. and McPhaul, W. A., 1939.

[13] Roman, E., 1939; Tsuchiya, H. and Rohlfing, E. H., 1932; Woodland, W. N. F., 1924.

[14] Kiribayashi, S., 1933.

[15] Shorb, D. A., 1933.

[16] Bacigalupo, J., 1929.

[17] Chandler, A. C., 1927.

History.—*Hymenolepis diminuta,* a common tapeworm of the mouse and rat, is also found in man. It was discovered by Olfers in 1766 in rats in Rio de Janeiro and was described in man by Weinland in 1858.

Geographical Distribution.—Cosmopolitan.

Morphology.—The adult worm (Fig. 146A), comprising 800 to 1,000 proglottides is from 10 to 60 cm. in length and has a maximal width of 4 mm. The small club-shaped

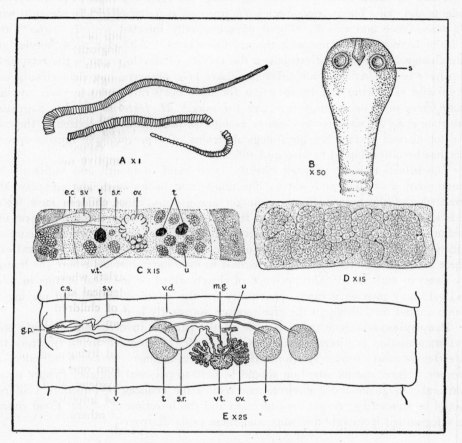

FIG. 146.—*Hymenolepis diminuta*

A, adult worm; *B,* scolex; *C,* proglottis with uterus developed and containing ova; *D,* proglottis containing fully developed ova; *E,* male and female reproductive organs.

c.s., cirral sac; *e.c.,* excretory canal; *g.p.,* genital pore; *m.g.,* Mehlis' gland; *ov.,* ovary; *s,* sucker; *s.r.,* seminal receptacle; *s.v.,* seminal vesicle; *t,* testis; *u,* uterus; *v,* vagina; *v.d.,* vas deferens; *vt.,* vitellarium (*A* redrawn with modifications from Weinland, 1861; *B* and *E* redrawn from Zschokke, 1889; *C* and *D* redrawn from Grassi, 1881).

scolex (Fig. 146B), 0.2 to 0.4 mm. in breadth, has a rudimentary apical unarmed rostellum and four small suckers. The mature proglottides (Fig. 146E), like those of *T. nana,* are broader than long with a similar quota and arrangement of reproductive organs. The slightly oval ovum (Fig. 147A) has a thick yellowish outer and colorless inner membrane, with a granular intermediate layer. It differs from the ovum of *H. nana* in the absence of filaments at the pointed poles of the inner membrane. The average length of the ovum is 72 μ (58 to 86 μ) and the size of the oncosphere 35 by 28 μ.

Life Cycle.—The natural definitive hosts are rats, mice, and other murine species. Man and dogs are accidental hosts. In order to complete its development, *H. diminuta* requires an intermediate host. Various species of larval and. adult insects, including 2 myriapods (*Fontaria virginiensis* and *Julus* sp.), 6 fleas (Chapter XLV) and 3 cockroaches, 11 beetles and 6 lepidopterans (Chapter XXXVIII), may act as intermediate hosts. The principal natural hosts are the rat fleas, *Ceratophyllus fasciatus* and *Xenopsylla cheopis,* which are infected in the larval stage, and the meal worm beetle, *Tenebrio molitor.*[18]

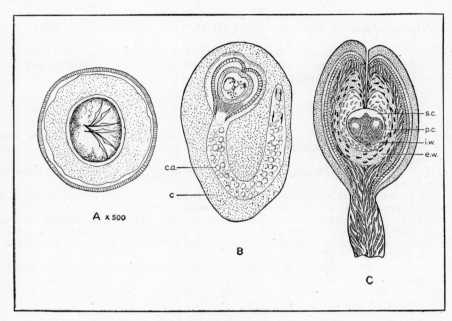

Fig. 147.—Larval Forms of *Hymenolepis diminuta*

A, ovum; *B,* encysted cercocystis; *C,* longitudinal section of cercocystis.

c, cyst; *c.a.,* caudal appendage; *e.w.,* external wall; *i.w.,* internal wall; *p.c.,* primary cavity; *s.c.,* secondary cavity (*A* redrawn from Bizzozero, 1889; *B* and *C* redrawn from Grassi and Rovelli, 1892).

The embryo hatches in the gut of these insects and by aid of its hooklets penetrates through the intestinal wall into the body cavity, where it undergoes metamorphosis into a cercocystis (Fig. 147B and C.)[19] When ingested by a rat, the liberated cercocystis attaches itself to the intestinal wall and becomes a mature adult in about 18 to 20 days.[20]

Pathogenesis.—Some 200 cases of infection have been reported in man, the majority in children under three years of age. *H. diminuta* produces the same pathology and symptomatology as *H. nana.*

Diagnosis.—Diagnosis is made by finding the ova or proglottides in the feces.

Prognosis.—Favorable.

Treatment.—Oleoresin of aspidium (Section **VII**, XIV, 29); any anthelmintic drug or even a strong cathartic readily removes the worms.

---

[18] Joyeux, C., 1920.
[19] Grassi, G. B. and Rovelli, G., 1892.   193
[20] Bacigalupo, J., 1926; Chandler, A. C.,

Epidemiology.—The incidence of human infection in the United States of America as determined by surveys, ranges from 0.03 to·0.07 per cent. An incidence of 10 to 15 per cent in rats and 2 per cent in mice has been reported in Australia.[5]

The ova are resistant to strong chemicals and urine, survive drying seven days, and remain viable for about a month in water.[21] They die immediately in water at 60° C. and within a few minutes at 50° C. Man is accidentally infected by food containing the intermediate hosts. Infected rat fleas may be transferred to the mouths of children by dirty hands.

Prophylaxis.—Cereals should be protected from meal-infesting insects, rats and mice. If necessary, measures for the control of rats and mice in homes should be instituted.

Drepanidotænia lanceolata (BLOCH, 1782) RAILLIET, 1892

Drepanidotænia lanceolata is a natural parasite of anseriform birds. The intermediate host is *Cyclops* or *Diaptomus*. Infection in man is purely accidental; a single infection in a German boy has been reported by Zschokke in 1902.

REFERENCES

BEARUP, A. J. and MORGAN, E. L.　The Occurrence of *Hymenolepis diminuta* (Rudolphi, 1819) and *Dipylidium caninum* (Linnæus, 1758) as Parasites of Man in Australia, M. J. Australia, 1939, 1 :104.

CHEN, H. T.　Reactions of *Ctenocephalides felis* to *Dipylidium caninum,* Ztschr. f. Parasitenk., 1934, 6 :603.

GRASSI, G. B. and ROVELLI, G.　Ricerche Embriologiche sui Cestodi, Atti Accad. Gioenia di sc. nat. in Catania (1891-92), An. 68, 4. s., v. 4, 2. mem. pp. 108.

RANSOM, B. H.　An Account of the Tapeworms of the Genus *Hymenolepis* Parasitic in Man, U. S. Pub. Health and Marine Hosp. Ser., Hyg. Lab. Bull. No. 18, 1904, pp. 138.

SHORB, D. A.　Host-parasite Relations of *Hymenolepis fraterna* in the Rat and the Mouse, Am. J. Hyg., 1933, 18 :74.

TSUCHIYA, H. and ROHLFING, E. H.　*Hymenolepis nana.* Report of Additional Cases and Experimental Transmission from Man to Rats, Am. J. Dis. Child., 1932, 43 :865.

VENARD, C. E.　Morphology, Bionomics and Taxonomy of the Cestode *Dipylidium caninum,* Ann. New York Acad. Sc., 1938, 37 :273.

[21] Narihara, N., 1934.

Chapter XXVII

THE SUPERFAMILY TÆNIOIDEA. THE GENERA TÆNIA AND MULTICEPS

FAMILY *TÆNIIDÆ* LUDWIG, 1886

Three species of the family TÆNIIDÆ are important parasites of man: the pork tapeworm, *Tænia solium;* the beef tapeworm, *T. saginata,* and the hydatid tapeworm, *Echinococcus granulosus.* The adult tænial worms are parasites of carnivorous or omnivorous animals and the larvæ of herbivorous or omnivorous animals. The scolex has four suckers and a well-devolped rostellum, unarmed or armed with a double row of alternate large and small hooks. The mature proglottides contain a single set of male and female reproductive organs and have irregularly-alternate lateral genital pores. The female genitalia, occupying the distal portion of the proglottis, comprise a median vitellarium, Mehlis' gland, a bilobed ovary, a vagina, and a median uterus, which when fully developed has characteristic lateral branches. The male genitalia, in the proximal portion of the proglottis, comprise numerous testes, vasa efferentia, vas deferens and cirral sac. The ova have a thick radially-striated inner case, the embryophore, and a thin deciduous outer shell. The adult worms are chiefly parasites of mammals and birds.

Tænia solium LINNÆUS, 1758

Synonyms.—*Tænia cucurbitina* Pallas, 1766; *Tænia pellucida* Goeze, 1782; *Tænia vulgaris* Werner, 1782; *Tænia dentata* Batsch, 1786; *Halysis solium* (Linnæus, 1758) Zeder, 1803; *Tænia armata humana* Brera, 1808.

Disease.—Tæniasis; pork tapeworm infection.

History.—The pork tapeworm has been known since ancient times. The larval stage in hogs, *Cysticercus cellulosæ,* was long recognized before its relation to the adult worm was ascertained. Van Beneden, Haubner and Leuckart were able to produce cysticerci in hogs by feeding gravid proglottides of *Tænia solium.* Küchenmeister in 1855-56 first established the relation between the larval worms in hogs and the adult worms in man by feeding cysticerci from hogs to a condemned criminal and four months later obtaining the adult worms. Cysticercal infection in man was first observed by Gessner in 1558.

Geographical Distribution.—Cosmopolitan. Human infection is especially prevalent in countries where raw or insufficiently cooked pork is consumed and its incidence depends upon gastronomic customs and sanitation. The adult parasite is extremely rare in man in the United States of America, although cysticerci are found occasionally in hogs. Human cysticercosis is probably more prevalent and serious than is ordinarily believed, judging from reports on British soldiers in India and Egypt.[1]

---

[1] MacArthur, W. P., 1933.

BIOLOGICAL CHARACTERISTICS

Morphology.—The adult worm is found in the upper part of the small intestine. It varies in length from 2 to 4 meters, occasionally reaching 8 meters, and when fully developed contains from 800 to 1,000 segments. The globular scolex (Fig. 126D), about 1 mm. in diameter, is equipped with four cup-shaped suckers, 0.5 mm. in diameter, and a low cushion-like rostellum with a double crown of from 25 to 30 hooks. The slender neck, about one-half the diameter of the scolex, is from 5 to 10 mm. in length. The immature segments are small and broader than long, the mature proglottides, about one meter from the scolex, are approximately square and the terminal gravid segments, about 12 mm. in length, are nearly twice as long as broad. At times abnormal fenestrated proglottides and scolices with a variable number and arrangement of hooks and suckers are encountered.

Each proglottis contains a single set of reproductive organs (Figs. 127 and 129A). The submedian, unilateral genital pores are irregularly alternate on consecutive segments. *Tænia solium* may be identified by the form of the gravid uterus with its 7 to 12 thick lateral branches (Fig. 133). Numerous small follicular testes, 150 to 200, are distributed throughout the dorsal portion of the mature proglottis. They communicate through minute vasa efferentia with the convoluted vas deferens, which enlarges at its distal end to form the cirral organ. The ovary consists of one small and two large lobes. The follicular vitellaria are concentrated in an elliptical band at the posterior margin of the proglottis. The uterus at first is a vertical club-shaped sac in the middle of the proglottis, but as it becomes distended with ova it forms lateral branches. The gravid proglottis contains from 30 to 50 thousand ova.[2] The original, thin, delicate shell membrane, which may have one or two filamentous extensions, is rarely retained after the ova leave the proglottis. The ova (Figs. 4 and 133), when liberated, consist of a fully-developed embryonic oncosphere with six hooklets surrounded by a light brown spherical or subspherical embryophore, 30 to 40 μ in diameter. The ova of *Tænia solium* and *T. saginata* for practical purposes are indistinguishable, 80 per cent of each falling within the range of 32 to 35 μ.[3] The embryophore is a thick-walled structure perforated with minute canals that give it a striated appearance.

Physiology.—The adult worm may live for years in the host; infections of 25 years have been recorded. Nourishment is obtained from the intestinal contents. The worm is hermaphroditic and fertilization takes place in the same proglottis or at times between neighboring proglottides. The terminal gravid proglottides separate from time to time from the strobila in groups of five or six. They are capable of independent movement and may even migrate through the anus, though usually they are passed in the feces. The ova are liberated by the rupture of the proglottis before or after leaving the host.

LIFE CYCLE

The life cycle involves an intermediate host. The ova are ingested in food or water by a susceptible intermediate host, usually the hog. The freed oncosphere

---

[2] Dixon, H. B. F. and Smithers, D. W., 1935.   [3] Maplestone, P. A., 1937.

penetrates the intestinal wall and develops into a cysticercus in the tissues. When infected pork is eaten by man the larva develops into the adult worm in the intestine (Fig. 148).

Man is the only natural definitive host, although the worm may undergo incomplete development in the dog.[4] The usual intermediate hosts are hogs and wild boars. Sheep, deer, dogs and cats are less frequently infected, and occasionally man and other primates.

The liberated ova, scattered in the feces, are usually ingested in small numbers by the intermediate host, but occasionally an overwhelming infection may result from eating an unbroken or partially disintegrated proglottis. In the intestine the

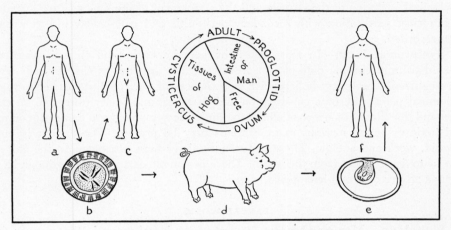

FIG. 148.—LIFE CYCLE OF *Tænia solium*

a, man infected with adult worm; *b*, ovum passed in feces; *c*, man infected with cysticercus; *d*, hog infected with cysticercus; *e*, cysticercus in pork; *f*, man infected by eating pork containing cysticercus.

oncosphere, freed from the embryophore, penetrates the intestinal wall with its hooklets and enters the portal vessels and lymphatics. It is carried by the blood stream to the tissues where the hooklets are lost and the larva develops into a cysticercus. Liquefaction of the central cells produces a central cavity filled with fluid and a small invagination, with a scolex equipped with hooks and suckers at the bottom, is formed in the wall (Fig. 132). Growth is fairly rapid, in three weeks the developing larva is from 1 to 6 mm. in length and the scolex is visible, and in nine to ten weeks it is a fully-developed infective bladder worm known as *Cysticercus cellulosæ* (Fig. 131D). The mature cysticercus is an ellipsoidal, translucent cyst, 10 by 5 mm., with an opaque invaginated scolex equipped with suckers and hooks.

In the hog cysticerci may invade all tissues but they are most frequently found in the striated muscles. The muscles of the tongue, neck and shoulder are most often infested; then in order of frequency the intercostal, abdominal, psoas, femoral, and

[4] Schwartz, B., 1928.

posterior vertebral muscles. In addition the liver, heart, lungs, brain and eye may be parasitized. When infected "measly pork" is eaten by man the cysticercus is dissolved by the action of the gastric juices. The worm passes into the upper part of the small intestine, attaches itself to the intestinal wall by its evaginated scolex and develops into an adult worm.

PATHOGENESIS

ADULT WORM

Pathology.—The adult parasite, usually a single specimen, causes no definite changes in the intestinal mucosa other than slight local inflammation from the mechanical irritation of the strobila and the attachment of the scolex. Rare instances of intestinal perforation with secondary peritonitis and gallbladder infection have been recorded.

Symptomatology.—In most cases the parasite evokes no clinical symptoms other than mild chronic digestive disorders and the presence of the worm is often unrecognized. There may be irregular disturbances of the appetite, headache, vague abdominal pains, alternate constipation and diarrhea, and faulty nutrition. In children and debilitated or nervous adults the digestive symptoms are more pronounced and toxic or reflex nervous manifestations may be present. The patient is often languid, weak and anemic. These disturbances have been attributed to the absorption of toxic products from the worm. There is sometimes a variable eosinophilia as high as 28 per cent and leukopenia.

LARVAL WORM

Pathology.—Man may become the host of the larval worm in three ways: (1) the ingestion of food or water contaminated by infected feces or by flies. (2) oral transmission by the unclean hands of carriers of the adult worm, and (3) autoinfection by the regurgitation of ova into the stomach by reverse peristalsis. Cysticerci may develop in any tissue or organ of the body and invasion is usually multiple, the optimal sites being above the level of the diaphragm. The invaded organs in order of frequency are the subcutaneous tissues, brain, eye, muscles, heart, liver, lung and peritoneum.

The size of the cysticercus depends upon its age and location in the host; in resistant tissues the cysts are small. In the subcutaneous tissues they appear as smooth, firm, oval, palpable nodules the size of a pea or larger. They produce an exudative tissue-reaction with lymphocytic infiltration that results in the production of a fibrous capsule. In the muscles there is degeneration and atrophy in the immediate vicinity of the parasite. On the death of the larva the nodules become more noticeable by an increase in fluid and a more pronounced tissue-reaction. Calcification ultimately results.

In the brain cysticerci are found in the meninges, cortex, cerebral substance and ventricles. They produce cerebral edema but there is a relative tolerance while the parasite is alive. The dead parasite acts as a foreign-body irritant and causes marked tissue-reaction and increased pressure by its toxic action. Encapsulation results from the proliferation of neuroglia tissue (Fig. 149) and the sclerosed neuroglia undergoes degenerative changes and necrosis.[5] Calcification is slower than in the muscles. Cysticerci are more frequent in the leptomeninges than in the parenchyma of the brain. In the pia-arachnoid they are more often at the base of the brain and in the sylvian fissures than over the convexity.[6] They may produce a purulent meningitis.[7] Meningo-encephalitis, encephalomalacia and endarteritis of the branches of the middle meningeal artery have been reported.[8]

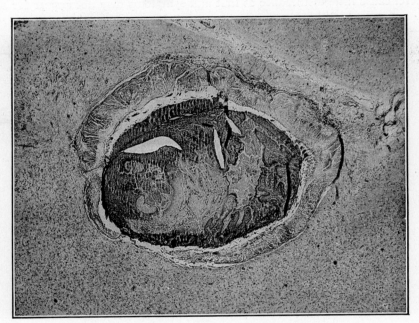

FIG. 149.—CYSTICERCUS OF *Tænia solium* IN HUMAN BRAIN

(From Hegner, Root, Augustine and Huff, *Parasitology*, 1938, D. Appleton-Century Company).

In the eye the cysticercus, usually single and 6 to 14 mm. in size, is subretinal or in the vitreous humor, where it appears as a free or attached sausage-shaped light gray body. The retina may be detached, the vitreous fluid slightly cloudy, the parasite surrounded by an inflammatory exudate, and the iris inflamed. Death of the parasite leads to iridocyclitis with pupillary occlusion and chemosis of the conjunctiva.

Symptomatology.—During the stage of invasion there may be no prodromal symptoms or only slight muscular pain and a mild fever. Unless the infection is heavy there are no symptoms since the cysticerci are well tolerated in the muscles and subcutaneous tissues. Muscular pain, particularly in the back of the neck,

[5] Dixon, H. B. F. and Smithers, D. W., 1934.

[6] Hare, C. C., 1938.

[7] Bucy, P. C. and Huff, C. G., 1938.

[8] Dolgopoz, V. B. and Neustaedter, M., 1935.

general muscular weakness, fatigue, cramps, loss of weight and nervousness may be present.[9] Extensive muscular involvement has been observed in an athlete with no apparent effect upon his athletic prowess (Fig. 150).[10]

Cerebral cysticercosis has been frequently observed in soldiers who have served in India or in countries where sanitation is lax. It is usually associated with an unrecognized general cysticercosis, but occasionally cysterci are found only in the brain. Invasion of the brain and nervous system produce grave symptoms. The cysticerci cause little disturbance at first and symptoms may not appear for several

FIG. 150.—ROENTGENOGRAM OF THIGH OF ATHLETE SHOWING NUMEROUS CYSTICERCI OF
Tænia solium

(After Evans, 1939).

years until the death of the parasite evokes toxic inflammatory reactions.[5] The symptoms are often vague and may simulate those of brain tumor, basal meningitis, general paralysis and hysteria. They may take the form of severe headaches, convulsions, epileptiform attacks, contractures and motor and sensory paralyses.[9] Recurrent epileptic attacks of the Jacksonian type occurring at irregular intervals are the most prominent symptoms, and range from petit mal with or without loss of consciousness to various stages of major epilepsy with aura.[11] Other cerebral manifestations are symptoms of brain tumor (vomiting, vertigo, muscular convulsions, hemiparesis, optic neuritis, and aphasia), encephalitis, disseminated sclerosis, psychical disturbances and mental deterioration. Involvement of the spinal cord may produce hyperesthesia and altered reflexes.

[9] Africa, C. M. and Cruz, J. S. S., 1937.   [11] Grieg, E. D. W., 1937.
[10] Evans, R. R., 1939.

Tænia solium is the most common larval tapeworm to invade the eye, which it reaches by chance through the retinal or uveal vessels. The patient may experience infra-orbital pain, flashes of light, grotesque shapes in the field of vision, and blurring and loss of vision. The cysticercus may be observed moving in the vitreous fluid. Involvement of the cardiac muscle may cause tachycardia, dyspnea, syncope and abnormal heart sounds. An eosinophilia of 5 to 12 per cent, but occasionally considerably higher, is a fairly constant but not invariable finding in cysticercosis.

IMMUNITY

There is no evidence of natural or acquired immunity against the adult worm. Investigations with the tænial worms of lower animals indicate that some degree of resistance is produced against cysticercal infection (Chapter XXIV), although the presence of various stages of cysticercal development in the same patient suggests that successive infections may occur. Precipitins have been demonstrated in a high percentage of infected hogs.[12] Precipitative, alexin-fixative and intracutaneous reactions with echinococcal and cysticercal antigens, representing a group reaction for tænial worms, have been observed in patients with cerebral cysticercosis.

DIAGNOSIS, PROGNOSIS AND TREATMENT

Diagnosis.—Specific diagnosis of intestinal infection depends upon finding the proglottides in the feces, since the ova cannot be readily differentiated from those of *T. saginata*. The gravid proglottis is distinguished by the smaller number, 7 to 12, of lateral branches of the uterus from that of *T. saginata* with 15 to 30 branches (Table 31 and Fig. 133). The scolex, if obtained, is identified by its hooks.

The diagnosis of cysticercosis is made by a biopsy of a palpable subcutaneous nodule and by the roentgen-ray; a history of intestinal tæniasis, the presence of multiple nodules and a moderate eosinophilia are suggestive. In cysticercosis of the brain and internal viscera, diagnosis is made by clinical symptoms and later by the roentgen-ray. If subcutaneous or muscular nodules are present with symptoms of cerebral involvement, the diagnosis of cysticercus of the brain is fairly definite, but it is necessary to await beginning calcification to obtain roentgenological evidence. In many cases final diagnosis is made only at autopsy. Cysticercosis must be differentiated from syphilis,[13] hereditary epilepsy,[14] and brain tumor. Serological and intracutaneous tests are of little diagnostic value, although occasionally they have proved useful in the recognition of cerebral cysticercosis.

Prognosis.—Prognosis for intestinal tæniasis is good. The prognosis for cysticercal infection depends upon the location of the larvæ. If the infection is limited to the muscles and subcutaneous tissues, the prognosis is favorable even with heavy infections, as the nodules in time become calcified; but if the cysticerci are present in the brain, heart or important viscera the prognosis is grave.

Treatment.—For the adult worm, treatment is similar to that for *Diphyllobothrium latum,* oleoresin of aspidium (Section **VII**, XIII, 29) being the drug of choice. Excision is sometimes used for accessible cysticerci, but their removal is

---

[12] Trawinski, A., 1936.

[13] Castellani, A. and Acanfora, A., 1938.

[14] MacArthur, W. P., 1934.

unnecessary unless they are dangerous to the patient. In involvement of the brain operative procedures are usually ineffective because of late diagnosis and multiple infections. Antimony compounds and arsenicals are ineffective against the larval parasite. Sedatives are useful in epileptiform conditions. The administration of calcium, parathormone and calcium, or vitamin D to accelerate calcification has been suggested, but is unsatisfactory and perhaps dangerous.

PREVENTION

Epidemiology.—The incidence of *T. solium* infection, usually a fraction of I per cent, varies throughout the world. In Armenia an incidence of 0.46 per cent was found in 3,000 persons.[15] Reports from various parts of Russia range from 0.2 to 1.5 per cent. In South Africa the incidence in hogs is about 25 per cent, about three-quarters of the animals showing heavy infection.[16] In some countries, however, cysticercosis in hogs is extensive but human infection is relatively low. Cysticercosis is more common than is generally believed, since many cases escape detection. It is a disease of adult life and is more prevalent in males than in females. It is more frequent among the poorer classes and is associated with insanitary surroundings and poor personal hygiene.[2] Its occurrence in persons harboring the adult worm indicates the danger of autoinfection. Tæniasis is acquired by eating raw or insufficiently cooked pork. A temperature of from 49° to 53° C. is required to kill the larval parasite and the methods of cooking that permit heat penetration give the greatest margin of safety. Pickling and smoking pork are usually not sufficient to destroy the cysticerci, but freezing of pork at — 10° kills the encysted larva in four days.[16]

Prophylaxis.—The control of *T. solium* infection comprises: (1) treatment of infected persons, (2) inspection of pork, and (3) thorough cooking of pork. The prompt treatment of infected persons not only reduces the sources of infection, but also eliminates the danger of autoinfection with cysticerci. Although governmental inspection of pork has lowered the incidence of human infection in countries where raw or insufficiently cooked pork is eaten, it does not include all pork. It is impossible to guarantee freedom from infection by any system of inspection, since to exclude porcine cysticercosis it would be necessary to cut the flesh into thin slices.[17] Refrigeration at — 10° C. for four or more days is a satisfactory procedure. Thorough cooking, however, is considered the most effective means of prophylaxis.

Tænia saginata GOEZE, 1782

Synonyms.—*Tænia solium* Linnæus, 1767, *pro parte; Tænia cucurbitina Pallas,* 1781, *pro parte; Tænia inermis* Brera, 1802; *Tænia dentata* Nicolai, 1830; *Tænia lata* Pruner, 1847; *Tænia mediocanellata* Küchenmeister, 1852; *Tænia zittavensis* Küchenmeister, 1852; *Tæniarhynchus mediocanellata* Weinland, 1858; *Tænia abietina* Weinland, 1858; *Tænia capensis* Moquin-Tandon, 1860; *Tænia tropica* Moquin-Tandon, 1860; *Tænia (Cystotænia) mediocanellata* Leuckart, 1863; *Tænia lophosoma* Cobbold, 1866; *Tænia fenestrata* Huber, 1896; *Tænia hominis* v. Linstow, 1902.

---

[15] Ananian, S. A., 1929.
[16] Viljoen, N. R., 1937.
[17] Morrison, W. K., 1936.

Disease.—Tæniasis; beef tapeworm infection.

History.—The beef tapeworm of man has been known since ancient times, but it was not until 1782 that it was identified as a distinct species by Goeze. Leuckart in 1861 established its relationship to the bladder worms of cattle by feeding gravid proglottides to a calf and obtaining the larval stage, *Cysticercus bovis.* Oliver in 1869, reversing this procedure, infected man with the cysticerci of cattle.

Geographical Distribution.—Cosmopolitan. It is especially prevalent in countries where raw beef is a staple article of diet.

BIOLOGICAL CHARACTERISTICS

Morphology.—The adult worm (Fig. 151), considerably larger than *T. solium* and possessing from 1,000 to 2,000 proglottides, is from 4 to 10 meters in length, but may reach 25 meters. The pyriform scolex (Fig. 126B), 1 to 2 mm. in diameter, has found prominent hemispherical suckers, but no rostellum or hooks. About

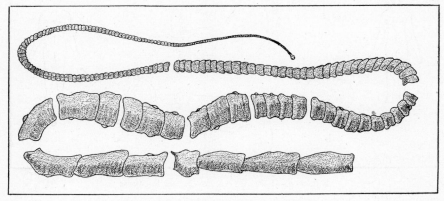

FIG. 151.—ADULT *Tænia saginata*
(Redrawn from Leuckart, 1863).

one-fifth of the scolices have a vestigial rostellum and over one-third are pigmented.[15] The mature proglottides, about 12 mm. broad and somewhat shorter, have irregularly alternate lateral genital pores and contain male and female reproductive organs similar to those of *T. solium.* However, there are twice as many testes, the ovary is bilobed and the vagina is equipped with a sphincter. The gravid proglottides, 16 to 20 mm. long by 5 to 7 mm. broad, are differentiated from those of *T. solium* by the uterus which has from 15 to 30 lateral branches (Fig. 133). Various types of abnormalities are common and these aberrant forms have caused considerable confusion by being identified as new species. The yellow-brown ovum (Fig. 130C), though usually considered slightly more oval, cannot be distinguished from that of *T. solium.* The radially-striated embryophore, 30 to 40 μ by 20 to 30 μ, surrounds a hexacanth embryo. In the uterus it is covered by an outer membrane with two delicate polar filaments, which is lost soon after the ovum leaves the proglottis. The gravid proglottis contains about 124,000 ova and the annual output of a worm has been estimated at 594,000,000 ova.[18]

Physiology.—Its physiology is similar to that of *T. solium*. The proglottides, usually detached singly, are capable of independent motion and may force their way through the anal sphincter. When first passed they are quite active and assume various shapes, but when quiescent they resemble pumpkin seeds.

LIFE CYCLE

The life cycle of *Tænia saginata* is similar to that of *T. solium* except that the development of the cysticercus takes place in cattle instead of hogs (Fig. 152). Man is the only definitive host. The cysticerci are found in cattle and have been reported

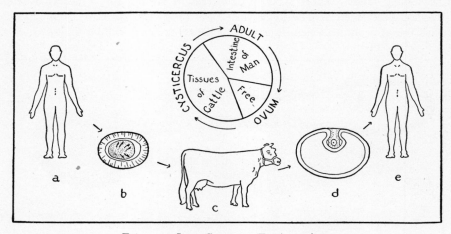

Fig. 152.—Life Cycle of *Tænia saginata*

a, man infected with adult worm; *b*, ovum passed in feces; *c*, cattle infected with cysticercus; *d*, cysticercus in beef; *e*, man infected by eating beef containing cysticercus.

infrequently from other mammals. Calves are more susceptible than older cattle. The cysticerci have been reported in man, but in most instances identification has been unsatisfactory.

The ova, infective when passed in the feces, are ingested by cattle and the oncospheres escape from their embryonal shell in the intestine. Hatching takes place *in vitro* if the ova are exposed to a pepsin-pancreatic sequence or to a lethal solution of sodium hypochlorite containing 0.5 per cent available chlorine, the dead ova hatching as readily as the living.[19] The embryo penetrates through the intestinal wall into the lymphatics or blood vessels and reaches the intramuscular connective tissues, where it develops into a *Cysticercus bovis* about 9 by 5 mm. in size. The hind limbs and hump of cattle are the selective sites,[16] but cysticerci are also found in the heart, diaphragm, tongue and other parts of the body. As a rule the infection is not heavy. Prenatal infection has been reported in calves. When the cysticercus

---

[18] Schapiro, M. M., 1937.   [19] Penfold, W. J., Penfold, H. B. and Phillips, M., 1937.

is ingested by man it develops in the intestine into an adult worm in from eight to ten weeks.

PATHOGENESIS

Pathology.—The adult worm causes a slight irritation of the intestinal mucosa by the mechanical action of the strobila. Usually only a single worm is present, but as many as ten have been reported.[20] Experiments *in vitro* suggest that *T. saginata* may produce a toxic substance with a strong hemolytic action.[21] Pancreatic necrosis from the penetration of the worm into the duct of Wirsung has been reported.[22]

Symptomatology.—The symptoms in 100 infected persons, who were passing segments of the worm in the stools, included epigastric pain, a sinking hungry feeling, vague discomfort with an empty, gnawing sensation, and awareness of the movements of the worm.[23] Over one-third of the patients complained of giddiness especially when hungry, but only 7 per cent experienced an increase in appetite. There was no appreciable loss of weight. Constipation and diarrhea were not significant and marked pruritus ani and irritability were observed in only a few individuals. In 20 of these patients the blood showed a mild anemia in 10 per cent, a relative lymphocytosis in 30 per cent and an eosinophilia of 6 to 13 per cent in 10 per cent. Severe attacks of hypogastric pain and an eosinophilia of 36 to 55 per cent have been observed in an infected woman.[24]

DIAGNOSIS, PROGNOSIS AND TREATMENT

Diagnosis.—Diagnosis is based on the recovery of the gravid proglottides or the ova in the feces. Specific diagnosis depends upon the appearance of the gravid proglottis with 15 to 30 lateral uterine branches (Fig. 133) or infrequently upon the characteristic hookless scolex.

Prognosis.—Prognosis is good, although it is difficult to eradicate the scolex.

Treatment.—Treatment is similar to that of *Diphyllobothrium latum*. Large doses of oleoresin of aspidium are reported to cure 90 per cent of patients, and seldom more than two courses of treatments are required.[25] Pelletierin, beta-naphthol, pumpkin seed, quassia and areca have also been used with more or less success.

PREVENTION

Epidemiology.—*Tænia saginata* has a world-wide distribution. Its incidence is considerably higher than that of *T. solium* in countries where beef is eaten. An incidence of 0.38 per cent has been found in 56,286 Chinese at Peiping.[26] Man acquires the infection by eating raw or imperfectly cooked beef containing cysticerci. Cattle are infected from grazing land contaminated either through fertilization with night soil or through sewage-laden water. Flooded pastures along the rivers are important sources of bovine cysticercosis. In these pastures the ova may remain

[20] Meserve, F. G. and Coatney, G. R., 1937.
[21] Penso, G., 1931.
[22] Itirnmanne, E., 1937.
[23] Penfold, H. B., 1937.
[24] Prümm, A., 1935.
[25] Penfold, H. B., 1936.
[26] Wu, L. S., 1939.

viable eight or more weeks.[19] The incidence of bovine cysticercosis varies: in the United States of America 0.37 per cent, in Holland 3.3 to 5.6 per cent,[27] and in South Africa 5.0 per cent.[16]

Prophylaxis.—Prophylactic measures comprise: (1) removal of sources of infection by treating infected individuals, (2) restriction of cattle from grazing on contaminated land, (3) inspection of beef for cysticerci, (4) refrigeration of beef, and (5) thorough cooking of beef. Human infection is not always readily detected and it is not practical in many instances to restrict grazing grounds. Inspection of beef, even if thorough, is not sufficient to combat the disease unless supported by vigorous eradication of infection in man. Cattle that have not been exposed to infection for over a year are usually considered safe for consumption, since by that time most of the cysticerci have become nonviable. Freezing at −10° C. kills the cysticerci within five days.[16] Heating at 71° C. for five minutes and pickling in 20 to 25 per cent salt solution for five days also destroys the cysticerci, but refrigeration at 0.5 to 1° C. is not completely effective even after 41 days.[28]

OTHER *TÆNIÆ* OF MAN

Several species of *Tænia* have been reported in man. These species are often variations or aberrant forms of *T. saginata*. *T. fusa* Collins, 1876 is characterized by absence of external segmentation. *T. fenestrata* Chiaje, 1825 has perforated or fenestrated proglottides.

Tænia confusa **Ward, 1896.**—This rare tapeworm has been identified seven times in man in the United States of America and has also been reported in Africa and Japan. It is probably identical with *T. bremneri* described by Stephens in northern Nigeria. The worm is from 5 to 8 meters in length, the scolex is unarmed, and the irregular lateral branches of the gravid uterus are constricted at their bases. The cysticerci mature in about 12 weeks in calves. It has been described as a distinct species by Faust.[29] Anderson, however, considers that it is a variety of *T. saginata,* since gross and histological studies show that the specific characteristics of *T. confusa* fall within the range of variation of *T. saginata*.[30]

Tænia africana **v. Linstow, 1900.**—This tapeworm was reported by Fülleborn from an East African native. It is distinguished by an unarmed scolex with a small extra apical sucker and a gravid uterus with radiating unbranched arms.

Tænia hydatigena **Pallas, 1766.**—The adult worm, sometimes known as *T. marginata,* is a natural parasite of dogs and wild carnivora. Its larval stage, *Cysticercus tenuicollis,* is found in sheep and less frequently in cattle, goats, deer and hogs, the chief site being the mesentery. The cysticercus of this parasite has been reported in the brain of man.[31]

COMMON *TÆNIÆ* OF DOMESTIC ANIMALS

Tænia pisiformis (Bloch, 1780) is a common tapeworm of dogs and less frequently of cats. The intermediate hosts are rabbits, chiefly the common cottontail. The larvæ first develop in the liver and in about 30 days migrate from the surface of the liver into the abdominal cavity, where they become attached to the mesentery and ultimately become

---

[27] Reitsma, K., 1931.
[28] Clarenburg, A., 1932.
[29] Faust, E. C., 1930.

[30] Anderson, M. G., 1934.
[31] Hausmann, M., 1921.

fully-formed cysticerci. Except in massive infections they cause little injury to the rabbit.[32]

Tænia ovis (Cobbold, 1869) is a common parasite of dogs. The larval *Cysticercus ovis* develops in three months in the intramuscular connective tissues of sheep, especially of the heart and diaphragm. The adult worm reaches maturity in dogs seven weeks after ingestion of the cysticercus. It is of economic importance because of the condemnation of carcasses and the mortality in sheep.[33]

Tænia tæniæformis (Batsch, 1786) commonly known as *T. crassicollis,* is a common parasite of the cat and wild felines. Its larval stage, *Cysticercus fasciolaris,* is present in rats and mice. The worm is of particular interest because of the association of its larva with sarcomatous growths in the liver of rats. Several investigators in cancer research have studied the sarcomata in infected rats and others have used this species for the study of cestode immunity (see cestode immunity). Various forms of fibro, osteo, chondro, mixed cell and spindle cell sarcoma arise from the encapsulating tissues. The fewer the parasitic cysts the longer is the time required to produce malignancy and the less likely it is to occur.[34] Malignancy is, therefore, associated with the susceptibility and length of life of the host.

GENUS *MULTICEPS*

Multiceps multiceps (Leske, 1780) Hall, 1910.—The adult worm, a common parasite of dogs, is 40 to 60 cm. in length and has a pyriform scolex about 1 mm. in diameter with a double crown of 22 to 32 large and small hooks. The gravid proglottis encloses a long medium uterus with 18 to 26 lateral branches on each side. The ova, 31 to 36 μ in diameter, are deposited in the dog's feces and are ingested in food or water by sheep, goats or other ruminants. In the intestine of the intermediate host the hexacanth embryo is freed from its shell, passes through the intestinal wall into the blood or lymph. Development to the cœnurus stage takes place only in the central nervous system; larvæ in other tissues usually fail to complete their development. The cœnurus (Fig. 131E) differs from the cysticercus by having multiple scolices invaginated from a thin, translucent wall. Each scolex is capable of producing an adult worm. Dogs acquire the parasite by eating infected sheep brains. The cysts may be as large as a hen's egg and may contain as many as 100 scolices.

The larvæ in the brain of sheep produce a fatal disease, characterized by somnolence, loss of weight, visual disturbances, and blind staggers. The single case of human infection had aphasia and epileptic symptoms, and at autopsy disclosed a degenerate cœnurus in the lateral ventricle.

Multiceps serialis (Gervais, 1845) Stiles and Stevenson, 1905.—The adult worm is a parasite of dogs and wild carnivora. The larva develops in the intermuscular connective tissues of rabbits, squirrels and other rodents. The cœnurus produces internal and external daughter bladders that develop numerous scolices. Two cases of human infection have been reported in France, with subcutaneous tumors containing characteristic cœnuri.

Multiceps glomeratus Railliet and Henry, 1915.—Only the larval worm is known. It was originally obtained from mouse-like rodents. It has been reported twice from natives, in northern Nigeria and the Belgian Congo.

REFERENCES

AFRICA, C. M. and CRUZ, J. S. S. *Cysticercus cellulosæ* in Man, J. Philippine M. Ass., 1937, 7:209.

[32] Whitlock, S. C., 1939.
[33] Ransom, B. H., 1913.

[34] Curtis, M. R., Dunning, W. F. and Bullock, F. D., 1933, 1934.

DIXON, H. B. F. and SMITHERS, D. W. Cysticercus (*Tænia solium*), J. Roy. Army Corps, 1935, 64:91, 227, 300, 375; 65:28.

DOLGOPOZ, V. B. and NEUSTAEDTER, M. Meningo-encephalitis Caused by *Cysticercus cellulosæ*, Arch. Neurol. & Psychiat., 1935, 33:132.

GRIEG, E. D. W. Cysticercosis and Epilepsy, Edinburgh M. J., 1937, 44:522.

MACARTHUR, W. P. Cysticercosis as Seen in the British Army with Special Reference to the Production of Epilepsy, Tr. Roy. Soc. Trop. Med. & Hyg., 1934, 27:343; J. Roy. Army M. Corps, 1934, 63:241.

PENFOLD, H. B. Diagnosis, Signs and Symptoms of *Tænia saginata* Infestation, M. J. Australia, 1937, 1:531.

VITJEON, N. R. Cysticercosis in Swine and Bovines, with Special Reference to South African Conditions, Onderstepoort J. Vet. Sc. & Animal Indust., 1937, 9:337.

Chapter XXVIII

THE SUPERFAMILY TÆNIOIDEA: THE GENUS ECHINOCOCCUS

Echinococcus granulosus (BATSCH, 1786) RUDOLPHI, 1801

Synonyms.—*Tænia echinococcus* (Zeder, 1803) v. Siebold, 1853; *Echinococcus multilocularis* Leuckart, 1863; *Echinococcus alveolaris* Klemm, 1883.

History.—Hydatid disease has been known as a clinical entity since ancient times. Its parasitic nature was recognized as early as 1684 by Redi, Hartmann and others. Goeze in 1782 pointed out that the scolices were of tænial origin and differentiated the hydatid cyst from the cysticercus and the cœnurus. The adult worm was observed in the intestine of dogs in 1808 by Rudolphi, but it was not until 1850 that it was recognized by Van Beneden as a distinct species, which he later named *Tænia nana*. In 1852 v. Siebold recovered the adult worm from dogs, which had eaten echinococcal cysts of cattle. In 1863 Naunyn in Germany and Krabbe and Finsen in Iceland in a like manner were able to produce adult worms with human hydatid cysts.

Disease.—Echinococcosis, hydatid disease, hydatid cyst.

Geographical Distribution.—Cosmopolitan. The areas of heavy infection are the sheep- and cattle-raising districts of South America, Australia, New Zealand, South Africa, Asia, central and north Europe, and the Mediterranean countries of Asia and Africa. In North America 482 cases of hydatid disease in man have been reported since 1808, only 22 of which were indigenous.[1]

BIOLOGICAL CHARACTERISTICS

Morphology.—The adult (Fig. 153A), which occurs chiefly in dogs, is the smallest tapeworm of medical importance, ranging from 3 to 8.5 mm. in length. It consists of a scolex, neck and three segments. The globular scolex, 0.3 mm. in diameter, bears a prominent rostellum with a double crown of 30 to 36 hooklets and four prominent, cup-like, oval suckers. The scolex narrows posteriorly to form a slender neck. The short first proglottis contains immature genital organs; the more elongated middle proglottis has fully developed reproductive organs (Fig. 153B), and the last or gravid proglottis consists largely of a median uterus with 12 to 15 or more lateral pouches filled with ova. This segment, over 2 mm. long and from 0.5 to 1 mm. wide, comprises about one-half the length of the worm. The nearly spherical ovum, from 30 to 37 μ in diameter, has a brown radially-striated embryophore surrounding a hexacanth embryo and is similar in appearance to those of other *Tænia*.

---

[1] Magath, T. B., 1937.

Physiology.—The physiology of the adult worm is similar to that of the other tapeworms. As a rule it does not harm the canine host, except by producing a catarrhal inflammation of the intestine in heavily infected animals.

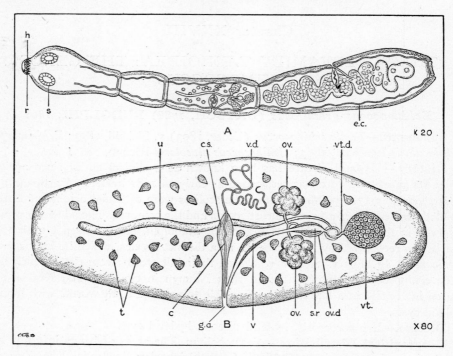

FIG. 153.—*Echinococcus granulosus*

A, adult worm; *B*, mature proglottis.

c, cirrus; *c.s.*, cirral sac; *e.c.*, excretory canal; *g.a.*, genital atrium; *h*, hooklets; *ov.*, ovary; *ov.d.*, oviduct; *r*, rostellum; *s*, sucker; *s.r.*, seminal receptacle; *t*, testes; *u*, uterus; *v*, vagina; *v.d.*, vas deferens; *vt.*, vitellarium; *vt.d.*, vitelline duct (Composite drawings).

LIFE CYCLE

The definitive hosts are dogs, wolves, jackals, coyotes and other CANIDÆ. Foxes have been experimentally infected. The common intermediate hosts are sheep, cattle, horses, other herbivorous animals, and hogs. The adult worms have been found in timber wolves and the larval hydatids in moose in the United States of America.[2] The larval worm is a parasite of man in regions where it is prevalent among animals.

Larval infection has been produced experimentally in animals by feeding ova or injecting scolices. Cysts, 2 to 5 mm. in size, have been found in lambs nine months after the ingestion of ova.[3] Secondary echinococcosis with sterile cysts has been established in a high percentage of mice by intraäbdominal injections of "echino-coccal sand" (scolices), the cysts reaching 20 mm. in size in 302 days.[4] The injec-

[2] Riley, W. A., 1933.
[3] Penfold, H. B., 1938.

[4] de Waele, A. and de Cooman, E., 1938; Coutelen, F., Lecroart, D. and Cochet, G., 1939.

tion of "hydatid sand" into the carotids of rabbits produces cerebral and intra-ocular cysts and a moniliform condition of the carotid, not unlike an aneurysm produced by a mechanical noninfectious embolus.[5]

The ova, evacuated in the feces, are ingested by man or other intermediate hosts. In the duodenum the embryo escapes from the embryophore and attaches itself by means of its hooklets to the intestinal mucosa. It penetrates the intestinal wall, passes into the lymphatics or mesenteric venules and is carried by the blood stream to various parts of the body. Most frequently it enters the portal vein and lodges in the liver, the first capillary filter. If it passes the liver, it reaches the lungs and other distant foci. It arrives at the liver within twelve hours after ingestion, where, if not destroyed by phagocytic cells, it develops into a hydatid cyst. The embryonic hooklets disappear, the larva undergoes central vesiculation and

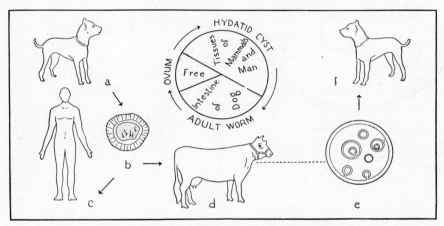

FIG. 154.—LIFE CYCLE OF *Echinococcus granulosus*

a, dog infected with adult worm; *b*, ovum in feces of dog; *c*, man infected with hydatid cyst; *d*, herbivorous animal infected with hydatid cyst; *e*, hydatid cyst in tissues; *f*, dog infected by eating hydatid cyst.

the cyst increases in size, attaining in the course of its growth a diameter of about 10 mm. in five months. The enveloping membrane is gradually differentiated into an external laminated layer and an internal nucleated germinal layer, while the surrounding tissues are infiltrated with endothelial cells, eosinophils, giant cells and fibroblasts. When the hydatid is eaten by a definitive host, such as the dog, it develops into a sexually mature worm in about seven weeks (Fig. 154).[6]

HYDATID CYST

Three types of primary hydatid cysts are found in man: (1) unilocular, (2) osseous, and (3) alveolar. The unilocular cyst, the most common form and practically the only form in lower animals, apparently represents the normal development of the larval parasite.

[5] Dévé, F., 1927.　　　　[6] Ross, I. C., 1929.

Unilocular Cyst.—Hydatid cysts grow slowly and require several years for development. The completely developed cysts vary considerably in size; in the hog they are usually 4 to 5 cm. in diameter and in man, with a longer period of growth, they may reach 15 to 20 cm. The cyst, if uninfluenced by pressure, is more or less spherical in shape. It has: (1) an external laminated cuticula, (2) an inner germinal layer, (3) fluid that causes distention of the limiting membrane, (4) brood capsules containing scolices, and (5) daughter cysts. It is walled off from the surrounding tissues by a fibrous adventitia.

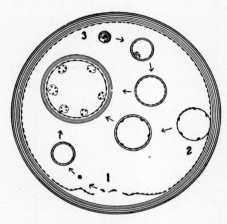

FIG. 155.— SCHEMATIC REPRESENTATION OF THE DEVELOPMENT OF ENDOGENOUS DAUGHTER CYSTS OF *Echinococcus granulosus*

1, from broken bits of germinative tissue; *2*, from a brood capsule; *3*, from a scolex (From Hegner, Root, Augustine and Huff, *Parasitology,* 1938, D. Appleton-Century Company).

The colorless or slightly yellowish hydatid fluid has a specific gravity of 1.012 and a pH of 6.7 to 7.2.[7] It contains albumin, creatinin, inosite, lecithin, urea, a small amount of dextrose, sodium chloride, phosphates, sodium sulphate and succinate of sodium and calcium. The chief enzymes are diastatic, but there are also a proteolytic enzyme, a lipase, a protease and oxydases.[8]

The external, nonnucleated, hyaline cuticula, about 1 mm. thick, that is formed by the germinal cells, acts as a support for the delicate inner germinal layer. It permits the entry of nutritive materials but excludes substances inimical to the parasite; the cystic fluid remains sterile when the cyst is placed in bacterial suspensions. When ruptured, this elastic membrane contracts, thus permitting the dissemination of its contents and making operative procedures difficult. The internal nucleated germinal layer, 22 to 25 μ thick, is a thin, delicate structure that is sparsely supplied with cells, rich in glycogen and contains some calcareous bodies.

The inner surface of a fertile cyst is studded with small papillæ, which are brood capsules in various stages of development (Figs. 131F and 155). These capsules, which arise by the proliferation of the nucleated cells, form minute single-layered vesicles, attached to the germinal membrane by a short pedicle. As the vesicle enlarges, from 5 to 20 or more small oval buds develop on its inner surface. These buds or scolices (Fig. 157), about 0.1 mm. in diameter, are equipped with suckers and a double crown of hooks. They represent the maturity of the larval parasite. When the brood capsule ruptures, the scolices may escape into the hydatid fluid, where they are known as "hydatid sand." The contractile anterior end is usually invaginated (Fig. 156A), but evagination (Fig. 156B) may occur. Hydatids without brood capsules and scolices are called sterile cysts or acephalocysts.

---

[7] Lemaire, G. and Ribère, 1935; de Waele, A. and de Cooman, E., 1938.

[8] Cameron, G. R., 1927.

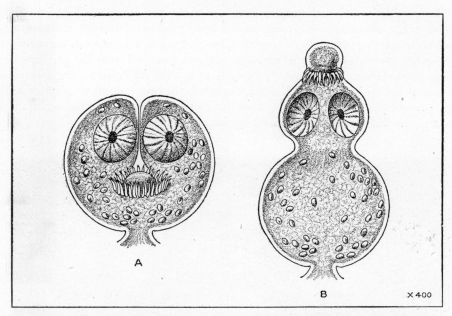

Fig. 156.—Scolices of Hydatid Cyst, Showing Hooklets and Suckers
A, invaginated; *B,* evaginated.

(Drawn from photomicrographs by Dr. M. L. Welcker, according to schema of Faust, 1939).

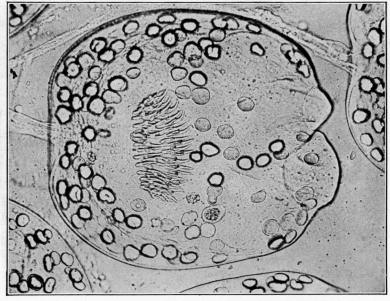

Fig. 157.—Invaginated Scolex of Hydatid Cyst (ca. ×750)

(Courtesy of Dr. Merrill L. Welcker, Worcester City Hospital, Worcester, Mass.)

The production of endogenous daughter cysts has been attributed to interference in the normal development of the larval parasite through mechanical or chemical trauma or through infection.[9] The phenomenon may be a defensive reaction when the vitality of the germinal cells is menaced and the production of scolices is curtailed. The daughter cysts have a thin transparent wall and often are free in the cystic fluid (Fig. 158). At times they may produce granddaughter cysts. Daughter cysts are rare in animals. In man they frequently occur in old hepatic cysts but are infrequent in pulmonary cysts.

FIG. 158.—HYDATID CYST REMOVED FROM HUMAN UTERUS
(Courtesy of Dr. Merrill L. Welcker, Worcester City Hospital, Worcester, Mass.)

Endogenous daughter cysts may arise (1) from the germinal membrane, (2) from brood capsules, or (3) from scolices (Fig. 155). The germinal membrane may rupture by trauma and the detached portions form small daughter cysts. Actively growing brood capsules may separate from the germinal layer, produce an outer protective membrane and become daughter cysts. Scolices develop into daughter cysts by vesiculation. Opinions vary as to whether the germinal membrane and brood capsules [10] or the scolices [11] are the chief source of daughter cysts.

The formation of exogenous daughter cysts has been attributed to intracuticular inclusion of bits of germinal layer, but they actually arise from herniation of the

[9] Dew, H. R., 1925.   [11] Dévé, F., 1927.
[10] Dew, H. R., 1926.

wall of ·the mother cyst as a result of trauma or unfavorable environmental conditions.[12] Both layers of the wall protrude through a weakened portion of the adventitia; the neck of the pouch becomes constricted and the fused germinal layer ultimately produces a complete laminated membrane; and the daughter cyst finally may be separated from the mother cyst. These eversions may be multiple and the daughter cysts may produce tertiary and even quaternary exogenous cysts.

When the scolices are maintained at 37° to 39° C. *in vitro* in·sterile hydatid fluid or in peptone solution plus exudates or extracts of organs, about 2 per cent undergo vesiculation; but the growth is of relatively short duration, the scolices attaining in about a month 25 to 30 times their original volume.[13] Daughter cysts have been kept alive 7 to 12 days in these media. Scolices cannot live in acidified or bacterially contaminated media and die in 2 to 3 minutes in 1:1,000 mercuric chloride or 1:200 formalin. *In vitro* tests at 37° C. indicate that scolices from the hydatid cysts of sheep and cattle are digested by the intestinal juices of man, rats, rabbits, sheep and cattle, but not by those of cats and dogs.[14] Thus digestive juices may play an important rôle in determining susceptibility to infection with adult *Echinococcus granulosus*.

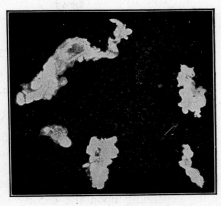

FIG. 159.—HYDATID CYST DISSECTED FROM DECALCIFIED BONE

Multiple pouchings along the bony canals may become cut off with the formation of small cysts (After Dew, from Hegner, Root, Augustine and Huff, *Parasitology*, 1938, D. Appleton-Century Company).

Osseous Cyst.—In the bones development of the hydatid cyst is markedly altered, since the dense tissues do not permit the cyst to assume its normal spherical form. Growth follows the line of least resistance along the bony canals with erosion of the osseous tissues and invasion of the medullary cavity. The bony structure is slowly permeated with a gelatinous infiltration and replaced with small cysts so that spontaneous fracture is common. Small multiple pouchings, which may become cut off from each other, occur in the larger spaces, giving the appearance of exogenous daughter cysts (Fig. 159). For the most part there is no regular adventitia, but in places there is a pseudotuberculous tissue-reaction. There is little or no fluid so that the small cysts appear semisolid and, except in open spaces, there is no production of scolices. If the parasite extends into the extraosseous tissue it resumes its normal spherical form.[10]

Alveolar Cyst.—The alveolar cyst is found in man, particularly in certain parts of Europe and Siberia, and occasionally is encountered in cattle. Its growth is neoplastic and it gives rise to metastases in other organs by direct extension or through the lymphatics or blood stream. Some investigators believe that this type of cyst is produced by a different species or variety of the parasite; others

[12] Dew, H. F., 1926; Fairley, N. H. and Wright-Smith, R. J., 1929.

[13] Coutelen, F., 1927.
[14] Berberian, D. A., 1936.

consider that its form is due to the nature of the tissues which do not permit normal unilocular development; and still others believe that it is due to an abnormal excessive growth of the primitive germinal tissue. The cyst has an irregular, reticulate outline that is not sharply defined from the surrounding tissues. It has the appearance of a porous spongy mass of small irregular cavities or vesicles filled with a jelly-like matrix and separated from each other by connective tissue. The alveolar hydatid is usually sterile but occasionally it contains brood capsules and scolices. It shows more or less central necrosis and calcification.

PATHOGENESIS

The effect of the hydatid cyst on man depends upon its type (unilocular, osseous or alveolar) and its location.

PATHOLOGY

The unilocular cyst evokes an inflammatory reaction of the surrounding tissues that produces an encapsulating fibrous adventitia. Immediately around the cyst there is an infiltration of endothelials, eosinophils and giant cells, surrounded by a zone of fibroblasts, new blood vessels and fibrous tissue. The neighboring tissue cells, depending upon the density of the tissues, undergo atrophy and pressure necrosis as the cyst increases in size. The intimate fusion of the reactive and normal tissues often makes difficult the enucleation of the cyst. In osseous cysts there is no regular adventitia, but in places there is a pseudotuberculous reaction with foreign body giant cells. The alveolar cyst has no circumscribed boundaries and invades the tissues with a neoplastic type of growth.

Hydatid cysts may lodge in any organ of the body. In man the primary cysts are usually single, confined to one organ, and fertile; in the lower animals they are often multiple, in several organs and frequently sterile.[15] The liver is the chief site of the cyst in nearly three-quarters of all human infections. The lungs, abdominal cavity, muscles and subcutaneous tissues, kidney, spleen, and bones are often invaded, while cysts are less frequently found in the pleura, heart, brain, spinal cord, orbit and other regions.

Hydatid cysts of the liver usually range from 1 to 7 cm., although occasionally they reach a large size; Barnett's colossal abdominal cyst contained 42 liters of fluid.[16] Over three-quarters of hepatic cysts are found in the right lobe of the liver. The majority are located on the inferior surface so that they extend downward into the abdominal cavity. Abdominal cysts, largely secondary, tend to gravitate to the pelvis. Pulmonary cysts (12 per cent) are more frequently primary than secondary and are most often subpleural. About two-thirds are found in the right lung. Peribronchial cysts, which rupture into a bronchus, undergo spontaneous cure in 80 to 90 per cent of such cases. Subpleural cysts may break through the pleura, but seldom undergo spontaneous cure. Kidney cysts (2 per cent) are usually single and located in the parenchyma of the cortex. In the majority of cases they rupture into the pelvis. The cyst usually assumes a goblet or crescent

---

[15] Businco, A. and Padronetti, R., 1927.   [16] Carmalt-Jones, D. W., 1929.

shape resting on the extremity of one calix.[17] Splenic cysts (2 per cent) are usually primary and single. Cerebral cysts (0.6 per cent) are chiefly primary and single in children, whereas secondary cysts are multiple. Osseous cysts (0.9 per cent) are most frequently found in the ilium. The cortex of the bones may be thickened by osteoblastic reaction, the cancellous tissues distorted and coarse trabeculæ observed in roentgenograms. Spinal involvement may result from vertebral infection. Cardiac cysts may perforate into the pericardium [18] or give rise to the dissemination of germinal tissue throughout the blood vessels producing thrombi, emboli and aneurysms.[19]

Secondary pyogenic infection may occur through the blood stream, biliary ducts or bronchioles. *E. typhosa,* various *Salmonella* and pyogenic bacteria have been isolated from hepatic cysts. The infection may render the cyst sterile, if no daughter cysts are present, or it may cause rupture and secondary echinococcosis. Rupture of the hydatid cysts sets free scolices, bits of germinal membrane, brood capsules and daughter cysts, which may reach other tissues through the blood or by direct extension and develop into secondary cysts. Rupture may occur from coughing (pulmonary cysts), muscle strain, blows, aspiration or operative procedures. Secondary abdominal echinococcosis from a ruptured primary hepatic cyst is not uncommon. Hepatic cysts may also rupture into the gallbladder, biliary ducts or through the diaphragm into the pleural cavity. Rupture into the hepatic veins often produces secondary cysts in the lungs. A primary cyst of the right heart may produce metastasis in the lung, and of the left heart in the brain, spleen, kidney, liver and other organs of the body.

SYMPTOMATOLOGY

The symptoms, comparable to those of a slowly-growing tumor, depend upon the location of the hydatid. In the abdomen the cysts give rise to increased discomfort, but symptoms do not appear until the cysts have attained a considerable size. Pulmonary cysts may cause bronchitis with attendant dry cough and hemoptysis, and a ruptured pulmonary cyst may simulate bronchiectasis. In the brain the tumors produce symptoms of intracranial pressure and Jacksonian epilepsy. A kidney cyst may cause intermittent pain, hematuria and kidney dysfunction and in case of rupture hydatid material may be present in the urine. A splenic cyst may cause dull pain and bulging of the ribs, while pelvic cysts may show spotty areas of dulness and resonance on percussion.

Infection is usually acquired during childhood, but, unless the brain or orbit is infected, symptoms do not usually appear until later in life. In one case a primary cardiac cyst required 5 to 10 years to develop and after rupture a 2- to 5-year period of latency before signs of secondary echinococcosis appeared in the pericardium and brain.[20]

The mortality rate is higher in secondary echinococcosis and in infected cysts than in uncomplicated cysts. When the cyst ruptures the escape of fluid may give

---

[17] Surraco, L. A., 1939.
[18] Dougal, N., 1938.

[19] Bacaloglu, C. N., Ballif. L. and Vasilescu, C., 1929.
[20] Dew, H. R., 1929.

rise to allergic manifestations. The usual form ·is an urticarial rash. It may be accompanied by an irregular fever, gastro-intestinal disturbances, abdominal pain, dyspnea, cyanosis, syncope, delirium and mania.[21] If a quantity of hydatid material suddenly enters the blood stream serious anaphylactic symptoms or even sudden death may result, since many patients have become sensitized by absorbing material from the cyst.

A slight eosinophilia, not exceeding as a rule 6 per cent, is present in about one-half of infected individuals. General eosinophilia occurs when there is seepage of the cystic contents. The eosinophils neutralize the toxic products of protein degradation by deaminization and are the essential cellular elements in hydatid allergy.[22]

IMMUNITY

Certain species have an inherent resistance against the adult parasite and are not natural hosts. The action of the digestive juices has been suggested as a contributory factor.[14] In cats the parasite lives for a short time but does not develop to maturity.[23] Some animals are refractory to injection of the larval form. The resistance of rabbits is not entirely, though almost, absolute, the injection of scolices only occasionally producing infection.[24] The source of the injected material may be important; rabbits can be readily infected with the larval echinococcus of sheep but not with that of horses, while the reverse is true of white rats.[25] Such differences suggest a biological dissociation of the systemic species and the influence of physiological factors upon adaptation. In the experimental intraäbdominal injection of mice with echinococcal larvæ, the number of developing cysts depends not on the dose but on individual variations in the host.[26]

Sheep develop some degree of acquired natural immunity against the larval echinococcus.[27] Immunization by the injection of antigenic substances prepared from the fluid membranes and scolices of hydatid cysts (Section **VII**, IX, 16, 17) has been reported by several workers, but absolute protection against infection has not been achieved. Lack of protection has been found in rabbits against subcutaneous injection of scolices after 18 subcutaneous injections of 2 ml. of ovine hydatid fluid and 0.3 ml. of echinococcus sand;[28] in lambs against infective feeding after injections totalling 66 ml. of ground hydatid membrane suspended in carbolized hydatid fluid,[3] and in mice against intraäbdominal injections of scolices after five weekly inoculations of hydatid material.[29] Lambs, 21 to 170 days after immunization with dried scolices and membrane, showed partial protection against infective feedings.[30] At autopsy one year later in some experiments there were fewer cysts in the immunized than in the control animals. These cysts showed an abnormally thickened adventitia, heavy calcification of the cyst wall and degeneration of the germinal layer.

[21] Godfrey, M. F., 1937.
[22] Tanturi, C. A., 1933.
[23] Lorincz, F., 1933; Southwell, T., 1927.
[24] Dévé, F., 1938.
[25] de Waele, A., and de Cooman, E., 1938.
[26] Coutelen, F., Lecroart, D. and Cochet, G., 1939.
[27] Turner, E. L., Dennis, E. W. and Berberian, D. A., 1935(a).
[28] Dévé, F., 1927.
[29] Dévé, F., 1934.
[30] Turner, E. L., Berberian, D. A. and Dennis, E. W., 1937.

Partial protection against the adult parasite has been demonstrated in dogs that were fed cysts from 6 to 15 days after they had received five immunizing injections of an antigen of dried scolices and membrane, at 3- to 5-day intervals.[31] The control dogs were intensely infected, whereas the immunized dogs showed fewer adult parasites. Passive immunization of mice with the serum of dogs infected with various tænial worms has failed to protect against infection.

Antibodies.—Precipitative and alexin-fixative antibodies have been demonstrated in the blood and spinal fluid of infected persons and have been produced in laboratory animals by the injection of antigens. Sensitization has been shown by intracutaneous tests and the presence of circulating antibodies has been demonstrated by passive transfer of sensitiveness to the skin of normal individuals. Laboratory animals may be sensitized with antigens and specific sensitiveness demonstrated by the Schilltz-Dale method. Such antibodies have been demonstrated chiefly in hosts of the larval parasite. No correlation has been found between intracutaneous reactions and the presence of adult parasites in dogs.[32]

Antigens.—Numerous types of antigens have been used for precipitative, alexin-fixative and intracutaneous tests and for the immunization of experimental animals and the detection of antibodies. The following types have been prepared from hydatid cysts: (1) hydatid fluid obtained by aseptic methods, sterilized by passing through a Berkefeld filter or phenolized, (2) aqueous or alcoholic extracts of dried fluid, (3) concentrated purified fluid, (4) aqueous or alcoholic extracts of dried scolices, (5) aqueous or alcoholic extracts of cyst membranes, and (6) various combinations of fluid, scolices and membranes. The antigen prepared from purified hydatid fluid (Section **VII**, IX, 17) is probably the most potent.[33] Antigens from other adult and larval tænial worms of man and animals have also been used for diagnosis. The antigenic substances may be removed from hydatid fluid by ultrafiltration with pyroxylin membranes hardened in 50 to 60 per cent alcohol.[34] A polysaccharide scolex antigen free from protein has been recently reported.

Group Reactions.—With few exceptions most investigators consider that the precipitative, alexin-fixative and intracutaneous reactions are not specific, but represent a group-reaction for tænial worms. Cross alexin-fixation has been observed with both echinococcal and cysticercal fluid antigens in echinococcosis and intestinal tæniasis.[35] Patients with echinococcosis and tæniasis give positive intracutaneous reactions with both echinococcal and tænial antigens.[36] Positive cutaneous reactions have been reported in human echinococcosis [17] with cysticercal antigens of the animal parasites *T. hydatigena* [37] and *T. pisiformis*.[38]

Precipitative Reactions.—The results of precipitative tests do not show as good correlation with clinical echinococcosis as the alexin-fixative and intracutaneous tests. Most workers consider the test unsatisfactory for diagnosis because

---

[31] Turner, E. L., Berberian, D. A. and Dennis, E. W., 1936.

[32] Turner, E. L., Dennis, E. W. and Berberian, D. A., 1935(b).

[33] Dennis, E. W., 1937.

[34] Kellaway, C. H., Fairley, N. H., and Williams, F. E., 1928.

[35] Chung, H, and T'ung, T., 1939.

[36] Fairley, K. D., Fairley, N. H. and Williams, F. E., 1929; Outeiriño Nuñez, J. and Lopez, M. C., 1933.

[37] Morenas, L., 1932.

[38] Rose, H. M. and Culbertson, J. T., 1939.

of nonspecific reactions and failure to give more than 50 per cent of positive reactions in echinococcosis.

Alexin-fixative Reactions.—Most investigators have been able to detect alexin-fixing antibodies in the sera of man and other animals in hydatid infection. The percentage of positive reactions in human echinococcosis as determined by seven investigators varies from 17 to 92 per cent, in most instances between 84 and 90 per cent. Positive reactions have been obtained in 59 per cent of infected cattle and 16 per cent in uninfected.[39] The test is especially valuable in diagnosing residual cysts in patients after operation.[40]

Intracutaneous Reactions.—The intracutaneous test, first used by Casoni in 1911, has been extensively investigated. The reports of 14 investigators between 1920 and 1929 indicate that about 86 per cent (58 to 100 per cent) of infected persons give positive reactions. Uninfected persons as a rule do not give positive reactions, although the test involves a group reaction for tænial worms. False immediate reactions, however, have been obtained in 23 per cent of uninfected persons, but no false delayed reactions.[41] Positive reactions have been obtained in 86 per cent of infected cattle and in 18 per cent of uninfected.[39]

The immediate reaction (Section **VII**, X) gives a higher percentage of positives than the delayed reaction. Care should be taken to exclude pseudoreactions due to sheep serum in the antigen, traumatic sensitiveness of the skin and insufficient size of wheal.[42] A positive reaction is not conclusive evidence of active disease, since the cyst may not be viable and the reaction may persist for years after the removal of the cyst.[43] Absence of an immediate reaction, except for the first few weeks after operation when the patient may be desensitized, is valuable but not conclusive evidence of freedom from hydatid disease. The absence of an immediate reaction accurately indicated freedom from hydatid disease in 97 per cent of patients, and the absence of a delayed reaction proved correct in 80 per cent.[44]

DIAGNOSIS, PROGNOSIS AND TREATMENT

Diagnosis.—Previous to serological and roentgenological procedures correct clinical diagnoses were made in about 40 per cent of hydatid infections, but with modern laboratory methods the percentage has risen to 90 per cent.[21] Clinical diagnosis is based on the presence of cystic tumors. The hydatid thrill, indicative of fluid, is a diagnostic sign, provided it can be elicited. Hepatic and abdominal cysts require differentiation from malignancy, liver abscess, hepatic cirrhosis and syphilis; pulmonary cysts from tuberculosis, pulmonary abscesses, actinomycosis and malignancy; and osseous lesions from tuberculosis, osteomyelitis and sarcoma. Eosinophilia is suggestive but not diagnostic, since it is also present in other helminthic infections.

Roentgenological examinations are particularly useful in diagnosis and in locating cysts. The cysts are identified by their fluid contents, spherical shape,

---

[39] Goodale, R. H. and Krischner, H., 1930.
[40] Fairley, K. D. and Kellaway, C. H., 1933.
[41] Longo, D., 1932.
[42] Fairley, K. D., Fairley, N. H. and Williams, F. E., 1929.
[43] Dew, H. R., Kellaway, C. H. and Williams, F. E., 1925.
[44] Fairley, K. D., 1929.

dense outline if the adventitia is thickened, and alterations of the normal contour of the invaded organs. Stereoroentgenometry is the best method for localization.[45]

Laboratory diagnosis is made by finding the scolices, brood capsules or daughter cysts in the hydatid fluid, and by serological and intracutaneous tests. The exploratory puncture for the purpose of obtaining fluid is contraindicated as a dangerous diagnostic procedure, since leakage may cause secondary echino-coccosis and anaphylactic shock. Precipitative, alexin-fixative and intracutaneous tests have been used with more or less success (see Immunity). The last two are of considerable diagnostic importance in the absence of other tænial infections. The intracutaneous test gives the highest percentage of positive reactions and a negative reaction is of special value in excluding hydatid infection. Some investigators, however, prefer the alexin-fixative test, especially in evaluating postoperative results.

Prognosis.—The prognosis is good when the primary cyst is accessible to surgical treatment; it is less favorable when pyogenic infection is present and is grave in secondary echinococcosis and inoperable cases. Recurrences some years after operation are not uncommon. In Australia the mortality rate is one-sixth of the morbidity rate.[46] Fatalities in 28 per cent of children with pulmonary cysts have been reported.

Treatment.—Treatment of hydatid cyst is surgical. The location and nature of the cyst determine the surgical procedure and each case presents an individual problem. Unilocular cysts are amenable to surgery but alveolar cysts are usually inoperable. Whenever possible the cyst should be enucleated. Marsupialization because of its safety is the operation of choice, particularly in infected cases. The cyst is opened and walled off by bringing its edges to the external incision, its contents emptied, and the cavity sterilized and drained. At times the contents may be evacuated, the interior sterilized, the cavity filled with saline and both the cyst and wound closed. The preoperative injection of 2 to 4 per cent formalin is usually employed as a precaution against leakage during operation, but is of little value if daughter cysts are present. Aspiration *per se* is dangerous because it may lead to secondary echinococcosis and pyogenic infection. Pulmonary cysts, unless attached to the ribs, present a difficult operative problem. Primary cerebral cysts require operative interference, but secondary cysts are inoperable. Renal cysts may be treated radically by nephrectomy or conservatively by marsupialization and partial nephrectomy.

PREVENTION

Epidemiology.—The prevalence of human echinococcosis depends upon the intimate association of man with infected dogs. The percentile incidence of the adult worm in dogs is reported as: Iceland 25 to 28, Palestine 25, New South Wales 20, South Australia 40 to 50 and Punjab (India) 29. Dogs are seldom infected in North America or in the British Isles, although hydatid infection is by no means uncommon in cattle and other domestic animals in Great Britain. The infection in dogs depends upon the dog-sheep or dog-cattle relationship in grazing

---

[45] Johnson, C. R., 1935.   [46] Barnett, L., 1936.

countries in respect to canine consumption of the offal and carcasses. The incidence of hydatid infection is somewhat greater in sheep than in cattle, but the ratio varies in different countries. The percentile incidence in sheep is variously given as: Iceland 12, Australia 36, north Prussia 27 to 51, Syria and Palestine 70 and Bulgaria 75; that in cattle as: Australia 36, north Prussia 37 to 64, Syria and Palestine 40, Bulgaria 33 and Punjab (India) 90; and that in hogs in north Prussia 5 to 13.

The percentile infection in man has been reported as: New South Wales 0.45, Bulgaria 0.75, southern Australia 0.2 to 0.26, Iceland 2.0 (1867) and 0.04 (1920), Syria 0.5, and in some parts of Argentina and Uruguay among the primitive peons 50 per cent. Of the 22 indigenous North American cases only 3 have been found in the United States. Infection usually takes place in childhood, the period of relatively unhygienic habits, but clinical symptoms are not manifest until adult life. Infection may persist for many years; a duration of 56 years has been recorded.[47]

The ova are usually transmitted to man by contact with infected dogs. Transmission is a hand-to-mouth affair, largely due to the contamination of the hands with ova from the fur and to manual uncleanliness. Dogs may contaminate eating utensils. Although ova are killed rapidly by direct sunlight, they may remain alive for three weeks in moist shady places.[6] Infection is less common in tropical than in temperate climates, since the ova are unable to resist high temperatures. Infection from soil, vegetables and water, except under special insanitary conditions, is probably a relatively unimportant factor.

Prophylaxis.—The marked decline in hydatid disease in Iceland since 1867 illustrates the value of prophylactic measures. Since the dog is the chief source of human infection, attention should be directed toward reducing canine infection and intimate contact between man and dogs. In endemic areas dogs should be barred from slaughter houses and should not be fed uncooked offal; the refuse from slaughtered animals should be burned or sterilized; stray dogs should be eliminated; and all dogs should be given teniafuges once or twice each year. The public should be informed regarding the method of transmission, warned concerning the danger of intimate contact with dogs, and instructed in personal cleanliness. Food should be prepared under hygienic conditions and in certain localities all vegetables should be cooked and all drinking water boiled.

REFERENCES

DEW, H. R. The Mechanism of Daughter Cyst Formation in Hydatid Disease, M. J. Australia, 1926, 1:451.
——— Some Aspects of *Echinococcus* Disease, Surgery, 1937, 2:363.
FAIRLEY, K. D., FAIRLEY, N. H. and WILLIAMS, F. E. Some Fallacies on the Intradermal Test for Hydatid Disease, M. J. Australia, 1929, 2:320.
GODFREY, M. F. Hydatid Disease. Clinical, Laboratory and Roentgenographic Observations, Arch. Int. Med., 1937, 60:783.
MAGATH, T. B. Hydatid (*Echinococcus*) Disease in Canada and the United States, Am. J. Hyg., 1937, 25:107.
TURNER, E. L., BERBERIAN, D. A. and DENNIS, E. W. The Production of Artificial Immunity in Dogs Against *Echinococcus granulosus,* J. Parasitol., 1936, 22:14.
——— Production of Artificial Immunity in Sheep, J. Parasitol., 1937, 23:43.

[47] Lawson, T. C., 1939.

Section V

THE TREMATODA OR FLUKES

Chapter XXIX

THE TREMATODA

The flukes are parasitic worms of the class TREMATODA of the phylum PLATY-HELMINTHES. Their parasitic existence has brought about a specialized development of the organs of reproduction and attachment, and a corresponding reduction in the organs of locomotion, sensation and digestion in contrast to their free-living relatives, the TURBELLARIA. Their structure and life cycles vary with the type of parasitic existence, ranging from ectoparasitism on aquatic hosts to extreme endoparasitism in the vascular system of vertebrates. As a rule, the **monogenetic** species have relatively simple life cycles without asexual development, whereas the endoparasitic **digenetic** forms have more complicated life cycles involving alternation of generations and hosts. All species parasitic in man belong to the digenetic group, in which sexual reproduction in the adult is followed by asexual multiplication in the larval stages.

CLASSIFICATION

The older classifications of the TREMATODA Rudolphi, 1808 have proved unsatisfactory, since they are based upon external and internal morphological characteristics that are frequently the result of parasitic adaptations and, therefore, are not indicative of genetic relationship. The excretory organs, which apparently maintain a constant pattern throughout larval and adult life, furnish an additional basis for modern classifications [1] and are of value in identifying larvæ with adults and in establishing the relationship between species.

SUBCLASS *MONOGENEA* V. BENEDEN, 1858

Ectoparasites or parasites of bladder or respiratory passages; one or more suckers, the posterior one well developed, chitinous anchors or hooks usually present; intestine absent or simple; excretory pores anterior; uterus short, usually containing a single ovum; vagina single or double; life cycle simple and direct with a single host; adults parasites of fishes, turtles and amphibians.

Order MONOPISTHOCOTYLEA Odhner, 1912.—Posterior sucker single; vagina single; gastro-intestinal tract absent; adults ectoparasites on skin and gills of fishes.

Order POLYOPISTHOCOTYLEA Odhner, 1912.—Posterior sucker multiple; vagina double; gastro-intestinal tract present; adults parasites of fishes, turtles and amphibians.

---

[1] La Rue, G. R., 1926; Stiles, C. W., and Hassall, A., 1926; Fuhrmann, O., 1928; Pearse, A. S., 1936; Price, E. W., 1937; Dubois, G., 1938.

SUBCLASS *ASPIDOGASTREA* FAUST AND TANG, 1936

Endoparasites; anterior sucker absent or poorly developed, posterior well developed, frequently divided into a series of sucking cups; intestine a simple blind sac; life cycle direct or with alternation of hosts; flame-cell pattern of larva "1 + 1 + 1"; adults parasites of tissues of mollusks and intestines of poikilothermal vertebrates.

SUBCLASS *DIGENEA* V. BENEDEN, 1858

Endoparasites; one or two suckers, anterior sucker single and median, no chitinous anchors or hooks; excretory pore posterior; intestine a simple sac; uterus long with numerous ova; life cycle complex with three or more generations and with alternation of hosts; flame-cell pattern of larva "1" or "1 + 1"; adults parasites of vertebrates. All the trematode parasites of man belong in this subclass.

Order PROSOSTOMATA Odhner, 1905.—Mouth at or near anterior extremity, usually surrounded by oral sucker; ventral sucker on ventral surface or at posterior end; flame-cell pattern of miracidium "1"; adults hermaphroditic; cercariæ with unforked tails.

Order STRIGEATOIDEA La Rue, 1926.—Anterior sucker almost always and one or more ventral suckers usually present; flame-cell pattern of miracidium "1 + 1"; cercariæ with forked tails; adults uni- or bisexual; parasites of circulatory system and intestines of vertebrates.

Table 32 gives the arrangement of the digenetic trematodes of man followed in this text.

TABLE 32

DIGENETIC TREMATODES OF MAN

Order	Sub-order	Superfamily	Family	Genus	Species
PROSOSTOMATA	DISTOMATA	FASCIOLOIDEA	FASCIOLIDÆ	*Fasciola*	*F. hepatica*
				Fasciolopsis	*F. buski*
		OPISTHORCHOIDEA	OPISTHORCHIDÆ	*Clonorchis*	*C. sinensis*
				Opisthorchis	*O. felineus*
		HETEROPHYOIDEA	HETEROPHYIDÆ	*Heterophyes*	*H. heterophyes*
				Metagonimus	*M. yokogawai*
		TROGLOTREMATOIDEA	TROGLOTREMATIDÆ	*Troglotrema*	*T. salmincola*
				Paragonimus	*P. westermani*
		DICROCŒLIOIDEA	DICROCŒLIIDÆ	*Dicrocœlium*	*D. dendriticum*
				Eurytrema	*E. pancreaticum*
		ECHINOSTOMATOIDEA	ECHINOSTOMATIDÆ	*Echinochasmus*	*E. perfoliatus*
				Echinostoma	*E. ilocanum*
				Paryphostomum	*P. sufrartyfex*
	AMPHISTOMATA	PARAMPHISTOMOIDEA	GASTRODISCIDÆ	*Gastrodiscoides*	*G. hominis*
			PARAMPHISTOMIDÆ	*Watsonius*	*W. watsoni*
STRIGEATOIDEA	SCHISTOSOMATA	SCHISTOSOMATOIDEA	SCHISTOSOMATIDÆ	*Schistosoma*	*S. hæmatobium* *S. japonicum* *S. mansoni*

MORPHOLOGY

Adult digenetic trematodes are usually flat, elongated, leaf-shaped worms, but may be ovoid, conical or cylindrical. The exact form depends upon the state of contraction. Flukes vary in size from less than 1 mm. to several centimeters. Certain external features are characteristic: an oral and in most species a ventral sucker, the acetabulum, are conspicuous; an excretory pore is located at the posterior extremity; a genital pore opens near the anterior border of the ventral sucker; and in some species a small pore, the opening of Laurer's canal, is present on the middorsal surface. The principal internal organs include a blind, bifurcate intestinal tract, an excretory system, prominent male and female reproductive

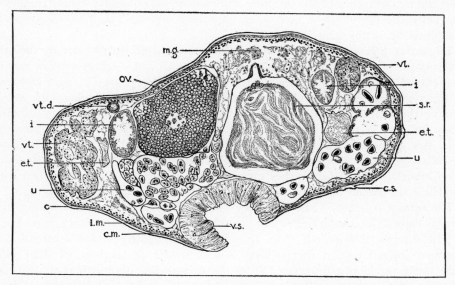

Fig. 160.—Cross Section of a Digenetic Trematode in Region of Ventral Sucker

c, cuticle; *c.m.*, circular muscles; *c.s.*, cuticular spine; *e.t.*, excretory tubule; *i*, intestine; *l.m.*, longitudinal muscles; *m.g.*, Mehlis' gland; *ov.*, ovary; *s.r.*, seminal receptacle; *u*, uterus; *v.s.*, ventral sucker; *vt.*, vitellaria; *vt.d.*, vitelline duct (Redrawn with modifications from Hegner, Root, Augustine and Huff, *Parasitology*, 1938, D. Appleton-Century Company).

organs, and a primitive nervous system. The arrangement, shape and size of these organs are characteristic for different species.

Integument.—The worm is covered by a noncellular, homogeneous layer, the cuticle (Fig. 160), which is secreted by subcuticular cells. In many species the cuticle is covered entirely or partially with spines, tubercles or ridges.

Suckers.—The worms are attached to the host by means of suckers, which sometimes possess spines or hooklets (Figs. 160 and 161). These suckers, cup-shaped disks with well-developed muscles, vary in size and position in the different species. An **oral** sucker is situated at the anterior end of the worm, while in most species a larger **ventral** sucker or **acetabulum** is located on the ventral surface somewhat posterior to the oral sucker. In the genus *Heterophyes* a third sucker, the **genital,** surrounding the genital pore, lies posterior to and to one side of the ventral sucker.

Muscular System.—There are three layers of muscles beneath the cuticle: (1) an outer circular, (2) a middle oblique, and (3) an inner longitudinal (Fig. 160). Transverse bands of muscles cross the body from the dorsal to the ventral cuticle. These muscles serve to alter the form of the worm.

Parenchyma.—There is no body cavity. The intervening space between the various organs and muscles is filled with fluid and a network of connective tissue cells and fibers, the mesenchymal parenchyma.

Lymph.—The vascular or lymph system embraces two to four main channels along the two branches of the intestine with numerous subsidiary canals supplying principally the reproductive and other important organs. The flow of lymph is maintained by bodily contractions.

Digestive System.—A terminal or subterminal mouth, surrounded by the oral sucker, opens into a muscular, globular pharynx (Fig. 161). A short, narrow esophagus extends from the pharynx to the intestine. The pharynx and esophagus are lined with an extension of the cuticle. They receive through ducts the secretions of the unicellular salivary glands. The intestine usually bifurcates immediately into two ceca, which may be straight or undulating and end blindly except in the few species that possess an anus. The ceca in some species extend almost the entire length of the body while in others they are shorter. They may have lateral branches (*Fasciola*) or they may unite (*Schistosoma*). They are lined with cylindrical epithelium and have thin longitudinal and circular muscle fibers.

Excretory System.—The excretory system includes numerous diffusely distributed flame-cells, capillaries, collecting tubes, bladder and excretory pore (Fig. 161). The terminal flame-cell (Fig. 161) is a large hollow cell with a tuft of cilia streaming inward toward the capillary end. Through the activity of these cilia liquid waste products are excreted from the surrounding tissues into the tubular excretory system. The capillaries of the flame-cells unite in tubules, and these coalesce to form lateral collecting tubes that enter the anterior part of the bladder. In the parasitic digenetic trematodes the bladder is usually located in the median line of the posterior part of the body and opens on the ventral surface at the posterior extremity by a small subterminal pore controlled by a muscular sphincter.

The pattern of the excretory system is always the same for a given species or for closely-related species. For this reason it is an important means of determining the relationship of species and of identifying larvæ with adults. The simplest arrangement is found in the miracidium. Two groups are present in the digenetic trematodes, one with a single flame-cell on each side of the body, a "1" pattern, and the other, two flame-cells, a "1 + 1" pattern. In the succeeding larval stages the flame-cells increase in number and multiply still further in the adult. The flame-cell pattern is most readily observed in the cercaria where there is a single or a double pair of excretory cells on each side, expressed in the latter case as $(1 + 1) + (1 + 1)$ or as $2 [(1 + 1) + (1 + 1)]$, where the "2" represents the bilateral

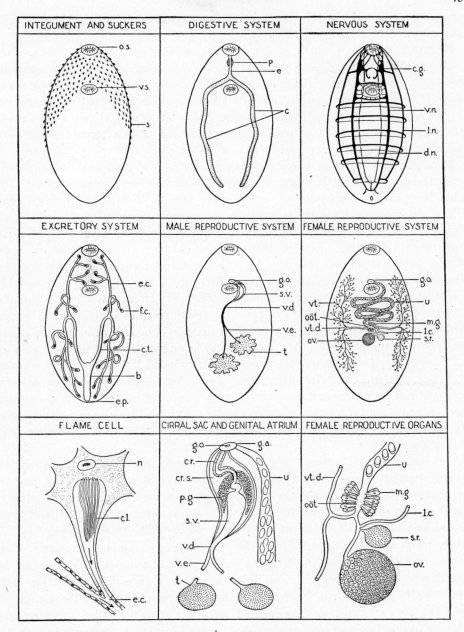

FIG. 161.—SCHEMATIC REPRESENTATION OF MORPHOLOGY OF A TYPICAL TREMATODE

b, bladder; *c*, ceca; *c.g.*, cephalic ganglia; *cl.*, cilia; *cr.*, cirrus; *cr.s.*, cirral sac; *c.t.*, collecting tube; *d.n.*, dorsal nerve trunk; *e*, esophagus; *e.c.*, excretory capillary; *e.p.*, excretory pore; *f.c.*, flame-cell; *g.a.*, genital atrium; *g.o.*, genital opening; *l.c.*, Laurer's canal; *l.n.*, lateral nerve trunk; *m.g.*, Mehlis' gland; *n*, nucleus; *oöt.*, oötype; *o.s.*, oral sucker; *ov.*, ovary; *p*, pharynx; *p.g.*, prostatic gland; *s*, spines; *s.r.*, seminal receptacle; *s.v.*, seminal vesicle; *t*, testis; *u*, uterus; *v.d.*, vas deferens; *v.e.*, vas efferens; *v.n.*, ventral nerve trunk; *v.s.*, ventral sucker; *vt.*, vitellaria; *vt.d.*, vitelline duct.

arrangement and the "$(1+1)$" each pair of cells. In the adult the number of cells is a multiple of the cercarial cells.

Nervous System.—There is a primitive nervous system (Fig. 161). Two lateral ganglia in the region of the pharynx are connected by dorsal commissures. From each ganglion arise three anterior and three posterior longitudinal nerve trunks. The latter, connected by numerous commissures with each other and the opposite set, occupy a dorsal, ventral and lateral position respectively on each side of the worm. The presence of sensory organs in adult endoparasites has not been satisfactorily demonstrated.

Reproductive System.—With the exception of the unisexual blood flukes, the SCHISTOSOMATIDÆ, the trematodes parasitic in man are hermaphroditic. The highly-developed and conspicuous reproductive organs lie between the two ceca.

The male reproductive organs comprise testes, vasa efferentia, and vas deferens (Fig. 161). The conspicuous testes, usually two but ranging from four to eight in the schistosomes, are most frequently located in the posterior half of the body between the intestinal ceca, but may be near the anterior end. Their form may be globular, lobate, tubular or dendritic depending on the species. They may lie side by side, diagonally or in tandem formation. The vasa efferentia, arising from the testes, unite in the vas deferens that passes anteriorly into the cirral sac before opening into the common genital atrium. The terminal portion within the cirral sac is divided into three parts: (1) a seminal vesicle ranging from a simple widening to a retort-shaped dilatation; (2) a portion surrounded by a cluster of prostatic cells; and (3) a muscular terminal portion, the cirrus, which serves as a copulatory organ and can be evaginated into the common genital atrium and into the female genital pore by the contraction of the muscular cirral sac. In this way spermatozoa may enter the uterus and travel to the seminal receptacle, thus producing self-fertilization.

The female genital organs (Fig. 161) comprise a single ovary, an oviduct, a seminal receptacle, two vitelline glands and ducts, Mehlis' gland, uterus, and in many species Laurer's canal. The rounded, lobed or dendritic ovary is anterior to and smaller than the testes. It is a vesicular organ, containing unfertilized eggs in various stages of development. A short oviduct leads from the ovary to the oötype, receiving Laurer's canal and the duct from the seminal receptacle. The function of Laurer's canal, which opens on the dorsal surface in some species, is not definitely known. It may be a vestigial vagina, through which fertilization may be effected by spermatozoa from another worm, or it may permit the escape of excess spermatozoa and yolk. The seminal receptacle is a thin-walled, saccular out-pocketing of the oviduct for storing the spermatozoa that have reached it by passing up the uterus. The vitellaria, usually located in the midlateral part of the body, are yellowish grape-like glands of various sizes. Their tubules converge in two longitudinal canals, and these in turn into transverse ducts, which unite to form the common vitelline duct. This joins the oviduct between the seminal receptacle and the oötype, a muscular dilatation of the oviduct surrounded by Mehlis' gland.

The cells of Mehlis' gland secrete a lubricative fluid for the ova.[2] The uterus arises from the oötype and extends forward as a long tortuous tube, often massed with ova. It terminates beside the cirral sac in the common genital atrium, which

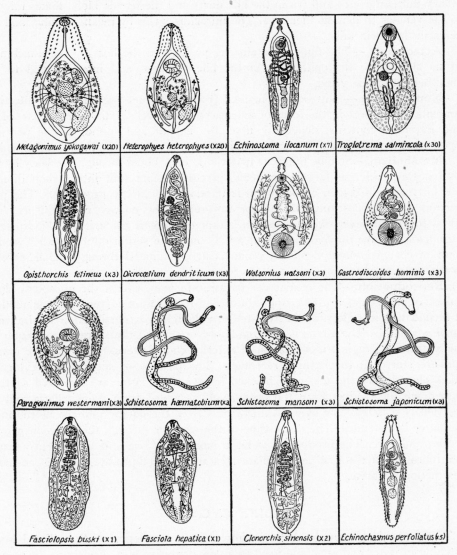

Metagonimus yokogawai (x20) *Heterophyes heterophyes* (x20) *Echinostoma ilocanum* (x7) *Troglotrema salmincola* (x30)

Opisthorchis felineus (x3) *Dicrocœlium dendriticum* (x3) *Watsonius watsoni* (x3) *Gastrodiscoides hominis* (x3)

Paragonimus westermani (x3) *Schistosoma hæmatobium* (x3) *Schistosoma mansoni* (x3) *Schistosoma japonicum* (x3)

Fasciolopsis buski (x1) *Fasciola hepatica* (x1) *Clonorchis sinensis* (x2) *Echinochasmus perfoliatus* (x5)

FIG. 162.—TREMATODES OF MAN

opens to the exterior by the genital pore. At first the uterus is straight and its terminal portion, the **metraterm,** acts as a vagina.

Trematodes of Man.—The more important trematodes parasitic in man are given in Figure 162.

_____

[2] Kouri, P. and Nauss, R. W., 1938.

PHYSIOLOGY

Movement.—The adult flukes move by contraction, elongation and flexion. The biliary flukes move to and fro in the bile ducts and the female blood flukes migrate to the venules to deposit their ova. The miracidia swim by means of cilia, and the cercariæ by their tails.

Attachment.—The fluke maintains its position in the host by the attachment of its suckers to the epithelium of the bile passages and intestine and to the endothelium of the veins.

Nourishment.—Nutrition is obtained from the tissues, secretions and intestinal contents of the host in the form of mucus, epithelial cells, biliary secretions, blood and intestinal contents, depending upon the habitat and species of the parasite. Species without an anus discharge undigested products through the oral opening.

Metabolism.—Soluble nutritive material is distributed through the body by the lymph. Respiration is largely anærobic, glycogen being split into carbon dioxide and fatty acids. Oxygen consumption is unrelated to energy production. The production of ova constitutes the major portion of the energy requirements. The larval forms, however, require oxygen. Adult *Clonorchis sinensis* and *Schistosoma japonicum* survive for five months at 37° C. in horse serum diluted with Tyrode's solution changed weekly.[3] Waste products are eliminated through the flame-cells of the excretory system.

Reproduction.—The trematodes parasitic in man, except the unisexual blood flukes, *Schistosoma,* are hermaphroditic. Self-fertilization is the common method of fecundation in endoparasitic trematodes, although cross-fertilization via Laurer's canal is possible. The cirrus is the copulatory organ and the spermatozoa, entering the metraterm (vaginal modification of anterior end of uterus), traverse the uterus and are stored in the seminal receptacle. The passage of spermatozoa evidently takes place before the uterus is blocked by ova. The latter are fertilized as they pass down the oviduct from the ovary, yolk is added from the vitellaria and an eggshell is secreted. The assembled ova pass from the oötype into the uterus until the latter is distended. The ova escape to the exterior through the common genital atrium and pore. The production of large numbers of ova and subsequent asexual multiplication in the first intermediate host tend to compensate for the enormous destruction of larvæ.

LIFE CYCLE

Ectoparasitic trematodes have a simple direct development, the ciliated larva hatching in water and attaching itself to a new definitive host. Endoparasitic trematodes have complicated life cycles involving alternation of generations and hosts. In the definitive host, usually a vertebrate, multiplication takes place sexually with the production of ova and in the intermediate molluscan host by asexual generations. The exact nature of the latter is still under discussion and is variously referred to as parthenogenesis, metagenesis, heterogenesis, pædogenesis, and even sexual re-

---

[3] Hoeppli, R., Feng, L. C., and Chu, H. J., 1938.

production.[4] The available evidence implicates the mollusk as the original host and the vertebrate as a later adaptation.

DEVELOPMENTAL CYCLE

Figure 163 shows in diagrammatic form the typical life cycle of digenetic trematodes. The fertilized ova escape from the body via the intestinal, genito-urinary or pulmonary tracts (Fig. 164). When discharged they may be fully

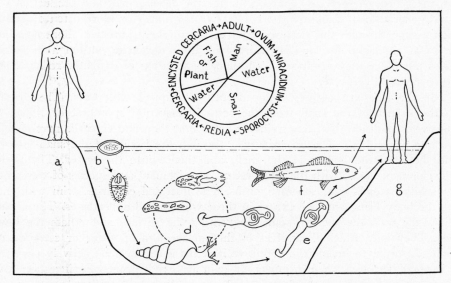

FIG. 163.—LIFE CYCLE OF A TYPICAL TREMATODE OF MAN

a, man infected with adult trematode; *b*, ovum discharged into water; *c*, free-swimming miracidium penetrates snail; *d*, sporocyst, redia and cercaria in gastropod host; *e*, free-swimming cercaria liberated from mollusk; *f*, metacercaria encysted in secondary intermediate host (fishes, crustacea and snails) or on aquatic plants; *g*, man infected through skin by cercaria or by ingestion of secondary intermediate hosts or infested aquatic plants.

developed (*Clonorchis, Opisthorchis, Dicrocœlium, Heterophyes, Metagonimus*) or may require subsequent development outside the host before hatching (*Fasciola, Fasciolopsis, Paragonimus, Echinostoma*). Hatching takes place in fresh water, the operculum springing open. In *Fasciola hepatica* the intake of water in a sub-opercular fluid vacuole causes the operculum to pop open.[5] In the nonoperculate ova the energetic movements of the larva and the presence of a hypotonic medium split the weakened shell.

A ciliated larva, the **miracidium**, escapes from the shell, remains momentarily quiescent, and then swims actively in the water. When it approaches an appropriate species of gastropod, it is attracted by a chemotactic stimulus, probably from the mucus of the snail, and penetrates the exposed portions. The avenues of

---

[4] Brooks, F. G., 1930; Woodhead, A. E.,   [5] Mattes, O., 1926.
1931; Anderson, M. G., 1935; Chen, P., 1937.

entrance are through the gills (*Fasciola*), through head, tentacles and foot (*Schistosoma*), and in other instances (*Clonorchis*) the ova apparently hatch in the intestine of the snail. Unless the miracidium finds the snail host within a few hours it perishes. Penetration of tissues is accomplished by a boring motion aided by the glandular secretions of the miracidium. The cilia disappear after the organism enters the snail.

Within the tissues of the snail the miracidium undergoes metamorphosis into an irregular sac-like **sporocyst.** Nourished by absorption of liquid food from the host, the sporocyst serves as a brood sac for the development and production of a second generation of daughter sporocysts (*Schistosoma*) or more often of **rediæ,** which escape through the ruptured wall of the mother sporocyst. The rediæ and sporocysts similarly develop into third-generation **cercariæ,** although in certain species the rediæ may produce an additional generation of daughter rediæ, which in turn produce cercariæ.

The cercariæ are highly-developed forms equipped with tails. They escape into the tissues of the snail from the second-generation sporocyst or rediæ. So extensive is multiplication that as many as several thousand cercariæ may develop from one miracidium. The cercariæ pass through the tissues of the snail into the cavity between the body and the shell, and thence into the water. The period of development varies with the temperature, nourishment and species of trematode, but usually extends over several months. The liberated cercariæ swim with their tails, the body being anterior except in those with forked appendages. The aquatic habits vary with the species, some frequenting the surface and others the lower levels. They may attach themselves to the surface film of water or settle to the bottom. In order to invade the definitive host the cercariæ must actively penetrate the exposed surfaces (*Schistosoma*) or gain passive entrance by ingestion after encystment as **metacercariæ** in a second intermediate host (fishes, crustacea and snails) or on aquatic plants (Fig. 164).

The definitive and intermediate hosts and the larval stages of the common trematodes of man are given in Table 33.

LARVAL FORMS

The larval forms of the digenetic trematodes include the developing ovum, miracidium, sporocyst, redia, cercaria and metacercaria.

Ovum.—The so-called ovum (Fig. 165A) consists of the fertilized ovum proper, a more or less constant number of nutrient yolk globules, a vitelline membrane and a shell. The shape and size of the shell, although subject to minor variations, are reasonably constant and diagnostic for each species. The shell ranges from a rotund oval to an elongate spindle and from 29 to 145 μ in length. In most trematodes there is a cap-like, polar operculum that rests in a rim of varying prominence and at the time of hatching pops open like a lid to permit the escape of the larva, whereas the nonoperculate shells split longitudinally. The shell is unornamented except for certain characteristic knobs or spines that are useful for the identification of species. The shell and lining membrane are probably derived

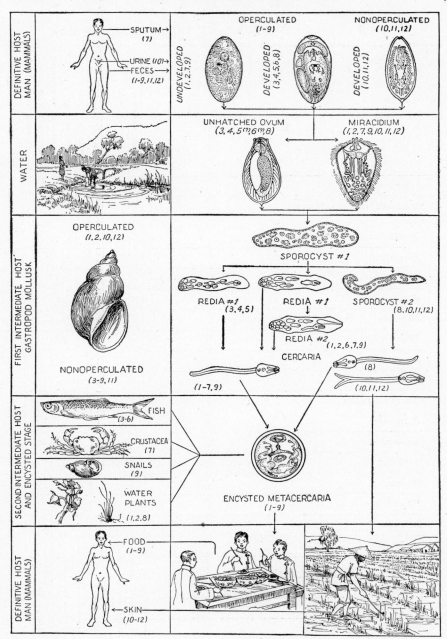

FIG. 164.—TRANSMISSION AND LIFE CYCLES OF IMPORTANT TREMATODES OF MAN

1, *Fasciola hepatica;* 2, *Fasciolopsis buski;* 3, *Opisthorchis felineus;* 4, *Clonorchis sinensis;* 5, *Heterophyes heterophyes;* 6, *Metagonimus yokogawai;* 7, *Paragonimus westermani;* 8, *Dicrocœlium dendriticum;* 9, *Echinostoma ilocanum;* 10, *Schistosoma hæmatobium;* 11, *Schistosoma japonicum;* 12, *Schistosoma mansoni.* The life cycle of each of the above trematodes may be traced by following its number and the appropriate arrows in the chart. The sporocyst stage in *Echinostoma ilocanum* is apparently absent.

TABLE 33

LIFE CYCLES OF IMPORTANT TREMATODES OF MAN

	Fasciola hepatica	Fasciolopsis buski	Opisthorchis felineus	Clonorchis sinensis	Heterophyes heterophyes	Metagonimus yokogawai	Paragonimus westermani	Dicrocoelium dendriticum	Echinostoma ilocanum	Schistosoma hæmatobium	Schistosoma japonicum	Schistosoma mansoni
First Intermediate Host												
Genera of Gastropods (number of species serving as hosts)												
Order PECTINIBRANCHIATA												
Brotia						6	7					
Pirenella					I							
Pomatiopsis							I					
Assiminea							I					
Hemibia											2	
Blanfordia											2	
Parafossarulus				I								
Bulimus			2	2								
Order PULMONATA												
Planorbis		I								I		10
Segmentina		5										
Gyraulus									I			
Bulinus										6		
Physopsis	I									3		
Helicella								3				
Cochlicella								I				
Zebrina								I				
Lymnæa	21											
Torquilla								I				
Stages in Gastropod Host												
Primary sporocyst	+	+	+	+	+	+	+	+		+	+	+
Secondary sporocyst							+			+	+	+
Mother redia	+	+	+	+	+	+	+		+			
Daughter redia	+	+				+	+		+			
Cercaria	+	+	+	+	+	+	+	+	+	+	+	+

TABLE 33—Continued

LIFE CYCLES OF IMPORTANT TREMATODES OF MAN

	Fasciola hepatica	Fasciolopsis buski	Opisthorchis felineus	Clonorchis sinensis	Heterophyes heterophyes	Metagonimus yokogawai	Paragonimus westermani	Dicrocoelium dendriticum	Echinostoma ilocanum	Schistosoma haematobium	Schistosoma japonicum	Schistosoma mansoni
First Intermediate Host—Continued												
Entry into Snail as:												
Ovum			+	+	?	?		+				
Miracidium	+	+					+		+	+	+	+
Secondary Intermediate Host												
Fishes			+	+	+	+						
Crustacea							+					
Gastropod mollusks									+			
Aquatic vegetation	+	+							+			
None										+	+	+
Definitive Host												
Natural Mammalian Hosts other than Man												
Domestic animals												
Cat			+	+	+	+	+	+			+	
Dog	+	+	+	+	+	+	+	+	+		+	
Equines	+							+			+	
Hog		+		+		+	+	+			+	
Ruminants	+							+			+	
Wild animals												
Fur-bearing carnivora (felines)							+	+				
Fur-bearing carnivora (other)						+	+	+				
Marsupials	+											
Rodents	+		+						+	+	+	
Primates										+	+	+
Ruminants	+							+				

from the yolk cells. In some species the ovum, on leaving the host, may be sufficiently mature to hatch soon after reaching water, while in other species it may require a developmental period.

Miracidium.—The miracidium (Fig. 165C) is a pyriform organism, covered with a ciliated ectodermal layer. It has a nonfunctional, primitive, pouch-like digestive tract with an anterior opening. Secretory glands, usually paired, open at the anterior end. There is a simple paired excretory system with flame-cells, a nervous system with ganglia, and a collection of germinal cells attached to the body wall or lying free in the posterior body cavity.

Sporocyst.—After penetrating the tissues of an appropriate snail the miracidium loses its cilia; its internal organs, except the germinal cells, gradually disappear; and it becomes a simple sac-like sporocyst (Fig. 165D and E). The sporocyst, eventually situated in the lymph spaces near the liver, increases in size by the absorption of nourishment from the tissues of the snail. The germinal cells develop until they fill the sporocyst as newly-developed larvæ (Fig. 165F). When the primary sporocyst matures these daughter embryos, liberated by the rupture of the parent sporocyst, become either secondary sporocysts (*Schistosoma*) or, in most species of trematodes, rediæ, which in turn give rise to a brood or successive broods of cercariæ.

Redia.—The redia (Fig. 165G and H) is equipped with an oral sucker, a pharynx and simple primitive gut, an excretory system with flame-cells and collecting tubules, and germinal cells that develop into cercariæ or daughter rediæ. In some species the rediæ may have a birth pore or may possess evaginated appendages. The rediæ usually produce cercariæ, but at times in certain species an additional generation of daughter rediæ may intervene before cercariæ are formed.

Cercaria.—The cercariæ (Fig. 165I and J) are liberated from the daughter sporocyst or rediæ by rupture of the wall or through the birth pore. They vary in size, shape and internal structure according to species. The typical cercaria has an elliptical body; an elongate caudal appendage for swimming; oral and ventral suckers; a digestive tract consisting of mouth, pharynx and bifurcated intestine; germinal cells; an excretory system; various spines or stylets; and unicellular secretory cephalic glands with ducts opening in the vicinity of the oral sucker. The lytic secretions of these glands enable the cercaria to penetrate the skin of definitive hosts (*Schistosoma*) or enter the tissues of secondary intermediate

---

Fig. 165 (*continued*).—*A*, immature ovum; *B*, miracidium in eggshell; *C*, miracidium ready to enter snail; *D*, a very young sporocyst, immediately after completion of metamorphosis; *E*, young sporocyst undergoing transverse fission; *F*, adult sporocyst with rediæ; *G*, immature redia; *H*, redia with developing cercariæ and one daughter redia; *I*, cercaria; *J*, body of cercaria; *K*, encysted metacercaria; *L*, excysted metacercaria.

ap., appendages; *b*, excretory bladder; *b.p.*, birth pore; *c*, ceca; *c.c.*, cystogenous cells; *cl.*, cilia; *col.*, collar; *e*, esophagus; *e.s.*, eye-spots; *f.c.*, flame-cells; *g.a.*, germinal area; *g.c.*, germinal cells; *i*, digestive tract; *m.c.*, mucoid cap; *o*, operculum; *o.s.*, oral sucker; *p*, pharynx; *pa.*, papilla; *t*, tail; *v.s.*, ventral sucker; *y*, yolk (*A* to *J* redrawn from Thomas, 1883; *K* adapted from Hegner, Root, Augustine and Huff, *Parasitology*, 1938, D. Appleton-Century Company; *L* redrawn from Leuckart, 1882).

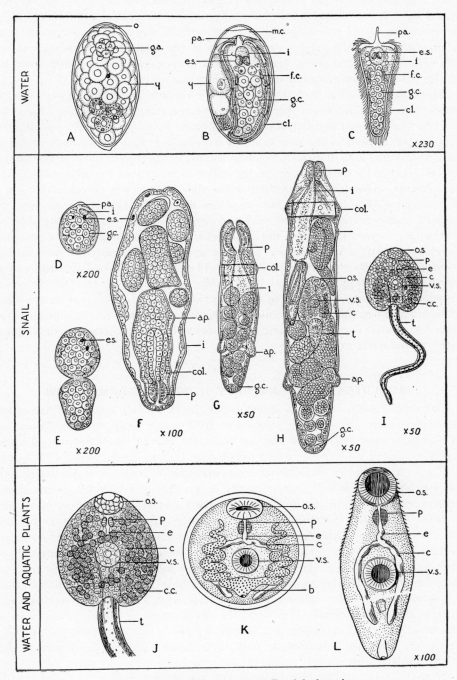

FIG. 165.—LARVAL FORMS OF *Fasciola hepatica*

hosts. Special cystogenous glands are present in species that encyst in secondary animal hosts or on plants. These glands secrete substances for attachment and for the formation of the true cyst wall. Of the cercarial organs only the suckers, and the digestive and excretory systems persist in the adult worm. Encystment may occur after penetration of the secondary intermediate host, in the water soon after leaving the snail and in rare instances in the snail itself.

Metacercaria.—The encysted stage of the cercaria is commonly known as the metacercaria. Save for those species where the cercaria directly invades the definitive host the encysted metacercaria is the infective form. In a broad sense the term metacercaria applies to the developing and migrating adolescent worm or adolescaria after entry into the definitive host either by the penetration of the skin by the cercariæ or by the ingestion of the encysted larva and its subsequent excystment. In the secondary intermediate hosts the metacercaria increases in size by the absorption of nourishment, but on plants there is no appreciable growth. The encysted metacercaria possesses oral and ventral suckers; a bifurcate digestive tract with pharynx, esophagus and ceca; inconspicuous genital cells; a prominent excretory system; a true cyst wall; and in secondary intermediate hosts an outer covering formed by the tissues of the host. The temporary larval structures of the cercaria, such as tail, spines and lytic glands, have disappeared. The changes in the adolescent worm during its migration to its normal habitat and its growth to sexual maturity in the definitive host are chiefly enlargement of the digestive tract, expansion of the excretory system, modification of the suckers and development of the reproductive organs.

MOLLUSCAN INTERMEDIATE HOSTS OF TREMATODES

Gastropod mollusks act as intermediate hosts for all species of trematodes parasitic in man. Only certain species of fresh-water snails serve as hosts, and their identification and control play an important rôle in the prevention of human infection.

The best method of establishing a given species of mollusk as a suitable intermediate host is to infect experimentally a susceptible uninfected mammal with cercariæ obtained from the snail or with their metacercariæ in secondary hosts in order to produce identifiable adult trematodes. Another method is to infect the snail with the miracidia of known parasites and observe the production of cercariæ, but it is open to the objection that the snail may already be infected with other morphologically-similar cercariæ. The least satisfactory method is to obtain from the snail larval forms with the distinguishing morphological characteristics of a definite species of trematode, a difficult task when other closely-related species occur in the same mollusk. Moreover, the development of larval forms in an experimentally-infected snail does not necessarily prove that the particular species of snail is an important intermediate host, since factors such as prevalence, ecology and habits determine natural hosts.

Nomenclature.—The identification and the correct nomenclature of the different molluscan species leave much to be desired. Identification in medical papers is often questionable, since this task requires the services of skilled malacologists and even then differences of opinion may arise. The confusion in generic names is bewildering and will require years for clarification. The names given below, though subject to change, suffice for the present.

Specificity.—The various species of trematodes have become adapted to a single or at most a few species of snails. They either fail to penetrate others or else do not complete their larval development. Even when many species of snails are capable of experimental infection, only a few may act as natural hosts, e.g., *Fasciolopsis buski* requires the genus *Planorbis* or the closely related *Segmentina; Metagonimus yokogawai* and *Paragonimus westermani* usually the genus *Brotia; Schistosoma hæmatobium* the genera *Bulimus* and *Physopsis; S. mansoni* the genus *Planorbis;* and *S. japonicum* the genera *Hemibia* and *Blanfordia*. The presence and ecological requirements of the different species of snails explain the geographical distribution of diseases due to trematodes.

Migration in Snail.—The miracidium is attracted to the snail by some fraction of the tissue juices or mucous secretions. Actual penetration is a matter of a few minutes. The miracidium digests the mesenchymatous tissue by the secretion of its lytic glands, forming a space which is soon connected with the lymphatic system.

Eventually the developing sporocysts reach the vicinity of the liver either by penetrating the respiratory tissues or the head, tentacles and foot. The fascioloid and echinostomatoid flukes prefer the former route and the schistosomes the latter. The migratory route of the larvæ of *Schistosoma mansoni* in *Planorbis guadeloupensis* (Fig. 166) proceeds from the head, tentacles and foot upward through the lymph spaces past the cephalic ganglia and salivary gland along the digestive tract to the liver.[6] By the eighth day small immature sporocysts are found at the several levels of the esophageal tissues and by the tenth day at the level of the seminal vesicle. They penetrate the septum from the twelfth to the fifteenth day. Rapid growth occurs in the vicinity of the stomach and secondary sporocysts erupt from the primary sporocyst in from 18 to 20 days. Cercariæ develop in the secondary sporocyst in the region of the liver and are found in numbers in the tissues after 27 to 35 days, ready to leave the snail.

Unsuitable species of snails apparently exert an injurious effect upon the miracidium. Observations upon the miracidia of *Fasciola hepatica* in contact with an unsuitable snail of the genus *Planaria* indicate that the mucus and outer covering of the snail first paralyze and then kill the miracidia.[5] Snails apparently develop some immunity against infection. Varieties of *Lymnæa stagnalis* acting as secondary intermediate hosts to *Cotylurus flabelliformis,* when infested with sporocysts of this species, showed an immunity, though not absolute, to the penetration of cercariæ of this strigeid.[7] Infection with *Schistosomatium douthitti* produced a partial nonspecific immunity against subsequent infection with *C. flabelliformis,* fewer and smaller metacercariæ developing than in normal snails.

Classification.—Of the 80,000 or more living species of mollusks, scarcely 60 species have been associated with helminthic disease in man. The mollusks that

---

[6] Faust, E. C. and Hoffman, W. A., 1934.

[7] Winfield, G. F., 1932; Nolf, L. O. and Cort, W. W., 1933.

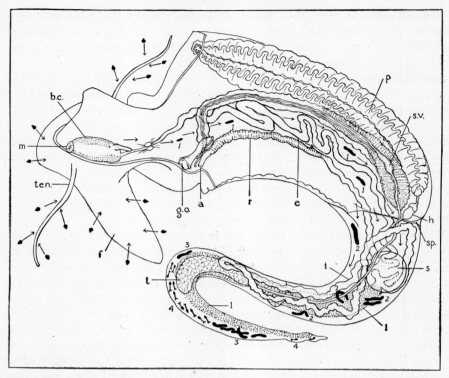

Fig. 166.—Migration and Development of Larval *Schistosoma mansoni* in the Snail, *Planorbis guadeloupensis*

1, immature primary sporocysts migrating through lymph spaces along digestive tract; 2, mature primary sporocysts in vicinity of stomach and liver; 3, secondary sporocysts in region of liver; 4, cercariæ in region of liver.

a, anus; *b.c.*, buccal cavity; *e*, esophagus; *f*, foot; *g.o.*, genital opening; *h*, heart; *i*, intestine; *l*, liver; *m*, mouth; *p*, pulmonary organ; *r*, rectum; *s*, stomach; *sp.*, septum; *s.v.*, seminal vesicle; *t*, ovotestis; *ten.*, tentacle (Redrawn with modifications from Faust and Hoffman, 1934).

serve as intermediate hosts of trematodes are terrestrial and fresh-water forms of the class GASTROPODA. The more important families that act as hosts of the trematodes of man are listed below.

Order PULMONATA.—Terrestrial or fresh-water snails and slugs without a confining operculum. Most species breathe through lungs. The intermediate hosts for the trematodes of man are chiefly the fresh-water species.

Family LYMNÆIDÆ.—Usually dextral, prominent raised acute spires. Genus *Lymnæa*.
Family PLANORBIDÆ.—Sinistral, secondary gills. Genera: *Planorbis, Segmentina, Bulinus* and *Physopsis*.

Order PECTINIBRANCHIATA.—Fresh-water snails with a calcareous or corneous operculum. Breathe chiefly through gills.

Family MELANIIDÆ.—Moderate or large size, dextral, often turreted and sculptured. Genera: *Brotia*.

Family AMNICOLIDÆ.—Small size, dextral, ovateconic, smooth, usually umbilicate. Genera: *Parafossarulus, Bulimus, Blanfordia* and *Hemibia*.

Geographical Distribution.—The principal geographical habitats of the several genera of snails that serve as intermediate hosts for the trematode parasites of man are listed below:

Order PULMONATA
    Family LYMNÆIDÆ
       Lymnæa—Cosmopolitan
    Family PLANORBIDÆ
       Planorbis—Central and South America, West Indies, southern Europe, North and Central Africa, southern Asia
       Segmentina—Eastern Asia.
       Bulinus—North, Central and South Africa
       Physopsis—Central and South Africa

Order PECTINIBRANCHIATA
    Family MELANIIDÆ
       Brotia—South and eastern Asia
    Family AMNICOLIDÆ
       Parafossarulus—Eastern Asia
       Bulimus—Eastern Asia, eastern Europe
       Blanfordia—Eastern Asia
       Hemibia—Eastern Asia

Ecology.—The distribution and habitat of the several families determine the prevalence and distribution of diseases due to trematodes.

Family LYMNÆIDÆ.—The numerous species of this common pond snail have a cosmopolitan distribution. They live in stagnant shallow-water ponds, ditches or brooks with muddy bottoms and abundant aquatic vegetation. Since they possess lungs, they can leave the water or temporarily withstand drought. On the other hand, they need not come to the surface to breathe. The eggs, laid in gelatinous masses on submerged stones, sticks and leaves, are readily destroyed by drought.

Family PLANORBIDÆ.—The species of this air-breathing family have the same habitat and general habits as the LYMNÆIDÆ and are frequently found together.

Family MELANIIDÆ.—The many species of these operculate gastropods prefer clean running water or the shores of deep lakes. Although unable to breathe air, they are better able to withstand prolonged drought than either the LYMNÆIDÆ or PLANORBIDÆ because of the tightly-closed operculum, and consequently are more difficult to eradicate.

Family AMNICOLIDÆ.—The several genera of this family have divergent habits in different parts of the world. *Parafossarulus* and *Bulimus* are found buried in the mud of slightly-polluted shallow ponds. They are able to withstand drying for months. *Blanfordia* and *Hemibia* spend part of the time in the shallow margins of clear still bodies of water and part on mossy banks protected from sunlight.

Control.—Control of gastropod vectors is often essential in preventing the diseases produced by trematodes. Effective control measures depend upon a knowledge of the ecology of the particular gastropod. The two principal methods of attack are drainage and chemical poisons, although other measures are sometimes employed (Section **VII**, XI).

Most of the species of snails that serve as intermediate hosts for the important trematodes of man are listed in Table 34, although the enumeration is not complete and several questionable host-species are omitted. The gastropod hosts of the less important trematodes are given under the descriptions of these parasites.

TABLE 34

GASTROPOD MOLLUSKS AS INTERMEDIATE HOSTS OF TREMATODES OF MAN

Order	Family	Genus	Species	Geographical distribution	Fasciola hepatica	Fasciolopsis buski	Opisthorchis felineus	Clonorchis sinensis	Heterophyes heterophyes	Metagonimus yokogawai	Paragonimus westermani	Dicrocoelium dendriticum	Echinostoma ilocanum	Schistosoma haematobium	Schistosoma japonicum	Schistosoma mansoni
PECTINIBRANCHIATA	MELANIIDÆ	*Brotia (Melania)*	*B. ebenina*	China						+						
			B. extensa	Korea						+	+					
			B. gottschei	Korea						+	+					
			B. libertina	China, Formosa, Japan, Korea						+	+					
			B. multicincta	Korea							+					
			B. nodiperda	Korea						+	+					
			B. obliquegranosa	Formosa						+	+					
			B. paucicincta	Korea							+					
	CERITHIIDÆ	*Pirenella*	*P. conica*	North Africa					+							
	AMPULLARIIDÆ	*Ampullaria*	*A. luteostoma*	Venezuela							?					
		Pila	*P. luzonica*	Philippines									+			
	HYDROBIIDÆ	*Pomatiopsis*	*P. lapidaria*	North America							+					
	ASSIMINEIDÆ	*Assiminea*	*A. lutea*	China							+					

Order	Family	Genus	Species	Locality						
PECTINIBRANCHIATA (Cont.)	AMNICOLIDÆ	*Hemibia*	*H. hupensis*	China		+				
		Hemibia	*H. quadrasi*	Philippines		+				
		Blanfordia (Oncomelania)	*B. formosana*	Formosa		+				
		Blanfordia (Oncomelania)	*B. nosophora*	China		+				
		Parafossarulus	*P. striatulus*	China, Formosa, French Indo-China, Japan, Korea				+		
		Bulimus (Bithynia)	*B. fuchsiana*	China				+		
		Bulimus (Bithynia)	*B. longicornis*	China				+		
		Bulimus (Bithynia)	*B. tentaculata*	Eastern Europe					+	
		Bulimus (Bithynia)	*B. leachi*	Eastern Europe					+	
PULMONATA	PLANORBIDÆ	*Planorbis*	*P. adowensi*	Central Africa	+					
		Planorbis	*P. alexandrinus*	North Africa	+					
		Planorbis	*P. antiguensis*	West Indies	+					
		Planorbis	*P. boissyi*	North Africa	+					
		Planorbis	*P. centimetralis*	Brazil	+					
		Planorbis	*P. cænosus*	China, Formosa, French Indo-China, India						+
		Planorbis	*P. dufourii*	North Africa, Portugal, Spain			+			
		Planorbis	*P. herbeni*	North Africa	+					
		Planorbis	*P. olivaceus*	Brazil, Dutch Guiana	+					
		Planorbis	*P. pfeifferi*	Central and West Africa	+					
		Planorbis	*P. guadeloupensis*	South America, West Indies	+					
		Planorbis	*P. sudanicus*	North Africa	+					

[1] Secondary intermediate host.

Table 34—Continued

GASTROPOD MOLLUSKS AS INTERMEDIATE HOSTS OF TREMATODES OF MAN

Order	Family	Genus	Species	Geographical distribution	Fasciola hepatica	Fasciolopsis buski	Opisthorchis felineus	Clonorchis sinensis	Heterophyes heterophyes	Metagonimus yokogawai	Paragonimus westermani	Dicrocoelium dendriticum	Echinostoma ilocanum	Schistosoma hæmatobium	Schistosoma japonicum	Schistosoma mansoni
PULMONATA (Cont.)	PLANORBIDÆ (Cont.)	Segmentina	S. calathus	China		+										
			S. hemisphærula	China, Formosa		+										
			S. nitidella	China, Japan		+										
			S. schmackeri	China		+										
			S. trochoideus	China		+										
		Gyraulus	G. prashadi	Philippines									+			
		Bulinus	B. brochii	North and Central Africa										+		
			B. contortus	North and Central Africa, Asia Minor										+		
			B. dybowskii	North Africa										+		
			B. forskali	East and Central Africa										+		
			B. innesi	North Africa										+		
			B. tropicus	South Africa										+		?
		Physopsis	P. africana	Central and South Africa	+									+		?
			P. globosa	Central and West Africa										+		
			P. nasuta	Central Africa										+		

HELICIDÆ	*Helicella*	*H. candidula*	Germany	+
		H. ericetorum	Germany	+
		H. itala	Scotland	+
	Cochlicella	*C. acuta*	Scotland	+
	Zebrina	*Z. detrita*	Germany	+
	Torquilla	*T. frumentum*	Germany	+
LYMNÆIDÆ	*Lymnæa*	*L. stagnalis, L. truncatula*	Cosmopolitan	+
		L. natalensis	South Africa	+
		L. brazieri	Australia	+
		L. plicatula	China	+
		L. suzuki, L. swinhoei	Formosa	+
		L. oahuensis, L. rubella	Hawaii	+
		L. acuminata, L. gedrosiana	India	+
		L. japonica, L. pervia	Japan	+
		L. cubensis, L. viator, L. viatrix	South America	+
		L. bulimnoides, L. bulimnoides var. techella, L. columella, L. ferruginea, L. modicella	North America	+

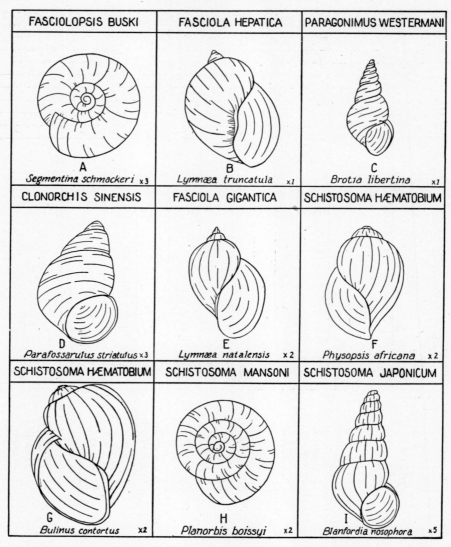

FASCIOLOPSIS BUSKI	FASCIOLA HEPATICA	PARAGONIMUS WESTERMANI
A	B	C
Segmentina schmackeri x3	*Lymnæa truncatula* x1	*Brotia libertina* x1
CLONORCHIS SINENSIS	FASCIOLA GIGANTICA	SCHISTOSOMA HÆMATOBIUM
D	E	F
Parafossarulus striatulus x3	*Lymnæa natalensis* x2	*Physopsis africana* x2
SCHISTOSOMA HÆMATOBIUM	SCHISTOSOMA MANSONI	SCHISTOSOMA JAPONICUM
G	H	I
Bulinus contortus x2	*Planorbis boissyi* x2	*Blanfordia nosophora* x5

Fig. 167.—Some Molluscan Intermediate Hosts of the Trematodes of Man

SECONDARY INTERMEDIATE HOSTS

Fishes.—Fresh-water or brackish-water fishes serve as intermediate hosts for at least seven genera of the well-known trematodes of man: the opisthorchoid and heterophyoid flukes, *Clonorchis, Opisthorchis, Heterophyes,* and *Metagonimus,* and also *Echinochasmus, Troglotrema* and *Echinostoma. Clonorchis sinensis* has been found in 40 species of cyprinoid fishes, of which the two most concerned with the transmission of clonorchiasis in man in China are *Ctenopharyngodon idellus* (Fig. 168A) and *Mylopharyngodon æthiops.*[8] *Opisthorchis felineus* has been re-

---

[8] Hsü, H. F. and Khaw, O. K., 1937.

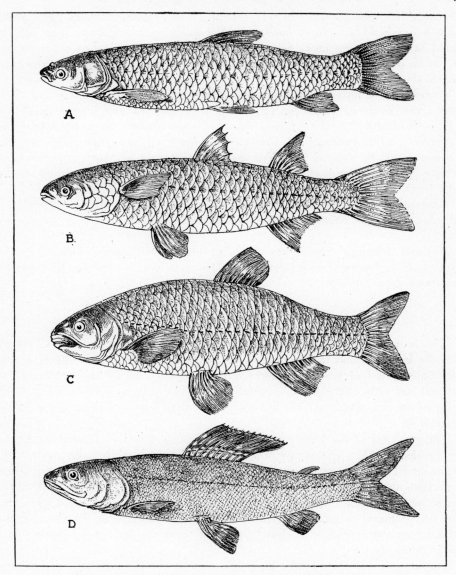

FIG. 168.—SOME PISCINE INTERMEDIATE HOSTS OF TREMATODES OF MAN

A, Ctenopharyngodon idellus, host of *Clonorchis sinensis* (× ⅓); *B, Mugil cephalus,* host of *Heterophyes heterophyes* (×¼); *C, Idus melanotus,* host of *Opisthorchis felineus* (× ⅓); *D. Plecoglossus altivelis,* host of *Metagonimus yokogawai* (× ⅓) (*A* redrawn from Hsü and Chow, 1937).

ported in eight genera of cyprinoid fishes of which *Idus melanotus* (Fig. 168C) and *Tinca tinca* are the chief sources of infection in man. *Heterophyes heterophyes* infects the brackish-water mullet, *Mugil cephalus* (Fig. 168B). *Metagonimus yokogawai* has been observed in the salmonoid *Plecoglossus altivelus* (Fig. 168D) and the cyprinoid *Leuciscus hakuensis*. *Echinochasmus perfoliatus* has been reported in some 19 cyprinoid fishes and one of the family ESOCIDÆ; *Troglotrema salmincola* in Pacific salmon and trout and *Echinostoma malayanum* in the cyprinoid *Barbus stigma*.

Crustacea.—*Paragonimus westermani* encysts in eastern Asia in the freshwater crabs, *Eriocheir japonicus* (Fig. 213C), *E. sinensis, Potamon dehaani* (Fig. 213B), *P. rathbuni, P. denticulatus, Parathelphusa sinensis, Sesarma dehaani* and *S. sinensis,* and in Venezuela *Pseudothelphusa iturbei*. It also encysts in crayfishes, in eastern Asia in *Astacus japonicus* and *A. similis* and in North America in ten or more species of Cambarus (Fig. 213A). Of these crustacea *Eriocheir japonicus* and *Potamon dehaani* are the species ordinarily eaten by man.

Gastropod Mollusks.—*Echinostoma ilocanum* encysts in *Pila luzonica, E. malaynum in Lymnæa leuteola* and *E. revolutum* in eight or more diverse genera of snails.

Aquatic Plants.—The flukes encysting on aquatic plants include: *Fasciola hepatica, F. gigantica, Fasciolopsis buski, Dicrocœlium dendriticum* and possibly *Eurytrema pancreaticum*.

PATHOLOGY

The lesions produced by flukes depend upon their location in the host and upon the irritating and toxic action of the parasites. The systemic effects are due to the absorption of toxic substances with allergic reactions on the part of the host and indirectly to the injury of vital organs. The severity depends upon the invasion of the ova, larvæ or adult worms into the tissues as well as upon the number of parasites.

The parasites of the biliary tract and liver cause a progressive hyperplasia of the bile ducts with adenomatous proliferation, thickening of the walls, cystic dilatations, and infiltration of connective tissue. In heavy infections or with continuous reinfections there is an extensive replacement of the liver parenchyma with fibrous connective tissue and eventually a portal cirrhosis. The same pathological conditions are produced by *Clonorchis sinensis, Opisthorchis felineus, Fasciola hepatica* and *Dicrocœlium dendriticum,* but in the last three the incidence of infection in man is relatively low.

The lungs are invaded by the lung fluke, *Paragonimus westermani* and at times by immature and mature schistosomes and their ova. In paragonimiasis there is a generalized or localized fibrosis, cystic dilatation of the bronchi, and tuberculoid lesions. Pulmonary lesions are not uncommon in schistosomiasis, the ova and adult worms producing arteriolar and focal pneumonic changes.

The schistosomes or blood-flukes inhabit the portal and mesenteric vessels. Their ova and to a lesser extent the adult parasites produce lesions of the intestine and bladder, while the migration of the immature worms causes minor lesions in diverse organs. *Schistosoma hæmatobium* chiefly affects the bladder and *S. japonicum* and *S. mansoni* the lower intestine.

The flukes that inhabit the intestinal tract are usually less harmful than those that invade the tissues. As a rule little injury results except in heavy infections. The worms injure the mucosa, produce hemorrhage and pave the way for secondary bacterial infection. *Fasciolopsis buski,* the large intestinal fluke, produces the most severe symptoms, advanced cases showing continuous diarrhea, anemia and ascites. *Heterophyes heterophyes, Metagonimus yokogawai* and *Echinostoma ilocanum* and other less common intestinal flukes also cause various intestinal disorders, diarrhea and general symptoms.

IMMUNITY

Parasites that invade the tissues or blood call forth the greatest immunological response, since they produce more tissue damage and provide greater opportunity for absorption than do parasites of the intestinal lumen. Hence immunity is largely confined to those flukes that have a larval or an adult somatic existence. With few exceptions the study of immunity in trematode infections has been confined to schistosomiasis (Chapter XXXV) and fascioliasis (Chapter XXX).

In man, age-resistance cannot be readily differentiated from acquired immunity or from the effects of customs and habits, although schistosomiasis is not often found in persons over 40 years of age. Age-resistance against the cloacal trematode, *Parorchis acanthus,* has been noted in herring gulls [9] and against the ectoparasitic monogenetic trematode, *Epibdella melleni,* in the black angel fish, *Pomacanthus arcuatus.*[10]

Previous infection tends to produce a certain degree of immunity, rarely absolute, as indicated by epidemiological evidence and by animal and human experimentation in schistomiasis (Chapter XXXV). This immunity appears to be a group-response to all species of schistosomes. Previous infection does not protect the herring gull against reinfection with *Parorchis acanthus* [9] and does not confer an appreciable resistance in snappers to *Hamacreadium mutabile* or *H. gulella,* although the brief existence of the secondary parasites in heavily-infected fish suggest some immune response.[11] Partial immunity against *Fasciola hepatica* in rabbits and against schistosomes in dogs has been produced by injecting suspensions of dried larval or adult parasites. The production of alexin-fixative antibodies, precipitins and allergic sensitizing antibodies has been reported in both man and animals by a number of investigators. The normal serum of certain vertebrates contains a highly labile substance, which has an antagonistic action against the cercariæ of various trematodes.[12]

REFERENCES

BEQUAERT, J. Mollusks of Importance in Human and Veterinary Medicine, Am. J. Trop. Med., 1928, 8:165; 215.

BROOKS, F. G. Studies on the Germ Cell Cycle of Trematodes, Am. J. Hyg., 1930, 12:299.

[9] Cable, R. M., 1937.
[10] Nigrelli, R. F. and Breder, C. M., Jr., 1934.
[11] McCoy, O. R., 1930.
[12] Culbertson, J. T. and Talbot, S. B., 1935.

FUHRMANN, O.   Zweite Klasse des Cladus Plathelminthes. Trematoda, In: Kükenthal's Hand-
    buch der Zoologie, Berlin und Leipzig, 1928, 2:1.
HOEPPLI, R., FENG, L. C. and CHU, H. J.   Attempts to Culture Helminths of Vertebrates in
    Artificial Media, Chinese M. J. Suppl., 1938, 2:343.
LA RUE, G. R.   Studies on the Trematode Family Strigidæ (Holostomidæ) No. III Rela-
    tionships, Tr. Am. Micr. Soc., 1926, 45:265.
PEARSE, A. S.   Zoological Names. A List of Phyla, Classes and Orders, Duke Univ. Press,
    1936, 1-24.
PILSBRY, H. A. and BEQUAERT, J.   The Aquatic Molluscs of the Belgian Congo, Am. Museum
    Nat. Hist., 1927, 53:69.
STILES, C. W. and HASSALL, A.   Key-catalogue of the Worms Reported for Man, Hyg. Lab.
    Bull. 142, 1926, Washington.
STUNKARD, H. W.   The Physiology, Life Cycles and Phylogeny of the Parasitic Flat Worms,
    Am. Museum Novitiates, 1937, 908, 27 pp.

Chapter XXX

THE SUPERFAMILY FASCIOLOIDEA

SUPERFAMILY *FASCIOLOIDEA* (STILES AND GOLDBERGER, 1910) FAUST, 1929

All members of the superfamily FASCIOLOIDEA belong to the family FASCIOLIDÆ Railliet, 1895. They are moderately large, flattened, leaf-like trematodes, usually with a spiny cuticle, lobed or branching ovary and testes, a short uterus anterior to the ovary, an elongated excretory bladder with numerous branching ducts, diffuse vitellaria extending along the lateral margins, and a ventral sucker in close proximity to the oral sucker. The large, operculate ova, in the early stages of segmentation at oviposition, hatch in water. The miracidia invade snails, in which they metamorphose into sporocysts, usually one or more generations of rediæ, and large cercariæ with simple tails. The liberated cercariæ encyst on vegetation or in fishes, and are thus ingested by the definitive hosts. The adult worms are parasites of the bile ducts and intestines of mammals. One species, *Fasciolopsis buski,* is an important intestinal parasite of man. Two other species, *Fasciola hepatica* and *Fasciola gigantica,* are accidental parasites of man.

Fasciola hepatica LINNÆUS, 1758

Synonyms.—*Distoma hepaticum* Linnæus, 1758; *Distomum hepaticum* Retzius, 1786; *Planaria latiuscula* Goeze, 1782; *Cladocœlium hepaticum* (Linnæus, 1758) Stossich, 1892.

Disease.—Fascioliasis, "liver rot."

History.—The sheep liver fluke, the first trematode to be described, was discovered by Jehan de Brie in 1379. Its intricate life cycle has interested many investigators.

Geographical Distribution.—Cosmopolitan, throughout the sheep-raising areas of the world. It is most prevalent in low wet pastures where suitable species of snails are indigenous. In the United States of America it occurs along practically all the coastal streams. At least 130 cases of human infection have been reported from Venezuela, Chile, Argentina, Cuba, Puerto Rico, Salonika, Turkey, France, Hungary, Italy, Rumania, Scotland, Russia, Algeria, French Somaliland, Turkestan, Syria, China, and Australia. About 25 cases have been reported from Cuba since 1931.

BIOLOGICAL CHARACTERISTICS

Morphology.—*Fasciola hepatica* (Fig. 169) is a large, flat, brownish, leaf-shaped trematode measuring from 2.0 to 3.0 cm. in length by 0.8 to 1.3 cm. in breadth. A cephalic cone, 0.4 to 0.5 cm. in length, gives a characteristic shouldered appearance to the worm. The integument is covered by scales, but the posterior surface may be smooth. Hemispherical oral and ventral suckers of equal size are present at the apex and base of the cephalic cone. The intestinal tract has a well-developed pharynx, a short esophagus, and two divergent intestinal ceca with numerous lateral diverticula. There is a posterior, elongate bladder with lateral branches.

The highly-dendritic testes are situated one behind the other in the middle of the body. The vasa efferentia unite in a vas deferens just before reaching the cirral sac, which encloses the seminal vesicle, prostatic portion, and cirral organ. The ejaculatory

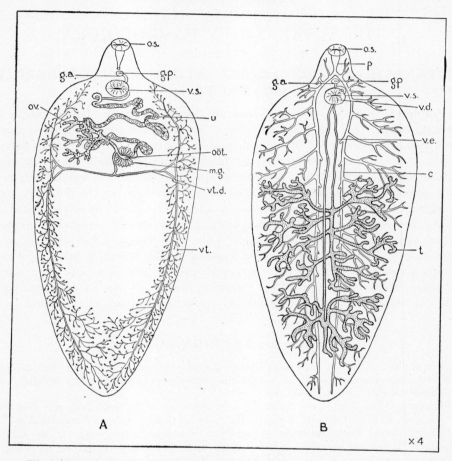

FIG. 169.—SCHEMATIC REPRESENTATION OF MORPHOLOGY OF *Fasciola hepatica*

A, female reproductive organs, ventral view; *B,* male reproductive organs and digestive tract, ventral view.

c, ceca; *g.a.,* genital atrium; *g.p.,* genital pore; *m.g.,* Mehlis' gland; *oöt.,* oötype; *o.s.,* oral sucker; *ov.,* ovary; *p,* pharynx; *t,* testes; *u,* uterus; *v.d.,* vas deferens; *v.e.,* vas efferens; *v.s.,* ventral sucker; *vt.,* vitellaria; *vt.d.,* vitelline duct (Adapted from Sommer, 1880 and from Leuckart, 1863).

duct terminates in a genital atrium midway between the oral and ventral suckers. The multilobed ovary lies anterior to the testes to the right of the median line. The diffusely-branched vitellaria fill the entire lateral and posterior portions of the body. The typical female reproductive organs, except a seminal receptacle, are present. The coiled tubular uterus opens into the genital atrium to the left of the male orifice.

Physiology.—*Fasciola hepatica* has an anaerobic metabolism. It obtains its nourishment from the biliary secretions. A longevity of three years in rabbits and at least five years in sheep has been reported.

LIFE CYCLE

Hosts.—The adult fluke is a natural parasite of sheep and cattle but also may infect the horse, goat, camel, llama, elephant, buffalo, ass, dog, rabbit, guinea pig, squirrel, beaver, deer, antelope, kangaroo, monkey, and man. Its intermediate hosts are some 21 species of *Lymnæa* (Table 34), of which *Lymnæa truncatula*, a snail that inhabits temporary bodies of water and sluggish brooks, is the most important. Species of the genera *Galba, Fossaria, Succinea, Pseudosuccinea, Practicolella, Bulinus, Bulimus,* and *Ampullaria* have also been incriminated.

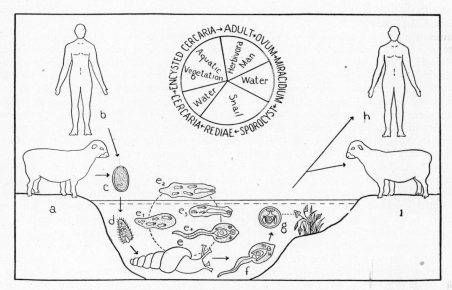

FIG. 170.—LIFE CYCLE OF *Fasciola hepatica*

a, definitive animal host, the chief source of infection; *b,* man infected with adult worm; *c,* ovum passed in feces; *d,* free-swimming miracidium; *e,* metamorphosis in snail (*e₁,* sporocyst; *e₂,* mother redia; *e₃,* daughter redia; *e₄,* cercaria); *f,* free-swimming cercaria; *g,* metacercaria, usually encysted on aquatic vegetation; *h,* man infected by accidental ingestion of metacercariæ; *i,* herbivorous animal infected by grazing on vegetation infested with metacercariæ.

Developmental Cycle.—After leaving the host the ovum hatches in a moist environment, releasing the active free-swimming miracidium, which, upon penetrating an appropriate species of snail, metamorphoses successively into sporocyst, mother rediæ, daughter rediæ, and cercariæ. The liberated cercariæ, after a brief free-swimming existence, encyst on various grasses and water plants. When these grasses are ingested by grazing animals, the larvæ excyst in the duodenum, pass through the intestinal wall into the abdomen, penetrate the liver, and eventually reach the biliary passages where they grow to maturity (Fig. 170).

Larval Forms.—The large, oval, yellowish-brown, operculate unsegmented ova (Fig. 165A), 130 to 150 μ in length by 63 to 90 μ in breadth, are laid in the biliary ducts, pass to the intestine, and are evacuated in the feces. The numerous yolk cells, besides supplying nutritive substances for the fertilized ovum, contribute material for the shell.

Malformed ova are produced regularly during the early stages of generative activity, and their presence is often indicative of recent infection.[1]

The ovum completes its development in water after leaving the host, but it does not necessarily hatch until five or more days after the mature miracidium is formed. Hatching is accomplished by the opening of the operculum through the intake of water in the fluid vacuole situated just inside the operculum.[2] Increased acidity of the water, often occasioned by rain, accelerates hatching. At an optimal temperature of 23° to 26° C. hatching takes place in from 10 to 15 days after the ovum leaves the host, at 11° to 18° C. in from 20 to 40 days, and at lower temperatures only after long periods.[3]

The resistant ova remain viable in moist feces for nine months or more. The most favorable hydrogen-ion concentration for their existence is pH 7.5 to 8.0. They are killed by desiccation and by temperatures below — 4° C.[2] The free-swimming ciliated miracidium (Fig. 165C), 130 by 27 μ, has a cephalic papilla, eye-spots, two flame-cells, and a rudimentary digestive tract. It perishes unless it penetrates a suitable species of snail within eight hours.

Metamorphosis into sporocysts (Fig. 165D-F) takes place in the lymph spaces of the snail. The sporocysts develop rediæ, which in turn produce other rediæ or cercariæ. The redia (Fig. 165G and H), 1.5 mm. in length when mature, has a digestive tract, excretory system, lateral appendages, and a birth pore. In cold weather, when development is slow, daughter rediæ are formed, which in turn produce cercariæ; but in summer, when growth is more rapid, only cercariæ are produced by the mother rediæ.[4] Mature cercariæ are produced in 32 to 54 days at 24° to 32° C.[5] Below 10° C. development is inhibited. In the lowlands of North Germany the maximal swarming of cercariæ occurs in August and September. Snails containing cercariæ have been found in March, showing that the larvæ survive the severe cold of winter.[6]

The cercariæ (Fig. 165I and J) have an unforked tail about 700 μ in length and a spinose body, 280 to 350 μ in length by 250 μ in breadth, containing the usual cercarial organs and numerous cystogenous cells. They emerge from the snail late in the evening and within eight hours undergo encystment. This process takes place rapidly; the body assumes a rounded form, a mucous envelope of considerable thickness is secreted by the cystogenous cells in a few minutes, and the tail is discarded. The encysted cercariæ (Fig. 165K) are found as small white spherical bodies on grasses, plants, bark, soil or even floating in the water. The cercariæ rarely settle on objects more than 4.5 cm. below the surface of the water. Thus epidemics in grazing animals are more prevalent in years of floods, since the receding waters expose large areas of infested grass. The danger from infection from dry hay is evidently slight, since desiccation kills the metacercariæ within 44 days.

When the cysts dissolve in the duodenum, the excysted metacercariæ (Fig. 165L) penetrate the intestinal wall into the peritoneum, whence they usually pass through the liver capsule and tissues to the biliary tract. They may also enter the mesenteric veins and lymphatics and reach the liver through the general circulation. At least twelve weeks are required to produce mature egg-producing flukes.

PATHOGENESIS

Pathology.—In heavy infections the migrating larvæ may produce extensive destruction of the liver in animals. The pathological processes in the biliary passages result from the mechanical, irritative and toxic actions of the parasites. There is hyperplasia of the biliary epithelium with adenomata and cystic dilatation of the biliary passages, leukocytic infiltration with many eosinophils, and periductal deposition of connective

---

[1] Taylor, E. L., 1934.
[2] Mattes, O., 1926.
[3] Thomas, A. P. W., 1883; Lievre, H., 1932; Luhrs, E., 1933; de Jesus, Z., 1935.
[4] Wright, W. R., 1927; Ross, I. C., 1930.
[5] Ross, I. C., 1930; Krull, W. H., 1933; de Jesus, Z., 1935.
[6] Noller, W. and Schmid, F., 1927.

tissue. Deposits of ova in the tissues set up multiple centers of inflammation. Hepatic enlargement is followed by portal cirrhosis with atrophy of the hepatic cells and portal vessels. Secondary bacterial invasion may occur. Occasionally the parasites are found in abnormal locations in other tissues.

Symptomatology.—About one-fourth of the infections in man have been reported from Cuba. The symptoms include hepatic colic, rigidity of the abdominal wall with pain on pressure, urticaria, eosinophilia, jaundice, irregular fever, a more or less persistent diarrhea, and rarely hemoglobinuria. Cases of acute cholecystitis, obstruction of the common duct, and biliary cirrhosis have been reported. An eosinophilia as high as 68 per cent and a leukocytosis of 23,000 have been recorded. The patient may show a profound toxemia with cachexia and anemia from absorption of the toxic products of the living and dead worms. A unique form of infection has been observed in Syria, in which symptoms of suffocation have resulted from the pharyngeal attachment of adult worms, ingested in raw livers.

Immunity.—Humoral antibodies in the blood serum of infected animals have been demonstrated by a number of investigators using precipitative, alexin-fixative, and cutaneous tests. Animals have been sensitized locally by intracutaneous injections of extracts of adult flukes.[7] Partial immunity has been obtained in rabbits by successive injections of an aqueous antigen of dried *Fasciola hepatica,* as evidenced by calcification of the flukes and absence of ova in the feces in some of the immunized animals.[8]

DIAGNOSIS, PROGNOSIS AND TREATMENT

Diagnosis.—Diagnosis is made by finding the ova in the feces or in material obtained by biliary drainage. The ova require differentiation from those of *Fasciolopsis buski.* Their presence in the feces of persons who have recently eaten infected liver may lead to an erroneous diagnosis, since the ova pass undamaged through the intestinal tract.[9]

Several investigators have employed precipitative, alexin-fixative and intradermal tests for the diagnosis of fascioliasis in man, sheep and cattle using aqueous and alcoholic extracts of the adult flukes as antigens (Section **VII**, IX, 10 to 15). These tests are inferior to the detection of ova in the feces, since they do not reveal light or recent infections (68 to 90 per cent positive), yield a high percentage of positive reactions in uninfected animals (5 to 78 per cent), and in man give pseudopositive reactions in syphilis and cross-reactions in schistosomiasis. However, specific precipitative reactions, which were more pronounced in acute liver damage than in chronic disease and were independent of the stage of development of the parasite, have been reported in infected sheep and cattle.[10]

Prognosis.—Prognosis is grave in heavy infections. When few worms are present, destruction of liver tissue is slight and symptoms are mild. The presence of the flukes predisposes to secondary bacterial infection.

Treatment.—Oleoresin of aspidium (Section **VII**, XIII, 29), administered in two doses of 0.1 ml. per kilogram of body weight 24 hours apart, has proved effective for sheep and cattle. It kills the adult flukes, but does not destroy the immature worms in the smaller bile ducts. Carbon tetrachloride (Section **VII**, XIII, 21) has also proved successful with sheep. Intramuscular injections of 0.03 to 0.04 gm. of emetine hydrochloride (Section **VII**, XIII, 14) daily for 18 days is recommended for hepatic infection in man, but it is ineffective for parasites elsewhere in the body.[11]

PREVENTION

Epidemiology.—Herbivorous animals are infected in low, damp pastures, where the vegetation is infested with metacercariæ. Man is believed to contract the disease acci-

---

[7] Curasson, M. G., 1935.
[8] Kerr, K. B. and Petkovich, O. L., 1935.
[9] Strom, Z. K., 1927; Kulagin, S. M., 1929.

[10] Trawinski, A., 1937.
[11] Kouri, P. and Arenas, R., 1932; Rodrí-guez-Molina, R. and Hoffman, W. A., 1938.

dentally by ingesting vegetation or, possibly, water containing the encysted cercariæ. Only sporadic cases of infection are found in man, the highest reported incidence being 0.7 per cent in Tiflis, Russia.[12] The incidence in sheep and cattle, however, may be very high; for instance, in Esthonia 57.3 per cent of the sheep and 71.7 per cent of the cattle and in Transcaucasia 48 per cent of the sheep are infected.

Prophylaxis.—The control of the disease in sheep and cattle calls for treating infected animals at the beginning of winter, when there is no danger of fresh infection; the use of uncontaminated drinking water; the destruction of the snails that act as intermediate hosts by drainage or chemical agents (Appendix XI); and the destruction of ova or metacercariæ by copper sulphate, 1 to 2 p.p.m., applied to infected waters and low pasture land every two or three months.[13] In man prevention depends upon the washing and cooking of raw vegetables and the boiling of drinking water.

Fasciola gigantica COBBOLD, 1856

The giant liver fluke is a natural parasite of the biliary tract of cattle and water buffaloes and is also found in other herbivorous animals in Africa and the Orient. Only three cases of infection in man have been reported, from Africa, Indo-China and the Uzbek Republic, Central Asia.

The adult worm is distinguished from *Fasciola hepatica* by its greater length, more elongate shape, shorter cephalic cone, larger ventral sucker, more anterior location of the reproductive organs, and the larger ova, 150 to 190 μ by 70 to 90 μ. Its life cycle and pathology resemble those of *Fasciola hepatica*. The ova hatch in 14 days at 26° to 28° C., the development in the snail requires 39 days, and the incubational period in the definitive host is 77 to 84 days.[14] Its intermediate gastropod hosts are *Lymnæa natalensis, L. acuminata, Fossaria ollula* and *Physopsis africana*. Diagnosis may be made from the large operculate ova in the feces or bile. Treatment and prevention of infection are similar to the measures employed with *Fasciola hepatica*.

Fasciolopsis buski (LANKESTER, 1857) ODHNER, 1802

Synonyms.—*Distoma crassum* Busk, 1859; *Distomum rathouisi* Poirier, 1887; *Fasciolopsis rathouisi* (Poirier, 1887) Ward, 1903; *Fasciolopsis fülleborni* Rodenwaldt, 1909; *Fasciolopsis goddardi* Ward, 1910; *Fasciolopsis spinifera* Brown, 1917.

Disease.—Fasciolopsiasis.

History.—*Fasciolopsis buski,* the large intestinal fluke, was discovered in 1843 by Busk in a Lascar sailor in London. Lankester in 1857 described the parasite under the name of *Distoma buskii,* but it was renamed *Distoma crassum* and more fully described in 1859 by Cobbold. In 1899 Looss created the genus *Fasciolopsis*. Several species of *Fasciolopsis* from man have been described under various names, but their distinguishing morphological characteristics, chiefly cuticular spines, are no greater than the variations that result in a single species from handling and preservation. Hence it is now believed that there is but one species in man.

Geographical Distribution.—The parasite is found in man and the hog in Central and South China as far north as the Yangtze valley, Formosa, Assam,

---

[12] Karibov, N., 1929.
[13] Luhrs, E., 1933.
[14] Alicata, J. E., 1938.

Siam, Annam, Tonkin, Bengal, Borneo, Sumatra, and the Malay Peninsula (Fig. 171). The chief endemic area is in the Kwanghung and Chekiang Provinces of China where its high incidence creates an important public health problem.

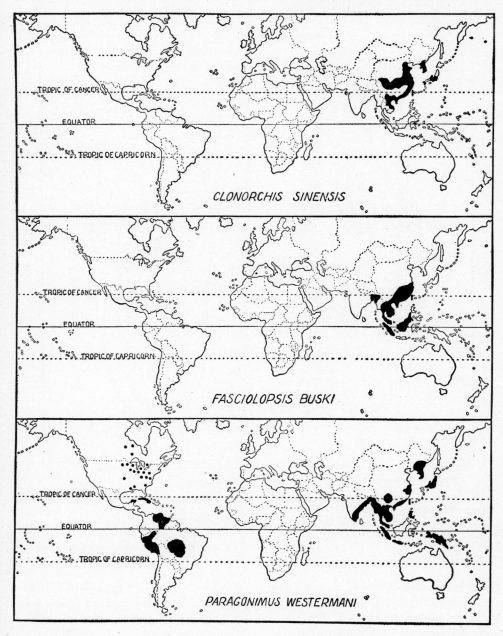

CLONORCHIS SINENSIS

FASCIOLOPSIS BUSKI

PARAGONIMUS WESTERMANI

FIG. 171.—GEOGRAPHICAL DISTRIBUTION OF *Clonorchis sinensis, Fasciolopsis buski* AND *Paragonimus westermani*

BIOLOGICAL CHARACTERISTICS

Morphology.—The adult fluke (Fig. 172) is a thick, fleshy, ovate, flesh-colored worm. The younger specimens are usually more rounded, have more compact testes, a more rotund ovary, and a distinct oral sucker.[15] It is the largest of

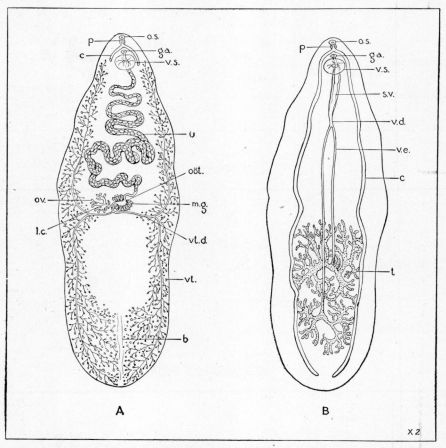

FIG. 172.—SCHEMATIC REPRESENTATION OF MORPHOLOGY OF *Fasciolopsis buski*

A, female reproductive organs, ventral view; *B,* male reproductive organs and digestive tract, ventral view.

b, bladder; *c,* ceca; *g.a.,* genital atrium; *m.g.,* Mehlis' gland; *l.c.,* Laurer's canal; *oöt.,* oötype; *o.s.,* oral sucker; *ov.,* ovary; *p,* pharynx; *s.v.,* seminal vesicle; *t,* testes; *u,* uterus; *v.d.,* vas deferens; *v.e.,* vas efferens; *v.s.,* ventral sucker; *vt.,* vitellaria; *vt.d.,* vitelline duct (Adapted from Odhner, 1902).

the parasitic trematodes of man, varying from 2.0 to 7.5 cm. in length by 0.8 to 2.0 cm. in breadth, and is about 0.2 cm. thick. The average length is about 3 cm. and the average breadth 1.2 cm. The size varies in different patients and decreases with the intensity of infection.

[15] Hung, S. L., 1933.

The cuticle is covered with transverse rows of small spines, which are especially numerous about the ventral sucker, but since these spines are susceptible to the action of the digestive juices, they are often absent. The subterminal oral sucker is one-fourth the size of the nearby ventral sucker. The intestinal tract comprises a short prepharynx, a bulbous pharynx, a short esophagus and a pair of unbranched ceca which pass to the posterior end of the worm with two characteristic indentations, one at the forward border of the anterior testis, the other between the testes (Fig. 172B). The two highly-branched testes are situated one behind the other in the middle of the posterior half of the body. The two vasa efferentia unite in the middle of the anterior half of the body to enter the posterior of two seminal vesicles in a long cylindrical cirral sac, which also contains the ejaculatory duct and cirral organ and opens through the precirral canal into the genital atrium at the anterior border of the ventral sucker.

The branched ovary (Fig. 172A) is situated in the middle of the body to the right of the midline. The oötype, surrounded by a well-developed Mehlis' gland, also lies in the midsection. The vitellaria extend from the level of the ventral sucker along the lateral fields to meet at the posterior end of the body. Their ducts converge into transverse tubes that form the common vitelline duct at the posterior aspect of Mehlis' gland. From the oötype the uterus follows a convoluted course to open into the genital atrium.

Physiology.—The fluke inhabits the small intestine particularly the duodenum, but sometimes may be found in the stomach or in the large intestine. It attaches itself to the mucosa by its ventral sucker or lies buried in the mucous secretions, its spines and oral extremity giving additional anchorage. It usually remains stationary, but keeps up a more or less continuous extension and contraction. It obtains its nourishment from the intestinal contents and secretions. The daily production of ova per fluke ranges from 15,000 to 48,000 with a mean output of between 21,000 and 28,000.[16]

LIFE CYCLE

Hosts.—*Fasciolopsis buski* lives normally in the small intestine of man and the hog; dogs, monkeys and rabbits may be infected, but the worms do not develop to maturity in these animals.[17] The intermediate molluscan hosts (Table 34) are *Planorbis cœnosus, Segmentina calathus, S. hemisphœrula, S. nitidella, S. schmackeri, S. trochoideus.* Larval forms have been found also in *Hippeutis cantori* and *Gyraulus saigonensis* but their rôle as natural hosts still awaits proof.[18] The plants (Fig. 174) on which the cercariæ encyst include the water caltrop, *Trapa natans, T. bispinosa* and *T. bicornis;* the water hyacinth, *Eichhornia crassipes;* the water chestnut, *Eliocharis tuberosa;* the water bamboo, *Zizania aquatica; Salvinia natans; Spirodela (Lemna) polyrhiza;* and species of *Vallisneria.* The cercariæ, however, show little selective specificity and seem able to encyst on all sorts of aquatic vegetation in stagnant ponds.[18]

[16] Stoll, N. R., Cort, W. W. and Kwei, W. S., 1927.

[17] Young, S., 1936.
[18] Wu, K., 1937.

Developmental Cycle.—The life cycle of *Fasciolopsis buski* (Fig. 173), which was first worked out by Nakagawa in 1921 in the hog, and in man by Barlow in 1925, closely resembles that of *Fasciola hepatica*. The miracidium after escaping from the shell, swims actively in the water. Usually within two hours, it penetrates a suitable molluscan host or perishes after 5 to 56 hours. Within the snail it metamorphoses successively into sporocyst, mother and daughter rediæ and cercariæ. After 30 or more days the cercariæ leave the snail and following a brief free-swimming existence encyst on aquatic plants. The encysted

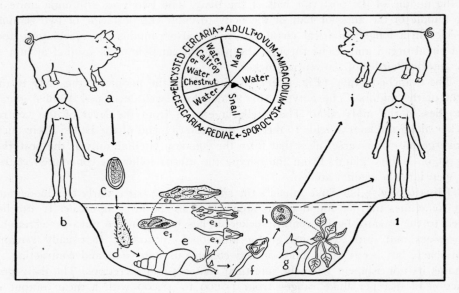

FIG. 173.—LIFE CYCLE OF *Fasciolopsis buski*

a, reservoir host, the hog; *b,* man infected with adult worm; *c,* ovum in feces; *d,* free-swimming miracidium; *e,* metamorphosis in snail (*e₁,* sporocyst; *e₂,* mother redia; *e₃,* daughter redia; *e₄,* cercaria); *f,* free-swimming cercaria; *g,* water caltrop or other aquatic plants; *h,* metacercaria encysted on aquatic plants; *i,* man infected by eating uncooked plants infested with metacercariæ; *j,* hog infected in similar manner.

parasite is ingested by man, when infested plants are eaten raw. In the duodenum the cyst wall is dissolved by the digestive juices and the excysted metacercaria attaches itself to the mucosa of the upper intestine, where it becomes an adult worm.

Ova.—The yellowish-brown, ellipsoidal ova have a clear thick shell with a small operculum at one end (Fig. 174A). They measure from 130 to 140 μ in length by 80 to 85 μ in breadth and, when evacuated in the feces, are undeveloped. The granules in the yolk cells are uniformly distributed, whereas in *Fasciola hepatica* ova they are accumulated around the nucleus.[19] The ova of *Echinochasmus perfoliatus,* although smaller, resemble those of *Fasciolopsis buski.*

The fertilized ovum divides at first into an ectodermal cell and a propagatory cell; the former giving rise to the enveloping membranes and the latter to the

---

[19] Kamisaka, T., 1930.

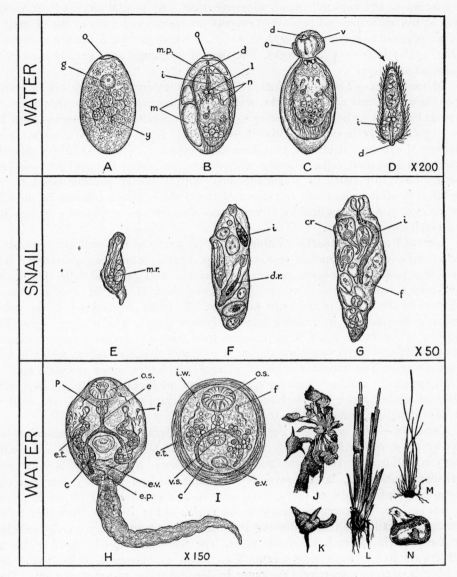

FIG. 174.—LARVAL FORMS OF *Fasciolopsis buski*

A, undeveloped ovum; *B,* miracidium in eggshell; *C,* hatching of miracidium; *D,* miracidium; *E,* sporocyst; *F,* mother redia; *G,* daughter redia; *H,* cercaria; *I,* metacercaria; *J,* water caltrop, *Trapa natans; K,* fruit of *Trapa natans; L,* water bamboo, *Zizania aquatica; M,* water chestnut, *Eliocharis tuberosa;* N, tuber of *Eliocharis tuberosa.*

c, ceca; *cr.,* cercaria; *d,* dimple; *d.r.,* daughter redia; *e,* esophagus; *e.p.,* excretory pore; *e.t.,* excretory concretions; *e.v.,* excretory vesicle; *f,* flame-cell; *g,* germinal area; *i,* primitive digestive tract; *i.w.,* inner cyst wall; *l,* optic lens; *m,* oil masses; *m.p.,* mucoid plug; *m.r.,* germ ball from which mother redia develops; *n,* neurone; *o,* operculum; *o.s.,* oral sucker; *p,* pharynx; *v,* vitelline membrane; *v.s.,* ventral sucker; *y,* yolk (*A* to *J* redrawn from Barlow, 1925; *K* to *N* redrawn from Wu, 1937).

primordia of the cephalic gland, digestive tract and genital organs.[20] A mucoid plug at the opercular end probably prevents premature loosening of the operculum. At an optimal temperature of 27° to 32° C. it develops into a mature miracidium (Fig. 174B) in from 3 to 7 weeks. The time of hatching varies greatly even in the same batch of ova.

Miracidium.—The miracidium (Fig. 174D) emerges through the opercular opening and swims actively in the water with a counter-clockwise movement for a period of 6 to 52 hours, depending upon the temperature. It is covered with five tiers, each of six hexagonal, ciliated, ectodermal plates, and has a spined head, pigmented eye-spot, neurones, two flame-cells, cephalic gland, a primitive digestive tract, and germinal cells. Usually within two hours the miracidium penetrates the exposed soft parts of a suitable snail with a boring motion aided by the suctorial headpit, spines and secretions of the cephalic gland, meanwhile shedding its ciliated plates. Occasionally it may pass through the respiratory orifice into the respiratory chamber.

Larval Forms in Snail.—Within the lymph spaces of the snail, the miracidium metamorphoses into a mobile sporocyst (Fig. 174E), which has a digestive tract without a pharynx, eye-spots, an excretory system and germinal cells. The sporocyst grows rapidly until it reaches an average size of 400 by 110 μ, when it migrates to the region of the heart and liver. The rediæ, formed within the sporocyst, are liberated by its rupture into the lymph spaces. The mother redia (Fig. 174F), 700 by 150 μ, has a large digestive tract with a pharynx, a muscular collar, a birth pore and locomotor appendages. It produces daughter rediæ, which in turn form cercariæ. The daughter redia (Fig. 174G) is larger, more sacculate and has a proportionally smaller digestive tract than the mother redia. In 13 days after infection mother rediæ both free and in the sporocysts are present in the snail, in 22 days daughter rediæ, and in 30 days cercariæ.[20]

Cercaria.—The cercaria (Fig. 174H) has a straight slender muscular tail, 500 by 57 μ, and a heavy body, 195 by 145 μ. It is equipped with a muscular pharynx, bifurcated ceca, oral and ventral suckers, a muscular bladder with vesicular concretions, large convolute collecting tubules, probably four pairs of flame-cells, two groups of cystogenous glands, and small spines on its head and ventral surface. The cercariæ remain in the region of the liver for some time before leaving the snail. The free-swimming stage is brief and ordinarily merely sufficient for the cercaria to reach a suitable plant. The cercaria swims by lashing the tail and crawls like a measuring worm. Two kinds of cystogenic cells, round and rhabdoidal, secrete respectively the outer friable and inner resistant cyst wall. During encystment, which occupies from one to three hours, the tail is cast off. The average time between infection of the snail and encystment is 49 days.

Metacercaria.—The metacercariæ (Fig. 174I) are attached to the integument of plants, but do not penetrate into the tissues. The cysts are subspherical, the outer wall measuring about 216 by 187 μ and the inner 148 by 138 μ. The outer wall is friable and is easily detached from the plant. The inner wall resists hydrochloric acid but dissolves in the intestinal juices. The number of cysts on the red water

---

[20] Yoshio, I., 1934.

caltrop, *Trapa natans,* is often large, as many as 1,000 being present on a single fruit.[18] The cysts resist cold and show no deterioration after a year at 5° C., although they survive best at a temperature of 42° C. Desiccation, however, is fatal, death occurring in a few minutes at summer temperatures.

When infected plants are peeled with the teeth, the cysts are swallowed. In the duodenum the inner cyst is dissolved and the activated larva breaks out of its membrane, attaches itself to the mucosa of the upper intestine, and grows to an adult worm in about 25 to 30 days.

PATHOGENESIS

Pathology.—Localized foci of inflammation occur at the site of attachment in the duodenum and upper small intestine. These lesions may involve the capillaries of the intestinal wall, producing hemorrhage or abscesses with infiltration of small round cells and eosinophils. Large numbers of worms (as many as 3,721 have been recovered from a nine-year-old girl) may cause intestinal stasis and produce intoxication.

Symptomatology.—Symptoms usually develop in 30 to 60 days after exposure, especially in massive infections. The gradual onset and increasing severity of symptoms have been described by Barlow, who became infected with 124 flukes after experimentally ingesting 132 metacercariæ.[21] Epigastric pain and hunger preceding meals were observed in 41 days. These symptoms subsided after a few days and then returned with increased severity. After 73 days there was severe, griping hypogastric pain every morning, lasting until half an hour after eating, and short periods of diarrhea with intervening mushy stools containing some mucus. A severe diarrhea with intermittent, intense, griping pains and large quantities of gas began at the eighty-fourth day and lasted for a week. Infected persons do not always show noticeable symptoms. They are usually absent in light infections, but at times persons harboring few worms may develop symptoms and those with numerous worms manifest none.

Three stages have been described: [22] (1) a latent period with no marked symptoms corresponding to the developmental stage of the parasite, (2) a period of several months with abdominal pain and sometimes diarrhea, and (3) a final period of edema and anasarca.

In severe infections the symptoms are abdominal discomfort, nausea, abdominal pain with tenderness in right upper quadrant, diarrhea, anemia and edema. The gnawing abdominal pains may simulate those of gastric ulcer. They are relieved by food, thus increasing the chances of repeated infection among workers in the field through eating raw water caltrops. The diarrhea is nondysenteric in type and tends to be persistent with greenish-yellow fermenting stools containing incompletely digested food. It is not a constant symptom and may alternate with constipation. There is no jaundice, and no blood in the feces.

In heavy infections edema may appear early. In the third stage of the disease it becomes distressing especially in children (Fig. 175) and undernourished patients. In most fatal cases there is edema with ascites and extensive anasarca, but the chest

[21] Barlow, H. C., 1925.   [22] Goddard, F. W., 1919.

is rarely involved. The abdomen in children is frequently distended. The skin is harsh and dry. There is extreme prostration and death results from intoxication and exhaustion.

The red blood cells show little change. The apparent anemia is due to the asthenia resulting from the intoxication and to the masking of the blood vessels by the overlying edema. There is a relatively high leukocytosis in about one-half of the patients with clinical fasciolopsiasis and an absolute eosinophilia which may reach 34 per cent.[23] However, there may be a leukopenia or at times a lymphocytosis.

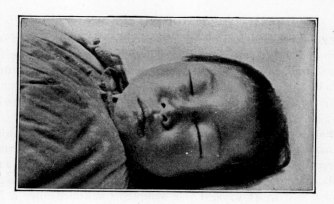

FIG. 175.—PATIENT WITH FASCIOLOPSIASIS, SHOWING EDEMA OF CHEEKS AND ORBITAL AREA

(From Faust, *Human Helminthology,* Second Edition, 1939. Courtesy Lea and Febiger, Philadelphia).

DIAGNOSIS, PROGNOSIS AND TREATMENT

Diagnosis.—The clinical symptoms of fasciolopsiasis, while not diagnostic, are sufficiently characteristic to arouse suspicion when they occur in an endemic area. Final diagnosis is based in finding in the feces the characteristic ova, which must be differentiated from those of *Fasciola hepatica, F. gigantica* (larger) and *Echinochasmus perfoliatus* (smaller). Adult flukes are sometimes vomited or passed in the feces.

Prognosis.—Except in cases of severe anasarca prognosis is good provided treatment is given. The patient usually undergoes an uneventful recovery after the elimination of the worms.

Treatment.—Beta-naphthol (Section **VII**, XIII, 26) and carbon tetrachloride (Section **VII**, XIII, 21) have been used successfully in fasciolopsiasis. The latter is more effective but less safe and requires careful supervision in the treatment of children. Tetrachlorethylene (Section **VII**, XIII, 22), a safer drug than carbon tetrachloride, should prove equally efficient. In children under 7 years hexylresorcinol (Section **VII**, XIII, 23) has produced cures in about half the cases and reduced the intensity of infection in half the remainder.[24] Tetrachlorethylene and hexylresorcinol are the drugs of choice in the treatment of this infection.

[23] Young, S., 1935.   [24] McCoy, O. R. and Chu, T. C., 1937.

PREVENTION

Epidemiology.—Human infection usually results from the ingestion of metacercariæ on the raw fruit, bulbs and stems of edible water plants. The chief plants in the dissemination of human infection are the water caltrop, *Trapa natans* in Chekiang Province and in Canton, China; *T. bicornis* in India and *T. bispinosa* in Formosa; the so-called water chestnut, *Eliocharis tuberosa,* in South China and Formosa; and the water hyacinth, *Eichhornea crassipes,* in Formosa. The red water caltrop, *Trapa natans,* is most heavily infested, since it thrives in ponds fertilized by night soil, while the other plants live in the canals that receive night soil only indirectly. The pods of the water caltrop and the bulbs of the water chestnut are sold in the Chinese markets in the fresh state from mid-July to September and later in dried form. When eaten raw, they are peeled with the teeth, thus rupturing the fragile outer wall of the cysts and permitting the detached metacercariæ to reach the mouth. Since desiccation kills the metacercariæ only the fresh plants are dangerous.

Prophylaxis.—The control of fasciolopsiasis involves: (1) reduction of the sources of infection by treatment; (2) destruction of the ova and larval forms in night soil, water and soil; (3) reduction of the gastropod hosts; and (4) most important of all, thorough cooking of edible plants infested with metacercariæ.

Clinics for the treatment of fasciolopsiasis will reduce human but not the porcine sources of infection. Ideally, areas where water caltrops and chestnuts grow should be kept free from fecal contamination. Since the economic necessity of using night soil as a fertilizer makes such a step impractical, the ova should be destroyed by prolonged storage of night soil in vats or by treatment with unslaked lime. In soil and water, ova, miracidia and cercariæ may be killed by unslaked lime 100 p.p.m. or copper sulphate 1 p.p.m. The intermediate hosts, the snails, may be destroyed in various ways (Section **VII,** XI). The abolition of the custom of eating raw aquatic plants would soon eliminate infection in man, but this would require educating the public to the danger of this practice. Such measures, though simple in theory, demand fundamental changes in the eating habits, customs and economic conditions of the people. Nevertheless, since the endemic area is limited, fasciolopsiasis may ultimately be controlled.

REFERENCES

ALICATA, J. E. Observations on the Life History of *Fasciola gigantica,* the Common Liver Fluke of Cattle in Hawaii, and the Intermediate Host, *Fossaria ollula,* Hawaii Agric. Exper. Sta. Bull. 80, 1938, 22 pp.

BARLOW, C. H. The Life Cycle of the Human Intestinal Fluke, *Fasciolopsis buski* (Lankester), Am. J. Hyg., Monographic Series, 1925, No. 4, 98 pp.

GODDARD, F. W. *Fasciolopsis buski;* a Parasite of Man as Seen in Shaohing, China, J. Parasitol., 1919, 5 :141.

DE JESUS, Z. *Lymnaea philippinensis,* an Intermediate Host of *Fasciola hepatica* in the Philippines, With Some Observations on the Bionomics of the Parasite, Philippine J. Sc., 1935, 58 :299.

LEUCKART, R. Zur Entwicklungsgeschichte des Leberegels (*Distomum hepaticum*), Arch. f. Naturgesch., 1882, 48 :80.

McCoy, O. R. and Chu, T. C. *Fasciolopsis buski* Infection Among School Children in Shaohing and Treatment with Hexylresorcinol, Chinese M. J., 1937, 51:937.

Thomas, A. P. W. The Life History of the Liver Fluke (*Fasciola hepatica*), Quart. J. Micr. Sc., 1883, 23:99.

Wright, W. R. Studies on Larval Trematodes from North Wales; Observations on the Redia, Cercaria, and Cyst of *Fasciola hepatica*, Ann. Trop. Med., 1927, 21:47.

Wu, K. Deux nouvelles plantes pouvant transmettre le *Fasciolopsis buski*, Revue générale, Ann. de parasitol., 1937, 15:458.

Young, S. The Blood Picture in Fasciolopsiasis (*F. buski*), Tr. 9th Congr. Far Eastern Assn. Trop. Med., 1935, 1:563.

Chapter XXXI

THE SUPERFAMILY OPISTHORCHOIDEA

FAMILY *OPISTHORCHIDÆ* LÜHE, 1901

All known species of the superfamily OPISTHORCHOIDEA belong to the family OPIS-
THORCHIDÆ. They have elongate, flat, transparent, flabby bodies, tapering anteriorly. The
integument may be smooth (*Opisthorchis, Clonorchis*) or spinous (*Metorchis*).
The weakly-developed oral and ventral suckers are close together in the anterior end. The
lobed or branched testes are situated one behind the other in the posterior third of
the body. There are no cirral sac, cirral organ or prostatic glands. The excretory bladder
is Y-shaped with unequal arms and a median anterior pouch. Flame-cell pattern 2(2+2+
2+2+2+2). The small operculate ova are fully developed at oviposition. The first
intermediate host is a snail and the second a fresh-water fish. The adult worms live in
the biliary passages of mammals and birds. The species parasitic in man are *Clonorchis
sinensis, Opisthorchis felineus, O. viverrini* and *O. noverca*.

Clonorchis sinensis (COBBOLD, 1875) LOOSS, 1907

Synonyms.—*Distoma sinense* Cobbold, 1875; *D. spathulatum* Leuckart, 1876; *D.
hepatis innocuum* Baelz, 1883; *D. hepatis endemicum* Baelz, 1883; *D. endemicum* Ijima,
1886; *Opisthorchis sinensis* Blanchard, 1895; *Clonorchis endemicus* Looss, 1907, *pro
parte.*

Disease.—Clonorchiasis.

History.—The Chinese or oriental liver fluke was discovered by McConnell
in 1875 in the biliary tract of a Chinese at Calcutta and was given the name *Distoma
sinense* by Cobbold. Several cases were found among Chinese in Mauritius and in
India. In 1883 Baelz described a small and a large species in Japan. At first he considered only the smaller of pathological significance, but later he decided that both
forms were a single species. Likewise Looss in 1907 and Verdun and Bruyant in
1908 differentiated two types of *Clonorchis sinensis,* a major and minor, a belief
that persisted until Kobayashi in 1917 and Ch'en Pang in 1923 proved that the difference in size was merely species variation. Blanchard in 1895 created the genus
Opisthorchis, in which the parasite remained until 1907, when Looss established the
genus *Clonorchis.*

Saito in 1898 first observed the miracidia and Kobayashi, in his studies on the
pathology of the disease between 1911 and 1917, produced adult worms in mammals by experimental feedings of fresh-water fishes containing encysted cercariæ.
Muto in 1918 identified the first intermediate host by finding the cercariæ in fresh-
water snails. Faust and Khaw in 1927 made a comprehensive investigation of the
biology of the parasite and epidemiology of the infection in China, while Hsü and

Khaw in 1936 and 1937 contributed further studies on the metacercaria, secondary intermediate hosts and epidemiology.

Geographical Distribution.—The fluke is a parasite of fish-eating mammals in Japan, China, Formosa, Korea and French Indo-China (Fig. 171). The chief foci of human infection are in Japan, southern Korea, Kwangtung Province in China, and the Red River delta in French Indo-China. The disease is clinically important only in the Okayama Prefecture, although more or less distributed throughout Japan. It is prevalent in eastern South China, occurs occasionally in Central China and is practically nonexistent in North China. No foci of infection have been established by immigration in other parts of the world because of the lack of suitable intermediate hosts, although many cases of infection in Cantonese immigrants have been reported in Cuba and elsewhere.[1] The presence of the disease in native Hawaiians has been attributed to infected fish imported from China or Japan.[2]

BIOLOGICAL CHARACTERISTICS

Morphology.—The adult fluke is a flat, elongate, aspinous, flabby worm tapering anteriorly and somewhat rounded posteriorly (Fig. 176). The living worm is a transparent, opalescent gray, but when discolored by bile has a deep brown color. In light infections it ranges in size from 11.5 to 20.1 mm. in length by 2.8 to 4.6 mm. in breadth with a mean length of 16.5 mm.[3] The great variation in size apparently depends upon the number of parasites, the location in large or small bile ducts and the size of the mammalian host. The oral sucker is directed anteriad and the small ventral sucker is one quarter the length of the body from the anterior end. The digestive tract (Fig. 177) consists of a small globose pharynx behind the oral sucker, a short esophagus and two somewhat dilated ceca that terminate blindly near the posterior end of the worm. A long sacculate bladder with a terminal excretory pore, lying in the posterior part of the body, receives collecting tubules from a branching network of capillaries on each side of the body.

The deeply-lobed testes lie one in front of the other in the posterior part of the body. The two vasa efferentia join to form the vas deferens which soon enlarges into the seminal vesicle. The latter ascends to the genital atrium in front of the acetabulum, where it opens through a poorly-developed ejaculatory duct without cirral pouch, cirrus or prostatic glands. The small faintly-lobate ovary lies in the midplane at the upper level of the posterior third of the body near the anterior end of the bladder. The vitellaria, a collection of minute follicles in the lateral midportion of the body, drain into a common vitelline duct that joins the oviduct between the common opening of Laurer's canal and the seminal receptacle and the oötype surrounded by Mehlis' gland. A closely-coiled, convoluted uterus, arising from the oötype, lies in the middle of the body and terminates in the genital atrium.

Physiology.—The worm moves sluggishly, its anterior fourth probing about with a restless, rotary movement. Although equipped with two suckers and well-developed muscles, it usually lies unattached in the distal portion of the biliary

---

[1] Kouri, P. and del Frade, A., 1935.　　　[3] Faust, E. C. and Khaw, O. K., 1927.
[2] Binford, C. H., 1934.

tract, particularly the left lobe of the liver. It may fold transversely or longitudinally and even roll up in the dilated biliary passages. During life it is not found in the common bile duct and duodenum and rarely invades the gallbladder. Apparently it cannot survive the action of the intestinal ferments for more than six hours, although after death the worms may crowd the common duct and even enter the

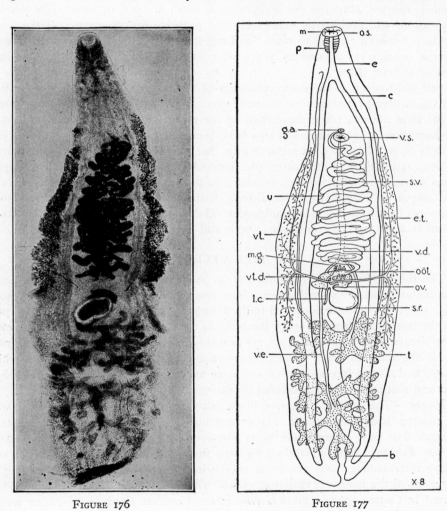

FIGURE 176   FIGURE 177

FIG. 176.—*Clonorchis sinensis* (From Smith and Gault, *Essentials of Pathology*, 1938, D. Appleton-Century Company).

FIG. 177.—SCHEMATIC REPRESENTATION OF MORPHOLOGY OF *Clonorchis sinensis*

b, excretory bladder; *c*, ceca; *e*, esophagus; *e.t.*, excretory tubules; *g.a.*, genital atrium; *l.c.*, Laurer's canal; *m*, mouth; *m.g.*, Mehlis' gland; *oöt.*, oötype; *o.s.*, oral sucker; *ov.*, ovary; *p*, pharynx; *s.r.*, seminal receptacle; *s.v.*, seminal vesicle; *t*, testes; *u*, uterus; *v.d.*, vas deferens; *v.e.*, vas efferens; *v.s.*, ventral sucker; *vt.*, vitellaria; *vt.d.*, vitelline duct.

duodenum and pancreatic duct. The worm probably feeds upon the secretions from the mucosa of the upper biliary ducts, although erythrocytes and leukocytes have been observed in its digestive tract.

The adult worm will survive for five months outside the host, if kept at 37° C. in diluted sera changed weekly; but without change of medium survival *in vitro* is much shorter, although the addition of a small amount of mercurochrome-220 or prontosil will prolong its existence.[4] The probable life expectancy of the worm in man is between 15 and 20 years,[3] and ova have been recovered from the feces of Chinese immigrants 20 and 25 years after leaving China.[5] Worms in dogs have lived up to four years.[6]

Self-fertilization is the common means of fecundation, although cross-fertilization via Laurer's canal may occasionally occur. Well-advanced embryos are formed by the time the ova reach the middle of the uterus. Egg-laying is independent of egg-formation. In cats imperfect ova have been observed in the uterus as early as 14 days after infection with metacercariæ, but ova are not usually recovered from the feces until 28 to 30 days after infection.[3] Once begun, the process of egg-laying seems continuous. The variable numbers in the stools are due to irregularities in fecal output, to differences in consistency of the stools, and to temporary retention of the ova in the bile ducts or gallbladder. The average daily output per parasite in the cat is 2,400; in the guinea pig, 1,600; and in the dog, 1,100.[3]

LIFE CYCLE

The life cycle of *Clonorchis sinensis* involves snails as first intermediate hosts, fresh-water fishes as second intermediate hosts and mammals as definitive hosts (Fig. 178). The ova are deposited in the biliary passages of the definitive host, pass into the intestinal tract and leave the body in the feces. Susceptible snails in water contaminated with fecal discharges are probably infected through the digestive tract. Within the snail the larva develops through successive stages into cercariæ, which emerge and after a free-swimming existence encyst in fresh-water cyprinoid fishes. Man and mammals become infected by eating raw or imperfectly-cooked fish.

Hosts.—The natural definitive hosts other than man are dog, cat, hog, wild cat, marten, badger and mink. The guinea pig and rabbit may be experimentally infected. The first intermediate hosts are operculate snails of the family AMNICOLIDÆ, *Parafossarulus striatulus, Bulimus fuchsiana* and *B. longicornis*. The secondary intermediate hosts are some 40 species of fresh-water fishes belonging to 23 genera of the family CYPRINIDÆ, of which 24 species have been incriminated in China.[7] In Canton the two most heavily infected species, *Ctenopharyngodon idellus* (Fig. 168A) and *Mylopharyngodon æthiops* are used in raw fish dishes and four other species are cultivated in ponds and sold for food. In Peiping *Ctenopharyngodon idellus* and *Culter aburnus* are the two most important food fishes involved.

Ova.—The light yellowish-brown ova average 29 by 16 μ, ranging from 27 to 35 μ in length and from 12 to 20 μ in breadth (Fig. 179A). The shell resembles in

[4] Hoeppli, R., Feng, L. C. and Chu, H. J., 1938; Chu, H. J., 1938.
[5] Moore, D., 1924.
[6] Muto, M., 1922.
[7] Hsü, H. F. and Chow, C. Y., 1937.

shape an old-fashioned carbon filament electric light bulb with the operculum at the smaller end. The operculum rests in a rim with pronounced shoulders in such a position that its contour does not follow the curvature of the shell. The surface of the shell has an arabesque polygonal pattern apparently produced by irregularities of the outer layer. At the thickened posterior end is a small median protuberance, usually comma shaped. The embryo is fully developed at oviposition, has the characteristic structures of the miracidium and is surrounded by mucoid padding. Two

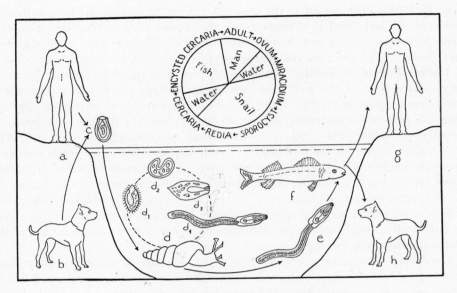

FIG. 178.—LIFE CYCLE OF *Clonorchis sinensis*

a, man infected with adult worm; *b*, animal reservoir host; *c*, ovum in feces; *d*, metamorphosis in snail (*d₁*, miracidium after hatching in intestine of snail; *d₂*, sporocyst; *d₃*, redia; *d₄*, cercaria); *e*, free-swimming cercaria; *f*, fresh-water fish with encysted metacercariæ; *g*, man infected by eating raw or insufficiently cooked fish; *h*, reservoir animal host infected in similar manner.

types of abnormal eggs are found: (a) anomalous eggs with neither miracidium nor operculum formed continuously throughout the life of the parasite; and (b) operculate eggs without miracidium occurring in young and old worms or during anthelmintic treatment.[8]

The mature ovum will live for six months in the ice box, for one month at 26° C., for three weeks at 37° C., for one hour at 50° C., and for only a few minutes at 58° C. It is readily killed by desiccation. In old putrefying feces it succumbs within 48 hours at 26° C. and in five days in the ice box. In fresh urine it survives for two days at 37° C. and for five minutes in 1:1,000 corrosive sublimate.

Although the ova contain mature embryos, they do not hatch upon reaching the water except under abnormal conditions such as an abrupt change in temperature,

[8] Youmoto, Y., 1936.

alternate freezing and thawing, mechanical pressure or a temporary increase in the tonicity of the medium followed by a return to normal.

Miracidium.—The miracidium (Fig. 179D) is a top-shaped organism, 32 μ in length and 17 μ in breadth. It is larger than the unhatched embryo which is only 25 x 12 μ. The ectodermal sheath is covered with cilia while a blunt solid spine, 1.6 μ in length, crowns the small head papilla. A bladder-like, primitive digestive tract containing coarse granules opens by a short duct ventrad to the spine. A sausage-shaped, finely-granular secretory gland fills the ventral side of the body and opens by a long duct dorsad to the spine. A pair of flame-cells in the dorsal mid-section of the body lead to a single trunk that opens dorsally one-third the body length from the posterior end. A small mass of nerve cells is ventrad to the digestive tract. Some 8 to 25 germinal cells are scattered through the body cavity.

Larval Forms in Snail.—Available evidence indicates that the ova hatch in the digestive tract of the snail and then penetrate into the lymph spaces where they become sporocysts (Fig. 179E, F). The immature, oval sporocyst migrates along the peri-intestinal lymph sinuses, elongates, becomes inactive and produces a number of rediæ (Fig. 179G-I), which break out through the thin wall. The active rediæ migrate to the interhepatic lymph sinuses where they reach maturity. They are elongate bodies with a muscular covering, prominent pharynx, yellowish-brown cecum and a core of germinal epithelium, but are distinctive in having no lateral appendages and no birth pore, so typical of many trematodes. Within each redia 6 to 8 cercariæ develop which eventually break out of the mother redia into the interhepatic lymph spaces. At maturity they penetrate the tunica propria of the snail and escape into the water.

Cercaria.—The mature cercaria (Fig. 179J, K) has an ellipsoidal body from 130 to 170 μ by 60 to 80 μ and a tail, 330 to 380 μ by 33 to 42 μ, equipped with a sheath and a dorsoventral keel. The body has an oral sucker, an ovoidal ventral sucker, a primitive digestive tract, penetration glands, a bladder and excretory system, and a genital primordium. The cercaria leads a free-swimming existence for 24 to 48 hours, but when inactive sinks to the bottom. Unless it encounters a fish within this period it perishes.

Fig. 179 (*continued*).—*A*, ovum with miracidium; *B*, miracidium in eggshell, showing detailed structure, viewed from left side; *C*, miracidium in act of hatching, viewed from right side; *D*, free-swimming miracidium; *E*, early sporocyst; *F*, mature sporocyst with rediæ; *G*, young redia; *H*, redia with early cercariæ; *I*, redia with developing cercariæ; *J*, cercaria, lateral view; *K*, body of cercaria, ventral view; *L*, metacercarial cyst in muscles of fish, with long axis parallel to muscle fibers; *M*, encysted metacercaria in ellipsoidal cyst; *N*, excysted metacercaria, ventral view.

b, excretory bladder; *c*, ceca; *c.c.*, cystogenous cells; *c.g.*, cephalic penetration glands; *c.s.*, cuticular sheath; *d.m.*, dorsal membrane; *e*, esophagus; *e.p.*, excretory pore; *e.s.*, eye-spot; *f.c.*, flame-cell; *g.b.*, germ balls; *g.c.*, germinal cells; *o*, operculum; *o.s.*, oral sucker; *ov.*, anlage of ovary, seminal receptacle and Laurer's canal; *p*, pharynx; *p.c.*, pigment cells; *p.g.*, primitive gut; *s*, papillary spine; *s.g.*, skin glands; *s.h.*, sensory hairs; *t*, anlage of testes; *tl.*, tail; *u*, anlage of uterus; *v.m.*, ventral membrane; *v.s.*, ventral sucker; *y*, yolk (*A* to *I* redrawn from Faust and Khaw, 1927; *J* and *K* redrawn from Yamaguti, 1935; *L*, drawn from a photograph by Faust and Khaw, 1927; *M*, drawn from a photograph by Hsü and Khaw, 1936; *N*, redrawn from Hsü and Khaw, 1937).

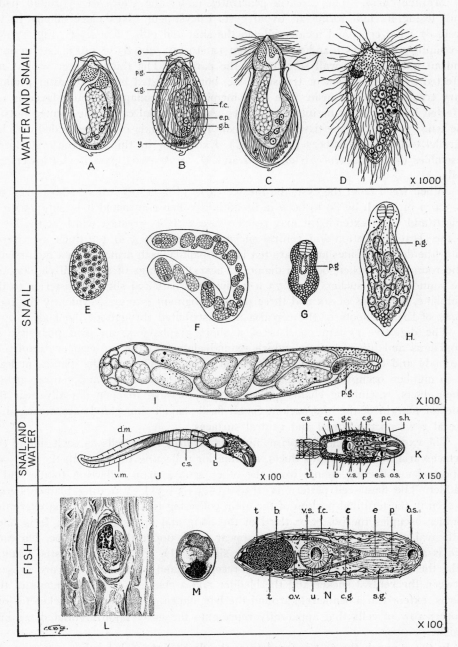

FIG. 179.—LARVAL FORMS OF *Clonorchis sinensis*

Metacercaria.—The cercaria penetrates under the scales of cyprinoid fishes and, losing its tail, forms an ovoid cyst. Encystment takes place chiefly in the flesh, 87.4 per cent, and incidentally in the skin and gills.[9] The cyst (Fig. 179M) averaging 138 by 115 μ and ranging from 121 to 150 μ by 85 to 140 μ, has an outer and an inner hyaline wall secreted by the parasite. The thicker outer wall is not affected by either pepsin or trypsin alone, but is digested by trypsin after preliminary treatment with pepsin. The thin, membranous, collapsible inner layer is unaffected by the gastric or intestinal juices. An additional capsule is formed outside the true cyst wall by the tissues of the fish. The long axis of the imbedded cyst lies parallel to the muscle fibers (Fig. 179L). Except for its thin wall the cyst closely resembles those of *Metorchis orientalis* and *M. taiwanensis,* parasites of lower animals.

When freed from the cyst, the metacercaria (Fig. 179N) at rest measures 300 to 320 μ in length by 80 to 90 μ in breadth.[10] When contracted it is only 150 μ in length and when extended it may reach 500 μ with its greatest width at the levels of the cecal bifurcation and ventral sucker. The cuticle, 3 to 4 μ thick, is covered with fine delicate spines and bears ten lateral papillæ each armed with a tactile hair. The round oral sucker, 60 μ in diameter, bears two rings of six small papillæ and the round ventral sucker, 70 to 73 μ in diameter, situated slightly posterior to the midplane, two rings of six and three papillæ. Pigment granules, evidently the remnants of the eye-spots of the cercaria are distributed throughout the body.

The digestive system consists of a short prepharynx, an oval pharynx, an esophagus and bifurcate ceca, which extend almost to the posterior extremity of the body and contain transparent discoidal particles. The cephalic glands, at least 12 in number, occupy the triangle formed by the intestinal ceca and ventral sucker. Their ducts, resembling chains of beads, pass forward to open dorsally near the anterior margin of the oral sucker. Small flask-shaped skin glands are arranged in lateral rows on the dorsal and ventral surfaces.

The excretory system comprises five sets of three flame-cells on each side of the metacercaria, their excretory ducts, an anterior collecting tubule from the first set, a posterior collecting tubule from the other sets, a main collecting tubule and a bladder. The flame-cell pattern is $2[3+(3+3+3+3)]$. Vibrating filaments may be seen in the terminal portion of the main collecting tubules. The oblong excretory bladder occupies the posterior third of the body and opens terminally. It is filled with oval or round concretions that appear black under the microscope. On each side is a shallow depression in which is situated the anlage of the testis. Genital cells, the anlage of the ovary, seminal receptacle and Laurer's canal, are present between the ventral sucker and the bladder and a chain of cells, the anlage of the uterus, extends in a semicircle around the left margin of the ventral sucker to join another row of cells that apparently represents the early undifferentiated seminal vesicle.

In the stomach the cyst is freed from the flesh of the fish by the gastric juices. In the duodenum the outer layer of the true cyst is dissolved by trypsin, while the inner layer is ruptured by the activity of the metacercaria. The freed larva within

---

[9] Hsü, H. F. and Khaw, O. K., 1936.   [10] Hsü, H. F. and Khaw, O. K., 1937.

a few hours migrates to the common bile duct and passes to the distal biliary capillaries where it matures. Here the worm loses its metacercarial characteristics. The bladder empties itself of concretions and the spines disappear gradually until they are entirely absent in 32 days, but the cephalic glands are present up to the adult stage. The vitellaria are first noticed in 10 to 12 days. Growth is rapid, though dependent upon the number of worms. In experimental animals ova appear in the uterus in from 12 to 15 days after infection and are found in the feces in from 26 to 28 days.

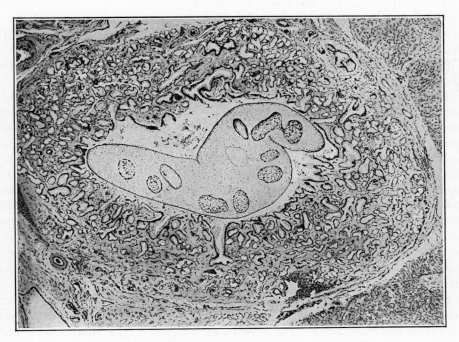

FIG. 180.—*Clonorchis sinensis* IN BILE DUCT (× 29)

Wall of bile duct is thickened showing numerous glandular structures, and in higher magnification lymphoid cells and eosinophils (Drawn from photomicrograph by Hoeppli, 1933).

PATHOGENESIS

Pathology.—The pathological changes produced by *Clonorchis sinensis* are localized in the distal biliary passages, particularly of the left lobe of the liver. The injury to the host depends upon the number of worms, a few parasites causing little damage, but large numbers producing serious and progressive hepatic disease. As many as 21,000 flukes have been found at autopsy.

Mechanical obstruction of the bile ducts with biliary stasis is uncommon and seldom produces jaundice. The chief lesions are caused by the irritative action of the parasite and its toxic secretions. The irritative action produces an adenomatous proliferation of the biliary epithelium with thickening of the walls of the ducts and crypt formation (Fig. 180). These cavities are often filled with parasites and brownish amorphous material with ova, leukocytes and lymphocytes. There is marked hyperplasia of the walls of the ducts and of the periportal connective tissues with infiltration of lymphoid cells and eosinophils, an increasing deposition of fibrous connective tissue and a resulting atrophy of the hepatic cells. These changes appear to be the result of toxic secretions as well as of the irritative action of the flukes, since they occur in bile capillaries not invaded by the worms. Superimposed bacterial infection may produce ulceration.

The condition progresses with the duration of the infection. In the early stages there is a proliferation of the biliary epithelium with leukocytic infiltration around the portal and interlobular spaces and a gradual deposition of connective tissue in the walls of the biliary passages. Later the walls become greatly thickened and the pressure of the connective tissue produces atrophy of the neighboring hepatic cells. With continuous reinfection an advanced stage of cirrhosis with extensive destruction of the liver parenchyma may finally result.

In 66 clonorchiasis patients, mostly under 40 years of age, who came to autopsy from other causes, there was an increase of periportal tissue in 74 per cent, infiltration of eosinophils in 56 per cent, fatty changes in the liver cells with central atrophy in 30 per cent, central fibrosis in 8 per cent and thickening of the arterial walls in 7 per cent.[11] Many cases with mild or even negligible clinical symptoms may show marked histological changes in the liver. In severe infections the liver is enlarged, the spleen is hypertrophied and ascites may occur. In heavily-infected experimental rabbits the spleen is enlarged from the passive congestion that results from liver injury.[12] Invasion of the pancreatic duct at times occurs. It is believed that the disease predisposes to the development of malignancy.[13] In guinea pigs there is a portal cirrhosis involving the liver lobules with periportal and adenomatous hyperplasia of the lining of the bile ducts, but jaundice and ascites are seldom produced.[14]

Symptomatology.—The disease as a rule follows an insidious and chronic course with periodic improvement. Early light infections, involving first-degree changes in the liver, are without appreciable symptoms. The characteristic early symptoms are indigestion, epigastric distress unrelated to meals, enlargement of liver with or without ascites, leukocytosis, eosinophilia and night blindness.[15] With second-degree lesions symptoms of diarrhea, edema and enlargement of the liver may occur. In severe infections these symptoms are aggravated by the involvement of the hepatic circulation and ascites and cachexia may develop.

Experimentally there is evidence of transitory hyperplasia of the bone marrow and changes in the reticulo-endothelial system. Light infections in rabbits cause slight or transitory changes in the hematopoietic system; no leukocytosis, mild eosinophilia below 10.5 per cent and no definite changes in the red blood cells.[12] Human cases may show a marked leukocytosis and high eosinophilia.[15] Impairment of the detoxifying properties of the liver may induce a systemic toxemia with palpi-

[11] Hoeppli, R., 1933.
[12] Young, S., 1931.
[13] Porter, A. and Pirie, J. H. H., 1922; Oldt, F., 1927; Nauck, E. G. and Liang, B., 1928; Hoeppli, R., 1933; Kourí, P., Basnuevo, J. G., Alveré, L. and Lescano, O., 1936; Swalin, W. A., Gault, E. S. and Morrison, L. M., 1938.
[14] Khaw, O. K., 1930.
[15] Bercovitz, Z., 1931.

tation, tachycardia, vertigo, tremors, tetanic cramps, and at times mental depression.[16]

DIAGNOSIS, PROGNOSIS AND TREATMENT

Diagnosis.—Clinical diagnosis is based on hepatic symptoms in patients from endemic areas who give a history of having eaten raw fish. The more advanced cases must be differentiated from malignancies of the liver, hydatid cyst, beriberi, and other forms of hepatic cirrhosis. Actual diagnosis is based on finding the characteristic ova in the feces. It is necessary to differentiate the ova from those of *Opisthorchis felineus, Heterophyes heterophyes* and other heterophyid flukes.

Prognosis.—Patients seldom die from clonorchiasis, but because of lowered resistance may succumb to superimposed diseases. Mild infections cause little harm. In advanced cases with definite impairment of liver function, the parasite may be a direct cause of death but only in prolonged, heavy infections. The disease is usually progressive in highly endemic areas.

Treatment.—Treatment is not particularly satisfactory. Intravenous administrations of tartar emetic (Section **VII**, XIII, 6) or alternate treatment with arsphenamine and tartar emetic have caused the disappearance of ova from the feces in some patients.[17] Malachite green, Nile blue sulphate and gentian violet 1:40,000 kill *Clonorchis sinensis in vitro* in 24 hours, gentian violet being most effective.[18] Gentian violet (Section **VII**, XIII, 27) given orally or intravenously will cure early light infections and will reduce the number of worms in chronic infections by 50 to 100 per cent.[19] The effectiveness of this dye probably depends upon its accumulation in the biliary passages. Some success has been reported from the intravenous injection of gold salts.[20] Nonsurgical biliary drainage under careful supervision is of value in removing toxic materials.[15]

PREVENTION

Epidemiology.—Man and animal reservoir hosts are usually infected by eating fresh-water fish containing metacercariæ. Cysts discharged by fish may occasionally be ingested in drinking water and fish handlers may transfer metacercariæ to their mouths from their contaminated hands. The intensity of human infection does not always coincide with the prevalence of the parasite in reservoir hosts but rather is dependent upon the custom of consuming raw or partly cooked fish. In North China, where little or no raw fish is eaten except in Cantonese restaurants, autochthonous human cases are rare, 0.38 per cent in 45,318 patients at the Peiping Union Medical College Hospital (1928 to 1935), although from 25 to 35 per cent of the cats and dogs are infected.[21] In Central China human infection is uncommon in the indigenous population, although 75 to 100 per cent of the cats and dogs are infected. In Southern China human infection is high, but there are no important

[16] Otto, I. H., 1935.

[17] Shattuck, G. C., 1924; Reed, A. C. and Wyckoff, H. A., 1926; Faust, E. C. and Yao, K. F., 1926.

[18] Chu, H. J., 1938.

[19] Faust, E. C., Yao, K. F., Khaw, O. K. and Chao, Y. A., 1926; Faust, E. C. and Yao, K. F., 1926; Kawai, T., 1937.

[20] Otto, I. H. and Tschan Tsching Ji, 1935.

[21] Hsü, H. F. and Khaw, O. K., 1936, Faust, E. C., 1925.

reservoir hosts.[3] In Kwangtung Province the ancient customs are particularly favorable for the transmission of the parasite. In the highly-endemic centers of this Province the incidence of infection, as determined by stool examination, ranges from 3 to 36 per cent of the population. A single examination of the feces of 4,033 patients admitted to the Canton Hospital revealed an incidence of 11.4 per cent.[7] Fish is served in thin raw slices either with vegetables and condiments or, more popularly, among the poorer classes with hot rice congee or gruel. The rearing of fresh-water fishes in ponds is an important industry. These ponds are fertilized and the fish fed on various waste products including night soil, so that a constant supply of *Clonorchis* ova contaminates the waters where snails abound. The fishes are not only sold locally, but are shipped to outside markets, thus spreading the disease.

Under five years of age, the incidence of infection is low, since small children do not partake of raw fish. It increases with age, the heaviest infections being found in the 55- to 60-year group. Males are more frequently infected than females.[22] The disease is equally prevalent in the well to do and the poor and in the illiterate as well as the educated, since the custom of eating raw fish is not confined to any particular class.

In slices of fish 2 to 3 mm. thick the metacercariæ are killed at 70° C. in 8 seconds; at 60° C. in 15 seconds and at 50° C. in 15 minutes.[23] Therefore, there is less danger in eating raw fish congee, in which the slices of raw fish are dipped in hot rice gruel at 68° to 73° C., than in eating cold raw fish with vegetables and condiments, but the danger is not eliminated. Moreover, cooking the larger fish may not always kill the metacercariæ, since they may retain viable cysts after heating for one hour at 80° C.[3] Neither are the metacercariæ killed by refrigeration, salting or the addition of vinegar or sauce.

Prophylaxis.—The prevention of clonorchiasis depends chiefly upon reducing the consumption of raw or imperfectly cooked fish. Other methods of attack, though useful, are less effective. Possible measures include: (1) reduction of sources of infection (carriers), (2) sterilization of feces, (3) protection of fish ponds from contamination with night soil, (4) control of snail hosts and (5) educational propaganda regarding the danger of eating raw fish.

The ineffectiveness of therapeutic measures and the prevalence of animal reservoir hosts make the elimination of carriers of doubtful value. However, the feeding of dogs and cats with fish waste can be curtailed. *Clonorchis* ova in night soil may be destroyed by storage or by mixing with ammonium sulphate; one part of a 0.7 per cent solution of this salt to ten parts of feces kills the ova in 30 minutes. Latrines should be removed from the vicinity of fish ponds, and the use of night soil as fish food and for fertilizing fish ponds prohibited. Attempts to eradicate snails have not proved effective owing to inadequate biological knowledge. Chemicals sufficiently strong to kill snails will destroy fish and other aquatic life. Removal of weeds that protect the eggs and young snails from the fish may aid in the reduction of this intermediate host.

Legislation prohibiting the serving of raw fish in restaurants is but partially effective, since raw fish congee is a household dish and Chinese housewives are

---

[22] Uttley, K. H., 1935. [23] Hsü, H. F. and Wang, L. S., 1938.

ignorant of the danger from this source. In districts where it is customary to eat raw fish, educational propaganda stressing the importance of thoroughly cooking all fresh-water fish appears to be the most effective means of preventing clonorchiasis.

Opisthorchis felineus (RIVOLTA, 1884) BLANCHARD, 1895

Synonyms.—*Distoma conus* Gurlt, 1831, *nec* Creplin, 1825; *D. lanceolatum felis cati* v. Siebold, 1836; *D. felineum* Rivolta, 1884; *D. lanceolatum canis familiaris* van Tright, 1889; *D. sibiricum* Winogradoff, 1892; *D. winogradoffi* Jaksch, 1897; *O. tenuicollis* (Rudolphi, 1819), Ejsmont, 1937.

Disease.—Opisthorchiasis.

History.—The first cases from man were reported from Tomsk, Siberia, by Winogradoff in 1892.

Geographical Distribution.—*Opisthorchis felineus* is prevalent in cats and dogs in central and eastern Europe, and Siberia. In the highly-endemic areas of East Prussia, Poland and the Ob Basin of Siberia it is also found in man. Cases have likewise been reported in the Philippines, India, Annam, Japan and French Indo-China, but it is not endemic in the localities where *Clonorchis sinensis* is prevalent.

BIOLOGICAL CHARACTERISTICS

Morphology.—The adult is a flat, elongate, lanceolate trematode, 0.7 to 1.2 cm. in length by 0.15 to 0.3 cm. in breadth, with a rounded posterior and a tapering anterior end (Fig. 181). During life it has a transparent reddish-yellow color. The integument is smooth, although immature forms may possess spines. The oral sucker, 0.025 cm., is subterminal and the ventral sucker of similar size is situated one-fifth of the body length from the anterior end. From the oral sucker a small bulbous pharynx leads into a short esophagus which bifurcates to form two ceca, extending to the posterior end of the body. The prominent excretory bladder, a long tubule in the midline of the posterior fourth of the body, terminates in an excretory pore at the caudal extremity.

The two lobate testes are situated in the posterior quarter of the worm, the anterior to the right of the bladder. Two vasa efferentia unite in the middle of the body into a vas deferens. The latter enlarges to form the seminal vesicle that terminates in an ejaculatory duct at the genital atrium near the anterior border of the ventral sucker. The female reproductive organs of the typical trematode are present. The ovary is a small, oval, slightly-lobulate body in the midline anterior to the excretory bladder. The transversely-compressed follicles of the vitellarium lie in the lateral middle third of the body. The uterus, a markedly-coiled tubule, terminates in the genital atrium near the opening of the ejaculatory duct.

Physiology.—The habitat and habits of the parasite resemble those of *Clonorchis sinensis*. It lies in the distal bile ducts, particularly those of the left lobe of the liver, but occasionally is found in the pancreatic duct and in the intestine.

LIFE CYCLE

The adult fluke is a natural parasite of dogs, cats, foxes and hogs. Man is an accidental host. The first intermediate hosts are *Bulimus leachi* and *B. tentaculata* (Table 34). The second intermediate hosts are cyprinoid fishes, including the chub, *Idus melanotus;* the bream, *Abramis brama;* the barbel, *Barbus barbus;* the tench, *Tinca tinca* and *T. vulgaris;* the carp, *Cyprinus carpio; Blicca bjorkna; Leuciscus rutilus* and *Scardinius erythophthalmus.* The chub and the tench are most frequently infected.

The yellowish-brown ova (Fig. 182A) are elongate, ovoid bodies measuring 30 by 12 μ. An operculum sets in a shouldered thickening of the shell at the anterior end and a small pointed projection is present at the opposite pole. At oviposition the ovum contains a ciliated miracidium with asymmetrical structures (Fig. 182B). The ovum, like that of *Clonorchis sinensis,* does not hatch after reaching the water until ingested

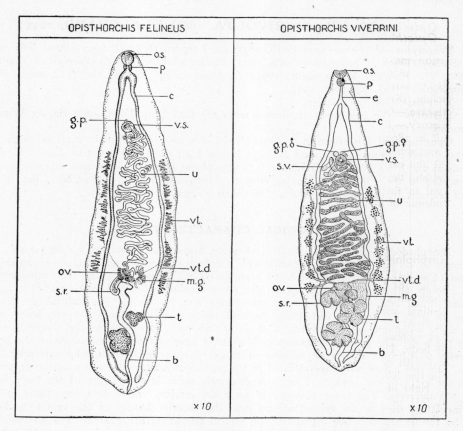

FIG. 181.—*Opisthorchis felineus* AND *O. viverrini*

b, bladder; *c,* ceca; *e,* esophagus; *g.p.,* genital pore; *m.g.,* Mehlis' gland; *o.s.,* oral sucker; *ov.,* ovary; *p,* pharynx; *s.r.,* seminal receptacle; *s.v.,* seminal vesicle; *t,* testes; *u,* uterus; *v.s.,* ventral sucker; *vt.,* vitellaria; *vt.d.,* vitelline duct (*O. felineus* redrawn from Stiles and Hassall, 1894; *O. viverrini* redrawn from Leiper, 1915).

by a snail. In the snail the sporocysts (Fig. 182C, D) develop near the lower intestine and in about one month form rediæ, which migrate to the region of the digestive gland. The rediæ (Fig. 182E) produce cerceriæ which emerge while still immature.[24] In about two months mature cercariæ leave the snail.

The liberated cercaria (Fig. 182F, G) is characterized by pigmented eye-spots, ten pairs of penetration glands with ducts opening dorsal to the mouth and a flame-cell formula of $2[5+(5+5+5+5)]$. Its body measures from 132 to 172 μ in length by 41 to 48 μ in breadth and the tail has a length of 400 to 500 μ. The unforked tail has a

---

[24] Vogel, H., 1934.

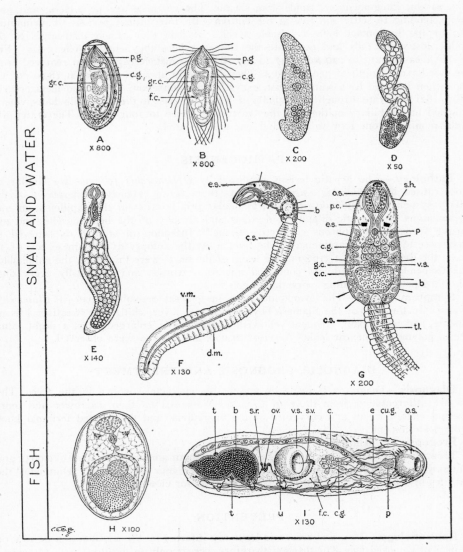

SNAIL AND WATER

FISH

FIG. 182.—LARVAL FORMS OF *Opisthorchis felineus*

A, miracidium in eggshell; *B,* miracidium; *C,* young sporocyst; *D,* older sporocyst with immature rediæ; *E,* young redia with germinating cercariæ; *F,* free-swimming cercaria, lateral view; *G,* body of cercaria, ventral view; *H,* young encysted metacercaria dissected from fish ten days after infection; *I,* excysted metacercaria, ventral view.

b, excretory bladder; *c,* ceca; *c.c.,* cystogenous cells; *c.g.,* cephalic gland; *c.s.,* cuticular sheath; *cu.g.,* cuticular glands; *d.m.,* dorsal membrane; *e,* esophagus; *e.s.,* eye-spot; *f.c.,* flame-cell; *g.c.,* genital cells; *gr.c.,* large granular cell; *o.s.,* oral sucker; *ov.,* anlage of ovary; *p,* pharynx; *p.c.,* pigment cell; *p.g.,* primitive gut; *s.h.,* sensory hair; *s.r.,* anlage of seminal receptacle; *s.v.,* anlage of seminal vesicle; *t,* testicular anlage; *tl.,* tail; *u,* anlage of uterus; *v.m.,* ventral membrane; *v.s.,* ventral sucker (*A* to *I* redrawn from Vogel, 1933).

transparent, integumentary, rudder-like sheath. The cercariæ are phototactic and geo-tactic, tending to settle and live at the bottom with intermittent periods of swimming. On coming in contact with a suitable species of fish, they attach themselves to the scales, lose their tails and penetrate the tissues, where they encyst. The cysts (Fig. 182H) measure 213 to 230 μ by 147 to 197 μ and the metacercariæ when removed from the cyst have a length of 340 to 590 μ. They mature in about six weeks at 18 to 20° C., and, when ingested by a suitable host, excyst in the duodenum. The freed metacercariæ (Fig. 182I) migrate through the ampulla of Vater and pass to the distal bile ducts, where, attached to the biliary epithelium, they mature in three to four weeks. The entire life cycle requires from four to four and one-half months.

PATHOGENESIS

Pathology.—The hepatic lesions produced by *Opisthorchis felineus* are similar to those caused by *Clonorchis sinensis*. In cats there is an extensive hyperplasia of the biliary system, multiplication of ducts, glandular proliferation of the papillomatous and adenomatous type, cystic dilatation, necrosis and atrophy of the hepatic cells, and extensive formation of fibrous connective tissue.[25] Infection in animals is believed to predispose to primary carcinoma of the liver.[26] At the autopsy of a Siamese boy of 17 years, the liver weighed 1,310 gm., the walls of the ducts were thickened, the gallbladder was tremendously dilated and contained numerous worms, and practically every duct contained parasites, totaling more than 1,000.[27]

Symptomatology.—The symptomatology in general resembles that of *Clonorchis sinensis*. In the case of the Siamese boy cited above fever, chills and sweating, loss of appetite, abdominal pain, frequent yellowish watery stools, enlarged liver, a slight jaundice, a polymorphonuclear leukocytosis of 21,600, and anemia were observed.

DIAGNOSIS, PROGNOSIS AND TREATMENT

Diagnosis.—Diagnosis is made by finding the characteristic ova in the feces. The ova are differentiated from those of *Clonorchis sinensis* by their narrower and more tapering ends, the rim and curvature of the operculum, and the pointed terminal knob at the posterior end.

Prognosis.—Unknown.

Treatment.—Fuadin (Section VII, XIII, 11), in an amount equivalent to 0.0034 gm. antimony per kilogram of body weight divided over four days usually eliminates the parasites in cats.[28] Treatment in man is the same as for clonorchiasis.

PREVENTION

Epidemiology.—Man and reservoir hosts are infected by the consumption of raw or insufficiently cooked fish. The disease, therefore, occurs only in localities such as central Siberia and East Prussia, where the fishes that serve as second intermediate hosts are eaten raw. While infection is usually limited to lower animals, in endemic districts the parasite occurs not infrequently in man, an incidence of 8 per cent being reported in children near the Bay of Courland, East Prussia. The chief reservoir of infection is the cat. Intermediate hosts are infected by feces deposited on the sandy shores and washed into the streams.

Prophylaxis.—Prevention depends upon curtailing the eating of raw fish in endemic localities and in general is similar to that of *Clonorchis sinensis*.

[25] Essex, H. E. and Bollman, J. L., 1930; M., 1929.
Bohl, B. K. and Jakowlew, J. J., 1931. [27] Prommas, C., 1927.
[26] Ruditzky, M. G., 1928: Hoogland, H. J. [28] Eichholtz, F. and Erhardt, A., 1934.

Opisthorchis viverrini (POIRIER, 1886) STILES AND HASSALL, 1896

Opisthorchis viverrini (Fig. 181) is a natural parasite of the civet cat. It has been reported in prisoners in northern Siam and in about 25 per cent of the population of the Lao country as determined by stool examination. *O. viverrini* differs slightly from *O. felineus* in having the testes nearer the ovary, in possessing more deeply lobulated testes and in the distribution and appearance of the vitellaria. The ova are shorter and broader than those of *O. felineus* and more nearly resemble those of *C. sinensis*. Infection is incurred through eating raw fish.

Opisthorchis noverca BRAUN, 1903

This parasite, sometimes known as *Amphimerus noverca*, has been reported twice from man in India. It differs from the two other species of *Opisthorchis* in the small size of the ventral sucker, the close proximity of the two suckers, the more extensive distribution of the vitellaria, and the larger ova. It commonly occurs in the pariah dogs of India and has also been reported from the wolverine and the hog.

OTHER SPECIES OF *OPISTHORCHIDÆ*

Amphimerus pseudofelineus Ward, 1901, is fairly common in cats and coyotes in the United States of America. *Pseudamphistomum truncatum* (Rudolphi, 1819) Lühe, 1908, has been reported in the dog, cat, fox, wolverine and seal. It has a spinous integument and a pseudosucker-like posterior end. *O. wardi* Wharton, 1921, has been reported in cats in the Philippine Islands. *Parametorchis complexus* Stiles and Hassall, 1894, and *P. noveboracensis* Hung, 1926, have been found in cats in New York City.

REFERENCES

BERCOVITZ, Z. Clinical Studies on Human Infestations with the Liver Fluke (*Clonorchis sinensis*), Am. J. Trop. Med., 1931, 11 :43.

ESSEX, H. E. and BOLLMAN, J. L. Parasitic Cirrhosis of the Liver in a Cat Infected with *Opisthorchis pseudofelineus* and *Metorchis complexus*, Am. J. Trop. Med., 1930, 10:65.

FAUST, E. C. and KHAW, O. K. Studies on *Clonorchis sinensis* (Cobbold), Am. J. Hyg., Monographic Series, 1927, No. 8, 284 pp.

———— and YAO, K. F. Specific Therapeusis in *Clonorchis* Infections, Arch. f. Schiffs- u. Tropen-Hyg., 1926, 30:383.

HOEPPLI, R. Histological Changes in the Liver of Sixty-six Chinese Infected with *Clonorchis sinensis*, Chinese M. J., 1933, 47 :1125.

HSÜ, H. F. and CHOW, C. Y. Studies on Certain Problems of *Clonorchis sinensis*. II. Investigation in the Chief Endemic Center of China, the Canton Area, Chinese M. J., 1937, 51 :341.

———— and KHAW, O. K. Studies on Certain Problems of *Clonorchis sinensis*. I. On the Cysts and Second Intermediate Hosts of *C. sinensis* in the Peiping Area, Chinese M. J., 1936, 50 :1609.

———— and KHAW, O. K. Studies on Certain Problems of *Clonorchis sinensis*. III. On the Morphology of the Metacercaria, Festschr. Bernhard Nocht, 1937, 4 :216.

———— and WANG, L. S. Studies on Certain Problems of *Clonorchis sinensis*. IV. Notes on the Resistance of Cysts in Fish Flesh, the Migration Route, and the Morphology of the Young Worm in the Final Host, Chinese M. J. Suppl., 1938, 2 :385.

OTTO, I. H. Clinical Pathophysiological and Therapeutic Aspects of Human Clonorchiasis, Tr. 9th Congr. Far Eastern Assoc. Trop. Med., 1935, 1 :543.

PROMMAS, C. Case of *Opisthorchis felineus* in Siam, Ann. Trop. Med., 1927, 21 :9.

SHATTUCK, G. C. Treatment of Clonorchiasis, Am. J. Trop. Med., 1924, 4 :507.

VOGEL, H. Der Entwicklungszyklus von *Opisthorchis felineus* (Riv.), nebst Bemerkungen über die Systematik und Epidemiologie, Zoologica, 1934, 33 :1.

YAMAGUTI, S. Ueber die Cercariae von *Clonorchis sinensis* (Cobbold), Ztschr. f. Parasitenk., 1935, 8 :183.

Chapter XXXII

THE SUPERFAMILY HETEROPHYOIDEA

SUPERFAMILY *HETEROPHYOIDEA* FAUST, 1929

The members of the superfamily HETEROPHYOIDEA are small oval pyriform or elongated trematodes resembling the OPISTHORCHOIDEA, but often possessing a more or less prominent sucker-like structure around the genital pore. The species parasitic in man belong to the family HETEROPHYIDÆ.

FAMILY *HETEROPHYIDÆ* ODHNER, 1914

The HETEROPHYIDÆ are small, elongated, somewhat flattened, oval or pyriform trematodes, rounded posteriorly and attenuated anteriorly. The cuticle is covered with fine scale-like spines that are less numerous posteriorly. A sucker-like structure, surrounding the genital pore, may be present near the ventral sucker. Oval or slightly-lobed testes are situated in the extreme posterior part of the body. A cirral sac is absent. An oval ovary lies anterior to the testes in the midline; the vitellaria are confined to the lateral lower third of the body; a seminal receptacle and Laurer's canal are present; and the loosely coiled ovary descends to the testes. The adult worms are parasites of mammals and fish-eating birds, and their life cycle involves snails and fresh-water fishes as intermediate hosts. Practically all species are potential parasites of man and fourteen species have been found in man, of which *Heterophyes heterophyes* and *Metagonimus yokogawai* are the most important.

Heterophyes heterophyes (v. SIEBOLD, 1852) STILES AND HASSALL, 1900

Synonyms.—*Distoma heterophyes* v. Siebold, 1852; *Distoma heterophyes hominis* Diesing, 1855; *Dicrocœlium heterophyes* Weinland, 1858; *Fasciola heterophyes* Moquin-Tandon, 1860; *Heterophyes ægyptiaca* Cobbold, 1866; *Mesogonimus heterophyes* Railliet, 1890; *Cœnogonimus heterophyes* Looss, 1899; *Cotylogonimus heterophyes* Lühe, 1899; *Heterophyes nocens* Onji and Nishio, 1915.

Disease.—Heterophyiasis.

History.—The worm, discovered in 1851 by Bilharz in Cairo in the intestine of an Egyptian boy, was named *Distoma heterophyes* by von Siebold. Cobbold in 1866 established the genus *Heterophyes* and Looss in 1894 gave the first detailed description of the type species. The incidence in man was considered negligible until Looss in 1896 pointed out that the parasite was fairly common in Egypt, since many cases were overlooked because of the small size of the ovum. Its presence in the Orient was established by Leiper, who found two infected sailors, a Chinese and a Japanese, in a London hospital, and by Onji and Nishio, who in 1915 described an almost identical parasite in Japan under the name *Heterophyes nocens*.

Geographical Distribution.—The parasite is found in Egypt, Palestine, Central and South China, Japan, Korea, Formosa, and the Philippines.

BIOLOGICAL CHARACTERISTICS

Morphology.—*Heterophyes heterophyes* (Fig. 183) is an elongated, oval, grayish trematode from 1 to 1.7 mm. in length by 0.3 to 0.7 mm. in breadth. The cuticle is covered with close-set, fine, scale-like spines that are most numerous toward the anterior end. The oral sucker, 90 μ in diameter, is much smaller than the

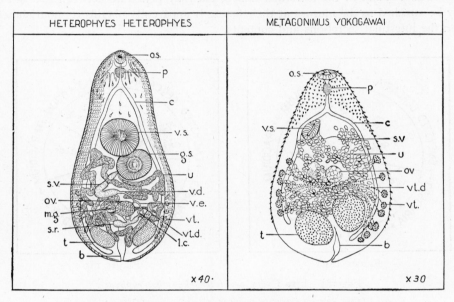

FIG. 183.—*Heterophyes heterophyes* AND *Metagonimus yokogawai*

b, excretory bladder; *c*, ceca; *g.s.*, genital sucker; *l.c.*, Laurer's canal; *m.g.*, Mehlis' gland; *o.s.*, oral sucker; *ov.*, ovary; *p*, pharynx; *s.r.*, seminal receptacle; *s.v.*, seminal vesicle; *t*, testes; *u*, uterus; *v.d.*, vas deferens; *v.e.*, vas efferens; *v.s.*, ventral sucker; *vt.*, vitellaria; *vt.d.*, vitelline duct (*Heterophyes heterophyes* redrawn from Looss, 1894; *Metagonimus yokogawai* redrawn from Leiper, 1913).

ventral sucker, 230 μ, which is located in the anterior middle third of the body. A protrusible, nonadhesive genital sucker or gonotyle, 150 μ in diameter, lies close to the left posterior margin of the ventral sucker. It bears a circlet of 60 to 90 cone-shaped plates, about 20 μ in length, which is broken for a short distance on the side toward the ventral sucker. The digestive tract consists of a capillary prepharynx, a minute bulbous pharynx, a capillary esophagus, and two intestinal ceca, which terminate blindly near the rounded extremity of the worm. The excretory bladder, an elongate tube in the midline of the posterior fifth of the body, receives two lateral collecting tubules and opens at the posterior extremity of the body.

The two ovoid testes lie opposite each other in the posterior fifth of the body, the left slightly in advance. The vasa efferentia unite in front of the ovary to form the vas deferens, which enlarges as a coiled, retort-shaped seminal vesicle, then forms a muscular ejaculatory duct surrounded by prostatic glands, and terminates within the genital sucker. There is no cirrus or cirral sac. The subglobose ovary lies in the midline of the upper posterior third of the body. There is a full complement of female reproductive organs. The long, coiled uterus opens beside the male pore in the genital sucker. The vitellaria consist of some 14 large, polygonal follicles on each side of the posterior third of the body.

Physiology.—The adult worm inhabits the middle part of the small intestine. It is usually found in the intestinal lumen, but may penetrate between the villi or may be attached to the mucosa at their bases. It apparently obtains its nourishment from the intestinal secretions and contents.

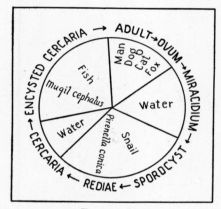
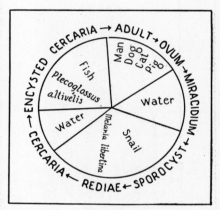

FIGURE 184   FIGURE 185

FIG. 184.—LIFE CYCLE OF *Heterophyes heterophyes*
FIG. 185.—LIFE CYCLE OF *Metagonimus yokogawai*

LIFE CYCLE

Hosts.—The adult worm is a natural parasite of man, cats, dogs, foxes and probably other fish-eating mammals. The first intermediate hosts are the snails, *Pirenella conica* (Egypt and Japan) and *Tympanotonus microptera* (Japan). The second intermediate hosts are the fishes, *Mugil cephalus* and *Tilapia nilotica* in Egypt and *Mugil japonicus* and species of *Acanthogobius* in Japan. Other fishes may be experimentally infected.

Development Cycle.—The ovum, probably ingested by the snail, develops successively into sporocysts, rediæ and cercariæ. After leaving the snail the lophocercous cercaria encysts on the scales, fins, tail, gills or, less frequently, in the muscles of the brackish-water mullet. When this fish is eaten raw or imperfectly cooked the metacercaria escapes from the cyst and develops into the adult worm in the small intestine (Fig. 184). Growth is rapid, mature ova being formed in 7 to 8 days after infection of the definitive host.[1]

---

[1] Cort, W. W. and Yokogawa, S., 1921.

Larval Forms.—The light brown, thick-shelled, operculate ova (Fig. 186A), from 28 to 30 μ by 15 to 17 μ, contain fully-developed miracidia at oviposition. They have a slight "shoulder" thickening at the rim of the operculum and sometimes a knob at the posterior pole resembling, though less pronounced, that of *Clonorchis sinensis*. They may be differentiated from *Clonorchis* ova by their broad operculate ends and indistinct "shoulders" and with greater difficulty from those of *Metagonimus yokogawai*, which have a light yellow color and thin shell.

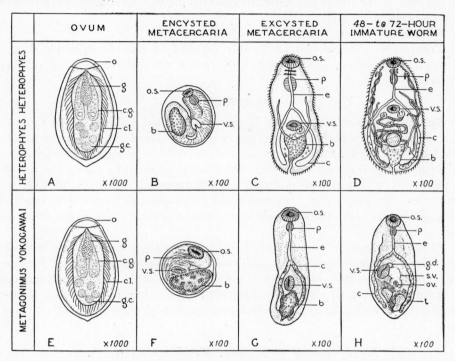

FIG. 186.—LARVAL FORMS OF *Heterophyes heterophyes* AND *Metagonimus yokogawai*

b, excretory bladder; *c*, ceca; *c.g.*, cephalic glands; *cl.*, cilia; *e*, esophagus; *g*, primitive gut; *g.c.*, genital cells; *g.d.*, genital disk; *o*, operculum; *o.s.*, oral sucker; *ov.*, ovary; *p*, pharynx; *s.v.*, seminal vesicle; *t*, testes; *v.s.*, ventral sucker (*A* and *E* adapted from various sources; *B* to *D* redrawn from Yokogawa, 1913; *F* to *H* redrawn after Onji and Nishio, 1915, from Cort and Yokogawa, 1921).

The metacercaria is enclosed in a two-layered cyst, 163 by 136 μ (Fig. 186B). The excysted larva (Fig. 186C), 340 by 150 μ, has a triangular excretory bladder filled with concretions, flame-cells, oral and ventral suckers, digestive tract, lytic glands, and genital cells. The 48-hour immature worm (Fig. 186D) shows the early differentiation of the reproductive organs.

PATHOGENESIS

The parasites, except in heavy infections, apparently cause no appreciable mechanical or toxic injury to the small intestine, and as a rule produce no marked symptoms. Chronic, intermittent, bloody diarrhea; nausea; abdominal discomfort with colicky pains and tenderness; and neurasthenia have been reported.[2] There is an eosinophilia but no anemia.

DIAGNOSIS, PROGNOSIS AND TREATMENT

Diagnosis.—Diagnosis is made by finding the ova in the feces. They require differentiation from those of *Clonorchis sinensis,* the various species of *Opisthorchis,* and the heterophyid flukes.

Prognosis.—Good.

Treatment.—The worms are readily expelled by such anthelmintic drugs as oleoresin of aspidium, tetrachlorethylene, carbon tetrachloride and oil of chenopodium.

PREVENTION

Epidemiology.—The parasite is prevalent around Lake Manzala near Port Said, Egypt, where at Mataria 88 per cent of 60 school children were infected.[3] The local fishermen continually pollute the water, hence a high percentage of mullets in the Cairo market are infected. Infection is acquired by eating the raw flesh of the mullet, which, though primarily a fresh-water fish, frequents brackish water during the spawning season. The raw salted fish, known as "fessikh," is eaten after being pickled for three days, but the metacercariæ are not killed in less than seven days.

Prophylaxis.—The elimination of foci of infection is impracticable because of the difficulty of detecting carriers and enforcing sanitary measures and because of the presence of reservoir hosts. Nor is the destruction of the intermediate gastropod hosts feasible. The most practical method of preventing human infection is to curtail the practice of eating raw or imperfectly-cooked fish in endemic areas.

Metagonimus yokogawai KATSURADA, 1912

Synonyms.—*Heterophyes yokogawai* Katsurada, 1912; *Loxotrema ovatum* Kobayashi, 1912; *Tocotrema yokogawai* Katsurada, 1912; *Metagonimus ovatus* Yokogawa, 1913; *Yokogawa yokogawai* Leiper 1913; *Loossia romanica* Ciurea 1915; *Loossia parva* Ciurea, 1915; *Loossia dobrogiensis* Ciurea, 1915; *Metagonimus romanicus* Lopez-Neyra and Pozo, 1932.

Disease.—Heterophyiasis.

History.—In 1911 Yokogawa discovered a larval trematode encysted in the gills, scales and muscles of fresh-water salmonoid fishes in Formosa. This parasite, *Metagonimus yokogawai,* was first described in 1912 by Katsurada, who produced the adult worm by feeding experiments, noted that the ova were similar to those found in human feces, and called attention to its wide distribution in Japan. Reports by Kobayashi in 1912 from Korea, Yokogawa in 1913 from Formosa, and Ciurea in 1915 from Rumania soon established its prevalence.

---

[2] Khalil, M., 1933, 1934.　　　　　　　[3] Khalil, M., 1933.

Geographical Distribution.—*Metagonimus yokogawai* is a common fluke in the Orient. It has been found in Japan, China, Korea, Formosa, Siberia, Dutch East Indies, Palestine, Russia, the Balkans and Spain.

BIOLOGICAL CHARACTERISTICS

Morphology.—The adult fluke (Fig. 183) has a mean size of 0.14 cm. by 0.06 cm., ranging from 0.10 to 0.25 cm. in length and from 0.04 to 0.075 cm. in breadth. Its shape is pyriform with a rounded posterior and a tapering anterior end. It is covered with minute scale-like spines, more closely set at the anterior end and particularly prominent around the oral sucker. The ventral sucker, 130 by 90 μ, lies to the right of the midline and the oral sucker, 80 μ in diameter, lies at the anterior end of the body. There is a short prepharynx, a globose pharynx, an esophagus, and paired intestinal ceca that extend to the posterior extremities of the body. The tubular excretory bladder has two lateral horns, into which the collecting tubules empty, and a posterior excretory pore.

The oval testes, the right more posterior than the left, are in the posterior third of the worm. The seminal vesicle is retort-shaped and the ejaculatory duct opens into the genital atrium at the anterior border of the ventral sucker. The globose ovary is in the midline at the juncture of the middle lower third of the body. The coarse vitellaria are arranged in a fan-like distribution in the posterior lateral fields. The uterus follows a tortuous course and terminates beside the ejaculatory duct in the genital atrium.

Physiology.—The adult worm inhabits the upper and middle part of the jejunum, rarely the duodenum, ileum and cecum. The worms are embedded in the mucus or in the folds of the mucosa.

LIFE CYCLE

Hosts.—The definitive hosts are man, dog, cat, hog, the pelican and probably other fish-eating birds. The first intermediate hosts are *Brotia libertina* and some five other species of *Brotia* (Table 34). The second intermediate hosts are the salmonoid, *Plecoglossus altivelis,* and the cyprinoids, *Richardsonium hakuensis* and *Odontobutis obscurus.*

Developmental Cycle.—The ovum with mature miracidium is probably ingested by the snail and hatches in the intestine. In the tissues of the snail it develops successively into sporocyst, mother redia, daughter redia and cercaria. The cercariæ, after leaving the snail, encyst in the tissues of the scales, fins, tail and gills, and rarely in the muscles of a fish. When the encysted cercariæ are ingested by the definitive host, the gastric juice digests away the outer capsule formed by the tissues of the fish. In the duodenum the true outer cyst wall is dissolved by the intestinal juices, and the activated larva ruptures the inner membrane. Mature adult worms develop in the small intestine in from 7 to 10 days (Fig. 185).

Larval Forms.—The yellow-brown, thick-shelled, operculate ova (Fig. 186E), 27 to 28 μ in length by 16 to 17 μ in breadth, at oviposition contain fully-developed, bilaterally-symmetrical miracidia. They have a nodular thickening at the posterior end and resemble the ova of *Clonorchis sinensis,* but the operculum does not set in a groove as in the latter species. They are differentiated with difficulty from the ova of *Heterophyes heterophyes* and other heterophyid flukes.

The cercaria that emerges from the snail has an elongate, spinous body attenuated anteriorly and a long lophocercous tail with dorsoventral flutings. It has two eye-spots, masses of golden pigment, several circlets of hook-shaped spines on the oral sucker, 14 penetration glands, a triangular excretory bladder with two lateral and one caudal tubules, a digestive system consisting of a prepharynx, pharynx, esophagus and ceca, and a poorly-developed ventral sucker situated behind the excretory bladder. After a short free-swimming existence it penetrates beneath the scales of an appropriate species of fish, casts off its tail and encysts.

The true cyst wall has a thin outer hyaline and a thin inner membranous layer. The cysts (Fig. 186F) vary in shape according to their location. In the gills they are ellipsoidal, measuring 150 by 100 μ, under the scales and in the muscles spherical with a diameter of 140 μ, and on the fins and tail spherical with a diameter of 225 μ and a hyaline membrane 40 μ thick. During encystment the larva increases in size, depending upon the available food supply. The excretory bladder becomes more distinct as it fills with concretions. Upon excystation the metacercaria (Fig. 186G) measures from 400 to 470 μ, has a small ventral sucker near the bifurcation of the ceca, and already shows the anlage of the reproductive organs anterior and lateral to the excretory bladder. As the immature worm (Fig. 186H) increases in size, the reproductive organs develop early.

PATHOGENESIS

Pathology.—Similar to that of *Heterophyes heterophyes.*
Symptomatology.—Similar to that of *Heterophyes heterophyes.*

DIAGNOSIS, PROGNOSIS AND TREATMENT

Diagnosis.—Diagnosis is made by finding the characterisitc ova in the feces. They are difficult to differentiate from the ova of *Clonorchis sinensis,* various species of *Opisthorchis, Heterophyes heterophyes,* and other heterophyid flukes.
Prognosis.—Favorable except in systemic invasion by the ova.
Treatment.—Same as that of *Heterophyes heterophyes.*

PREVENTION

Epidemiology.—Infection is acquired by man and other mammals by the ingestion of raw infected fish. The parasite is fairly common in countries where this custom prevails. In Japan *Plecoglossus altivelis* and *Richardsonium hakuensis* are the principal sources of human infection. The waters inhabited by these fishes are contaminated by the fecal discharges of man and other mammals.
Prophylaxis.—Infection may be avoided by not eating raw or imperfectly cooked fish.

OTHER SPECIES OF *HETEROPHYIDÆ* IN MAN

Nearly all the HETEROPHYIDÆ parasitic in mammals and birds are potential parasites of man. At least twelve species have been found in man. Their life cycles involve species of *Brotia* or other snails as first intermediate hosts and fresh-water or brackish-water fishes as second intermediate hosts.

SPECIES

Heterophyes katsuradai Ozaki and Asada, 1926.—From man in Japan. Piscine host *Mugil cephalus*. Broad round worm with large ventral sucker and vitellaria in posterior part of body. Ova 25.6 by 14.7 μ.

Heterophyes brevicæca Africa and Garcia, 1935.—From man in Philippines. Small pear-shaped worm, 0.065 by 0.033 cm., with short ceca, ventral sucker slightly larger than oral, globular or ovoid testes opposite each other, vitellaria consisting of five or six large follicles on each side, and excretory bladder with two long lateral arms. Ova 16 by 10 μ.

Monorchotrema taichui Nishigori, 1924.—Formosa and Philippines. Natural definitive hosts: dog, cat, man and, experimentally, laboratory animals. Molluscan host, *Brotia obliquegranosa*. Piscine hosts: CYPRINIDÆ, SILURIDÆ and COLITIDÆ. Adult worm, 0.072 by 0.031 cm., has a single testis and a genital sucker fused with ventral sucker and surrounded by a half-circlet of hooklets. Light yellow ova, 21.4 by 10.6 μ with inconspicuous "shoulder."

Monorchotrema taihokui Nishigori, 1924.—Formosa and Philippines. Natural definitive hosts: dog, cat, night-heron, man and, experimentally, laboratory animals. Molluscan host, *Brotia reiniana* var. *hidachiensis*. Piscine hosts: CYPRINIDÆ, SILURIDÆ and COLITIDÆ, *Arius manilensis* in Philippines. Adult worm, 0.057 by 0.035 cm., has a single testis and fusion of genital and ventral suckers. Yellow-brown ova, 27.0 by 13.5 μ with distinct "shoulder."

Monorchotrema yokogawai Katsuta, 1932.—From dog and cat in Formosa and the Philippines. Man experimentally infected. Ventral sucker bears 70 to 74 hooklets. Ova 31.7 by 15.6 μ.

Monorchotrema microrchia Katsuta, 1932.—From dog and cat in Formosa. Man experimentally infected. Piscine host fishes of the genus *Mugil*. Adult worm, 0.058 by 0.023 cm., has ventral sucker with 46 to 48 hooklets. Ova 28.6 by 15.7 μ.

Stamnosoma armatum Tanabe, 1922.—Mammals and night-heron in Japan. Man experimentally infected. Piscine hosts, cyprinoid fishes.

Stamnosoma formosanum Nishigori, 1924.—Dog, cat, night-heron and man in Formosa. Piscine hosts, several species of cyprinoid and other fishes.

Diorchitrema pseudocirrata Witenberg, 1929.—From man and dog in the Philippines and Hawaii. Piscine hosts, fishes of the genus *Mugil*.

Diorchitrema formosanum Katsuta, 1932.—Formosa. Molluscan hosts, *Brotia obliquegranosa, B. libertina, B. reiniana* var. *hidachiensis* and *B. hahajimana*.

Diorchitrema amplicæcale Katsuta, 1932.—Formosa.

Metagonimus minutus Katsuta, 1932.—Formosa. Piscine hosts, fishes of the genus *Mugil*.

PATHOGENESIS

Pathology.—The intestinal lesions produced by the adult worms are similar for all heterophyid flukes. No marked pathological changes, other than a slight atrophy of the epithelium, are caused by the worms, which are attached by their suckers to the intestinal mucosa. Apparently there is some invasion of the intestinal mucosa, especially by immature and young worms, which are frequently found imbedded in the villi.

In the Philippines a general secondary invasion of the heart, brain, spinal cord and other organs by ova has been reported in patients harboring adult *Monorchotrema tai-*

hokui, M. taichui, Heterophyes brevicœca and *Diorchitrema pseudocirrata*.[4] The ova, deposited in the mucosa or submucosa, gain access to the general circulation either through the central lacteals of the intestinal villi and the thoracic duct, or by erosion into the venules of the portal system. Because of their small size they invade the capillaries of the various viscera, particularly the heart and brain.

In the heart the ova produce a "cardiac heterophyiasis" with marked congestion, subepicardial hemorrhages, edema, fragmentation of the cardiac muscle, embolism and sclerosis of the mitral valves with subsequent calcification. There are various grades of fibrotic lesions in the myocardium and valves and a final massive flooding of the cardiac vessels with ova without the usual infiltrative or proliferative inflammatory reactions.

In the brain capillary hemorrhages have been observed with ova and focal accumulations of endotheliocytes and histiocytes in a framework of connective tissue similar to the cardiac lesions. The capillaries, plugged with ova, rupture and the spilled material undergoes organization. Islands of circumscribed reactive tissue and hemorrhagic areas punctuated with ova have also been observed in the cord.

Symptomatology.—Symptoms arising from the adult flukes are usually negligible. In heavy infections vague digestive disturbances and diarrhea may occur. Cardiac heterophyiasis resembles the cardiac picture of beriberi with edema, dilatation of the heart and cardiac failure. The cerebral symptoms are those of cerebral hemorrhage.

DIAGNOSIS, PROGNOSIS AND TREATMENT

Diagnosis.—Diagnosis depends upon finding the ova in the feces. The small, lemon-yellow, ovoid ova, varying in length from 15 to 35 μ in the different species, have a moderately thick shell, a slight but distinct thickening of the opercular rim and a short knob-like thickening at the posterior pole. The shell contains a fully-developed miracidium.

Prognosis.—Favorable, except in systemic invasion by the ova.

Treatment.—Similar to that of *Heterophyes heterophyes*. Because of the danger of systemic invasion by the ova, treatment of infected individuals is advisable, although the worms tend to leave the host without treatment.[5]

PREVENTION

Infection in man may be prevented by thoroughly cooking fish. The encysted cercariæ of *Monorchotrema taihokui* are killed by heating at 55° C. for 10 minutes, in Ilocano vinegar in 3 hours, in salt in 4 hours and in the icebox in 2 to 3 days.[6]

REFERENCES

AFRICA, C. M., DE LEON W. and GARCIA, E. Y. Heterophydiasis. III. Ova Associated with Fatal Hemorrhage in Right Basal Ganglia of Brain, J. Philippine Islands M. A., 1936, 16:22.
—— Heterophydiasis. IV. Lesions Found in the Myocardium of Eleven Infested Hearts Including Three Cases with Valvular Involvement, Philippine J. Pub. Health, 1936, 3:1.
CORT, W. W. and YOKOGAWA, S. New Human Trematode from Japan, J. Parasitol., 1921, 8:66.
FAUST, E. C. and NISHIGORI, M. The Life Cycles of Two New Species of Heterophyidæ, Parasitic in Mammals and Birds, J. Parasitol., 1926, 13:91.
KHALIL, M. The Life History of the Human Trematode Parasite *Heterophyes heterophyes* in Egypt, Lancet, 1933, 2:537.
YOKOGAWA, S. Ueber einen neuen Parasiten *Metagonimus yokogawai*, der die Forellenart *Plecoglossus altivelis* (Temminck) zum Zwischenwirt hat. Bildung einer neuen Gattung, Zentralbl. f. Bakt., 1913, 72:158.

---

[4] Africa, C. M., Garcia, E. Y. and de Leon, W., 1935; Africa, C. M., de Leon, W. and Garcia, E. Y., 1935, 1936, 1937.

[5] Faust, E. C. and Nishigori, M., 1926.
[6] Garcia, E. Y., 1936.

Chapter XXXIII

THE SUPERFAMILY TROGLOTREMATOIDEA

All members of the superfamily TROGLOTREMATOIDEA belong to the family TROGLOTREMATIDÆ.

FAMILY *TROGLOTREMATIDÆ*

The TROGLOTREMATIDÆ are small to medium-sized, oval, compact flukes with flattened ventral and arched dorsal surfaces, covered with cuticular spines. The suckers are poorly-developed and the ventral sucker is sometimes absent. The lobed or coarsely-branched testes lie side by side. The cirral sac, often absent, encloses the seminal vesicle and pars prostatica. The ovary is lobed, the seminal receptacle is small, Laurer's canal is present, the highly-developed vitellaria fill the lateral fields, and the coils of the uterus usually lie lateral to the ventral sucker. The excretory bladder is a triangular or tubular pouch extending to the anterior portion of the worm. The flame-cell formula is $2 [2+2+2]$. The large, broadly-oval ova have a wide opercular cap and slightly-thickened shoulder at oviposition. The bilaterally-symmetrical miracidia develop in snails into sporocysts, rediæ and small cercariæ with a short knob-like tail and oral stylet. The cercariæ encyst in arthropods or fishes. The adult worms are parasitic in carnivorous mammals and birds, generally occurring in pairs in cyst-like cavities in the respiratory tract or connective tissues. The species parasitic in man are *Troglotrema salmincola* and *Paragonimus westermani*.

Troglotrema salmincola (CHAPIN, 1926) WITENBERG, 1932

Synonyms.—*Nanophyes salmincola* Chapin, 1926; *Distomulum oregonensis* Ward and Mueller, 1926; *Nanophyetus salmincola* Chapin, 1927; *Nanophyetus schikhobalowi* Skrjabin and Podjapolskaja, 1931.

Disease.—Salmon poisoning of dogs.

History.—The salmon poisoning of dogs and other CANIDÆ was first reported by Suckley in 1855 on the Pacific Coast of North America. The disease was attributed to the eating of salmon and at first believed to be caused by an amœba. Donham in 1925 found the fluke in the intestines of dogs dying from the disease, and in 1931 Simms, Donham and Shaw were able to produce the disease experimentally in dogs. Chapin in 1926 named the parasite *Nanophyes salmincola,* but Witenberg in 1931 decided that it belonged to the TROGLOTREMATIDÆ rather than the HETEROPHYIDÆ and gave it the present name of *Troglotrema salmincola.*

Geographical Distribution.—The northwest Pacific Coast of North America and Siberia.

BIOLOGICAL CHARACTERISTICS

Morphology.—The adult fluke (Fig. 187) has a small pyriform body somewhat flattened dorsoventrally. The size is variously given as 0.08 to 0.11 cm. by 0.03 to 0.05 cm.[1]

---

[1] Witenberg, G., 1932.

and 0.05 by 0.03 cm. for the Siberian species *Nanophyetus schikhobalowi*, which is evidently identical.[2] The unarmed ventral and oral suckers are well developed, the ventral, slightly smaller than the oral, lying just above the equatorial plane of the body. The digestive tract consists of a pharynx, an esophagus, and two large ceca that extend to the midregion of the testes. The sac-shaped excretory bladder lies posterior to and between the oval testes, which are situated symmetrically in the posterior half of the body. The cirral sac, containing the pars prostatica and the large seminal vesicle, lies behind the ventral sucker to the left of the ovary, which is at the right of the midline. There is no seminal receptacle and Laurer's canal opens dorsally at the level of the esophagus. The uterus, after forming two posterior coils, passes forward to a tube-like genital sinus near the posterior edge of the ventral sucker. It usually contains from 10 to 15 ova. The irregular vitelline follicles are scattered through the main dorsal part of the body.

LIFE CYCLE

The definitive hosts are dog, coyote, fox, raccoon, lynx, cat, wildcat and man. The gastropod host on the Pacific Coast is *Galba plicifera silicula* (*Goniobasis plicifera* var. *silicula* Gould). The piscine hosts are species of the SALMONIDÆ.

The yellowish, broadly-oval, operculate, thick-shelled ova measure from 60 to 80 μ by 34 to 50 μ. The ovum hatches in about 75 to 90 days and the miracidium penetrates the snail, where it develops into sporocyst, rediæ and cercariæ. The liberated cercaria, 270 by 80 μ, has a simple stylet, six penetration glands, and a microcercous tail. It encysts throughout the tissues of salmonoid fishes. Mammals are infected by eating raw fish. The excysted metacercariæ, attached to the intestinal mucosa of the definitive host, develop to maturity in five or more days.

PATHOGENESIS

Pathology.—Heavy infections in dogs produce a local or general hemorrhagic enteritis. The parasites are found in the mucosa and beneath the muscularis mucosæ. The ileocecal valve, colon, ileum and rectum are most severely affected. There is superficial necrosis of the mucosa with polymorphonuclear and eosinophilic infiltration and hyperplasia of the ileocecal mesenteric lymph glands.

Symptomatology.—Symptoms appear in dogs in 6 to 10 days. There is loss of appetite, marked depression and high fever. On the second to third day there is orbital edema, rapid loss of weight, persistent vomiting and bloody diarrhea. From the fifth to seventh day the temperature may become normal or subnormal, and between the sixth and twentieth day there is general progressive weakness, usually followed by death. Such symptoms have not been observed in man. The possibility of an associated viral infection in dogs must be considered.

Immunity.—Apparently there is no natural immunity to salmon poisoning and immunization has not been successful. However, dogs that have recovered from one attack of the disease are protected against reinfection.

DIAGNOSIS, PROGNOSIS AND TREATMENT

Diagnosis.—Diagnosis in dogs is made from the characteristic symptoms and the presence of the ova in the feces by the fifth to the seventh day.

Prognosis.—Unfavorable in dogs when more than 100 flukes are present.[3]

Treatment.—No satisfactory medical treatment has been found. Apomorphine has proved beneficial in animals, if used early.

---

[2] Skrjabin, K. J. and Podjapolskaja, W. P., 1931.

[3] Simms, B. T., Donham, C. R., and Shaw, J. N., 1931.

PREVENTION

Epidemiology.—The disease is acquired by eating raw or imperfectly cooked infected salmonoid fishes. The incidence in man is slight.

Prophylaxis.—Infection in man may be prevented by thorough cooking of fish. Dogs should not be allowed to feed on raw fish.

Paragonimus westermani (KERBERT, 1878) BRAUN, 1899

Synonyms.—*Distoma westermani* Kerbert, 1878; *Distoma ringeri* Cobbold, 1880; *Distoma pulmonum* Baelz, 1880; *Distoma pulmonale* Baelz, 1883; *Distoma westermani* Leuckart, 1889; *Paragonimus kellicotti* Ward, 1908.

Disease.—Paragonimiasis.

History.—The oriental lung fluke, discovered in 1877 by Westerman in a tiger at the Zoological Gardens of Amsterdam, was described by Kerbert in 1878 under the name *Distoma westermani*. It was found in 1879 by Ringer in the lungs of a Portuguese in Formosa and named *Distoma ringeri* by Cobbold in 1880. In the same year Manson found its operculate ova in the sputum of a Chinese resident of Formosa, who was suffering with hemoptysis. Between 1880 and 1883 several investigators observed the parasite and its ova in Chinese and Japanese and recognized the infection as a distinct disease. Ward in 1894 discovered the American form, *Paragonimus kelicotti,* in a cat in Michigan.

The identity of the oriental and the American forms has been disputed. Ward and Hirsch in 1915 concluded from a study of the size, shape and arrangement of cuticular spines that there were three species: the tiger form, *P. westermani;* the human, *P. ringeri;* and the American, *P. kelicotti.* Vevers in 1923 added a fourth species, *P. compactus,* which was described in India by Cobbold in 1859. Kobayashi in 1919 found, however, that the individual variations were greater than the specific differences listed by Ward and Hirsch and concluded that the name *Paragonimus westermani* should be given to all the described species. Ameel in 1934 also concluded that the variation in cuticular spines was not a suitable criterion for the differentiation of species.

The life history of *P. westermani* was first studied in 1915 by Nakagawa, who obtained the adult fluke by feeding experimental animals with the fresh-water crab, *Potamon obtusipes,* containing the encysted larvæ. Further investigations between 1915 and 1921 by Nakagawa, Yokogawa, Kobayashi, Miyairi and Ando in Japan, and more recent studies by Vogel, Wu and Watt in 1935 and by Chen in 1937 in China, and by Ameel in 1934 in North America have added materially to our knowledge of the life history of this parasite.

Geographical Distribution.—*Paragonimus westermani* has a wide geographical distribution (Fig. 171). In the Orient it is found in Japan, Korea, Manchuria, Formosa, China (principally Chekiang Province), French Indo-China, the Philippine Islands, Siam, the Malay Peninsula, Assam, India, New Guinea, Java and Sumatra. In Africa two questionable cases of human infection have been reported in French West Africa and Tripoli. In South America it is present in the Mato Grosso region of Brazil, Peru and Venezuela. One case has been found in Cuba and another in Yucatan. Only a single autochthonous case in man has been discovered in North America, but the adult parasite has been found in mammals in Minnesota, Wisconsin, Michigan, Ohio, Mississippi, Kentucky, South Carolina and northern Canada, and in addition the larval forms have been observed in crayfish in Illinois, Indiana, Iowa, Louisiana, Missouri, Pennsylvania, Virginia, West Virginia and Ontario, Canada.

BIOLOGICAL CHARACTERISTICS

Morphology.—The living worm, reddish-brown when removed from the host but turning a slate gray on exposure, has an indefinite shape owing to its constant expansion and contraction. The distended worm is ribbon-like or spoon-shaped

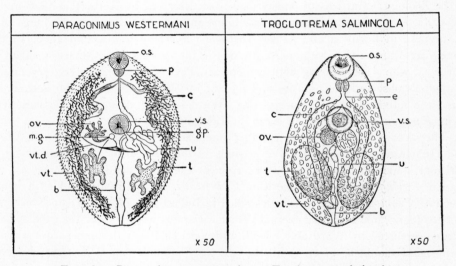

FIG. 187.—*Paragonimus westermani* AND *Troglotrema salmincola*

b, bladder; *c*, ceca; *e*, esophagus; *g.p.*, genital pore; *m.g.*, Mehlis' gland; *o.s.*, oral sucker; *ov.*, ovary; *p*, pharynx; *t*, testes; *u*, uterus; *v.s.*, ventral sucker; *vt.*, vitellaria; *vt.d.*, vitelline duct (*Paragonimus westermani* adapted from Leuckart, 1863; *Troglotrema salmincola* redrawn from Witenberg, 1932).

with one end contracted and the other elongated. When completely contracted it is spherical. The preserved parasite (Fig. 187) is a fleshy, plump, oval fluke resembling a coffee bean, with an abruptly rounded anterior and a somewhat tapering posterior end. Its size ranges from 0.8 to 1.6 cm. in length by 0.4 to 0.8 cm. in breadth and from 0.2 to 0.5 cm. in thickness. The integument is covered with encircling groups of scale-like, simple or toothed spines. The ventral sucker, 0.08 cm. in diameter, situated in the midline just anterior to the equatorial plane of the body, is often completely invaginated. The oral sucker is of equal size. The digestive tract consists of a short prepharynx, a globose pharynx, a short esophagus, and two ceca that extend in a zigzag manner to the caudal portion of the body. There is a long convoluted bladder extending forward in the midline to the level of the pharynx.

The testes are irregular, lobed organs situated somewhat obliquely to each other in the posterior third of the body. The vasa efferentia unite in a common vas deferens which forms the seminal vesicle. There is no cirral sac, but the terminal part of the seminal vesicle is modified into a prostatic portion and an ejaculatory duct, which empties through a common opening with the metraterm into the genital atrium. The genital pore, often indistinct, lies close to the posterior margin of the ventral sucker.

The lobed ovary, slightly larger than the testes, lies to the right or the left of the midline somewhat posterior to the ventral sucker. Mehlis' gland, a small seminal receptacle, and Laurer's canal opening on the dorsal surface are present. The vitellaria are situated in the extreme lateral fields from the level of the pharynx to the caudal end of the worm. The uterus forms a series of knotted coils behind the ventral sucker on the side opposite the ovary, before it joins the ejaculatory duct to enter the genital atrium.

Physiology.—The adult worms, bathed in a purulent exudate, are enclosed in cystic cavities in the tissues. In man there is usually a single worm per cyst, but in mammals two or more are often present. The worms obtain nourishment from the tissues and produce ova which are retained within the cyst until it ruptures. The span of life is about six years.

LIFE CYCLE

Hosts.—The definitive hosts are man, dog, cat, wildcat, tiger, mountain lion, fox, martin, badger, mink, rat, muskrat, weasel, wolf, goat and hog. Monkeys have been experimentally infected, but in experimentally infected rabbits, guinea pigs, rats and mice the worms do not reach sexual maturity.

At least seven species of fresh-water snails of the genus *Brotia* (*Melania*) serve as the first intermediate hosts in the Orient (Table 34), of which *B. libertina* and *B. gottschei* are the most important. Other gastropod hosts are *Assiminea lutea* in China, *Ampullaria luteostoma* (?) in Venezuela, and *Pomatiopsis lapidaria* in North America. The second intermediate hosts (Fig. 213) are the fresh-water crabs *Eriocheir japonicus*, *E. sinensis*, *Potamon dehaani*, *P. rathbuni*, *P. denticulatus*, *Sesarma dehaani*, *S. sinensis*, and *Parathelphusa sinensis*; the crayfishes *Astacus japonicus* and *A. similis* in the Orient; ten and probably most species of the crayfish *Cambarus* in North America; and the crab *Pseudothelphusa iturbei* in Venezuela.

Developmental Cycle.—Undeveloped ova are passed in the sputum or feces. They hatch in the water at an optimal temperature of 27° C. in about 21 days. The liberated miracidium enters a suitable species of snail and develops successively into sporocyst, mother rediæ, daughter rediæ and cercariæ. The cercariæ emerge from the snail in the late afternoon or at night and lead a crawling, stationary or floating existence until they encyst in the heart, muscles or gills of a crustacean. Man and mammals are infected by eating the raw or partially cooked flesh of the crustacean host (Fig. 188).

Larval Forms.—The oval, yellowish-brown, thick-shelled ova (Fig. 189A) have a mean size of 85 by 53 μ and vary from 73 to 118 μ in length and from 46 to 67 μ in breadth. The maximal breadth is toward the operculate pole. The

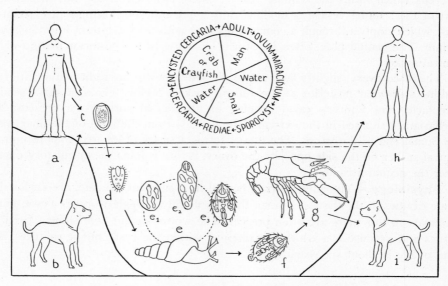

FIG. 188.—LIFE CYCLE OF *Paragonimus westermani*

a, man infected with adult fluke; *b,* reservoir animal host; *c,* ovum in sputum or feces; *d,* free-swimming miracidium; *e,* metamorphosis in snail (*e₁,* sporocyst; *e₂,* redia (two generations) ; *e₃,* cercaria) ; *f,* cercaria in water; *g,* crayfish or fresh-water crab infected with metacercaria; *h,* man infected by eating raw or imperfectly cooked crustacea; *i,* animal host infected in the same manner.

opercular rim is distinctly thickened. At oviposition the ovum is in the single-celled stage and surrounded by five to ten coarsely-granular yolk cells. The ova are laid in cystic pockets in the lungs and, when these rupture, escape into the bronchi. They leave the host in the sputum or, if swallowed, in the feces. The ova are sus-

---

FIG. 189 (*continued*) *A,* ovum showing yolk cells and germinal area; *B,* miracidium showing excretory system and arrangement of ciliated epidermal cells; *C,* miracidium showing ganglionic mass and germ cells; *D,* mature sporocyst containing well-developed first generation rediæ 39 days after infection of snail; *E,* mature first generation redia containing well-developed second generation rediæ; *F,* mature second generation redia; *G,* cercaria after emergence from snail; *H,* cercaria after emergence from snail; *I,* metacercaria from crab, cyst wall not shown in drawing; *J,* mature excysted metacercaria.

b.p., birth pore; *c,* ceca; *col.,* collar; *e.b.,* excretory bladder; *e.p.,* excretory pore; *f.c.,* flame-cell; *g,* gut; *g.a.,* germinal area; *g.c.,* genital cells; *gl.c.,* gland cells; *m,* mouth; *n,* nervous system; *o,* operculum; *o.s.,* oral sucker; *p,* pharynx; *p.g.,* penetration glands; *s,* stylet; *t,* testes; *tl.,* tail; *v.s.,* ventral sucker (*A* to *F, H* and *J,* redrawn from Ameel, 1934; *G* and *I* redrawn from Chen, 1936).

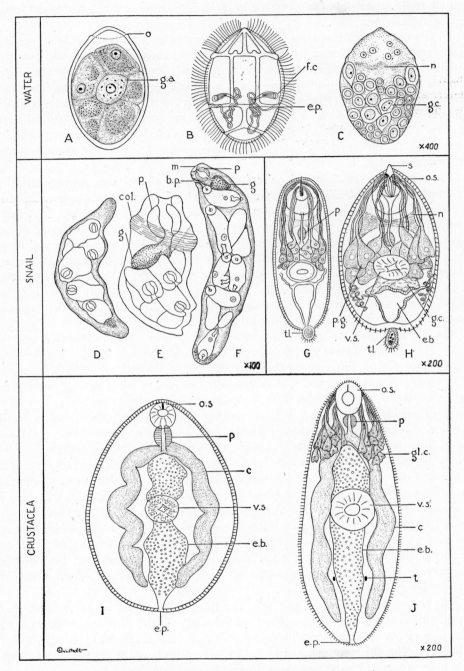

FIG. 189.—LARVAL FORMS OF *Paragonimus westermani*

ceptible to desiccation, but can survive in limited moisture and can withstand freezing for six minutes.

In North America immature miracidia are produced in two weeks at an optimal temperature of 27° C., and hatching takes place in three weeks, but the ova may remain dormant four to five months in the icebox.[4] The vitelline membrane bulges through the opercular opening before it is ruptured by the miracidium. The free-swimming miracidium (Fig. 189B and C), 80 by 40 μ, has 16 ciliated epidermal cells arranged in four rows, a conspicuous bilobed ganglionic mass, a pair of large flame-cells with excretory tubules, and germinal cells. It cannot survive over 24 hours at 25° C. unless it penetrates the head or mantle of a snail, but remains active for three days at 7° C.

The miracidium loses its ciliated epithelium either at the time of penetration or within the snail. It becomes first an ellipsoidal and later an elongate sacculated sporocyst (Fig. 189D), 400 by 160 μ, which contains 20 to 26 rediæ.[5] The first-generation rediæ (Fig. 189E), after escaping from the sporocyst as early as 26 days after infection, develop in the lymph sinuses near the digestive tract and liver. They are short and truncate with an invaginated posterior end, prominent collar, germinal cells, and digestive tract consisting of a pharynx, a short esophagus and an elongate intestine. In 63 days they produce a second generation of rediæ (Fig. 189F), which are larger and have sloping, rounded extremities, a birth pore and no collar. These daughter rediæ produce cercariæ.

The microcercous cercaria (Fig. 189G and H) has an ellipsoidal body, 225 by 80 μ, covered with spines, and an abbreviated cylindrical tail, 19 by 13 μ, bearing several large spines. The round or slightly-elongate, terminal oral sucker carries on its anterodorsal surface a simple, boring stylet. The smaller, oval ventral sucker lies slightly posterior to the middle of the body above the muscular, expansile, trigonate excretory bladder. The digestive tract consists of a slender prepharynx, a small pharynx, a short esophagus, and indistinct ceca that extend about half the body length. The genital cells occupy a small area between the ventral sucker and excretory bladder. A butterfly-shaped ganglionic mass is situated between the oral sucker and the pharynx. There are eight lateral and six smaller median penetration glands with ducts opening anteriorly near the stylet. Subcuticular glands are distributed over the entire body. The cercariæ that emerge from the snail about 13 weeks after infection travel with a leech-like motion, float rather than swim, and at times are anchored to objects by strands of mucus. They perish in 24 to 48 hours at 22° C. unless they penetrate the articulations of a crustacean host. Encystment is completed within 25 minutes, except in the heart and internal viscera where it may require 24 hours.

The encysted cercariæ are found in the gills, muscles of the appendages and thorax, and viscera; in *Cambarus* they are especially in the pericardial region. The mean size of the spherical cysts varies from 245 to 450 μ according to various investigators. The thick, transparent cyst wall is surrounded by a closely adherent membrane produced by the tissues of the crustacean. The size of the encysted larvæ depends upon the abundance of the food supply. The fully-developed enclosed meta-

---

[4] Ameel, D. J., 1934.   [5] Ameel, D. J., 1934; Wu, K., 1935; Chen, H. T., 1936, 1937.

cercariæ (Fig. 189I), from 250 to 520 μ in length, are characterized by the large convoluted ceca with reddish globules and the large excretory bladder filled with highly-refractive granules. Metacercariæ removed from the cyst survive for five days at 12° to 21° C., succumb immediately in 10 per cent sodium chloride and 35 per cent alcohol, but live nearly three hours in 3 per cent alcohol.[4] They perish in five minutes at 55° C.[6]

After ingestion by the mammalian host the metacercaria excysts in the duodenum. The excysted worm (Fig. 189J), 625 by 240 μ, covered with small spines, has two well-developed suckers, a spherical pharynx, a short esophagus, broad ceca, 14 small glandular cells with large vesicular nuclei, a ganglionic mass with anterior and posterior rami, large excretory bladder, and genital primordia. The excysted metacercaria passes through the walls of the jejunum into the abdominal cavity and in three to four days penetrates through the diaphragm, chiefly in the region of the liver, into the pleural cavity. In 20 days it reaches the lungs, where, enclosed in a cystic capsule near the bronchi, it grows to an adult worm in five to six weeks. Excysted metacercariæ can penetrate wounds or mucous membranes but not intact skin.[7]

The route of the larval worms in the body is influenced by the resistance of the tissues. They may remain for a long time in the abdominal cavity and may be in advanced stages of development before they penetrate the tendinous portion of the diaphragm. They often enter the liver, penetrate for a short distance, and then escape, leaving blind tunnels. Not all the worms migrate through the diaphragm, and not all that reach the pleura penetrate the lungs. These excess worms lodge in other organs.

PATHOGENESIS

Pathology.—The chief habitat of the adult parasite is the lungs, although other organs are also invaded. The worms are enclosed in cystic cavities, which rupture into the bronchi, thereby permitting the ova to reach the sputum. Externally the lungs show little change except scattered areas of congestion, emphysematous edges, and an uneven surface with reddish-brown, superficial nodules. In man these nodules usually number less than 20 and do not as a rule project from the surface, but in mammals they are more numerous and stand out as dark-reddish-brown, irregularly-shaped bodies from 0.2 to 1.0 cm. in size. These nodules are composed of cysts with white fibrotic capsules, surrounded by congested and edematous tissue. The cysts (Fig. 190) contain one or more living, or dead, worms (usually only one in man) in a brownish, necrotic, gelatinous exudate containing ova and Charcot-Leyden crystals. In recent infections in animals the pleura shows plastic adhesions and in old infections focal areas of fibrosis.[8]

On section the cysts are found distributed throughout the lungs, but are more numerous near the pleural surface, in the posterior lobes, and near the hilum. In heavy infections the lungs in the neighborhood of the cysts appear atelectatic. In the infiltrated areas the cysts and burrows break down to form cavities that com-

---

[6] Nakagawa, K., 1917.   [8] Kau, L. S. and Wu, K., 1936.
[7] Yokogawa, S. and Suyemori, S., 1920.

municate with the bronchi. These cavities resemble dilated bronchi. The bronchial mucosa is congested, edematous and even desquamated. At times there is a peribronchitis, and the hilar lymph glands are enlarged.

There are four types of lesions:[9] (1) the nonsuppurative; (2) the tuberculosis-like; (3) the suppurative; and (4) the ulcerative. The nonsuppurative type with round cell and connective tissue proliferation is caused by the infiltration of ova.

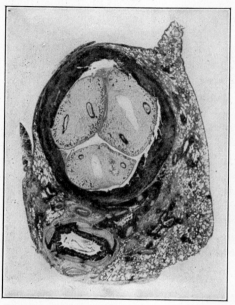

Fig. 190.—Section of Lung Showing Lesions Produced by *Paragonimus westermani*

(Copyright by General Biological Supply House, Chicago).

The inflammatory reaction about the encysted worm and ova may take the form of tuberculoid lesions or abscess formation with progressive fibrosis. In the ulcerative type permanent healing is infrequent.

The parasite may also be found, particularly in heavy infections, in other parts of the body including the abdominal and pleural cavities, spleen, liver, mesenteric lymph glands, omentum, pericardium, testes, intestines, brain, orbital cavity, muscles and skin. The lesions, though modified by the character of the special tissues, are essentially the same as in the lung. Infiltration of ova in the intestinal mucosa, a common site, gives rise to ulceration and the appearance of ova in the feces. Cutaneous lesions resulting from infected superficial lymph glands are usually ulcerative. In the internal viscera abscesses containing ova and pyogenic bacteria occur. The tumor-like lesions in the brain are nearly always in the temporal or occipital lobes.

Symptomatology.—The disease is a slowly progressing chronic condition with insidious onset, resembling in many respects tuberculosis. Four types have been described:[9] (1) general, (2) pulmonary, (3) abdominal, and (4) cerebral. The general type manifests a constant fever, enlargement of the superficial lymph glands, especially the axillary and inguinal, with occasional cutaneous ulceration, and in fatal cases muscular rheumatic pains. In the predominating pulmonary type the patients have a chronic cough, most pronounced on rising in the morning; an abundant, blood-stained, rusty-brown, purulent, tenacious sputum; and occasional attacks of hemoptysis, usually slight though at times severe. The physical signs, usually slight, may suggest lobular pneumonia or tuberculosis. The abdominal type is characterized by dull abdominal pains, rigidity, tenderness and, if ulceration of the intestinal mucosa is present, diarrhea with blood, mucus and ova. The liver, prostate, epididymis and mesenteric lymph glands may be involved. The cerebral

---

[9] Musgrave. W. E., 1907.

type produces a peculiar form of Jacksonian epilepsy with hemiplegia, monoplegia, aphasia, visual disturbances, and paresis of various degrees, resembling cerebral cysticercosis.

DIAGNOSIS, PROGNOSIS AND TREATMENT

Diagnosis.—The clinical symptoms are not sufficiently pathognomonic for definite diagnosis, but in endemic areas are suggestive. The pulmonary type must be differentiated from lobular pneumonia, tuberculosis, pulmonary spirochætosis and bronchiectasis; the general and abdominal type from leishmaniasis, schistosomiasis and amœbiasis; and the cerebral type from idiopathic epilepsy, cerebral tumors and cystocercal infection. Different opinions exist as to the value of roentgen-ray diagnosis in detecting infiltration in pulmonary paragonimiasis.[10] In endemic areas eosinophilia is an early sign of some value.

Definite diagnosis is established by finding the ova in the characteristic sputum, which is viscid and reddish-brown from the dark brown ova and red blood cells. It contains leukocytes, eosinophils and often Charcot-Leyden crystals. Ova may be found in the feces in about 40 per cent of the patients, either from swallowed sputum or from intestinal lesions. The unsegmented ova are identified by their size and shape (Fig. 189A). Alexin-fixation, using as antigen a saline extract of macerated adult worms from mammalian hosts, has proved useful in detecting nonpulmonary infection, where the worms are lodged in deep foci and the ova are not present in the subcutaneous tissues or in the excreta.[11]

Prognosis.—In light infections prognosis is good, although spontaneous cure may not occur. In heavy invasions, superimposed tuberculosis, secondary pyogenic infections, or cerebral involvement it is unfavorable.

Treatment.—No specific treatment is known. The removal of patients from endemic areas is advisable, since without reinfection the disease subsides within six years with the death of the worms. Treatment with emetine (Section **VII**, XIII, 14) reduces the sexual activity of the worms.[12] Tartar emetic (Section **VII**, XIII, 6) temporarily relieves pulmonary symptoms. Lipoidal injections of the bronchi have been employed.[13]

PREVENTION

Epidemiology.—The disease is transmitted to man by eating infected crabs or crayfishes, particularly the oriental custom of consuming these crustaceans raw in brine or wine. While the crabs are killed by this treatment, the metacercariæ survive for several hours and may be viable when ingested by man. Relatively little cooking is sufficient to destroy the metacercariæ, which are killed if the crabs are roasted until the muscles turn white or if heated in water at 55° C. for 5 minutes.[6]

Prophylaxis.—The most practical methods of preventing human infection are to avoid eating raw, freshly salted, pickled or imperfectly cooked crustacea and drinking unfiltered or unboiled river water in infected districts. The best line of attack is

[10] Anto, R., and Yamata, R., 1916; Wang, S. H. and Hsieh, C. K., 1937; Bercovitz, Z., 1937.

[11] Ando, R., 1917.
[12] Ando, R., 1918.
[13] Bercovitz, Z., 1937.

public education. Although the sputum and other excreta of man can be disinfected, the disease in endemic districts can not be easily eradicated, since the elimination of reservoir hosts, crustaceans and snails is impracticable.

REFERENCES

AMEEL, D. J. *Paragonimus,* its Life History and Distribution in North America and its Taxonomy (Trematoda: Troglotrematidæ), Am. J. Hyg., 1934, 19:279.

BERCOVITZ, Z. Clinical Studies on Human Lung Fluke Disease (Endemic Hemoptysis) Caused by *Paragonimus westermani* Infestation, Am. J. Trop. Med., 1937, 17:101.

CHEN, H. T. Further Notes on the Life History of *Paragonimus* From Rats, Chinese M. J., 1936, Supp. I; 368.

——— Some Observations on the Evolutionary Cycle of *Paragonimus* in the South of China, Ann. de parasitol., 1937, 15:155.

KAU, L. S. and WU, K. Preliminary Report on Histopathology of Paragonimiasis in Cats in China, Chinese M. J., 1936, Supp. 1:101.

NAKAGAWA, K. Pulmonary Distomiasis Caused by *Paragonimus westermanni,* J. Exper. Med., 1917, 26:297.

SIMMS, B. T., DONHAM, C. R. and SHAW, J. N. Salmon Poisoning, Am. J. Hyg., 1931, 13:363.

SKRJABIN, K. J. and PODJAPOLSKAJA, W. P. *Nanophyetus schikhobalowi* n. sp. ein neuer Trematode aus dem Darm des Menschen, Zentralbl. f. Bakt., 1931, 119:294.

WITENBERG, G. On the Anatomy and Systematic Position of the Causative Agent of So-called Salmon Poisoning, J. Parasitol., 1932, 28:258.

WU, K. Notes on Certain Larval Stages of the Lung Fluke *Paragonimus* in China, Chinese M. J., 1935, 49:741.

Chapter XXXIV

THE SUPERFAMILIES DICROCŒLIOIDEA, ECHINO-STOMATOIDEA AND PARAMPHISTOMOIDEA

SUPERFAMILY *DICROCŒLIOIDEA* FAUST, 1929

The members of the superfamily DICROCŒLIOIDEA are small to medium-sized, elongate, flattened or cylindrical flukes. The small ova, fully-developed at oviposition, hatch in the molluscan host. Cercariæ develop in second-generation sporocysts or rediæ and enter mollusks, other invertebrates or plants to be ingested, encysted or unencysted, by the final hosts. The species infecting man belong to the family DICROCŒLIIDÆ.

FAMILY *DICROCŒLIIDÆ* (LOOSS, 1907) ODHNER, 1910

The DICROCŒLIIDÆ are small, elongate, transparent, leaf-like or cylindrical trematodes, tapering at both extremities. The testes are situated between the ventral sucker and the ovary, the long uterus fills the body posterior to the ovary, and the vitellaria occupy the lateral midportion of the worm. The genital pore is midway between the oral and ventral suckers. The intestinal ceca do not extend to the posterior extremity. The simple tubular excretory bladder passes forward to the midplane of the body, and the fundamental flame-cell pattern is $2 \left[(2+2+2) + (2+2+2) \right]$. The relatively small, dark brown, thick-shelled ova have a thickened opercular rim. These flukes are parasites of the biliary tract, rarely of the pancreatic duct and intestine, of birds and mammals. The species parasitic in man are *Dicrocœlium dendriticum* and possibly *Eurytrema pancreaticum*.

Dicrocœlium dendriticum (RUDOLPHI, 1819) LOOSS, 1899

Synonyms.—*Fasciola lanceolata* Rudolphi, 1803 (*nec* Schrank, 1790); *Fasciola dendritica* Rudolphi, 1819; *Distomum lanceolatum* Mehlis, 1825; *Dicrocœlium lanceolatum* Dujardin, 1845; *Dicrocœlium lanceatum* Stiles and Hassall, 1896.

Disease.—Dicrocœliasis.

Geographical Distribution.—*Dicrocœlium dendriticum* has a more or less cosmopolitan distribution in sheep and other herbivorous animals. It is common in Europe and is found in northern Africa, Asia (Syria, Turkestan, Siberia and China) and in North and South America. Sporadic cases of human infection have been reported from eleven countries in Europe, Asia and northern Africa.

BIOLOGICAL CHARACTERISTICS

Morphology.—The adult fluke (Fig. 191G), has a slender, lancet-shaped, flat, aspinose body, 0.5 to 1.5 cm. in length and 0.15 to 0.25 cm. in breadth. The extremities are somewhat pointed, the posterior end being less attenuated than the anterior. The ventral sucker is more highly developed than the oral. The pharynx is globular, the esophagus delicate, and the unbranched ceca extend only to the posterior fifth of the body. The bladder is long and tubular.

The two large, slightly-lobed testes are situated obliquely to each other between the small subglobose ovary, which usually lies to the right of the midline of the body, and the ventral sucker. The vasa efferentia join at the base of the cirral sac near the anterior margin of the ventral sucker. The highly-coiled voluminous uterus fills the posterior two-thirds of the worm before it passes forward, ventral to the left testis, to terminate in the genital pore just anterior to the ventral sucker. The moderately-developed vitellaria occupy the lateral fields in the middle portion of the body below the level of the lower testis.

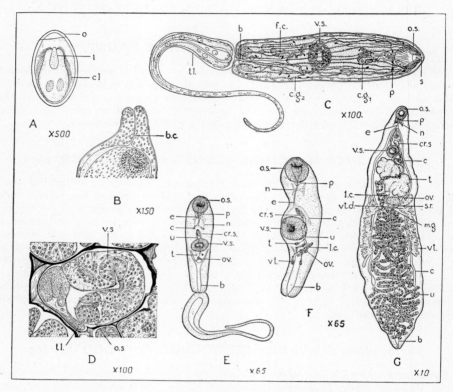

FIG. 191.—LARVAL AND ADULT FORMS OF *Dicrocœlium dendriticum*

A, miracidium in eggshell; *B*, anterior end of secondary sporocyst, showing birth-canal and part of maturing cercaria; *C*, cercaria; *D*, metacercaria encysted in slime ball; *E*, metacercaria freed from cyst; *F*, eight-day-old immature worm in definitive host; *G*, adult worm.

b, excretory bladder; *b.c.*, birth canal; *c*, ceca; *c.g.₁*, anterior cephalic glands; *c.g.₂*, posterior cephalic glands; *cl.*, cilia; *cr.s.*, cirral sac; *e*, esophagus; *f.c.*, flame cell; *i*, primitive gut; *l.c.*, Laurer's canal; *m.g.*, Mehlis' gland; *n*, nervous system; *o*, operculum; *o.s.*, oral sucker; *ov.*, ovary; *p*, pharynx; *s*, stylet; *s.r.*, seminal receptacle; *t*, testes; *tl.*, tail; *u*, uterus; *v.s.*, ventral sucker; *vt.*, vitellaria; *vt.d.*, vitelline duct (*B* redrawn from Mattes, 1936; *C* redrawn from Vogel, 1929; *D* redrawn from Neuhaus, 1936; *E* to *G* redrawn from Neuhaus, 1938).

LIFE CYCLE

Hosts.—The principal definitive host is the sheep, but the parasite has been found in cattle, goats, horses, asses, camels, deer, elk, hogs, rabbits, dogs and man. The intermediate hosts are the snails, *Helicella candidula*, *H. ericetorum*, *H. itala*, *Cochlicella acuta*, *Zebrina detrita* and *Torquilla frumentum*.

Developmental Cycle.—The transmission stage of the life cycle is not completely known, although the larval stages have been studied.[1] The ova, fully developed on leaving the definitive host, are ingested by snails. The miracidium hatches in the snail and metamorphoses into two generations of sporocysts and finally into cercariæ. After liberation from the sporocyst, the cercariæ migrate to the respiratory chamber of the snail where, without losing their tails, they agglomerate in groups of 200 to 400 in slime balls of secreted cystogenous material. The snails in crawling shed these slime balls on damp vegetation. When ingested by the definitive host the cercariæ excyst in the intestine, penetrate the intestinal wall, and are carried by the portal veins to the liver and bile ducts. Development to mature egg-producing flukes requires eleven or more weeks.

Larval Forms.—The dark brown, thick-shelled, operculate ova (Fig. 191A), slightly flattened on one side, measure 38 to 45 μ in length by 22 to 30 μ in breadth. At oviposition they contain an oval, fully developed miracidium. The ova are resistant to desiccation and survive freezing temperatures.[2] The cercaria (Fig. 191C) that develops from the second generation of sporocysts has an elongate, ovoidal, aspinose body, 400 to 700 μ in length, and a long tapering tail. It has a minute stylet at its anterior end, 6 anterior and 12 posterior lytic glands, two suckers, and an elongate bladder with a flame-cell pattern of $2[(2+2+2)+(2+2+2)]$. The metacercaria (Fig. 191E) does not lose its stylet or tail until it reaches the liver of the host.

PATHOGENESIS

Pathology.—The adult worm inhabits the biliary tract. The immature worms (Fig. 191F) first invade the biliary capillaries and later descend to the main ducts and gallbladder. The parasite in animals causes enlargement of the ducts, hypertrophy of the biliary epithelium, formation of periductal fibrous connective tissue, atrophy of liver cells, and finally portal cirrhosis. Infection in man is usually light and the hepatic changes are less pronounced.

Symptomatology.—Toxemia is less marked than in *Fasciola hepatica* infections. Digestive disturbances, flatulence, chronic constipation, diarrhea, enlarged liver, and toxic manifestations may occur.

DIAGNOSIS, PROGNOSIS AND TREATMENT

Diagnosis.—Diagnosis is made by finding the characteristic ova consistently present in the feces. Their temporary presence may result from the ingestion of raw infected liver.[3]

Prognosis.—Favorable.

Treatment.—The successful use of thymol (Section **VII**, XIII, 24) has been reported.[4]

PREVENTION

Epidemiology.—Infection in man is uncommon. Surveys based upon the presence of ova in the feces give an incidence of 0.2 per cent in Syria, but many cases are evidently spurious infections. Man is accidentally infected by the ingestion of plants or water containing the parasites encysted in slime balls. Infection of herbivorous animals occurs in warm dry meadows in contrast to low muddy flooded areas for *Fasciola hepatica*.

Prophylaxis.—In endemic areas persons should refrain from eating uncooked vegetables and from drinking unfiltered water.

[1] Vogel, H., 1929; Mattes, O., 1933; Neuhaus, W., 1936, 1938.

[2] Henkel, H., 1931.

[3] Yenikomshian, H. A., and Berberian, D. A., 1934.

[4] Galli-Valerio, B. and Bornand, M., 1931.

Eurytrema pancreaticum (JANSON, 1889) LOOSS, 1907

Eurytrema pancreaticum has been reported once from man in South China. It is a natural parasite of the pancreatic duct of hogs and the biliary tract of cattle and water buffaloes in the Orient. In animals it produces epithelial hyperplasia, hypertrophy of the ducts, and periductal fibrosis. The liver lesions, though less extensive, resemble those of *Fasciola hepatica*. It is a broad, thick, spinose fluke somewhat shorter than *Dicrocœlium dendriticum* with a large oral sucker, deeply lobed testes opposite each other, vitellaria confined to the lateral third quarter of the body, and a highly coiled uterus that fills the posterior half of the worm. The ova resemble those of *Dicrocœlium dendriticum*. Its life cycle is unknown.

SUPERFAMILY *ECHINOSTOMATOIDEA* FAUST, 1929

The members of the superfamily ECHINOSTOMATOIDEA belong to the family ECHINOSTOMATIDÆ Looss, 1902, which comprises more than thirty genera, parasitic in the intestinal and biliary tracts of vertebrates, chiefly mammals and birds. They are elongate, moderate-sized, spinose flukes with a reniform collar, armed with a single or double row of spines, surrounding the dorsal and lateral margins of the oral sucker. The larvæ metamorphose into rediæ and cercariæ in snails and the cercariæ encyst in mollusks, fishes and frogs, and on vegetation or in water.

THE *ECHINOSTOMATIDÆ* OF MAN

Some ten or more echinostomes have been reported in man, and, of these, six species have been described in detail (Fig. 192, Table 35). Since these parasites are of little pathological importance, they are discussed as a group, their differential characteristics tabulated, and a description of one, *Echinostoma ilocanum*, will suffice.

Species.—The six species include: (1) *Echinostoma ilocanum* (Garrison, 1908) Odhner, 1911 (Synonyms: *Fascioletta ilocanum* Garrison, 1908; *Euparyphium ilocanum* (Garrison, 1908) Tubangui and Pasco, 1933); (2) *Echinostoma malayanum* Leiper, 1911 (Synonyms: *Euparyphium malayanum* Leiper, 1911); (3) *Echinostoma jassyense* Léon and Ciurea, 1922; (4) *Echinostoma revolutum* Fröhlich, 1802 (Synonyms: *Fasciola revoluta* Fröhlich, 1802; *Distoma echinatum* Zeder, 1803; *Echinostoma mendax* Dietz, 1909); (5) *Paryphostomum sufrartyfex* (Lane, 1915) Bhalerao, 1931 (Synonyms: *Artyfechinostomum sufrartyfex* Lane, 1915; *Euparyphium malayanum* Leiper, 1911; *Echinostoma sufrartyfex* (Lane, 1915) Faust, 1929); and (6) *Echinochasmus perfoliatus* (v. Ratz, 1908) Dietz, 1910 (Synonyms: *Echinostomum perfoliatum* v. Ratz, 1908).

Single instances of human infection have been reported for the following species: *Echinostoma macrorchis* Ando and Ozaki, 1923, a natural parasite of the rat, in Japan in 1927; *Echinoparyphium paraulum* Dietz, 1909, a natural parasite of birds, in Russia in 1938; *Echinoparyphium recurvatum* v. Linstow, 1873 in Formosa in 1924; and *Himasthla muehlensi* Vogel, 1933, a possible parasite of gulls, in 1933 in a German, believed to have been infected by eating the lamellibranch, *Venus mercenaria*, in North America.

Morphology.—The echinostome flukes are distingushed from other trematodes by a horseshoe-shaped collar, bearing one or two rows of straight spines, which surrounds the dorsal and lateral sides of the oral sucker. Differentiation into subfamilies is based upon the dorsal continuity of this collar. They are elongate, moderate-sized trematodes with slightly tapering, rounded extremities. The cuticle bears minute scale-like spines, which usually cover the anterior portion of the body. The species differ in the extent and distribution of these spines as do individuals of the same species, because of the

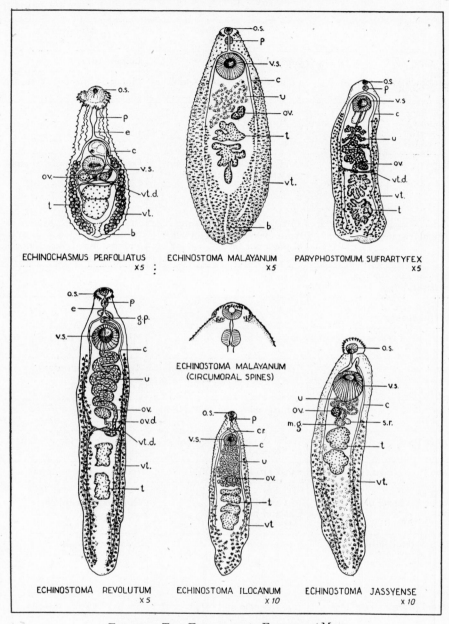

FIG. 192.—THE ECHINOSTOME FLUKES OF MAN

c, ceca; *cr.,* cirrus; *e,* esophagus; *g.p.,* genital pore; *o.s.,* oral sucker; *ov.,* ovary; *ov.d.,* oviduct; *p,* pharynx; *s.r.,* seminal receptacle; *t,* testes; *v.s.,* ventral sucker; *vt.,* vitellaria; *vt.d.,* vitelline duct. (*Echinochasmus perfoliatus* redrawn from Ujiie, 1936; *Echinostoma malayanum* redrawn from Odhner, 1913; *Paryphostomum sufrartyfex* redrawn from Lane, 1915; *Echinostoma revolutum* redrawn with modifications from Johnson, 1920; anterior end of *Echinostoma malayanum* redrawn from Leiper, 1913; *Echinostoma ilocanum* redrawn from Odhner, 1911; *Echinostoma jassyense* redrawn from Léon and Ciurea, 1922).

TABLE 35

THE PARASITIC

	Echinostoma ilocanum	*Echinostoma malayanum*
Discoverer	Garrison, 1908	Leiper, 1911
Geographical distribution	Philippines, Celebes, China	Malay Peninsula, India, China
Morphology Size (cm.) Length Breadth	0.25 to 0.65 0.11	1.2 0.13
Shape	Oval, rounded tapering ends, posterior more attenuate	Oval, bluntly rounded ends
Cuticular spines	Anterior portion to midlevel of posterior testis	On ventral surface to posterior end, on dorsal to anterior border of ventral sucker
Number of spines on circumoral disk	49 to 51	43
Ratio of size of oral to ventral sucker	1:2.3	1:3.5
Location of testes	Posterior half	High in posterior half, extend above midplane
Cirral sac	To center of ventral sucker	To posterior border of ventral sucker
Ovary	Transversely oval, in midline	
Upper level of vitellaria	Halfway between ventral sucker and ovary	Posterior margin of ventral sucker
Size of ova (micra)	83 to 116 by 53 to 82	120 to 130 by 80 to 90
Life cycle Definitive hosts other than man	Rat and dog Cat and monkey (experimental)	Dog (experimental)
First intermediate host	*Gyraulus prashadi*	*Lymnæa leuteola*
Second intermediate host	*Pila luzonica* and other fresh-water snails	Snails: *Lymnæa leuteola,* *Indoplanorbis exustis* Fish: *Barbus stigma*
References	Odhner, T., 1911 Tubangui, M. A. and Pasco, A. M., 1933 Hilario, J. S. and Wharton, L. D., 1917	Odhner, T., 1913

TABLE 35—Continued

ECHINOSTOMATIDÆ OF MAN

Echinostoma jassyense	*Echinostoma revolutum*	*Paryphostomum sufrartyfex*	*Echinochasmus perfoliatus*
Léon, 1916	Fröhlich, 1802	Lane, 1915	von Ratz, 1908
Rumania	Formosa (man) Cosmopolitan (birds)	Assam, India	Japan, Italy, Rumania, Russia
0.55 to 0.75 0.12	1.0 to 2.2 0.22	0.9 0.25	0.5 to 1.2 0.20
Elongate oval, tapering, rounded ends	Elongate, with tapering rounded ends	Oval, with bluntly rounded posterior end, ventral curvature, and at times a constriction at level of ventral sucker	Elongate, with tapering rounded ends
On lateral margins	Anterior portion	Entire ventral and anterior part of dorsal surface	Entire body, except middorsal and midventral portions
27	37	39 to 42	24
1:3.3		1:4.7	
Posterior part of anterior half	Posterior half	Posterior half	Posterior half
To somewhat behind midplane of ventral sucker	To anterior part of ventral sucker	Very large, extending to 0.05 cm behind ventral sucker	
Spherical, right of midline	Oval, midline	Subglobose, right of midline	Globose, right of midline
Midplane of ovary	Posterior margin of ventral sucker	Midplane of ventral sucker	Anterior margin of ventral sucker
132 to 154 by 79 to 85	90 to 126 by 59 to 71	90 to 125 by 60 to 75	90 to 135 by 55 to 95
Unknown	Water fowl Mouse and dog (experimental)	Hog	Cat, dog, hog, fox
Unknown	*Physa occidentalis* and various species of *Lymnæa, Planorbis, Segmentina* and *Paludina*	Unknown	*Parafossarulus striatulus* var. *japonicus* and other species of *Parafossarulus*
Unknown	Same as first intermediate hosts and also *Viviparus viviparus, Sphærium corneum,* and *Corbicula producta*	Unknown	19 cyprinoid and 1 species of ESOCIDÆ
Léon, N. and Ciurea, I., 1922	Anazawa, K., 1929 Johnson, J. C., 1920	Lane, C., 1915	Ujiie, N., 1936

ease with which the spines are rubbed off the body. The oral sucker is smaller and less muscular than the ventral sucker. The digestive tract comprises a pharynx, a relatively long esophagus, and two ceca that terminate in the posterior portion of the body. The excretory system consists of a Y-shaped, pouch-like excretory bladder, extending from the caudal extremity to the posterior testis. The genital pore lies between the ventral sucker and the bifurcation of the esophagus.

The more or less lobate testes occupy a tandem or slightly oblique position, usually in the posterior half of the worm but occasionally above the equatorial plane. The vasa efferentia pass forward to unite in a coiled seminal vesicle. The size of the cirral sac, which contains the seminal vesicle, cirral organ and prostatic portion of the ejaculatory duct, varies considerably in the different species. The globular ovary is situated in front of the anterior testis either in or slightly to the right of the midline. Mehlis' gland varies in size in the different species. The seminal receptacle is often absent, but has been recorded in some species. The looped uterus lies anterior to the ovary and passes to the genital pore to the left of the opening of the cirral sac. The vitellaria usually fill the lateral borders of the posterior two-thirds of the worm and extend from variable upper levels posteriorly into the intracecal region with a crescentic sweep.

Life Cycle.—The life cycles for the most part have been incompletely studied, the best known being those of *Echinostoma ilocanum, E. malayanum, E. revolutum* and *Echinochasmus perfoliatus*. The undeveloped ovum matures after leaving the host and, under favorable conditions of light and moisture, hatches in about three weeks. The miracidium enters a snail as the first intermediate host. Apparently the sporocyst stage is abortive and development takes place directly into mother redia, daughter rediæ and cercariæ. The cercariæ either escape to infect snails and fishes, or possibly to encyst on vegetation and in the water. They may also encyst in the tissues of the first intermediate host, even within the rediæ. *Echinostoma ilocanum* and *E. revolutum* require snails for their second intermediate hosts, *E. malayanum* snails or fishes, and *Echinochasmus perfoliatus* fishes. Infection is acquired by the ingestion of the metacercariæ by the definitive host.

Pathogenesis.—It is questionable whether the echinostomes are active pathogens. They are attached by the oral circlet of spines to the mucosa of the small intestine, particularly the jejunum, where they cause little damage other than irritation. Heavy infections with *Echinostoma ilocanum, E. malayanum, E. jassyense,* and possibly *E. revolutum* and *Echinochasmus perfoliatus* may produce a mild catarrhal inflammation of the intestinal mucosa, but infected persons usually manifest no noticeable symptoms. Heavy infections of *Paryphostomum sufrartyfex* in children, however, have been reported to cause a clinical syndrome of diarrhea, abdominal pain, anemia and edema similar to that of *Fasciolopsis buski*.

Diagnosis.—Diagnosis is made by recovering the ova in the feces or obtaining the adult worms after anthelmintic treatment. The operculate, ellipsoidal, yellow to yellow-brown, thin-shelled ova require differentiation from the undeveloped ova of other intestinal and biliary flukes. The size of the ovum differs with the species of echinostomes, although there is considerable overlapping.

Prognosis.—Prognosis is favorable. Only heavy infections produce symptoms and patients respond readily to treatment.

Treatment.—Any reliable vermifuge is effective. Oleoresin of aspidium (Section **VII,** XIII, 29) has been used successfully in infections with *Echinostoma ilocanum* and *Paryphostomum sufrartyfex*.

Prevention.—Mollusks, fishes, amphibians and plants are possible sources of infection. Thorough cooking of food and boiling of drinking water constitute proper safeguards, but salting or similar treatment of food is inadequate. Raw or insufficiently cooked snails should not be eaten in endemic areas of *Echinostoma ilocanum, E. malayanum* and *E. revolutum,* nor fresh-water fishes where *E. malayanum* and *Echinochasmus perfoliatus* are present.

Echinostoma ilocanum (GARRISON, 1908) ODHNER, 1911

History.—*Echinostoma ilocanum* was first described by Garrison in 1908 in a native of Luzon in the Philippines. Odhner after more detailed study placed it in the genus *Echinostoma* in 1911.

Geographical Distribution.—The parasite is present in mammals in the Philippines and China. Human infection is confined to the Philippines (Island of Luzon) and Celebes.

Morphology.—*Echinostoma ilocanum* (Fig. 192, Table 35) is a small, elongate, oval, reddish-gray fluke with tapering rounded ends more attenuated posteriorly. It averages 0.47 cm. in length and 0.10 cm. in breadth, ranging from 0.25 to 0.65 cm. by 0.075 to 0.135 cm. The anterior portion is partially or completely covered with scale-like spines. The circumoral collar bears two alternating rows of 49 to 51 spines uninterrupted dorsally. The oral sucker is about one-third the size of the ventral sucker. The digestive tract consists of a globular pharynx, a short esophagus, and two intestinal ceca of unequal length, which extend to the subcaudal regions. The two deeply-lobed testes are arranged in tandem fashion in the middle of the posterior half of the body behind the globular uterus. The seminal receptacle and prostatic portion of the male duct within the cirral sac are lacking. The coarse granular vitellaria occupy the lateral two-thirds of the body and extend posteriorly in the form of a crescent toward the midline. The tightly-coiled uterus fills the intracecal space between the ovary and the ventral sucker and opens to the left of the male ejaculatory duct.

Life Cycle.—The natural definitive hosts are dog, rat and man. Experimentally cats and monkeys have been infected. The first intermediate host is the snail, *Gyraulus prashadi*. The second intermediate host may be any fresh-water snail, but *Pila luzonica* is the most important in transmitting human infection.

The following life cycle has been observed.[5] The thin-shelled operculate ovum, 83 to 116 μ in length by 53 to 82 μ in width, is undeveloped (Fig. 193A) when passed in the feces. After leaving the definitive host it develops into a mature miracidium (Fig. 193B) in 6 to 15 days and hatches 3 to 5 days later.

The liberated miracidium (Fig. 193C), 85 x 35 μ, has a conical anterior papilla, 19 transverse epithelial plates in four transverse rows covered with cilia, pigmented eye-spots, two flame-cells, a small sacculated gut and germinal cells. Its average length of free-swimming life is 6.5 hours, since it dies unless it penetrates the mantle or pulmonary chamber of a suitable snail. In the tissues near the digestive glands of the latter it develops into a mother redia (Fig. 193D and E) with an anterior collar, a rhabdicele gut, and locomotor appendages. It contains from 3 to 20 daughter rediæ (Fig. 193F) which, when mature, enclose in turn 3 to 25 cercariæ.

The cercaria (Fig. 193G and H) has a body 180 to 300 μ in length by 100 to 130 μ in width and a tail 130 to 350 μ in length. It has two suckers, a spinous collar, a digestive tract with pharynx, esophagus and bifurcated ceca, genital cells, cystogenous glands, and flame-cells. In 42 to 50 days after infection of the snail the cercariæ escape during daytime into the water, where they swim or creep. Unless they reach a secondary snail host they die within ten hours. If successful, they encyst in the region of the pericardium, digestive tract or mantle. The metacercariæ (Fig. 193I) are enclosed in spheroidal or slightly oval double-walled cysts, measuring externally 120 to 133 μ by 108 to 129 μ. When infected snails are ingested by the definitive host the metacercaria excysts and develops in the intestinal tract into an adult worm.

Pathogenesis.—No appreciable damage to the intestinal tract and no marked intestinal symptoms are produced. Occasional headaches, dizziness and slight anemia have been reported.[6]

---

[5] Tubangui, M. A. and Pasco, A. M., 1933.   [6] Hilario, J. S. and Wharton, L. D., 1917.

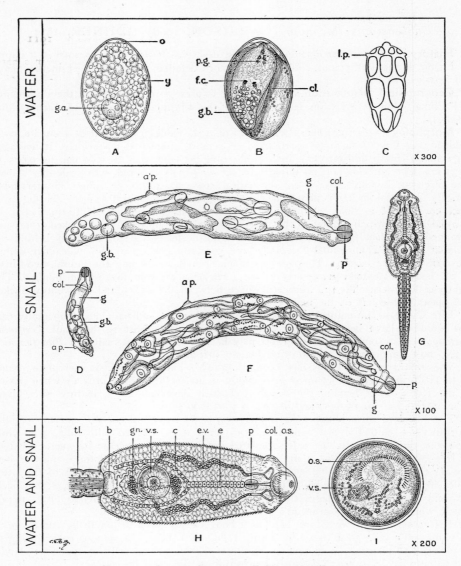

FIG. 193.—LARVAL FORMS OF *Echinostoma ilocanum*

A, freshly passed ovum in one-celled stage, showing yolk balls and germinal area; *B,* ovum with fully developed miracidium; *C,* diagram of miracidium showing epidermal plates and lateral processes; *D,* young mother redia with undifferentiated germ balls, ventral view; *E,* mature mother redia with young daughter rediæ, lateral view; *F,* mature daughter rediæ with cercariæ, lateral view; *G,* mature cercaria, ventral view; *H,* body of cercaria showing detailed structure; *I,* encysted metacercaria.

ap., appendages; *b,* excretory bladder; *c,* ceca; *cl.,* cilia; *col.,* collar; *e,* esophagus; *e.v.,* excretory vessel; *f.c.,* flame-cell; *g,* primitive gut; *g.a.,* germinal area; *g.b.,* germ balls; *gn.,* genital anlage; *l.p.,* lateral processes; *o,* operculum; *o.s.,* oral sucker; *p,* pharynx; *p.g.,* penetration glands; *tl.,* tail; *v.s.,* ventral sucker; *y,* yolk. (*A* to *I* redrawn from Tubangui and Pasco, 1933).

Diagnosis.—Diagnosis is made by finding the ova in the feces of natives in endemic areas.

Prognosis.—Good.

Treatment.—Oleoresin of aspidium (Section **VII**, XIII, 29).

Prevention.—Man is infected by ingesting snails containing the metacercariæ. The natives of Luzon are accustomed to eating the snail, *Pila luzonica,* raw, either directly from the shell in the field or with salt or vinegar in the home. The abolition of this custom will prevent infection in man.

SUPERFAMILY *PARAMPHISTOMOIDEA* STILES AND GOLDBERGER, 1910

The members of the suborder AMPHISTOMATA Bojanus, 1817, are included under the superfamily PARAMPHISTOMOIDEA. They are thick, muscular, somewhat flattened, aspinose flukes, often conical in shape and tapering anteriorly, with a highly-developed, terminal or subterminal ventral sucker. The genital pore is pre-equatorial, and the testes are usually anterior to the ovary. The basic flame-cell pattern is 2 [1+1+1]. The amphistomes are intestinal parasites of fishes, amphibians, reptiles, birds and mammals. Of the three families, (1) GASTRODISCIDÆ, (2) PARAMPHISTOMIDÆ, and (3) GASTROTHYLACIDÆ, the first two contain parasites of man.

FAMILY *GASTRODISCIDÆ* STILES AND GOLDBERGER, 1910

The GASTRODISCIDÆ are amphistome flukes with a discoidal body divided by a transverse constriction into a cephalic and a caudal portion, the latter bearing a sucking disk. The venter has many large papillæ. There is no ventral pouch. One species, *Gastrodiscoides hominis,* has been found in man.

Gastrodiscoides hominis (LEWIS AND McCONNELL, 1876) LEIPER, 1913

Synonyms.—*Amphistomum hominis* Lewis and McConnell, 1876; *Gastrodiscus hominis* Fischoeder, 1902.

History.—*Gastrodiscoides hominis* was discovered by Lewis and McConnell in 1876 in autopsy material from a native of Assam. It was placed in the genus *Gastrodiscus,* tentatively by Fischoeder in 1902 and definitely by Stephens in 1906, and finally in the genus *Gastrodiscoides* by Leiper in 1913.

Geographical Distribution.—Assam, India, Malay Peninsula, Cochin-China, and British Guiana (East Indian immigrants).

Morphology.—The aspinose, dorsally-convex adult worm (Fig. 194), reddish in color when alive, is divided into an anterior conical portion and an enlarged posterior disk with a thick, overhanging rim. The anterior part bears a small, globular oral sucker and a prominent genital cone, while the ventrally-concave disk is nonpapillate and has a ventral sucker on its posterior portion. It measures from 0.5 to 0.8 cm. in length by 0.3 to 0.5 cm. in breadth, but when extended may reach 1.0 cm. The digestive system consists of an elongate, somewhat tortuous pharyngeal tube with two lateral pouches and a pharyngeal bulb just above the cecal bifurcation, and two ceca that extend to the middle of the discoidal region. An elongate excretory bladder lies in the midline dorsad to the ventral sucker.

The large, lobate testes are situated obliquely in the anterior part of the disk just posterior to the bifurcation of the ceca. There is no cirral sac or prostatic portion, the seminal vesicle opening just orad to the female pore on the genital cone. The oval ovary lies posterior to the testes near the midline. The fine, fan-shaped, follicular vitellaria surround the intestinal ceca below the upper border of the posterior testis. There is a tortuous seminal receptacle, a Laurer's canal opening on the dorsal surface, and a loosely-coiled uterus terminating in the genital cone.

Life Cycle.—The natural host appears to be the hog. The parasite has also been reported in the Napu mouse deer and monkeys. Man is probably an accidental host. Its incidence in Assam and the development of the ovum and miracidium have recently been studied.[7] The greenish-brown, rhomboidal, operculate ova, 150 to 170 μ in length

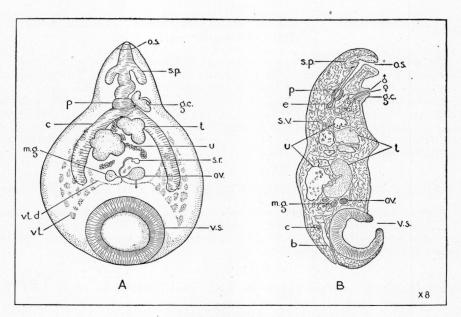

FIG. 194.—*Gastrodiscoides hominis*

A, ventral view; *B*, sagittal section.

b, excretory bladder; *c*, ceca; *e*, esophagus; *g.c.*, genital cone; *m.g.*, Mehlis' gland; *o.s.*, oral sucker; *ov.*, ovary; *p*, pharynx; *s.p.*, suctorial pouch; *s.r.*, seminal receptacle; *s.v.*, seminal vesicle; *t*, testes; *u*, uterus; *v.s.*, ventral sucker; *vt.*, vitellaria; *vt.d.*, vitelline duct (*A* redrawn from Khalil, 1923; *B* redrawn from Leiper, 1913).

by 60 to 70 μ in breadth, develop in 16 to 17 days at 27° to 34° C. The phototactic miracidium has a prominent apical papilla, a pair of penetration glands, a primitive gut, no eye-spots, and a pair of flame-cells. The life cycle is unknown, but is probably similar to those of amphistomes of lower animals, in which the miracidia develop into rediæ in snails and the liberated cercariæ encyst in amphibians or lower vertebrates.

Pathogenesis.—The fluke inhabits the cecum and ascending colon, where it causes inflammation and produces diarrhea.

Diagnosis.—Presence of ova in feces.

Prognosis.—Good.

Treatment.—Thymol (Section **VII**, XIII, 24) and soapsuds enemas have been used. Intestinal anthelmintics, such as tetrachlorethylene (Section **VII**, XIII, 22) should prove effective.

---

[7] Buckley, J. J. C., 1939.

Prevention.—The only appreciable incidence in man has been reported from Assam, where ova have been found in 41 per cent of the natives in the Kamrup district. Since its life cycle is unknown, prophylactic measures have not been devised.

FAMILY *PARAMPHISTOMIDÆ* (FISCHOEDER, 1901) EMEND. STILES AND GOLDBERGER, 1910

The PARAMPHISTOMIDÆ are amphistomes that have a venter without large papillæ and without a ventral pouch, and are undivided into a cephalic and caudal portion. Most species are parasites of domestic animals. One species, *Watsonius watsoni,* has been found in man.

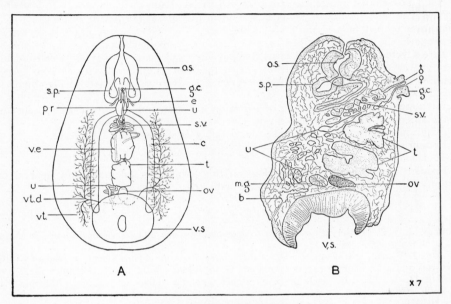

FIG. 195.—*Watsonius watsoni*

A, ventral view; *B*, sagittal section.

b, excretory bladder; *c*, ceca; *e*, esophagus; *g.c.*, genital cone; *m.g.*, Mehlis' gland; *o.s.*, oral sucker; *ov.*, ovary; *pr.*, pars prostatica; *s.p.*, suctorial pouch; *s.v.*, seminal vesicle; *t*, testes; *u*, uterus; *v.e.*, vas efferens; *v.s.*, ventral sucker; *vt.*, vitellaria; *vt.d.*, vitelline duct (*A* redrawn from Stiles and Goldberger, 1910; *B* redrawn from Leiper, 1913).

Watsonius watsoni (CONYNGHAM, 1904) STILES AND GOLD-BERGER, 1910

Synonyms.—*Amphistomum watsoni* Conyngham, 1904; *Cladorchis watsoni* (Conyngham, 1904) Shepley, 1905; *Paramphistomum watsoni* Manson, 1908; *Pseudodiscus watsoni,* Fukui, 1929.

History.—Conyngham first described *Watsonius watsonsi* in 1904 from numerous specimens obtained from the duodenum and jejunum of a West African Negro, who died from diarrhea and inanition in northern Nigeria. It has also been found in the cecum of monkeys in French Guiana by Railliet, Henry and Joyeux in 1912.

Geographical Distribution.—West Africa (man), French Guiana and Malay Peninsula (monkeys).

Morphology.—*Watsonius watsoni* (Fig. 195) is a reddish-yellow, translucent, pyriform trematode, 0.8 to 1.0 cm. in length and 0.4 to 0.5 cm. in breadth. The ventral surface is slightly concave and the cuticle is transversely ridged. At the anterior end is a deeply-recessed oral sucker with two lateral suctorial pouches. The esophagus, originating at the raised, inner, median portion of the oral sucker, bifurcates into two ceca that extend to the posterior fifth of the body.

The rectangular, fissured testes lie in tandem formation in the midline in the middle third of the body. The vasa efferentia unite anteriorly in a markedly coiled vas deferens with a posterior thin-walled and a shorter anterior muscular portion, followed by a bulbous prostatic part and a thin-walled ejaculatory duct that terminates in the genital cone. A small oval ovary is situated posterior to the testes slightly to the left of the midline. No seminal receptacle has been described. Laurer's canal leads to the dorsal surface. The finely-granular vitellaria extend in the lateral portion of the body from the bifurcation to just beyond the ends of the ceca. The coiled uterus extends forward to terminate in the genital cone just posterior to the ejaculatory duct.

Life Cycle.—The definitive hosts are monkeys and man. Man is an accidental host. The oval, operculate ova range from 122 to 130 μ in length and 75 to 80 μ in breadth. The life cycle is unknown. Probably cercariæ are formed in a fresh-water snail and encyst upon vegetation.

Pathogenesis.—Only one case of infection has been found in man. In this instance, a fatal infection, the patient had severe diarrhea and toxic inanition.

Diagnosis.—From the adult fluke and possibly from the ova in the feces.

Prognosis.—Unknown.

Treatment.—Unknown.

Prevention.—Since the epidemiology of this parasite is unknown, only general precautions for food and drinking water are indicated.

REFERENCES

BUCKLEY, J. J. C. Observations on *Gastrodiscoides hominis* and *Fasciolopsis buski* in Assam, J. Helminthol., 1939, 17:1.

HILARIO, J. S. and WHARTON, L. D. *Echinostoma ilocanum* (Garrison): A Report of Five Cases and a Contribution to the Anatomy of the Fluke, Philippine J. Sc., 1917, 12:203.

JOHNSON, J. C. The Life Cycle of *Echinostoma revolutum* (Froelich), Univ. California Publ. Zoöl., 1920, 19:335.

KHALIL, M. Description of *Gastrodiscoides hominis* from Napu Mouse Deer, Proc. Roy. Soc. Med., 1923, 16:8 (Sect. Trop. Dis.).

LANE, C. *Artyfechinostomum sufrartyfex*. A New Parasitic Echinostome of Man, Indian J. M. Res., 1915, 2:977.

LEIPER, R. T. Observations on Certain Helminths of Man, Tr. Roy. Soc. Trop. Med. & Hyg., 1913, 6:265.

MATTES, O. Der Entwicklungsgang des Lanzettegels *Dicrocœlium lanceatum*, Ztschr. f. Parasitenk., 1936, 8:371.

NEUHAUS, W. Untersuchungen über Bau und Entwicklung der Lanzettegel-cercarie (*Cercaria vitrina*) und Klarstellung des Infektionsvorganges beim Endwirt. Ztschr. f. Parasitenk., 1936, 8:431.

——— Der Invasionsweg der Lanzettegel-cercarie bei der Infektion des Endwirtes und ihre Entwicklung zum *Dicrocœlium lanceatum*, Ztschr. f. Parasitenk., 1938, 10:476.

STILES, C. W. and GOLDBERGER, J. A Study of the Anatomy of *Watsonius* (n.g.) *watsoni* of Man and of Nineteen Allied Species of Mammalian Trematode Worms of the Superfamily Paramphistomoidea, Hyg. Lab. Bull., No. 60, Washington, 1910, 264 pp.

TUBANGUI, M. A. and PASCO, A. M. Life History of the Human Intestinal Fluke, *Euparyphium ilocanum* (Garrison, 1908), Philippine J. Sc., 1933, 51:581.

UJIIE, N. Structure and Development of *Echinochasmus japonicus* and its Parasitism in Man, Taiwan igakkai zasshi (J. Med. A. Formosa), 1936, 35:545.

VOGEL, H. Beobachtungen über *Cercaria vitrina* und deren Beziehung zum Lanzettegelproblem, Arch. f. Schiffs-u. Tropen-Hyg., 1929, 33:474.

Chapter XXXV

THE BLOOD FLUKES OF MAN

The blood flukes, the most important trematodes of man, belong to the family SCHISTOSOMATIDÆ of the superfamily SCHISTOSOMATOIDEA of the order STRIGEATA. Three species of the genus *Schistosoma* produce serious human diseases: *Schistosoma hæmatobium* bilharziasis, *S. mansoni* intestinal schistosomiasis, and *S. japonicum* Asiatic intestinal schistosomiasis. These three diseases have long been recognized, but the parasitic species have been clearly differentiated only since about 1915. Their chief differential characteristics are given in Table 36. A few cases of human infection with *S. bovis,* a sheep and cattle schistosome, have been reported, and certain species parasitic in lower animals produce cercarial dermatitis in man.

SUPERFAMILY *SCHISTOSOMATOIDEA* STILES AND HASSALL, 1926

The members of the superfamily SCHISTOSOMATOIDEA are blood-inhabiting monecious or diecious flukes with or without suckers and without a pharynx. The ova are nonoperculate. The cercariæ have slender forked tails, a preoral suctorial organ for penetration, and invade the definitive host without passing through an encysted metacercarial stage. They are parasites of lower vertebrates, birds and mammals. The avian and mammalian parasites belong to the family SCHISTOSOMA-TIDÆ.

FAMILY *SCHISTOSOMATIDÆ* LOOSS, 1899

The SCHISTOSOMATIDÆ are parasites of the blood vessels of mammals and birds. The sexes are separate, anterior and ventral suckers are present, and the bifurcate intestinal ceca unite posteriorly. Most mammalian species belong to the genus *Schistosoma.*

SYNONYMS

Schistosoma hæmatobium (Bilharz, 1852) Weinland, 1858.—*Distoma hæmatobium* Bilharz, 1852; *Gynæcophorus hæmatobius* Diesing, 1858; *Bilharzia hæmatobia* Cobbold, 1858; *Bilharzia magna* Cobbold, 1859; *Thecosoma hæmatobium* Moquin-Tandon, 1860; *Bilharzia capensis* Harley, 1864; *Bilharzia ægyptiaca* Miyagawa, 1924.

Schistosoma mansoni Sambon, 1907.—*Schistosomum americanum* da Silva, 1909.

Schistosoma japonicum Katsurada, 1904.—*Schistosoma cattoi* Blanchard, 1905.

TABLE 36

DISTINGUISHING FEATURES OF SCHISTOSOMAL INFECTIONS OF MAN

	Schistosoma hæmatobium	*Schistosoma mansoni*	*Schistosoma japonicum*
Disease	Vesical schistosomiasis, bilharziasis, urinary schistosomiasis, endemic hematuria	Intestinal schistosomiasis	Oriental intestinal schistosomiasis, Katayama disease, Yangtze Valley fever, Hankow fever
Geographical distribution	Africa, western Asia, southern Europe, Australia	Africa, South America, West Indies	China, Japan, Formosa, Philippines, Celebes
Principal habitat of parasite in man Adult	Vesicoprostatic, pubic and uterine plexuses, vesical and mesenteric veins	Inferior and superior mesenteric veins, hemorrhoidal plexus	Same as *S. mansoni*
Ova	Bladder, prostate, male genitalia, less frequently intestine	Intestine, mesenteric lymph nodes, less frequently bladder	Intestine, mesenteric lymph nodes
Definitive host Natural	Man, monkey (*Cercocebus fubiguosus*)	Man, West Indian green monkey (*Cercopithecus sabæns*)	Man, dog, cat, hog, cattle, horses
Experimental	Laboratory animals	Laboratory animals	Readily transmitted to common laboratory animals and monkeys
Intermediate gastropod host (genera)	*Bulinus, Physopsis, Planorbis, Lymnæa* (?)	*Planorbis, Physopsis* (?), *Bulinus* (?)	*Blanfordia, Hemibia*

HISTORY

Early Egyptian records and its presence in Egyptian mummies (1250 to 1000 B.C.) indicate that schistosomiasis is an ancient disease. It was observed in the French army of occupation in Egypt in 1799 to 1801, but the discovery of the parasite did not occur until 1851.

Schistosoma hæmatobium.—Bilharz in 1851 discovered the adult parasite in the mesenteric veins of an Egyptian in Cairo, and later showed the relation of the parasite and its ova to the prevailing hematuria and dysentery among the native population. His work gave rise to the name of bilharziasis for the disease and established for the first time the rôle of a trematode in the production of human disease. The presence of two types of spined ova and of two clinical forms of the disease, the vesical and the intestinal, caused considerable confusion, until Sambon in 1907 demonstrated the existence of two species, *S. hæmatobium* and *S. mansoni*. The life cycle and method of transmission of these parasites were not discovered for many years. The early idea that mollusks served as intermediate hosts was not substantiated by the first experiments and it was believed that infection took place through the skin by the direct invasion of the miracidium. Leiper between 1915 and 1918 proved experimentally that both *S. hæmatobium* and *S. mansoni* required snails for intermediate hosts and that the vesical and the intestinal forms of schistosomiasis were produced by distinct species of schistosomes.

Schistosoma mansoni.—As early as 1902 to 1904 epidemiological investigations indicated that *S. mansoni* had a different geographical distribution in Africa than *S. hæmatobium*. Sambon in 1907 was able to separate the two species on the basis of differences in ova, habitat in the host, pathogenicity and geographical distribution. He gave the name *Schistosoma mansoni* to the worm that produced ova with lateral spines. The observations of Sambon and others were confirmed by the experimental work of Leiper in 1915 and later by other investigators.

Schistosoma japonicum.—The first description of oriental schistosomiasis or Katayama disease, was made by Fujii in 1847, although the disease is undoubtedly as ancient as Egyptian schistosomiasis. Between 1890 and 1904 Yamagiwa, Kurimoto and Fujinami found the ova in various organs at autopsy and Fujinami in 1904 discovered the adult worm in the mesenteric veins. Katsurada in 1904 found the ova in the feces of patients afflicted with Katayama disease and studied the infection in cats and dogs, obtaining both ova and the adult parasite which he described under the name *Schistosoma japonicum*. Following these early discoveries several Japanese investigators in their studies of the parasite and the disease demonstrated that dogs, cats, horses and cattle as well as man were natural hosts and that infection took place through the skin. In 1912 and 1913 Miyagawa traced the route of the immature parasite through the body. In 1913 and 1914, Miyairi and Susuki observed the hatching of the ovum, the penetration of the snail by the miracidium, and the development of the sporocysts and cercariæ in the snail. From 1905 to 1924, the symptomatology, pathology and distribution of the disease were studied by numerous workers in China.

GEOGRAPHICAL DISTRIBUTION

The distribution of the schistosomes of man is governed by the existence of suitable molluscan hosts (Table 34). *Schistosoma hæmatobium* and *S. mansoni* have become adapted to nonoperculate snails. The genera *Bulinus* and *Physopsis*, the hosts of *S. hæmatobium*, are common in Africa, southern Europe and western Asia. The genus *Planorbis*, host of *S. mansoni*, has a cosmopolitan distribution. The operculate snails of the genera *Blanfordia* and *Hemibia*, hosts of *S. japonicum*, are found only in the Far East. The original focus of *S. hæmatobium* and *S. mansoni* appears to be the valley of the Nile, while that of *S. japonicum* the Yangtze valley in China. At present the distribution of *S. hæmatobium* and *S. mansoni* coincides in many parts of Africa, but only *S. mansoni* is found in the Western Hemisphere and *S. japonicum* in the Far East (Fig. 196).

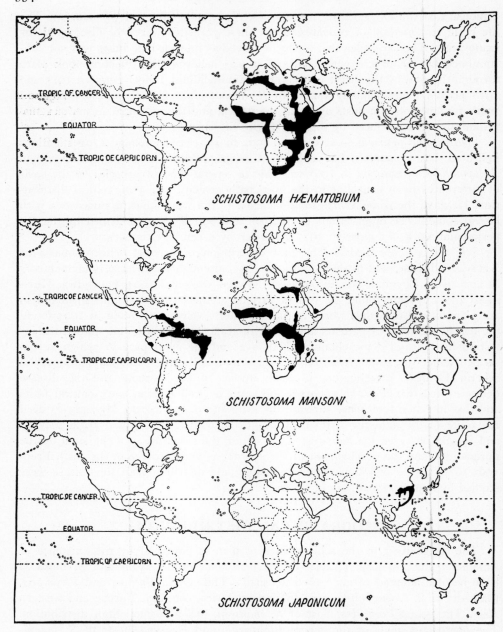

FIG. 196.—GEOGRAPHICAL DISTRIBUTION OF *Schistosoma hæmatobium*, *S. japonicum* and
S. mansoni

Schistosoma hæmatobium.—In Africa *S. hæmatobium* is highly endemic in the
valley of the Nile. It is found from Morocco to Egypt on the Mediterranean coast;
throughout Ethiopia and the Sudan; along the East Coast of Africa south of Italian

Somaliland; throughout Central Africa, including Uganda, Kenya, Tanganyika, Zanzibar, Nyasaland, and the Belgian Congo; on the West Coast of Africa from Senegal south to Angola, and in the Cameroons including the Lake Chad district and the upper Niger; and on the islands of Madagascar, Mauritius and Reunion. In Europe, foci of infection have been found in Portugal, Spain, Greece and Cyprus. In western Asia the parasite is present in Palestine, Syria, Arabia, Iraq and Meso-potamia. It has also been found in Australia.

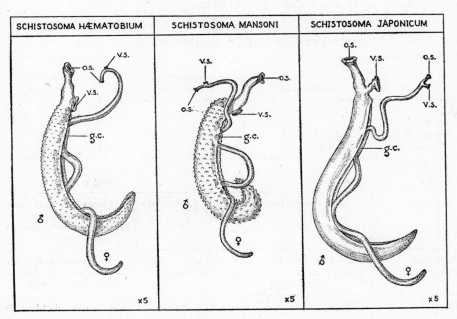

| SCHISTOSOMA HÆMATOBIUM | SCHISTOSOMA MANSONI | SCHISTOSOMA JAPONICUM |

FIG. 197.—SCHEMATIC REPRESENTATION OF IMPORTANT SCHISTOSOMES OF MAN

g.c., gynecophoric canal; *o.s.*, oral sucker; *v.s.*, ventral sucker.

Schistosoma mansoni.—In Africa, *S. mansoni* is found together with *S. hæma-tobium* and the distribution of the two species is somewhat confused. It is less prevalent than *S. hæmatobium* in South Africa, but more prevalent in the Belgian Congo. It is found in Egypt, Libya, the Sudan, Tanganyika, northern Rhodesia, Belgian Congo; on the East Coast of Africa from Italian East Africa and Zanzibar to the Zambesi River; on the West Coast in Senegal, Sierra Leone, French Guinea and inland to the Lake Chad district; and in Madagascar. It has also been reported in Arabia. In the Western Hemisphere, the parasite is found in northern Brazil, Venezuela and Dutch Guiana; and in the West Indies, including Martinique, Guadeloupe, Antigua, Santa Lucia, St. Kitts, Nevis, Montserrat, Vieques and Puerto Rico. It evidently was introduced here from Africa by slaves and upon finding suitable gastropod hosts became endemic in a new area.

Schistosoma japonicum.—The distribution of *S. japonicum* is confined to the Far East, endemic areas being present in Japan, China, Formosa, Celebes and the

Philippines. In Japan, there are five endemic centers in coastal river valleys, one northeast of Tokio, two near Mt. Fuji, one in Okayama and one in northern Kyushu. In China it occurs in the Yangtze River basin from Szechuan Province to the coast; the coastal regions from the Yangtze delta to Hong Kong; the North and West River districts above Canton; and in the upper Mekong basin of Yunnan. The most heavily infected areas are in the vicinity of the three lakes Taihu, Poyang and Tungting and the districts bordering the Yangtze River. An isolated endemic area is present in the Paloe district of Celebes.

TABLE 37

MORPHOLOGY OF ADULT SCHISTOSOMES OF MAN

	Schistosoma hæmatobium	*Schistosoma mansoni*	*Schistosoma japonicum*
Male Length (cm.) Mean Range	1.3 1.0 to 1.5	1.0 0.6 to 1.4	1.5 0.9 to 2.2
Breadth (cm.) Mean	0.09	0.11	0.05
Integument	Finely tuberculate	Grossly tuberculate	Nontuberculate except minute spines on suckers and gynecophoric canal
Intestinal ceca	Unite late, united intestine short	Unite early, united intestine long	Unite very late, united intestine very short, last fifth of body
Testes	4, large	8 (6 to 9), small	7, ovoid, slightly lobate, compressed in a single column
Female Length (cm.) Mean Range	2.0	1.4 1.2 to 1.6	1.9 1.2 to 2.6
Breadth (cm.) Mean	0.025	0.016	0.030
Ovary	Posterior half of body	Anterior half of body	Middle of body
Uterus	Long, voluminous, 20 to 30 ova	Short, 1 to 4 ova	Long, 50 to 300 ova

MORPHOLOGY

The differential morphological characteristics of the three species are given in Table 37. The larger male has a ventral gynecophoric canal, extending the entire length of the body from the ventral sucker, in which the slender female is held during copulation (Fig. 197). The male is a light gray or white, while the female is a darker color. The integument is smooth or tuberculate, depending upon the species. The oral and ventral suckers are located near the anterior end. The former

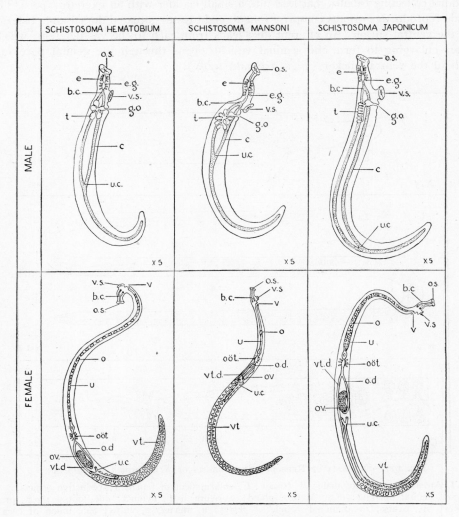

FIG. 198.—SCHEMATIC REPRESENTATION OF MORPHOLOGY OF IMPORTANT SCHISTOSOMES OF MAN

b.c., bifurcation of ceca; *c*, ceca; *e*, esophagus; *e.g.*, esophageal glands; *g.o.*, genital orifice; *o*, ova; *o.d.*, oviduct; *oöt.*, oötype; *o.s.*, oral sucker; *ov.*, ovary; *t*, testes; *u*, uterus; *u.c.*, union of ceca; *v*, vulva; *v.s.*, ventral sucker; *vt.* vitellaria; *vt.d.*, vitelline duct. The breadth of the female worms has been doubled.

is funnel-shaped and somewhat smaller than the pedunculate ventral sucker. The mouth is slightly ventral; there is no muscular pharynx; the esophagus is surrounded by glands; and the intestine anterior to the ventral sucker bifurcates into two ceca, which reunite in the posterior part of the body in a single stem. The length of the united portion, which ends blindly at the caudal end of the worm, varies in the three species (Fig. 198). The excretory system consists of two longitudinal collecting tubules that lead into a small bladder with an excretory pore. The male reproductive organs comprise four to eight testes, situated dorsal and posterior to the ventral sucker. An efferent duct leads from each to the vas deferens, which, after enlarging to form the seminal vesicle, opens through the genital pore just behind the ventral sucker (Figs. 198 and 199A).

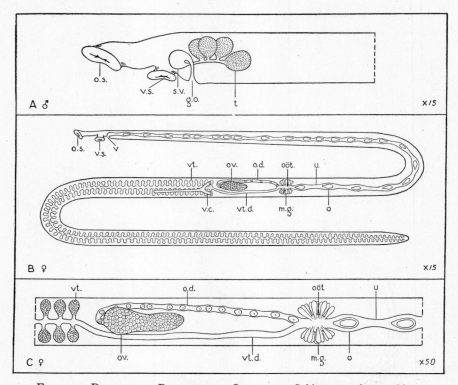

FIG. 199.—DIAGRAM OF REPRODUCTIVE ORGANS OF *Schistosoma hæmatobium*

A, Anterior portion of male; *B,* female; *C,* enlargement of female reproductive organs.

g.o., genital opening; *m.g.,* Mehlis' gland; *o,* ovum; *o.d.,* oviduct; *oöt.,* oötype; *o.s.,* oral sucker; *ov.,* ovary; *s.v.,* seminal vesicle; *t,* testes; *u,* uterus; *v,* vulva; *v.c.,* union of ceca; *v.s.,* ventral sucker; *vt.,* vitellaria; *vt.d.,* vitelline duct.

The slender female worms have a cylindrical shape with pointed ends (Fig. 198). They often lie in the gynecophoric canal of the male with the terminal portions free (Fig. 197). The integument is smooth except for minute papillæ on the anterior and posterior extremities. The oral and ventral suckers near the anterior end are of equal size. The pattern of the intestinal tract is similar to that of the male, the ceca uniting posterior to the ovary. The intestine is often reddish-black in color from ingested red blood cells. The female reproductive organs (Fig. 199B and C) consist of an elongate ovary, the position of which varies in the three species (Fig. 198). The oviduct, passing forward from the broad posterior pole of the ovary, is joined by the vitelline duct at the oötype, which is surrounded by Mehlis' gland. The uterus extends forward from the oötype, where fertilization takes place, to the genital pore just behind the ventral sucker. The length of the uterus and the number of ova are distinctive for the species (Table 37 and Fig. 198).

LIFE CYCLE

Man is the principal definitive host, but monkeys are also natural hosts of *S. hæmatobium* and *S. mansoni,* and dogs, cats, cattle, horses and hogs of *S. japonicum* (Table 36). For *S. hæmatobium* the gastropod hosts are species of the genera *Bulinus, Physopsis, Planorbis* and possibly *Lymnæa;* for *S. mansoni* the genera *Planorbis* and possibly *Bulinus* and *Physopsis;* and for *S. japonicum* the genera *Blanfordia* and *Hemibia* (Table 34).

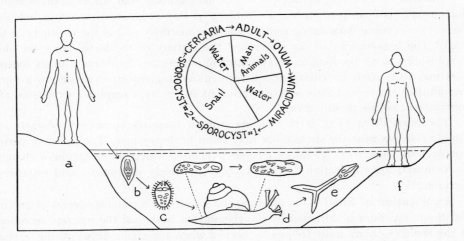

FIG. 200.—LIFE CYCLE OF A PARASITIC SCHISTOSOME OF MAN

a, man infected with adult worm; *b,* ovum passed in feces or urine; *c,* free-swimming miracidium; *d,* metamorphosis in snail with formation of primary sporocyst, secondary sporocysts and cercariæ; *e,* free-swimming cercaria; *f,* man infected by cercaria in water through skin.

DEVELOPMENTAL CYCLE

The life cycle (Fig. 200) comprises the passing of the ovum from the definitive host; its hatching in water with the liberation of a free-swimming miracidium; the penetration of a suitable species of snail by the miracidium; the metamorphosis of the larva into primary and secondary sporocysts and cercariæ in the snail; the eruption of free-swimming cercariæ into the water; the penetration of the skin of man by the cercaria; and the migration and growth of the immature worm in the blood vessels.

Oviposition.—When ready to deposit ova, the female worm moves against the blood stream to the small venules of the portal system. In these restricted quarters, the ova are deposited like a chain of beads, the female retreating successively in the direction of the current. The ova of S. mansoni and S. japonicum are usually deposited in the venules of the intestine and rectum, and those of S. hæmatobium in the venules of the bladder. The ova penetrate the venous capillaries and work their way through the wall of the intestine or bladder to escape from the body in the feces or urine. The ova of S. hæmatobium are usually passed in the urine and less frequently in the feces, those of S. mansoni usually in the feces and more rarely in the urine, and those of S. japonicum only in the feces.

Hatching.—In putrefying feces at 22° C. the unhatched ova (Fig. 201A) survive less than 24 hours, but in formed feces at 7 to 10° C. the majority remain viable for a week or more. In water, relatively free from fecal material, they survive over 30 days in cold weather. Ova of S. japonicum can withstand exposure for one hour at —10° to —17° C. without injury and remain viable at 4° C.[1] Desiccation proves rapidly fatal and a moderate amount of acid kills the ova.

The time of hatching depends upon the temperature, but under optimal conditions usually is from 2 to 16 hours (Table 38). For a single batch of ova hatching varies two or more days owing to differences in maturity and in the elasticity of the shell.[2] The hypotonicity of the water and the activity of the larva cause the shell to split open along the long axis. The miracidium escapes headfirst with its mucoid covering, frees itself by ciliary action from its entanglement, elongates to a paramecium-like shape, and after a short period of inactivity, except for expansion and contraction, swims rapidly away.

The miracidium (Fig. 201B) swims straight forward, but avoids obstacles. It usually remains near the surface but may swim in deep water. The infective period usually lasts from 16 to 32 hours (Table 38), after which the miracidium changes its form and loses its activity. It is probably positively phototactic and negatively thermotactic.

Penetration of Snail.—On reaching the vicinity of a suitable species of gastropod the miracidium is attracted by the chemotactic action of the mucous secretions of the snail.[3] Contact most frequently occurs when the snails crawl to the surface of the water. The most accessible portions of the snail, such as the head, foot, tentacles and mantle cavity, are attacked. Penetration is accomplished by a head-on, boring motion aided by the proteolytic ferments of the cephalic glands. The time required for penetration has been variously recorded as from 3 to 15 minutes.[4] After penetration the burrowing miracidium retains its cilia for 24 to 48 hours.

Metamorphosis in Snail.—Early development takes place in the tissues and lymph sinuses of the foot and head of the snail. After seven days the larva has lost its proteolytic glands and other miracidial characteristics and has become a primary sporocyst (Fig. 201C), an elongate thin-walled saccular creature containing closely-packed masses of germ cells. It migrates, usually through tissues but sometimes by the blood, to the vicinity of the liver, where it completes its development. Its rup-

[1] Faust, E. C. and Meleney, H. E., 1924.
[2] Faust, E. C. and Meleney, H. E., 1924; Faust, E. C. and Hoffman, W. A., 1934.
[3] Faust, E. C., 1924.

[4] Faust, E. C. and Meleney, H. E., 1924; Gordon, R. M., Davey, T. H. and Peaston, H., 1934.

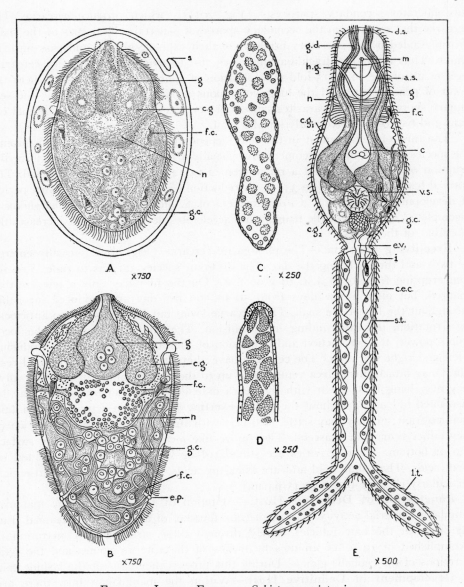

FIG. 201.—LARVAL FORMS OF *Schistosoma japonicum*

A, mature ovum, showing lateral knob-like spine; *B*, miracidium; *C*, primary sporocyst; *D*, portion of secondary sporocyst; *E*, cercaria.

a.s., anterior sucker; *c*, cecum; *c.e.c.*, caudal excretory canal; *c.g.*, cephalic glands; *c.g.*₁, cephalic glands anterior; *c.g.*₂, cephalic glands posterior; *d.s.*, duct spines; *e.p.*, excretory pore; *e.v.*, excretory vesicle; *f.c.*, flame-cell; *g*, gut; *g.c.*, genital cells; *g.d.*, gland ducts; *h.g.*, head gland; *i*, island of Cort; *l.t.*, lobe of tail; *m*, mouth; *n*, nervous system; *s*, spine; *s.t.*, stem of tail; *v.s.*, ventral sucker (*A* adapted from Faust and Meleney, 1924 and Tang, 1938; *B* and *E* redrawn from Tang, 1938; *C* and *D* redrawn from Faust and Meleney, 1924).

ture liberates secondary sporocysts (Fig. 201D), which produce cercariæ. The cercariæ that erupt from the secondary sporocyst penetrate the tissues of the snail, possibly aided by the secretory products of their cephalic glands, and pass into the water. Thus a single miracidium may give rise to tens of thousands of cercariæ, as a result of the 10 to 15-fold multiplication of sporocysts in the tissues near the point of penetration,[5] and the long, continuous production of cercariæ by the secondary sporocysts.[6] The parasites cause more or less injury to the liver, sexual organs and tissues, and frequently kill the snail.

The time of development in the snail depends upon the particular schistosome, the species of snail and the temperature. Usually 4 to 5 weeks are necessary for the eruption of the cercariæ, but a range from 2 to 12 weeks has been reported. The optimal temperature is 32° to 33° C.; a reduction of 5° C. doubles the usual period of development; and at 14° C. development of S. mansoni and S. hæmatobium is incomplete.[5] Elevation of the temperature accelerates development, but increases the mortality of the snails.

Free-living Cercariæ.—The phototactic cercariæ (Fig. 201E) usually emerge by twos and threes during the day. The different species vary as to time, S. mansoni erupting from 9:00 A.M. to 2:00 P.M.[6] On the first day only a few are discharged, but after a few days from 50 to 500 per day are produced, probably throughout the life of the snail. The cercariæ swim tail forward with an anticlockwise rotation, the furca aiding in propulsion. The tail stem furnishes the locomotor power, the contraction and expansion of the bipolar muscle cells producing a left and right vibration.[7] The cercariæ have alternate periods of activity and rest. They may attach themselves ventral side up to the surface film, tail bent dorsally; they may hang head down with the furca extended at the surface; they may be suspended tail up throughout the water, exerting just enough activity to maintain their position; or they may settle head first with furca curled to the bottom, where they either remain or reascend. They move like measuring worms on the surface film or bottom. Their activities are stimulated by weak alkalies and inhibited by weak acids. They shun cold and are killed by acids, essential oils and antiseptics, particularly chlorine 0.22 to 0.45 p.p.m.[8]

Penetration of Definitive Host.—Agitation of the water by any mammal stimulates cercarial activity. They penetrate the skin of a susceptible mammal usually between the hair follicles, rarely through these structures.[9] Penetration is accomplished in 10 to 15 minutes by means of the anterior spines and the lytic secretions of the cephalic glands. During this process they cast off the lashing tail.

Development in Definitive Host.—Within the mammalian host there are four developmental stages: (1) metacercariæ during their migration to liver, (2) immature forms in the liver, (3) adolescent forms migrating to the mesenteric or portal vessels and (4) maturing adult worms.

The cephalic glands and other cercarial structures degenerate soon after penetration. The larvæ enter the small blood vessels and lymphatics, are carried to the

[5] Gordon, R. M., Davey, T. H. and Peaston, H., 1934.
[6] Faust, E. C. and Hoffman, W. A., 1934.
[7] Tang, C. C., 1938.
[8] Witenberg, G. and Yofe, J., 1938.
[9] Koppisch, E., 1937.

heart through the venous or lymphatic systems, and reach the capillaries of the lungs. Hence they reach the liver and intrahepatic portal system; their actual path is still a subject of controversy. The most probable route is the vascular,[10] but some investigators believe that the metacercariæ more often leave the blood vessels, pass through the pulmonary tissues to the peritoneal cavity and finally penetrate the liver.[11] There is little growth until the larvæ reach the intrahepatic portal system. In the immature worm the anterior organ of the metacercaria becomes a true sucker, the digestive tract elongates and the two ceca join behind the

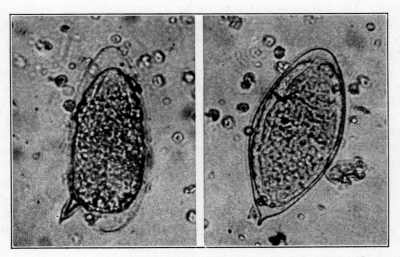

FIG. 202.—Ova of *Schistosoma mansoni* (LEFT) AND *S. hæmatobium* (RIGHT)
(Courtesy of Dr. H. K. Giffin, American Mission Hospital, Assiut, Egypt)

ventral sucker. During adolescence the rate of growth of the sexes differs, the gynecophoric canal is formed in the male, the ventral sucker becomes larger than the oral, and the ovary and testes are distinguishable when the worms are from 1.5 and 2.0 mm. in size. The time from infection to the production of ova is 28 days for *S. japonicum,* 37 to 44 days for *S. mansoni* and 30 to 60 days for *S. hæmatobium.*

LARVAL FORMS

Ovum.—The fertilized ovum, when deposited in the venules, is an ovoid hyaline body with yolk granules. The stage of development on leaving the host depends upon the time required for extrusion into the bladder or intestine, and immature as well as mature ova are found in the discharges. The mature ovum (Fig. 202) is larger than the immature owing to the development of the miracidium and the deposition of secretory and excretory products. It usually has a light yellowish-brown color, but may be colorless and translucent. Except at the poles a delicate

[10] Koppisch, E., 1937; Faust, E. C. and Meleney, H. E., 1924; Faust, E. C. and Hoff-man, W. A., 1934.
[11] Cort, W. W., 1921.

membrane, secreted by the mucous glands of the larva, lines the shell. The differential characteristics of the mature ova (Fig. 203) of the three important species of schistosomes are given in Table 38.

Miracidium.—The miracidium (Fig. 203) is an oval, pyriform, ciliated organism with a cone-shaped anterior end capped with a small papilla. Its greatest width is at the juncture of the first and second quarters. On cross section it is round. The body is covered with four rows of 6, 8, 4 and 3 ciliated ectodermal plates. The anterior cilia differ topographically, structurally and functionally from the long, delicate posterior cilia, and those just in front of the pores have a special sickle shape. The miracidium is covered by a thin, noncellular membrane with irregularly-distributed, adherent integumental cells. The mesodermal tissues, lining the body cavity, contain muscular elements. A transparent fluid surrounds the internal organs.

The internal organs are bilaterally symmetrical. The miracidium has a primitive digestive tract; anterior and lateral paired penetration glands; two pairs of flame-cells with collecting tubules opening on each side through a lateral pore; a nerve center; and a posterior mass of germinal cells. The miracidia (Fig. 203) of the three schistosomes are so similar that differentiation is almost impossible. The minor differences reported by several investigators are neither consistent nor sufficiently trustworthy for specific identification.

The primitive digestive tract, a rudimentary nonfunctioning pouch-like solid mass with a slight posterior bifurcation, extends from the oral opening for about one quarter the length of the miracidium. Posterior to the digestive pouch is the so-called nerve mass of compact cells with small nuclei. Nerve fibers, extending out of this mass, have been reported in *S. hæmatobium.* Dorsal, lateral and ventral chords with transverse commissures, have been observed.[1]

Two pyriform cephalic glands with vesicular nuclei, one on each side, open by ducts at the anterior end. One quarter the body length from the anterior end two small bulbous projections, one on each side, mark the outlets of two lateral ducts, which apparently have their origin in an ill-defined glandular mass of basophilic and mucoid cells. Refractile globules have been observed to exude from these ducts, and it is believed that they secrete the material lying between the embryo and vitelline membrane. Four flame-cells, two on each side, are present. The capillaries of the anterior and posterior flame-cells unite on each side in a tortuous tube leading to a lateral excretory pore situated one-fifth the body length from the posterior end. In the posterior two-thirds of the body are a few, or as many as 100, germ cells derived from the germinal epithelium. In *S. japonicum* the germinal portion is enclosed and separated from the rest of the body by a membranous sac.[7] It is possible that this sac rather than the entire miracidium may form the sporocyst.

Sporocysts.—The primary sporocyst (Fig. 201C), a sausage-shaped sacculate body, contains finely-granular cells, a central network of refractile granules and germ balls proliferated from the epithelial lining. Wavy movements along its long axis are produced by expansion and contraction. It travels from the tissues near the point of penetration to the lymph spaces around the digestive gland of the snail (Fig. 166), where it matures and on rupture liberates a second generation of sporocysts. The secondary sporocyst (Fig. 201D) is an elongate organism with a relatively thick wall, a narrow germinal cavity and a mobile snout-like protuberance. The germ balls, which proliferate at the aboral end, develop into cercariæ that escape through a break near the anterior end.

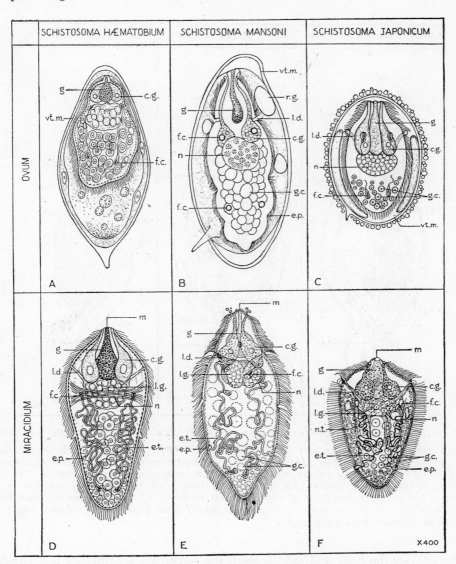

FIG. 203.—OVA AND MIRACIDIA OF IMPORTANT SCHISTOSOMES OF MAN

c.g., cephalic gland; *e.p.,* excretory pore; *e.t.,* excretory tubule; *f.c.,* flame-cell; *g,* gut; *g.c.,* germinal cells; *l.d.,* lateral duct; *l.g.,* lateral gland; *m,* mouth; *n,* nervous system; *n.t.,* nerve trunk; *r.g.,* refractile globule; *vt.m.,* vitelline membrane (*A* and *D* adapted from Looss, 1900; *B* redrawn from Gordon, Davey and Peaston, 1934; *C* and *F* redrawn from Faust and Meleney, 1924; *E* redrawn from Faust and Hoffman, 1934).

Cercaria.—The mature cercaria has an elongate pear-shaped body with rounded ends and a long tail with a terminal furca. Its shape and size vary with the state of contraction. The cuticle of both body and tail, except the anterior sucker and the tips of the furca, is covered with minute spines. Tactile hairs are irregularly dis-

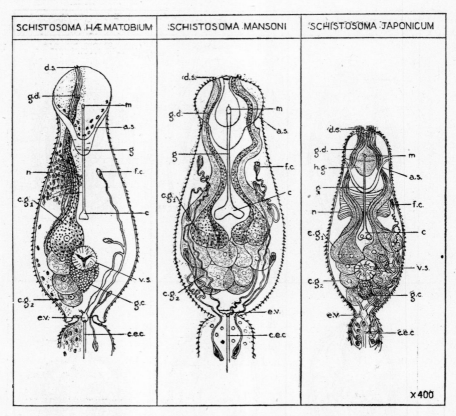

| SCHISTOSOMA HÆMATOBIUM | SCHISTOSOMA MANSONI | SCHISTOSOMA JAPONICUM |

×400

FIG. 204.—CERCARIÆ OF IMPORTANT SCHISTOSOMES OF MAN. DIAGRAM OF BODY STRUCTURE

a.s., anterior sucker; *c*, cecum; *c.e.c.*, caudal excretory canal; *c.g.₁*, cephalic glands, anterior; *c.g.₂*, cephalic glands, posterior; *d.s.*, duct spines; *e.v.*, excretory vesicle; *f.c.*, flame-cell; *g*, gut; *g.c.*, genital cells; *g.d.*, gland ducts; *h.g.*, head gland; *m*, mouth; *n*, nervous system; *v.s.*, ventral sucker. Ventral sucker, genital cells and nervous system not represented in diagram of *S. mansoni* but disputed sixth pair of cephalic glands is shown (*S. hæmatobium*, redrawn from Blacklock and Thompson, 1924; *S. mansoni* redrawn from Faust and Hoffman, 1934; *S. japonicum* redrawn from Tang, 1938).

tributed over the body and tail.[5] beneath the cuticle are longitudinal and circular muscles, and the stem of the tail is lined with bipolar muscle cells.

The cercariæ (Fig. 204) of the three important schistosomes of man are considered to have certain differential characteristics (Table 38). These morphological differences, however, are not sufficiently consistent for absolute identification and final proof depends upon producing the adult worm in experimental animals. The variable sizes reported by various workers are due to the difficulty of measuring living specimens, the contraction of fixed specimens, the stage of maturity of the cercariæ and possibly the variety.

The large anterior sucker is a pyramidal organ with a concave anterior base and a solid posterior portion with a thick muscular wall. It is pierced by the gut and ducts of the cephalic glands. The shape of the sucker and subterminal, ventral, funnel-shaped buccal cavity is asymmetrical.[11] The ventral sucker, one half the size of the anterior, is a well-developed, muscular, cup-shaped organ with a Y-shaped aperture, situated in the posterior fourth of the body. It serves as an attachment organ and is capable of protrusion. The rudimentary nonfunctioning digestive tract extends from the mouth in the midline of the body as an S-shaped capillary esophagus, which terminates anterior to the ventral sucker in a bifurcate pouch.

The excretory system includes lanceolate flame-cells; convoluted collecting tubules; an excretory vessel and a duct, which passes along the tail, bifurcates and terminates in papillæ at the tips of the furca. On each side there is an anterior and a posterior pair of flame-cells, one cell being in the proximal part of the tail. All observers agree as to the two flame-cells in the tail, but the number in the body is variously cited as from three to eight, although apparently it is six. Flagellated or ciliated areas variable in location have been observed near the ends of the main collecting tubules.

The five pairs of uninuclear cephalic glands fill most of the posterior half of the body. Their ducts pass forward in two lateral bundles, ventral to the nerve mass and digestive tract, penetrate the oral sucker and open at the anterior tip of the cercaria through hollow piercing spines. The glands have a loose texture, large nuclei, a compressible shape and apparently contain secretory products that function in penetration. Two types of glands, anterior and posterior, may be distinguished by structure, position and staining reactions. The acidophilic anterior glands are more spherical, have larger granules, and occupy a more ventral position closer to the midline than the basophilic posterior glands. The structure and number of these glands have been considered a differential characteristic between the three schistosomes (Table 38). There has been considerable dispute as to the number. Most observers agree on two anterior and three posterior pairs for *S. hæmatobium* and *S. japonicum* but in *S. mansoni* the number of posterior pairs is given as three by some investigators [12] and as four by others.[13] The anterior glands of *S. japonicum* have finer granules than those of the other two schistosomes and, except in staining reaction, more nearly resemble the posterior glands.[7]

A coarsely granular slightly basophilic head gland is present in *S. japonicum*. It develops earlier than the cephalic glands and degenerates immediately after invasion of the definitive host. It has not been observed in *S. hæmatobium* and evidence of its existence is conflicting in *S. mansoni*. The nervous system comprises two triangular cellular areas behind the anterior sucker with their bases at the

[12] Vogel, H., 1932; Archibald, R. G. and Marshall, A., 1932; Gordon, R. M., Davey, T. H. and Peaston, H., 1934.

[13] Porter, A., 1920; Faust, E. C., 1920 and 1926; Faust, E. C. and Hoffman, W. A., 1934.

TABLE 38

DIFFERENTIAL CHARACTERISTICS OF LARVAL FORMS OF THE IMPORTANT SCHISTOSOMES OF MAN

	Schistosoma hæmatobium	*Schistosoma mansoni*	*Schistosoma japonicum*
OVUM			
Size (micra) Mean	143 x 60	155 x 66	89 x 67
Range	112 to 170 x 40 to 73	114 to 182 x 45 to 73	74 to 106 x 55 to 80
Shape	Spindle-shaped with rounded anterior and conical posterior end	Elongate oval, some-times with slight S-like curve	Oval to rounded
Spine	Terminal, delicate with relatively blunt point	Lateral, long (20 μ)	Lateral, short some-times curved
Principal location in host	Bladder	Large intestine	Intestine
Exit from host	Urine, at times feces	Feces, occasionally urine	Feces
Time of hatching	A few hours	2 to 48 hours, usually within 16 hours	2 to 6 hours at 24° C., 28 days at 8° to 13° C.
MIRACIDIUM			
Size (micra)	130 x 60	140 x 66	97 x 35
Anterior penetration glands	Small, short	Large, extend beyond lateral ducts	Small, short
Lateral penetration glands	Two masses with median separation	Two masses, unsepa-rated in median line	Two masses, unsepa-rated in median line
Flame-cells	4, pyramidal with long axis at right angles to anteroposterior plane	4, rounded with long axis in anteroposterior plane	4, anterior pair di-rected toward neural surface, posterior pair toward glandular surface
Distribution in water	At all levels	Within 3 cm. of surface	Within 3 cm. of surface
Length of free-living existence	16 to 32 hours	Up to 24 hours	24 to 32 hours
SPOROCYSTS			
Migration in snail Remain in local tissues	21 to 28 days	7 days	13 days
Arrive liver	28 to 35 days	14 days	21 days
Size of mature primary sporocyst (micra)	130 x 60 (immature)	1500 x 150	400 x 50

TABLE 38—Continued

DIFFERENTIAL CHARACTERISTICS OF LARVAL FORMS OF THE IMPORTANT
SCHISTOSOMES OF MAN

	Schistosoma hæmatobium	*Schistosoma mansoni*	*Schistosoma japonicum*
SPOROCYSTS—Cont.			
Size of mature secondary sporocyst (micra)		1500 x 75	250 x 40
Temperature for development Optimal	32° to 33° C.	32° to 33° C.	
Range	14° to 37° C.	14° to 37° C.	
Period of development	35 to 42 days, earliest 21 days	22 to 28 days, earliest 15 days	49 to 63 days
CERCARIA			
Size (micra) Body Mean	175 x 62	194 x 73	125 x 49
Range	105 to 242 x 35 to 92	165 to 230 x 50 to 100	100 to 150 x 40 to 66
Tail Mean	222 x 36	232 x 53	148 x 27
Range	186 to 253 x 23 to 46	185 to 300 x 35 to 75	100 to 160 x 20 to 35
Furca Mean	86	92	60
Range	80 to 92	75 to 110	50 to 70
Cephalic glands	2 anterior pairs with large nuclei and coarse granular acidophilic cytoplasm 3 posterior pairs with smaller nuclei and fine granular basophilic cytoplasm	2 anterior pairs with large nuclei and coarse granular acidophilic cytoplasm 3 or 4 posterior pairs with smaller nuclei and fine granular basophilic cytoplasm (Number of glands controversial)	2 anterior pairs with large nuclei and fine granular acidophilic cytoplasm 3 posterior pairs with large nuclei and fine granular basophilic cytoplasm
Head gland	Absent	Questionable	Present
Germinal cells	Triangular cluster of 20 to 30 small cells posterior to ventral sucker	Triangular cluster of 20 to 30 small cells posterior to ventral sucker	Single oval cluster of small granular cells just behind ventral sucker
Length of life	48 to 54 hours	24 to 30 hours	30 to 72 hours
Resting position in water	Hangs head down from surface film furca extended	Uniformly distributed through water first 18 hours, caudal end up, then congregate at bottom. Not attached to surface film	Attached by ventral sucker to surface film of water or to other surfaces, tail bent dorsally, or hanging straight down

periphery and apices toward the midline. Transverse striations may be observed.[5] Some 20 to 30 small germinal cells lie behind the ventral sucker in *S. hæmatobium* and *S. mansoni* and a single oval cluster of small cells in *S. japonicum*. The differences noted between the germinal cells of *S. hæmatobium* and *S. mansoni* by some investigators do not appear to be well substantiated.

PATHOLOGY

The extruded ova, and to a lesser extent the adult worms, are responsible for the pathological changes produced by the three important schistosomes of man. The severity of the lesions depends upon the number of parasites, the frequency of reinfection and the duration of the infection. The disease comprises three stages: (1) the incubational period, representing the development of the cercaria into the sexually mature worm, (2) the period of oviposition and extrusion of the ova into the tissues, and (3) the period of proliferation and repair. The lesions produced by the three species are similar during the first stage and differ during the overlapping second and third stages only in tissue-selectivity. The site depends upon the egg-laying habits of the female worm; the ova of *S. hæmatobium,* deposited chiefly in the vesical plexuses, produce lesions in the bladder, genitalia and to a lesser extent the rectum; those of *S. mansoni,* deposited in the mesenteric venules, invade the intestinal wall from the ileum to the rectum, and at times the bladder; and those of *S. japonicum,* deposited in the mesenteric venules, affect only the intestine.

GENERAL PATHOLOGY

The pathological changes of the incubational stage include: (1) cutaneous lesions at the point of entry, (2) tissue reactions to the immature worms inside and outside the blood vessels and (3) toxic and allergic manifestations. Petechiæ resembling flea bites develop at the site of cercarial penetration, reach a maximum in 24 to 36 hours and disappear in three to four days with a transitory adenitis of the local superficial lymph glands.[14] The invasion of the tissues by the immature worms during their migration produces petechial hemorrhages and small foci of eosinophilic and leukocytic infiltration in the lungs, lymph nodes, kidneys, digestive tract, muscles and subcutaneous tissues. Toxic and allergic reactions may cause a generalized urticaria with subcutaneous edema, leukocytosis, eosinophilia as high as 50 per cent, asthmatic and respiratory disorders, and hemorrhagic congestion of the liver and spleen.

The deposited ova adhere to the inner lining of the venules and become embedded in the endothelium so that they lie next to the basement membrane. Their eruption into the tissues is brought about by pressure and an endothelial and subendothelial inflammatory reaction.[9] In the tissues the ova produce multiple foci of inflammatory cellular infiltration that develop into typical schistosomal abscesses or nonnecrotizing pseudotubercles. The initial reaction appears to be induced by the secretions disseminated through the eggshell. Granulation and connective tissue

---

[14] Watarai, J., 1936; Koppisch, E., 1937.

rapidly form about the ovum and an endothelial reaction with foreign-body giant cells is followed by a peripheral fibroblastic proliferation. The resulting pseudo-tubercle (Fig. 205) consists of a layer of epithelioid cells, fibroblasts and giant cells surrounded by a zone of plasma cells and eosinophils.

The adult worms to a lesser extent influence the pathological picture. In experimental rabbits as the result of eosinophilic and lymphocytic infiltration polyps form in the intima of the veins and, when the worms die, there is complete or partial replacement of the walls of the blood vessels by epithelioid cells.[9] These changes

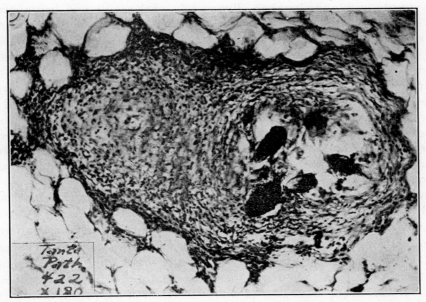

FIG. 205.—*Schistosoma mansoni* OVA IN TUBERCULOID FOCUS OF EPITHELIOID AND GIANT CELLS
(Courtesy of Dr. H. K. Giffin, American Mission Hospital, Assiut, Egypt).

are particularly marked in the liver and lungs. In the lungs aneurysmal dilatations, infarcts and areas of eosinophilic bronchopneumonia are found. The hematin, discharged from the alimentary tract of the parent worms, is engulfed by the phagocytic cells of the liver and spleen.

Liver.—Numerous ova are carried by the blood to the liver, where they break through the walls of the blood vessels into the tissues. They either form abscesses that increase in size without fibrous-tissue formation, or pseudotubercles. Passive congestion is produced by the embolic closure of the minute portal venules by the ova, particles of hematin accumulate in the endothelial cells of the capillaries and sinusoids and the liver cells are affected by the toxins secreted by the adult worms. Central necrosis was prevalent in the livers of patients with *S. mansoni* infections in Brazil.[15] The liver at first undergoes hyperplasia. In repeated and long-continued

[15] Davis, N. C., 1934.

infections the toxic secretions of the adult worms, the irritation of the ova and the passive congestion eventually produce a cirrhosis with thickening of the larger veins, fibrosis and hepatic degeneration. There is biliary involvement and more rarely invasion of the gallbladder, 15 per cent in S. mansoni infections.[16] With repeated infections there is a steady decrease in liver function.

Hepatic involvement is less marked with S. hæmatobium than with S. mansoni and S. japonicum. In late cases moderate to marked ascites may develop, dilated superficial abdominal and thoracic veins are often noticeable, and the pressure upon the thoracic viscera gives a cone-shaped appearance to the thorax. Egyptian splenomegaly, with a syndrome of splenomegaly, cirrhosis, anemia, leukopenia and often fever, in many instances has been attributed to S. mansoni.[17] Apparently it can be produced by the adult worms alone, since infections with male S. mansoni show practically no intestinal disturbances, but pass through toxemic, hepatomegalic and cirrhotic stages.[18]

Spleen.—The spleen at first shows congestion and later hypertrophy with a marked increase in fibrous reticular tissue. In rabbits, experimentally infected with S. mansoni, the changes in the spleen are attributable to toxemia and the deposition of pigment in the reticulo-endothelial system, since no ova are present.[9] Ova of S. hæmatobium, however, have been found in the spleen.[19] In Egypt repeated invasions of S. mansoni and S. hæmatobium produce splenomegaly with permanent hyperplasia and fibrosis and at times ascites.[20]

Lungs.—Ova and the adult worms may reach the lungs. In 282 Egyptians infected with S. hæmatobium ova were found at autopsy in the lungs in 33 per cent and adult flukes in 3.6 per cent.[21] The embolic ova produce a necrotizing arteriolitis and parenchymatous tubercles in the peribronchial tissues. Massive and repeated infections may induce extensive arteriolar changes that lead to passive congestion. Dead worms cause toxic necrosis of the arteries and a cicatrizing focal pneumonia. Similar lesions in the small arteries with obliteration of the lumen, destruction of the elastica and aneurysmal dilatation with attendant right heart hypertrophy have been observed in S. mansoni infections.[22] In a fatal case of S. mansoni infection obstruction of the pulmonary circulation was caused by numerous ova embedded in granulomatous nodules in the alveolar septa and arteries and by the occlusion of the arteries by the adult worms.[23]

Nervous System.—Occasionally the ova reach the brain and spinal cord, producing various nervous disorders including symptoms of Jacksonian epilepsy in S. japonicum infections.[24]

Other Organs.—The ova may set up inflammatory foci in numerous organs, especially in the mesenteric lymph nodes, which are enlarged, hyperplastic and show loss of lymphoid tissue. They have also been found in the pancreas, stomach, kidneys, suprarenals and myocardium, and even in the upper eyelid.

[16] Hashim, M., 1931.
[17] Bonnin, H., 1929.
[18] Girges, R., 1931, 1932.
[19] Onsy, A., 1929.
[20] Onsy, A., 1937.
[21] Shaw, A. F. B. and Ghareeb, A. A., 1938.
[22] Clark, E. and Graef, I., 1935.
[23] Day, H. B., 1937.
[24] Greenfield, J. G. and Pritchard, B., 1937.

SPECIAL PATHOLOGY

The location of the main depots of ova extrusion varies with the species, thus producing different pathological manifestations.

Schistosoma hæmatobium.—The ova pass from the venules of the vesical plexuses into the bladder wall where they are distributed in the submucosa and to a lesser extent in the muscularis and mucosa, while some occlude the blood vessels. The resultant inflammatory reaction leads to progressive changes in the bladder and neighboring tissues. The extent of these changes depends upon the number of ova and upon the duration of the infection.

The early changes in the bladder are a diffuse hyperemia from the injection of the small blood vessels and the appearance of minute vesicular or papular elevations of the mucosa. Later these coalesce into inflammatory patches consisting of sloughing tissue, phosphatic deposits and ova, that give the mucosa a sandy or granular appearance, especially on the trigone of the bladder. Papillomatous folds and polypoid excrescences develop as the disease progresses. Concretions of uric acid and oxalate crystals, later augmented by phosphatic deposits, form around the ova, blood clots and sloughed-off papillomata. There is a general hyperplasia of the wall of the bladder and reduced vascularity of the mucosa. The urine changes from an acid to án alkaline reaction and contains abundant mucus, pus and red blood cells.

The ureters may be obstructed by thickening of their walls and occasionally the pelvis of the kidney is affected. The urethra may be occluded, and the prostate and seminal vesicles of the male and the urethra and vagina of the female may become indurated from the infiltrating ova. The external male genitalia may assume an elephantoid appearance from obstruction of the scrotal lymphatics (Fig. 208). Secondary bacterial invasion may produce ulceration, perivesical and periurethral abscesses and fistulæ of the bladder, rectum, scrotum and penis.

Not infrequently the adult worms invade the lower large intestine and deposit ova in the venules of the inferior mesenteric vessels, producing, like *S. mansoni,* rectal papillomata (Figs. 206 and 207). The invading ova that penetrate the intestinal wall are passed in the feces. Infection of the rectum without bladder involvement has been reported.[25] Combined infections with *S. hæmatobium* and *S. mansoni* often occur with both vesical and intestinal involvement. Foci of inflammation and even partially calcified ova in the walls of the appendix have been observed. The intestinal lesions produced by *S. hæmatobium,* however, though similar are milder than those of *S. mansoni.*

The mechanical and toxic irritation of the ova evidently predisposes to malignancy.[26] The incidence of epithelioma of the bladder in patients with vesical schistosomiasis is 2 to 11 times that in uninfected persons.[27] Carcinoma of the intestine seems unduly prevalent in endemic regions of *S. japonicum* and has been noted in *S. mansoni* infections. The relationship of intestinal schistosomiasis to malignancy, however, is not as definite as that of vesical schistosomiasis.[27]

---

[25] Nessman, V. and Trensz, F., 1928.   [27] Brumpt, E., 1930.
[26] Fairley, N. H., 1931.

Schistosoma mansoni.—The invading ova after their escape from the mesenteric venules produce an intense cellular infiltration of the intestinal wall from the lower ileum to the rectum. The minute abscesses rupture into the intestine, discharging blood, pus and ova. Increase in connective tissue produces irregular thickenings of the intestinal wall with fibrous constrictions. The tearing-off of papillomata and secondary bacterial infection may cause ulceration. The entire intestinal wall in-

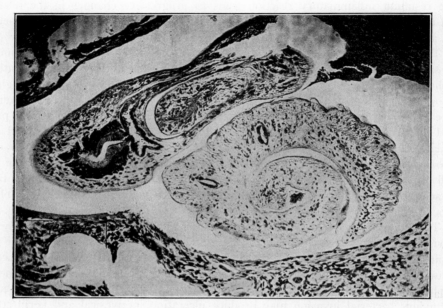

FIG. 206.—ADULT *Schistosoma hæmatobium* IN RECTAL POLYP

(Courtesy of Dr. H. K. Giffin, American Mission Hospital, Assiut, Egypt).

cluding the peritoneal surface may be included in the process and may be bound down with peritoneal adhesions. Simple thickenings of the mucosa or papillomata of various sizes and shapes, thickly or sparsely distributed, are formed. In advanced cases relaxation of the anal sphincter permits the prolapse of pedunculate papillomatous masses. Fistulæ may extend to the ischiorectal fossa, perineum, buttocks and bladder. At times the bladder may be invaded by the ova; 3.4 per cent of *S. mansoni* patients show ova in the urine.[27]

Schistosoma japonicum.—The ova are deposited in the mesenteric lymph nodes and mucosa of the intestinal wall. They are extruded with blood and pus into the intestinal lumen. Congestion and inflammation extend throughout the intestinal wall. The mesentery and omentum are often thickened and adhere to the colon in a firm mass. There is extensive fibrous tissue proliferation in the layers of the intestinal wall, formation of papillomata, and thrombosis of the mesenteric and portal vessels.[1] The bladder is usually not involved, as is sometimes the case in *S. mansoni* infections.

SYMPTOMATOLOGY

Schistosomal infection may be divided clinically into three stages: (1) incubational, (2) oviposition and extrusion, and (3) tissue proliferation and repair. The general symptoms, similar for all three species, correspond to the common pathological changes in the viscera, and the special symptoms, characteristic of the individual species, are determined by the particular tissues invaded, such as the bladder by *S. hæmatobium* and the intestine by *S. mansoni* and *S. japonicum*. During the incubational stage the symptoms are mild and may pass unnoticed. At the

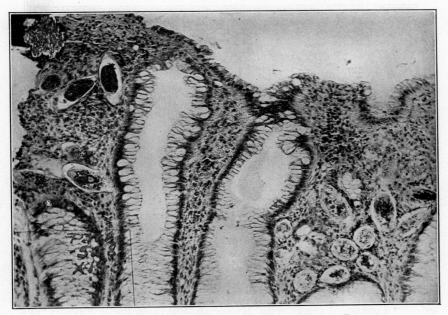

FIG. 207.—*Schistosoma hæmatobium* OVA IN RECTAL POLYP

(Courtesy of Dr. H. K. Giffin, American Mission Hospital, Assiut, Egypt)

time of infection there is a tingling sensation followed by a local dermatitis. (See cercarial dermatitis.) During the migration and development of the immature worms, toxic and allergic manifestations may appear. An urticarial rash with subcutaneous edema accompanied by intense itching usually occurs in about three weeks. Leukocytosis, eosinophilia, and occasionally asthmatic symptoms may be present. Other symptoms include headache, anorexia, malaise, vague muscular pains and a remittent fever.

Schistosoma hæmatobium.—The most characteristic symptom is a painless or painful hematuria, which may be present for years without other manifestations. The first symptoms are a burning sensation at micturition, increased frequency of urination and at times a dull pain in the suprapubic and perineal regions. Usually only the last few drops of urine contain blood, but sometimes the entire output may be blood-tinged. The urine contains mucoid flocculi, ova and sometimes blood clots. A few patients may show rectal involvement with blood and mucus in the feces. At the same time there may be toxic manifestations in the form of fever, slight hepatitis, splenitis and nephritis.

In mild cases without reinfection the hematuria gradually diminishes, but in severe infections a progressive cystitis develops. The frequency of urination increases, the output of urine at each period is reduced and finally little more than pus and blood are passed. The urine becomes alkaline, calculi form about the ova, papil-

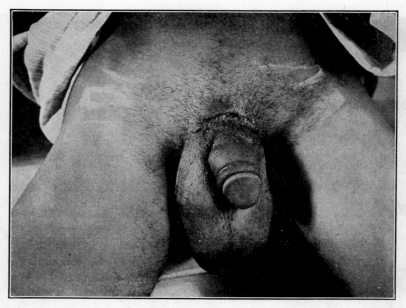

FIG. 208.—BILHARZIASIS PATIENT WITH HYDROCELE, ENLARGED RIGHT TESTICLE AND PUBIC ABSCESS. DURATION OF INFECTION FIVE YEARS

(Courtesy of Dr. H. K. Giffin, American Mission Hospital, Assiut, Egypt)

lomata develop and ulceration occurs. Secondary infection may produce a septic cystitis. The bladder becomes hypertrophied and contracted, the urethra may be obstructed, and involvement of the ureters and kidneys may produce hydronephrosis. The prostate and seminal vesicles may be affected, and lymph stasis may produce an elephantoid condition of the penis and scrotum (Fig. 208). Urinary fistulæ involving the perineum, scrotum and neighboring parts are frequent complications.

Interstitial pneumonia and, more rarely, epileptic or paralytic symptoms and appendicitis may arise from the involvement of lungs, brain and appendix. The hepatic lesions produce a serious cirrhosis with its accompanying symptoms. Early in the disease the leukocytes may be increased, but in the late stages there is leukopenia. The patient shows a chloritic anemia, progressive weakness and finally dies from exhaustion or secondary infection.

Schistosoma mansoni.—In the early stages of the infection, dysenteric symptoms with mucus, blood and frequent stools are present. The dysentery usually subsides, but at times frequent evacuations with tenesmus may persist. Occasionally a fatal choleraic type of dysentery develops. Fever, urticaria, abdominal pain, anorexia, leukocytosis, high eosinophilia and pulmonary symptoms may be present. Later, branching polypoid growths extending up to the sigmoid flexure are found, and with relaxation of the sphincter the papillomata may prolapse through the anus. Occasionally symptoms of appendicitis may be produced by the extrusion of ova in the appendix.

Some cases of Egyptian splenomegaly, with its syndrome of splenomegaly, hepatic cirrhosis, anemia, leukopenia and irregular, intermittent fever, have been attributed to infection with *S. mansoni*.[17] The spleen is enlarged, firm, and often extends to the umbilicus. The liver at first is enlarged, but later is cirrhotic, hard and shrunken. Vomiting, diarrhea, chloritic anemia and hematemesis frequently occur, but jaundice is rare. Ascites may develop if there is insufficient collateral circulation.

Schistosoma japonicum.—Oriental schistosomiasis is more severe than infection with *S. mansoni*. The stage of ova extrusion, about a month after infection, is accompanied by dysentery with ova in the feces and enlargement of the liver and spleen. There is daily fever, abdominal pain and tenderness, and loss of appetite and weight. In from three to ten weeks the fever disappears and the patient recuperates slowly, though subject to relapses. Severe or repeated infections, however, lead to cirrhosis of the liver and ascites (Fig. 209). Patients show low blood pressure, weakness, emaciation, marked anemia, extreme pallor, and various digestive symptoms. Young patients show retarded development. Death occurs from exhaustion, pneumonia or superimposed infections.

IMMUNITY

In Africa schistosomiasis is not often found in persons over 40 years of age and in China seldom after 50 years. This apparent age-resistance, however, may be the result of an immunity acquired by previous infection. In the highly-endemic districts of the Belgian Congo infection is largely confined to persons below 30 years of age with the highest in-

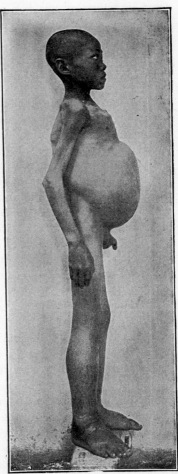

Fig. 209.—Patient with Severe *Schistosoma japonicum* Infection of Three Years' Duration

(After Jeffreys and Maxwell, from Stitt, *Diagnostics and Treatment of Tropical Diseases*, 1929. Copyright The Blakiston Company, Publishers).

cidence in children between five and nine years, whereas in districts of low incidence there is no age distinction.[28] The absence of infection in children under five years of age may be explained by the native custom of washing small children in warmed water instead of allowing them to bathe in streams and pools. In China most cases of *S. japonicum* are found in the 16- to 30-year group and few children under 15 years of age are infected.[29]

The production of an acquired immunity from previous infection is still unsettled, since experiments with animals and man have not given conclusive results, and some investigators question whether there is an acquired immunity to superinfection.[30] The experimental exposure of presumably immune natives to the cercariæ of *S. mansoni* produced only a few ova in the feces of one half the volunteers, while mice exposed to the same test-lot of cercariæ acquired adult worms.[31] Only 20 per cent of the test-dose of cercariæ developed in dogs that had been cured of previous *S. japonicum* infection by treatment with sodium antimony tartrate as compared with 45 per cent in normal control dogs, and also the worms in the immune dogs were abnormally small and degenerate.[32] Dogs that were artificially immunized by injecting suspensions of adult worms or cercariæ showed milder symptoms, and fewer, smaller and more degenerate worms than the control dogs. Previous infection partially protected dogs and rabbits against *S. japonicum;* but active immunization by antigenic extracts was unsuccessful in rabbits and gave only slight protection to dogs, while passive immunization was ineffective.[33]

Monkeys (*Macacus sinicus*) infected with *S. spindale* undergo spontaneous cure and only show the early developmental stages. The disappearance of the schistosomes is due either to an obscure immunity or to an inherent unsuitability of the blood for the adult worms.[34] Following recovery there is an enhanced refractiveness for three months during which the schistosomulæ fail to develop after penetrating the skin.

The presence of immune antibodies in infected and artificially immunized animals has been demonstrated by several investigators. Alexin-fixative antibodies were found in goats infected with *S. spindale,* a primary rise in antibody titer occurring in the second week and a secondary rise between the fifth and the ninth week.[35] The antibodies persisted for over one year, probably as long as the schistosomes were present. The rate of appearance of the antibodies depended upon the size of the infecting dose, being earlier in massive infections. In animals cured by antimony treatment the antibodies persisted for 4 to 28 weeks after the start of treatment. The injection of cercarial antigens of *S. spindale* in normal goats produced maximal alexin-fixative antibodies in 21 to 25 days, while in diseased animals there was a rapid rise to about nine times the titer produced in normal goats.[36] The injection of cercarial extracts increases the antibody content of the serum but fails to modify the course of the infection in monkeys.[37] In man and animals alexin-

[28] Dixon, P. K., 1934; Fisher, A. C., 1934.
[29] Kan, H. C. and Kyng, J. C., 1936.
[30] van den Berghe, L., 1934.
[31] Fisher, A. C., 1934.
[32] Ozawa, M., 1930.
[33] Tanaka, S., 1929.

[34] Fairley, N. H., Mackie, F. A. and Jasudasan, F., 1930.
[35] Fairley, N. H. and Jasudasan, F., 1930.
[36] Fairley, N. H., 1927.
[37] Fairley, N. H., 1926.

fixative antibodies,[38] precipitins,[39] and cutaneous sensitization,[40] have been recorded by several observers. These tests represent group-reactions for the various species of schistosomes.

DIAGNOSIS

Clinical.—During the incubational stage schistosomiasis may be suspected in patients from endemic areas with a history of cutaneous lesions after exposure to suspected water, or with urticaria, eosinophilia and pulmonary disorders. Differential diagnosis from typhoid fever and angioneurotic edema is necessary. Eosinophilia is helpful, but it is less likely to be present in the late stages. The use of antimony as a diagnostic procedure has been recommended, since it provokes a rise in eosinophils in schistosomiasis.[41]

In vesical schistosomiasis hematuria, cystitis, urinary calculi and other vesical symptoms are suggestive, but the disease must be differentiated from renal calculi, nephritis, tuberculosis, hemoglobinuria, and benign and malignant papillomata. Cystoscopic examination may show discrete grayish elevations, hemorrhagic papules around the trigone, sandy patches and papillomata. Roentgen-ray examination reveals *S. hæmatobium* infection when there is a sufficient deposition of calcified ova, and intravenous pyelography is useful in demonstrating complications.[42] Bilharziasis is shown by calcified demarcations or cloud-like shadows in any part of the urinary tract. This procedure is useful when the ova are imbedded so deeply that they do not reach the mucous surfaces or when the lesions are healed. In intestinal schistosomiasis dysentery, enlarged or cirrhotic liver and splenomegaly are suggestive, but require differentiation from amœbic or bacillary dysenteries, tuberculosis, typhoid fever, other splenomegalies, hepatic cirrhoses, and malignancies. Rectal examination, manual or by sigmoidoscope, may show the presence of pedunculated papillomata.

Ova.—The recovery of ova from the urine and feces is the most reliable method of diagnosis. The species of parasite may be determined by the characteristics of the ova (Table 38). Occasionally the ova assume unusual forms, but as a rule they maintain their characteristic appearance. In old infections the discharge of ova ceases with the death of the worms, and occasionally cases of infection with only male worms have been reported.

In *S. hæmatobium* infections the ova are found chiefly in the urine, less frequently in the feces. In old infections the number is reduced. When few in number, the last drops of urine should be examined or the bladder scratched with a sound. In latent cases, when ova are not found in the urine, a provocative intravenous injection of Bayer 205 has been recommended.[43]

---

[38] Fairley, N. H., 1926, 1933; Miyaji, S. and Imai, B., 1928; Fairley, N. H. and Jasudasan, F., 1930; Andrews, M. N., 1935; Salam, A. A., 1935.

[39] Miyaji, S. and Imai, B., 1928; Taliaferro, W. H., Hoffman, W. A. and Cook, D. H., 1928.

[40] Meleney, H. E. and Wu, H., 1924; Fairley, N. H. and Williams, F. E., 1927; Taliaferro, W. H. and Taliaferro, L. G., 1931; Khalil, M. and Hassan, A., 1932; Vogel, H., 1932; Kan, H. C. and Kyng, J. C., 1936; Kan, H. C., 1936.

[41] Mainzer, F., 1939.

[42] Afifi, M. A., 1934.

[43] Kunert, H., 1939.

In *S. mansoni* infections the ova are found chiefly in the feces and less frequently in the urine, and in *S. japonicum* infections only in the feces. The discharge of ova of *S. mansoni* in the feces is fairly constant.[44] They are present in flakes of mucus and are more readily obtained from the outside of fecal masses than in fluid stools. A combination of dilution egg-counts (three slides) and sedimentation is recommended, each of these methods giving alone about 85 per cent of the positives obtained by their combination.[45] When ova are scarce, the rectal swab method gives the maximal results.[46]

Chemical Tests.—Schistosomiasis produces an increase in euglobulin. Consequently, Napier's aldehyde test (Section **VII**, IX, 25) or similar tests may be used for confirmatory diagnosis, provided leishmaniasis and other infections can be excluded.[47] The test in *S. hæmatobium* and *S. mansoni* infections is more often positive in patients with enlarged spleens.

Serological and Intracutaneous Tests.—Serological and intracutaneous tests are of value in detecting asymptomatic cases, old infections where fibrotic changes in the tissues prevent the extrusion of ova, and early infections before the discharge of ova. They may disclose unisexual infections with male schistosomes. These tests are also useful in determining cure, since a persistent positive reaction is indicative of the presence of live schistosomes. Alexin-fixative, precipitative, and intracutaneous tests show a group-reaction for schistosomes with antigens prepared from cercariæ or adult worms (Section **VII**, IX, 10-14). The three human schistosomes produce antibodies that give cross-reactions with each other and also react with antigens prepared from the livers of snails infected with *S. spindale* and *S. bovis*, schistosomes of domestic animals.

Positive precipitative reactions were obtained in 82 per cent of 77 tests on persons infected with *S. mansoni* and in 71 per cent of 14 persons infected with *S. japonicum*.[39] Occasional pseudopositive reactions were noted in syphilitic patients. Alexin-fixative tests were positive in 86 per cent of 152 patients reported by five investigators.[38] A smaller percentage of positive reactions was obtained in those with infections of over two years' duration than in more recently infected patients, 73 vs. 88 per cent.[48] Positive reactions were encountered in a small percentage of uninfected persons, mostly syphilitics. The nature of the alexin-fixative test with alcoholic extracts tends toward the production of pseudopositive reactions in syphilitic sera.

The intracutaneous test has been used by several investigators for the diagnosis of schistosomiasis.[40] With cercarial antigens a control antigen prepared from snail livers should be employed. An immediate reaction is obtained in a high percentage of infected individuals. Positive reactions are also found in persons who have recovered from a past infection, and the reaction persists for a long time after chemotherapeutic cure. The test is useful in field work on *S. japonicum*, since only one per cent of infected persons fail to give positive reactions.[49] On the other

[44] Scott, J. A., 1938.
[45] Scott, J. A., 1937.
[46] Khalil, M. and El Din, M. S., 1930.
[47] Meleney, H. E. and Wu, H., 1924;

Khalil, M. and Hassan, A., 1932.
[48] Fairley, N. H., 1919.
[49] Kan, H. C., 1936.

hand, only 60 per cent of the persons giving positive intracutaneous reactions showed ova in the feces.

PROGNOSIS

The prognosis in *S. hæmatobium* infection depends upon the stage of the disease, the age of the patient, exposure to reinfection, and treatment. Provided treatment is given, prognosis is good in the toxemic and infiltrative stages of the disease; in the papillomatous stage favorable as to life except with superimposed septic infection; and in the cirrhotic and ulcerative stage extremely poor.[50] Mortality varies with age, the rate after the age of 45 years, increasing fourfold. In *S. mansoni* and *S. japonicum* infections, provided treatment is instituted, the prognosis is fairly good in early and light infections, but in late infections with extensive involvement of the liver and intestinal wall it is poor. *S. japonicum* infections, as a rule, are more severe than those of *S. mansoni,* since the female worms of the former produce a greater number of ova.

TREATMENT

Schistosoma hæmatobium.—The antimony compounds are specific in the treatment of bilharziasis. Potassium antimony tartrate (Section **VII,** XIII, 6) first used by Christopherson in 1918, has proved an effective drug and is commonly used. Sodium antimony tartrate, though more expensive and less stable, is preferred by some workers for intravenous administration. Fuadin, a trivalent antimony compound (Section **VII,** XIII, 11), is the drug of choice. It is as efficient as sodium antimony tartrate, is less toxic, and may be given intramuscularly. The oxyquinoline derivatives of antimony are reported to be superior to potassium antimony tartrate and fuadin.[51] Emetine hydrochloride (Section **VII,** XIII, 14) is temporarily beneficial, but does not produce permanent cure.[52]

Antimony treatment should be given as early in the disease as possible. In the first or toxemic stage and in the second or infiltrative stage specific treatment cures by killing the worms and ova. The condition of the patient improves; micturition is less frequent; dysuria is reduced; the congestion of the mucosa of the bladder is lessened; and hematuria, pyuria and albuminuria disappear.[53] The female worms are more susceptible to treatment than the males and the drugs also reduce the egg-laying capacity of the female.[37] Antimony treatment is also helpful during the papillomatous stage but is of no avail or even dangerous in the advanced cirrhotic stage, where only symptomatic treatment is indicated.

Surgical treatment is called for in complications such as calculi, periurethral abscess, fistulæ, stricture, incontinence of urine, acute urinary retention, malignancy, perineal tumors and hydronephrosis. Perineal cystotomy gives the most efficient drainage and facilitates nursing care.[53] Antiseptics in the form of irrigations or local

---

[50] Girges, R., 1930.   Giovannola, A., 1936.
[51] Cawston, F. G., 1936.   [53] Girges, R., 1932.
[52] Gordon, R. M. and Hicks, E. P., 1930;

applications are helpful in clearing up secondary pyogenic infections of the bladder and adnexa.

Schistosoma mansoni.—Potassium antimony tartrate (Section **VII**, XIII, 6) and fuadin (Section **VII**, XIII, 11) are the drugs of choice. Fuadin in experimental animals appears to be less efficient than potassium antimony tartrate. The more extensive liver involvement caused by this parasite requires greater precautions in administering treatment than in *S. hæmatobium* infections, and patients with advanced hepatic cirrhosis do not respond to treatment.

Schistosoma japonicum.—Potassium antimony tartrate (Section **VII**, XIII, 6) and especially sodium antimony tartrate are at present the favored drugs. Fuadin in experimental animals and man seems less effective,[54] although eventually it may prove the most satisfactory drug. These drugs are only of value in the early and moderately advanced stages of the disease. They are useless and even dangerous in advanced hepatic cirrhosis. The response of patients to treatment is shown by improvement in general condition, by diminution in the size of liver and spleen, and by reduction in the number of ova and their final disappearance from the feces. The extensive liver damage calls for greater care in their administration than in *S. hæmatobium* infections.

EPIDEMIOLOGY

The incidence of schistosomiasis in endemic areas is high. Extensive surveys indicate that of the 12 million rural inhabitants of Egypt one half are infected with *S. hæmatobium* and one quarter with *S. mansoni*.[45] In the Western Hemisphere the incidence of *S. mansoni* has been variously given as: Puerto Rico 12.2 per cent,[55] St. Kitts 25 per cent,[56] Guadeloupe 14.8 per cent,[57] and Brazil 5.4 per cent.[58] In Chekiang, China, an incidence of 30.8 per cent for *S. japonicum* has been reported.[29]

Schistosomiasis is more extensive in rural than in urban communities, is associated with agricultural pursuits and is more prevalent among the poorer classes. By reason of occupation men are more frequently infected than women; a ratio of 37:1 has been reported for *S. japonicum*.[29] The disease is most common in early adult life, is rare in young children and tends to disappear with age.

The endemicity of schistosomiasis depends upon the insanitary disposal of urine and feces, the presence of suitable snail-hosts and exposure to water infested with cercariæ. Waters are infected by promiscuous defecation and urination, latrine drainage and sewage disposal. The snails that act as intermediate hosts are sewage feeders and prefer slow-moving or stagnant bodies of water, especially artificial irrigation canals or ponds where plant life is abundant. The infestation of water by cercariæ depends upon the presence of these snails. The disease is contracted by persons working, washing clothes or bathing in infested waters. Unfiltered water supplies from such sources are also dangerous.

[54] Lee, C. U., 1932; Lee, C. U. and Chung, H. L., 1933.

[55] Faust, E. C., Hoffman, W. A., Jones, C. A. and Janer, J. L., 1934.

[56] Jones, S. B., 1932.

[57] Fabre, H. J. A., 1929.

[58] Davis, N. C., 1934.

The incidence of infection depends largely upon the distribution of the snail-hosts. The canals of the perennial irrigation system of the Nile delta and the Nile valley south to Assiut afford a favorable habitat, whereas the ancient system of basin irrigation farther south in the Nile valley is less suitable. The distribution of the specific host-species explains the different endemic areas of *S. hæmatobium* and *S. mansoni*. In the northern part of the Nile delta the incidence of *S. mansoni* is 60 per cent, in the southern 6 per cent and in the Nile valley south of Cairo 0 per cent, while that of *S. hæmatobium* is 60 per cent throughout the entire perennial irrigation area and 5 per cent in the basin irrigation area.[45] Floods bear vegetation laden with snails downstream, deposit them on the shores of the Nile and carry them into the branch irrigation canals. This replenishment complicates measures for snail destruction.[59]

In China the smaller irrigation canals or ditches are most heavily infested in the villages and rice fields, particularly the highly-fertilized rice nursery grounds. The amphibious oriental snails live on the vegetation on the edges of these ditches and flourish on soil enriched with humus and fecal débris. The limiting factors in the distribution of these snails are salinity, nitrogen load, currents, floods, humus content, and plant population, while mountain ranges, dams and large chasms act as barriers.[60]

PROPHYLAXIS

The prevention of schistosomiasis includes: (1) reduction of sources of infection, (2) the sanitary disposal of human wastes, (3) the control of snail-hosts, (4) the destruction of ova and cercariæ and (5) the protection of persons from exposure to infested waters.

Foci of infection may be reduced by the detection and treatment of infected persons, but because of constant reinfection mass therapy in Egypt has failed to control the disease. Likewise domestic and wild animal reservoir hosts make this method of little value for the control of oriental schistosomiasis; an incidence of 12.6 per cent in cattle and 18.7 per cent in water buffaloes has been reported.[61] The presence of *S. hæmatobium* and *S. mansoni* in monkeys may also reduce the effectiveness of this method of control.[62]

The sanitary disposal of feces would eradicate the disease, but its practice runs contrary to economic, racial and religious customs. In China night soil is used for fertilizer, and in Egypt and other Mohammedan countries the religious practices of cleansing the anal and urethral openings lead to urination and defecation in or near water supplies. Wherever sanitary disposal of human discharges has been accomplished the incidence of schistosomiasis has declined.

Ova in the feces may be destroyed by chemical treatment or through fermentation of night soil by storage for two weeks. Cercariæ in the water are killed by 1 p.p.m. of chlorine in 2½ to 3 hours in filtered water and by 1 p.p.m. chloramine

[59] Khalil, M., 1930; Helmy, M. M., 1929.   [61] Wu, K., 1938.
[60] Li, F. C., 1934.   [62] Cameron, T. W. M., 1928.

in 1 hour.[63] Chlorine 0.22 to 0.45 p.p.m., has also been reported as effective.[8] The acridine dyes,[64] copper sulphate and lime have a lethal effect.

The destruction of snails theoretically offers the best method of attack, but the practical application of control measures is far from satisfactory. Snails may be destroyed by chemicals, desiccation, collection, removal of vegetation, and natural enemies (Section **VII**, XI). Periodic clearance of plants and snails in Egyptian irrigation canals, a relatively inexpensive method, was effective in reducing the snail population over a period of three years.[65] Desiccation is ineffective unless the snails are kept dry over three months, but reduces their parasitic infestation. Winter closure of the canals with drying does not kill the majority of the snails, but does destroy their eggs.[66] Copper sulphate, 5 p.p.m., is lethal for snails and certain species of fish but not for mammals.[67] It is not effective against amphibious oriental snails that spend part of their existence on the canal banks. Lime has been used successfully in restricted areas in Japan, but chemical methods cannot be economically applied to the more extensive Chinese areas.

Agricultural workers may be protected by clothing and boots from exposure to water, but economic considerations, convenience of working, and ignorance tend to make such efforts impractical. Likewise prohibition of bathing in infected waters cannot be enforced.

Schistosoma bovis (SONSINO, 1876), BLANCHARD, 1895

S. bovis is a parasite of the portal and mesenteric veins of cattle, sheep and goats. It has also been found in horses, mules, antelopes and baboons. Its distribution includes Africa, southern Asia, Corsica and Sardinia. The adult worm resembles *S. hæmatobium*. The tuberculate males are from 1.5 to 2.2 cm. in length and the females 1.2 to 2.8 cm. The variable oval to spindle-shaped ova, usually passed in the feces, have a terminal spine and are longer and narrower than the ova of the *S. hæmatobium*, measuring 160 to 220 μ by 40 to 60 μ. The intermediate hosts are *Bulinus contortus* in Corsica, *Physopsis africana* in Rhodesia, Natal and the Belgian Congo, and *P. nasuta* in Kenya. The cercariæ, similar to those of *S. hæmatobium*, penetrate the skin and occasionally the oral mucosa of animals. Their bodies measure from 160 to 260 μ by 50 to 80 μ and their tail stems from 180 to 280 μ.

A few human infections have been reported in southern Rhodesia, Natal and the Belgian Congo.[68] These reports, based on ova in the feces and urine, require confirmation, and it is doubtful if *S. bovis* infects man.[69] Ova may occur in the faces when the intestines of infected animals are eaten, and in the urine abnormal ova of *S. hæmatobium* may be mistaken for those of *S. bovis*.

Schistosoma spindale, MONTGOMERY, 1906

S. spindale is a parasite of the mesenteric veins of cattle, sheep, goats, horses, antelopes and water buffaloes. It is found in India, Sumatra and Africa. In animals phlebitis of the branches of the mesenteric veins, mesenteric thrombosis, and toxic changes in the

[63] Griffiths-Jones, E., Atkinson, H. and Hassan, A., 1930.

[64] Oesterlin, M. and Krainick, H., 1934.

[65] Barlow, C. H., 1937.

[66] Barlow, C. H., 1935.

[67] Khalil, M., 1932.

[68] Blackie, W. E., 1932; Cawston, F. G., 1929, 1930; Brumpt, E., 1930.

[69] MacHattie, C., Mills, E. A. and Chadwick, C. R., 1933.

liver and kidneys occur before the deposition of ova, seven weeks after infection. The ova produce pseudotubercles and periportal cirrhosis in the liver but, although they freely invade the intestines, rarely produce macroscopical lesions.[70] The males range from 0.6 to 1.4 cm. in length and the females from 0.7 to 1.6 cm. The long, spindle-shaped ova with terminal spines range in size from 160 to 490 μ by 20 to 70 μ. They are passed in the feces, rarely in the urine. The intermediate host in Egypt and India is *Planorbis exustus,* and in South Africa *P. pfeifferi* and *Bulinus tropicus* have been incriminated. The cercariæ are more slender and longer than those of other mammalian schistosomes. Two questionable cases of human infection, based on ova in the urine, have been reported in South' Africa.[71] The cercariæ produce a dermatitis in workers in the rice fields of the Federated Malay States.

CERCARIAL DERMATITIS

The cercariæ of certain species of animal schistosomes produce in man a cercarial dermatitis, which has become a vexing problem on some fresh-water bathing beaches.

The dermatitis produced by the pathogenic species, though often overlooked, may be demonstrated experimentally with *S. hæmatobium* and *S. mansoni.*[72] Biopsy of the skin, two and one-half hours after penetration of cercariæ of *S. mansoni,* reveals infiltration of neutrophils and eosinophils around the cercariæ in the under-layers of the epidermis.[73] In repeated infections the reaction is more severe and probably represents an immune response. The more pronounced reaction in unnatural hosts is due to natural resistance and local destruction of the cercariæ.[74] "Kabure," a dermatitis observed in endemic districts of *S. japonicum,* is believed to be caused by schistosomes abnormal to man rather than by *S. japonicum.*[75]

Geographical Distribution.—Cercarial dermatitis has been observed in England, France, Germany, Switzerland, the Federated Malay States, Canada and the United States of America. In North America endemic centers have been found in Saskatchewan and Manitoba, and in Wisconsin, Michigan, Minnesota and Iowa. Reports of outbreaks have also been received from Illinois, North Dakota, Nebraska, Texas, Florida and Washington.

Species.—Six species of animal schistosomes have been associated with cercarial dermatitis: (1) *Cercaria elvæ,* (2) *C. stagnicolæ,* (3) *C. physellæ,* (4) *Schistosoma douthitti,* (5) *Trichobilharzia ocellata,* (6) *Schistosoma spindale.* The first four are found in the United States of America. The cercariæ of these species are characterized by prominent eye-spots and differ in this respect from the three schistosomes of man.

Cercaria elvæ (Miller, 1923) probably lives as an adult in birds. Its intermediate hosts are the snails, *Lymnæa stagnalis* vars. *appressa, perampla, lillianæ, sanctæmariæ* and *jugularis,* and *Stagnicola palustris elodes.*[76] Experimental observations have shown that the cercaria escapes from the snail in the early morning, swims vigorously, is phototactic and spends most of its time on the side of the container nearest the light.[77]

[70] Fairley, N. H. and Mackie, F. P., 1930.
[71] Porter, A., 1926.
[72] Barlow, C. H., 1936.
[73] Vogel, H., 1932.
[74] Cort, W. W., 1928; Vogel, H., 1932.
[75] Watarai, J., 1934.
[76] Talbot, S. B., 1936; Swales, W. E., 1936; Brackett, S., 1940.
[77] Cort, W. W., 1936.

Cercaria stagnicolæ (Talbot, 1936) probably lives as an adult in birds. Its intermediate hosts are *Stagnicola emarginata* vars. *angulata, emarginata, vilasensis, wisconsinensis* and *canadensis*.[76] The phototactic cercaria escapes from the snail in the early morning, and spends most of its free-living existence suspended in the water with body and tail extended.[77]

Cercaria physellæ (Talbot, 1936) probably lives as an adult in birds. Its intermediate hosts are *Physella parkeri* and *P. magnalacustris*.[76] The cercaria escapes from the snail in the early morning and tends to settle to the bottom, but is attracted towards the surface by light.

Schistosoma douthitti (Cort, 1914) is a parasite of the hepatic portal veins of the meadow mouse, *Microtus pennsylvanicus* in North America. The intermediate hosts are *Lymnæa stagnalis* vars. *appressa, jugularis, lillianæ, sanctæmariæ* and *perampla, L. palustris, L. reflexa* and *Physa ancillaria parkeri*. The cercariæ escape from the host at night and spend most of their free-living existence attached to the surface film of the water.[77]

Trichobilharzia ocellata (La Valette St. George, 1855) is a parasite of wild and domestic ducks in Europe. Its cercaria develops in *Lymnæa stagnalis* and *L. limosa*. It resembles in morphology and in behavior *Cercaria elvæ* but is a less vigorous swimmer and has a different resting position.[77] It produces a dermatitis in bathers in France.[78]

The cercaria of *Schistosoma spindale*, a cattle schistosome, causes "swamp itch" on the legs of workers in the paddy fields of the Federated Malay States.[79]

Pathology and Symptomatology.—The resistance of man, an abnormal host, to these cercariæ explains the severe reaction.[80] Its nature indicates that the cercariæ are walled off by the host and destroyed in the epithelial layers of the skin. Penetration of the skin occurs when the film of water evaporates. The cercariæ adhere with the ventral suckers and enter in about five minutes through the action of their anterior spines and lytic secretions, either between or through the pores. After 29 hours no cercariæ remain but the reaction persists around the burrows.[81] They evoke an acute inflammatory response with edema, early infiltration of neutrophils and lymphocytes, and later invasion of eosinophils. As the water evaporates a prickling sensation is followed by the rapid development of urticarial wheals, which subside in about half an hour leaving a few minute macules. After some hours severe itching, edema and the transformation of the macules into papules and occasional pustules occurs, reaching maximal intensity in two to three days (Fig. 210). The papular and sometimes hemorrhagic rash heals in a week or more, but may be complicated by scratching and secondary infection. Individuals vary in susceptibility and show slight or severe reactions.

Epidemiology.—The distribution and habits of the snail-host determine the endemic localities. *C. elvæ* and *C. physellæ*, found in swampy waters, produce "collectors' itch," while *C. stagnicolæ*, which frequents the shores of lakes, is more often the cause of "swimmers' itch." Persons in contact with aquatic vegetation are most likely to be infected with *C. elvæ* and *C. physellæ*. The affected beaches are usually near vegetation that furnishes a favorable habitat for snails. The cercariæ swarm in the shallow water or are swept toward the shore by wave action. They survive about 24 hours. Bathing is safe at night in waters infested with species

[78] Brumpt, E., 1931.
[79] Buckley, J. J. C., 1938.
[80] Vogel, H., 1930; Cort, W. W., 1936.
[81] Brackett, S., 1940.

of cercariæ that erupt from the snail in the early morning, but the reverse is true for the cercariæ of *S. douthitti* that leave the snail in the evening.

Prophylaxis.—The removal of snails from the vicinity of bathing beaches is the most practical method of combating "swimmers' itch." The snails may be destroyed by collection, removal of vegetation and, in small bodies of water, by the use of copper carbonate or sulphate. Copper carbonate is preferable to copper

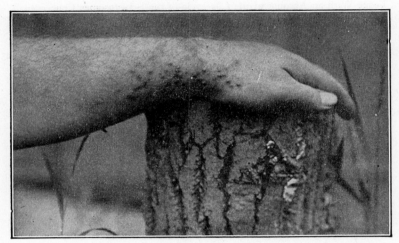

FIG. 210.—SCHISTOSOMAL DERMATITIS PRODUCED BY CERCARIÆ OF
SPECIES PARASITIC IN LOWER ANIMALS

(From Hegner, Root, Augustine and Huff, *Parasitology*, 1938, D. Appleton-Century Company).

sulphate since it is effective in smaller amounts, 2 p.p.m., and does not kill fish in alkaline waters.[82] In the larger lakes the spraying of formaldehyde on the surface of the water in the early morning in the vicinity of bathing beaches has been recommended for destroying the cercariæ. Vigorous rubbing of the body with a towel immediately after the bather leaves the water will prevent the cercariæ from penetrating the skin.

REFERENCES

BLACKLOCK, D. B. and THOMPSON, M. G. Human Schistosomiasis due to *S. hæmatobium* in Sierra Leone, Ann. Trop. Med., 1924, 18:211.

BARLOW, C. H. The Value of Canal Clearance in the Control of Schistosomiasis in Egypt, Am. J. Hyg., 1937, 25:327.

CORT, W. W. The Development of the Japanese Blood-fluke, *Schistosoma japonicum* Katsurada, in its Final Host, Am. J. Hyg., 1921, 1:1.

————, TALBOT, S. B., BRACKETT, S. *et al.* (individual papers). Studies on Schistosome Dermatitis, I-IV, Am. J. Hyg., 1936, 23:349, 372, 385; 24:318. V-VIII, Am. J. Hyg., 1940, Sec. D, 31:49, 65 and 32:33, 85.

FAIRLEY, N. H. and JASUDASAN, F. Studies in *Schistosoma spindale* Part VI. The Complement Fixation Reaction With Cercarial Antigen,—a Study in Experimental Serology, Indian M. Res. Mem., 1930, 17:73.

[82] Brackett, S., 1939.

FAUST, E. C., *et al.* Studies on Schistosomiasis mansoni in Puerto Rico. I-III. Puerto Rico J. Pub. Health & Trop. Med., 1933, 9:154, 228; 1934, 10:1, 133, and 1937, 13:1, 171.

———— and MELENEY, H. E. Studies on Schistosomiasis japonica, Am. J. Hyg. Monographic Series No. 3, 1924, 339 pp.

GIRGES, R. The Pathology, Treatment and Prognosis of Schistosomiasis mansoni, J. Trop. Med., 1930, 33:1, 45, 65.

———— Clinical Aspects, Pathology, Treatment and Prognosis of Schistosomiasis hæmatobium, J. Trop. Med., 1930, 33:145; 1931, 34:65, 342; 1932, 35:145.

GORDON, R. M., DAVEY, T. H. and PEASTON, T. The Transmission of Human Bilharziasis in Sierra Leone With an Account of the Life-cycle of the Schistosomes Concerned, *S. mansoni* and *S. hæmatobium,* Ann. Trop. Med., 1934, 28:323.

HOEPPLI, R. Histological Observations in Experimental Schistosomiasis japonica, Chinese M. J., 1932, 46:1179.

LEIPER, R. T. Researches on Egyptian Bilharziasis, J. Roy. Army Med. Corps, 1915, 25:1, 147, 253; 1916, 27:171; 1918, 30:235.

SCOTT, J. A. The Incidence and Distribution of the Human Schistosomes in Egypt, Am. J. Hyg., 1937, 25:566.

TANG, C. C. Some Remarks on the Morphology of the Miracidium and Cercaria of *Schistosoma japonicum,* Chinese M. J., 1938, Suppl. 2:423.

Section VI

ARTHROPODA

Chapter XXXVI

THE PARASITIC ARTHROPODS OF MAN

Medical Entomology.—The members of the widely distributed phylum AR-THROPODA are of medical interest, since they not only directly injure man and other animals but also serve as vectors of bacterial, viral and parasitic diseases. Their study is commonly known as Medical Entomology, although arthropods other than insects are involved. Not all arthropod vectors of disease can be classed as true parasites. The transient contact of a free-living, bloodsucking insect differs essentially from that of a parasitic helminth, which exists within the very body of its host. Certain arthropods, which are mechanical vectors of human disease (nonbiting flies) or intermediate hosts (crustaceans), though not actual parasites of man, are also included under Medical Entomology.

Medical entomology is complicated by the difficulty of distinguishing between those arthropods that are concerned with human diseases and the vast number of innocuous related species. The identification of harmful forms requires careful classification and painstaking study to establish their guilt. The following pages deal with systematic entomology only in so far as is necessary to identify suspected species and provide a logical presentation. Emphasis is placed rather upon the relation of arthropods to man and animals, and upon their distribution, seasonal prevalence, and capacity to transmit specific diseases.

PHYLUM *ARTHROPODA*

The phylum ARTHROPODA includes among its diversified forms more species than all other phyla of the animal kingdom. In general, its members are characterized by bilateral symmetry, metameric segmentation, the presence of jointed appendages, and a hardened exoskeleton. Only a small percentage of arthropods are parasites or vectors of disease. Those of medical importance range in size from minute insects to crabs.

Classification.—The ARTHROPODA are divided into five classes, of which the INSECTA and ARACHNIDA include most of the parasitic species or vectors of disease. The classification of the parasitic species is given later under their respective classes.

CRUSTACEA: Crabs, crayfishes, shrimps, copepods, etc.
ONYCHOPHORA: *Peripatus*
MYRIAPODA: Centipedes and millipedes
INSECTA: Six-legged insects
ARACHNIDA: Spiders, scorpions, ticks and mites

TABLE 39

ARTHROPOD VECTORS OF DISEASES OF MAN

Class	Order	Family	Genus	Species	Etiological Agent	Type of development in arthropod	Method of infection
CRUSTACEA	COPEPODA	DIAPTOMIDÆ	Diaptomus	D. gracilioides, D. gracilis, D. oregonensis, D. silicis, D. silicoides, D. vulgaris	Diphyllobothrium latum (C)	Cyclic	Oral (through fishes as secondary hosts)
				D. spinosus (?)	Drepanidotænia lanceolata (C)	Cyclic	Oral (through fishes as secondary hosts)
		CYCLOPIDÆ	Cyclops	C. bicuspidatus, C. coronatus, C. leuckarti, C. magnus, C. prasinus, C. quadricornis, C. serrulatus, C. strenuus, C. ternis, C. vernifer, C. vernalis, C. viridis	Dracunculus medinensis (N)	Cyclic	Oral (water)
				C. brevispinosus, C. prasinus, C. strenuus, C. vicinus	Diphyllobothrium latum (C)	Cyclic	Oral (through fishes as secondary hosts)
				C. bicuspidatus, C. serrulatus, C. strenuus	Drepanidotænia lanceolata (C)	Cyclic	Oral (through fishes as secondary hosts)
				Various species	Gnathostoma spinigerum (N)	Cyclic	Oral (through fishes and amphibians as secondary hosts)
				Various species	Diphyllobothrium erinacei (C)	Cyclic	Oral and cutaneous

Class	Order	Family	Genus	Species	Organism transmitted (and disease)	Type	Route
CRUSTACEA (Cont.)	DECAPODA	ASTACIDÆ	Astacus	A. japonicus, A. similis	Paragonimus westermani (T)	Cyclic	Oral
			Cambarus	Numerous species			
		POTAMONIDÆ	Parathelphusa	P. sinensis			
			Potamon	P. dehaani, P. denticulatus, P. rathbuni			
			Pseudothelphusa	P. iturbei			
		GRAPSIDÆ	Eriocheir	E. japonicus, E. sinensis			
			Sesarma	S. dehaani, S. sinensis			
INSECTA	ANOPLURA	PEDICULIDÆ	Pediculus	P. humanus	Borrelia recurrentis (S) (relapsing fever)	Cyclic (?)	Contamination of bite
					Rickettsia quintana (R) (trench fever)	Cyclic (?)	Contamination of bite
					Rickettsia prowazeki (R) (typhus fever)	Cyclic (?)	Contamination of bite
	SIPHONAPTERA	PULICIDÆ	Pulex	P. irritans	Pasteurella pestis (B) (bubonic plague)	Noncyclic	Contamination of bite
					Rickettsia prowazeki (?) (R) (typhus fever)	Cyclic (?)	Contamination of bite
					Dipylidium caninum (C)	Cyclic	Oral
					Hymenolepis diminuta (C)	Cyclic	Oral
			Xenopsylla	X. cheopis	Pasteurella pestis (B) (bubonic plague)	Noncyclic	Contamination of bite
					Rickettsia prowazeki (R) (typhus fever)	Cyclic (?)	Contamination of bite
					Hymenolepis diminuta (C)	Cyclic	Oral
		ARCHAROPSYLLIDÆ	Ctenocephalides	C. canis, C. felis	Dipylidium caninum (C)	Cyclic	Oral
					Hymenolepis diminuta (C)	Cyclic	Oral

TABLE 39—Continued

ARTHROPOD VECTORS OF DISEASES OF MAN

Class	Order	Family	Genus	Species	Etiological Agent	Type of development in arthropod	Method of infection
INSECTA (Cont.)	SIPHONAPTERA (Cont.)	DOLICHOPSYLLIDAE	Ceratophyllus	C. fasciatus	Pasteurella pestis (B) (bubonic plague)	Noncyclic	Contamination of bite
					Rickettsia prowazeki (R) (typhus fever)	Cyclic (?)	Contamination of bite
			Hoplopsyllus	H. anomalus	Hymenolepis diminuta (C)	Cyclic	Oral
		HYSTRICHOPSYLLIDAE	Ctenopsyllus	C. segnis	Hymenolepis diminuta (C)	Cyclic	Oral
	HEMIPTERA	CIMICIDAE	Cimex	C. hemipterus, C. lectularius	Capable of harboring organisms of bubonic plague, leprosy, tularemia, relapsing fever, American trypanosomiasis, leishmaniasis and Brazilian typhus, but natural human infection unproved	Noncyclic	
		REDUVIIDAE	Triatoma	T. infestans, geniculata, megista, sordida, etc.	Trypanosoma cruzi (P) (American trypanosomiasis)	Cyclic	Contamination of bite, occasionally by bite
			Rodnius	R. prolixus, R. pallescens, etc.	Trypanosoma cruzi (P) (American trypanosomiasis)	Cyclic	Contamination of bite, occasionally by bite
	ORTHOPTERA	BLATTIDAE	Blatta	B. orientalis	Hymenolepis diminuta (C)	Cyclic	Oral
			Blatella	B. germanica	Gongylonema pulchrum (N)	Cyclic	Oral
					Hymenolepis diminuta (C)	Cyclic	Oral
			Periplaneta	P. americana	Hymenolepis diminuta (C)	Cyclic	Oral
					Moniliformis moniliformis (N)	Cyclic	Oral

		Family	Genus	Species		Cyclic	Bite
INSECTA (Cont.)	DIPTERA	CULICIDÆ	Aëdes	18 species	Virus of yellow fever (V)	Cyclic	Bite
				A. ægypti	Virus of dengue (V)	Cyclic (?)	Bite
				8 species	Wuchereria bancrofti (N)	Cyclic	Invasion of bite
				5 species (experimental)	Virus of equine encephalitis (V)	Cyclic	Bite
			Anopheles	70 species	Plasmodium falciparum, P. malariæ, P. ovale, P. vivax (P) (malaria)	Cyclic	Bite
				3 species	Virus of yellow fever (V)	Cyclic	Bite
				A. albopictus	Virus of dengue (V)	Cyclic (?)	Bite
				22 species	Wuchereria bancrofti (N)	Cyclic	Invasion of bite
				2 species	Wuchereria malayi (N)	Cyclic	Invasion of bite
			Armigeres	A. perturbans	Virus of yellow fever (V)	Cyclic	Bite
				A. obturbans	Wuchereria bancrofti (N)	Cyclic	Invasion of bite
			Culex	2 species	Virus of yellow fever (V)	Cyclic	Bite
				5 species	Wuchereria bancrofti (N)	Cyclic	Invasion of bite
				5 species	Virus of yellow fever (V)	Cyclic	Bite
			Mansonia	6 species	Wuchereria bancrofti (N)	Cyclic	Invasion of bite
				6 species	Wuchereria malayi (N)	Cyclic	Invasion of bite
		CHIRONOMIDÆ	Culicoides	C. austeni, C. grahami	Acanthocheilonema perstans (N)	Cyclic	Invasion of bite
				C. furens, C. paraensis	Mansonella ozzardi (N)	Cyclic	Invasion of bite
		PSYCHODIDÆ	Phlebotomus	P. minutus, P. papatasii, P. perniciosus	Virus of pappataci fever (V)	Cyclic (?)	Bite

TABLE 39—Continued
ARTHROPOD VECTORS OF DISEASES OF MAN

Class	Order	Family	Genus	Species	Etiological Agent	Type of development in arthropod	Method of infection
INSECTA (Cont.)	DIPTERA (Cont.)	PSYCHODIDÆ (cont.)	Phlebotomus (cont.)	P. papatasii, P. sergenti	Leishmania tropica (P) (oriental sore)	Cyclic	?
				P. argentipes, P. chinensis, P. intermedius, P. longipennis, P. major, P. pernicosus	Leishmania donovani (P) (visceral leishmaniasis)	Cyclic	?
				P. intermedius, P. migonei, P. squamiventris (suspected vectors)	Leishmania braziliensis (P) (American leishmaniasis)	Cyclic	?
				P. noguchii, P. verrucarum	Bartonella bacilliformis (B) (Oroya fever)	Noncyclic	Bite
		SIMULIIDÆ	Simulium	S. callidum, S. damnosum, S. metallicum, S. neavei, S. ochraceum	Onchocerca volvulus (N)	Cyclic	Invasion of bite
				S. decorum kalmai	Pasteurella tularensis (B) (tularemia)	Noncyclic	Bite
		TABANIDÆ	Chrysops	C. discalis,	Pasteurella tularensis (B) (tularemia)	Noncyclic	Bite
				C. centurionis, C. dimidiata, C. distinctipennis, C. longicornis, C. silacea	Loa loa (N)	Cyclic	Invasion of bite

Class	Order	Family	Genus	Species	Pathogen (disease)	Cyclic/Noncyclic	Mode
INSECTA (Cont.)	DIPTERA (Cont.)	MUSCIDÆ	Stomoxys	S. calcitrans (experimental)	Pasteurella tularensis (B) (tularemia)	Noncyclic	Bite
					Trypanosoma gambiense and T. rhodesiense (P)	Noncyclic	Bite
					Leishmania tropica (P)	Noncyclic	Bite
					Virus of poliomyelitis (V)	Noncyclic	Bite
			Glossina	G. palpalis, G. tachinoides and less frequently G. fusca, G. morsitans, G. submorsitans, G. pallidipes	Trypanosoma gambiense (P) (Gambian sleeping sickness)	Cyclic	Bite
				G. morsitans, G. swynnertoni and less frequently G. brevipalpis, G. palpalis	Trypanosoma rhodesiense (P) (Rhodesian sleeping sickness)	Cyclic	Bite
			Musca	M. domestica and to a lesser extent other species of DIPTERA	Agents of various bacterial, protozoan and helminthic diseases, chiefly enteric	Noncyclic	Mechanical, chiefly contamination of food
		OSCINIDÆ	Hippelates	H. pallipes (experimental)	Treponema pertenue (S) (Yaws)	Noncyclic	Bite or contact
				H. pusio	Agent of infectious conjunctivitis	Noncyclic	Bite or contact
			Siphunculina	S. funicola	Agent of infectious ophthalmia	Noncyclic	Bite or contact
ARACHNIDA	ACARINA	ARGASIDÆ	Ornithodorus	O. turicata, O. parkeri	Pasteurella tularensis (B) (tularemia)	Noncyclic	Bite or contamination of bite
				O. moubata, O. rostrata (experimental)	Virus of yellow fever (V)	Cyclic (?)	Bite or contamination of bite

TABLE 39—Continued

ARTHROPOD VECTORS OF DISEASES OF MAN

Class	Order	Family	Genus	Species	Etiological Agent	Type of development in arthropod	Method of infection
ARACHNIDA (Cont.)	ACARINA (Cont.)	ARGASIDÆ (cont.)	Ornithodorus (cont.)	O. moubata and II other species	Borrelia duttoni and other varieties of B. recurrents (S) (relapsing fever)	Noncyclic	Bite or contamination of bite
				O. moubata (experimental)	Trypanosoma cruzi (P)	Cyclic	Bite or contamination of bite
			Amblyomma	A. americanum (experimental)	Rickettsia rickettsi (R) (Rocky Mountain spotted fever)	Cyclic (?)	Bite or contamination of bite
				A. cajennense	Rickettsia braziliensis (R) (São Paulo fever)	Cyclic (?)	Bite or contamination of bite
				A. cajennense (experimental)	Virus of yellow fever (V)	Cyclic (?)	Bite or contamination of bite
				A. cajennense (experimental)	Trypanosoma cruzi (P) (American trypanosomiasis)	Cyclic	Bite or contamination of bite
		IXODIDÆ	Dermacentor	D. andersoni, D. variabilis	Pasteurella tularensis (B) (tularemia)	Noncyclic	Bite or contamination of bite
				D. andersoni, D. marginatum (experimental), D. occidentalis, D. variabilis	Rickettsia rickettsi (R) (Rocky Mountain spotted fever)	Cyclic (?)	Bite or contamination of bite
				D. nuttalli	Rickettsia sp. (R) (Russian tropical typhus)	Cyclic (?)	Bite or contamination of bite
				D. andersoni	Rickettsia diaporica (R) (Montana Q. fever)	Cyclic (?)	Bite or contamination of bite
				D. andersoni (suspected)	Virus (?) of Colorado tick fever (V)		

Order	Suborder	Family	Genus	Species	Organism (disease)	Cyclic/Noncyclic	Transmission
ARACHNIDA (Cont.)	ACARINA (Cont.)	IXODIDÆ (cont.)	Dermacentor (cont.)	D. andersoni (experimental)	Virus of equine encephalitis (western type) (V)		Bite or contamination of bite
				D. silvarium	Virus of Russian spring and summer encephalitis (V)		Bite or contamination of bite
				D. andersoni (experimental)	Virus of lymphocytic choriomeningitis (V)		Bite or contamination of bite
			Hæmaphysalis	H. concinna	Virus of Russian spring and summer encephalitis (V)		Bite or contamination of bite
			Hyalomma	H. ægyptium (experimental)	Rickettsia sp. (R) (African tick fever)	Cyclic (?)	Bite or contamination of bite
				H. ægyptium (experimental)	Pasteurella tularensis (B) (tularemia)	Noncyclic	Bite or contamination of bite
			Ixodes	I. persulcatus	Virus of Russian spring and summer encephalitis (V)		Bite or contamination of bite
				I. ricinus	Pasteurella tularensis (B) (tularemia)	Noncyclic	Bite or contamination of bite
			Rhipicephalus	R. appendiculatus, and R. sanguineus (experimental)	Rickettsia sp. (R) (African tick typhus)	Cyclic (?)	Bite or contamination of bite
				R. sanguineus	Rickettsia braziliensis (R) (São Paulo fever)	Cyclic (?)	Bite or contamination of bite
				R. sanguineus	Borrelia duttoni, etc. (S) (relapsing fever)	Noncyclic	Bite or contamination of bite
				R. sanguineus (experimental)	Trypanosoma cruzi (P) (American trypanosomiasis)	Cyclic	Bite or contamination of bite
				R. sanguineus	Dermacentroxenus rickettsi (R) (Boutonneuse fever)	Cyclic (?)	Bite or contamination of bite
		DERMANISSIDÆ	Liponyssus	L. bacoti (experimental)	Rickettsia prowazeki (R) (typhus fever)	Cyclic	Bite or contamination of bite
		TROMBIDIIDÆ	Trombicula	T. akamushi	Rickettsia niponica (R) (tsutsugamushi fever)	Cyclic (?)	Bite or contamination of bite

B, bacteria; C, cestode; N, nematode; P, protozoa; R, rickettsia; S, spirochete; T, trematode; V, virus.

Morphology.—The body, usually encased in a chitinous exoskeleton, at times impregnated with lime, has three main divisions, head, thorax and abdomen. The paired appendages, covered by a thin cuticle, are divided into segments which are moved by special muscles. Growth, which takes place by molting, involves the complete shedding of the exoskeleton and the formation of a new cuticle.

The musculature consists of groups of striated muscles that are attached to the exoskeleton and pass from one segment to another. The tubular digestive tract is subdivided into a buccal cavity, muscular pharynx, esophagus, proventriculus, midgut and hindgut. The blood, usually colorless, is driven through the circulatory system by a tubular heart situated dorsad to the digestive tract. The body cavity does not correspond to a true cœlom, but to a hemocele developed from the circulatory system. Respiration is accomplished in the aquatic forms by gills and in the terrestrial by trachea, tubular extensions of the outer covering. The excretory system consists of long malpighian tubules that empty into the hindgut. The nervous system consists of a double chain of ventral ganglia, originally one pair in each segment. In the head are paired dorsal ganglia, representing the brain. The eyes are compound or simple. Sexes are usually separate and reproduction is generally sexual, though parthenogenesis may occur. Postembryonic development usually involves some form of metamorphosis.

Pathogenesis.—The injuries produced by parasitic arthropods are caused directly by the parasite or indirectly by the transmission of disease organisms. Direct lesions result from the biting, sucking, stinging or burrowing of the adult and larval parasites. A few adults (*Tunga penetrans*) burrow in the tissues and a few larvæ (*Auchmeromyia luteola*) are bloodsuckers. Bloodsucking species are distributed irregularly throughout the ARTHROPODA; some orders, such as the SIPHONAPTERA, are exclusively of this type. Their mouth parts, adapted to piercing the skin, are merely modifications of the oral appendages of the non-bloodsucking forms. Biting insects are so numerous that they render large areas uninhabitable and may even cause the death of domestic animals and man. Larvæ may invade wounds and external cavities of the body or may burrow in the tissues, producing myiases.

Biting and bloodsucking arthropods, in addition to mechanical injury, may inject poisonous or irritating substances. Bees, scorpions, centipedes and spiders may introduce venom by stings or bites. The body fluids of certain beetles and the hairs of some caterpillars may cause a dermatitis. Individuals differ in sensitiveness and degree of immunity to the bites and stings of arthropods. Numerous complications may ensue from scratching and secondary infection.

Arthropod parasites, however, are chiefly important in medicine because of the diseases which they transmit as mechanical vectors through biting or contamination or because they serve as intermediate hosts in the biological or cyclical transfer of animal parasites, filtrable viruses and spirochætes (Table 39). The causative agent of an infectious disease, particularly bacterial, may be carried on the proboscis, feet or body hairs, if the arthropod has been contaminated by contact with or by feeding on the exposed lesions or infectious discharges of the patient. Transfer to a new host may result from piercing the skin by the proboscis or from contamination of the skin or food by the body or discharges of the arthropod. The biological or cyclical method of transmission requires a developmental period in which the disease-producing agent undergoes changes culminating in an infectious form. The causative agents of certain protozoan diseases (malaria), helminthic infections (filariasis), and probably viral diseases (yellow fever) require such development.

Chapter XXXVII

THE CLASSES ONYCHOPHORA, MYRIAPODA AND CRUSTACEA

The classes of ARTHROPODA other than the INSECTA and ARACHNIDA are seldom associated with the diseases of man. The poisonous centipedes of the MYRIAPODA produce trivial and occasionally serious injuries by their bites, while among the CRUSTACEA the copepods, *Cyclops* and *Diaptomus,* and fresh-water crabs and crayfishes of the order DECAPODA are the intermediate hosts of certain helminthic parasites.

CLASS *ONYCHOPHORA*

The ONYCHOPHORA are tracheate arthropods with a thin, soft cuticle and a muscular body wall. All species belong to the genus *Peripatus* and probably closely resemble the primitive ancestral arthropod. They are not parasites of man or intermediate hosts for disease-producing agents.

CLASS *MYRIAPODA*

The MYRIAPODA are elongated, terrestrial, tracheate arthropods with numerous segments bearing legs and tracheal stigmata. The well-defined head has a pair of antennæ, a palpless mandible, at least one pair of maxillæ, and ocelli. The two principal orders are the CHILOPODA (centipedes) and the DIPLOPODA (millipedes). Millipedes of the genus *Julus* and *Fontaria* have been incriminated as hosts of the cestode, *Hymenolepis diminuta.* The poisonous centipedes may be distinguished from the nonpoisonous millipedes by the following characteristics:

	Centipedes	Millipedes
Body	Flattened dorsoventrally	Cylindrical
Jaws	One pair of mandibles; two pairs of maxillæ	One pair of mandibles; one pair of maxillæ
Claws of first body segment	Poisonous	Nonpoisonous
Legs	Single pair on each segment of body except last two	Single pair on first four segments behind head (thorax), two pairs on double segments of rest of body (abdomen)
Trachea	Anastomosing	Nonanastomosing
Gonads	Dorsal to gut	Ventral to gut
Genital opening	Posterior end	Third segment behind head
Diet	Carnivorous	Herbivorous

Centipedes (Fig. 211A) are active animals that usually live in damp localities under bark, rubbish or stones, and feed on insects and small animals. They have long, narrow, flattened bodies, enabling them to squeeze into cracks and crevices. The six-segmented head bears jointed antennæ, toothed mandibles, first maxillæ with inner and outer lobes, and fused, jointed, palp-like second maxillæ. The genital opening on a posterior segment is guarded by a pair of modified appendages, the **gonopods**. The appendages of the first body segment bear poison claws (Fig. 211B) with openings at the tips for the expulsion of a paralyzing venom.

The small centipedes of temperate climates are often incapable of penetrating the skin, and their bites seldom produce more than mild, local symptoms in man. In the Southern United States two species, *Scolopendra heros* and *S. morsitans,* 10 to 15 cm.

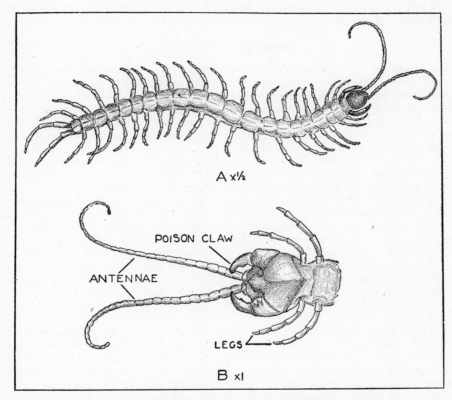

FIG. 211.—SCHEMATIC REPRESENTATION OF CENTIPEDE (*Scolopendra*)

A, Dorsal view of centipede; *B,* ventral view of head.

in length, inflict painful bites. The larger tropical species, such as *S. gigantea,* 25 to 30 cm. in length, in addition to causing necrotic local lesions, may produce general symptoms of lymphangitis, fever, vomiting and headache. Questionable instances of death in children bitten by centipedes have been reported.

The local irritation may be relieved by strong ammonia or wet baking soda, followed by iodine or some other disinfectant to prevent secondary infection. There is no satisfactory method for controlling centipedes, but their presence in houses may be minimized by reducing available hiding places through the removal of débris, by filling cracks and by screening.[1]

---

[1] Back, E. A., 1939.

CLASS *CRUSTACEA*

The CRUSTACEA are mostly aquatic arthropods in which the original appendages of the multisegmented ancestral form have been modified for locomotion, feeding, respiration, and reception of sensory stimuli. The body has been shortened with corresponding loss of appendages and somites; and in many species a special structure, the carapace, covering the anterior part of the body, has been developed. The CRUSTACEA are divided into two subclasses of distinctive characteristics: (1) the ENTOMOSTRACA, with the orders BRANCHIOPODA, OSTRACODA, CIRRIPEDIA and COPEPODA; and (2) the MALACOSTRACA, with several orders including the important DECAPODA. Species of copepods and decapods are intermediate hosts of parasites of man.

ORDER *COPEPODA*

The copepods, the largest division of the CRUSTACEA, include both free-living and parasitic forms. They are small, graceful, symmetrical, usually distinctly segmented animals from 0.5 to 10 mm. in size, and may be transparent or brilliantly colored. The body comprises a cephalothorax, in which the head and the first two thoracic segments are fused, and a slender abdomen of three to five segments. The last abdominal segment bears a pair of caudal rami, and the last thoracic segment the genital apertures and external egg cases. The head bears six pairs of appendages: two antennæ, one mandible, two maxillæ and one maxillipede. Two pairs of well-developed antennæ aid in locomotion or prehension. Fertilization is by spermatophores. The body anterior to the movable articulation is called the **metasome,** and the posterior part, the **urosome.**

The classification of genera and species is based upon (1) the shape, number of segments, and ornamentation of the first antennæ; and (2) the fifth feet, the caudal rami, and the egg case. The COPEPODA are divided into eight suborders: [2] (1) ARGULOIDA, (2) CALANOIDA, (3) HARPACTICOIDA, (4) CYCLOPOIDA, (5) NOTODELPHYOIDA, (6) MONSTRILLOIDA, (7) CALIGOIDA, and (8) LERNÆOPODOIDA. The species that are intermediate hosts for parasites of man belong to the genus *Diaptomus* of the family DIAPTOMIDÆ of the suborder CALANOIDA, and to the genus *Cyclops* of the family CYCLOPIDÆ of the suborder CYCLOPOIDA.

GENUS *CYCLOPS*

Morphology.—The body (Fig. 212C) is slender with a movable articulation between the fourth and fifth thoracic segments. The metasome, wider than the urosome, is narrowed posteriorly. The margins of the body have a jagged appearance. The first antennæ have seventeen segments and the second antennæ have four segments without an exopod. The eggs are carried in two subcylindrical ovisacs attached to the lateral but never to the ventral surface of the genital segment. The rudimentary fifth legs, alike in both sexes, have two segments, the terminal having a long, apical seta and a short, inner spine.

Habitat.—Species of *Cyclops* are widely distributed throughout fresh and salt waters but are most abundant in still water. Certain species are predominately littoral, others limnetic, and some both. The littoral types are relatively short and stout, have short, caudal rami, and are often deeply colored red, blue and purple, while the limnetic species are long and slender, have long caudal rami, and are usually colorless. Species vary in their seasonal prevalence but are usually most abundant in the summer. Many species are cosmopolitan, but others are restricted to certain regions. Temperature largely governs their distribution, some species preferring cold water and others warm. The more primitive forms are found in northern waters; the more specialized in southern.

Life Cycle.—A flat, oval nauplius larva hatches from the egg. Its body is not divided into a cephalothorax and abdomen and only the first and second antennæ and mandibles are present. The larva molts several times, acquiring maxillæ, maxillipedes, and the first

---

[2] Wilson, C. B., 1932.

two swimming feet (metanauplius stage) before it reaches the first cyclops stage, in which the thorax and abdomen are divided and the third and fourth swimming feet appear, but the appendages behind the third pair of swimming limbs and some urosome somites of the adult are still lacking. It passes through five cyclops stages before it becomes an adult.

Pathogenesis.—Species of *Cyclops* have been found to be intermediate hosts of the guinea worm, *Dracunculus medinensis,* the fish tapeworm, *Diphyllobothrium latum,* the

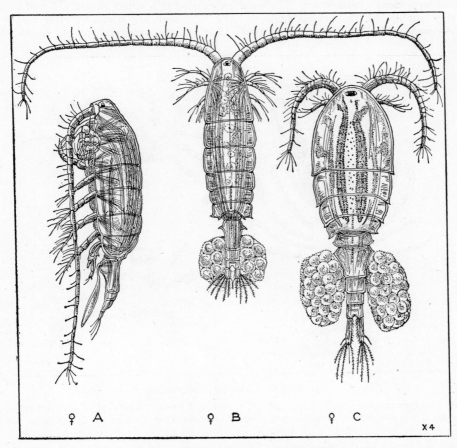

FIG. 212.—COPEPOD HOSTS OF HELMINTHIC PARASITES

A, Diaptomus gracilis, female, lateral view; *B, Diaptomus gracilis,* female, dorsal view; *C, Cyclops strenuus,* female, dorsal view (*A* and *B* redrawn from Sars, 1911; *C* redrawn from Sars, 1918).

cestode, *Drepanidotænia lanceolata,* and the nematode, *Gnathostoma spinigerum* (Table 39). Among the species associated with *Dracunculus medinensis* are *Cyclops bicuspidatus, C. cornatus, C. leuckarti, C. magnus, C. prasinus, C. quadricornis, C. serrulatus, C. strenuus, C. ternis, C. vermifer, C. vernalis* and *C. viridis.* Among these associated with *Diphyllobothrium latum* are *C. brevispinosus, C. prasinus, C. strenuus* and *C. vicinus;* with *Drepanidotænia lanceolata, C. bicuspidatus, C. serrulatus* and *C. strenuus;* and with *Gnathostoma spinigerum,* various species.

GENUS *DIAPTOMUS*

Morphology.—The body (Fig. 212A and B) is slender with a well-defined, dorsal, midcervical depression and a movable articulation between the fifth and sixth thoracic segments. The metasome is wider than the three-segmented urosome, which narrows abruptly. The posterior corners are biangular with a minute spine at each angle. The elongate first antennæ have many more joints than those of *Cyclops*. The second antennæ are biramose, usually with a two-segmented endopod and a longer, two-lobed exopod armed with many plumose setæ. The eggs are carried in a single ovisac attached to the ventral surface of the genital segment. The fifth legs are normally made up of a two-segmented basipod and one- or two-segmented rami, carrying in the female two

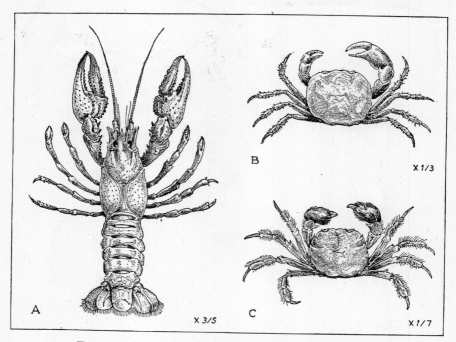

Fig. 213.—Crustacean Hosts of *Paragonimus westermani*

A, Cambarus virilis (North America) ; *B, Potamon dehaani* (Japan) ; *C, Eriocheir japonicus* (Japan) (*A* redrawn from Hagen, 1870; *B* and *C* adapted from photographs by Yoshida, 1916).

spines and in the male a long, curved, denticulate claw on the exopod of the right leg. Its habitat and life cycle in general are similar to those of *Cyclops*.

Pathogenesis.—Among the species of *Diaptomus* incriminated as first intermediate hosts of *Diphyllobothrium latum,* the fish tapeworm, are *Diaptomus oregonensis, D. silicis* and *D. silicoides* in North America and *D. vulgaris, D. gracilis* and *D. gracilioides* in Europe. *D. spinosus* may serve as an intermediate host of *Drepanidotænia lanceolata* (Table 39).

ORDER *DECAPODA*

The DECAPODA include the large crustaceans, such as prawns, shrimps, lobsters, crabs and crayfishes. They have a five-segmented head with compound eyes, typically stalked, usually a carapace covering, a thorax of eight somites, and an abdomen of six or rarely

seven segments with appendages on every segment except the last. The first three pairs
of thoracic appendages are modified into biramous maxillipedes and the last five into
conspicuous uniramous legs. The mandibular palp, if present, is uniramous. There is
great diversity of form among the numerous species.

Pathogenesis.—Fresh-water crabs and crayfishes serve as secondary intermediate
hosts of the lung fluke, *Paragonimus westermani* (Table 39). Among the crayfishes are
Astacus japonicus and *A. similis* in Japan and Korea and numerous species of the genus
Cambarus (Fig. 213A) in North America. Among the oriental fresh-water crabs, occasionally found in brackish water, are *Potamon dehaani* (Fig. 213B), *P. denticulatus* and
P. rathbuni; Parathelphusa sinensis; Pseudothelphusa iturbei; Eriocheir japonicus
(Fig. 213C) and *E. sinensis;* and *Sesarma dehaani* and *S. sinensis*. The lung fluke is
transmitted to man and other mammals through the consumption of raw or imperfectly
cooked crabs and crayfishes.

REFERENCES

BACK, E. A. Centipedes and Millipedes in the House, U. S. Dept. Agriculture, Leaflet No. 192,
    1939.
SARS, G. O. An Account of the Crustacea of Norway. Copepoda, Vol. 4, 1911; Vol. 6, 1918,
    Bergen Museum, Bergen, Norway, Alb. Cammermeyers Forlag, Christiania.
WILSON, C. B. The Copepods of the Woods Hole Region, Massachusetts, U. S. Nat. Mus.
    Bull. 158, 1932, Smithsonian Institution, Washington, D. C.

Chapter XXXVIII

CLASS INSECTA (HEXAPODA)

Insects are tracheate arthropods with three distinct divisions of the body: head, thorax and abdomen. They abound under diverse conditions and possess a variety of forms. The numerous species, far outnumbering those of all other animals, play an important rôle in the economic life of man. Many species are beneficial, fertilizing plants and serving as a direct or indirect source of food for animals; others are of no economic importance; and still others cause extensive damage to crops and domestic animals. Relatively few species are parasites of man or act as vectors of human disease, but these few are intimately concerned with the welfare of man.

CLASSIFICATION

Of the many orders of insects, eight contain species that are parasitic, produce injury, or act as vectors of disease in man. Numerous species of these and other orders are parasites of lower animals or are vectors of animal diseases. Classification is based upon (1) the type of development; (2) the modification of the mouth parts; (3) the antennæ; (4) the number and venation of the wings; (5) the male external genitalia; and (6) the location of various hairs and bristles. The insects of special interest as parasites of man belong to four orders: DIPTERA (flies); HEMIPTERA (bugs); SIPHONAPTERA (fleas); ANOPLURA (lice). Four other orders contain species that affect man to a minor degree either by direct injury or as vectors of disease: COLEOPTERA (beetles); HYMENOPTERA (bees, wasps, hornets, ants, etc.); LEPIDOPTERA (butterflies and moths); ORTHOPTERA (grasshoppers, locusts, crickets and cockroaches).

MORPHOLOGY

The primitive insect (Fig. 214) had three well-defined regions: (1) the six-segmented head; (2) the three-segmented thorax bearing three pairs of legs and two pairs of wings; and (3) the eleven-segmented abdomen. The segmentation of the ancestral form is evident only in the abdomen of present-day insects.

Integument.—The body is encased in a more or less rigid, noncellular, chitinized integument that forms a protective exoskeleton strengthened by pit-like internal extensions. The integument consists of hard, highly chitinized plates or **sclerites** connected by flexible, mobile, slightly-chitinized membranes. These plates are so greatly modified in the various species that it is difficult to determine their relationship to those of the primitive insect. Less than one-half the weight of the integument consists of chitin, a stable, amber-colored substance secreted by an underlying

606

layer of chitinogenous cells. Like other arthropods, insects shed their integument from time to time, the cuticle usually splitting along the back.

Appendages.—The appendages of the primitive arthropod are greatly reduced in insects. Those of the head have been converted into sensory and masticatory organs; those of the abdomen are entirely suppressed or extremely modified; and those of the thorax are retained for locomotion. The hairs, bristles and scales, useful in the classification of the DIPTERA, are outgrowths from the exoskeleton. The sensory hairs of the proboscis, palps and antennæ contain delicate nerve filaments, but the function of the other hairs is unknown.

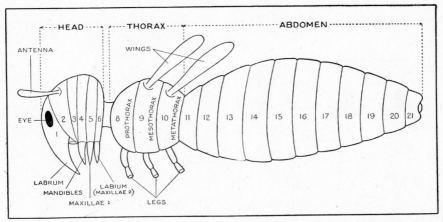

FIG. 214.—DIAGRAM OF PRIMITIVE INSECT, SHOWING SEGMENTATION OF HEAD, THORAX AND ABDOMEN

The numbering includes 20 segments and the neck piece. (Adapted from Patton and Cragg, 1913, after Berlese).

HEAD

The head is enclosed in a box-like exoskeleton consisting of several paired and unpaired sclerites without definite relation to the primitive segmentation, which is indicated only by the appendages and nerve ganglia. The appendages of the original segments form the antennæ, the compound eyes and the mouth parts. The various external regions of the head have received special names for descriptive purposes. In the relatively-primitive cockroach the head, viewed from in front, is pear-shaped and, from the side, flat with a rounded top. Two dorsal **epicranial plates** meet in the midline and extend over the top and back; a large **clypeus** or facial plate occupies the greater part of the frontal region; two antennæ arise between the eyes; a **labrum** or upper lip of the mouth parts forms a movable flap at the lower edge of the clypeus; two mandibles are lateral and posterior to the labrum; and large, compound eyes and **genæ** or cheeks cover the sides (Fig. 215A and B).

In the more specialized orthorrhaphous flies the angle at the junction of the anterior and superior surfaces is known as the **occiput**; the region in front of this angle, the **vertex**; the upper portion of the frontal area between the eyes, the **frons**, the anterior end of which bears the antennæ; the oblong lower portion of the frontal area, the clypeus; and the lateral regions the genæ (Fig. 220A). In the highly-specialized muscoid flies these areas are further modified and subdivided (Fig. 220B).

Antennæ.—The multijointed antennæ are sensory organs. Their structure is useful for the classification of the different genera of DIPTERA (Fig. 221).

Eyes.—The external surface of the compound eyes is composed of a large number of hexagonal facets, varying from fifty to several thousand in different insects. In addition to the compound eyes one to three ocelli, or simple eyes, may be situated on the vertex.

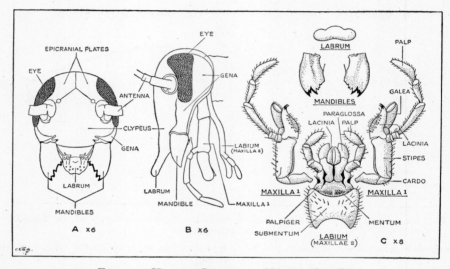

FIG. 215.—HEAD OF COCKROACH (*Blatta orientalis*)

A, front view of head; *B,* lateral view of head; *C,* mouth parts (Adapted from Miall and Denny, 1886).

Mouth Parts.—The structure of the mouth parts varies greatly, depending upon the feeding habits. In the highly-specialized DIPTERA the mouth parts have been greatly modified for sucking and piercing. The simplest form is the chewing or biting mouth, as represented by the cockroach. The mouth parts of this insect (Fig. 215C) consist of an upper lip or labrum, a pair of horny, toothed mandibles or jaws, a pair of maxillæ, and a **labium** formed by the fusion of a pair of maxilla-like appendages. The labrum, a small transverse flap in front of the mandibles, is attached to the clypeus by a movable joint. The single-jointed mandibles and the two pairs of maxillæ serve as cutting or clasping organs. Each maxilla consists of a basal segment, the **cardo**; a square-like central portion, the **stipes**; and three distal parts, the single, toothed **lacinia**, the two-segmented flexible **galea**, and the five-segmented maxillary palp. The labium forms the posterior boundary of the mouth and consists of the basal **submentum** and **mentum**, the paired **paraglossæ** (galeæ) the laciniæ, and the three-segmented labial palps. There is no **epipharynx** in the cockroach and the **hypopharynx** is represented by a small chitinous fold in the floor of the mouth, into which the salivary duct opens.

THORAX

The thorax is composed of three segments, each of which bears a pair of legs. The first is known as the prothorax, the second as the mesothorax, and the third as the metathorax (Fig. 214). Each segment is protected by a dorsal plate or **notum,** a ventral plate or **sternum,** and a lateral plate or **pleuron.** The nota are designated by segments, respectively as the pronotum, mesonotum and metanotum, and the sterna as prosternum, mesosternum and metasternum. The relative size of the three segments depends upon the development of the wings; in wingless forms

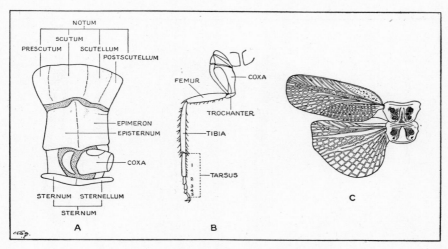

FIG. 216.—THORAX AND THORACIC APPENDAGES OF AN INSECT

A, schematic representation of lateral view of a typical mesothoracic segment; *B,* hind leg of cockroach (*Blatta orientalis*); *C,* wings and wing covers of male cockroach (*Blatta orientalis*) (*B* and *C* redrawn from Miall and Denny, 1886).

all three are of uniform size, while in winged insects those bearing the wings are proportionately larger.

In some of the thoracic segments the notum may be divided by sutures into **prescutum, scutum, scutellum** and **postscutellum;** the sternum into **sternum** and **sternellum;** and the pleuron into an anterior **episternum** and a posterior **epimeron** (Fig. 216A).

Legs.—The three pairs of legs vary in size and shape in different insects. Each leg (Fig. 216B) is divided into a broad, basal **coxa;** a small **trochanter;** a straight **femur** narrowed at both ends; a **tibia** armed with stiff spines; and a **tarsus,** usually five-jointed and bearing at its extremity a pair of claws. At the base of the leg are several chitinous plates, forming a hinge-like, rotatory joint between the leg and thorax.

Wings.—The anterior pair of wings or wing covers of the cockroach are borne by the second thoracic segment or mesothorax and the membranous posterior or true wings are attached to the third thoracic segment or metathorax (Fig. 216C). The denser, anterior wings protect the true wings when the cockroach is at rest. Various modifications are present in different types of insects. In the DIPTERA the posterior wings have degenerated to rudimentary **halteres.** The venation of the wings is an important characteristic for differentiating genera in the DIPTERA.

ABDOMEN

The abdomen is composed of eleven nonspecialized segments, the first often fused with the thorax and not readily visible. The number of abdominal segments varies in different insects, being reduced in the more specialized forms. The last segments

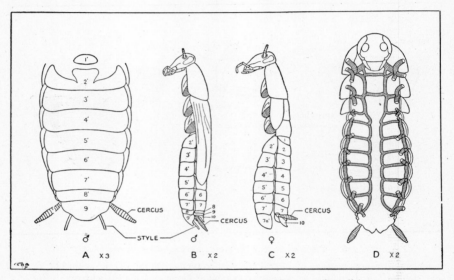

FIG. 217.—ABDOMEN OF COCKROACH (*Blatta orientalis*)

A, ventral view of male; *B*, lateral view of male; *C*, lateral view of female; *D*, tracheal system, showing dorsal tracheal communications after removal of ventral integument and viscera (Redrawn from Miall and Denny, 1886).

may be modified for sexual purposes into the **hypopygium** of the male and the **ovipositor** of the female. Each segment has a small, dorsal **tergum** and a ventral **sternum,** connected by a pleural membrane and often referred to as tergites and sternites. Aside from the terminal segments adapted for copulation and oviposition, the abdomen is usually devoid of appendages, although they may be present in the larvæ of some species.

In the male cockroach ten abdominal terga and nine sterna are visible (Fig. 217A and B). In the female eight terga and seven sterna may be seen, while two more may be demonstrated by extending the abdomen (Fig. 217C). The rudimentary first sternum is a small oval plate. The external visible appendages are the paired, sixteen-jointed **cerci** which project beneath the edge of the tenth tergite and, in the male, the paired subanal **styles.**

INTERNAL STRUCTURES

Respiratory System.—The respiratory organs of insects consist of a system of tracheal tubes communicating with the exterior by **spiracles.** The cockroach has ten pairs of spiracles, two in the thorax and eight in the abdomen (Fig. 217D). The two pairs of thoracic spiracles lie one in front of the mesothorax and the other in front of the metathorax. The abdominal spiracles are in the first eight abdominal segments between the terga and the sterna. Their number is variously reduced in different insects. A pair of large chitinous tracheal trunks extends the length of the

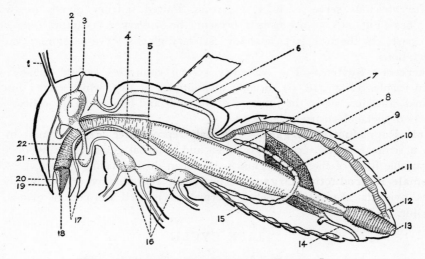

FIG. 218.—INTERNAL STRUCTURE OF A TYPICAL INSECT

1, antennæ; 2, supra-esophageal ganglion; 3, ocellus; 4, esophagus; 5, salivary gland; 6, aorta; 7, midgut; 8, gonad; 9, malpighian tubule; 10, dorsal pulsating vessel; 11, intestine; 12, rectum; 13, anus; 14, gonaduct; 15, abdominal nerve ganglion; 16, thoracic nerve ganglia; 17, maxillæ; 18, mandible; 19, labrum; 20, mouth; 21, subesophageal ganglion; 22, pharynx (From Hegner, Root, Augustine and Huff, *Parasitology,* 1938, as redrawn from Berlese "Gli Insetti," D. Appleton-Century Company).

body and communicates with the spiracles directly or by short side branches. These trunks send off branches that subdivide until tracheal capillaries reach all the tissues of the body. In certain insects the tracheæ dilate into air sacs. The exact mechanism of respiration is not clearly understood, but expiration is believed to be effected by muscular contraction and inspiration by the elastic recoil of the tracheal wall.

Circulatory System.—The poorly developed circulatory system consists of a closed and an open portion. The closed part includes a dorsal organ (Fig. 218, 6 and 10), comprising an aorta and a pulsating vessel, which receives blood posteriorly and ejects it anteriorly. The open portion is the body cavity (hemocele), in which the blood comes in direct contact with the tissues.

Nervous System.—The nervous system (Fig. 218, 2, 15, 16 and 21) is represented by a chain of ventral ganglia connected by commissures, and sub- and supra-esophageal ganglia. The primitive insect had a pair of ganglia in each segment. The esophageal ganglia represent the fusion of the ganglia of the several head segments of the primitive insect, while the number of the abdominal ganglia has been reduced by fusion. Nerves pass from the ganglia to the tissues and sensory appendages.

Digestive System.—The highly-developed digestive system consists of pharynx, slender esophagus, proventriculus (a valvular expansion of the esophagus anterior to the stomach in some insects), distensible stomach or midgut, intestine or hindgut, rectum and anus (Fig. 218, 22, 4, 7, 11, 12, 13). In bloodsucking insects the muscular pharynx acts as a sucking pump. The stomach and at times the proventriculus serve as food reservoirs. Paired salivary glands of two or three lobes (Fig. 218, 5) are usually present, the salivary ducts terminating in the mouth parts. In the true bugs accessory salivary glands serve as storage vats for the secretions.

Excretory System.—The excretory system comprises several slender malpighian tubules (Fig. 218, 9), usually in multiples of two, which empty into the intestinal canal just above the juncture of the mid- and hindgut. They collect waste products of metabolism from the blood.

Male Reproductive Organs.—The male reproductive organs consist of two testes, a seminal vesicle, accessory glands, and external genitalia or hypopygium. The variable form of the hypopygium is useful in distinguishing genera.

Female Reproductive Organs.—The female reproductive organs include the ovaries, oviducts, seminal receptacle (spermatheca), shell and cement glands, and ovipositor.

LIFE CYCLE

Insects are both oviparous and viviparous. The three different types of life cycle that are found among insects afford a basis for classification. In the uncommon direct development, confined to the primitive order THYSANURA, the newly hatched insect is a small replica of the parent. The two common types are incomplete and complete metamorphosis. The more primitive insects of the orders ORTHOPTERA (grasshoppers and cockroaches) and HEMIPTERA (true bugs) undergo incomplete metamorphosis, wherein the larvæ differ from the adults only in size, proportion, and absence of wings and external genitalia. The larval insect gradually attains the parental form by passing through a series of molts. In the highly-specialized insects, which undergo complete metamorphosis, the worm-like larvæ differ in feeding habits from the adults and pass through several molts without essential change of form. Prior to the last molt the larva becomes a nonfeeding pupa, from which after a variable interval of a few days to years the adult emerges.

During the superficially quiescent pupal stage the larval structures are remodeled into those of the adult. The larva and pupa possess characteristic hairs, bristles and appendages that aid in the differentiation of genera and species. The duration of life in both larval and adult stages varies with species and with environment.

The adult life may be brief, usually terminating after the production of eggs, while the larval life may be as long as two years. A favorable environment, particularly optimal temperature conditions, shortens the life cycle.

ORDER *COLEOPTERA*

The order COLEOPTERA comprises thousands of species of carnivorous and herbivorous beetles. These insects have chewing mouth parts, forewings modified into horny sheaths (elytra) covering the membranous hind wings, a large, mobile prothorax, and a reduced mesothorax.

Beetles are found in water, soil, dung and plants. They undergo complete metamorphosis. In some species the active, predaceous larvæ have well-developed heads, biting mouth parts, legs, and a chitinized exoskeleton, while in others, as the weevils, which live in the soft tissues of plants, legs are absent and mouth parts are reduced. Certain species, such as the boll weevil of cotton and the death-watch beetle of lumber, cause serious economic loss.

Beetles are facultative or incidental parasites of man. Canthariasis of the digestive tract, urinary system, nasal passages and sinuses, and skin have been reported. This relatively rare condition results from the ingestion of eggs, larvæ or adult beetles, or from their entrance into wounds or natural cavities of the body. The blister beetles (MELOIDÆ) produce cantharidin, a toxic, volatile, vesicating substance.[1] It is present throughout the body, but is most abundant in the elytra. The commercial preparation, obtained from the Spanish fly, *Lytta vesicatoria* and species of the genus *Mylarbris*, is used as a rubefacient, diuretic and aphrodisiac (U. S. Pharmacopœia), although its internal administration is somewhat dangerous. Vesicating lesions are produced by another toxic substance in species of rove beetles of the family STAPHYLINIDÆ.

The larvæ and adults of many species serve as intermediate hosts for such rare helminthic parasites of man as the cestode, *Hymenolepis diminuta;* the nematode, *Gongylonema pulchrum;* and the acanthocephalids, *Moniliformis moniliformis* and *Macracanthorhynchus hirudinaceus.*

Hymenolepis diminuta.—Family ANOBIIDÆ: *Anobium paniceum;* family DERMESTIDÆ: *Dermestes peruvianus, Dermestes vulpinus;* family SCARABÆIDÆ: *Aphodius distinctus, Geotrupes sylvaticus;* family TENEBRIONIDÆ: *Akis spinosa, Scaurus striatus, Tenebrio molitor, Tenebrio obscurus, Tribolium castaneum, Ulosonia parvicornis.*

Gongylonema pulchrum.—Family HYDROPHILIDÆ: *Sphæridium* sp; family SCARABÆIDÆ: *Aphodius fimetarius* and other species of the genus, *Caccobius schreberi, Onthophagus taurus* and other species of the genus; family TENEBRIONIDÆ: *Blaps appendiculata.*

Moniliformis moniliformis.—Family TENEBRIONIDÆ: *Blaps gigas, Blaps mucronata;* family CURCULIONIDÆ: *Calandra orizæ.*

Macracanthorhynchus hirudinaceus.—Family ALLECULIDÆ; *Omophlus rugosicollis;* family HYDROPHILIDÆ: *Tropisternus collaris;* family SCARABÆIDÆ: *Amphimallon solstitialis, Anisoplia segetum, Anomala vitis, Cetonia aurata, Diloboderus abderus, Epicometis hirta, Gromphas lacordairei, Lachnosterna arcuata, Melolontha vulgaris; Melolontha melolontha, Phanæus splendidulus, Phyllophaga fervens, Phyllophaga rugosa, Phyllophaga vehemens, Polyphylla fullo, Scarabæus sacer, Strategus julianus, Xylorictes satyrus.*

ORDER *HYMENOPTERA*

The order HYMENOPTERA, which includes the bees, wasps, ants and sawflies, is remarkable for specialization of structure and the development of social life. Its members

---

[1] Hinman, E. H., 1933.

possess two pairs of membranous wings and mouth parts adapted for chewing, licking and sucking plants. The ovipositor is modified for piercing, sawing or stinging.

The venom is injected by the stinging apparatus at the end of the abdomen. The sting has a barbed sheath, a pair of serrated lancets, and a pair of lateral palps. The venom, secreted by glands, is forced down the canal formed by the sheath and lancets of the sting. The exact nature of the active principle of the venom is unknown, but it is believed to be a complex nonspecific poison of moderate toxicity. During the act of sting-ing the ovipositor is cast off by the honeybee and some wasps, but is retained by other species.

Bee stings cause pain, edema and local inflammation. Ordinarily the symptoms dis-appear after a few hours, but at times there may be marked swelling and inflammation, depending upon the location and number of the stings. Supersensitive persons manifest mild to severe systemic reactions, depending upon the degree of sensitiveness and the rapidity of absorption of the venom. Evidently insect proteins are atopens similar to those of plants and animals and their injection may induce constitutional, atopic manifes-tations.[2] A number of ·cases of severe systemic reactions from single stings, in some instances with fatal termination, have been reported in medical literature.[3] Such indi-viduals manifest symptoms of anaphylactic shock with respiratory and cardiac impair-ment, general edema, and urticaria. The stinging ants of the temperate zones cause little injury, but the large, tropical species give rise to considerable pain and local in-flammation, and, if stings are numerous, may even endanger life. The foraging ants of India and Africa bite viciously with their mandibles.

The treatment of stings requires the removal of the stinging apparatus, when left in the wound, and the application of soothing lotions. In cases of atopic systemic mani-festations the administration of adrenalin, calcium, and respiratory stimulants may be required. Extreme sensitiveness may be eliminated for a period of years by a series of specific injections.[4] Extracts of the bee (*Apis*) will also hyposensitize man against wasps (*Vespa*).[5]

ORDER *LEPIDOPTERA*

Butterflies and moths have a sucking proboscis, two pairs of membranous wings, and are covered with flattened scales. They undergo complete metamorphosis. The larvæ have three pairs of thoracic legs and often five pairs of conical, retractile prolegs on the abdomen. The pupæ are free or immured in cocoons and earthen cases. The adults live on the nectar of flowers, but the voracious larvæ destroy plants.

The larval caterpillars of some fifty species have poisonous hairs that produce a transient, though painful, urticarial dermatitis in man. These hairs are of two types: (1) the venom being secreted by a single glandular cell at the base of the hair (tussock moths), and (2) by cells forming the chitinized, sharply pointed spines (flannel moths).[6] They may be distributed in isolated groups or scattered diffusely among other hairs. The exact chemical composition of the venom is unknown, but it is probably proteic or linked with a protein. The venom of the brown-tail moth is destroyed at 115° C., is soluble in alkalies, and causes hemolysis of erythrocytes.[7] No immunity appears to be acquired. Poisoning is caused by contact with caterpillars or their nests, or by wind-blown hairs settling upon the exposed body or upon drying underclothing.

The severity of the dermatitis varies with the species of caterpillar, the site and extent of the exposure, and the sensitiveness of the victim. The lesions may be local or diffuse, according to the type of exposure. Within a few minutes to several hours the exposed skin shows a vesicular erythema accompanied by an early burning or prickling sensation

---

[2] Coca, A. F., Walzer, M. and Thommen, A. A., 1931.

[3] Beck, B. F., 1935.

[4] Benson, R. L., 1939.

[5] Prince, H. E. and Secrest, P. G., 1939.

[6] Gilmer, P. M., 1925.

[7] Tyzzer, E. E., 1907.

with numbness and pronounced itching. There is necrosis of the epidermal cells around the nettling hairs, the formation of vesicles, and inflammatory changes about the vessels of the corium.[7] In sensitive persons edema, urticaria and systemic symptoms may occur. Wind-blown hairs may produce an irritative tubercular ophthalmia [8] or serious inflammation of the respiratory tract.

Treatment is palliative; some relief is afforded by local applications of calamine lotion, warm baking soda, carbolated vaseline or ammonia. In susceptible individuals supportive treatment may be necessary. Repeated contacts are believed to increase susceptibility. Prevention requires the avoidance of localities frequented by these caterpillars and the destruction, where possible, of their nests and nesting grounds. Caterpillars may be destroyed by arsenical sprays or by the application of creosote to the egg-masses. It is advisable for workers to protect their eyes against hairs by wearing glasses. Insect predators and parasites also destroy caterpillars.

The caterpillars of at least one family of butterflies and several families of moths have poisonous hairs.[9] The more important species belong to the four-footed butterflies (NYMPHALIDÆ) of North America and Europe; the flannel moths (MEGALOPYGIDÆ) of North and South America; the slug-caterpillar moths (EUCLEIDÆ) of North America, Africa and the Orient; the processionary caterpillar moths (THAUMETOPŒIDÆ) of Europe and Africa; the tussock moths (LYMANTRIIDÆ) of North America, Europe and the Orient; the tiger moths (ARCTIIDÆ) of North America; the owlet moths (NOCTUIDÆ) of North America; and the giant silkworm moths (SATURNIIDÆ) of North America. In the eastern United States a common form of caterpillar dermatitis is the "brown-tail rash" caused by the brown-tail moth, *Euproctis chrysorrhœa*, of the family LYMANTRIIDÆ. *Automeris io* of the family SATURNIIDÆ is the most generally known moth with poisonous hairs in the eastern and central United States.[10]

The following lepidopterans are intermediate hosts of the cestode, *Hymenolepis diminuta: Aglossa dimidiata, Anisolabis annulipes, Aphornia gularis, Asopia farinalis, Tinea granella* and *T. pellionella*.

ORDER *ORTHOPTERA*

The ORTHOPTERA includes the grasshoppers, locusts, crickets, and cockroaches. These large, terrestrial insects have biting mouth parts, narrow hardened forewings, membranous hind legs for running and jumping, and often stridulent and auditory organs.

COCKROACHES

The cockroaches (family BLATTIDÆ) are swift-running, omnivorous insects with legs of approximately equal length. Their morphology has previously been described.

Species.—The oriental cockroach, *Blatta orientalis*, a dark brown insect about 2.5 cm. in length, has spread from the Far East throughout the world. The male (Fig. 219A) has wing covers (elytra), wings, styles and a rounded supra-anal plate. The female (Fig. 219B) has rudimentary wing covers and wings, no styles, and a notched, supra-anal plate. The smaller, light brown German cockroach, *Blatella germanica* (Fig. 219C), known as the Croton bug in the United States of America, is about 1.3 cm. in length and has well-developed wings in both sexes. The large reddish-brown American cockroach, *Periplaneta americana* (Fig. 219D), about 3.8 cm. in length, also has well-developed wings in both sexes. The Australian cockroach, *Periplaneta australasiæ*, about 2.6 cm. in length, may be distinguished from the American species by its smaller size and the yellow marginal bands on the thorax.

---

[8] Cheverton, R. L., 1936; Viallefont, H., 1936.

[9] Craig, C. F. and Faust, E. C., 1937.

[10] Hegner, R., Root, F. M., Augustine, D. L. and Huff, C. G., 1938.

Habits.—The oriental and German cockroaches frequent homes and food-handling establishments; the American and Australian species prefer ships, warehouses, sugar refineries and hothouses. The two species are seldom found together. The cockroach is nocturnal, shuns bright sunlight, and seeks concealment during the day in cracks and crevices. It is common in basements where heat, dampness and a liberal food supply create an ideal environment. Both nymphs and adults are omnivorous with a partiality

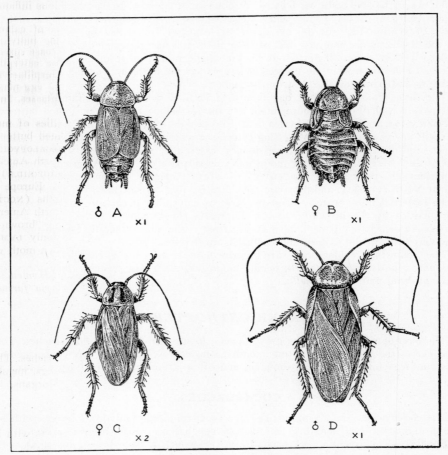

FIG. 219.—THE COCKROACH

A, oriental cockroach, *Blatta orientalis*, male; *B*, oriental cockroach, *Blatta orientalis*, female; *C*, German cockroach, *Blatella germanica*, female; *D*, American cockroach, *Periplaneta americana*, male (Redrawn from Laing, 1938).

for sweetened food. Roaches may infest a building by their introduction in food supplies or by migrating along plumbing fixtures.

Life Cycle.—The female cockroach begins egg-laying 10 to 12 days after fertilization. Two rows of eggs are enclosed in a hard capsule. Egg-laying habits differ slightly in the several species. The oriental cockroach at intervals deposits in crevices from one to eight cases each containing 16 eggs and plasters them with mud and débris; the German cockroach lays five cases of 40 eggs each, the cases adhering to the female for over two weeks until just before the young hatch; and the American cockroach may lay as many as 50 cases of 14 to 28 eggs each.[11]

At a temperature above 23° C. the eggs of the oriental cockroach hatch in 6 to 12 weeks, those of the American in 3 to 10 weeks, and those of the German soon after the case is deposited. The case ruptures along the dorsal ridge and the larvæ, after freeing themselves from their individual membranous capsules, run actively away. Roaches develop by incomplete metamorphosis. Under optimal conditions of temperature, food and moisture the larva, at first white and later brown, passes through six molts to become a nymph and thence through a seventh molt to the adult stage. The complete cycle in the oriental cockroach requires 8 to 11 months, in the American 8 to 19 months, and in the German 2 to 3 months. The females are more than three times as numerous as the males. The oriental cockroach dies in July after breeding, the length of adult life averaging 40.2 days for males and 43.5 days for females.[12]

Pathogenesis.—The cockroach is a household pest. Its omnivorous habits cause damage to books, woolen goods and leather, and it leaves a persistent "roachy" odor from gland secretions that spoils all food with which it comes in contact. Little evidence of its association with human disease has been found. The oriental, German and American cockroaches have been incriminated as intermediate hosts of the cestode, *Hymenolepis diminuta,* the German of the nematode, *Gongylonema pulchrum* and the American of the acanthocephalid, *Moniliformis moniliformis.* Through its dual contact with filth and food, pathogenic bacteria, protozoan cysts and helminthic ova may be transmitted mechanically by its appendages and feces.

Control.—The shy, wary habits of the cockroach make methods of control difficult. Cleanliness in kitchens and protection of stored food are primary essentials. Other preventive measures call for the repair of the cracks and crevices that serve as favorable habitats and tight-fitting installations where pipes penetrate the walls, in order to prevent the passage of cockroaches into and through buildings. When present, these pests may be eradicated by poisonous powders, sprays, fumigation, heat and traps. A mixture of three parts sodium fluoride and one part pyrethrum is an effective antiroach powder, and pyrethrum extract in kerosene with an added scent is a useful spray.[11] These substances kill by penetrating the cuticle. They should be spread about the haunts of cockroaches with care so as not to contaminate food. When cockroaches are abundant and conditions are suitable, fumigation with sulphur dioxide (2 pounds of sulphur being burned to 1,000 cubic feet) or with hydrocyanic acid gas may be used to advantage. Dry or moist heat over 55° C. may be employed to drive cockroaches from their hiding places to areas impregnated with poisonous powders. When other measures are impracticable, traps baited with bananas have proved effective.

REFERENCES

BENSON, R. L. Diagnosis of Hypersensitiveness to the Bee and to the Mosquito with Report on Successful Specific Treatment, Arch. Int. Med., 1939, 64:1306.

BERLESE, A. Gli Insetti, Vol. I. Embriologiæ Morphologia, Societá Editrice Libraria, Milano, 1909, pp. 1004.

CHEVERTON, R. L. Irritation Caused by Contact with the Processionary Caterpillar, Tr. Roy. Soc. Trop. Med. & Hyg., 1936, 29:555.

GILMER, P. M. A Comparative Study of the Poison Apparatus of Certain Lepidopterous Larvæ, Ann. Entomol. Soc. Am., 1925, 18:203.

HINMAN, E. H. The Use of Insects and Other Arthropods in Medicine, J. Trop. Med., 1933, 36:128.

LAING, F. The Cockroach. Its Life History and How to Deal with It, Brit. Mus. (Nat. Hist.) Economic Series No. 12, 1938.

---

[11] Laing, F., 1938. [12] Rau, P., 1924.

MIALL, L. C. and DENNY, A.   The Structure and Life-History of the Cockroach (*Periplaneta orientalis*), Lovell Reeve and Co., Leeds, Eng., 1886, pp. 224.

PRINCE, H. E. and SECREST, P. G., Jr.   Use of Whole Bee Extract in Sensitization to Bees, Wasps and Ants, J. Allergy, 1939, 10:379.

RAU, P.   The Biology of the Roach, *Blatta orientalis* Linn., Tr. St. Louis Acad Sc., 1924, 25:27.

Chapter XXXIX

THE ORDER DIPTERA (FLIES)

The DIPTERA from a medical standpoint is the most important order of arthropods. It embraces many species of bloodsucking and non-bloodsucking flies, some of which are intermediate hosts of animal parasites and others mechanical vectors of bacterial, viral and parasitic diseases.

MORPHOLOGY

The general morphology is similar to that previously described for insects. Numerous modifications of the head, thorax, abdomen and appendages are present in the various species. Certain structures are of value for classification; namely, antennæ, mouth parts, external male genitalia, venation of wings, and type and distribution of hairs and bristles.

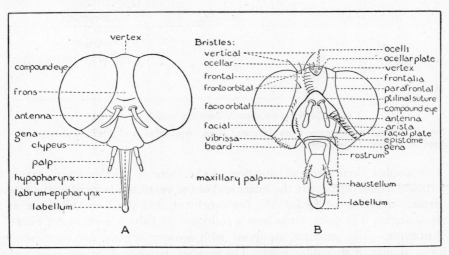

Fig. 220.—Diagrammatic Representation of Heads of Dipterous Flies (Frontal View)
A, orthorrhaphous fly; *B,* cyclorrhaphous fly.

HEAD

The relatively large head covered with chitinous sclerites is separated from the thorax by a cervical constriction. It bears two conspicuous compound eyes that meet in the midline (holoptic) or are separated by a frontal space (dichoptic). In the more primitive orthorrhaphous flies the dorsal region between the eyes is known as the **vertex** and the posterior superior surface the **occiput** (Fig. 220A).

619

In front between the eyes is the **frons,** bearing the antennæ at its anterior end, while below these is the **clypeus** or face, flanked by the **genæ** or cheeks.

In the more specialized cyclorrhaphous flies these structures are greatly modified (Fig. 220B). Small **ocelli** or simple eyes, usually three in number, are arranged in the form of an inverted triangle in a plate slightly behind and between the compound eyes. Between the ocellar plate and the **ptilinal suture** is the frontal plate or frons, which is divided into a central **frontalia** and lateral **parafrontals.** The arched ptilinal suture, the residual scar of the ptilinal sac, encloses the facial plate in which the antennæ lie in grooves, separated by the **facial carina.** Between the antennæ and ptilinal suture are the **facial ridges** which terminate in the **vibrissal angles.** Between the ptilinal suture and the eyes are the **parafacials.** Below the facial plate is a small mesial plate, the **epistoma,** in front of the oral orifice through which passes the upper part of the extended proboscis.

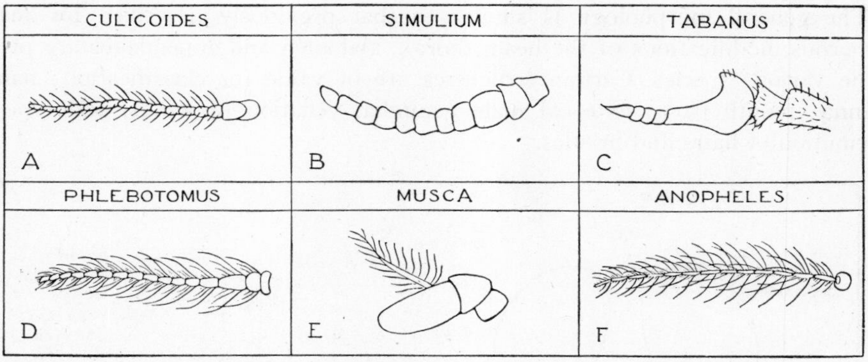

CULICOIDES	SIMULIUM	TABANUS
A	B	C
PHLEBOTOMUS	MUSCA	ANOPHELES
D	E	F

FIG. 221.—ANTENNÆ OF VARIOUS GENERA OF DIPTERA

(*A, B, C* and *E* redrawn from Hegner, Root, Augustine and Huff, *Parasitology,* 1938. D. Appleton-Century Company).

The number, structure and situation of the hairs or bristles are of taxonomic importance. These bristles are the **inner** and **outer vertical,** the **ocular,** the **frontal,** the **fronto-orbital,** the **facial,** the **facio-orbital,** and the large **vibrissæ** at the vibrissal angles. The genæ often bear a collection of hairs known as the **beard.**

Antennæ.—The antennæ, equipped with sensory organs, are composed of a series of similar or dissimilar joints. The number, shape and hirsute adornment of these joints are characteristic for various genera (Fig. 221). The more primitive flies have long antennæ with numerous joints, while the more highly-developed species have short antennæ with fewer and heavier joints. In the highly-specialized muscoid flies the antenna has become modified into the **scape** with three joints and the **arista** that rises from the base of the distal joint. The arista may be bare, covered with short hairs, or lined with dorsal or both dorsal and ventral bristles.

Mouth Parts.—The mouth parts, designed for sucking liquids, vary greatly with the sex and the genus. Various adaptations enable flies to feed upon the blood and body juices of animals, the nectar of flowers, fruit juices, other liquids, or food that may be liquefied by their digestive secretions. The bloodsucking flies have mouth parts modified for piercing. The apposition of the ventrally grooved epipharynx and the flattened hypopharynx creates a food-channel. Suction is produced by a strong traction exerted by the muscles attached to the chitinous walls of the first part of the alimentary canal. The labrum may be fused to the **epipharynx,** and the **hypopharynx** conveys the salivary secretions. The length, shape and position of the sucking mouth parts comprising the cylindrical proboscis are important in distinguishing genera and species.

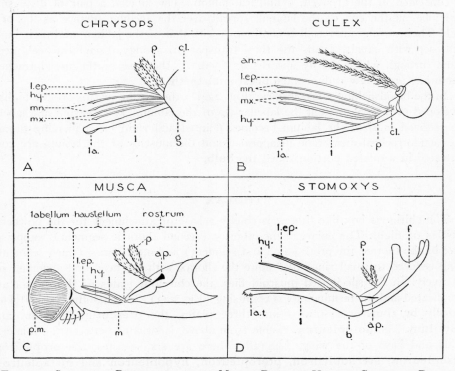

FIG. 222.—SCHEMATIC REPRESENTATION OF MOUTH PARTS OF VARIOUS GENERA OF DIPTERA

Orthorrhaphous flies: *A, Chrysops* (bloodsucking) ; *B, Culex* (bloodsucking). Cyclorrhaphous flies: *C, Musca* (non-bloodsucking) ; *D, Stomoxys* (bloodsucking).

an., antennæ; *ap.,* apodeme of labrum; *b,* bulb; *cl.,* clypeus; *f.,* fulcrum; *g,* gena; *hy.,* hypopharynx; *l,* labium; *la,* labella; *l.ep.,* labrum-epipharynx; *la.t.,* labellar teeth; *m,* mentum; *mn.,* mandibles; *mx.,* maxillæ; *p,* palps; *p.m.,* pseudotracheal membrane.

In the less specialized bloodsucking flies of the suborder ORTHORRHAPHA the mouth parts include: (1) the upper lip or labrum; (2) the epipharynx, usually combined with the labrum; (3) the hypopharynx, containing the salivary duct; (4) two mandibles; (5) two maxillæ, equipped with palps; and (6) the labium, or lower lip, which serves as a sheath for the other appendages and bears at its tip the **labella** (Fig. 222A and B). The penetration of the skin is accomplished by the saw-like mandibles and file-like maxillæ.

In the more specialized muscoid flies of the suborder CYCLORRHAPHA both mandibles and maxillæ have disappeared, while the maxillary palps have become attached to the basal **rostrum** or beak that contains the sucking apparatus. In the non-bloodsucking species the bluntly-pointed proboscis consists of three parts : the rostrum, **haustellum** and two labella (Fig. 222C). The protrusible and retractile rostrum, shaped like an inverted truncated pyramid, is a prolongation of the head, containing the pharynx and buccal cavity. The haustellum consists of the labrum-epipharynx, hypopharynx and the labium. The first two, forming the sucking tube, lie concealed in the grooved, cylindrical labium. The labella, a pair of distensible oval lobes at the end of the labium, spread over the feeding surface as the **oral disk.** Their strong outer wall is continuous with that of the labium, and their inner wall, set with canals, forms the thin, transparent, spongy, pseudotracheal membrane through which the fly absorbs its food. At the base of the pseudotracheal membrane are a few rudimentary **prestomal teeth.**

In the bloodsucking muscoid flies (Fig. 222D) the cutting organs are the highly-developed prestomal teeth at the labellar tip of the labium. The rostrum and labella are reduced in size; the labium becomes pointed and rigid for a piercing organ; the pseudotracheal membrane disappears; and the muscles of the labium are concentrated in a dilated portion called the **bulb.**

THORAX

The chitinous box-like thorax is chiefly a base of attachment for the powerful muscles of flight. The enlarged mesothorax (second thoracic segment) comprises most of the thorax, the prothorax (first segment) and metathorax (third segment) being reduced to small rings that unite the thorax with the head and abdomen respectively. In the specialized muscoid flies, the chitinous plates of the thorax are complicated and the terminology is confusing (Fig. 223). The mesothorax is divided dorsally by transverse sutures into three plates, the **prescutum, scutum** and **scutellum.** The **notopleuron,** visible from above, is situated between the humeral callus and base of the wing. Laterally, there are six sclerites, the **propleuron, mesopleuron, sternopleuron, pteropleuron, hypopleuron** and **metapleuron.** The **prothoracic spiracle** of the tracheal system is situated between the prothorax and mesothorax and the **postthoracic spiracle** on the metathorax. The number and location of the bristles (macrochætes) on the various sclerites and calli are useful for classification (Fig. 223). Each thoracic segment bears a pair of legs, while the wings are attached to the mesothorax and the **halteres** to the metathorax.

Legs.—The fairly long legs variously colored and adorned with spines and hairs in different species, are composed of: coxa, trochanter, femur, tibia and tarsus (Fig. 226). The **coxa** is a short, stout, oval segment which is attached to the thorax. The **trochanter** is small and the cylindrical **femur** and **tibia** are usually long. The **tarsus** consists of a proximal **metatarsus** and four **tarsi.** The foot bears a pair of toothed claws of various shapes and sizes, the claws of the forelegs often differing from those of the other two legs. At the bases of the claws are the **pulvilli,** elongate hairy pads that secrete a sticky substance. The **empodium,**

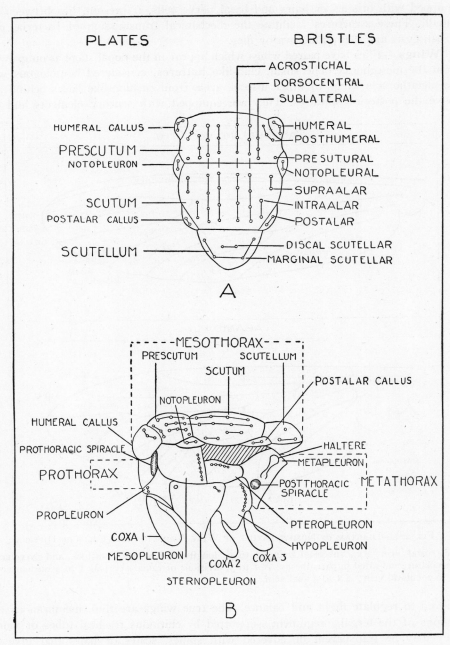

FIG. 223.—THORAX OF MUSCID FLY, SHOWING PLATES AND BRISTLES

A, dorsal view; B, lateral view (Redrawn with modifications from Hegner, Root, Augustine and Huff, *Parasitology,* 1938, D. Appleton-Century Company).

equipped with bristles or hairs and basal nerve cells, if present, lies between the pulvilli. These structures facilitate the mechanical transmission of bacteria, protozoan cysts and helminthic ova by flies.

Wings.—Flies have paired wings which appear in the pupal stage as outgrowths from the mesothorax. The small, club-like **halteres,** considered homologous with the metathoracic wings of other insects, arise from cushion-like bases behind and above the posterior spiracles. They are equipped with sensory elements and are

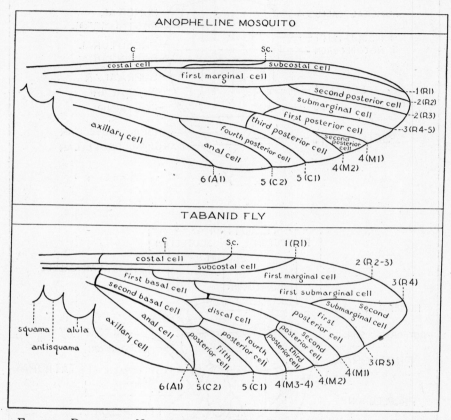

FIG. 224.—DIAGRAM OF NOMENCLATURE OF WING VENATION AND CELLS OF DIPTERA

c, costal vein; *s.c.,* subcostal vein; 1 to 6, longitudinal veins. Comstock and Needham's nomenclature indicated in parentheses: *R* 1 to 5, divisions of radial vein; *M* 1 to 4 median vein; *C* 1 to 2, cubical vein; *A* 1 to 3 anal vein.

believed to regulate flight and balance. The true wings are thin, membranous extensions of the tergal integument, supported by chitinous tracheal tubes or veins. They may be transparent or covered with spines, scales or hairs that give an iridescent or mottled appearance. They have a straight anterior border, a rounded apex and a convex posterior border. The proximal portion of the posterior border is indented in a series of lobes known respectively as the **alula, antisquama** and **squama** (Fig. 224).

The venation of the wings is of value in identifying genera and species. A heavy vein, the **costa**, passes along the anterior edge either extending entirely around the wing or ending near the tip. Another vein, the **subcosta**, lies beneath the costa and joins it along the anterior margin. **Longitudinal veins**, connected at intervals by **cross veins**, radiate from the base of the wing. The spaces between the veins are called cells.

Two principal systems of nomenclature are ordinarily employed to designate the veins: (1) the older empirical system applicable only to the DIPTERA, and (2) the system of Comstock and Needham (1898-99) adapted to insects in general. In the former the veins are designated from front to back as costal, subcostal and six or occasionally seven longitudinal veins, while the cells are named according to their position (Fig. 224). The cross veins, connecting the longitudinal veins, are

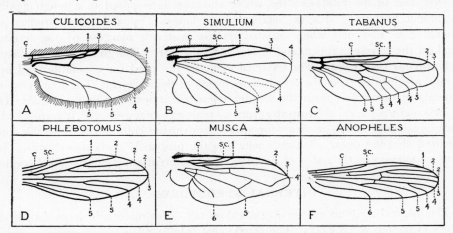

FIG. 225.—WING VENATION OF CERTAIN GENERA OF DIPTERA OF MEDICAL IMPORTANCE

c, costal vein; *s.c.*, subcostal vein; 1 to 6, longitudinal veins (*A, B, C* and *E* redrawn with modifications and *D* and *F* redrawn from Hegner, Root, Augustine and Huff, *Parasitology*, 1938, D. Appleton-Century Company).

the **humoral** between the costal and subcostal, the **upper** between the second and third longitudinal, the **middle** between the third and fourth longitudinal, and the **posterior** between the fourth and fifth longitudinal. The **discal** cell, a convenient landmark when present, is bounded by the fourth longitudinal vein. The cells formed by the bifurcation of a vein are sometimes known as **forked** cells.

In the Comstock-Needham classification (Fig. 224) the anterior trachea divides into the **costal, subcostal, radial** (R 1-5) and **median** (M 1-4); and the posterior into the **cubital** (C 1-2) and **anal** (A 1-3). The cross veins include: the **humeral** between the costal and subcostal veins, the **axillary** between the anterior group of veins at the insertion of the wing, the **radial-median** between the fifth radial and the first median veins, the **median** between the branches of the median vein, and the **median-cubital** between the fourth median and the first cubital veins.

In the transition from the simpler to the more highly-specialized flies there is a general tendency toward a reduction in the number of veins by fusion, thus producing types of venation characteristic of different genera (Fig. 225). The number and position of the veins and enclosed cells and the distribution of hairs or scales on the veins and margins of the wing are of taxonomic value.

ABDOMEN

The first two of the abdominal segments are atrophied and are not easily observed. The remaining segments are not always visible while in the more specialized species only four or five may be noted. Each segment bears a pair of transversely elongate, overlapping plates, the **tergite** and the **sternite,** connected by a loose pleural membrane. Each plate overlaps its successor. The anal opening lies between the last tergite and sternite. In the higher DIPTERA the sternites are greatly reduced, and in the PUPIPARA the whole abdomen is enclosed in a tough flexible integument without plates or segmental markings. The abdominal bristles are designated as marginal when situated on the posterior margins of the tergites, discal on the tergites proper, and lateral near the lateral margins of the segments.

External Genitalia.—The external genitalia designed for copulation and oviposition are formed from the terminal segments of the abdomen. The four terminal segments in many flies form the slender telescopic **ovipositor** of the female. The last two segments form the **hypopygium** or male external genitalia. It consists of a series of bilateral hooks or claws for attachment during coitus, usually in the form of paired clasping organs, between which is the protrusile ensheathed penis. This structure varies greatly and is of importance in differentiating closely-allied species.

INTERNAL STRUCTURES

The internal anatomy of the DIPTERA does not differ materially from that of the insects (Chapter XXXVIII). The pharyngeal tube is adapted for suction; a food reservoir or diverticulum, is usually situated ventrally in the anterior abdomen; the proventriculus is absent in a few genera; the malpighian tubules number from two to five; and the paired salivary glands are well developed. In the more specialized flies there is some fusion of the nerve ganglia of the head, thorax and abdomen. The closed portion of the circulatory system consists of a heart and an anterior aorta, from which the colorless blood passes to the hemocele. In some species the tracheal system has expansible air sacs.

LIFE CYCLE

The majority of DIPTERA are oviparous; a few species deposit larvæ in various developmental stages. These larvæ are elongated, segmented, worm-like, legless creatures with or without well developed heads. The tracheal spiracles, the sclerites of the head, the shape of the body and the distribution of hairs are of value in classification. The larvæ lead an aquatic or terrestrial existence. They feed voraciously on organic material or become adapted to a parasitic existence in small animals. After a series of three or four molts they become quiescent, nonfeeding pupæ that eventually develop into adult flies.

In the more primitive orthorrhaphous flies the pupa is enclosed in its own chitinous skin, whence the adult emerges through a longitudinal dorsal slit over the thorax. In the more specialized cyclorrhaphous flies the pupa is enclosed in a chitinous, yellow to dark brown, oval **puparium** formed from the last larval skin. The adult escapes by forcing open a circular cap at the anterior and by the expansion and contraction of the **ptilinum,** a vesicular structure protruding from the anterior surface of the head. The arched scar on the face of the adult fly that results from the withdrawal within the head of the sac-like ptilinum is called the **ptilinal suture.**

CLASSIFICATION

The order DIPTERA is divided into the suborders ORTHORRHAPHA and CYCLORRHAPHA according to the type of the pupal stage. The former includes the more primitive and the latter the more specialized flies.

SUBORDER *ORTHORRHAPHA* BRAUER, 1885

The larva has a distinct head and a chitinous head capsule, and the pupa is free or is enclosed in its own chitinous pupal skin. The imago escapes through a T-shaped anterior dorsal slit. Its head is without a ptilinal suture. The suborder is divided into two sections, the NEMATOCERA and the BRACHYCERA according to the structure of the antennæ, wing venation and larval morphology.

NEMATOCERA

The various species of NEMATOCERA are small flies. The long antennæ are composed of more than six joints. The tips of the sixth and posterior branch of the fifth longitudinal veins of the wings are widely separated. The larvæ have biting or rudimentary mouth parts. The families of medical interest are: the CULICIDÆ, PSYCHODIDÆ, CHIRONOMIDÆ and SIMULIIDÆ.

CULICIDÆ *Stephens, 1829 (mosquitoes).*—Small flies with slender abdomen and long proboscis; antennæ plumose in males, pilose in females; wings long and narrow with one or more cross veins at or beyond the middle of the wing, no extra seventh vein and a marginal fringe of scales as well as a patterned distribution on the veins; ocelli absent; mesonotum divided into scutum, scutellum and postscutellum.

PSYCHODIDÆ *Bigot, 1854 (moth flies).*—Minute flies with short proboscis; body, legs and wings clothed with long hairs and occasionally scales; antennæ long and beaded; venation of broad wings well developed, nine or more veins or branches reaching margin; ocelli absent.

CHIRONOMIDÆ *Westwood, 1840 (midges).*—Small delicate flies; antennæ slender, most segments bearing circlets of long hairs, especially noticeable in males; wing venation reduced, less than nine veins or branches reaching margin; veins sometimes hairy but lacking scales.

SIMULIIDÆ *Latreille, 1804 (black flies).*—Short thick flies; antennæ stout without circlets of long hairs on most segments; wing venation reduced, less than nine veins or branches reaching margin; wings without hairs or scales.

BRACHYCERA

The BRACHYCERA as a rule are usually large flies. The short antennæ are composed of three or four joints, the last being simple with either a terminal bristle or a dorsal arista, or divided into annuli. The tips of the sixth and posterior branch of the fifth longitudinal veins of the wings are close together or fused. The larvæ have rudimentary mouth parts. The TABANIDÆ is the only family of medical interest.

TABANIDÆ *Leach, 1819 (horse flies)*.—Medium to large thick-set flies with brilliantly colored eyes; last segment of the three-jointed antennæ divided into two, four or eight annuli, without arista; squamæ of the wings large, discal cell longer than broad.

SUBORDER *CYCLORRHAPHA*, BRAUER, 1885

The larva has no distinct head or chitinous head capsule and the pupa is enclosed in a chitinous oval puparium derived from the last larval skin. The imago emerges through a circular opening at the anterior end. Its head bears a ptilinal suture. The suborder CYCLORRHAPHA is divided into the ASCHIZA, with frontal lunule but without frontal suture and the SCHIZOPHORA with both frontal lunule and suture. The cyclorrhaphous flies of medical importance belong to the SCHIZOPHORA which is subdivided into the ACALYPTRATÆ and the CALYPTRATÆ. The PUPIPARA are degenerate parasite forms.

ACALYPTRATA

The folded wings do not conceal the halteres. Squamæ of wings are small or rudimentary and the subcostal vein is often reduced. Thorax has no complete suture. This group contains one family of medical importance, the OSCINIDÆ.

OSCINIDÆ *Latreille, 1804 (eye flies)*.—Small flies; mouth parts modified so that the tips of the labella act as cutting edges; antennæ short with bare arista; wings short and bare.

CALYPTRATA

Squamæ of the wings are large and the subcostal vein is always well developed. Thorax has a complete suture. This group contains several families and many species of medical importance.

ANTHOMYIDÆ *Robineau-Desvoidy, 1830 (lesser house flies)*.—Mouth parts well developed and mouth large; tip of fourth wing vein straight; hypopleura bare with fine hairs.

ŒSTRIDÆ *Latreille, 1804 (botflies)*.—Large, stout flies; mouth parts poorly developed and mouth small; antennal arista spinous on anterior side.

SARCOPHAGIDÆ *Hagen, 1881 (flesh flies)*.—Large flies with gray or black bodies; antennal arista plumose for half its length; postscutellum with single concavity; abdomen bristly near tip.

CALLIPHORIDÆ *Robineau-Desvoidy, 1830 (blow flies)*.—Medium to large flies; body color usually metallic blue or green; antennal arista plumose nearly to tip.

MUSCIDÆ *Latreille, 1802 (house, stable and tsetse flies)*.—Medium to large bloodsucking and nonbloodsucking flies; tip of fourth wing vein angled and curved toward third.

HIPPOBOSCIDÆ *Gray, J. E., 1832 (tick flies)*.—The PUPIPARA are pupiparous bloodsucking ectoparasites of mammals and occasionally of birds, with highly developed toothed claws and tough integument; sac-like abdomen without distinct segmentation; wings reduced or absent; and larvæ ready to pupate when laid. The HIPPOBOSCIDÆ unlike other families of the PUPIPARA do not have the head folded back on the dorsum of the thorax and the palpi are neither broad nor leaf-like.

TABLE 40
DIPTERA OF MEDICAL IMPORTANCE

Suborder	Section	Family	Genus	Species
ORTHORRHAPHA	NEMATOCERA	CULICIDÆ	Aëdes	A. ægypti and other species
			Anopheles	A. maculipennis and other species
			Culex	C. fatigans and other species
			Mansonia	M. uniformis and other species
		CHIRONOMIDÆ	Culicoides	C. austeni C. furens C. grahami
		PSYCHODIDÆ	Phlebotomus	P. papatasii and other species
		SIMULIIDÆ	Simulium	S. callidum S. damnosum S. metallicum S. neavei S. ochraceum
	BRACHYCERA	TABANIDÆ	Chrysops	C. centurionis C. dimidiata C. discalis C. distinctipennis C. longicornis C. silacea
CYCLORRHAPHA	ACALYPTRATA	OSCINIDÆ	Hippelates	H. pallipes H. pusio
			Siphunculina	S. funicola
	CALYPTRATA	ŒSTRIDÆ	Dermatobia	D. hominis
			Gasterophilus	G. hæmorrhoidalis G. intestinalis G. nasalis
			Hypoderma	H. bovis H. lineatum
			Œstrus	Œ. ovis
			Rhinœstrus	R. purpureus
		CALLIPHORIDÆ	Auchmeromyia	A. luteola
			Calliphora	C. erythrocephala C. vomitoria
			Chrysomyia	C. bezziana
			Cochliomyia	C. americana C. macellaria
			Cordylobia	C. anthropophaga
			Lucilia	L. cæsar L. serenissima
			Phormia	P. regina

TABLE 40—Continued
DIPTERA OF MEDICAL IMPORTANCE

Suborder	Section	Family	Genus	Species
CYCLORRHAPHA (Cont.)	CALYPTRATA (Cont.)	SARCOPHAGIDÆ	Sarcophaga	S. carnaria S. fuscicauda S. hæmorrhoidalis
			Wohlfahrtia	W. meigeni W. magnifica W. vigil
		ANTHOMYIDÆ	Fannia	F. canicularis
		MUSCIDÆ	Glossina	G. morsitans, G. palpalis and other species
			Musca	M. domestica
			Muscina	M. stabulans
			Stomoxys	S. calcitrans

Chapter XL

THE SUBORDER ORTHORRHAPHA: THE FAMILY CULICIDÆ (MOSQUITOES)

Mosquitoes are slender, delicate flies of evil reputation. Of the 1,400 species throughout the world at least 50 have been found in the United States of America. The family CULICIDÆ includes the bloodsucking subfamily CULICINÆ and the non-bloodsucking subfamilies DIXINÆ and CHAOBORINÆ. The true mosquitoes of the subfamily CULICINÆ, distinguished from the other subfamilies by a conspicuous proboscis, are important transmitting agents of viral, protozoan and helminthic diseases of animals and man. They are distinguished from other DIPTERA by (1) the elongated mouth parts of the females adapted, with few exceptions, for piercing and sucking blood; (2) the long antennæ, plumose in the males and pilose in the females; and (3) the characteristic wing venation with flat striated scales on the longitudinal veins and posterior borders.

Geographical Distribution.—Mosquitoes range from the polar regions to the equator. Unlike most insects they predominate in northern countries where, although perhaps not carriers of disease, their bites render them a pest to man and animals. Because of their depredations, many hunting and camping grounds are closed to the public and vast regions remain uninhabited.

MORPHOLOGY

The body of the mosquito (Fig. 226) may be separated into three main divisions: the head which bears the eyes, antennæ and mouth parts; the thorax, the wings and legs; and the abdomen, the external genitalia.

HEAD

The roughly spherical head (Figs. 226 and 227C) is almost covered by a pair of compound eyes that nearly meet. On their surfaces are numerous octagonal corneal facets, each an optical lens. The snout-like clypeus projects from the frons to articulate distally with the proboscis.

Mouth Parts.—The proboscis is a sheath or scabbard enclosing the mouth parts which differ in the sexes. In the female these parts consist of the grooved lower lip or labium, which protects the lancet-like penetrating organs; the upper lip or labrum-epipharynx, horseshoe shaped in cross section; the hypopharynx; the paired mandibles and the maxillæ (Fig. 227A and B). The hypopharynx is a flat, tongue-like blade traversed like a hypodermic needle by a minute canal, the salivary duct, the pathway of the malarial sporozoites. The mandibles and the distally serrated maxillæ are lancets which penetrate the victim's skin to permit the entrance of the labrum-epipharynx and hypopharynx. The gutter-shaped labium, which terminates in two small labella, does not enter the wound but bends in a loop to steady the piercing instruments. During the process of biting the labrum-epipharynx, when

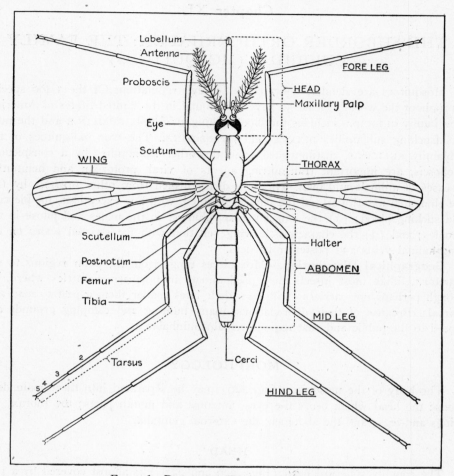

Fig. 226.—Diagram of Mosquito (Female)

Dorsal view, showing nomenclature of parts (Adapted from MacGregor, 1927, and Marshall, 1938).

closed by the underlying hypopharynx, forms a tube through which blood is sucked by the pharyngeal pump and the salivary secretions are injected into the wound. The arrangement of the male mouth parts varies in the subgenera, but they cannot penetrate the skin; hence, male mosquitoes feed chiefly on fruit and flower juices. Maxillæ and mandibles are present in the genus *Anopheles* and in most species of *Culex* but not in *Aëdes*.[1]

---

[1] Marshall, J. F., 1938.

The maxillary palps of the female mosquitoes are slender and bare; those of the anophelines being about as long as the proboscis and those of the culicines one-fifth to one half as long (Fig. 227C). The long palps of the male are ornamented with tufts of hair, the fourth segment only in the anophelines and the last three segments in the culicines.

Antennæ.—The antennæ lie immediately above the base of the clypeus. Their basal segments are narrow, ring-like structures at the margin of the eye concealed beneath a conspicuous, goblet-shaped second segment. The remaining thirteen segments comprise the flagellum, each being ornamented with a whorl of hairs, longer and more numerous in the males. The hirsute adornment of the palps and antennæ gives a plumed appearance to the head of the male that readily distinguishes the sexes (Figs. 227C and 231).

THORAX

The rigid thorax is formed by the fusion of three segments: the prothorax, bearing the forelegs; the mesothorax, the midlegs and wings; and the metathorax, the hind legs and vestigial hind wings. The upper surface of the large mesothorax is covered by the scutum save for a narrow posterior three-lobed portion, the scutellum (Fig. 226). Posterior to the scutellum is the dome-shaped postnotum, separated from the first abdominal tergite by the narrow metanotum. Viewed laterally the thorax is wedge-shaped and its lateral surface is covered with plate-like sclerites usually bearing groups of bristles (Fig. 227H). The coloration and pattern of the thoracic scales and bristles are useful in differentiating genera and species.

Legs.—There are three pairs of long slender legs: the fore, mid and hind legs, which join the undersurface of the thorax by short conical protuberant coxæ (Figs. 226 and 227E). The fifth metatarsus is short and bears two claws, simple in some species, in others toothed (Fig. 227F). Between the claws is a small pad of minute hairs, the empodium, while some species carry two large pads, the pulvilli, at the bases of the claws (Fig. 227G).

Wings.—A single pair of strong wings is attached to the mesothorax, and a pair of halteres or vestigial wings, sometimes called balancers, to the metathorax. The wings consist of a delicate transparent chitinous membrane supported by chitinous veins of characteristic arrangement which distinguish the mosquito from other insects (Fig. 224). The spaces enclosed by the veins and the margin of the wing are referred to as cells. The most important for the determination of species are the second marginal and second posterior, sometimes known as the anterior and posterior forked cells. The anterior margin is relatively straight, while the posterior is convexly curved and near the wing base is deeply indented at two points, forming a small lobe, the alula, and a thoracic portion, the squama.

The surface of the wing is longitudinally corrugated with alternate ridges and furrows, and each longitudinal vein has a ridge and a furrow side. The veins are covered with scales that vary in shape, size, structure and distribution in different species. They may be separated into squamæ scales, which are shaped somewhat like an oar blade and lie flat against the surface of the wing, and long, narrow plume scales, which project from the surface. The scaling is uniformly dark in many species, including most culicines, but in others, particularly anophelines, it gives a characteristic spotted appearance, depending upon the color, size and number of the scales at the venous junctions (Fig. 227D).

ABDOMEN

There are ten segments in the abdomen, although the last two are not readily visible. Each segment consists of two chitinous plates, a dorsal tergite and a ventral sternite, connected by a flexible pleural membrane. The tergites and sternites of the ninth and tenth segments are modified to form the external reproductive organs.

Female Genitalia.—In the female a pair of appendages, the cerci, protrude from the tenth tergite, and a small postgenital plate from the tenth sternite (Fig. 227K). The cerci are relatively inconspicuous except in *Aëdes*.

Male Genitalia.—In the male the ninth and tenth segments are modified into the male genitalia or hypopygium (Fig. 227J). Within 24 hours after the imago emerges from the pupa the last three abdominal segments rotate 180° to an upside-down position.[1] The tergite and sternite of the ninth abdominal segment form a nearly complete ring. The sternite bears the paired clasping organs, each consisting of a coxite and a style, usually with a terminal claw (Fig. 227I). Anopheline mosquitoes have stout spines at the base of the coxite and a ventral two- or three-lobed claspette. The modifications of the hypopygium are useful in classifying mosquitoes, but this method is inconvenient for field work.

INTERNAL ANATOMY

The chief internal structures of the female mosquito are (1) salivary glands, (2) alimentary tract, (3) reproductive organs, and (4) fat body.

FIG. 227 (*continued*) *A*, mouth parts of a female mosquito; *B*, cross section of mouth parts of male and female anopheline mosquito; *C*, head of male and female culicine mosquito; *D*, wing of anopheline mosquito showing venation, scales and maculations; *E*, hind leg of female *Aëdes*; *F*, distal segments of foretarsus of male *Theobaldia annulata*; *G*, tip of fifth tarsal segment of *Culex pipiens* showing claws, empodium and pulvilli; *H*, lateral view of thorax of *Psorophora*, showing location of sclerites and groups of bristles (dots); *I*, hypopygium of *Anopheles maculipennis*; *J*, abdomen of male mosquito, dorsal view; *K*, abdomen of female mosquito, lateral view.

an., antenna; *c*, claw; *ce.*, cercus; *cl.*, clypeus; *cp.*, claspette; *cx.*, coxa; *cxi.*, coxite; *e*, eye; *em.*, empodium; *fe.*, femur; *hy.*, hypopharynx; *i.m.*, intersegmental membrane; *i.sp.*, internal spine; *in.t.*, intercranial tunnel; *l*, labium; *la.*, labella; *l.ep.*, labrum-epipharynx; *lm.*, lateral metasternal sclerite; *m*, mesonotum; *me.*, mesepimeron bearing upper- and midmesepimeral bristles; *mn.*, mandible; *mp.*, mesopleura bearing postspiracular bristles; *ms.*, muscles; *mx.*, maxilla; *oc.*, occiput; *pa.*, palp; *pg.p.*, postgenital plate; *pl.*, pleuron; *pn.*, postnotum; *p.p.*, pharyngeal pump; *ppl.*, propleuron bearing propleural bristles; *ppn.*, posterior pronotum bearing pronotal bristles; *p.sp.*, parabasal spine; *pt.l.*, prothoracic lobe bearing prothoracic bristles; *pu.*, pulvillus; *s*, sternite; *sc.*, scape; *sct.*, scutellum; *sp.*, spiracle; *sp.s.*, spiracular sclerite bearing spiracular bristles; *st.*, style; *stp.*, sternopleuron bearing prealar, upper sternopleural and lower sternopleural bristles; *t*, tergite; *ta.*, tarsus; *tb.*, tibia; *to.*, torus; *tr.*, trochanter; *v*, vertex (*A* adapted from Marshall, 1938, after Patton; *B* adapted from Nuttall and Shipley, 1901; *C*, *E* to *G* and *I* to *K* redrawn from Marshall, 1938; *H* redrawn from Hegner, Root, Augustine and Huff, *Parasitology*, 1938, D. Appleton-Century Company).

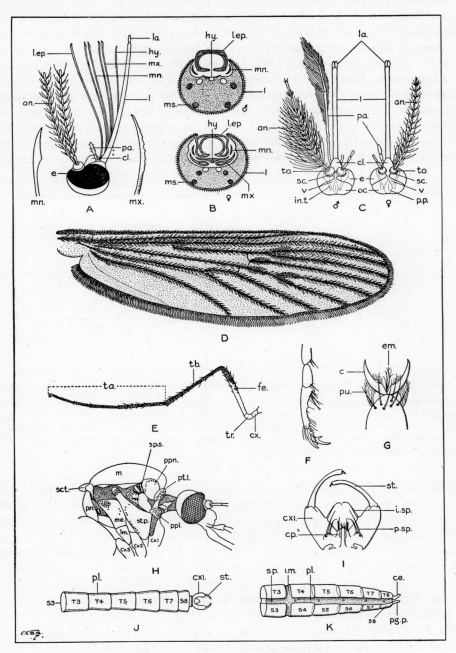

FIG. 227.—MORPHOLOGY OF MOSQUITO

Salivary Glands.—The paired salivary glands (Fig. 228) lie within the prothorax immediately above the forelegs. Each gland has one short and two long tubules lined with a single layer of secretory cells. The efferent ducts unite to form the common salivary duct that traverses the hypopharynx. Near the base of the latter the duct passes through a conical muscular chamber which acts as a pump.

Alimentary Tract.—The alimentary tract (Fig. 228) comprises: foregut, midgut and hindgut. The chitinous foregut is divided into pharynx and esophagus. The suction of the pharyngeal pump, an expansile chamber formed by three oval externally concave plates united by a flexible membrane, propels liquids through the esophagus to the midgut. The posterior extremity of the esophagus is connected with a large ventral and two dorsal diverticula, which act as food reservoirs.

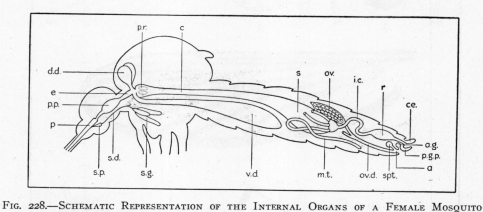

FIG. 228.—SCHEMATIC REPRESENTATION OF THE INTERNAL ORGANS OF A FEMALE MOSQUITO

a, atrium; *a.g.*, accessory gland; *c*, cardia or midgut; *ce.*, cercus; *e*, esophagus; *d.d.*, dorsal diverticula; *i.c.*, ileum-colon; *m.t.*, malpighian tubules; *ov.*, ovary; *ov.d.*, oviduct; *p*, pharynx; *p.g.p.*, posterior genital plate; *p.p.*, pharyngeal pump; *pr.*, proventriculus; *r*, rectum; *s*, stomach; *s.d.*, salivary duct; *s.g.*, salivary gland; *s.p.*, salivary pump; *spt.*, spermatheca; *v.d.*, ventral diverticulum (Redrawn from Marshall, 1938).

Posterior to the diverticular ducts the invagination of the esophagus into the midgut forms a two-way valve or proventriculus. The selective action of this valve admits ingested blood into the midgut and shunts vegetable nourishment into the diverticula.

The midgut resembles an elongate flask, the neck or cardia lying within the thorax, and the expanded portion or stomach in the first five abdominal segments. The malpighian tubules, usually five in number, enter just anterior to the junction of the mid- and hindgut. The latter is a tortuous tube which enlarges to form the papillate rectum. The anus opens between the tenth tergite and sternite.

Reproductive Organs.—The two ovaries (Fig. 228) lie dorsad to the stomach below the fourth and fifth tergites, but in a gravid female they fill most of the abdominal cavity. Each ovary has an outer membrane and an inner layer of follicular tubes within which the eggs are formed. The egg follicle develops in two stages, the second commencing only after the blood meal. Each ovary communicates with the common oviduct, which opens at the posterior border of the eighth abdominal segment after expanding into an atrium that receives ducts from the spermatheca and accessory cement glands. The spermatheca comprise one to three small sub-spherical reservoirs (one in *Anopheles*) within the eighth segment. In impregnated females these are filled with spermatozoa that fertilize the eggs in transit. In *Culex* the accessory gland provides a secretion which cements the eggs together in rafts, but in other mosquitoes its function is unknown. The male reproductive organs consist of a pair of spindle-shaped testes, long vasa deferentia with distal seminal vesicles, and a common chitinous ejaculatory duct, that receives the secretions of the accessory glands and even serves as a penile organ.

Fat Body.—The fat body consists of layers of cells partly beneath the body wall and partly surrounding the alimentary tract. The fat stored in globules provides nourishment for hibernating mosquitoes.

Respiratory System.—The paired spiracular openings of the trachea are present on the second and third thoracic and the first eight abdominal segments.

HABITS

Feeding of Adult.—The male mosquito and also the bloodsucking female feed upon the nectar of flowers and juices of fruit. Some bloodsucking species, possibly attracted by the odor of the host, confine their activities almost exclusively to the lower animals, rarely attacking man. While a fertilized female usually cannot produce fertile eggs without ingesting blood, at least three species are able to deposit the first batch of eggs without a blood meal.[1] Peculiar feeding habits have been observed: *Culex pipiens* feeding on milk and a local species of *Culex* in Santa Lucia that acquired a fondness for port wine. Nearly all anopheline mosquitoes are aggressive biters at twilight, but are inactive in bright daylight and on dark nights, the hours of evening activity varying with the species. In houses mosquitoes bite at any time and certain forest species, as *Anopheles braziliensis,* are diurnal biters.

Feeding of Larva.—The voracious larvæ have elaborate mouth parts, which enable them to obtain and masticate algæ, fungal spores, microsclerotia, bacteria and particulate matter. The anopheline larvæ feed at the surface, the culicine larvæ below. Culicine larvæ are of two types, with different mouth brushes, one obtaining nourishment by sweeping particles near the surface, and the other, including most species of *Aëdes,* by nibbling decaying material on the bottom.

Swarming and Mating.—The males dance in swarms in sheltered places in the evening. The females wander about singly, dart into the swarm and seize partners, and the couples then retire. The swarm, thereupon, resumes its movement and awaits the arrival of another female. Copulation usually takes place in an end-to-end position.[2] The males are able to mate upon the rotation of the hypopygium which occurs 12 to 24 hours after they emerge from the pupa. The mouth parts of the female become sufficiently hard for bloodsucking on the second day after the pupal stage. Both mating and the blood meal are the result of chance encounters, but usually occur within the first two or three days except in certain hibernating

---

[2] Howard, L. O., Dyar, H. G. and Knab, F., 1915.

domestic species. In the latter group oviposition of the last of several generations is postponed until the following spring.

Flight.—The flight range is important in mosquito control. The direction and velocity of the wind are determining factors, since some species fly with, others against, and still others across the wind. The range of *Anopheles* is usually within a half mile, though occasionally it may extend over one mile or even four miles.[3] *Aëdes vexans* is credited with a flight range of 10 miles or more,[4] while salt-marsh mosquitoes in America have invaded towns at least 30 miles inland for blood meals then returned to the coast to lay their eggs.[5]

Oviposition.—*Anopheles* and *Culex* deposit their eggs in water, and *Aëdes* in shaded localities on ground subject to intermittent flooding. The number of eggs laid at any one time varies widely. The maximum for five water-laying species ranged from 208 to 433 and for dry-laying species 104 to 240.[1] Most species lay two or more batches of eggs, when blood meals are obtainable, after a single mating. Many anopheline species produce 800 to 1,000 eggs during their lifetime. The interval between the blood meal and egg laying barely exceeds a week.

Hibernation.—Most domestic species are able to hibernate as adults, the females mating in the autumn and ovipositing the following spring. The males die in the late fall and the females hibernate in the dark corners of cellars, sheds, houses or in the field. Nourishment is obtained from the fat body and blood meal. A few species, such as *Anopheles bifurcatus* of Europe, hibernate as larvæ.

LIFE CYCLE

Mosquitoes undergo complete metamorphosis. The eggs produce voracious, rapidly-growing larvæ that molt four times before they enter the nonfeeding pupal stage, from which the fully-developed insect emerges. The hatching time varies widely. Eggs deposited in water mature within a few days. The eggs of *Aëdes*, laid upon the ground, may remain viable for months unless exposed to excessive sunlight. When once flooded with water, hatching ensues as with the water-laid eggs, but only a certain percentage of the eggs hatch at each flooding. The duration of the larval stage depending upon the food supply and temperature varies from 10 days to 6 months. The nonfeeding pupal stage lasts from 4 to 5 days, but may be prolonged to 10 days at low temperatures. The minimal period from egg to adult is about two weeks.

Egg.—The shell is composed of three layers: a thin, vitelline, inner membrane; a hard, opaque, middle **endochorion**; and a flexible, transparent, outer **exochorion,** covered with minute protuberances. The freshly laid egg is white but later darkens. Near the anterior extremity is a rosette-shaped membrane with a stoppered, funnel-shaped passage, the **micropyle,** through which the spermatozoon enters.

The eggs of *Anopheles* (Figs. 229A and 230), 0.7 mm. in length, are laid separately in the water. They resemble boats, the under surface convex, the upper slightly concave, and bear a pair of lateral, ribbed, exchorionic **floats** and a project-

---

[3] Boyd, M. F., 1930; Wallace, R. B., 1939; Adams, P. C. G., 1940.

[4] Herle, E., 1926.
[5] Mitchell, E. G., 1907.

ing **frill** that extends around the egg from one float to the other. The under surface
is sculptured in an irregular polygonal pattern. The tapering eggs of *Culex* (Figs.
229C and 230) float in raft-like masses. The smaller end is bluntly pointed, and the
larger rounded end at the lower surface of the raft, has a cup-shaped **corolla**. The

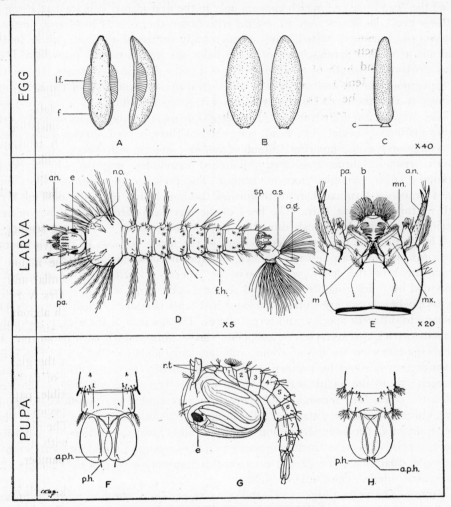

FIG. 229.—LARVAL FORMS OF MOSQUITO

A, egg of *Anopheles maculipennis*, dorsal and lateral views; B, egg of *Aëdes geniculatus*,
dorsal and lateral views; C, egg of *Culex pipiens* with attached corolla; D, larva of *Anopheles
maculipennis*, dorsal view (the anal segment rotated so as to display the dorsal and ventral
brushes); E, head of fourth-instar larva of *Anopheles maculipennis*, ventral view; F, terminal
abdominal segment of pupa of *Anopheles maculipennis*; G, pupa of a mosquito; H, terminal
abdominal segment of pupa of *Culex pipiens*.

a.g., anal gills; an., antenna; a.p.h., accessory paddle hair; a.s., anal segment; b, brush;
c, corolla of culicine egg; e, eye; f, frill or flange of egg; f.h., float hair; l.f., lateral floats of
anopheline egg; m, mentum; mn., mandible; mx., maxilla; n.o., notched organ; pa., palp;
p.h., paddle hair; r.t., respiratory trumpets; sp., spiracle (Redrawn from Marshall, 1938).

elliptical, polygonally-sculptured eggs of *Aëdes* (Fig. 229B), 0.75 mm. in length, are deposited separately, usually on shaded ground subject to flooding. They succumb to drying but may survive for some time in moist mud.

Larva.—The larva breaks out of the egg by using a sharp projection on its head called the "egg breaker," which appears only in the first instar. It is then an elongate, limbless grub, about 1.5 mm. in length, with broad thorax and head and simple or transversely-branched, tufted hairs symmetrically arranged along its whole length. The character and arrangement of these hairs are of taxonomic importance. The larva grows to a length of about 10 mm. and casts its skin four times. In molting the integument of the thorax splits in the dorsal midline and that of the head horizontally so that the larva emerges through a Y-shaped opening.

The larva of the fourth instar (Fig. 229D) is most frequently examined for the determination of species. The head, composed of three curved scleritic plates, bears the compound eyes; tapering, hirsute antennæ; and mouth parts, consisting of mouth brushes, labrum-epipharynx, flattened mandibles, maxillæ with truncated maxillary palps, hypopharynx and labium. The presence of two saber-like spines and a branched terminal hair distinguishes the anopheline from the culicine larvæ with its three tapering hairs. The head of the larva also carries a number of symmetrically-paired hairs, which differ for genera and species.

The thorax, the most conspicuous part of the larva, consists of three segments, prothorax, mesothorax and metathorax, but the divisions are obscure save for the arrangement of the hairs, which serve for species identification. The abdomen is divided into nine roughly cylindrical segments. The first seven are similar and in the anopheline larvæ are dorsally ornamented with palmate or float hairs, varying in shape in different species, and tergal plates. The dorsum of the eighth abdominal segment carries two spiracles, in anopheline larvæ almost flush with the surface but in culicine larvæ on the top of a long, tubular, hairy siphon (Fig. 230). The influx of water is prevented by protective valves and an oily secretion from the glands. On each side of the eighth segment of the culicine larva is a collection of flattened scales, the comb. The terminal anal aperture is surrounded by four flexible, papilliform, chitinous processes, the anal gills, of variable length in different species. Their chief function is probably absorption of water, rather than respiration. The digestive tract comprises a foregut, including pharynx and esophagus; a midgut, with stomach and eight dilatations, the gastric ceca; and a hindgut, with pyloric chamber, five malpighian tubules, colon and rectum.

Pupa.—The pupa (Figs. 229G and 230) resembles a question mark, with head and thorax at the top and abdomen beneath. The tail terminates in a pair of paddles which assist the pupa to dive rapidly with jerky motions when not resting on the surface. An air vesicle, situated between the future wings of the adult, not only supplies buoyancy but also keeps the apertures of the divergent respiratory trumpets in contact with the surface of the water. The cephalothorax is marked by the future compound eye of the adult accompanied by a smaller pupal eye and contains a number of flexible, chitinous sheaths within which the mouth parts, antennæ, wings, legs and other adult appendages develop. The terminal ninth segment of the abdomen carries a pair of overlapping oval paddles with terminal hairs. In the anopheline pupa an accessory hair arises from the ventral surface of each paddle immediately above the main paddle hair, whereas in the culicine pupa the two hairs lie side by side on the dorsal surface (Fig. 229F and H).

In hatching, air from the vesicle spreads out under the pupal skin, and a portion is aspirated orally into the midgut, where it forms a narrow bubble reaching back-

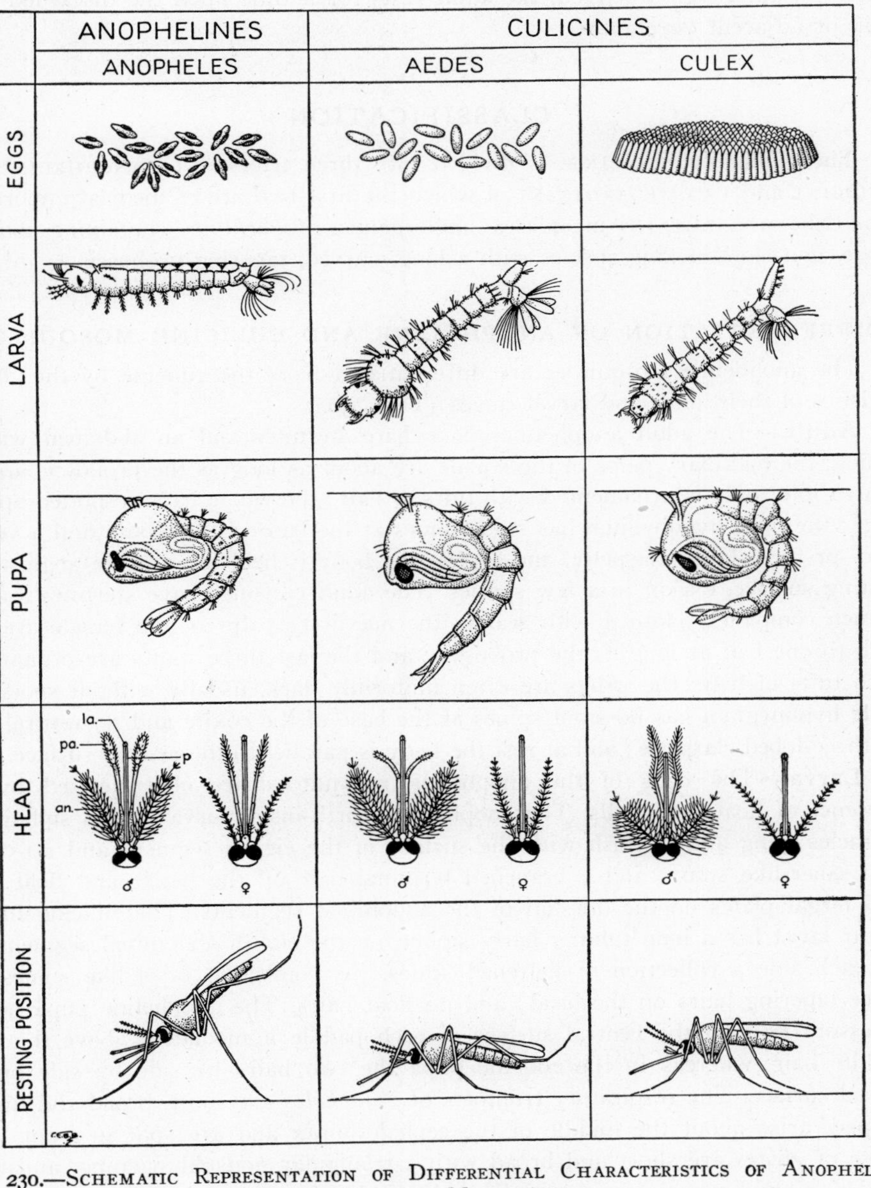

FIG. 230.—SCHEMATIC REPRESENTATION OF DIFFERENTIAL CHARACTERISTICS OF ANOPHELENE AND CULICINE MOSQUITOES

an., antenna; *la.*, labella; *p*, proboscis; *pa.*, palp.

ward to the fourth abdominal segment. Air and muscular action push the thorax forward until it ruptures the pupal skin. Air is now swallowed more rapidly, and alternate movements of the legs and abdomen facilitate emergence. As soon as the midlegs are nearly withdrawn, the body of the adult, which has retained a roughly vertical position, bends forward until the forelegs reach beyond the water surface. After the hind legs are freed, the adult rests for a time upon the discarded pupal skin or adjacent vegetation.

CLASSIFICATION

The subfamily CULICINÆ is divided into three tribes: (1) ANOPHELINI, (2) CULICINI and (3) MEGARHININI of which the first two are of medical importance. The tribe MEGARHININI includes a single genus, *Megarhinus,* containing about 50 large, non-bloodsucking species with a long, curved, tapering proboscis.

DIFFERENTIATION OF ANOPHELINE AND CULICINE MOSQUITOES

The anopheline mosquitoes are differentiated from the culicine by the characteristics of their adult and larval stages (Fig. 230).

Adult.—The adult anophelines have bare sternites and an abdomen without scales; the maxillary palps of the female are about as long as the proboscis and the fourth joint only is ornamented with tufts of hair; the wings have a spotted appearance; the male hypopygium has stout spines at the base of the coxite and a ventral two- or three-lobed claspette, and at rest the body is held at an acute angle to the resting surface, except in a few species. The adult culicines have sternites and abdomen completely clothed with scales; the maxillary palps of the female are one-fifth to one-half as long as the proboscis; and the last three joints are ornamented with tufts of hair; the wings are often uniformly dark, usually without spots; the male hypopygium has no stout spines at the base of the coxite and no ventral two- or three-lobed claspette; and at rest the body is parallel to the resting surface.

Larva.—The eggs of the anopheline mosquitoes are characterized by the presence of floats and frills. The anopheline fourth-instar larva has no siphon, the spiracles lying almost flush with the surface of the eighth segment and no comb; two saber-like spines and a branched terminal hair on the head; and float hairs and tergal plates on the dorsum of the abdominal segments. The culicine fourth-instar larva has a long tubular hairy siphon on the eighth abdominal segment and on each side a collection of flattened scales, the comb; no saber-like spines and three tapering hairs on the head; and no float hairs. The anopheline pupa has an accessory hair on the ventral surface of each paddle immediately above the main paddle hair, whereas in the culicine pupa the two hairs lie side by side on the dorsal surface. The respiratory trumpets of *Anopheles* are short, broad and funnel-shaped, arise about the middle of the cephalothorax and are split in front while those of *Aëdes* are short and broad with a triangular nonsplit opening, and those of *Culex* are long, slender, nonsplit and attached to the posterior portion of the cephalothorax.

IDENTIFICATION OF MOSQUITOES

Identification of species is essential for effective mosquito control, since usually only a few species are prevalent in a locality and it is important to know their particular habits. The differentiation of genera and species is based upon a variety of characteristics in both adult and larva. The identification of mosquitoes is given in detailed keys in books on mosquitoes, to which the reader is referred.

Anopheline Mosquitoes.—The differential characteristics of the adult include (1) the coloration and pattern of the thoracic scales and bristles, (2) the form of the second marginal and second posterior cells of the wing and the color, shape, size, structure and distribution of the scales, and (3) the diversity of structure of the male hypopygium. Although anopheline larvæ closely resemble each other, many species may be identified by certain characteristics. In the fourth-instar larva these include (1) shape and relative dimensions, (2) distribution and type of hairs and bristles, and (3) the various appendages. The more important hairs are the clypeal, frontal and basal hairs of the anterior head, the inner of the three anterior, submedian, thoracic hairs, the palmate and lateral abdominal hairs, and the saddle hair of the anal segment. The length and arrangement of the teeth of the pecten of the eighth abdominal segment and the shape and dimensions of the tergal plates of the abdomen are also useful.

Culicine Mosquitoes.—The adults are differentiated by (1) the coloration and pattern of the thoracic and abdominal scales and bristles, (2) the scale-covering and veins of the wings, (3) the presence or absence of pulvilli, (4) the structure of the male hypopygium, and (5) the color and ornamentation of the legs. The species of fourth-instar larvæ are distinguished by (1) the position and type of the post-clypeal and frontal hairs of the head, (2) the shape, length, pecten and hirsute adornment of the respiratory siphon, (3) the ventral brush, anal gills and dorsal tuft of hairs of the anal segment, and (4) the comb-scales of the eighth abdominal segment.

TRIBE *ANOPHELINI*

The tribe ANOPHELINI includes the large genus *Anopheles,* divided into three subgenera *Anopheles, Nyssorhynchus* and *Myzomyia;* and two small genera *Chagasia* and *Bironella.*

Genus Chagasia.—Hypopygium with a lobe bearing two or more spines on inner side of side-piece; wings without definite light and dark spots; and white-banded tarsi.

Genus Bironella.—Hypopygium with massive spur near base of ventral surface of side-piece.

Genus Anopheles.—Hypopygium with one to six parabasal spines near base of ventral surface of side-piece.

SUBGENUS *ANOPHELES*

Hypopygium with two (rarely one to three) parabasal spines near base of ventral surface of side-piece.

Anopheles Group.—Wings without definite light and dark spots; tarsi dark.

Arribalzagia Group.—Wings with definite light and dark spots; sixth vein with four or more small dark spots.

Patagiamyia Group.—Wings with definite light and dark spots; sixth vein with one to three dark spots; costa with light areas at tip of first vein or at tips of first vein and subcosta.

SUBGENUS *NYSSORHYNCHUS*

Hypopygium with one basal and two accessory spines on ventral surface of side-piece; wings with definite light and dark areas.

Kerteszia Group.—Second, fourth and sixth veins of wings entirely dark without light areas.

Myzorhynchella Group.—Second, fourth and sixth veins of wings with some light areas; sixth vein with one to three dark spots; costa with more than two light areas; third vein nearly all dark or with three distinct spots.

Nyssorhynchus Group.—Second, fourth and sixth veins of wings with some light areas; sixth vein with one to three dark spots; costa with more than two light areas; third vein mainly white with dark spot near each end.

SUBGENUS *MYZOMYIA*

Hypopygium with four to six parabasal spines on ventral surface of side-piece.

The following key for the identification of adult American anopheline mosquitoes is abridged from that given in Hegner, Root, Augustine and Huff, *Parasitology*, 1938.

KEY TO ADULT FEMALES OF IMPORTANT AMERICAN ANOPHELINE MOSQUITOES

SUBGENUS *ANOPHELES*

1. Hind tibia all dark, wings with four indistinct dark spots.......................... 2
2. Wing fringe all dark...*A. quadrimaculatus*
   Wing fringe coppery or yellowish at tip of wing....................*A. maculipennis*
3. Sixth vein with one to three dark spots.
   Costa of wing with light areas only at tip of first vein or at tips of first vein and
   subcosta 4
4. Costa white only at tip of first vein; sixth vein with three dark spots....*A. crucians*
5. Costa white at tips of first vein and subcosta; sixth vein with only one or two dark areas 6
6. Sixth vein with two dark areas; third vein dark, except sometimes at tip; palpi dark
   A. punctipennis
   Sixth vein with one dark area, third vein extensively white in middle; palpi with
   narrow white rings......................................*A. pseudopunctipennis*
7. Sixth vein with four or more dark spots; third and fourth hind tarsals with at least
   two white rings each.
   Fifth hind tarsal with a black ring; dark area at tip of wing about the same size
   as the dark area between it and the large dark area just beyond the tip of the subcosta.
   A. punctimacula
   Fifth hind tarsal with a black ring; dark area at tip of wing decidedly larger than
   the dark area between it and the large dark area just beyond the tip of the subcosta 8
8. Third vein extensively white in middle; broadest wing scales about one-third as broad
   as long...*A. pseudomaculipes*
   Third vein with numerous light and dark areas; broadest wing scales nearly half as
   broad as long, enlarged, with rounded tips....................*A. intermedius*
   Third vein either extensively white in middle or with many small light and dark
   areas; broadest wing-scales nearly half as broad as long, not enlarged, truncate
   at tip..*A. apicimacula*

SUBGENUS *NYSSORHYNCHUS*

9. Wings with definite light and dark spots produced by alternate light-scaled and
   dark-scaled areas; second, fourth and sixth veins of wing with some light-scaled
   areas; sixth vein with one to three dark spots; costa with more than two light-
   scaled areas; third vein mainly white with a small dark spot near each end........ 10

10. Third, fourth and fifth hind tarsals all white; white spot on costa near humeral cross-vein smaller than the black spot just basal to it.....................*A. darlingi*

White spot on costa near humeral cross-vein larger than black spot just basal to it.... 11

11. Midtarsi with definite white rings; second hind tarsal joint usually with much more white than black...*A. argyritarsis*

12. Fifth hind tarsal with black ring, third and fourth white; white spot on costa near humeral cross-vein larger than the black spot just basal to it...................... 13

13. Next to last joint of female palpi mainly black; second hind tarsal joint usually more black than white..*A. albimanus*

Next to last joint of female palpi mainly white; second hind tarsal joint usually more white than black...*A. tarsimaculatus*

KEY TO THE LARVÆ OF THE GENUS *ANOPHELES* OCCURRING IN THE UNITED STATES [6]

1. Abdomen with plumose lateral hairs on first six segments; head hairs simple..*A. barberi*

Abdomen with plumose lateral hairs on first three segments only; head with plumose hairs 2

2. Outer clypeal hairs simple, unbranched; elements of dorsal abdominal palmate hairs with long slender apical portion...............................*A. pseudopunctipennis*

Outer clypeal hairs branched; inner clypeal hairs simple, branched, or feathered; elements of dorsal palmate tuft notched toward tip.............................. 3

3. Outer clypeal hairs with few (5 to 8) branches; inner clypeal hairs usually divided into two or more branches toward tip; occipital hairs simple............*A. atropos*

Outer clypeal hairs thickly branched, fan-like..................................... 4

4. Abdominal segments 4 and 5 with two conspicuous hairs anterior to the palmate tuft (these are of approximately equal size and each has from 4 to 9 branches)
   A. crucians (fresh-water race)

Abdominal segments 4 and 5 with but one conspicuous hair anterior to the palmate hairs (this may be single or with 2 or 3 branches)................................. 5

5. Abdomen with palmate tufts on segments 3 to 7 inclusive of similar form but those on segments 3 and 7 noticeably smaller than the others; posterior clypeal hairs long, usually single; antennal branched hair long, being approximately one-half the length of the segment from which it arises; tubercles of inner anterior clypeal hairs wide or close..*A. crucians* (brackish-water race)

Abdomen with the palmate tufts on segments 3 to 7 inclusive, of approximately equal size 6

6. Tubercles of inner anterior clypeal hairs separated by at least the width of one of these tubercles; antepalmate hairs on segments 4 and 5 usually single, palmate tufts on segment 2 usually well developed...........................*A. quadrimaculatus*

Tubercles of inner anterior clypeal hairs so close together that another tubercle of similar size could not be placed between them.................................... 7

7. Inner anterior clypeal hairs not minutely feathered toward tip; antepalmate hairs of abdominal segments 4 and 5 usually double or triple.............................. 8

Inner anterior clypeal hairs minutely feathered toward tip; antepalmate hairs of abdominal segments 4 and 5 usually single..................................... 9

8. Antepalmate hairs of abdominal segments 4 and 5 usually with two branches, rarely one or three; posterior clypeal hairs usually with two branches from near base; inner anterior clypeal hairs single, unbranched......................*A. punctipennis*

Antepalmate hairs of abdominal segments 4 and 5 usually with three branches, rarely two or four; posterior clypeal hairs usually long, with apical branching; inner anterior clypeal hairs unbranched or with two to three branches beyond middle
   A. maculipennis

9. Hairs 1 and 3 of submedian prothoracic group of approximately equal length; hair 0 on abdominal segments 2 to 6 poorly developed, usually single or having one to three branches....................................*A. walkeri* (northern race)

Hair 1 of submedian prothoracic group approximately twice as long as hair 3; hair 0 on abdominal segments 2 to 6 fairly well developed and having three to seven branches....................................*A. walkeri* (southern race)

[6] Bradley, G. H., 1936.

TABLE 41

GEOGRAPHICAL DISTRIBUTION OF SOME ANOPHELINE VECTORS OF MALARIA

Subgenus	North America	Central and South America and West Indies	Europe	Africa	Asia and East Indies	Oceania and Australia
Anopheles	A. crucians A. maculipennis A. punctipennis A. pseudopunctipennis A. qua rimaculatus	A. crucians A. pseudopunctipennis A. apicimacula A. intermedius A. pseudomaculipes A. punctimacula	A. hyrcanus A. maculipennis	A. maculipennis A. umbrosus	A. hyrcanus A. maculipennis A. umbrosus	
Nyssorhynchus		A. albimanus A. albitarsis A. argyritarsis A. darlingi A. tarsimaculatus				A. annulipes
Mysomyia		A. gambiæ (imported)	A. hispaniola A. superpictus	A. funestus A. gambiæ A. hispaniola A. pharensis A. superpictus	A. barbirostris A. culicifacies A. fluviatilis A. maculatus A. minimus A. philippinensis A. stephensi A. superpictus	A. punctulatus

A. albimanus.—This medium-sized black mosquito with yellow spots on its wings is found in Mexico, Central America, the West Indies and northern South America. It breeds in streams, swamps and marshes. It is an important vector of malaria in the humid regions of Mexico and the Caribbean countries.

A. annulipes.—This mosquito is found in Australia and New Hebrides, where it is suspected epidemiologically of being a malarial carrier. It breeds in swamps and stagnant pools.

A. argyritarsis.—This mosquito with white spots on the costa of the wing is found in Central America, the West Indies and South America, where it is recognized as a malarial carrier.

A. crucians.—This medium-sized black mosquito with mottled wings is found in the South Atlantic and Gulf States of the United States of America. There are two varieties, one breeding in brackish and the other in fresh water. It is a relatively unimportant vector of malaria.

A. culicifacies.—This mosquito, found in Arabia, India and Siam, is considered the most important malarial vector in India. It breeds in clear, fresh and brackish waters.

A. darlingi.—This mosquito is prevalent in Brazil and British Guiana. It is a domestic species, being almost exclusively the only species of anopheline mosquitoes caught in houses.[7] It breeds in ditches, shallow pools and small swamps on the coast in sugar and rice plantations, and in the interior in seepage swamps. It is an important malarial carrier since it is androphilous, whereas *A. albitarsis* and *A. tarsimaculatus* though abundant and potential carriers in the same areas, are zoophilous.

A. funestus.—This mosquito has a wide distribution in tropical Africa. It breeds in clear, sluggish streams and is an important vector of malaria.

A. gambiæ.—This mosquito has a wide distribution in tropical Africa and southern Arabia. It has been introduced into Brazil, probably from Dakar, Africa. It breeds in stagnant pools and sluggish streams and frequents human habitations. It is an important vector of malaria.

A. hyrcanus.—This mosquito ranges from southern Europe to China and Japan. In China the variety *sinensis* is considered an important malarial carrier. The varieties *nigerrimus* and *sinensis* are vectors of *Wuchereria bancrofti* and *W. malayi*.

A. maculatus.—This mosquito is found in India, southeastern Asia, and the East Indies. It is recognized as a malarial carrier in Malaya and the Dutch East Indies. It breeds in clear streams.

A. maculipennis.—This medium-sized mosquito (Fig. 231) has a wide distribution in North America on the Pacific coast and northern border of the United States and in Canada; throughout Europe; in northern Africa and in northern, western and central Asia. It is an important vector of malaria, but its rôle in this respect varies greatly with different varieties or races. In Europe certain varieties feed almost entirely on domestic animals (zoophilous) and others have a preference for human blood (androphilous). The zoophilous races are a minor factor in the transmission of malaria, unless domestic and wild animals are so scarce that they are forced to feed on man. The androphilous races because of their domestic habits and tendency to winter in houses are the main vectors of malaria. In England and northern Europe the zoophilous and androphilous variety *atroparvus,* chiefly a coastal form breeding in waters of slight to moderate salinity, is the important vector, whereas, the zoophilous variety *messeæ,* an inland form breeding in cold fresh water, is of little consequence. In the Mediterranean area malaria is not endemic in districts where the varieties *maculipennis* and *messeæ* are present, is of low endemicity where *atroparvus* is found and is highly endemic where *sacharovi* and *labranchiæ,* brackish-water breeders, are abundant. In the Steppe region of Russia *atroparvus, messeæ* and *maculipennis,* because of the small number of domestic animals, may act as vectors. Experiments in the selection of hosts have demonstrated that the animal-to-man ratio of *atroparvus* is 12:1, *labranchiæ* 1:2.2 and *sacharovi* 1:2.4.[8]

---

[7] Giglioli, G., 1939.   [8] Van Thiel, P. and Bevere, L., 1939.

A. punctipennis.—This medium-sized mosquito is widely distributed in Canada, the United States and Mexico. It breeds in streams, ponds and small pools. It prefers to feed upon large animals and is a relatively unimportant vector of malaria.

A. pseudopunctipennis.—This medium-sized black mosquito with white spotted wings is found in the southwestern United States, Mexico, Central America, West Indies and South America. It breeds in pools, streams and springs. It is unimportant in the United States, but is considered an important vector of malaria in the dry regions of southern Mexico and in Argentina.

A. punctimacula.—This mosquito is found in Central America, Colombia and Trinidad. It breeds mainly in jungle pools. It probably is one of the most common vectors of malaria in the Panama Canal Zone.[9]

A. quadrimaculatus.—This medium-sized black mosquito is found throughout the United States of America east of the Rocky Mountains. It is the principal vector of malaria in the southern United States.

A. stephensi.—This mosquito is found in Arabia, Mesopotamia, India and French Indo-China. It is an urban species breeding in wells, cisterns and small pools. It is an important vector of malaria.

TRIBE *CULICINI*

The large tribe CULICINI contains five groups of wild and domestic species. The various American genera may be identified by the following keys from Hegner, Root, Augustine and Huff, *Parasitology* (1938) as modified from Edwards (1932).

Sabethes Group.—Formerly classed under tribe SABETHINI; large mosquitoes of many genera in the Eastern and Western Hemispheres; mostly tropical; breed in water collected by plants; genus *Wyeomyia* most common in the eastern United States; not vectors of human disease.

Uranotænia Group.—Formerly classed under tribe URANOTÆNINI; small mosquitoes with patches of brilliant blue scales on thorax and base of certain wing veins; breed chiefly in ground pools and marshes; larvæ have superficial resemblance to those of *Anopheles;* species of the single genus *Uranotænia* mainly tropical; *U. sapphirinus* only species in the eastern United States; not vectors of human disease.

Theobaldia-Mansonia Group.—A loosely-related group including the genera *Theobaldia, Orthopodomyia, Mansonia, Aëdeomyia* and *Ficalbia,* of which the last is not found in the Western Hemisphere; certain species vectors of human disease.

Aëdes Group.—Includes the genera *Aëdes, Psorophora, Hæmagogus, Eretmopodites, Armigeres, Heizmannia,* and *Opifex,* of which the last four are not found in the Western Hemisphere; breed in temporary pools or depressions that will be flooded with water; certain species vectors of human disease.

Culex Group.—Includes the large genus *Culex* and the nonbiting genus *Deinocerites;* breed in permanent bodies of water; certain species vectors of human disease.

KEYS TO THE AMERICAN GENERA OF TRIBE *CULICINI* [10]

A. BY ADULT CHARACTERS

1. Squama fringed (usually completely); 6th vein reaching well beyond fork of 5th vein 2
   Squama bare or rarely with 1-4 short hairs.................................... 13
2. Pulvilli present; pleural hairs well developed but spiracular and post-spiracular bristles
   absent 3
   Pulvilli absent or rudimentary.. 4

---

[9] Simmons, J. S., 1936.

[10] Hegner, R., Root, F. M., Augustine, D. L. and Huff, C. G., *Parasitology,* 1938.

3. Second antennal segment short in both sexes; antennæ of male nearly always plumose ....*Culex*
   Second antennal segment elongate in both sexes; antennæ of male not plumose
   Deinocerites
4. Post-spiracular bristles absent; claws of female simple (except in *Hæmagogus*)   5
   Post-spiracular bristles present (even if only one or two); claws of female usually
   toothed, dorsocentral and upper sternopleural bristles nearly always well developed   11
5. Spiracular bristles present (sometimes only one or two)..........................   6
   Spiracular bristles absent..   8
6. Several upper sternopleural bristles; subcostal vein basal to humeral cross-vein usually
   hairy beneath..*Theobaldia*
   At most one or two upper sternopleural bristles; subcostal vein basal to humeral
   cross-vein bare beneath...   7
7. Clypeus with setæ...........................*Trichoprosopon* (*Joblotia*)
   Clypeus bare...*Goeldia*
8. Dorsocentral and prescutellar bristles absent; pronotal lobes approximated.*Hæmagogus*
   Dorsocentral and prescutellar bristles well developed; pronotal lobes well separated   9
9. All segments of female antenna, and last two of male antenna short and thick; middle
   femora with scale-tuft......................................*Aëdeomyia*
   Antennæ normal, slender; middle femora without scale-tuft.........................   10
10. First segment of front tarsi longer than the last four together, fourth very short in
    both sexes..*Orthopodomyia*
    First segment of front tarsi not longer than last four together; fourth not shortened
    in female...*Mansonia*
11. Spiracular bristles present, even if few..............................*Psorophora*
    Spiracular bristles absent...   12
12. Wing-scales generally mostly narrow (or if all broad, female claws toothed); usually
    a few hairs on upper surface of subcostal stem basal to humeral cross-vein (stem vein)
    Aëdes
    Wing-scales all very broad; female claws simple, subcostal stem basal to humeral
    cross-vein (stem vein) bare.....................................*Mansonia*
13. Wing-membrane without microtrichia (or only visible at high magnification); second
    marginal cell (R_2) shorter than its stem; 6th vein ends basal to fork of 5th vein
    Uranotænia
    Wing-membrane with distinct microtrichia...   14
14. Middle legs with "paddles" formed of very long erect scales.................*Sabethes*
    Middle legs without "paddles"...   15
15. Clypeus with hairs; large species, with long palpi in male..*Trichoprosopon* (*Joblotia*)
    Clypeus bare, or with scales only...   16
16. Hind tarsi with long suberect scales; large species, with long palpi in male..*Goeldia*
    Hind tarsi with appressed scales only; smaller species with short palpi in male......   17
17. No bristles on sub-alar knob; pronotal lobes large and almost in contact; mesonotal
    scales all metallic...*Sabethoides*
    Bristles present on sub-alar knob; pronotal lobes more widely separated; mesonotal
    scales rarely metallic...   18
18. Spiracular area with scales only; hind tarsus with one claw..............*Limatus*
    Spiracular area with 1-4 bristles; hind tarsus with two claws...........*Wyeomyia*

B. BY LARVAL CHARACTERS

1. Anal segment with ventral brush of at least four separate hairs....................   2
   Anal segment with one pair of ventral hairs.......................................   13
   Anal segment without ventral hairs...*Culex*
2. Eighth segment with lateral chitinous plates, with one row of comb-teeth on its margin;
   mouthbrushes normal...................................*Uranotænia*, *Aëdeomyia*
   Eighth segment without lateral plates (except sometimes in *Psorophora*)............   3
3. Air-tube with pecten, teeth usually denticulate (pecten rarely reduced)..............   4
   Air-tube without pecten or rarely with a few simple teeth.........................   10
4. Air-tube with several pairs of hair-tufts, or else very long and slender..............   5
   Air-tube with one pair of hair-tufts, and never very long...........................   7

5. Mouthbrushes forming matted prehensile tufts.....................*Culex* (*Lutzia*)
   Mouthbrushes normal 6
6. Mandibles with hairy projection at base...............................*Deinocerites*
   Mandibles without such projection..........*Culex, Theobaldia* (*Culicella, Climacura*)
7. Hair-tuft on air-tube basal ....*Theobaldia*
   Hair-tuft on air-tube near middle, often beyond.................................. 8
8. Mouthbrushes forming matted prehensile tufts.....................*Psorophora, Aëdes*
   Mouthbrushes normal 9
9. Anal segment with ring complete.........................*Psorophora, Uranotænia*
   Anal segment (except rarely) with ring incomplete...............*Aëdes, Hæmagogus*
10. Valves of air-tube highly modified for piercing...........................*Mansonia*
    Valves of air-tube not modified... 11
11. Abdominal segments 6-8 normally with dorsal chitinous plates..........*Orthopodomyia*
    Abdomen without plates on segments 6-8....................................... 12
12. Antennæ very large and flattened.......................................*Aëdeomyia*
    Antennæ nearly round 13
13. Eighth abdominal segment without comb, but with small lateral plate bearing a simple
    bristle ....*Trichoprosopon* (*Joblotia*)
    Eighth abdominal segment with lateral comb as usual............................ 14
14. Eighth segment with a pair of dorsal chitinous hooks.....................*Sabethoides*
    Eighth segment without dorsal hooks.. 15
15. Maxilla large, ending in two strong articulated horns.......................*Goeldia*
    Maxilla without such horns 16
16. Maxilla with slender spine or tooth at its tip............................*Sabethes*
    Maxilla hairy at tip 17
17. Lateral comb of eighth abdominal segment consisting of a few separate scales..*Limatus*
    Comb scales numerous, sometimes attached to a lateral plate..............*Wyeomyia*

GENUS *THEOBALDIA*

Species largely confined to north temperate regions of world; fairly large mosquitoes; *T. inornata* most common species in the eastern United States; not vectors of human disease.

GENUS *ORTHOPODOMYIA*

Small genus of medium-sized mosquitoes of cosmopolitan distribution; resemble *Aëdes;* breed in tree-holes and water held by plants; *O. signifera* only species in the United States of America; not vectors of human disease.

GENUS *MANSONIA*

Adults have white-banded legs and usually a mixture of black and white scales on wings; cosmopolitan distribution but largely tropical; eggs are deposited in clumps on leaves of aquatic plants (*Pistia*), and larvæ obtain oxygen from the air cavities in the roots and food from suspended organic matter; *M. perturbans* is only species found outside of Florida in the United States; certain species are intermediate hosts of filarial parasites of man.

GENUS *AËDEOMYIA*

The three species of *Aëdeomyia* are distributed in the tropical regions of the Eastern and Western Hemispheres. These small mosquitoes, resembling *Mansonia,* breed in ponds with dense surface vegetation. They are not vectors of human disease.

GENUS *AËDES*

Numerous species of small to medium-sized mosquitoes with white-banded legs and thorax with stripes, or patches of silver or gold scales; divided into many subgenera mainly on hypopygial characters; breed in tree holes, temporary pools of fresh surface or tidal water; cosmopolitan distribution; certain species act as vectors of yellow fever, dengue, equine encephalitis and filariasis; many species are noxious and troublesome biters in North America, including among others *A. vexans,* a freshwater breeder, and the salt marsh mosquitoes *A. sollicitans, A. tæniorhynchus, A. dorsalis, A. squamiger* and *A. aldrichi.*

Aëdes ægypti.—*Aëdes ægypti* (Fig. 231) is a small, blackish-brown mosquito with silver stripes on thorax (lyre markings), abdomen and legs, a black proboscis and white-tipped palpi. It breeds in the immediate environment of man in artificial collections of water and is urban rather than rural in distribution. The females bite during the day and less frequently at night. It is the principal vector of yellow fever and dengue, and also transmits equine encephalitis, lymphocytic choriomeningitis (experimentally), herpes encephalomyelitis and filariasis.

Aëdes albopictus.—In the Orient *A. albopictus,* distinguished by a single silvery stripe down the middle of the thorax, is a vector of dengue, yellow fever (experimentally) and equine encephalitis.

Aëdes variegatus.—This species, which resembles *A. albopictus* but has white bands only on the sides of the abdominal segments, is widely distributed in the Pacific islands, where though a day-biter it is an important intermediate host of *Wuchereria bancrofti.*

GENUS *PSOROPHORA*

Species of the genus *Psorophora,* found only in America, comprise several subgenera and range from small mosquitoes superficially resembling *Mansonia* to large bluish mosquitoes often with white hind tarsi. Certain species are passive carriers of the larvæ of the botfly, *Dermatobia hominis,* to man and other mammals and have been incriminated as vectors of the jungle type of yellow fever.

GENUS *HÆMAGOGUS*

These metallic blue or purple mosquitoes, comprising only a few species, are confined to tropical America and breed in tree holes and cut bamboo. They are not vectors of human disease.

GENUS *DEINOCERITES*

The genus *Deinocerites,* closely allied to *Culex,* includes a few tropical American species that breed only in crab-holes and do not bite man.

GENUS *CULEX*

Large genus of small and medium-sized mosquitoes; many subgenera distinguished by hypopygial characteristics; cosmopolitan distribution; breed mostly in permanent bodies of water, the eggs being deposited in rafts, although a few species breed in temporary bodies of water and tree-holes.

Culex fatigans (quinquefasciatus).—*Culex fatigans* (Fig. 231), the most important intermediate host of *Wuchereria bancrofti,* is a medium-sized reddish-brown mosquito. The legs and proboscis have black scales; the abdomen is black above with white basal segmental bands, separated from the lateral spots; and the wings have dark, narrow, hair-like scales. It has become a common domestic mosquito, breeding in ground pools and artificial receptacles near human habitations, throughout the tropics and subtropics. Its range in America is from 35° N to 35° S latitude.

Culex pipiens.—*Culex pipiens,* similar in habits to *C. fatigans,* is the common house mosquito of the temperate regions of the world. It is also a vector of filariasis. Several varieties of *C. pipiens* and other species such as *C. subpictus, C. sundaicus* and *C. vagans* also transmit filariasis.

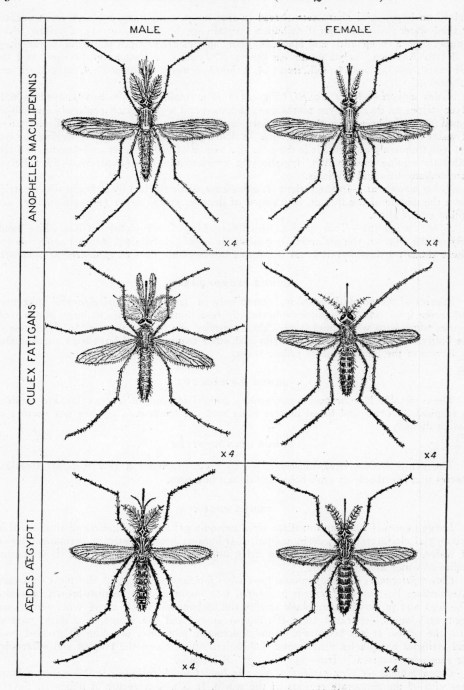

FIG. 231.—*Anopheles maculipennis, Culex fatigans* AND *Aëdes ægypti*
(Adapted from various sources).

PATHOGENESIS

The effect of the bite varies with the species of mosquito and with the susceptibility of the individual, some bites causing little and others extreme irritation. Occasionally persons manifest severe local symptoms of an allergic nature. The ordinary bite is followed by the appearance of wheals with erythema, swelling and itching lasting from a few hours to several days. Vesicular bullæ may appear and secondary infection may supervene.

The irritation is commonly believed to result from the salivary secretions injected into the wound. The problem is more complicated than the mere presence of toxic substances in the saliva, since many parts of the mosquito, including the salivary glands, esophageal diverticula, malpighian tubules, stomach and ovaries, when introduced into the skin, will produce similar reactions.[11]

Many remedies, namely, alcohol, iodine, ammonia, phenol, camphor, soap, etc., may give some relief from mosquito bites. The immediate application of a disinfectant, however, will not prevent infection with malaria or yellow fever, although it may prevent subsequent entrance of filarial larvæ.

MOSQUITOES AS VECTORS OF DISEASE

Mosquitoes serve as intermediate hosts in the transmission of four important diseases of man: (1) malaria, (2) yellow fever, (3) dengue, and (4) filariasis. Equine encephalomyelitis, a disease of man as well as equines, has been transmitted experimentally by eight species of *Aëdes,* but since the virus is readily transferred by the nasal route, means of transmission other than by mosquitoes are probable.[12] *Aëdes ægypti* has been shown to transmit the western type;[13] *Aëdes sollicitans,* the saltmarsh mosquito, both the eastern and western types;[14] and *Aëdes albopictus* the western type experimentally.[15] *Aëdes ægypti* also is the experimental vector of the neurotropic virus of herpes encephalomyelitis,[15] and of the virus of lymphocytic choriomeningitis 4 to 15 days after the infective blood meal.[16] Culicine mosquitoes of the genera *Culex* and *Aëdes* have been proved vectors of avian malaria and fowl pox (epithelioma contagiosum). Mosquitoes of the genus *Psorophora* carry the eggs of the botfly, *Dermatobia hominis,* to human skin which is penetrated by the larvæ. Likewise, staphylococcal, streptococcal and fungal infections and tularemia may be transmitted mechanically by mosquitoes. Species of *Aëdes, Anopheles* and *Mansonia* harbored *Pasteurella tularensis* for a month and were able to produce tularemia in sheep and rodents by their bites.[17]

MALARIA

Anopheline mosquitoes are the intermediate hosts of the plasmodia of human and simian malaria. Of the 150 or more recognized species some 70 have been

---

[11] Manalang, C., 1931.
[12] Riley, W. A., 1938.
[13] Kelser, R. A., 1933.
[14] Merrill, M. H., Lacaillade, C. M., Jr. and Ten Broeck, C., 1934.
[15] Simmons, J. S., Reynolds, F. H. K., and Cornell, V. H., 1936.
[16] Coggeshall, L. T., 1939.
[17] Olsuf'ev, N. G., 1939.

incriminated as potential carriers, of which 19 are of major and 24 of minor importance, while the remaining species are not natural carriers. The aptitude of a species or variety of anopheline mosquito for transmitting malaria is determined by its habits and susceptibility to the malarial parasite. It must breed and live near human habitations and must prefer human blood. The topography of the country must provide such breeding places, and the climate not only must favor its propagation but also permit the normal development of the parasite within the mosquito. Changes in local conditions may transform a species from a negligible to an important malarial carrier. Furthermore, the problem of malarial transmission is complicated by the different species of *Plasmodium,* the production of gametocyte carriers, and the social, economic and racial status of the population (Chapter XIII). Hence, a species that may be an important transmitter in one country may be relatively unimportant in another. The habits of species and even of varieties differ, thus explaining the absence of malaria in localities where suitable species of *Anopheles* are present. For instance, malaria is indigenous in certain coastal districts of Europe where *Anopheles maculipennis* var. *atroparvus* and other species breed in brackish water and hibernate in dwelling houses and barns, but is absent in areas where the zoophilous *Anopheles maculipennis* var. *messeæ* or var. *maculipennis* breeds in inland waters.

Anopheline Surveys.—The methods usually employed to determine whether a particular species of *Anopheles* is an important vector in a locality are: (1) epidemiological index; (2) experimental index; and (3) natural index. It is sometimes possible to obtain presumptive epidemiological evidence by correlating the presence of a particular species with the presence of malaria. Laboratory-hatched species may be allowed to feed on malarial patients and later dissected in order to determine whether an appreciable percentage (25 to 50 per cent) have become infected. This experimental method, however, indicates only the species that are potential carriers, irrespective of whether they normally feed on man. The index of natural infection may be determined by dissecting female mosquitoes collected from houses. Since the natural index is usually less than 5 per cent and in most instances a fraction of 1 per cent, large numbers of mosquitoes must be dissected. A combination of the experimental feeding method and the determination of the species feeding on man or present in human habitations often provides the most practical line of attack.

Malarial parasites may be found in infected mosquitoes as oöcysts in the stomach wall or as sporozoites in the salivary glands. The latter is the more reliable index, since it signifies the complete development of the parasite in the mosquito. The salivary glands and stomach may be examined directly in cover-glass mounts with the high-power compound microscope, or they may be fixed and stained (Section **VII,** XII, 10 and 11).

In determining the prevailing species of anopheline mosquitoes in a district, both adults and larvæ should be obtained. The adults may be collected in their daytime resting places in houses, barns, hollow trees and under protecting barriers, or baited with domestic animals at dusk. Larvæ may be collected from the breeding grounds, especially where aquatic plants are abundant, by skimming the surface with dippers. They may be reared in the laboratory, but require regular change of water and feeding with powdered insect tissue, blood serum or algæ. Since *Anopheles* breed in widely different locations, careful records of the localities where larvæ are present should be made.

YELLOW FEVER

Yellow fever is a viral disease of high mortality, at times producing epidemics in nonimmune populations. Its original focus was the West Coast of Africa but it has spread over tropical and subtropical regions. It is confined chiefly to the Atlantic seacoast although there are foci on the Pacific coast of Central and South America. Epidemics have been recorded ever since the fifteenth century. Several cities in Central and South America and the West Indies were the endemic centers, from which the disease was once carried by ships to the cities of the Atlantic coast of the United States of America. The pioneer work of Findlay and the experiments of Reed, Carroll, Agramonte and Lazear (1900) proved that *Aëdes ægypti* was the transmitting agent. The elimination of the disease in Havana, Cuba, and in the Canal Zone by mosquito-control substantiated this finding. The mosquito can only be infected by biting the patient during the first three days of the disease; the virus requires an incubation of 12 days before the mosquito becomes infective; and the mosquito remains infective all its life.

Since 1928 some 33 species of mosquitoes other than *Aëdes ægypti* in Africa, South America and the Orient have been found to be experimental vectors of yellow fever; 3 *Anopheles;* 16 *Aëdes;* 6 *Mansonia;* 2 *Culex;* 2 *Psorophora;* 2 *Wyeomyia;* 1 *Limatus;* and 1 *Eretmopodites*.[18] More recently the jungle mosquitoes, *Aëdes leucocelænus* and *Hæmagogus capricorni,* have been naturally infected near Rio de Janeiro, Brazil.[19] Undoubtedly, many other species may harbor the virus, some without transmitting it by their bite, and others transmitting it poorly. Probably few of the experimental vectors play an important rôle in the transmission of the disease. The rural and jungle types of yellow fever in Brazil, Colombia and Bolivia are present without the presence of *Aëdes ægypti*. The existence of these types, with a possible animal reservoir, renders the complete elimination of yellow fever improbable.

DENGUE

Dengue is an endemic viral disease of the tropics and subtropics that at times becomes epidemic. The disease lasts from three to eight days and has a low fatality rate. It is an acute febrile disease that is characterized by an abrupt onset, and intense muscular and joint pains. The virus is transmitted chiefly by *Aëdes ægypti*. but *Anopheles albopictus* and *Armigeres perturbans* have also been found to be vectors in the Orient. Infection is acquired by the mosquito during the first three days of the patient's illness and an incubation period of eight to ten days is required before the mosquito becomes infective for life.

[18] Biraud, Y., 1935.

[19] Shannon, R. C., Whitman, L. and Franca, M., 1938.

FILARIASIS

Mosquitoes are the vectors of two filarial parasites of man: (1) *Wuchereria bancrofti* and (2) *W. malayi* (Chapter XXI).

Wuchereria bancrofti.—*Culex fatigans,* a night-biting mosquito is the most common intermediate host of the prevailing nocturnal form of *Wuchereria bancrofti* but *Aëdes variegatus,* a day-biting mosquito, is an important host in the Pacific islands. Other species are susceptible to infection, but the microfilariæ do not complete their development. The determination of these hosts for the most part has been made by allowing the mosquitoes to feed on heavily-infected persons and observing the development of the larval worms. Some 41 or more species in various parts of the world have shown complete development of the microfilariæ, but most of these are unimportant as natural carriers. Complete development has been recorded in 22 species of *Anopheles* (*albimanus, albitarsis, algeriensis, amictus, bachmanni, barbirostris, coastalis, fuliginosus, funestus, hyrcanus* var. *nigerrimus* and var. *sinensis, ludlowi, pallidus, philippinensis, pseudojamesi, punctulatus, rhodesiensis, rossi, squamosus, stephensi, subpictus, sundaicus, tarsimaculatus* and *varuna*); 8 species of *Aëdes* (*albopictus, ægypti, chemilpœnis, koreicus, ochraceus, scutellaris, togoi,* and *variegatus*); 5 species of *Culex* (*fatigans, pipiens* and *pipiens* var. *pallens, tripiliformis, vagans* and *whitmori*); and 6 species of *Mansonia* subgenus *Mansonioides* (*annulata, annulifera, juxtamansonia, longipalpis, pseudotitillans,* and *uniformis*).

Wuchereria malayi.—The mosquitoes that have been incriminated as vectors of *W. malayi* include *Anopheles barbirostris* and *A. hyrcanus* var. *nigerrimus* and var. *sinensis; Armigeres obturbans;* and six species of *Mansonia* (*annulatus, annuliferus, annulipes, indiana, longipalpis* and *uniformis*). The principal carriers belong to the genus *Mansonia.*

MOSQUITO CONTROL

The problem of mosquito control involves the habits of the particular species; the topography and climate of the country; and the racial, social and economic status of the population. When such control aims to prevent disease rather than to eliminate a nuisance, the problem centers upon determining the offending species. The cost of control measures must be kept within limits commensurate with the financial status of the community.

Mosquito control is primarily directed against the larvæ. Permanent results are attained by destroying breeding grounds by drainage and other measures, and temporary results by the destruction of the larvæ. Although both methods are usually employed, the type of control is necessarily governed by the topography of the district and the available funds. The permanent reduction of breeding grounds through drainage involves a high initial and a subsequent maintenance cost, while larvicidal measures, though less expensive, require an annual outlay. Since the flight of most species is restricted, partial control is of value even when limited to breeding grounds near human habitations. In each locality the measures adopted should give the maximal results for the available funds.

PROTECTION AGAINST ADULT MOSQUITOES

Natural Enemies.—Dragonflies, birds such as swallows, swifts and night-hawks, and bats are natural enemies of adult mosquitoes. Parasitic mites, protozoa (microsporidia), bacteria and fungi also attack them. Although results from the propagation of bats by erecting "bat roosts" in Texas are encouraging, the elimination of mosquitoes by such methods seems hardly practicable.

Personal Protection.—In mosquito-infested districts the individual may be protected during the day by headnets, gloves, high boots and clothing and at night by 18-mesh mosquito nets over the bed. The application of repellents to the exposed skin is a popular, but because of rapid evaporation, not a particularly effective protective measure. A mixture of two parts oil of citronella, two parts spirits of camphor and one part oil of cedar by weight, is recommended.

Protection of Buildings.—The elimination of mosquitoes from dwelling houses is important. Light, airy rooms with white walls attract these pests less readily than dark, damp rooms. Doors and windows should be tightly screened, preferably with 18-mesh bronze wire screening, since most species cannot penetrate screen openings less than .046 inch (16 meshes). Cloth netting, though more impenetrable to mosquitoes than wire screens, is easily damaged, less durable, and tends to exclude breezes. Chimneys and cracks should also be carefully blocked or screened. In highly-malarial districts double screening of doorways is advisable. Mosquito bars of fine-mesh cloth over beds are especially effective if kept in repair and hung in such a manner that the sleeper does not come in contact with the netting. Special frames are manufactured for campers.

Screening should be supplemented by the destruction of mosquitoes that pass the barrier. Mosquitoes may be killed with "fly swatters" or captured by holding a cup of kerosene below those resting on walls or ceilings. Mosquito traps, boxes with dark-colored interiors, from which the mosquitoes do not readily escape, have been used with some success. Fumigants and lethal sprays are most effective, however, in ridding houses of mosquitoes. Those hibernating in vacant houses may be destroyed by fumigation with hydrocyanic gas or sulphur, although the latter impairs metals and other household furnishings. Insect powders, such as pyrethrum (dried flower heads of certain species of chrysanthemums) may be dusted around doors, in corners, recesses and fireplaces. Pyrethrum sprays are effective, particularly with a high temperature and low humidity (Section **VII**, XIII, 36). Carbolic acid, gum camphor, cresol, arsenic and various commercial preparations, are also helpful. In camps, smudges afford some relief.

Airplanes:—Attention has recently been directed to the transportation of dangerous species of mosquitoes and other insects from tropical countries by airplane. Five species of mosquitoes, including *Culex fatigans* and *Anopheles albimanus,* and a variety of flies, gnats, bugs, beetles, cockroaches, wasps and moths have been found in airplanes arriving at Miami, Florida.[20] Various methods of fumigation during flight or at the ports of call have been tried, not always with complete success, living insects having been found in 17 out of 44 planes.[21] Both interior and exterior

---

[20] Welch, E. V., 1938.   [21] Rosso, G. A. P., 1938.

hiding places should be treated. Insects lodged in the interior of the wings and rudder present perhaps the more difficult problem. An aqueous base pyrethrum spray (150 c.c. of 1 :30 insecticide for 1,000 cubic feet) applied by a Phantomyst sprayer is sufficient to kill mosquitoes inside airplanes (Section **VII**, XIII, 36).[22]

Animal Barriers.—Diverting disease-carrying mosquitoes from man to animals presents an interesting biological problem. Such natural barriers may prove effective in satisfying the blood-meal requirements of certain varieties of *Anopheles maculipennis*. The incidence of malaria fell from 32 to 7.5 per cent in two years following the erection of pigsties around an Italian village.[23]

DESTRUCTION OF BREEDING GROUNDS

Permanent elimination of mosquitoes requires the destruction of their breeding grounds. Here knowledge of the species involved is essential. Certain species, such as *Aëdes ægypti, Culex fatigans, C. pipiens, Anopheles albopictus* and *A. stephensi,* are domestic, breeding in cisterns, gutters and miscellaneous water containers. Other species, such as *Anopheles quadrimaculatus,* use bodies of relatively clean, quiet water. Still others utilize brackish water, flowing streams, tree holes, swamps, marshes and jungles. In different countries the same species may have different breeding places; for example, brackish water for one variety and fresh water for another. As a rule, most species breed in the shade but a few prefer sunlight. Drainage is applicable to species that breed in quiet pools, while damming and changing the water level in streams by intermittent flushing is useful for species that breed in flowing water.

Local Measures.—Since many species have a limited flight range, it is important to destroy all local breeding grounds. This may be accomplished by emptying containers of stagnant water, filling in depressions and pools, screening cisterns and other bodies of water that cannot be drained, and clearing weeds and grasses bordering water.

Drainage.—Drainage of mosquito breeding grounds is an engineering problem. Successful operation depends upon biological knowledge of the species concerned, the topography of the country, and the available funds. Ill-advised drainage has even increased the breeding grounds of *Anopheles quadrimaculatus*. Extensive drainage operations are seldom practicable, but at carefully selected sites they have produced surprising results.

Various forms of drainage have been tried. Straight surface-draining ditches with gradual curves and narrow bottoms readily kept free from accumulated vegetation may be dug by hand or ditching machines. The flow of stagnant streams may be accelerated by deepening the channel. The water level may be lowered by tile or pipe subsoil drainage. Marshes may be drained into artificially created central ponds. These and similar operations should be supplemented by filling depressions in which water may collect.

Removal of Vegetation.—The removal of aquatic vegetation from the banks of streams and ponds and the clearance of jungle growths reduce the breeding

---

[22] Mackie, F. P. and Crabtree, H. S., 1938.   [23] Escalar, G., 1934.

grounds of many species and render the larvæ of others susceptible to fishes and oil films.

Flooding.—Intermittent sluicing or flushing of streams, thus periodically altering the water level, and agitating the water, tends to prevent breeding in flowing streams.

DESTRUCTION OF LARVÆ

Mosquito larvæ may be destroyed by natural enemies, by oiling the waters, or by toxic chemicals.

Natural Enemies.—Among natural enemies are the western newt (*Notophthalmus torosus*), beetles, various aquatic predaceous larvæ, larvæ of water mites of the genus *Arrenurus,* water fowl and fishes. In brackish-water breeding grounds the killifishes (*Fundulus*) and other species are efficient destroyers of larvæ and pupæ. The viviparous top minnow (*Gambusia affinis*) is especially effective in fresh-water pools, but less so in waters clogged by weeds and grasses or when larger predaceous fishes are present. *Gambusia,* however, propagates only in warm climates. In India *Panchax panchax* is reported to be more effective than *Gambusia* or *Lebistes*.

Oil.—Oil, a contact larvicide, forms a film, toxic for surface-inhabiting larvæ. Gasoline is the most toxic, but it is expensive and its film does not persist. Heavy crude oil, when sprayed, must be heated or mixed with kerosene. The addition of castor oil enables it to spread farther and more rapidly. Oil films are less effective where aquatic vegetation is abundant. Light fuel oil, one ounce to 15 square feet of surface, in still waters, will produce a film that lasts for about ten days.[2] Heavier oils require less frequent application but inspections of larvæ-infested localities should be made at weekly intervals. Oil is most frequently sprayed by portable hand machines, but airplanes have been employed in some districts. Oil-soaked sawdust is desirable for waters with thick aquatic vegetation and oil may be applied with mops to puddles and swamps. In running streams, oil-soaked sawdust or cotton may be placed in containers or "drip-cans" may be employed.

Poisons.—Where oil films are impracticable because of evaporation, excessive vegetation, or heavy rains, other substances poisonous to the larvæ may be tried. Paris green is used extensively in Italy, where the fine powder, diluted 1:100 with dust, is scattered over the surface of the water by hand or by blowers. It is effective only when eaten, and so, while deadly to surface-feeding anopheline larvæ, it is unsuited for the bottom-feeding culicine larvæ. It does not kill the eggs and pupæ or prevent oviposition as do oil films, but it is useful in heavy vegetation. It should be repeated in from 7 to 10 days. Automatic dusting machines for streams have been devised.[24] Airplanes have been employed effectively in Russia for dusting peat bogs, reed beds, and rice and cotton fields with their network of irrigation ditches. Powdered paraform, trioxymethylene and calcium arsenate may be used like Paris green.[25] Agitation of the water makes the poisons sink to lower levels where they may be ingested by culicine larvæ. A liquid resin soap, of caustic soda, resin and crude carbolic acid, known as the Panama larvicide, makes an emulsion with water

[24] Russell, P. F. and Eaton, L. S., 1934.   [25] Roubaud, E., 1920, 1926.

in a 1 :10,000 dilution that kills larvæ as well as algæ, other vegetation and fishes; consequently, it cannot be used in supplies of drinking water. Cresote, cresol and borax have also been used.

CONTROL OF MALARIAL VECTORS

Malaria is transmitted by numerous species of anopheline mosquitoes that vary in their habits and efficacy as vectors. Certain species are natural carriers of malaria, others are of minor importance. Thus, a species may be the most prominent vector in a country where topography, climate and racial customs are favorable and play only a minor rôle elsewhere. Species of anopheline mosquitoes, and even varieties of the same species, differ in their breeding places, their preference for human or animal blood, their natural hiding places, and their susceptibility to the malarial parasites. An efficient malarial vector must readily attack man and its habits must bring it in contact with human habitations.

The many anopheline species, some with a wide and others a restricted range, select a variety of breeding places. The majority prefer standing pools of fresh water, as ponds, swamps and marshes. Peculiar breeding sites, however, are selected by certain species: holes in trees by *Anopheles barberi;* cut bamboo stems by *A. asiaticus;* leaves of plants by *A. cruzi* of Brazil; swift-flowing streams by *A. maculatus* and *A. willmori* in the Orient; polluted water by *A. subpictus* in India; flood pools near rivers by *A. walkeri;* sea water by *A. litoralis* of the Philippines; and brackish water marshes by *A. atropos* and one variety of *A. crucians.* In the United States of America *A. quadrimaculatus,* an important malarial mosquito, breeds in fresh-water ponds, and another, *A. punctipennis,* has a wide range of ponds, springs, streams, ditches and marshes. Such variations show the necessity of knowing the habits of any species in order to apply control measures.

The eradication of malaria does not demand complete extermination of malarial mosquitoes. The continuous transmission of the disease requires a relatively high mosquito index per person. Reduction of this index to a minimal level is sufficient to prevent effective transmission. Numerous instances where partial control measures have eliminated malaria may be cited. Among the most striking are those at the Suez Canal, the Panama Canal Zone, Havana in Cuba, Vera Cruz in Mexico, and certain districts in Italy. In the extensive swamp land of the Southern United States, however, the disease can never be eradicated without large-scale and expensive drainage operations.

CONTROL OF YELLOW FEVER AND DENGUE VECTORS

Aëdes ægypti, the principal vector of yellow fever, is a "domesticated" species, frequenting the vicinity of houses and preferring human blood. It breeds in all manner of domestic water receptacles, the larvæ thriving as bottom feeders in clean or foul water containing organic material. It seldom travels beyond a few hundred yards and hides in houses. Yellow fever may be prevented by adequate screening of infected patients and healthy persons, by killing potentially-infected mosquitoes by fumigation, and by destroying breeding places and larvæ. Hence.

cisterns should be screened, small containers eliminated, and top-minnows introduced into storage tanks.

The extermination of *Aëdes* mosquitoes in a locality is unnecessary to control yellow fever. Reducing the number to a point where they no longer can transmit the disease effectively is usually sufficient. Control measures should be continued, however, for at least a year after the termination of all local cases of yellow fever. No satisfactory methods have been devised against the nondomestic and jungle species in Africa and South America.

CONTROL OF FILARIAL VECTORS

The destruction of local breeding grounds usually suffices to control *Culex fatigans, C. pipiens, Aëdes ægypti, A. variegatus* and *Anopheles stephensi,* the more important vectors of *Wuchereria bancrofti.* The measures employed are those for malarial and yellow fever mosquitoes. Where the domestic species, *Culex fatigans, C. pipiens, Anopheles stephensi* and *Aëdes ægypti,* are the carriers, local control is indicated with special attention to polluted water. In Oceania eliminating the natural breeding places of *Aëdes variegatus,* such as cocoanut shells, cavities in trees and cocoa pods is a more difficult task. In Malaya the chief means of protection against *Wuchereria malayi* is to prohibit persons from working in swamps after dark, since the elimination of the breeding places of the *Mansonia* mosquitoes is impractical. In some localities destruction of the water plant, *Pistia stratiotes,* upon which these mosquitoes breed, is an effective method of control.[26]

REFERENCES

DE BEAUREPAIRE, ARAGAO, H.   Mosquitoes and Yellow Fever Virus, Mem. Inst. Oswaldo Cruz, 1939, 34:565.

BIRAUD, Y.   Present-day Problems of Yellow-Fever Epidemiology, Epidem. Rept. Health Sec. League of Nations, 1935, 179:103.

HACKETT, L. W. and MISSIROLI, A.   The Varieties of *Anopheles maculipennis* and Their Relation to the Distribution of Malaria in Europe, Riv. di Malariol., 1935, 14:45.

HOWARD, L. O., DYAR, H. G. and KNAB, F.   The Mosquitoes of North and Central America and the West Indies, Carnegie Inst., Washington, 1915.

KUMM, H. W.   The geographical Distribution of the Malaria Carrying Mosquitoes, Am. J. Hyg. Monographic Series No. 10, 1929, 178 pp.

——— The Geographical Distribution of the Yellow Fever Vectors, Am. J. Hyg. Monographic Series No. 12, 1931, 110 pp.

MACGREGOR, M. E.   Mosquito Surveys. A Handbook for Anti-Malarial and Anti-Mosquito Field Workers, London, 1927, 282 pp.

MARSHALL, J. F.   The British Mosquitoes, British Museum, London, 1938, 341 pp.

MATHESON, R.   A Handbook of the Mosquitoes of North America, Springfield, Ill., 1929, 268 pp.

SILER, J. F., HALL, H. W. and HITCHINS, A. P.   Dengue: its History, Epidemiology, Mechanism of Transmission, Etiology, Clinical Manifestations, Immunity and Prevention, Philippine J. Sc., 1926, 29:1.

WHITFIELD, F. G. S.   Air Transport, Insects and Disease, Bull. Ent. Research, 1939, 30:365.

---

[26] Sweet, W. C. and Pillai, V. M., 1937.

Chapter XLI

THE SUBORDER ORTHORRHAPHA; THE FAMILIES CHIRONOMIDÆ, PSYCHODIDÆ, SIMULIIDÆ AND TABANIDÆ

The families of the suborder ORTHORRHAPHA other than the CULICIDÆ that contain species of medical importance are the CHIRONOMIDÆ, PSYCHODIDÆ and SIMULIIDÆ of the section NEMATOCERA (small flies) and the TABANIDÆ of the section BRACHYCERA (large flies).

FAMILY *CHIRONOMIDÆ*

The numerous and widely-distributed species of the family CHIRONOMIDÆ are small midges of nocturnal habits. The bloodsucking members of this family belong to the subfamily CERATOPOGONINÆ, which is rated by some authorities as an independent family, the CERATOPOGONIDÆ.

SUBFAMILY *CERATOPOGONINÆ*

The subfamily CERATOPOGONINÆ includes several genera and many species of small flies 1 to 2 mm. in length. They are variously called midges, gnats, punkies and no-see-ums. The head is rounded posteriorly; the proboscis is relatively short; the antennæ have 14 segments adorned with whorls of hairs; the palpi have usually four to five joints; the strongly convexed thorax with few exceptions does not project over the head; the mouth parts are complete and the mandibles are usually well developed in both sexes; both body and wings are more or less hairy but are without scales; the flat wings are superimposed over the back when the fly is resting; and the venation of the wings is characterized by the absence of the second longitudinal vein, the more pronounced first and third veins, the presence of a transverse connecting vein between the third and fourth veins and none between the fourth and fifth.

GENUS *LASIOHELEA*

Several species, chiefly tropical, bite mammals, but the majority probably feed on large insects. The larvæ are terrestrial, frequenting moist, decomposing, organic material. The wings are covered with dense macrotrichia and the costal vein extends to about the middle of the wing. The empodium is as long as the claws.

GENUS *LEPTOCONOPS*

All species of this genus, mostly tropical or subtropical, are biters. They are uniformly colored with unspotted wings. The first and third veins of the wings are indistinct and more or less fused, a fold resembling a simple vein is present between the third and fourth veins, and the anterior or radio-median cross vein is absent. The empodium is short or absent.

GENUS *CERATOPOGON*

The bloodsucking species attack man and animals in large numbers. The larvæ are aquatic or terrestrial, the latter being deposited under bark, leaves and wood. The wings, whitish without dark markings, are finely punctate but without distinct microtrichia. The claws of the female are equal and the empodium is almost as long as the claws.

GENUS *CULICOIDES*

The genus *Culicoides* includes several hundred species, many of which are aggressive biters. From a medical standpoint it is the most important genus of the subfamily CERATOPOGONINÆ.

Geographical Distribution.—Cosmopolitan except Patagonia and New Zealand.

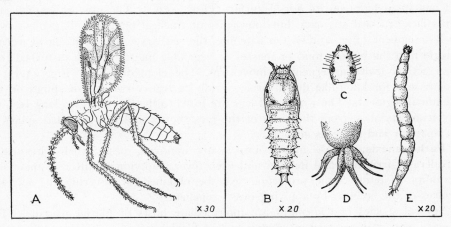

FIG. 232.—THE GENUS *Culicoides*

A, Culicoides austeni, adult female; *B,* pupa of *C. kiefferi; C,* head of larva of *C. kiefferi; D,* last segment of larva of *C. kiefferi* showing tracheal gills extruded; *E,* larva of *C. kiefferi* (*A* redrawn from Sharp, 1928; *B* to *E* redrawn from Patton, 1913).

Morphology.—The *Culicoides* are small, delicate, brown or black flies from 1 to 1.5 mm. in length (Fig. 232A). The thorax is slightly humped and projects forward over the head; the long fourteen-jointed antennæ (Fig. 221A) are plumose in the male and pilose in the female; the proboscis is short and the maxillary palps are long; and the short broad wings, covered entirely or in part with delicate hairs, are often marked with dark spots and light clear circles in transverse rows of three or more. The genus *Culicoides* is distinguished from the other genera of the subfamily CERATOPOGONINÆ by the presence of conspicuous humeral pits, the poorly-developed empodium but one half the length of the small equal claws of the female, and the extension of the costal vein well beyond the middle of the wing (Fig. 225A). The species are differentiated by the number, type and distribution of the hairs (macro- and microtrichia) on the wings.

Habits.—Midges swarm during the day near ponds and swamps. Many species rest with their front legs elevated. Only the female has mouth parts adapted for bloodsucking. Although attracted by light, they bite most actively at dusk or in the shade during daytime.

Life Cycle.—The small, oval eggs are deposited in a single row or in masses on plants or vegetable matter in shallow water. In about three days they produce elongate larvæ that lead an aquatic existence in shallow deposits of water such as weedy margins of ponds, puddles, tree holes, retained water of plants and crab holes. The larvæ have also become adapted to modified terrestrial habitats such as tree sap, moist vegetation and manure. Several species including *C. furens* live in brackish water. In from 6 to 12 months the larva passes into the pupal stage from which the adult fly emerges in about three days.

The larva (Fig. 232E) has a smooth vermiform twelve-segmented body nearly devoid of hairs. The head is equipped with curved, chitinous, toothed mandibles and has small hairs on its dorsal surface (Fig. 232C). The nine abdominal segments lack tracheal stigmata, but four pairs of tracheal or anal gills project from the last segment (Fig. 232D). On hatching, the red larvæ, known as blood worms, wriggle into the bottom mud or masses of vegetable matter. When disturbed they swim actively with a serpentine movement. The elongate pupa (Fig. 232B) is smooth save for knob-like dorsal processes and a transverse row of spines on the abdominal segments. The wings and legs are fused to the thorax. Two long respiratory trumpets arise from the sides of the mesothorax and two terminal spines at the posterior end serve as anchors.

Pathogenesis.—These minute insects are annoying pests; their bites cause considerable irritation and itching, and even fever. Individuals differ in their susceptibility to bites. Some protection may be obtained by covering the exposed surfaces of the body or by applying insect repellents.

Several species of *Culicoides* are intermediate hosts of filarial parasites. The species involved in the transmission of human filarial diseases (Chapter XXI) are: *C. austeni* and *C. grahami* for *Acanthocheilonema perstans* in Africa, and *C. furens* and probably *C. parœnsis* and other species for *Mansonella ozzardi* in the Western Hemisphere.[1] *C. nubeculosus* has been incriminated as the intermediate host of *Onchocerca cervicalis,* a parasite of horses in England, and other species have been associated with filarial parasites of animals. Even parasitism of anopheline mosquitoes by species of *Culicoides* has been reported.[2]

Control.—Methods of control are unsatisfactory. Their efficiency depends upon a knowledge of the biology of the particular species and the topography of the locality. The installation of trap tide gates on small coastal streams in which the brackish water species breed and the spraying of the soil near the margin of the water in salt marshes with a mixture of 1 part crude carbolic acid and 90 parts of creosoted pine sap are recommended by the Bureau of Entomology of the United States Department of Agriculture. Local breeding grounds may be reduced by drainage and filling operations. The use of electric light traps in dwellings has been suggested. Flies may be excluded from houses by applying a mixture of concentrated pyrethrum extract and oil to screens.[3]

---

[1] Buckley, J. J. C., 1934; Dampf, A., 1936. [3] Hull, J. B. and Shields, S. E., 1939.
[2] Galliard, H. and Gascher, H., 1937.

FAMILY *PSYCHODIDÆ*

The members of the family PSYCHODIDÆ, commonly called moth flies or owl midges, are small moth-like flies. The arched thorax and cylindrical abdomen are covered with hairs and the stumpy or long legs with hairs and scales. The large, oval or lanceolate wings are either arched over the abdomen or held erect in repose, the wing veins are covered with hairs and scales, and the margins of the wings are fringed with long hairs. The second longitudinal vein may have one or two forks, the fourth one fork, and the third terminates near the tip of the wing, while the indistinct cross veins are situated toward the base of the wing. The proboscis in most species is short and unadapted for biting. The beaded, sixteen-jointed antennæ and the recurved palps of four or five joints are adorned with hairs.

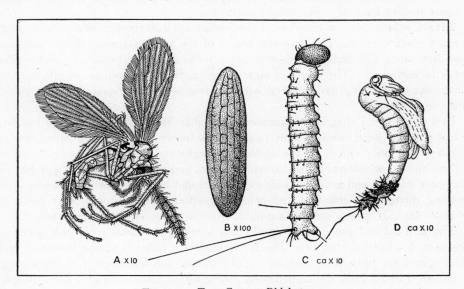

FIG. 233.—THE GENUS *Phlebotomus*

A, adult fly; *B*, egg of *P. papatasii*; *C*, larva of *P. papatasii*; *D*, pupa of *P. papatasii* (*A* redrawn from Hegner, Root, Augustine and Huff, *Parasitology*, 1938, D. Appleton-Century Company; *B* to *D* redrawn from Newstead, 1911).

GENUS *PHLEBOTOMUS*

Geographical Distribution.—Southern Europe, southern Asia, Africa and tropical America.

Morphology.—The numerous species of *Phlebotomus* are small, slender, yellowish or buff-colored flies about 3 mm. in length with hairy bodies (Fig. 233A). The characteristics that distinguish them from the other genera of the family PSYCHODIDÆ are: longer and more slender bodies, wings and legs; long proboscis with biting mouth parts; wings hairy, but devoid of scales; forking of the second longitudinal vein near the middle instead of the base of the wing and subsequent forking of the anterior branch before reaching the margin; and erect position of wings in repose. Differentiation of species depends chiefly upon slight variation in wing venation, length of palpal segments, armature of the buccal cavity and pharynx, structure of the spermatheca in the female, and type of hypopygium in the male, particularly the distribution of spines on the terminal segment of the dorsal pair of claspers.

Habits.—Most species are nocturnal feeders and are active after twilight, especially on warm, humid nights. They are repelled by sunlight, though attracted by feeble artificial light, and hide in crevices during the day. They are usually found in regions where old stone, concrete and hard earth constructions provide damp retreats. Inability to fly against the slightest wind limits their flight range. Their small size enables them to pass through 18-mesh screening. Usually only the females feed on mammals and occasionally on lower vertebrates, but the males of some species have piercing mouth parts.

Life Cycle.—After a blood meal the female explosively deposits 40 to 50 eggs in moist, dark crevices. The breeding places of the various species differ: rubbish, loose dirt, sandy soil, damp cracks, crevices of rocks and ruined masonry, and broken places in earthwork. The elongate eggs (Fig. 223B), 0.4 mm. in length, at first translucent but turning dark-colored within a few hours, are covered with a viscid, adhesive substance.

In 6 to 12 days a sluggish, segmented, caterpillar-like larva (Fig. 233C) hatches. It has a large head, armed with heavy, dark-brown, dentate mandibles, and a grayish-white body. Each of the abdominal segments bears a transverse row of toothed spines, which vary in different species, and the terminal segment has an inner pair of long and an outer pair of short caudal bristles. The larva feeds upon decaying nitrogenous material and before pupation passes through four molts in about 26 days. It cannot survive sunlight, desiccation or excessive moisture.

The buff-colored pupa (Fig. 233D) has a triangular head with long antennal sheaths and a curved abdomen. The last larval skin adheres to the posterior end. Small spines are present on the sides of the thorax and abdomen. The pupal stage lasts from 6 to 10 days, the adult finally emerging on a humid night. The life span of the adult is short, 7 to 14 days, and usually but one blood meal is required. The entire period from egg to adult averages about seven weeks.

Pathogenesis.—The bite produces an itching, rose-colored papule surrounded by an erythematous area 1 to 2 cm. in diameter. In sensitive individuals the local lesions are more pronounced and may be accompanied by nausea, fever and malaise.

Pappataci fever, sometimes known as sandfly or three-day fever, is transmitted by *Phlebotomus papatasii* and probably by *P. perniciosus* and *P. minutus*. This viral disease, most prevalent in the Mediterranean countries and southern Asia, resembles dengue. A developmental period of 7 to 10 days is required before the fly becomes infective.

The exact rôle of *Phlebotomus* in the transmission of oriental sore and kala-azar is still uncertain. The leishmanian organisms pass through a developmental cycle to infective forms in the flies, but experimental transmission to man by bites has been inconclusive (Chapter XI). *Leishmania tropica* is believed to be carried by *P. sergenti* and *P. papatasii* and *Leishmania donovani* by *P. major* in Greece, *P.*

papatasii in Spain, *P. perniciosus* in southern Europe and northern Africa, *P. argentipes* in India, and *P. chinensis* in China. The transmission of *Leishmania donovani* to dogs by *P. chinensis* has been demonstrated in China. The etiological agent of Brazilian visceral leishmaniasis undergoes cyclic development in *P. intermedius* and *P. longipalpis*. In South America *P. intermedius*, *P. squamiventris* and *P. migonei* are suspected intermediate hosts of *Leishmania braziliensis*. There is some evidence that Oroya fever may be transmitted by *P. verrucarum* and *P. noguchii* in South America.

Control.—Persons may be protected by the use of repellent ointments, and dwelling houses may be kept free from these flies by screens of fine mesh or by installing electric fans so as to produce strong air currents at the windows and doors. Elimination of nearby breeding grounds is a satisfactory method of control, since these flies have a short flight range. Drainage and filling operations produce an unfavorable dry environment. Stone walls may be faced with mortar or cement to eliminate crevices, and cracks in the ground may be filled in or sprayed with larvicides.

FAMILY *SIMULIIDÆ*

The members of the family SIMULIIDÆ are small, short, thick-set flies, characterized by stout almost hairless antennæ, reduced wing venation, and the absence of hairs and scales on the wings. They are popularly known as blackflies, buffalo gnats, turkey gnats and Kolumbatz flies. The 100 or more species of SIMULIIDÆ are frequently placed in the single genus *Simulium*. Four genera have been made on the basis of wing venation [4]: (1) *Simulium,* in which the first vein is bare between the humeral cross vein and the cross vein between the third and fourth longitudinal veins, (2) *Parasimulium,* in which the first vein is hairy throughout its length and joins the middle of the costal vein, (3) *Prosimulium,* in which the first vein is hairy throughout its length and joins the costal vein near its tip, and (4) *Eusimulium,* in which the first vein is hairy throughout its length and joins the costal vein near its tip, but the second and third veins are fused.

Geographical Distribution.—Cosmopolitan.

Morphology.—The various species of *Simulium* are small robust brown or black flies 2 to 3 mm. in length, with a semicircular head, conspicuous compound eyes, humped thorax, short stout legs and a short proboscis with piercing mouth parts (Fig. 234A). The body is covered with short, golden or silver hairs, giving a longitudinally-striped appearance. The thoracic pattern differs in sexes and species. The eleven-jointed antennæ are short and bare (Fig. 221B). The wings are broad and unspotted. The costal vein does not extend to the tip, the second and third veins are often fused; the costal, subcostal, first, second, third, and the base of the fourth vein are prominently grouped near the anterior margin, while the other veins are poorly defined (Fig. 225B). The male has an inconspicuous hypopygium.

Habits.—Although not strictly forest insects, the flies abound in the vicinity of clear wooded streams. They shun bright sunlight and do not readily venture

---

[4] Dyar, H. G. and Shannon, R. C., 1927.

into the open. Most species rarely migrate far from their breeding grounds except when borne by the wind or on animals, but flights of four miles per day and wanderings within a 60 mile radius have been reported.[5] The females usually bite

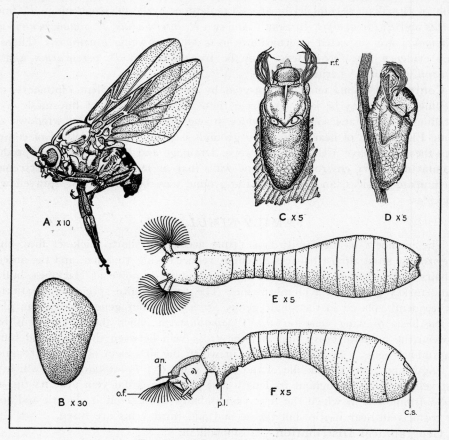

FIG. 234.—THE GENUS *Simulium*

A, adult fly; *B*, egg; *C*, cocoon and pupa of *S. mexicanum*, dorsal view; *D*, lateral view of same; *E*, larva, dorsal view; *F*, larva, lateral view.

an., antenna; *c.s.*, caudal sucker; *p.l.*, proleg of thorax; *o.f.*, oral fan; *r.f.*, respiratory fila-ments (*A, E* and *F* redrawn from Hegner, Root, Augustine and Huff, *Parasitology*, 1938, D. Appleton-Century Company; *C* and *D* redrawn from Bequaert, 1934).

man and other mammals during the day, particularly in the early morning just after sunrise and toward evening. Although they do not enter houses, they bite man on shady porches or in the vicinity of dwellings.

Life Cycle.—The eggs are deposited under water in swiftly flowing streams. Uneven masses of 300 to 500 eggs are attached by a gelatinous secretion to rocks, plants and débris. The triangular shaped egg (Fig. 234B), at first yellowish and then black, is pointed at one end. In three to five days a yellowish-green, cylindrical

---

[5] Baranov, N., 1939.

larva emerges from the egg and attaches itself, usually in an upright position, to rocks, aquatic vegetation or débris. The larva (Fig. 234E and F) has a rectangular head with small lateral eyes; long three-jointed antennæ; mandibular mouth parts with two, long, fan-like, hairy processes; a short, ventral, conical, prothoracic proleg armed with hooklets; and a broad posterior end terminating in three finger-like anal gills and a large armed subcylindrical sucker. It feeds on plankton and molts seven times within 13 days. Before pupation the larva, with silken threads from its salivary glands, spins a cocoon resembling an open pocket. The dark brown pupa (Fig. 234C and D) is attached within the cocoon by two posterior hooklets and entangling silken threads. Long respiratory filaments, diversely branching in different species, are attached to each side of the thorax and emerge from the open top of the cocoon. An accumulation of gas splits the pupal case along the midline and the bubble carries the imago to the surface. The females live only a few weeks; 23 days is the longest recorded period in captivity.

Pathogenesis.—The bite, at first painless except for a slight prickling sensation, later produces an ulcer-like sore due to the salivary toxin. In susceptible individuals there may be marked inflammation, local swelling and general incapacity. Exposed portions of the body such as head, neck and legs are most frequently attacked and the flies also have the habit of crawling beneath the clothing. They are a pest to fishermen and woodsmen and may incapacitate both man and animals. Large numbers of cattle, horses and other domestic animals have perished from the depredations of these flies in Europe and America.

Simulium damnosum and possibly *S. neavei* are the intermediate hosts of the filarial worm, *Onchocerca volvulus* in Africa and *S. metallicum, S. ochraceum* and *S. callidum* are involved in the transmission of Central American onchocerciasis (Chapter XXI). *S. decorum katmai* is reported to be a vector of tularemia.[6] Other species have been found to transmit protozoan diseases of birds and onchocerciasis of cattle.

Control.—The control of these flies is problematical. Robber flies, dance flies, dragon flies, aquatic beetles, caddis fly larvæ and fishes are natural enemies. The removal of submerged objects decreases the available places for attachment of the eggs and larvæ in streams, but except in limited areas this procedure is not practicable. In North America phinotas oil has been used to destroy the larvæ and the spraying of kerosene in the vicinity of hunting camps at times has appeared effective. Individuals may be protected to some extent by fine netting and the copious application of chemical repellents.

FAMILY *TABANIDÆ*

The tabanid flies have many common names: horseflies, deer flies, mangrove flies, breeze flies, green-headed flies, clegs and seroots. The family, most numerous of the DIPTERA, comprises some 60 genera and nearly 2,500 species. The important species are cosmopolitan but many have a local distribution. The only species associated with the transmission of disease in man belong to the genus *Chrysops*.

[6] Parker, R. R., 1933.

Morphology.—The TABANIDÆ are thick-set, bulky, often beautifully-colored flies, usually larger than the common housefly. The head, as wide as the thorax, bears large, brilliantly-colored compound eyes, which meet in the midline in the males but are separated in the females by a broad white band. Ocelli are present in the subfamily PANGONINÆ. The antennæ have three segments, the third or distal joint with a large basal portion and three to seven small divisions. The number of annuli in the third segment and the relative length of the first and second segments are useful in differentiating genera (Fig. 235D to G). The mouth parts (Fig. 235C), complete in the female, comprise an awl-shaped, tubular epipharynx, a grooved hypopharynx, paired blade-like mandibles, paired serrated maxillæ with coarse two-segmented palps at their bases, and an enclosing proboscis sheath or labium tipped with two labella. The proboscis is usually short but in some species may exceed the body length.

The three-segmented thorax is stout, usually hairy, and black, brown or yellowish. It bears three pairs of legs, a pair of wings, and a pair of halteres. The strong legs end in two claws and a hairy pad. Spine-like spurs adorn the tibia of the middle legs and in the subfamily PAGONINÆ the hind legs also. The wing structure distinguishes the TABANIDÆ from other families. The wings may be completely clear, covered with dark pigment or mottled with patterns characteristic of certain genera or species. The third longitudinal vein is forked and the fourth, which encloses the discal cell, terminates in three branches. Five posterior cells are always present (Fig. 224). Generally the lower extremities of the fifth and sixth longitudinal veins unite. The seven-segmented abdomen may show definite whitish or dark markings and sexual differences in coloration. The last segment bears the anal opening and the sexual orifices.

Habits.—The adult flies frequent stagnant water, hovering near the surface during the day. As a rule, they prefer sunlight, although the deer flies, *Chrysops,* are found in shady woodland. The males have mouth parts adapted exclusively to sucking plant juices, but the females of many species are voracious bloodsuckers. Only the smaller species habitually attack man; the larger prey upon domestic and wild animals. The mouth parts of the female are adapted for piercing and sucking. The blade-like mandibles pierce the skin, while the protrusion and retraction of the toothed rod-like maxillæ further lacerate the tissues. The blood is sucked through a tube improvised by the apposition of the grooved epipharynx and the flat hypopharynx. *Chrysops* attacks man most actively from sunrise to 10:00 A.M. and from 4:00 P.M. to dusk.

Life Cycle.—The female deposits 200 to 800 eggs in masses on aquatic plants, grasses and rocks overhanging water. Oviposition requires nearly an hour, the eggs forming a single adhesive layer with their long axes in one plane. The spindle-shaped eggs (Fig. 235H), which gradually turn brown along the sides and black at the tip, are coated with a cement-like covering white at first but later dark gray. Hatching occurs in five or more days, the egg splitting lengthwise and the larva falling into the mud or water. The carnivorous larvæ grow rapidly and pass through six molts during the summer. They feed nocturnally upon insect larvæ, snails, worms and other small animals. As they grow they seek drier areas and after six

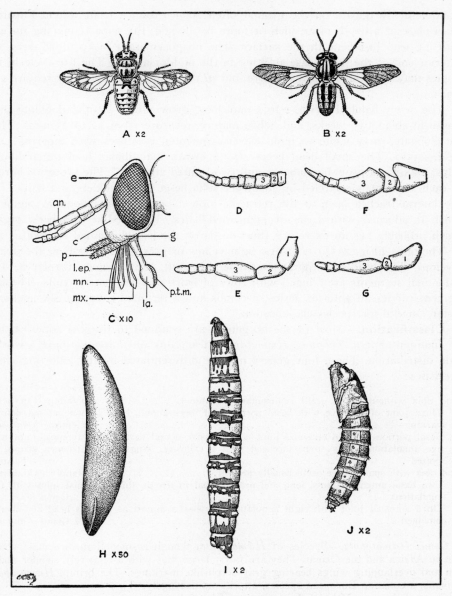

FIG. 235.—TABANID FLIES

A, Chrysops discalis; B, Chrysops dimidiata; C, mouth parts of *Chrysops discalis; D,* antenna of *Pangonia; E,* antenna of *Chrysops; F,* antenna of *Tabanus; G,* antenna of *Hæmatopota; H,* egg of *Tabanus; I,* larva of *Tabanus insignis; J,* pupa of *Tabanus variabilis.*

an., antenna; *c,* clypeus; *e,* compound eye; *g,* gena; *l,* labium; *la.,* labella; *l.ep.,* labrum-epipharynx; *mn.,* mandibles; *mx.,* maxillæ; *p,* palps (*A* redrawn and *C* adapted from Stitt, Clough and Clough, *Practical Bacteriology, Hæmatology and Animal Parasitology,* 1938, P. Blakiston's Son and Company; *B* redrawn from colored plate by Austen, 1909; *D* to *F* redrawn from Hegner, Root, Augustine and Huff, *Parasitology,* 1938, D. Appleton-Century Company; *I* and *J* redrawn from Neave, 1915).

months finally pupate on the ground often some distance from water. Pupation takes place at a depth of an inch or more in the soil, the pupa remaining upright with its head just beneath the surface. The imago emerges in 10 to 18 days, the anterior end of the pupal case splitting in the middorsal line. The life cycle in the tropics may run four months or more, but in the temperate zones may require two years.

The newly hatched larvæ, 2 to 4 mm. long, grow slowly at first, doubling their length in about two weeks, and, when mature, measure from 22 to 25 mm.[7] They are elongate, dirty white to pink, eleven-segmented creatures with tapering ends (Fig. 235I). The small head bears strong brown mandibular hooks, mandibular palps, maxillæ, a prow-like labium, and two-jointed antennæ.[8] The posterior border of each segment is encircled by small propodia beset with hooklets and hairs. The two lateral trachea open at the retractile siphon on the last abdominal segment, which is adorned with areas of pigmented hairs. The sac-like Graeber's organ, which probably has an excretory function, is on the last abdominal segment.

The pupa (Fig. 235J) is at first light yellow or green but darkens as the imago develops. The head and thorax resemble the adult, the abdomen the larva. The abdominal segments are fringed with rows of hairs and bear lateral tufts. The last segment carries an anterior series of combs and a terminal group of six hooks or "aster," useful for species classification.[9]

Classification.—Most of the 60 genera are confined to tropical America, but the common genera, *Tabanus, Hæmatopota, Chrysops* and *Pangonia* have a world-wide distribution. These four genera may be differentiated by the following characteristics:

Hind tibia without spurs, ocelli rudimentary or absent..................Subfamily TABANINÆ
    Third joint of antennæ with basal portion and three annuli, body brown without definite markings ....Genus *Hæmatopota*
    Basal portion of third antennal joint with massive dorsal tooth, third antennal joint with five annulations, body stout, forehead with a callosity, wings clear, abdomen striped or spotted ....Genus *Tabanus*
Hind tibia with spurs, three ocelli usually present.....................Subfamily PANGONINÆ
    Two basal antennal joints, long and nearly equal in length, third antennal joint with five annulations ....Genus *Chrysops*
    Third antennal joint with eight annulations, proboscis almost as long as head and thorax combined ....Genus *Pangonia*

Genus Hæmatopota.—Species of *Hæmatopota*, though cosmopolitan, are most abundant in Africa and the Orient. They are fairly large flies with a relatively slender abdomen and overlapping wings bearing gray scroll-like markings. The brimp, *Hæmatopota pluvialis,* a common European species, attacks man savagely.

Genus Tabanus.—Most of the 1,200 species, mainly cosmopolitan, are stout large flies that feed on domestic animals, although some smaller forms attack man, inflicting painful bites that itch for long time. The nonoverlapping wings are usually clear but in some species are mottled black and in a few uniformly dark. Species of *Tabanus* serve as intermediate hosts of *Trypanosoma theileri,* a nonpathogenic parasite of cattle in Europe.

Genus Chrysops.—Species of *Chrysops* have a world-wide distribution, but are particularly abundant in temperate and tropical America. The flies are small tabanids with

---

[7] Hine, J. S., 1906.
[8] Schuurmans-Stekhoven, J. H., Jr., 1926.
[9] Neave, S. A., 1915.

conspicuous markings, long slender antennæ, and brilliantly-colored eyes chiefly green. The ovoid abdomen has yellow bands and dark stripes. The widely-separated wings are usually clear with a dark band along the anterior margin and a broad dark cross band at the level of the discal cell. The color pattern of the wings is helpful in distinguishing species; C. discalis is named from its characteristic nonpigmented discal cell.

Genus Pangonia.—The Pangonia, cosmopolitan in distribution, are large, elongate, slender flies with a long, more or less horizontal proboscis. The wings may be clear or dusky. The front of the female is narrow.

Pathogenicity.—The bite of Chrysops is not immediately painful, although the act of withdrawing the mouth parts is usually noticeable, but within a few hours there is considerable local irritation and often extensive swelling, which may persist for days. The flies usually attack the ankles, back of leg, and outerside of hand. Tabanid flies are of medical importance, not only as biting pests, but also because certain species transmit diseases to man and animals. As mechanical vectors they may carry pathogenic organisms on their mouth parts and bodies. Trypanosomal infections in animals may thus be transmitted if feeding on an infected animal is interrupted and the fly within ten minutes bites a second animal. Only the genus Chrysops is concerned with the transmission of disease in man; members of the other three common genera serve as mechanical vectors of anthrax and trypanosomal infections of animals.

Chrysops discalis, the western deer fly, can transfer Pasteurella tularensis to both man and animals and remains infective for at least two weeks.[10] The filarial worm, Loa loa, is transmitted by Chrysopa silacea and C. dimidiata (Chapter XXI). Normal development of the microfilaria of Loa loa has also been reported in C. centurionis, C. longicornis and C. distinctipennis.

Control.—Domestic animals may be given some protection by nets, smudges, repellent dips or sprays. Oiling pools with kerosene kills the hatching larvæ of some species but is ineffective with others.[7] The extermination of larvæ, however, seems impossible because of the varied and widely distributed breeding places. The natural enemies are spiders, the bald-faced hornet and the fossorial wasp.

REFERENCES

AUSTEN, E. E. African Blood-Sucking Flies Other Than Mosquitoes and Tsetse-Flies, 1909, Brit. Museum, London, 229 pp.

DYAR, H. G. and SHANNON, R. C. The North American Two-Winged Flies of the Family Simuliidæ, Proc. U. S. Nat. Mus., 1927, 69, Art. 10:1.

EDWARDS, F. W., OLDROYD, H. and SMART, J. British Blood-Sucking Flies, 1936, Brit. Museum, London, 156 pp.

HINE, J. S. Habits and Life Histories of Some Flies of the Family TABANIDÆ, U. S. Dept. Agric. Bull. Entomology, 1906, Tech. Series, No. 12, Part II.

—— Second Report Upon the Horseflies of Louisiana, Agric. Exp. Sta. of Louisiana State Univ. and A. and M. College, 1907, Bull. 93.

NEAVE, S. A. The TABANIDÆ of Southern Nyasaland with Notes on Their Life-Histories, Bull. Ent. Research, 1915, 5:287.

NEWSTEAD, R. The Papataci Flies (Phlebotomus) of the Maltese Islands, Bull. Ent. Research, 1911, 2:47.

---

[10] Francis, E. and Mayne, B., 1922.

ROOT, F. M. and HOFFMAN, W. A.   The North American Species of *Culicoides,* Am. J. Hyg., 1937, 25 :150.

SCHUURMANS-STEKHOVEN, J. H., JR.   The Bloodsucking Arthropods of the Dutch East Indian Archipelago. VII. The Tabanids of the Dutch East Indian Archipelago, Treubia (Instituto Scientifiques de Buitenzorg's Lands Plantentuin, 1926) 6 Suppl. I, 552 pp.

SINTON, J. A.   Notes on Some Indian Species of the Genus *Phlebotomus.* Part III. Provisional Diagnostic Table of the Males of the Species and Varieties Recorded from India and Ceylon, Indian J. M. Res., 1924, 11 :807.

STRONG, R. P., SANDGROUND, J. H., BEQUAERT, J. C. and OCHOA, M. M.   Onchocerciasis With Special Reference to the Central American Form of the Disease, Harvard Univ. Dept. Trop. Med. and Inst. Trop. Biol. & Med. Com. No. VI, 1934, Cambridge, Mass., 234 pp.

Chapter XLII

THE SUBORDER CYCLORRHAPHA: THE BLOODSUCK-ING FLIES OF THE FAMILIES MUSCIDÆ AND HIPPOBOSCIDÆ

FAMILY *MUSCIDÆ*

Bloodsucking species are found in relatively few genera of the family MUSCIDÆ. These range from simple to specialized flies and fall into three subfamilies: PHILÆMATOMYINÆ, STOMOXYDINÆ and GLOSSININÆ. Many species are found in Africa and in the Orient, but only two, the stable fly *Stomoxys calcitrans* and the horn fly *Hæmatobia irritans,* have a cosmopolitan distribution.

SUBFAMILY *PHILÆMATOMYINÆ*

The flies of the genus *Philæmatomyia,* the only one in the subfamily PHILÆMATO-MYINÆ, resemble the housefly, but the haustellum of the proboscis is well chitinized and the prestomal teeth are large and prominent. The bloodsucking species prey chiefly on cattle and horses.

SUBFAMILY *STOMOXYDINÆ*

The STOMOXYDINÆ are medium-sized, grayish or brownish, oviparous flies with four brownish-black longitudinal thoracic stripes, a banded or spotted abdomen and a long conspicuous proboscis.

Genus Stomoxys.—The slender palpi are shorter than the proboscis; the antennal arista is pectinate with bristles only on upper surface; and the first and third veins of the grayish wing have hairy bases, while the fourth is nearly straight with a slight upward curvature. The species are popularly known as stable flies, since they frequent buildings occupied by domestic animals. The ten or more species are difficult to identify because of variations in individual markings. They are chiefly distinguished by (1) the width of the frons in relation to that of the head, (2) the width of the light median strip on the thorax and (3) the color of the legs. Most species are found in Asia and Africa, but the well-known *Stomoxys calcitrans* has an almost world-wide distribution.

Genus Hæmatobia.—The palpi are as long or longer than the proboscis; the antennal arista has bristles on the upper surface; the bases of the first and third veins of the wing are bare; the fourth vein is feebly curved upward; and the abdomen has a central longitudinal stripe. These grayish flies are of a relatively small size. The horn fly, *Hæmatobia (Lyperosia) irritans,* probably introduced from Europe, is the common American species.

Genus Stygeromyia.—The palpi are as long as the proboscis; the antennal arista has bristles on the upper surface; the base of the first vein of the wing is bare and that of the second hairy; and the fourth vein is strongly curved upward.

Genus Bdellolarynx.—The palpi are strongly spatulate and as long as the proboscis; the antennal arista has bristles on both sides; the bases of the first and third veins of the wings are bare; the fourth vein curves slightly upward; and the yellow abdomen has a central, brown, longitudinal stripe.

Genus Hæmatobosca.—The slightly spatulate palpi are as long as the proboscis; the antennal arista has bristles on both sides; the bases of the first and third veins of the wings are bare; the fourth vein has a strong upward curve; the body is slender; and the abdomen has a central longitudinal band.

STOMOXYS CALCITRANS

Stomoxys calcitrans is an annoying pest to man and domestic animals. It is the common stable fly, storm fly or stinging fly.

Geographical Distribution.—Cosmopolitan. It was probably introduced into North America from Europe.

Morphology.—This, oval, grayish fly (Fig. 236 A), 6 to 8 mm. in length, resembles the common house fly. It may be distinguished, however, by its more

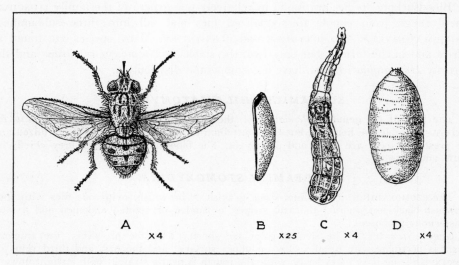

Fig. 236.—*Stomoxys calcitrans*

A, adult female; *B*, egg; *C*, larva; *D*, puparium (*A* redrawn from Austen; *B* to *D* redrawn from Newstead).

robust appearance, darker color, divergent spread of wings in repose, curve of the fourth longitudinal vein of the wing, and long narrow proboscis. The thorax has four dark longitudinal stripes and the abdomen dark variable bands. The proboscis is bent almost at a right angle near its base and projects forward like a bayonet. Unlike that of other biting flies, the labium, which usually forms a sheath for the piercing mouth parts (Fig. 222D), is itself a piercing organ.[1]

Habits.—The flies usually frequent stables and farmyards, attracted by animals and moist decaying straw, hay or other vegetable material, in which they breed. They feed on fruits, straw and manure as well as on animals, and bask in the sun on railings, plants and grass near grazing animals. Both males and females attack domestic animals and occasionally man during the day, usually after 9:00 A.M.

[1] Stephens, J. W. W. and Newstead, R., 1907.

They are particularly annoying to man when they invade houses during and after a rainstorm. Their activity is diminished below 60° F. and ceases below 45° F., while they perish at 8° F. In the southern United States they are present the year round and are extremely abundant in some years, but in the northern United States they appear only during the late summer and fall. The average length of adult life is 17 days; a few flies live as long as 29 days.[2]

Life Cycle.—The flies breed in moist decaying vegetable matter in barnyards, gardens, marshy ground or on the banks of streams. The female deposits batches of 20 to 50 eggs in the evening, rarely during the day. Oviposition begins about nine days after the fly emerges from the puparium and continues for some days. The maximal total production rarely exceeds 278 eggs, but the high figure of 820 has been recorded.[3] The elongate, creamy-white, banana-shaped egg (Fig. 236B), 1 mm. in length, is deeply furrowed on its straight side. Creamy-white, footless, translucent larvæ hatch in 1 to 3 days and mature in 7 to 21 days, depending upon season and food. Semidarkness and abundant moisture are necessary for development.[4] The mature larva (Fig. 236C), 20 mm. long, resembles that of the common house fly, but may be distinguished by its small black stigmal plates and circular, widely-separated posterior stigmata. When ready to pupate the larva forsakes moist sand or dung for drier ground. The barrel-shaped puparium (Fig. 236D), 5 to 7 mm., changes in color from red to chestnut-brown a few days before the fly emerges. The pupal stage lasts from 6 to 26 days, depending upon the temperature. The average time for larval development under favorable conditions is from three to four weeks.

Pathogenesis.—The fly is a vicious biter, sucking blood for two to five minutes or longer until its abdomen bulges. The anterior third of the proboscis is driven vertically into the flesh and during feeding this organ is moved slowly up and down with a semirotary motion.[4] Man is usually bitten on the ankles or shins even through woolen socks. The initial pain is sharp with two subsequent pricks as irritating as the first, but after the extraction of blood there is little discomfort. A drop of blood collects at the puncture and a small roseola with a scarlet center persists for a long time. The flies feed repeatedly on animals, since at least three blood meals are required for egg-production. Cattle and horses, subjected to frequent and heavy attacks, lose flesh, are unable to work and may even die.

Their habit of leaving one animal to resume feeding upon another makes stable flies ideal mechanical carriers of disease-producing agents. They have been accused of transmitting poliomyelitis, anthrax, infectious anemia of horses, trypanosomiasis and leishmaniasis. Poliomyelitis has been transmitted by this fly from monkey to monkey, but this method is not the natural mode of transmission.[5] The fly is a fortuitous transmitter of anthrax in animals, though definite proof is lacking.[6] Like the tabanid flies it may also mechanically transmit trypanosomal diseases in animals. This has been proved for *Trypanosoma evansi* (surra) [6] and experimentally for *T. brucei, T. gambiense* and *T. rhodesiense. Leishmania tropica,* the etio-

[2] Bishopp, F. C., 1913.
[3] Mitzmain, M. B., 1913.
[4] Newstead, R., 1906.

[5] Rosenau, M. J. and Brues, C. T., 1912.
[6] Mitzmain, M. B., 1914.

logical agent of oriental sore, has been experimentally transmitted to man by this vector.[7]

Control.—The control of stable flies requires the destruction of their breeding places. Decaying vegetable matter in the form of garbage, manure, wet hay and straw should be removed, dried or burned. Chemical treatment of manure will destroy the larvæ without impairing its value as fertilizer. A mixture of borax, 100 ounces and crude calcium borate, 120 ounces, in 25 gallons of water or hellebore powder, 5 pounds in 100 gallons of water, may be used for every 100 cubic feet of manure. Stables may be screened and fly traps installed. Cattle may be partially protected by a repellent consisting of fish oil 1 gallon, pine tar oil 2 ounces, pennyroyal 2 ounces and kerosene 1 pint. Robber flies, wasps, spiders and beetles are natural enemies.

HÆMATOBIA IRRITANS

Hæmatobia irritans, a dark or yellowish-gray fly found in Africa, Europe and America, was introduced in the United States about 1885. It feeds on the backs and flanks of cattle and has the habit of resting on the horns. It lays its eggs in fresh cow dung, from which the dirty white larvæ, resembling those of *Stomoxys calcitrans,* migrate when ready to pupate.

SUBFAMILY *GLOSSININÆ*

The GLOSSININÆ are large, elongate, yellowish or dark-brown viviparous flies with a narrow hairy body, slender proboscis, mottled thorax and brown-banded abdomen.

GENUS *GLOSSINA*

The genus *Glossina* includes some 20 or more African species of tsetse flies. Several are intermediate hosts of trypanosomes of mammals. Two species, *Glossina palpalis* and *G. morsitans,* are of special importance in the transmission of African sleeping sickness.

Geographical Distribution.—The tsetse flies are almost entirely confined to equatorial Africa from 18° north to 31° south latitude, except one species, *G. tachinoides,* which is also found in southern Arabia. *Glossina palpalis* is confined to western and central Africa from Senegal to Angora on the west coast and inland to Lake Victoria and Lake Albert. *G. morsitans* has a wider range in eastern, western and central Africa extending south to Rhodesia and north to the Sudan. Its distribution is extremely irregular, being limited to the so-called "fly belts."

Morphology.—Tsetse flies are yellow, yellowish-brown, dark brown or black flies with narrow bodies from 6 to 13 mm. in length. They are distinguished from other bloodsucking flies by (1) the resting position of the wings, which fold over each other like the blades of scissors completely concealing the abdomen and projecting beyond it; (2) the slender, horizontally-projecting proboscis with its bulbose base (Fig. 237G); (3) the branched, curved bristles on the upper side of the three-jointed antennal arista and (4) the distinctive venation of the light brown wings, chiefly characterized by the curvature of the fourth longitudinal vein, which imparts an irregular appearance to the discal cell (Fig. 237H).

---

[7] Berberian, D. A., 1938.

The head is narrower than the thorax and the compound eyes are separated in both sexes. The slightly-arched, quadrate thorax is partly covered with minute black hairs and mottled with gray or brown streaks or blotches. The males have longer claws and pulvilli than the females. The dorsal surface of the flattened tapering six-segmented abdomen has dark brown bands interrupted in the midline and is covered with short black hairs and long posterior bristles (Fig. 237A). The

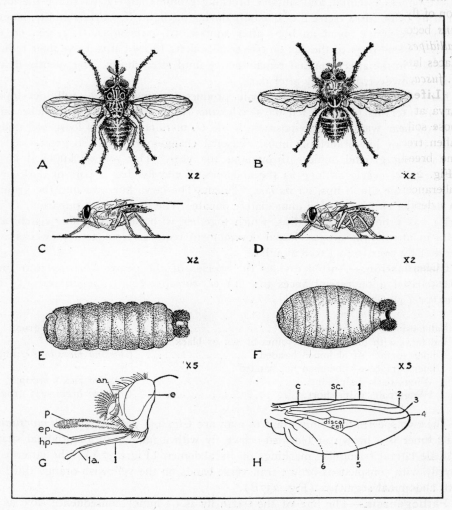

FIG. 237.—TSETSE FLIES

A, *Glossina palpalis*, male; *B*, *G. morsitans*, female; *C*, *G. palpalis*, lateral view, before feeding; *D*, *G. palpalis*, lateral view, after blood-meal; *E*, larva of *G. palpalis*; *F*, puparium of *G. pallidipes*; *G*, head and mouth parts of *G. palpalis*; *H*, wing of *G. palpalis*, showing venation. *an.*, antenna; *c*, costal vein; *s.c.*, subcostal vein; *e*, eye; *ep.*, epipharynx; *hp.*, hypopharynx; *l*, labium; *la*, labella; *p*, palps; 1 to 6, longitudinal veins (*A* to *D* and *F* redrawn from Austen, 1911; *G* redrawn from Surcouf and Gonzalez-Rincones; *H* adapted from Hegner, Root, Augustine and Huff, *Parasitology*, 1938, D. Appleton-Century Company).

sexes may be distinguished by the male hypopygium that forms a conspicuous, oval, knob-like protuberance beneath the end of the abdomen.

Habits.—*Glossina palpalis* and allied species frequent the neighborhood of water and dense undergrowth. Their favorite localities are hot, damp areas on the borders of rivers or lakes. Species of the *G. morsitans* group are less dependent upon water and are found in wooded and brush country that provides moderate shade. Cover is more or less essential, and suitable breeding grounds largely determine the location of fly belts. Most tsetse flies bite only during daylight. *G. palpalis* and *G. morsitans* become active about an hour after sunrise. *G. brevipalpis, G. fusca* and *G. pallidipes* spend most of the day on tree trunks along forest paths, leave their hiding places late in the afternoon and remain active until after sunset. The silently flying *G. fusca,* however, bites only after dark.

Life Cycle.—The pregnant female produces a single large, fully-developed larva at intervals of about ten days. *Glossina palpalis* selects sandy beaches and loose soil near water for larviposition, while *G. morsitans* prefers loose soil under fallen trees or low-branching limbs. Seasonal changes are often so great that no one breeding ground suffices throughout the year.[8] The yellow, knobbed larva (Fig. 237E), nearly as long as the abdomen of the fly, has a pair of dark protuberances, the tumid lips, on its last segment. The larva burrows into the ground to a depth of two inches and immediately pupates. The dark brown puparium (Fig. 237F) has prominent tumid lips, which together with the intervening notch, are useful in identifying species. Pupal development requires from 3 to 12 weeks and the adult fly lives from 4 to 8 months.

Classification.—Austen divides the species of the genus *Glossina* into four groups based upon resemblances to: (1) *G. palpalis,* (2) *G. morsitans,* (3) *G. fusca,* or (4) *G. brevipalpis.*[9]

Hind tarsi brown or black.............................*Glossina palpalis* group
Hind tarsi with only last two joints brown or black
   Upper surface of abdomen banded.....................*Glossina morsitans* group
   Upper surface of abdomen not banded
      Wings dark, palpi long...........................*Glossina fusca* group
      Wings pale, palpi short..........................*Glossina brevipalpi* group

The two species most important to man are *Glossina palpalis* and *G. morsitans.* The former is a brown or blackish-brown fly with a faint gray longitudinal stripe and pale lateral triangular markings on its abdomen (Fig. 237A). The latter is a gray fly with conspicuous brown transverse bands on the yellowish-orange third to sixth abdominal segments (Fig. 237B).

Pathogenesis.—The bite of the tsetse fly is of minor consequence save as it serves to transmit disease to man and animals (Chapter XI). Seven species of *Glossina,* particularly *G. morsitans,* are vectors of trypanosomal infections of domestic animals. *G. morsitans* and the closely related *G. swynnertoni* are vectors of *Trypanosoma rhodesiense* the causative agent of Rhodesian sleeping sickness, and this trypanosome has also been observed to develop in *G. palpalis* and *G. brevipalpis.*

[8] Nash, T. A. M., 1939.   [9] Austen, E. E., 1911.

G. palpalis and in certain districts the smaller *G. tachinoides* are the main vectors of *Trypanosoma gambiense,* the causative agent of Gambian sleeping sickness, while *G. morsitans, G. submorsitans, G. pallidipes* and *G. fusca* at times have been recorded as additional vectors.

Control.—The protection of the individual is determined by the habits of the flies (Chapter XI). Travel through infested districts should take place at night, while during daytime persons should be protected by special clothing and fly nets. Trains passing through infested regions should be thoroughly screened. The destruction of adult flies has been attempted with some success by various traps, such as adhesive fly paper on the backs of men; traps resembling quadrupeds [10] and operating through visual impression; and strips of white cloth set at an angle over a container and placed at that elevation most frequented by the flies in their flight. The advisability of destroying the wild game animals upon which the flies feed, thus reducing the flies through starvation, is questionable. The destruction of local habitats and breeding grounds by the removal of the underbrush along waterways is effective for *G. palpalis,* but the large scale deforestation and burning of underbrush and grass required for *G. morsitans* are not always practical.

FAMILY *HIPPOBOSCIDÆ*

The HIPPOBOSCIDÆ are pupiparous flies, ectoparasitic on mammals and birds. These degenerate species, known as tick or louse flies, have toothed claws, a sac-like abdomen and a leathery integument. They are larviparous, the larvæ remaining in the body until nearly ready to pupate. When the fly emerges from the puparium the wings are well developed, but may become rudimentary after it reaches its host. The various species are confined to the Old World. They may serve as vectors of hemoprotozoan parasites of animals. *Hippobosca rufipes* and *H. maculata* transmit *Trypanosoma theileri* of cattle and the wingless *Melophagus ovinus,* the common sheep tick or ked, is the vector of *T. melophagium,* a nonpathogenic trypanosome of sheep. Certain species parasitic on birds transmit *Hæmoproteus* infections.

REFERENCES

AUSTEN, E. E. A Handbook of the Tsetse-Flies, 1911, Brit. Museum, London, 110 pp.

BISHOPP, F. C. The Stable Fly, U. S. Dept. Agric. Farmers Bull, No. 1097, 1939, 23 pp.

BROWN, A. A. F. *Trypanosomiasis gambiensis.* Some Observations in Uganda, and Their Bearing on Prophylaxis, J. Trop. Med. & Hyg., 1938, 41 :200, 220, 234, 247, 265, 281, 296.

EDWARDS, F. W., OLDROYD, H. and SMART, J. British Blood-Sucking Flies, 1936, Brit. Museum, London, 156 pp.

MITZMAIN, M. B. I. Collected Studies on the Insect Transmission of *Trypanosoma evansi.* II. Summary of Experiments in the Transmission of Anthrax by Biting Flies, U. S. Public Health Serv. Hyg. Lab. Bull. No. 94, 1914, 53 pp.

NASH, T. A. M. The Ecology of the Puparium of *Glossina* in Northern Nigeria, Bull. Ent. Research, 1939, 30 :259.

[10] Harris, R. H. T. P., 1931, 1939.

Chapter XLIII

THE SUBORDER CYCLORRHAPHA: THE NON-BLOOD-SUCKING FLIES OF THE FAMILIES OSCINIDÆ, ŒSTRIDÆ, SARCOPHAGIDÆ, CALLIPHORIDÆ, MUSCIDÆ AND ANTHOMYIDÆ

The non-bloodsucking flies affect the health of man by the mechanical transmission of disease-producing organisms and by the parasitic activities of their larvæ.

FLIES AS MECHANICAL VECTORS OF DISEASE

The domestic species are the most important mechanical vectors. Pathogenic bacteria, protozoa and helminthic ova are carried on the external structures (hairs, feet, legs and mouth parts) and in the intestinal tract. Experiments have demonstrated that pathogenic bacteria may pass unharmed through the intestine or may be regurgitated, and that the typhoid bacillus may remain viable in the intestine 6 days, the tubercle bacillus 10 days and the anthrax bacillus 20 days. Spore-forming bacteria, ingested by larvæ, may even survive through the pupal to the adult stage. The ova of various helminths have also been observed to pass unharmed through the intestines of flies.

Flies that feed on fecal matter transmit enteric diseases by contaminating food and water. Several species, especially the common house fly, *Musca domestica*, have been incriminated on experimental or epidemiological evidence as transmitters of typhoid, bacillary and amœbic dysenteries and cholera. In several instances their control has been responsible for the decline in typhoid epidemics in army camps and elsewhere. Flies that feed on suppurating wounds and discharges are believed to spread nonenteric infections. Tuberculosis, plague, tularemia, anthrax and undulant fever have been associated with the common house fly, and trypanosomal, leishmanial and spirochætal diseases with other flies. Species of the genus *Hippelates* transmit acute conjunctivitis and yaws.

MYIASIS

Myiasis is the term applied to the invasion of living tissues of man and other mammals by dipterous larvæ. Clinically it may be classified according to the regions of the body affected: (1) cutaneous, when the larvæ live in or under the skin; (2) intestinal, when they are present in the stomach or intestine; (3) atrial, when they invade the oral, nasal, aural, ocular, sinusal, vaginal and urethral cavities; (4) wound, when they enter artificial lesions; and (5) external, when they are bloodsuckers. A regional classification is unsatisfactory, since one species may invade various parts of the body, and since all manner of gradations may occur, ranging from the accidental invasion by nonparasitic larvæ to the penetration of the tissues of definite hosts by host-specific forms.

A more satisfactory method groups the myiasis-producing flies by their ovi- or larvipositing habits into three classes: (1) specific, (2) semispecific and (3) accidental.[1] The specific myiasis-producing flies deposit eggs or larvæ in or near living tissues, where the larvæ inevitably become parasites. This group may be subdivided into (1) flies that deposit their larvæ in the habitat of the host; (2) those that lay their eggs or larvæ on the hairs or body of the host, whence the larvæ invade the local tissues and external atria or migrate to selective tissues; and (3) those that deposit their eggs or larvæ in wounds and diseased tissue, where the larvæ cause cutaneous, atrial and wound myiasis without penetrating unbroken skin. The semispecific myiasis-producing flies usually deposit their eggs or larvæ in decaying flesh or vegetable matter, and less frequently in diseased tissues and neglected wounds, although a few species have acquired a purely parasitic habit. The large number of larvæ thus deposited often causes extensive tissue destruction. The accidental myiasis-producing flies of diverse genera and habits deposit their eggs and larvæ in excrement or decaying organic material and at times in food. Their larvæ produce intestinal and urinary myiasis.

The myiasis-producing flies of importance in human and veterinary medicine fall in the first two groups and belong to the families ŒSTRIDÆ, CALLIPHORIDÆ and SARCOPHAGIDÆ. The clinical types of the specific (1) and the semispecific (2) myiases of the important genera are given below. The locations of deposition of the eggs and larvæ are designated as (A) hairs and body of host, (B) external habitat of host, and (C) wounds of host.

Family ŒSTRIDÆ
    Dermatobia   (1B) cutaneous
    Gasterophilus   (1A) atrial, intestinal, cutaneous
    Hypoderma   (1A) cutaneous
    Œstris   (1A) atrial
    Rhinœstrus   (1A) atrial
Family CALLIPHORIDÆ
    Auchmeromyia   (1B) bloodsucking
    Calliphora   (2C) wounds
    Chrysomyia   (1C) atrial, wounds
    Cochliomyia   (2C) atrial, cutaneous, wounds
    Cordylobia   (1B) cutaneous
    Lucilia   (2C) wounds
    Phormia   (2C) wounds
Family SARCOPHAGIDÆ
    Sarcophaga   (2C) wounds
    Wohlfahrtia   (1C) atrial, cutaneous, wounds

Intestinal Myiasis.—Intestinal myiasis in man is largely accidental, although some 30 species of dipterous larvæ have been found in the digestive tract. These

[1] Patton, W. S. and Evans, A. E., 1929.

accidental invaders are from flies that breed in decaying organic matter such as: *Fannia canicularis,* the lesser house fly; the *Eristalis tenax,* the rat-tailed maggot; *Aphiochæta ferruginea* and *A. scalaris* of the family PHORIDÆ; *Hermetia illucens,* the soldier fly, and *Piophila casei,* the cheese skipper. The intestine, however, is the normal environment of the parasitic ·*Gasterophilus* larvæ. The larvæ of the flesh flies of the genus *Sarcophaga* may gain entrance through the anus when the eggs are deposited at the anal orifice of infants. Many larvæ are destroyed by the digestive juices, but others are able to live in the intestinal tract and may produce intestinal distress. The extracorporeal contamination of feces should be differentiated from the actual presence of larvæ in the intestine.

Urinary Myiasis.—The larvæ of seven species of flies have been found in the urine. The larvæ of *Psychoda albipennis,* one of the simpler flies of the family PSYCHODIDÆ, have been recovered from the bladder of a boy, infestation probably resulting from migration through the tissues from the rectum. Urethral infections are presumably due to the invasion of larvæ from eggs deposited in purulent material on the genitals.

Cutaneous Myiasis.—The larvæ of some 36 species of flies have been associated with cutaneous myiasis. They are able to burrow through necrotic or healthy tissues with their chitinous mandibular hooks, usually following the line of least resistance. Their progress is facilitated by secondary bacterial infection and possibly by their proteolytic secretions.

Diagnosis.—The identity of the parasite causing a particular myiasis may be determined (1) by rearing the adult fly from the larva, except in obligatory parasites that cannot be separated from the host, and (2) from the morphology of the larva, particularly the characteristic posterior spiracles. The part containing the spiracles should be removed from the larva, treated over night with sodium or potassium hydrate, washed, dehydrated and mounted in balsam for microscopical examination.

Control of Myiasis.—Many and varied methods have been employed for the control of myiasis-producing flies. The destruction of carcasses and the disposal of offal reduce the breeding grounds of certain species. Fly traps, baited with carcasses of small animals or albuminous material in water, with or without poison, at times are effective. Screening of susceptible young domestic animals, treatment of wounds and the use of insect repellents, are also useful measures. Persons with catarrhal or suppurative lesions should not sleep in the open. The larvæ paralyzed with chloroform may be extracted by manual pressure or by forceps. Anthelmintic drugs may be used for intestinal forms. The eggs and larvæ on hairs or skin may be destroyed by kerosene, phenol, nicotine, derris powder or iodoform.

MAGGOTS IN SURGERY

The beneficial effect of maggots in the healing of suppurating wounds has been observed on the battlefields of the last century, but their use in the treatment of osteomyelitis was first introducd by Baer in 1929. The beneficial results have been ascribed to the ingestion of necrotic tissue and bacteria by the larvæ and to the action of excreted substances, which produce an alkaline reaction, digest necrotic tissue and stimulate healing. Allantoin, a urinary constituent of the larvæ, even in the absence of maggots, stimulates healing by granulation and restores the normal resistance of the tissues.[2] The maggots commonly used are the larvæ of the blow-flies, *Lucilia cæsar, L. sericata* and *Phormia regina.* They ordinarily live on necrotic tissues, but at times they have been observed to attack normal tissues.[3] For therapeutic use methods of breeding maggots under sterile conditions have been developed.

IDENTIFICATION OF CYCLORRHAPHOUS LARVÆ

The larvæ of cyclorrhaphous flies have certain structures that are useful in differentiating genera and species: (1) general shape and ornamentation, (2) structure of the anterior end, (3) anterior spiracles, and (4) posterior spiracles. These

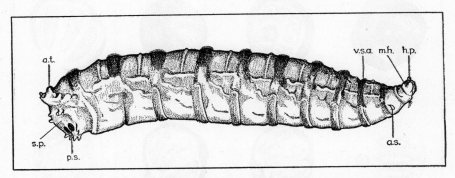

FIG. 238.—MATURE LARVA OF A MUSCID FLY

a.s., anterior spiracles; *a.t.,* anal tubercle; *h.p.,* head papillæ; *m.h.,* mouth hooks; *p.s.,* posterior spiracles; *s.p.,* stigmal plate; *v.s.a.,* ventral spinose area (Redrawn from Hegner, Root, Augustine and Huff, *Parasitology,* 1938, D. Appleton-Century Company).

characteristic structures are most readily recognizable in the mature third-stage larva. The larva (Fig. 238) has a broad truncated or rounded posterior and a narrow anterior end, and each segment may bear spinose areas that sometimes girdle the body. The tapering anterior end carries paired or fused dark hook-like processes and a pair of projecting papillæ. The anterior spiracles, small fan-like structures with a variable number of branches, extend from the lateral surfaces of the second segment.

The ventral surface of the posterior segment bears the anus and the anal tubercle and the dorsal surface the two posterior spiracles, the most important structures for differentiating genera and species. The dark chitinous stigmal plates of the posterior spiracles may be depressed in a slight pit ridged with several pairs of tubercles or may be invaginated to form a pocket. Each spiracle consists of a completely or nearly closed chitinous ring, a small, round, often perforated, chiti-

---

[2] Robinson, W., 1935, 1937.   [3] Stewart, M. A., 1934.

nous button, and usually three slits. The button may be inside of but attached to the ring, may form an integral part of it, or may appear indistinctly in the broken section of the ring. The slits are straight, tortuous or with transverse divisions, except in some species of œstrid larvæ which have numerous small, round, oval or

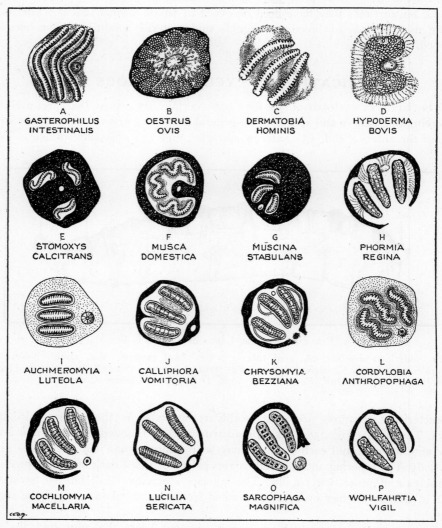

Fig. 239.—Schematic Representation of the Posterior Spiracles of Third-stage Larvæ of Representative Cyclorrhaphous Flies (Right Spiracular Plate Only)

sinuous apertures. The type of slit, the position of the button and the form and completeness of the ring serve to differentiate species (Fig. 239). The following key for identifying larvæ is taken from Hegner, Root, Augustine and Huff, *Parasitology*, 1938.

KEY TO THE THIRD-STAGE LARVÆ OF SOME OF THE MUSCOID FLIES

1. Larvæ of the normal muscoid shape, i.e., slender, cylindrical, tapering anteriorly, more or less truncate posteriorly, without lateral or posterior processes................. 2
   Larvæ either large, stout and more or less flattened dorsoventrally or else with lateral or posterior processes 7
2. Posterior spiracles with button area well chitinized and ring complete............... 3
   Posterior spiracles with button area very slightly chitinized and ring incomplete 6
3. Button area a part of the ring; slits nearly straight
                    Calliphora, Lucilia, Anastellorhina, Neopollenia
   Button area within ring... 4
4. Slits only slightly bent ....*Muscina*
   Slits sinuous, much curved 5
5. Posterior spiracle D-shaped; each slit thrown into several loops
             Musca, Philæmatomyia, Hæmatobia, Cryptolucilia, Morellia, etc.
   Posterior spiracle triangular with rounded corners; each slit S-shaped
                    Stomoxys, Bdellolarynx, Hæmatobosca
6. Inner slits sloping downward and outward; middle slits nearly vertical; outer slits sloping downward and inward.......................*Sarcophaga, Wohlfahrtia,* etc.
   All of the slits sloping downward and inward
                    Cochliomyia, Chrysomyia, Phormia, Photophormia
7. Larvæ large, stout, more or less flattened dorsoventrally, usually without processes
                                               (ŒSTRIDÆ)   9
   Larvæ short, stout, cylindrical, with a very long, tubular process posteriorly
                                    Eristalis (SYRPHIDÆ)
   Larvæ with fleshy or spinose lateral processes.................................... 8
8. Posterior spiracles placed in a depressed stigmal field
                    Chrysomyia albiceps, varipes and villeneuvii
   Posterior spiracles elevated on short tubercles............................*Fannia*
9. Posterior spiracles each with three distinct slits.............................. 10
   Posterior spiracles each with a large number of small apertures.................. 13
10. Slits of posterior spiracles nearly straight.................*Dermatobia, Cobboldia*
    Slits of posterior spiracles decidedly curved or sinuous........................ 11
11. Each slit bent at its middle.....................................*Gasterophilus*
    Each slit thrown into several loops... 12
12. Slits separate and not parallel to each other.............*Cordylobia* (CALLIPHORIDÆ)
    Slits close together and parallel to each other.........................*Gyrostigma*
13. Each posterior spiracle a single solid plate; its apertures without obvious cross-bars 14
    Each posterior spiracle more or less distinctly divided into several plates; its apertures small, curved, cross-barred slits.................................*Cuterebra*
14. Button area a part of the spiracular plate.......*Œstrus, Rhinœstrus, Gedœlstia,* etc.
    Button area separate, lying in an indentation of the spiracular plate.................. 15
15. Button area strongly chitinized, lying in a deep indentation of the spiracular plate
                                               Hypoderma
    Button area weakly chitinized, lying in a shallow indentation............*Cephalopsis*

FAMILY *OSCINIDÆ* (EYE FLIES)

The OSCINIDÆ are small acalyptrate flies about 2 mm. in length, with short antennæ, bare aristæ, dark thorax, short, dark bare wings, and pale legs. They breed in decaying vegetable matter and feces. The developmental cycle of *Hippelates pusio* (Fig. 240) averages 18.5 days; and the egg is 0.5 mm., the third-stage larva 3.3 mm. and the reddish-brown pupa 2.3 mm. in length.[4] Those species that attack man and other mammals use the tips of the pseudotracheal rings of the labella as incising instruments

---

[4] Hall, D. G., Jr., 1932.

for cutting granulation tissue and conjunctival epithelium, thus providing a pathway for secondary infection.

The eye gnat, *Hippelates pusio,* spreads an acute seasonal conjunctivitis prevalent among children during the summer in California, and in Georgia and other Southern States.[5] The control of this disease requires the removal of waste material suitable for the breeding places of the flies near human habitations and personal cleanliness to eliminate the ocular discharges that attract the flies. *Siphunculina funicola,* the eye fly of India, and other species of ŒSTRIDÆ that feed on sores, wounds and conjunctival exudates in Asia and Africa, are believed to be responsible for transmitting certain forms of ophthalmia. Yaws has been transmitted from man to rabbits by *H. pallipes.*[6]

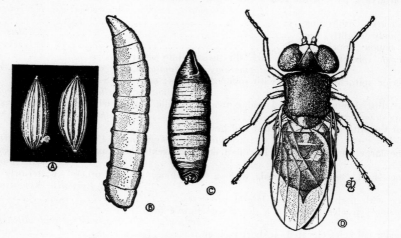

FIG. 240.—*Hippelates pusio,* THE EYE GNAT
A, eggs; *B,* larva; *C,* puparium; *D,* adult (From Hall, 1932).

FAMILY *ŒSTRIDÆ* (BOTFLIES)

The non-bloodsucking flies of the family ŒSTRIDÆ are known as botflies, warble flies or breeze flies. They have medium- to large-sized, thick-set, often hairy bodies, large heads, rudimentary mouth parts, relatively small eyes, short three-jointed antennæ concealed in facial grooves, a thorax with a distinct transverse suture, and wing venation of the muscoid pattern. The family includes a heterogeneous collection of genera, difficult to classify, of which *Dermatobia hominis* is the most important parasite of man. The adults inhabit the open country, resting upon leaves or on the ground along roads and pathways. The young twelve-segmented larvæ have oral hooks, but only certain species retain these appendages in the later larval stages. They undergo two molts and when ready to pupate leave the host for the ground. The larvæ of the various species are parasites of the subcutaneous tissues, nasal cavities, and intestinal tract of herbivorous and carnivorous mammals including the primates.

GENUS *GASTEROPHILUS*

The fourth longitudinal vein is straight, not reaching the margin of the wing; antennal arista bare; mouth parts vestigial; ovipositor elongate; larvæ, with inner and outer pairs of chitinous jaws, last abdominal segment broadly attached, posterior spiracles with three long slits (Fig. 239); geographical distribution cosmopolitan.

---

[5] Bengston, I. A., 1933.   [6] Kumm, H. W. and Turner, T. B., 1936.

Three species of botflies attack equines: *G, intestinalis,* a brown fly with rows of black spots on lower borders of abdominal segments and pale wings with dark central transverse bands; *G. hæmorrhoidalis,* the small red-tailed botfly with an orange tip to its abdomen; and *G. nasalis,* the chin fly. The eggs, pointed at the posterior and operculate at the anterior end, are laid singly on the shafts of hairs. Each species selects a preferential site: *G. nasalis* and *G. hæmorrhoidalis* the lower lips or jaw, and *G. intestinalis* the inner side of the legs and the abdomen. Friction and moisture from the tongue of the host appear necessary for hatching, which occurs about the fourteenth day, and for the transfer of the larvæ to the mouth. The larvæ invade the perioral skin and migrate to the stomach and intestine, where they mature in 8 to 12 months. The site of the attachment is marked by local inflammation and fibrosis, and heavily-infected animals are in poor condition. When ready to pupate the larvæ pass to the ground in the feces. In man the larvæ infest the cutaneous and subcutaneous tissues, causing slight pain and inconvenience. Their migrations produce a creeping eruption like that caused by larvæ of the dog hookworm, *Ancylostoma caninum.*

GENUS *ŒSTRUS*

The fourth longitudinal vein of the wing curves forward at tip closing the first posterior cell; the body is bare; the facial grooves near together below; larva with one pair of hooklets, an oval body, strongly convex anteriorly and flat below, segments bearing spindle-shaped hooks, and posterior spiracles with numerous small oval openings (Fig. 239); geographical distribution cosmopolitan.

Œstrus ovis, the botfly of sheep, deposits its newly hatched larvæ in the nostrils, whence they migrate to the frontal sinuses, attaching themselves by hooks to the mucosa. Heavy infestations may cause extensive mortality in sheep. The third-stage larvæ attain a length of 30 mm. before passing to the ground for a pupal stage of two months. They cause painful ocular and nasal myiasis in man.

GENUS *RHINŒSTRUS*

These large, dark gray flies have dark spots on the dorsum of the thorax and abdomen and a moderate growth of light brown hair. The larvæ are deposited in the nares, on the conjunctiva and occasionally in the mouths of mammals. *R. purpurens,* the Russian gadfly, is found in Europe, Asia and Africa. Its larvæ invade the nasopharyngeal regions of equines and less frequently of cattle, becoming attached to the mucosa of the sinuses. It occasionally causes naso- and ophthalmomyiasis in man.

GENUS *HYPODERMA*

The fourth longitudinal vein curves forward at the tip narrowing the first posterior cell; antennal arista is bare; proboscis reduced; palpi absent; facial grooves well-separated below; larva has no oral hooklets and its posterior spiracles have numerous, small, oval apertures (Fig. 239); geographical distribution Northern Hemisphere.

The larvæ of *H. bovis* and *H. lineatum,* the hairy yellow and black warble or heel flies, are parasites of cattle, causing grubby hides during the spring and early summer. Heavy financial losses result from the destruction of hides. The yellowish-white eggs are deposited singly on the hairs usually of the dewlap, legs and flanks. The larvæ penetrate the skin and migrate through the thoracic and abdominal cavities to the subcutaneous tissues of the back. The path of migration, though usually sterile, is marked by edema and hemorrhage. Involvement of the spinal cord may produce paralysis. The larvæ have numerous minute spines on all segments and when mature in about six months, are about 25 mm. in length. The second- to fifth-instar larvæ encapsulate beneath the skin of the host, causing painful subcutaneous swellings and perforation of the hide. When ready to pupate they work their way out and fall to the ground. A dry soil with less than 22 per cent moisture is necessary for pupal development,[7] which requires 22 days at 12° C.[8] Cattle over four years old are relatively immune.

Instances of human infection in workers in animal husbandry have been reported in North America, Europe and Asia. The subcutaneous tissues and eyes are usually involved. The larva may be removed by incising the furunculous lesion.

GENUS *DERMATOBIA*

The fourth longitudinal vein curves forward narrowing the first posterior cell; alulæ of wings are of moderate size; antennal arista pectinate; mouth parts vestigial; tarsi slender and not very hairy; third joint of antennæ elongate; larva club-shaped, more slender posteriorly; geographical distribution tropical America.

Dermatobia hominis.—The tropical warble fly, *Dermatobia hominis* (Fig. 241D), sometimes known as *D. cyaniventris,* is found in the damp forests of Central and South America, where its larvæ cause cutaneous myiasis of mammals. It is a large, thick-set fly, about 15 mm. in length, with a prominent triangular head, small antennæ, bluish-black thorax, a narrow thoracicoabdominal junction, a diamond-shaped bluish abdomen and orange-colored legs.

The eggs, 15 to 20 in number, enclosed in an adhesive substance, are attached to the abdomen of mosquitoes (chiefly the genera *Janthinosoma* and *Psorophora*) and, less frequently, other flies and ticks. When a mosquito bearing these eggs feeds on a mammal, the body heat of the latter apparently stimulates hatching. The larvæ crawl onto the skin, which they penetrate by means of their mandibular hooks in about 30 minutes, frequently utilizing the puncture-wound made by the mosquito, and then burrow in the subcutaneous tissues.

In its burrow the larva first assumes a club-shaped form, ver macaque (Fig. 241E), and when mature after two molts a cylindrical shape, torcel or berne (Fig. 241F). It has well-developed oral hooks and is encircled by several rows of segmental spines that anchor it in its burrow. The two posterior spiracles each with three curved slits (Fig. 239) lie in small deep clefts. The larva produces a tumor-like subcutaneous swelling with a small orifice at the surface. The narrow posterior extremity of the larva is directed toward this aperture for respiration. In 7 to 12 weeks the mature third-stage larva, 18 to 25 mm. in length, escapes to pupate in the soil for 22 to 24 days.[9]

Many domestic and wild animals and occasionally birds are hosts for this larva. In man it penetrates beneath the skin in various parts of the trunk and extremities. Its presence produces a furuncular swelling the size of a pigeon egg which breaks down and discharges a seropurulent fluid containing the dark feces of the larva. Considerable discomfort and local pain result, particularly when the larva moves. The larva may be extracted with forceps or squeezed out of its burrow after the injection of chloroform.

FAMILY *CALLIPHORIDÆ* (BLOWFLIES)

The CALLIPHORIDÆ are medium to large flies of a bright, uniform, metallic or yellowish color with round, oval or rarely elongate abdomens. The eyes are bare or pubescent and the aristae are usually plumose to tip, rarely bare. The fourth vein of the wings has an angular or sharply-rounded bend. These oviparous flies usually deposit their eggs in decaying organic matter, but some species, attracted by blood or offensive discharges, lay their eggs in cutaneous sores and abrasions.

GENUS *AUCHMEROMYIA*

Large, robust, brownish-yellow flies with elongate abdomen; cheeks broad and prominent; several rows of hair on parafacials; front wide in male; distinct pleropleural and well developed abdominal bristles; geographical distribution, Africa.

---

[7] Bruce, W. G., 1938.   [8] Ono, S., 1938.   [9] Dunn, L. H., 1930.

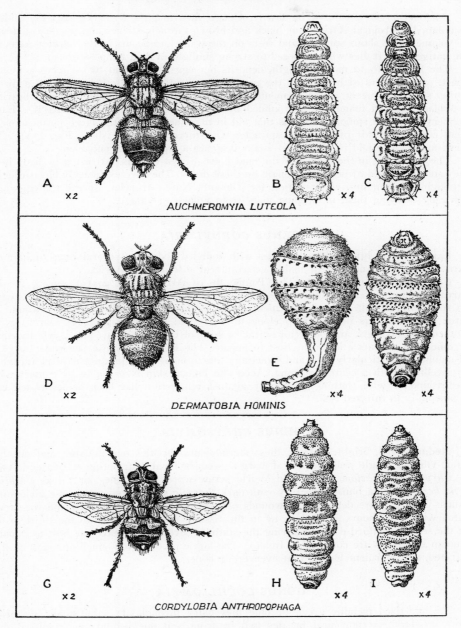

FIG. 241.—MYIASIS-PRODUCING FLIES

Auchmeromyia luteola: A, adult female; B, dorsal view of larva; C, ventral view of larva. *Dermatobia hominis:* D, adult female; E, young larva ("ver macaque"); F, old larva ("torcel"). *Cordylobia anthropophaga:* G, adult female; H, dorsal view of larva; I, ventral view of larva (A, D and G redrawn from Manson-Bahr's *Manson's Tropical Diseases*, 1936; B, C, H and I redrawn from Brumpt's *Précis de Parasitologie*, 1913; E and F redrawn from Blanchard).

Auchmeromyia luteola.—The tawny, Congo floor-maggot fly (Fig. 241A), widely distributed in tropical Africa, has black and brown thoracic stripes and unequal abdominal segments. It shuns sunlight and rests on the walls and beams in the darkest parts of the native huts. It dies when exposed to strong sunlight or to a temperature of 45° C.

The female, to 12 mm. in length, deposits her eggs, usually in two batches a month apart, on the floors of huts or on the ground. In about two days there emerges a dirty-white, semi-translucent, seven-segmented larva with a protrusible anterior end, bearing two black, curved mandibles surrounded by minute spicular teeth (Fig. 241B). Each segment has three spinous footpads that aid in movement, while the large posterior segment contains a pair of posterior spiracles with three transverse slits (Fig. 239). The larva molts twice and in about two weeks becomes a dark brown puparium.

The larvæ live in the cracks of the mud floors of native huts. Attracted by body heat they suck the blood of persons sleeping on these floors. They are exclusively bloodfeeders, although they can survive starvation for a month. Native travelers spread the eggs and larvæ by carrying them in sleeping mats from village to village.

GENUS *CORDYLOBIA*

Large, robust, brownish-yellow flies with rounded abdomen; several rows of hair on parafacials; front narrow in male; geographical distribution Africa.

Cordylobia anthropophaga.—The Tumbu fly of Africa (Fig. 241G), except for its narrow front and rounded abdomen, resembles *Auchmeromyia luteola*. It deposits its eggs on soil polluted with animal excrement or on clothing saturated with perspiration. In three days the eggs develop into elongate segmented larvæ (Fig. 241H and I) with toothed oral hooklets, and posterior spiracles without chitinous rim (Fig. 239). In eight or nine days the larvæ leave the host to pupate. The first-stage larvæ penetrate the skin of mammals, particularly rats, and sometimes attack man. They produce painful furuncular swellings with a central opening. Access to human skin is probably by contact with the ground or with clothing. Immunity against reinfection has been demonstrated experimentally in infected rats.[10]

GENUS *CHRYSOMYIA*

Medium-sized, bright, metallic flies; sternopleural bristles one in front and one behind; vibrissal angle well above oral margin; geographical distribution Africa and Asia.

Chrysomyia bezziana.—The Old World screw worm, sometimes known as *Cochliomyia bezziana,* is a bluish-green fly with dark thoracic stripes and transverse abdominal bands. The eggs are deposited in wounds or external atria of mammals, and the larvæ hatch within ten hours. They burrow in the tissues, develop rapidly to the third instar on the second or third day and during the sixth or seventh day leave the host to pupate. Human infections are common in India.[11] The larvæ produce foul-smelling, secondarily-infected, mucopurulent lesions that even erode bone.

GENUS *COCHLIOMYIA*

Medium-sized metallic green or blue flies hairy throughout; palpi small; posterior spiracles dark; sternopleural bristles two in front and one behind; geographical distribution America.

Cochliomyia macellaria.—The common American screw worm fly, 8 to 10 mm. in length, has a metallic blue to green color, three black longitudinal thoracic stripes and an abdomen covered with black hairs. It lays its eggs in decaying carcasses or in diseased

---

[10] Blacklock, D. B. and Gordon, R. M., 1927.　　[11] Patton, W. S., 1920.

tissues of cattle, horses and sheep. The dirty-white larva has circlets of spines on each
of its twelve segments, and the dark-brown puparium has rudimentary spines.

Cochliomyia americana.—*Cochliomyia americana* (*C. hominivorax*), less common
than *C. macellaria,* is found in southwestern United States and in greater numbers in
tropical America. It is an obligatory parasite of mammals, and human infestations are
now considered to be due to this species rather than to *C. macellaria.* It is responsible
for 86 to 90 per cent of wound infestation by larvæ in the mammals of the United States
of America.[12] The eggs are deposited in small batches on the intact skin of domestic
and wild animals, particularly of cattle, when the flies are attracted by purulent discharges and suppurating wounds. The larvæ hatch in a few hours, penetrate the skin,
produce deep festering wounds and leave the animal to pupate in the soil in 6 to 25 days.
They can penetrate healthy tissues, even cartilage. The turbinates and nasal septum may
be destroyed, the sinuses infested and even the brain invaded through the middle ear.
The fatality rate in man is about 8 per cent.[13]

GENUS *CALLIPHORA*

Medium to large, metallic black, blue and green flies; prothoracic spiracles brownish-
red; sternopleural bristles two in front and one behind; base of third longitudinal vein
of wing bare above, subcostal sclerite with minute hairs only and upper side of lower
squama hairy; geographical distribution cosmopolitan.

The larvæ of the common blow flies, *C. vomitoria* and *C. erythrocephala,* are essentially scavengers of animal refuse. The female deposits 450 to 600 small eggs on the
bodies of dead animals. Occasionally the larvæ develop in the neglected wounds of man
and other mammals, causing extensive tissue destruction.

GENUS *LUCILIA*

Medium-sized, metallic green or blue flies; prothoracic spiracles black; sternopleural
bristles two in front and one behind; base of first vein bare above, subcostal sclerite with
minute hairs only, and upper side of lower squama bare; geographical distribution cosmopolitan.

The female fly usually deposits her eggs on meat and dead animals, but at times on
the skin of debilitated mammals. *L. cæsar,* a common European species, and *L. serenis-
sima,* a bazaar fly of south India, may occasionally cause myiasis in man. The larvæ of
L. sericata, the sheep maggot fly, penetrate the living tissues, and are a serious menace
to sheep raising in South Africa and Australia.

GENUS *PHORMIA*

Metallic black, blue or green flies; prothoracic spiracle light orange; vibrissal angle
at same level as oral margin; base of first vein of wing hairy above, subcostal sclerite
with small black bristles and disk of upper squama bare. The larva of *Phormia regina*
has been reported to produce myiasis in man.

FAMILY *SARCOPHAGIDÆ* (FLESH FLIES)

The SARCOPHAGIDÆ are medium to large, thick-set, grayish, larviparous flies that are
usually found in the vicinity of latrines or near decaying animal or vegetable matter.
The aristæ are plumose to the middle; the abdomen has four visible segments; the first
posterior cell of the wing is closed by the forward curve of the fourth longitudinal vein,
and the male hypopygium is prominent. The numerous species are difficult to identify.

---

[12] Brennan, J. M., 1938; Knipling, E. F.,   [13] Cushing, E. C. and Patton, W. S., 1933.
1939.

GENUS *SARCOPHAGA*

These large grayish flies, 10 to 14 mm. in length, with four dorsal longitudinal, thoracic stripes and a light- and dark-checkered abdomen, have an almost world-wide distribution. The larvæ live in animal and vegetable matter or as parasites of open sores and discharges. They produce cutaneous and nasal myiasis in animals. The third-stage larva has a narrow posterior end, segments banded with transverse spinous swellings, finger-like anterior spiracles; prominent bifid anal swellings and depressed posterior stigmata (Fig. 239). The dark brown, oval puparium has depressed spiracular pits. Larvæ of *S. hæmorrhoidalis* and *S. carnaria* have been found in the human intestine following ingestion and also in the rectum when deposited near the anus, while those of *S. fuscicauda* have been observed in ulcerated tissues.

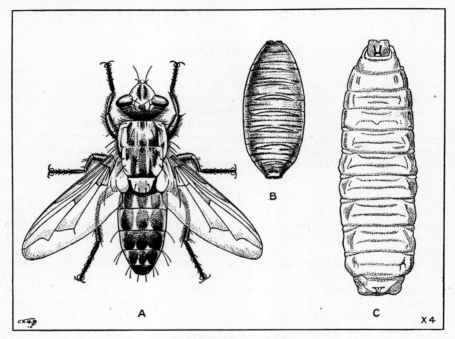

Fig. 242.—*Wohlfahrtia vigil*

A, adult male; *B,* puparium, ventral view; *C,* mature larva (Redrawn from Walker, 1920).

GENUS *WOHLFAHRTIA*

These flies are similar in appearance and habits to those of the genus *Sarcophaga,* but their abdomens have a spotted pattern. Their larvæ, identified by the posterior spiracles (Fig. 239), are frequently deposited in cutaneous lesions and atrial discharges and sometimes cause extensive tissue destruction. *Wohlfahrtia magnifica,* the Old World flesh fly of Europe, Africa and Asia, deposits numerous larvæ in cutaneous lesions, nasal and aural cavities, eyes and vagina. In North America the larvæ of *W. vigil* and *W. meigeni* produce cutaneous lesions in mammals. About 180 cases of larval infestation of mink, dogs, cats, ferrets, rabbits and foxes have been reported.[14] *W. vigil* is found in Canada and the northern United States from Nova Scotia to the Rocky Mountains and further west is replaced by *W. meigeni.* The adult (Fig. 242A), about 11 mm. in

[14] Kingscote, A. A., 1934.

length, deposits larvæ upon the skin. The mature larva (Fig. 242C) measures 17 to 18 mm. and puparium (Fig. 242B) 9 to 10 mm.[15] In summer the larvæ develop in from 7 to 9 days and puparia in from 10 to 12 days. The entire life cycle requires 30 to 36 days and the adults live 30 to 40 days.[16] Extensive superficial lesions of the cheek, neck, arms and chest of infants due to these burrowing larvæ have been reported by several investigators. These cases have nearly all occurred in June in infants sleeping unscreened out of doors. The larvæ appear unable to penetrate the skin of adults, but they can penetrate the tender skin of infants and produce furunculous lesions, 1.0 to 2.5 cm. in diameter, with round or elliptical openings. Surgical removal of the larvæ may be necessary to prevent disfiguration.

FAMILY *ANTHOMYIDÆ*

The ANTHOMYIDÆ are small- to medium-sized, gray or dark-brown flies of the muscoid type. The antennal aristæ are either plumose or bare, first posterior cell of wing wide open, and the abdomen has four or five visible segments.

GENUS *FANNIA*

The lesser house fly, *Fannia canicularis,* a domestic species, breeds in dung and on carcasses. The adult, 5 to 6 mm. in length, has three dark longitudinal thoracic stripes, and the antennal aristæ are bare. About one day after oviposition dorsoventrally-flattened larvæ with branched fleshy lateral extensions emerge. The larval and the pupal stages each require about one week. The larva has been found in the intestinal tract of man.

FAMILY *MUSCIDÆ*

The flies of the family MUSCIDÆ include both bloodsucking and non-bloodsucking species. The latter group contains both bloodfeeding and non-bloodfeeding species. They act as mechanical vectors of disease-producing organisms. They are small- to medium-sized, dark gray or black flies. The eyes are bare or pubescent; the antennal artistæ are bare or plumose; the proboscis is short and stout with fleshy labella adapted to licking or rasping; the thorax has usually two or more dark longitudinal bands; the front is narrow in the male; and the fourth longitudinal vein curves forward with a sharp or rounded bend leaving the first posterior cell open or closed.

GENUS *MUSCA*

Eyes almost contiguous in male; palpi cylindical; hastellum of proboscis weakly chitinized and prestomal teeth minute; thorax usually with four longitudinal stripes: wings hyaline with yellowish border, and tip of the fourth longitudinal vein with more or less rounded angle; middle tibiæ without prominent bristles on innerside of distal half; most species oviparous, some larviparous; larva cylindrical with widely-separated posterior spiracles; geographical distribution cosmopolitan.

MUSCA DOMESTICA

The common house fly, the most abundant species of the MUSCIDÆ, infests human habitations throughout the world.

Morphology.—The dark-gray adult with four black stripes on its back (Fig. 243A) is from 6 to 7 mm. in length. The fourth longitudinal vein bends forward at a rather sharp angle, and the arista is feathered with straight hairs both dorsally and ventrally.

---

[15] Walker, E. M., 1920.   [16] Ford, N., 1936.

The eyes are close together in the male, far apart in the female. The mouth is equipped for sucking liquids, but not for biting.

Life History.—The eggs (Fig. 243B), some 125 in number, are laid in masses in manure or other refuse, where they hatch in from 24 to 36 hours. The white, translucent, cylindrical, legless larvæ (Fig. 243C) have two mandibular hooks, two antennæ and bear stigmal plates on the posterior abdomen (Fig. 239). In warm weather the larval stage continues for seven days but may be prolonged to ten, when the larva is transformed into a barrel-shaped puparium (Fig. 243D). The pupal stage terminates in about three days with the emergence of the adult fly. The entire life cycle occupies from 10 to 14 days, while the adult fly normally lives about a month.

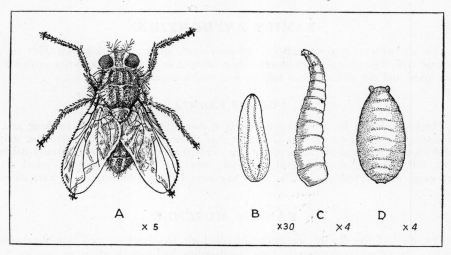

FIG. 243.—*Musca domestica* (COMMON HOUSE FLY)

A, adult fly; *B,* egg; *C,* larva; *D,* puparium (*A* redrawn from Philip, 1937; *B* redrawn from Philip, 1937, after Hewitt; *C* and *D* redrawn from Howard, 1906).

In tropical countries house flies are present throughout the year, but in dry climates the larvæ perish in times of maximal heat and drought. In temperate countries flies disappear in winter and are most numerous in early autumn. Some, however, survive the winter either as larvæ or pupæ or by continuous breeding in warm places.

Pathogenesis.—Apart from causing an occasional intestinal myiasis, the common fly does no direct damage. It menaces health, however, as a mechanical carrier of pathogenic bacteria, protozoa and helminthic ova or larvæ, chiefly those of enteric diseases.

Control.—Control is a community not an individual measure, since flies travel considerable distances; a record flight of 13 miles in a few days has been reported. Careful screening or continual trapping helps protect the individual. Fly traps, fly paper, poisons such as a 2 per cent solution of formalin in milk or sweetened water, fumigation or spraying with insecticides may be employed. Adequate control depends upon the elimination of breeding places in deposits of animal excrement, garbage and decaying vegetable matter.[17] Such material should be burned, buried or enclosed in screens. Manure may be rendered unsuitable as a breeding place for flies by spreading thin, rapidly-drying layers on fields, by constructing compost heaps or by chemical treatment with 0.62 lbs. of borax or 0.75 lbs. crude calcium borate to each 8 bushels of manure. Various expedients have been developed to eliminate larvæ during their migratory period, such as storing

---

[17] Philip, C. B., 1937.

manure in perforated bins so that the larvæ drop into water, or covering the manure with earth or canvas to induce destructive fermentation. The principal natural enemies of the house fly are the fly fungus, *Empusa muscæ,* the red mite, *Acarus muscarum,* and the chalcidoid wasps.

GENUS *MUSCINA*

Muscina stabulans, the nonbiting stable fly, resembles *Musca domestica.* There are four indistinct stripes on the thorax and the fourth longitudinal vein curves forward gradually leaving open the first posterior cell. Its larvæ have been found in the human intestinal tract.

REFERENCES

BLACKLOCK, D. B. and GORDON, R. M. The Experimental Production of Immunity Against Metazoan Parasites, Lancet, 1927, 1:923.

DUNN, L. H. Rearing the Larvæ of *Dermatobia hominis* Linn. in Man, Psyche, 1930, 37:327.

FORD, N. Further Observations on the Behavior of *Wohlfahrtia vigil* (Walker) With Notes on the Collection and Rearing of These Flies, J. Parasitol., 1936, 22:309.

HALL, D. G., JR. Some Studies on the Breeding Media, Development and Stages of the Eye Gnat *Hippelates pusio* Loew. (Diptera: Chloropidæ), Am. J. Hyg., 1932, 16:854.

KNIPLING, E. F. A Key for Blowfly Larvæ Concerned in Wound and Cutaneous Myiasis, Ann. Ent. Soc. America, 1939, 32:376.

—— and RAINWATER, H. T. Species and Incidence of Dipterous Larvæ Concerned in Wound Myiasis, J. Parasitol., 1937, 23:451.

PHILIP, C. B. The Transmission of Disease by Flies, U. S. Pub. Health Rep., 1937, Supp. No. 29, Washington, 22 pp.

ROBINSON, W. The Healing Properties of Allantoin and Urea Discovered Through the Use of Maggots in Human Wounds, Smithsonian Inst. Rep., 1937, Publication 3471:451.

Chapter XLIV

THE PARASITIC LICE OF MAN

Lice are small, degenerate, dorsoventrally flattened, wingless insects, lacking true metamorphosis. They are parasites of birds and mammals. The order ANO-PLURA (lice) includes two suborders: (1) MALLOPHAGA (biting lice) and (2) SIPHUNCULATA (sucking lice). The species parasitic on man belong to the family PEDICULIDÆ of the suborder SIPHUNCULATA.

SUBORDER *MALLOPHAGA* (BITING LICE)

The biting lice are ectoparasites of birds, less frequently of mammals. Their mouth parts are adapted to mastication. They never suck blood directly, but feed on cuticular material, hair and feathers. They are neither parasites of man nor vectors of human disease. The dog louse, *Trichodectes canis,* however, is an intermediate host of the cestode, *Dipylidium caninum,* and transmits this parasite from dog to dog.

SUBORDER *SIPHUNCULATA* (SUCKING LICE)

The sucking lice have mouth parts modified for piercing and sucking. The thoracic segments are fused, the head is narrower than the thorax, and the thoracic spiracular openings are dorsally located. They are ectoparasites of mammals. The suborder comprises four families: (1) the ECHINOPTHIRIIDÆ of aquatic mammals, (2) the HÆMATO-MYZIDÆ of elephants, (3) the HEMATOPINIDÆ of wild and domestic mammals, and (4) the PEDICULIDÆ of mammals. Over 120 species of the family PEDICULIDÆ have been classified and described.

The parasitic lice of man are (1) *Pediculus humanus* var. *capitis* de Geer, 1778 (head louse), (2) *Pediculus humanus* var. *corporis* de Geer, 1778 (body louse), and (3) *Phthirus pubis* Linnæus, 1758 (crab louse). The three forms confined almost exclusively to man and primates, differ somewhat in their habitats, characteristics and habits. *Phthirus pubis,* the crab louse, is morphologically a distinct species, but the head and body lice are apparently varieties of a single species. The latter, though larger and less dark, is believed to have been derived from the former when man acquired the habit of wearing clothing. The two varieties interbreed, their descendants are fertile, and their morphological differences overlap. Some authorities, however, distinguish separate types for the primary races of mankind: white, black, red and yellow and a distinctive species peculiar to African Negroes, *Pediculus maculatus,* has been reported.[1]

Disease.—Pediculosis.

History.—Infestations with lice have been known since ancient times in all parts of the world. Their presence in Peruvian mummies was reported by Küchenmeister

---

[1] Ferris, G. F., 1935.

in 1855. From a medical standpoint they have played an important rôle in spreading epidemics of typhus.

Geographical Distribution.—Cosmopolitan.

BIOLOGICAL CHARACTERISTICS

Morphology.—The elongate body (Fig. 244A) has three distinct parts: an angular ovoid head, a fused thorax, and a segmented abdomen over three-fifths the body length. The male is smaller than the female. The head bears a pair of simple lateral eyes, anterior to which are a pair of short five-jointed antennæ. The frons lies

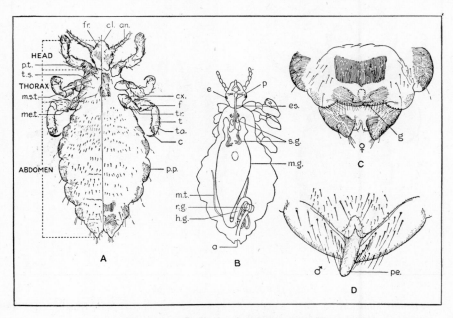

Fig. 244.—*Pediculus humanus corporis*

A, external anatomy of female; *B,* internal anatomy; *C,* posterior end of female; *D,* posterior end of male.

a, anus; *an.,* antenna; *c,* claw; *cl.,* clypeus; *cx.,* coxa; *e,* eye; *es.,* esophagus; *f,* femur; *fr.,* frons; *g,* gonopod; *h.g.,* hindgut; *m.g.,* midgut; *m.t.,* malpighian tubule; *me.t.,* metathorax; *ms.t.,* mesothorax; *p,* pharynx; *pe.,* penile organ; *p.p.,* pleural plate; *p.t.,* prothorax; *r.g.,* rectal glands; *s.g.,* salivary glands; *t,* tibia; *ta,* tarsus; *t.s.,* thoracic spiracle; *tr.,* trochanter (*A, C* and *D* redrawn from Ferris, 1935; *B* redrawn from Sikora, 1916).

between the eyes and the antennæ, and in front of the frons is the projecting clypeus. The oral opening at the anterior end of the clypeus is encircled by six pairs of **prestomial hooklets** that serve to attach the louse to the skin during feeding. Below the buccal opening is an extensile piercing proboscis with three slender stylets and a supporting labium. The median stylet, the hypopharynx, contains the salivary duct through which the salivary secretions are introduced into the wound. While feeding, the chitinous pharynx acts as a sucking organ.

The three fused segments of the thorax are covered with heavy, chitinous, lateral plates. Each segment bears a pair of short, strong five-segmented legs. The terminal unjointed tarsus of each leg terminates in a single hook-like claw, which by opposing a thumb-like tibial process, enables the louse to maintain a firm hold on hairs or fibers. The middle thoracic segment bears a pair of respiratory spiracles.

The elliptical abdomen has nine segments; the anterior may be fused and the last two modified for sexual purposes. The heavy, lateral, pleural plates, which are useful in species identification, bear the openings of the six abdominal spiracles.

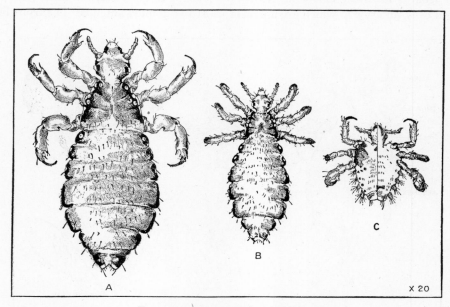

FIG. 245.—PARASITIC LICE OF MAN

A, Pediculus humanus corporis, female; *B, Pediculus humanus capitis,* female; *C, Phthirus pubis,* female (Redrawn from Ferris, 1935).

The last segment of the male, narrower and more rounded than that of the female, bears on its dorsal surface a terminal chitinized **ædeagus** with a penile organ (Fig. 244D). In the female the last segment bears a median, dorsal genital opening and two lateral blunt **gonopods,** which clasp the hairs during oviposition (Fig. 244C).

The digestive tract (Fig. 244B) consists of a buccal funnel, a muscular pharynx, a long narrow esophagus, a broad anterior and a narrow posterior midgut, a narrow hindgut which receives the malpighian tubules, a rectum with a distended ampulla, and an anal opening on the dorsal surface of the eighth segment. Four salivary glands in the thorax empty into two lateral ducts that pass to the salivary duct in the proboscis. The male reproductive organs include paired double testes, vasa deferentia, seminal vesicles, accessory glands, and an ejaculatory duct and penis. The female reproductive organs comprise paired ovaries, oviducts, accessory glands, and a common oviduct and vagina leading to a median genital opening.

The morphological differences in the three lice parasitic to man are shown in Table 42 and Figure 245.

Habits.—Body and head lice can move fairly rapidly and pass from host to host during contact. The crab louse changes its position infrequently and moves only for a short distance. They maintain a temporary position on the body of the host by clasping the hairs with their claws. The favorite site for the head louse is the hairs of the back of the head, that of the crab louse the pubic hairs, and that of the body louse the fibers of clothing and the hairs of the chest and axilla.

TABLE 42

DIFFERENTIATION OF LICE PARASITIC TO MAN

	Pediculus humanus var. *corporis* (body louse)	*Pediculus humanus* var. *capitis* (head louse)	*Phthirus pubis* (crab louse)
Size of adults (mm.) Male	2.0 to 3.0	1.0 to 1.5	0.8 to 1.0
Female	2.0 to 4.0	1.8 to 2.0	1.0 to 1.2
Shape	Elongate	Elongate	Oblong, turtle-shaped
Color	Grayish-white	Grayish-white with dark margins	Grayish-white
Head	Diamond-shaped	Diamond-shaped	Rectangular, neck not constricted
Abdomen Shape	Elongate, wider than thorax	Elongate, wider than thorax	Short
Segments	Distinct	Distinct	Indistinct
Size of claws	Medium	Medium	Large, heavy
Eggs Deposited on	Clothing, less frequently hairs	Hairs	Hairs
Length (mm.)	0.8	0.6	0.8
Principal habitat	Body	Head	Pubic region

Lice are dependent upon their hosts for food. Well-nourished body and head lice can survive for ten days at 5° C. without food, but the crab louse dies in two days if separated from its host. They suck blood for long periods but apparently never become engorged. During feeding the feces are a dark red in color. In experimental investigations as to the rôle of lice in the transmission of disease, uncontaminated lice may be kept in small, gauze-covered, pillbox-sized glass-bottomed containers, which are strapped like a wrist watch to the wrist, gauze surface down, during feeding periods, thus bringing the lice in direct contact with the skin of the host.[2]

During oviposition the female clasps a hair between the two gonopods and the body so that the shaft is in contact with the genital opening (Fig. 246A). The eggs, called "nits," are firmly attached to the hairs or, in the case of the body louse, to fibers of the clothing by a durable chitin-like cement. The ellipsoidal, distally-operculate white egg (Fig. 246B) is about 0.8 mm. in length. Those of the head and body lice are similar, but those of the crab louse are slightly more conical and

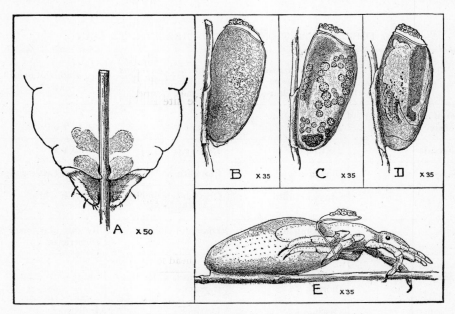

FIG. 246.—DEVELOPMENT OF *Pediculus humanus capitis*

A, hair clasped by female at oviposition; *B* to *D* development of embryo in egg case attached to hair; *E,* nymph emerging from egg (Redrawn from Nuttall, 1917).

have a larger quantity of cementing material. Eggs remain viable on clothing and blankets for a month. The eggs are deposited soon after the female reaches maturity and becomes impregnated. The total number produced by a female varies with the temperature and food supply, and is estimated as a maximum of 300 for the body louse, 140 for the head louse and 50 for the crab louse. Under experimental conditions the daily average was 6.4 for the body louse and 3.7 for the head louse,[2] but under optimal natural conditions the body louse averages 9.7 eggs per day.[3]

LIFE CYCLE

Lice have a high host-specificity. *Pediculus humanus,* however, has been found on monkeys and apes and *Pthirus pubis* occasionally on dogs.

---

[2] Bacot, A., 1917.   [3] Nuttall, G. H. F., 1917.

The time of incubation of the ova, depending upon the temperature, averages 8 to 9 days and varies from 5 to 11 days for *Pediculus humanus* and is approximately the same for *Phthirus pubis,* but the eggs may lie dormant for 35 days. The nymph (Fig. 246B-D) develops within the egg-case and when ready to hatch emerges through the opened operculum (Fig. 246E). The young louse, which resembles the adult in shape and feeding habits, undergoes three moults within two weeks. The second- or third-stage larva is also known as a nymph. Unless fed it lives little more than one day. It also perishes in two days if held at a temperature of –2.3° to 1.1° C.

The life cycle of *Pediculus humanus* from egg to adult averages 16 days, ranging from 12 to 28 according to temperature and available food, and that of *Phthirus pubis* is 15 days. The young *Phthirus pubis* seldom moves from the locality of hatching, attaches itself to the base of the hairs and is helpless if removed from the host. The life span of female *Pediculus humanus corporis* averages 34 days and the extreme limit is 46 days, while that of *P. humanus capitis* is 27 and 38 days respectively.[2] The average life span of the female *Phthirus pubis* is approximately 35 days. The females live longer than the males. The length of life of *P. humanus* without food varies with the temperature; ten days at 5° C., seven days at 20° C. and two days at 27° C.

PATHOGENESIS

Pathology.—Characteristic cutaneous lesions are produced by the bites of both young and adult lice, the location varying with the three types. Those due to the head louse occur most frequently on the back of the head and neck, although they may be present anywhere on the scalp; those due to the body louse on the parts of the body in close contact with clothing; and those due to the crab louse in the pubic region, but at times appearing on the hairy parts of the abdomen, thorax, axilla and head.

The irritating saliva, injected during feeding, produces a roseate elevated papule accompanied by severe itching. Individuals vary in sensitivity, and in chronic infestations, owing to immunizaton against the salivary secretion, the reaction may be slight. Patients with pale delicate skin show patches from 2 to 15 mm. in size. Scratching increases the inflammation and may lead to secondary bacterial infection with the sequelæ of pustules, crusts, suppurative processes and matted hair. Severe infestations may lead to scarring, induration and pigmentation of the skin and even ulceration. Infestation of the eyelashes through secondary infection leads to phlyctenular conjunctivitis and keratitis.[4]

Symptomatology.—The symptoms are those of cutaneous irritation, loss of sleep and psychological depression. Itching is the earliest and most prominent symptom and with the crab louse is especially severe at night. The sequelæ of scratching are the most characteristic signs. Old and debilitated individuals are most severely affected and death may occasionally result.

---

[4] de Font-Réaulx, P., 1912; Hudson, A. C., 1914.

DIAGNOSIS, PROGNOSIS AND TREATMENT

Diagnosis.—The diagnosis of pediculosis depends upon finding the adult or the "nits" of the head and crab louse attached to hairs. It is more difficult to find the eggs of the body louse, which are most often hidden in the seams of clothing. The adult body lice also tend to congregate in these locations. The differential diagnosis between the three forms is given in Table 42.

Prognosis.—Favorable under treatment.

Treatment.—In civil life the treatment of the individual or small groups of patients presents no serious problem, but in wartime and in typhus-infected populations under insanitary conditions the application of mass control is more complicated.

In combating head lice, prevalent among schoolgirls, the head should be thoroughly rubbed with a mixture of equal parts of kerosene or crude petroleum and olive oil. After several hours 2.5 per cent phenol or 1 per cent lysol may be applied for one to two hours and the head wrapped in a towel overnight. The following morning a soap shampoo is administered, and the hair is combed with a fine-toothed comb to remove the "nits." Treatment should be repeated in ten days to destroy newly-hatched lice. In severe infestations it is advisable to cut the hair short.

Body lice are destroyed by sterilizing all clothing and bedding by dry heat, dry cleansing or laundering and by thorough cleansing of the body after applying kerosene or crude oil to the hairy parts. Shaving these areas is sometimes advisable. Itching may be relieved by applying a 1 per cent alcoholic solution of thymol to the irritated areas. A naphthalene powder (naphthalene 96 parts, creosote 2 parts and iodoform 2 parts) dusted into the seams of clothing serves as a repellent.

The areas infested by crab lice may be treated by shaving and the application of a petroleum-olive oil mixture or 10 per cent thymol in olive oil followed after several hours by washing with soap and water. Blue mercuric ointment or a 1 per cent mercuric chloride in glycerin may also be used. Skin irritation may require a bland, soothing lotion.

Mass delousing is required when large groups are infested with body lice. After removing all clothing, the individuals undergo hair-clipping, thorough bathing with insecticidal soap, and revestment in sterilized clothing. Infested articles may be disinfected by heat, chemicals or storage. The eggs are more resistant than the larvæ and adults. Steam sterilization is the most practical method of treating infested clothing. However, it causes wrinkling and shrinking of woolen goods. Moist heat destroys the eggs at 60° C. in 15 to 30 minutes and at 100° C. in 1 minute, and is more efficient than dry heat because of its penetrating powers. Dry heat should be used for leather goods and fabrics injured by steam, although a high temperature tends to damage woolen fibers. Chemicals, such as kerosene, gasoline, cresol, naphthalene and acetic acid may be used for leather goods, felts and webbing. Dry storage for 30 days also destroys the eggs. Ironing of seams and folds in clothing with a hot iron is a useful procedure. Various types of delousing plants for handling large numbers of individuals have been devised. The usual plant includes steam or hot air disinfectors, rooms for disrobing, bathing, inspection and treatment, and facilities for reissuing disinfested clothing.

PREVENTION

Epidemiology.—The incidence of pediculosis varies with personal hygiene. It is high in persons of unclean habits, in cold climates where heavy clothing is required and bathing is infrequent, in flop-houses frequented by beggars and itinerants, in jails, in children living in crowded or filthy tenements, in soldiers during wartime, and in groups of persons subjected to crowding in an unclean environment.

The head louse is the most common and the crab louse the least common of the three lice of man. The head louse is easily transmitted by brushes, combs and hats. It is endemic where personal cleanliness is neglected, is most prevalent in children, particularly girls, and may become epidemic in schools and institutions. The body louse is transmitted by contact, by clothing or personal effects, on which eggs may remain viable for at least a month. The crab louse is usually transmitted through coitus and less frequently through toilet seats, clothing and bedding. The tendency of the adult crab louse to cling to two hairs prevents its ready transfer to another host, and infection usually occurs by the transfer of "nits" or broken hairs.

Prophylaxis.—Mass delousing methods are designed not only to exterminate the lice and their eggs but also to control the diseases transmitted by lice. The methods employed for troops may be used to advantage in delousing a civil population in regions where typhus is epidemic. Individuals may be protected by wearing silk or rubber outer garments fastened tightly at wrists, ankles and neck, and houses may be disinfected by hydrocyanic gas.

HUMAN DISEASES TRANSMITTED BY LICE

The body louse is the vector of typhus, trench and European relapsing fever. The head louse is a less important vector, while the crab louse has never been incriminated. Temperatures above the normal body heat of man are unfavorable for lice. For this reason they tend to leave febrile patients and seek other hosts, thus increasing the chance of spreading infection.

Typhus Fever.—Typhus fever, caused by *Rickettsia prowazeki,* occurs in epidemics in crowded jails, armies or during famines. Lice become infected by ingesting the blood of a diseased person. The parasites multiply in the intestinal epithelium of the midgut of the louse and are passed in the feces after the second day or reach the proboscis after the sixth. The louse remains infective throughout its life. Man acquires the infection through contamination of the bite by the feces or the crushed body of the infected louse, or when bitten by a contaminated proboscis.

Trench Fever.—Trench fever, caused by *Rickettsia quintana,* is an incapacitating disease that was prevalent during the First World War. When the infected blood is ingested by the louse the parasites multiply in the lumen of the midgut of the louse, which becomes infective in from five to nine days. Infection of a new host occurs as in typhus fever, the contaminative method being the more common.

Relapsing Fever.—The European form of relapsing fever is caused by the Spirochæta, *Borrelia recurrentis.* The organisms are ingested with blood by the louse, multiply and are distributed throughout its body within six days. Man is infected by the contaminative method, the crushed body of the louse coming in contact with the bite or broken skin.

ANIMAL DISEASES TRANSMITTED BY LICE

Other species of lice transmit diseases among the lower animals. Tularemia is spread in rabbits, plague in marmots, bartonella infections in mice and rats, and *Dipylidium caninum* infection in dogs.

REFERENCES

BACOT, A. A Contribution to the Bionomics of *Pediculus humanus* (*vestimenti*) and *Pediculus capitis,* Parasitology, 1917, 9:228.

BUXTON, P. A. The Louse, an Account of the Lice Which Infest Man, Their Medical Importance and Control, 1939, London, 115 pp.

FERRIS, G. F. Contributions Toward a Monograph of the Sucking Lice, Part VIII. Stanford Univ. Pub. Biol. Sc., 1935, 531 pp.

KEILIN, D. and NUTTALL, G. H. F. Icogonographic Studies of *Pediculus humanus,* Parasitology, 1930, 22:1.

NUTTALL, G. H. F. The Part Played by *Pediculus humanus* in the Causation of Disease, Parasitology, 1917, 10:43.

—— The Biology of *Pediculus humanus,* Parasitology, 1917, 10:80.

—— Combating Lousiness Among Soldiers and Civilians, Parasitology, 1918, 10:411.

—— The Biology of *Phthirus pubis,* Parasitology, 1918, 10:383.

SIKORA, H. Beiträge zur Anatomie, Physiologie und Biologie der Kleiderlaus (*Pediculus vestimenti* Nitzsch.). I. Anatomie des Verdauungstraktes, Arch. f. Schiffs-u. Tropen-Hyg., 1916, 20: Beihefte 1:5.

WOLBACH, S. B., TODD, J. L. and PALFREY, F. W. The Etiology and Pathology of Typhus; Being the Main Report of the Typhus Research Commission of the League of Red Cross Societies to Poland, 1922, Harvard Univ. Press, 222 pp.

Chapter XLV

THE SIPHONAPTERA OR FLEAS

Fleas are ectoparasites that for feeding purposes temporarily infest mammals and birds. These small, apterous, laterally-compressed, brownish insects undergo complete metamorphosis. The various species tend to be host-specific, but their activity and method of life permit the infestation of animals other than the preferred hosts. Their geographical distribution, often cosmopolitan, is determined by the range of their principal hosts. The larval fleas are not parasitic, although they live in the habitations of the hosts. Man is the principal host of two species, but occasionally is infested with the fleas of other mammals. Flea dermatitis may result from their bites and one burrowing species, *Tunga penetrans,* produces festering, cutaneous sores. Certain genera are of medical importance; particularly the rodent species that transmit bubonic plague and typhus fever.

BIOLOGICAL CHARACTERISTICS

Morphology.—Fleas (Fig. 247) are small insects from 2 to 2.5 mm. in length with laterally-compressed bodies. The males are smaller than the females. The relatively-small chitinous head is usually longer than wide and simple eyes are often present in front of or below the fossæ that contain the closely-fitting, three-jointed, club-shaped antennæ. Below or in front of each eye is an ocular bristle. The suctorial apparatus consists of an anterior pair of maxillary palps, a posterior pair of labial palps, two triangular distally-serrated maxillæ, two needle-like mandibles, and a pointed stylet-shaped epipharynx. Blood is carried to the buccal cavity and saliva secretions are discharged in the channel formed by the epipharynx and mandibles. Conspicuous rows of stout spines known as combs (Fig. 248) are present in some species on the ventral margin of the head (genal comb) and on the posterior margin of the first thoracic segment (pronotal comb).

The thorax is composed of three distinct segments each bearing a pair of powerful legs terminating in two curved claws. The posterior pair, adapted for leaping, are greatly elongated. The laterally-compressed abdomen has ten segments, the last two modified for sexual purposes. Each segment has a dorsal tergite and a ventral sternite. The rows of segmental bristles are of taxonomic importance.[1] At the posterior portion of the seventh tergite are the stout antepygidial bristles. Posterior to these bristles is a small hairy pad, the **pygidium,** which probably possesses a sensory function, and still further back is the anus. The male may be distinguished by the claspers of the ninth segment and a conspicuous, coiled cirrus

---

[1] Fox, I., 1940.

extending inward and forward from the junction of the ninth and tenth segments (Fig. 247). In the female the vulva is situated at the posterior extremity and in cleared specimens the chitinous seminal receptacle or spermatheca may be observed. The characteristics of the genitalia are useful for differentiating species.

The digestive tract consists of a muscular pharynx, a long esophagus, a proventriculus with chitinous teeth, a dilated midgut, a narrow hindgut and a pouch-like rectum. Four malpighian tubules enter at the juncture of the mid- and hindgut. There are two pairs of salivary glands and a pair of long salivary ducts that unite at the base of the mouth parts. The male reproductive organs comprise two

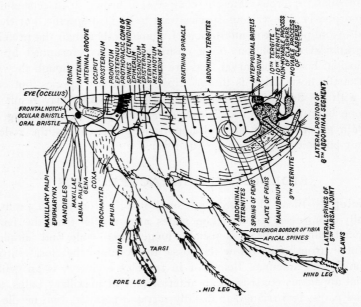

FIG. 247.—EXTERNAL ANATOMY OF A MALE FLEA (*Ceratophyllus fasciatus*)

(From Stitt, Clough and Clough, *Practical Bacteriology, Hæmatology and Animal Parasitology,* 1938. Copyright The Blakiston Company, Publishers).

testes, two vasa deferentia, a seminal vesicle, four accessory glands, an ejaculatory duct and a complicated penial organ. The female reproductive organs include two lobulate ovaries, a common oviduct, a seminal receptacle and a vagina.

Habits.—The adult fleas feed on their hosts, while the larvæ live on any nutrient débris, particularly dried blood and the feces of adult fleas. In biting the flea thrusts the labrum beneath the skin, enlarges the hole by working the mandibles back and forth and injects an anticoagulative salivary secretion. Fleas have unusual leaping powers which enable them to transfer readily from host to host; *Pulex irritans* has been known to leap for a distance of 13 inches and to a height of 7¾ inches.[2]

---

[2] Mitzmain, M. B., 1910.

The span of life of the adult flea, under favorable conditions, is about a year, although *Pulex irritans* has been observed to live 467 days [2] and 513 days.[3] Cool, but not cold, moist temperatures favor longevity. Unfed fleas may live several months; the human flea about two months, the dog flea somewhat less and the stick-tight flea still less.[4] The maximal survival period off the host is 125 days for *P. irritans,* 95 days for *C. fasciatus,* 38 days for *X. cheopis* and 58 days for *Ct. canis.*[3] One male flea is able to impregnate at least 13 females, but in order to produce a large number of eggs females must copulate more than once and take frequent blood meals. Cold weather inhibits egg-production.

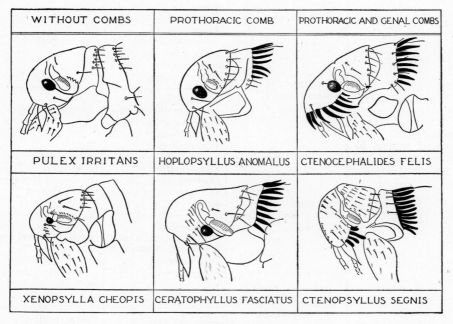

FIG. 248.—SCHEMATIC REPRESENTATION OF HEADS OF VARIOUS FLEAS, SHOWING DIFFERENTIAL CHARACTERISTICS OF SHAPE, COMBS, EYES AND ANTENNÆ

CLASSIFICATION

The order SIPHONAPTERA includes two suborders: (1) the INTEGRICIPITA of which the genera *Pulex, Xenopsylla, Ctenocephalides, Ceratophyllus* and *Tunga* are concerned with the diseases of man and (2) the FRACTICIPITA of which only the genus *Ctenopsyllus* is of medical interest. The differential morphological characteristics of the more common species associated with the diseases of man are set forth in Table 43 and Figure 248. Classification is based chiefly on the presence, size and position of the eyes; the location of the ocular bristles; presence and arrangement of combs; structure of head, genitalia, antennæ, and appendages; and ornamentation.

---

[3] Bacot, A. W., 1914.   [4] Bishopp, F. C., 1915.

TABLE 43

COMMON FLEAS OF MAN AND MAMMALS

Suborder	Family	Genus	Species
INTEGRICIPITA (antennal grooves incomplete, frons and occiput fused dorsally)	HECTOPSYLLIDÆ (without combs)	*Tunga* (hind coxa without spinules)	*T. penetrans* (jigger of man)
		Echidnophaga (hind coxa with spinules)	*E. gallinacea* (chicken flea)
	PULICIDÆ (without combs)	*Pulex* (mesosternite with one internal rod-like thickening, ocular bristle anterior to eye)	*P. irritans* (human flea)
		Xenopsylla (mesosternite with two internal rod-like thickenings, ocular bristle ventral to eye)	*X. cheopis* (Indian rat flea)
	DOLICHOPSYLLIDÆ (combs only on prothorax)	*Ceratophyllus* (rostrum extending to and beyond trochanters)	*C. fasciatus* (rat flea of Europe and United States)
		Hoplopsyllus (rostrum short, scarcely one-half distance to anterior coxæ)	*H. anomalus* (ground squirrel flea)
	ARCHAROPSYLLIDÆ (combs on genæ and prothorax)	*Ctenocephalides*	*Ct. canis* (dog flea) (short head, front tooth of genal comb shorter than second) *Ct. felis* (cat flea) (long head, front tooth of genal comb same length as second)
FRACTICIPITA (antennal grooves divide head completely)	HYSTRICHOPSYLLIDÆ (combs on genæ and prothorax; eyes absent or vestigial)	*Ctenopsyllus*	*C. segnis* (mouse flea)

LIFE CYCLE

The female lays small, ovoid, white or cream-colored eggs (Fig. 249A), about 0.5 mm. in length, in the hairs or in the habitat of the host. In houses they are deposited in small batches in cracks of the floor and under rugs. Those deposited on the host are not attached and usually drop off before hatching. The number of eggs varies both with the species and with climatic conditions; a female *Pulex irritans* has been observed to lay over 448 ova in a period of three months.[2]

Fleas develop by complete metamorphosis, passing through a larval and a pupal stage. The time of incubation of the egg varies from 2 to 12 days.[4] The minimal temperature for hatching is 41° F. for *C. fasciatus,* 46° for *P. irritans,* and 55° for *X. cheopis.* The larva (Fig. 249 B-D) is an active, wormlike, white, eyeless, legless, bristled creature of 14 segments approximately 4.5 mm. in length.[5] It avoids light and seeks crevices. The larval period, depending upon food, temperature and

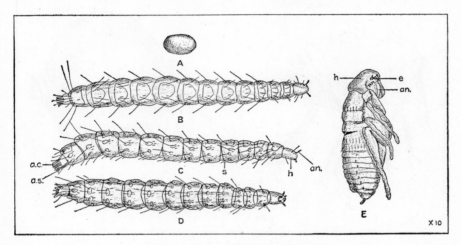

FIG. 249.—LIFE CYCLE OF FLEA

A, egg; *B,* larva of *Xenopsylla cheopis,* dorsal view; *C,* same, lateral view; *D,* same, ventral view; *E,* pupa of *Ctenocephalides canis.*

a.c., anal comb; *an.,* antenna; *a.s.,* anal strut; *e,* eye; *h,* head; *s,* seta (*B* to *D* redrawn from Bacot and Ridewood, 1914; *E,* adapted from Bishopp, 1915).

humidity, usually lasts from 7 to 30 days but may be prolonged for months. The maximal duration for *P. irritans* is 202 days, for *C. fasciatus* 114, *X. cheopis* 84, and for *Ct. canis* 142.[3] The larvæ of *P. irritans* and *X. cheopis,* unlike those of *C. fasciatus,* cannot survive below 40° F. The larva undergoes two and sometimes three molts, the last being within the cocoon. The mature larva prepares for pupation by constructing an enveloping, white or brownish, silky cocoon. The surface of the cocoon is covered with sand, dust or fine fragments. The prepupal and pupal stage usually lasts from 14 to 21 days but may range from 3 days to over a year, low temperatures prolonging the period. When the development of the nymph (Fig. 249E) is completed, the flea breaks out of the cocoon.

FLEAS ASSOCIATED WITH MAN

Man is the principal host of *Pulex irritans,* an important host of *Tunga penetrans* and an incidental host of several species parasitic to other mammals.

---

[5] Bacot, A. W. and Ridewood, W. G., 1914.

Tunga penetrans, Linnæus, 1758.—The chigoe, jigger or nigua is a parasite of man, hogs and dogs in tropical America and Africa. Man is infected by contact with soil infested with immature fleas. The site of infection is usually the feet and sometimes the hands. The mature female burrows into the skin. It is differentiated from the other fleas by its large, pointed, double-curved head, and shortened thorax (Fig. 250).

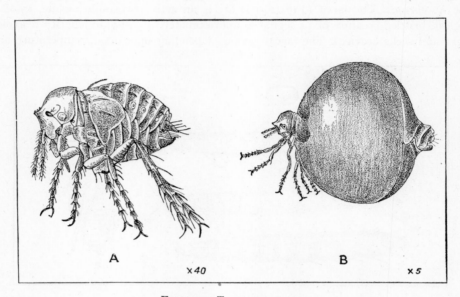

A   B
×40   ×5

FIG. 250.—*Tunga penetrans*

A, unengorged female; *B,* engorged female (Redrawn from Moniez, 1889).

Echidnophaga gallinacea (Westwood, 1875) Jordan and Rothschild, 1906.—The stick-tight or southern chicken flea, the most important live stock species, infests dogs, cats and rats as well as birds and occasionally man. It is found in the tropics and sub-tropics and less frequently in the temperate zone, its range extending in the United States of America as far north as Kansas. Its burrowing habits are similar to those of *Tunga penetrans.*

Pulex irritans Linnæus, 1758.—The human flea (Fig. 251C and D) is the most common flea found on man in houses in Europe and western United States. It also infests hogs, dogs, rats and other small mammals.

Xenopsylla cheopis Rothschild, 1909.—The Indian rat flea (Fig. 251B) is the most abundant rat flea in tropical and subtropical regions. It resembles *Pulex irritans* except for minor structural differences. It is the most important flea associated with the trans-mission of bubonic plague. It attacks man and other mammals as well as its natural host, the rat.

Ctenocephalides canis (Curtis, 1826) Banks, 1905 and *Ct. felis* (Bouche, 1835) Banks, 1910.—These fleas infest dogs and cats but may attack man and other mammals. They closely resemble each other and are more or less interchangeable. Their distribution is cosmopolitan. In eastern and southern United States they are the most common species found in house infections.

Ceratophyllus fasciatus (Bosc, 1801) Fox, 1910.—The common rat flea (Fig. 251A) of Europe and North America is distributed throughout the temperate zones. Its principal host is the brown rat, *Rattus norvegicus*. Other species of this genus infest rats and other rodents.

Hoplopsyllus anomalus Baker, 1904.—This species is one of the common fleas of ground squirrels and related rodents in western United States.

Ctenopsyllus segnis (Schönherr, 1811) Stewart, 1903.—The mouse flea is a common parasite of the house mouse, rat and other small rodents.

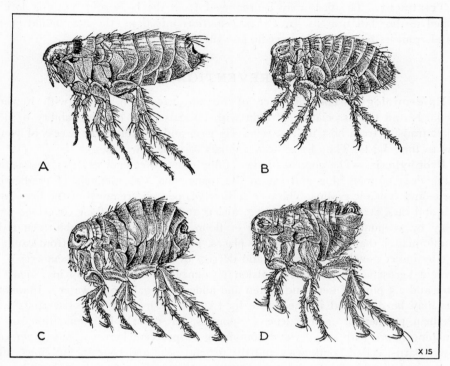

FIG. 251.—ADULT FLEAS

A, Ceratophyllus fasciatus, female; *B, Xenopsylla cheopis*, female; *C, Pulex irritans*, female; *D, Pulex irritans*, male (*A, C* and *D* redrawn from Bishopp, 1915; *B* redrawn from Patton and Cragg, 1913).

PATHOGENESIS

The cutaneous irritation caused by the salivary secretions of fleas varies with different persons. Some show no reaction, others a raised, roseate, slightly-edematous lesion at the site of the bite and susceptible individuals more extensive inflammation and even papular rashes.

The female jigger, *Tunga penetrans*, after fertilization burrows into the skin usually about the toes, soles of the feet, finger nails or interdigital spaces, and after engorging herself with blood becomes distended with eggs. The lesion, at first characterized by a central black spot in a tense pale area, becomes a festering sore. Secondary bacterial infection may produce an extensive painful ulcer, sometimes crippling the host.

DIAGNOSIS, PROGNOSIS AND TREATMENT

Diagnosis.—Diagnosis is suggested by the bites and confirmed by finding the fleas.

Prognosis.—Favorable.

Treatment.—The fleas may be removed from the body and soothing lotions applied to the bitten areas. In *Tunga penetrans* infections, the flea should be removed from its burrow with a needle and the wound disinfected.

PREVENTION

Epidemiology.—The incidence of human infestation varies with hygienic standards and the association of man with animals. The jumping ability of fleas makes transfer from host to host relatively easy and facilitates the access of young fleas to their hosts. They leave dead animals to seek new hosts.

Prophylaxis.—The control of fleas falls into two categories: (1) destruction of the fleas of man, dog and cat in the home, and (2) methods of eradicating plague and endemic typhus. The former involves periodic removal of the fleas from dogs and cats, sterilization of bedding, airing and cleaning of floor coverings preferably by vacuum cleaner, scrubbing of floors, and removal of rubbish and dry organic matter that serve as breeding places. Fleas may be removed from cats and dogs by insect powders (pyrethrin and derris) or by baths of 3 per cent cresol, 10 per cent kerosene or kerosene emulsion (2 ounces of washing soap in 1 quart of water and 2.5 pints of kerosene beaten and added to 5 gallons of water). Immature fleas may be destroyed in the house by treating floors and floor coverings with pyrethrin powder or naphthalene (5 pounds per room), by fumigation, or by scrubbing floors with soapy water containing 10 per cent kerosene and 5 per cent cresol. Barns, cellars, outhouses and the ground near and beneath buildings, after the removal of rubbish, may be sprayed with creosote oil or crude petroleum.

The control of rodent fleas that transmit plague and endemic typhus requires the destruction of the rodent hosts. Effective measures include fumigation with hydrocyanic gas, trapping and rat proofing of buildings. The clothing of infected individuals should be burned.

FLEAS AS VECTORS OF DISEASE

Fleas are of medical interest chiefly in connection with the transmission of plague and endemic typhus from rodents to other rodents or man. *Dipylidium caninum* is carried from dog to dog or man and *Hymenolepis diminuta* among mice and rats and occasionally to man.

Plague.—The bubonic and septicemic types of plague, due to *Pasteurella pestis,* is transmitted from rat to rat and thence to man by fleas. Plague is primarily an endemic disease of wild rodents in Asia, South Africa and in the western United States. Epidemics among these wild rodents give rise to infection in rats. The spread of the disease in man is chiefly due to the rats associated with human habitations, such as the brown rat, *Rattus norvegicus,* and the black rat, *Rattus rattus.* On the death of the rat the infected fleas seek new hosts, either man or other rats.

The incidence of plague is not regulated by the number of fleas on rats but rather by the species of fleas.[6] The Indian rat flea, *X. cheopis,* the principal and most efficient vector, is three times as susceptible to infection with *Pasteurella pestis* as other fleas. When infected it has a short life, averaging 16 days, whereas other species may live for months. *Pulex irritans* and at least nine species of the genera *Xenopsylla, Ctenocephalides, Ceratophyllus, Hoplopsyllus* and *Ctenopsyllus* may also spread the disease. The flea may inoculate a new host by mechanical transfer of the bacilli by its infected mouth parts, by regurgitation of blood or of bacteria, when they are numerous enough to block the proventriculus,[7] or by contaminating the wound with its infected feces. The most dangerous fleas are those susceptible to infection and to bacterial obstruction of the proventriculus, but the feces of all diseased fleas are infectious. Ground squirrel fleas do not readily transmit the disease to man.

Typhus Fever.—Endemic typhus, a mild form of *Rickettsia prowazeki* infection occurring sporadically in the United States of America and in other countries of the Western Hemisphere, is transmitted by fleas from rat to rat and from rat to man. The common insect vectors are *Ceratophyllus fasciatus* and *Xenopsylla cheopis.* The organism of murine typhus may remain viable for at least 651 days in the infected feces of the flea.[8] Its long extracorporeal existence may explain the endemicity of the disease. Infection occurs by contamination rather than by the bite of the flea.

Cestode Infections.—*Ctenocephalides canis, Ct. felis* and *Pulex irritans* act as intermediate hosts of *Dipylidium caninum.* The rat fleas, *Ceratophyllus fasciatus, C. wickhami* and *Xenopsylla cheopis,* the mouse flea, *Ctenopsyllus segnis,* the dog flea, *Ctenocephalides canis,* and the human flea, *Pulex irritans,* are hosts of *Hymenolepis diminuta.*

REFERENCES

BACOT, A. W. A Study of the Bionomics of the Common Rat Fleas and Other Species Associated with Human Habitations with Special Reference to the Influence of Temperature and Humidity at Various Periods of the Life History of the Insect, J. Hygiene, Plague Supplement III, 1914, 13:447.
—— and RIDEWOOD, W. G. Observations on the Larvæ of Fleas, Parasitology, 1914, 7:157.
BISHOPP, F. C. Fleas and Their Control, U. S. Dept. Agric. Farmers' Bull, No. 897, 1937, 16 pp.
ESKEY, C. R. Recent Developments in Our Knowledge of Plague Transmission, U. S. Pub. Health Rep., 1938, 53:49.
—— Fleas as Vectors of Plague, Am. J. Pub. Health, 1938, 28:1305.
FOX, I. Fleas of Eastern United States, Iowa State College Press, Ames, Iowa, 1940, 192 pp.

[6] Eskey, C. R., 1938.
[7] Bacot, A. W. and Martin, C. J., 1914.
[8] Blanc, G. and Baltazard, M., 1940.

Chapter XLVI

ORDER HEMIPTERA: TRUE BUGS

The insects of the order HEMIPTERA are primarily of agricultural importance, since they feed on plants and small invertebrates. A few genera of the families CIMICIDÆ and REDUVIIDÆ that feed on the blood of vertebrates are of parasitological interest. Their mouth parts, modified for piercing and sucking, consist of a hinged labrum, barbed maxillæ, and doubly-grooved blade-like mandibles enclosed in a ventrally-flexed, three-jointed labial sheath. There are two pairs of wings, the forewings with a thickened basal and a membranous apical portion and the membranous hind wings. The forewings serve as a protective covering for the more delicate hind wings. The head is often inconspicuous; the antennæ, usually long, have four or five joints; the eyes are prominent; and two or three ocelli may be present. The thorax consists of a large prothorax and a small meso- and metathorax. Eight abdominal segments are usually discernible, the ovipositors are long, and the conspicuous male genitalia have large claw-like claspers. Reproduction is by incomplete metamorphosis.

FAMILY *CIMICIDÆ* (BEDBUGS)

The bedbugs have oval, dorsoventrally-flattened bodies, short broad heads without ocelli; vestigial wings (hind wings absent, forewings reduced to small pads), four-jointed antennæ, a four-jointed proboscis and three-jointed tarsi. Only the genus *Cimex* contains important bloodsucking species. Several species are ectoparasites of birds and bats.

THE BEDBUGS OF MAN

The common bedbug, *Cimex lectularius,* and the oriental bedbug *C. hemipterus,* are parasites of man. The former has a cosmopolitan distribution, although it is outnumbered in the tropical countries of the Old World by the latter, which is also found in tropical America. *C. hemipterus* is chiefly distinguished from *C. lectularius* by a less deeply indented anterior border, lesser anterolateral wing-like projections and a greater lateral extension of the dorsal convexity of the prothorax (Fig. 254). It also has a shorter, narrower head and a less orbicular abdomen with its greatest width at the second rather than the third segment.

BIOLOGICAL CHARACTERISTICS

Morphology.—*Cimex lectularius* has a broad, oval, dorsoventrally-flattened, chestnut-brown body covered with short, stout, simple or serrated hairs (Fig. 252).

716

The female, slightly larger than the male, has an average length of 5.5 mm., a width of 3 mm. and a thickness of 0.5 mm. When fed its length may increase to 8 mm. and its thickness to 2 mm.[1] Its flattened, pyramidal head bears prominent compound eyes, slender four-jointed antennæ and specialized mouth parts in a long proboscis flexed backward ventrally when not in use. The mouth parts consist of a two-jointed, flap-like triangular labrum; two inner chitinous mandibles that join to form the sucking tube and salivary canal; two outer blade-like, cutting maxillæ with finely-toothed, pointed distal ends; and a four-jointed, grooved labium that ensheaths the mandibles and maxillæ.

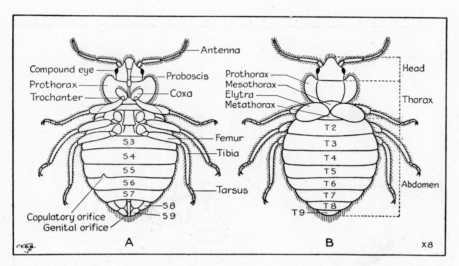

FIG. 252.—SCHEMATIC REPRESENTATION OF EXTERNAL ANATOMY OF THE BEDBUG, *Cimex lectularius*

A, ventral surface of female; *B,* dorsal surface of female.

The prothorax is large and conspicuous, its concave anterior border and rounded lateral horns giving the head a sunken appearance. The small mesothorax is visible dorsally as the triangular mesonotum carrying the pad-like forewings or elytra, which partially conceal the metanotum. Each of the three thoracic segments bears a pair of legs with three tarsi, terminating in a pair of simple claws. The abdomen, with eight visible segments and additional sclerites for the genitalia, is broad and oval in the female and more pointed in the male. The asymmetrical eighth segment in the male has a notch on the left side to accommodate the curved, saber-like penial organ that is extended through a chitinous ring (Fig. 253B). The genital orifice at the modified tip of the female abdomen is evidently used only for oviposition (Fig. 253A). A curious longitudinal slit on the lower right side of the fifth (apparently the fourth) abdominal sternite leads to a blind pouch, consisting of an ectodermal structure, Ribaga's organ and an inner enveloping mass of cells, the organ of

---

[1] Murray, C. H., 1914.

Berlese, into which spermatozoa are introduced during copulation. Thence clusters of spermatozoa penetrate through the hemocele to the walls of the oviducts and to the ovarioles.[2]

The digestive system (Fig. 253C), comprises a small, muscular pharynx; a narrow thin-walled esophagus without diverticula or proventriculus; a midgut with a dilated anterior and a tubular posterior portion, and a hindgut with a sacculate rectum and four malpighian tubules. Two pairs of salivary glands supply the anti-coagulative salivary secretions. The tracheal system has paired thoracic and abdominal spiracular openings. Stench glands, in various parts of the body, secrete a clear, volatile liquid, which imparts the characteristic, objectionable "bedbug" smell.

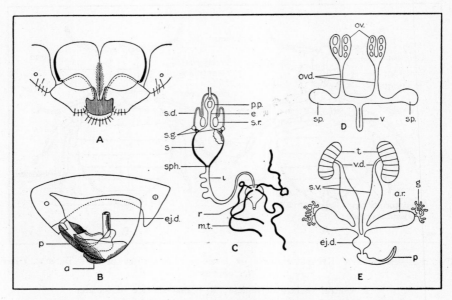

FIG. 253.—THE DIGESTIVE TRACT AND REPRODUCTIVE ORGANS OF *Cimex lectularius*

A, anal segments of female; *B,* anal segments of male; *C,* alimentary tract; *D,* female reproductive organs; *E,* male reproductive organs.

a, anus; *a.r.,* accessory reservoir; *e,* esophagus; *ej.d.,* ejaculatory duct; *g,* male accessory gland; *i,* intestine; *m.t.,* malpighian tubule; *ov.,* ovaries; *ov.d.,* oviduct; *p,* penis; *p.p.,* pharyngeal pump; *r,* rectum; *s,* stomach; *sph.,* sphincter; *s.d.,* salivary duct; *s.g.,* salivary glands; *sp.,* spermatheca; *s.r.,* salivary reservoir; *s.v.,* seminal vesicles; *t,* testes; *v,* vagina; *v.d.,* vas deferens (Redrawn from Murray, 1915).

The male reproductive organs (Fig. 253E) consist of a pair of lobulate testes, short vasa deferentia, branched accessory glands, a common collecting chamber and a muscular penial organ. The female reproductive organs (Fig. 253D) comprise a pair of ovaries with seven digitate ovarioles, short oviducts along which the spermatozoa mass as a pseudospermatheca, a common uterine duct and a copulatory pouch or organ of Berlese.

---

[2] Cragg, F. W., 1923.

Habits.—Bedbugs flourish in warm climates and are more abundant in plains and valleys than in mountainous regions. The common bedbug has spread over the entire world from its probable original habitat in the eastern Mediterranean countries. It was first reported in 1503 in England, whence it migrated to America with the early colonists. It can travel distances of 46 meters or more at the rate of 1 to 2 cm. per second, passes readily from house to house via walls, pipes or gutters, and is easily transported in clothing and baggage. In cold weather the bedbug remains inactive in its hiding places. *C. hemipterus* succumbs more rapidly than *C. lectularius* when exposed to 0° C.: eggs 14 *vs.* 21 days, first instar nymphs 7 *vs.* 49 days, last four instar nymphs 7 *vs.* 21 days, and adults 7 *vs.* 175 days.[3]

FIG. 254.—COMMON AND ORIENTAL BEDBUGS

A, common bedbug, *Cimex lectularius,* female; *B,* oriental bedbug, *Cimex hemipterus,* female (Adapted from various sources).

Bedbugs are nocturnal in their habits, concealing themselves during the day in the crevices of wooden bedsteads, in wainscoting or under loose wall paper. They feed at night on man and small mammals, such as rats and mice. Nymphs as well as adults feed upon blood. There is no definite evidence that they are attracted by body odor or heat except for short distances.[1] They probably obtain additional nourishment from the juices of moist wood and dust. They survive starvation for over a year, thus accounting for their presence in houses long unoccupied.

In sucking blood the proboscis moves from a horizontal to a vertical position, the distal end of the labium is bent back to permit penetration by the mandibles and maxillæ, and through the tube formed by the maxillæ, saliva is injected and blood is aspirated. The bedbug exhibits a violent trembling motion as it enlarges the opening by the alternating gliding movements of the mandibles and maxillæ.[1]

[3] Omori, N., 1938.

The feeding process requires from three to eight minutes. Females engorge more frequently than males.

Both sexes are fully mature after the first molt and the female may be impregnated before either sex has fed. Copulation takes place frequently, not less than once a day and one male can fertilize at least three females within 24 hours.[2] Oviposition takes place the third or fourth day of adult life, but only a few eggs are laid prior to a blood meal, which appears essential to the production of the normal quota. A single impregnation does not enable a female to lay fertile eggs indefinitely.

LIFE CYCLE

The common bedbug lays an average of two eggs per day for a considerable period.[2] Under favorable conditions up to 200 eggs may be deposited.[4] The tropical bedbug has been observed to lay as many as 429 eggs within 94 days.[5] The white,

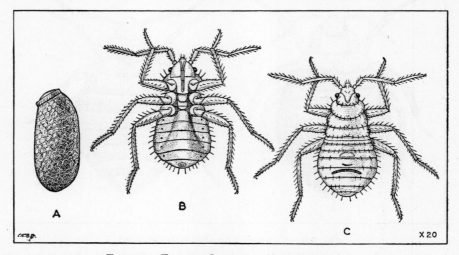

Fig. 255.—Egg and Larva of *Cimex lectularius*

A, egg; *B,* newly hatched larva, ventral view; *C,* newly hatched larva, dorsal view (Redrawn from Marlatt, 1907).

ovoid eggs (Fig. 255A), about 1 mm. in length, have an oblique, projecting collar-like ring with an operculum at the anterior end. They are coated with an adherent, gelatinous substance. The embryo, already far advanced at oviposition, emerges through the operculum in 4 to 10 days. The lowest temperature at which complete development of *C. lectularius* takes place is 13° C.[6]

Development is by incomplete metamorphosis. The larval bedbug (Fig. 255B and C), at first yellowish-white and nearly transparent but later deepening to brown, passes through five (occasionally six) molts at intervals of about a week to become a sexually-mature adult. This stage is usually reached in seven weeks, the time varying with warmth and food. The larvæ of *C. hemipterus* suck blood within two

---

[4] Cummings, B. F., 1917.
[5] Dunn, L. H., 1924.
[6] Johnson, C. G., 1940.

days after emerging from the egg. The majority molt first on the fourth day, and with intervening blood meals pass through successive nymphal molts at intervals of 3 to 6 days. The adult lives perhaps six months to one year.

PATHOGENESIS

The bite of the bedbug ordinarily produces red itching wheals and causes loss of sleep. Some persons show no reaction, others have more or less urticaria, and still others manifest allergic symptoms. Asthma has been caused by *C. lectularius*.[7] Ammonia, sweet oil and menthol relieve the irritation and alcoholic tincture of iodine is a good local disinfectant.

The rôle of the bedbug in the transmission of human disease is problematical. It may act as a mechanical carrier, but it is not a proved vector of human diseases. The anatomy of its digestive tract prevents the regurgitation of infected blood when it bites a second host. Laboratory experiments have shown that it is capable of harboring and transmitting the organisms of plague, leprosy, tularemia, relapsing fever, Chagas' disease, leishmanian infections and yellow fever. Bedbugs fed on mice infected with paratyphoid bacilli harbor the organisms in the intestine and feces for three weeks.[8] Tularemia has been transmitted to healthy guinea pigs by rubbing on the intact skin the crushed bodies of bedbugs that had fed on infected guinea pigs, and in one instance by their bites.[9] *Borrelia recurrentis* has been transmitted to mice by the consumption of bedbugs that had fed on infected monkeys.[10] The virus of yellow fever has been experimentally transmitted to animals through the feces of infected bedbugs.[11] Inoculations of *C. lectularius* from an infected mouse has produced Brazilian exanthematic typhus in a guinea pig.[12]

PREVENTION

The natural enemies of the bedbug are the red ants, reduviid bugs and mice. Recent investigations disprove the prevailing belief that cockroaches are important enemies.[13] Methods of extermination in inhabited dwellings include (1) substitution of iron for wooden bedsteads, (2) liberal application of kerosene, turpentine, benzine or petroleum oils with small brushes or syringes to crevices in wooden bedsteads, furniture, floors and walls, (3) repair of cracked plaster and wallpaper, (4) dry cleaning of infected mattresses and repainting of iron beds with flaming of joints, and (5) daily inspection of beds, bedding and crevices. Boiling water is an effective agent if it can be applied without damage to furniture. In cases of heavy infestation, where houses may be temporarily vacated, fumigation is recommended. Sulphur, 2 pounds per 1,000 cubic feet, may be burned after removal of furnishings with metallic surfaces. Hydrocyanic acid gas is more effective, though dangerous except in the hands of experts. It kills bedbugs in six hours at 0.086 per cent by volume (1 ounce per 1,000 cubic feet) at 15 to 20° C., but tends to be

[7] Sternberg, L., 1929.
[8] Braun, H. and Caspari, E., 1938.
[9] Kamil, S. and Bilal, S., 1938.
[10] Francis, E., 1938.
[11] Monteiro, J. L., 1930.
[12] Dias, E. and Martins, A. M., 1937.
[13] Johnson, C. G. and Mellanby, K., 1939.

absorbed and dissipated so gradually that it may injure man (0.0026 per cent) even after aeration for 24 hours.[14] Coal tar naphtha distillates may be diffused by a foot pump with screens of cotton cloth close to the walls to maintain the concentration.[15] Hot air disinfection also destroys bedbugs, if a temperature over 55° C. is maintained for six hours by an oil heater with a motor for circulating the air.

FAMILY *REDUVIIDÆ*

The reduviid bugs have long narrow heads with prominent compound eyes, usually two ocelli, four-jointed antennæ and a three-segmented ventrally-folded proboscis; an obvious neck; a long, rather narrow and flattened body; functional wings on the prothorax, and elongate legs with three-jointed tarsi.

KEY FOR THE CLASSIFICATION OF THE GENERA OF THE *REDUVIIDÆ*
(Modified from Pinto, 1927)

1. Rostrum does not extend beyond the eyes..............................*Linshcosteus*
   Rostrum extends beyond the eyes... 2
2. First joint of rostrum longer than second.. 3
   First joint of rostrum one-half length of second.................................... 4
   First joint of rostrum two-thirds length of second................................. 5
3. First joint of antenna long, passing the anterior end of head..............*Adricomius*
4. Antennæ arise near anterior end of head...........................*Rhodnius* (Fig. 256D)
5. Antennæ inserted near the eyes or at the middle of the anteocular region.............. 6
6. Spine on posterior angles of pronotum....................................*Eratyrus*
   No spine on posterior angles of pronotum.........................*Triatoma* (Fig. 256C)

BIOLOGICAL CHARACTERISTICS

Morphology.—Species of *Triatoma* and *Rhodnius* are called "cone-nosed" bugs because of the pointed head, "barbers" because they bite the face, "assassin bugs," and "flying bedbugs." They are dark brown with red or yellow markings on the thorax, wings and sides of abdomen (Fig. 257). In the bloodsucking species the proboscis is long, straight and slender, while in those that feed on insects it is short, stout and bent. The anterior coxæ are short; the thorax is constricted anteriorly; the apex of the scutellum bears a single spine or none at all; and two ocelli are situated behind the compound eyes (Fig. 256C and D).

Habits.—Several species of reduviid bugs frequent houses, especially native huts with dirt floors. Other species infest the burrows of rodents and armadillos, and chicken houses. They hide during the day in crevices and dark recesses and feed at night. They move rapidly both in flight and on foot. Most species feed on insects, but occasionally bite man and other mammals. The latter habit is especially true of those species of *Triatoma* and *Rhodnius* that frequent houses and nests of animals.

---

[14] Page, A. B. P., Lubatti, O. F. and Gloyns, F. P., 1939.   [15] Hughes, A. W. M., 1938.

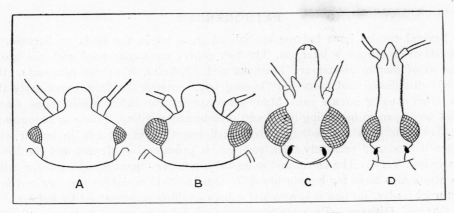

FIG. 256.—HEADS OF BEDBUGS AND REDUVIID BUGS

A, Cimex lectularius; B, Cimex hemipterus; C, Triatoma megista; D, Rhodnius prolixus
(Adapted from Hegner, Root, Augustine and Huff, *Parasitology,* 1938, D. Appleton-Century
Company).

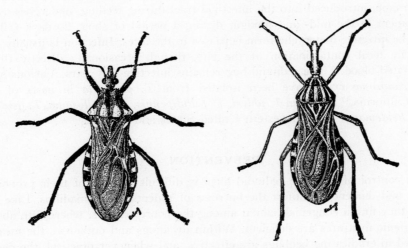

FIG. 257.—ADULT MALES OF *Triatoma megista* (LEFT) AND *Rhodnius prolixus* (RIGHT)

(After Brumpt, from Hegner, Root, Augustine and Huff, *Parasitology,* 1938, D. Appleton-
Century Company).

LIFE CYCLE

The female lays about 200 eggs in batches of 8 to 12. The white or yellowish-
pink, unattached eggs usually hatch in from 20 to 30 days. Development is by
incomplete metamorphosis. The larva obtains its first blood meal within five days
and the young bugs, with habits similar to the adult, undergo a lengthy metamorphosis with blood meals during the 40 to 50 days intervening between each
molt, the entire life cycle requiring a year or more.

PATHOGENESIS

Several species have become specialized parasites in the nests or burrows of animals or in human habitations. The two genera most concerned with the transmission of human disease are *Triatoma* and *Rhodnius*. *Reduvius personatus,* the widely distributed and notorious "kissing bug," attacks the face, particularly the lips, often causing intense pain. Many other species also inflict painful bites, sometimes accompanied by oozing blood and pronounced swelling. *Triatoma sanguisuga,* the Texas or Mexican bedbug, a brownish insect about 2.5 cm. in length with flattened head and relatively thick rostrum, is prevalent in Mexico and the lower Mississippi Valley. The larval and nymphal forms prey upon insects, but the adult has acquired a taste for human blood. It remains hidden during the day and is a nocturnal feeder. Its bite is severe and causes swelling accompanied by itching.

Chagas' Disease.—Probably all species of *Triatoma* and *Rhodnius,* and even those of *Eratyrus* and the several other related genera, are capable of transmitting *Trypanosoma cruzi*. The most important disease-transmitting species are *Triatoma megista* and *T. sordida* in Brazil, *T. infestans* in Argentina and Paraguay, *Rhodnius prolixus* in Venezuela, *T. geniculata* and *R. pallescens* in Panama. The trypanosome, introduced into the intestinal tract during feeding, undergoes a cyclic development in the mid- and hindgut during a period of about 20 days (Chapter XI). The infective metacyclic form is passed in the feces. Infection is usually transmitted by fecal contamination of the bite, though occasionally directly through regurgitated blood.[16] The reduviid bug remains infective for years. Various strains of *Trypanosoma cruzi* have been isolated from *T. protracta* in nests of wood rats in California,[17] and from *T. uhleri, T. pallidipennis, T. phyllosoma, T. gerstakeri* and *T. heidemanni* in southwestern United States and Mexico.

PREVENTION

The control of parasitic reduviid bugs is difficult because of their pronounced activity and tendency to infest the burrows of rodents and armadillos. Like other vermin they find a congenial habitat among the poorer classes, where filth abounds and hygienic measures are deficient. Within dwellings and outhouses the measures employed in eradicating bedbugs are effective, and whenever practical, the destruction of animal hosts is advisable.

REFERENCES

BRUMPT, E.   Mode de transmission de la maladie de C. Chagas, Ann. de parasitol., 1939, 17:320.
CARDOSA, F. A.   Sur les mécanismes de la transmission de la maladie de Chagas, Ann. de parasitol., 1938, 16:341.
CRAGG, F. W.   Observations on the Bionomics of the Bedbug *Cimex lectularius* L. with Special References to the Relation of the Sexes, Indian J. M. Res., 1923, 11:449.
DUNN, L. H.   Life History of the Tropical Bedbug *Cimex rotundatus* in Panama, Am. J. Trop. Med., 1924, 4:76.

---

[16] Cardosa, F. A., 1938.   [17] Wood, S. F., 1938.

JOHNSON, C. G. Development, Hatching and Mortality of the Eggs of *Cimex lectularius* (Hemiptera) in Relation to Climate, with Observations on the Effects of Preconditioning to Temperature, Parasitology, 1940, 32:127.

KASSIANOFF, L. Étude morphologique et biologique de la famille des cimicides, Ann. de parasitol., 1937, 15:97, 385.

MARLATT, C. L. The Bedbug (*Cimex lectularius*), U. S. Dept. Agric. Bur. Ent., 1907, Bull. No. 4, 32 pp.

MURRAY, C. H. Notes on the Anatomy of the Bedbug (*Acanthia lectularia* L.), Parasitology, 1914, 7:278.

Chapter XLVII

THE CLASS ARACHNIDA

The arachnids differ from insects in the absence of wings and antennæ, the presence of four pairs of legs, and the fusion of head and thorax into a cephalothorax. Of the eleven orders the spiders (ARANEIDA) and the scorpions (SCORPIONIDA) are harmful to man by their bites and stings, while the ticks and mites (ACARINA) in addition are vectors of human diseases.

ORDER *ARANEIDA*

Many of the numerous genera and species of spiders use venom to paralyze their prey. Man rarely suffers from their bites save for individual idiosyncrasies or secondary infection. The common spiders are seldom able to penetrate the skin, or, if successful, produce but a mild local erythema. A few species, however, cause serious symptoms.

Morphology.—The unsegmented body consists of a cephalothorax and a sacculated abdomen covered by a tough hairy integument. The head bears several pairs of eyes. The mouth parts include a rostrum or upper lip, an epipharynx, a median lower lip, a pair of six-jointed **pedipalps** (modified in males for transferring spermatozoa), and a pair of **cheliceræ** (Fig. 258D). Venom from paired glands in the cephalothorax is discharged through the tips of the claw-like distal segments of the cheliceræ. The thorax, with four pairs of seven-segmented legs, is separated from the abdomen by a slender stalk and from the head by a superficial furrow. The silk-spinning glands of the web, usually three, open on the subcaudal ventral surface of the abdomen. There are one or two pairs of ventral spiracles and in front of the spinnerets a single, at times paired, spiracle.

Habits.—Spiders spin their webs in all manner of recesses or out-of-the-way places. They leap upon their entangled prey, paralyze them with venom and devour them at leisure.

Life Cycle.—Spiders develop by incomplete metamorphosis. The eggs are laid in masses and are usually encased in a cocoon, in which young remain for long periods sometimes through the winter. The spiderlings pass through eight or nine molts before becoming mature adults.

SPIDERS INJURIOUS TO MAN

The large, hairy, ferocious-looking tarantulas of the tropical family AVICULARIIDÆ, although sometimes capable of killing small animals, inflict only slight or at most painful injury to man. *Lycosa tarantula* of southern Europe may cause edema of the eyelids and fever in susceptible persons and *Chætopelma olivacea* of North Africa produces an acute local inflammation. The small black spiders of the genus *Latrodectus,* of the family THERIDIIDÆ, however, possess a potent venom that does produce serious symptoms. Various species of this genus are found in Europe, Australia, New Zealand, the Philippines, Africa, the West Indies, South America and the United States of America. Species of *Atrax* in Australia, *Lycosa* and *Ctenus* in Brazil and *Glyptocranium* in Peru are also considered venomous.

BLACK WIDOW SPIDER

The black widow, *Latrodectus mactans,* sometimes called the hour-glass, shoe-button or po-ko-moo spider, is the most dangerous species in the United States of America, where 380 cases of spider bite and 17 deaths have been reported.[1] It ranges from southern Canada to Chile and is most abundant in the far western and southern parts of the United States.

Morphology.—The female (Fig. 258A and C) is about 13 mm. in length and the male (Fig. 258B) considerably smaller, 6 mm. The thorax is brown or black, the long, slender legs dark brown or black, and the abdomen jet black. The legs and body are covered with short, black hairs. The female has a variable, median, orange or red spot in the form of an hour-glass or Maltese cross on the ventral surface of her glossy, globose abdomen, and at times additional red markings on the dorsal surface. The males are distinguished by their small size, full-tipped "feelers," and by broken rows of red spots, diagonal yellowish stripes and straw-colored markings on the dorsal surface of the abdomen. The markings of immature females vary between those of the male and female.[2]

Habits.—The spider infests lumber heaps, rail fences, stumps, undersides of privy seats, outbuildings, cracks in basements, and even houses. It spins a loosely-woven, irregular web of coarse, tough strands with a strong-walled tube into which the active female retires. The spider avoids strong light and usually bites only when disturbed. It preys on insects but can survive without food for a month or more. The aggressive female frequently devours the male after copulation, but sometimes the male escapes to mate with other females.[3] Its natural enemy is the wasp.

Life Cycle.—During the summer the female lays several masses of 100 to 600 translucent eggs, about 1 mm. in diameter, in a spherical or pyriform cream-colored cocoon attached to her web. The small, gray, active, cannibalistic spiderlings (Fig. 258E) hatch in two to four weeks. After a series of molts (male 3 to 6, female 6 to 9) at intervals of 15 days or more, depending upon the food supply, they become adults, usually the following spring. Their creamy-white or reddish-brown abdomens are first flecked with white and later with orange, red and black markings.[4]

Pathogenesis.—The females alone are dangerous as the small males are too feeble to harm man. The nonhemolytic venom, probably a toxalbumin, affects the nerve endings. It is a transparent, oily, lemon-colored liquid that is insoluble in

---

[1] Bogen, E., 1932.
[2] Gowanlock, J. N. and Leeper, B. F., 1935.
[3] Kaston, B. J., 1937.
[4] Blair, A. W., 1934.

ether, nondialyzable, opalescent when mixed with water, and made innocuous by heating to 75° C. for 20 minutes or by the enzymes of the digestive tract.[5]

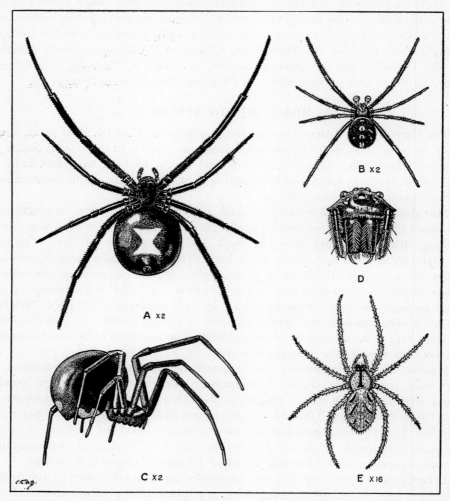

FIG. 258.—BLACK WIDOW SPIDER (*Latrodectus mactans*)

A, adult female, ventral view; *B,* adult male, dorsal view; *C,* adult female, lateral view; *D,* head of female, front view; *E,* spiderling just prior to first molt (*A* adapted, *B* and *D* redrawn from Hayward, 1935; *C* adapted from Kaston, 1937; *E* redrawn from Blair, 1934).

Symptoms vary with the location of the bite and the amount of injected venom. The most frequent sites are the buttocks or penis; 80 per cent of all affected persons are males and genital bites are three times as frequent as elsewhere.[6] The bite may be accompanied by a sharp, slightly smarting pain or may pass unnoticed. The site

[5] D'Amour, F. E., Becker, F. E. and Van Riper, W., 1936.

[6] Vail, A. D., 1939.

shows a minute, nonelevated bluish-red spot with a white areola that speedily disappears, or it may become red and swollen. An urticarial rash may be present.

Systemic symptoms, however, follow a uniform progressive course, corresponding to the stages of (1) lymphatic absorption, (2) vascular dissemination and (3) elimination of the toxin.[4] Lymphatic absorption is evidenced by the proximal progress of throbbing, lanceolating pains and numbness in the affected part. In from 15 minutes to several hours agonizing muscular pains increasing in intensity spread over the abdomen, chest, back and extremities. When the bite is below the waist, cramping pains extend up the abdomen and down the thighs. There is a board-like rigidity and spastic contraction of the abdominal muscles simulating acute, surgical, abdominal conditions. When the bite is in the upper extremities the pains radiate to the shoulders, back and abdomen.[7] The patient shows symptoms of shock. He becomes dizzy, weak, thirsty and nauseated; there is profuse perspiration, slow pulse, headache, rapid, shallow and labored breathing, and fall in blood pressure. In cases of profound shock delirium follows and death may ensue in 18 to 36 hours. The elimination of the toxin is characterized by recovery from shock, increased blood pressure, diminished muscular pain, leukocytosis, slight fever, diaphoresis, and an acute toxic nephritis. Urinary retention has been observed.[8]

Diagnosis.—Arachnidism is differentiated from acute, surgical, abdominal conditions, particularly ruptured gastric or duodenal ulcers, by the history of the spider bite, the spreading course of the cramping muscular pains and the faster pulse rate. The spider is identified by her characteristic abdominal markings.

Prognosis.—Fairly good. Mortality rate is 4 to 5 per cent. Children are more susceptible than adults.

Treatment.—The wound, usually noticed too late for incision and suction, may be washed with potassium permanganate 1 :4,000 or with iodine, but such measures seldom check the absorption of the venom. The patient should be placed in bed and hot baths freely administered for the relief of pain. Measures to restore capillary tone and combat shock call for sedation with morphine and the administration of calcium gluconate (10 per cent) both intravenously and intramuscularly, or magnesium sulphate (10 per cent) combined with glucose (50 per cent) intravenously. During the eliminative stage the kidneys should be rested by not forcing fluids and by sweating. Spinal puncture has been used to relieve pain and urinary retention. Convalescent serum has not proved satisfactory and antivenom is not commercially available.

Prophylaxis.—Man is usually bitten by accidental contact with spiders. Summer and autumn are the dangerous seasons. Outdoor privies, a favorite habitat of the black widow spider, should be carefully inspected. Children are more likely to be bitten than adults, and should be taught to be careful when playing in localities frequented by this spider. Creosote has a lethal and repellent action.

---

[7] Ginsberg, H. M., 1937.   [8] Robinson, H. M., Jr., 1938.

ORDER *SCORPIONIDA*

The small scorpions of the temperate zones are not often dangerous to man, but the stings of the larger tropical species may cause severe reactions.

Morphology.—Scorpions (Fig. 259) are elongated terrestrial arachnids with large pedipalps terminating in stout claws, a nonsegmented cephalothorax with four pairs of legs, and an elongate abdomen with a broad, seven-segmented anterior and an attenuate six-segmented posterior portion. The caudal extremity bears a hooked stinger for the discharge of venom. Most species have a pair of median eyes and from two to five lateral eyes. The males are distinguished by their broad claws and long posterior abdomen. A pair of combs is attached to the ventral part of the second abdominal segment. The respiratory organs, four pairs of book-lungs, are located on the ventral side of the third to sixth abdominal segments.

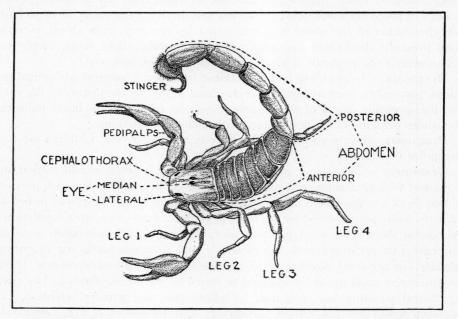

FIG. 259.—SCHEMATIC REPRESENTATION OF SCORPION WITH ARCHED ABDOMEN

Habits.—Scorpions seize their prey in their claws and by a backward-downward thrust of the tail-like abdomen insert the stinger. The paralyzed prey, usually spiders or insects, is then crushed and eaten. Scorpions, nocturnal in their activities, invade human habitations concealing themselves in the dirt floors of adobe huts, and during the rainy season in the tropics even enter houses.

Life Cycle.—Scorpions are viviparous and the young are carried for some time on the back of the female.

SCORPIONS INJURIOUS TO MAN

Species.—Of the numerous species of scorpions throughout the world some twenty or more are found in the Southern United States and many more in Mexico. Some of the larger scorpions injurious to man are: *Buthus quinquestriatus* of northern Africa and southern Europe, *Centruroides suffusus* and *C. noxius* of Mexico, and *C. sculturatus* of Arizona.

Pathogenesis.—Man is usually stung when his bare feet or hands unexpectedly come in contact with scorpions. The small species are unable to pierce the skin or at most cause only a slight local redness like a bee-sting. The larger species, however, produce serious and even fatal systemic reactions, most frequently observed in young children. Numerous deaths from scorpion stings have been reported from North, Central and South America, India, northern Africa, and the Orient. A 60 per cent mortality among children under five years is reported in Egypt, and 38.5 per cent in India; while 25 deaths have occurred in Arizona within a period of six and a half years.[9]

Scorpion venom is a clear, colorless toxalbumin, containing a variety of toxic substances. It produces paralysis, nervous disturbances, convulsions, and pulmonary disorders in mice,[9] and is toxic to horses and most laboratory animals, but the hedgehog, desert rat and other animals seem immune.

The local symptoms are relatively mild. A small, red spot at the site of the sting is followed by slight swelling and excruciating pain that last several hours and subside the following day. Nervous reactions are often severe, with throbbing and muscular twitching of the fingers, toes, ears, nose and chin accompanied by itching and paresthesia.[10] Other symptoms are: headache, giddiness, nausea and vomiting, profuse perspiration, cold extremities, subnormal or slightly elevated temperature and feeble pulse. Fatal cases show accelerated respiration and death results from pulmonary edema.[11]

Treatment.—A ligature should be applied immediately and the incised wound washed with potassium permanganate. Pain may be relieved by the local application of ammonia and the subcutaneous injection of novocaine and adrenalin.

Systemic treatment, primarily designed to prevent shock, includes: raising the foot of the bed, application of heat to the extremities, saline and glucose intravenously, and the administration of morphine and adrenalin. Intravenous glucose, intramuscular calcium and atrophine sulphate may be given for pulmonary edema.[11] Chloroform inhalations may relieve restlessness. Antitoxic serum has a prophylactic and curative action.

Prophylaxis.—Precautions against contact with scorpions constitute the most practical means of prevention. Attempts to reduce the scorpion population have not proved particularly effective.

---

[9] Stalinke, H. L., 1938.
[10] Ball, C. R., 1938.

[11] Basu, U. P., 1939.

ORDER *PENTASTOMIDA (LINGUATULIDA)*

The members of this small group of arthropods are bloodsucking endoparasites of mammals, birds, reptiles and fishes. These degenerate, worm-like arthropods, although not closely related to any group, were formerly placed in the ARACHNIDA and by some authorities in the order ACARINA. The species of medical interest belong to the family LINGUATULIDÆ (tongue worms)

FAMILY *LINGUATULIDÆ*

The tongue worms have white, elongate, annulate, vermiform, flattened or cylindrical bodies that have lost practically all appendages. A broad rounded cephalothorax merges into an elongate, tapering abdomen. An oval, chitinous mouth on the anterior ventral surface is armed on each side with a pair of retractile chitinous hooks for penetration and anchorage. There is a rudimentary digestive tract and a nervous system, but no definite circulatory and respiratory systems. The genital opening of the smaller male is near the posterior end and that of the female just behind the cephalothorax. The adults live in the pulmonary tract and the larvæ and nymphs in the alimentary tract, viscera and body cavities of their hosts. Species of the genera *Linguatula* and *Porocephalus* are parasites of man.

LINGUATULA SERRATA

Linguatula serrata is found in the adult and nymphal stages in the nose and paranasal sinuses of dogs and other carnivorous mammals, and as larvæ and encapsulated nymphs in herbivorous mammals. Human infection with the adult is rare but larval infections have been reported not infrequently in Europe, Africa, and South and Central America.

Morphology.—The female (Fig. 260D) has a yellowish pyriform body, 8 to 10 cm. in length, with about 90 fine annulations. The white male, 1.8 to 2 cm. in length, is similar in appearance.

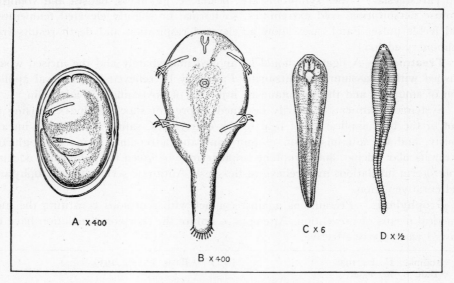

FIG. 260.—*Linguatula serrata*

A, embryonate ovum; *B,* acariform embryo; *C,* nymph; *D,* adult (*A* and *B* redrawn from Leuckart, 1860; *C* adapted from Darling and Clark, 1912; *D* adapted from various sources).

Life Cycle.—The hard-shelled eggs (Fig. 260A), 90 x 70 μ, containing developed embryos, are discharged in the nasal secretions. When ingested by a mammalian host, the eggs develop into four-legged larvæ (Fig. 260B), 130 μ in length, that pass through the intestinal wall and penetrate the liver, mesenteric glands and other organs. In about six months after several molts they become encysted nymphs (Fig. 260C), 6 to 8 mm. in length, similar to adults except for minute spines on the annular rings. The nymphs pass to the nasal passages of the same host or reach those of another host by ingestion or by some other means. Here they molt into adults.

Pathogenesis.—Both adult and larval forms have been found in man; the rare adult in the lungs and the larvæ and nymphs in the lungs, liver, spleen and intestinal wall. Symptomatology is unknown. Inflammation of the nasal passages and bleeding sometimes occur.

POROCEPHALUS ARMILLATUS

The genus *Porocephalus* contains about 20 species, many of which are imperfectly known. They are distinguished from the *Linguatula* by their cylindrical, ringed bodies. Two species, *P. armillatus* of Africa and *P. moniliformis* of Asia, and possibly others, have been found in man.

Geographical Distribution.—Africa and southern Arabia.

Morphology.—The adult has a yellowish, elongate, more or less cylindrical, vermiform body, tapering to a bluntly-pointed cone and encircled at intervals with bracelet-like, oblique rings that give it a screw-like appearance. The male (Fig. 261A), 3 to 4.5 cm. in length, has 16 to 17 rings and the female (Fig. 261B), 9 to 12 cm. in length, has 18 to 22 rings.[12] The dorsally-convex, ventrally flattened cephalothorax extends to the first ring. The circular, ventral mouth (Fig. 261C), 1 mm. from the anterior end, has two hooks and two anterior papillæ on each side. The female genital aperture is on the mid-ventral surface anterior to the anus and the male genital opening is at the level of the first ring. The digestive tract extends as a straight tube from mouth to anus.

Habits.—The adult is a parasite of the lungs, trachea and nasal cavities of the West African and royal pythons and three species of puff adders. The nymph is found in primates and various wild and domestic mammals.

Life Cycle.—The elliptical, double-shelled eggs, 108 x 80 μ, containing developed embryos, are enclosed in a transparent bladder. They are discharged in the nasal secretions and may remain viable in water or on the ground for six months. When the egg is ingested by a suitable host, usually in drinking water, an acariform larva, 92 x 72 μ, is liberated. The larva has four legs that terminate in a pair of claws, an anterior perforating apparatus and a tapering terminally-spined tail. It pierces the intestinal wall and is carried by the blood or lymph to the mesenteric glands, liver or other parts of the body, where it encysts, losing its penetrating apparatus and claws. After a series of molts it becomes in a year or more a full-grown, closely-coiled, encysted nymph (Fig. 261D) that resembles the adult. When ingested by a snake, the nymphs develop into sexually-differentiated adults.

Pathogenesis.—Human infection with the larvæ and nymphs is fairly common in Africa, particularly in the Belgian Congo. The nymphs are found on the surface of the liver, in the intestinal mucosa, in the peritoneal cavity and in the lung. The disease is chronic and its severity depends upon the intensity of the infection. The terminal symptoms are emaciation, weakness, bronchitis, hepatitis and peritonitis. Pulmonary involvement simulates tuberculosis. There is no known treatment and the prognosis is serious.

Prevention.—Boiling or filtering drinking water should prevent infection.

Other Species.—*P. moniliformis*, an Asiatic species, is more slender and has a greater number of annular rings, 26 to 31, than *P. armillatus*. Its definitive hosts are pythons and its intermediate hosts are primates and wild animals. A few cases of human

---

[12] Sambon, L. W., 1910.

infection have been recorded. *P. crotali,* a parasite of the tropical rattlesnake of Central and South America, and other species possibly may cause porocephaliasis in man.

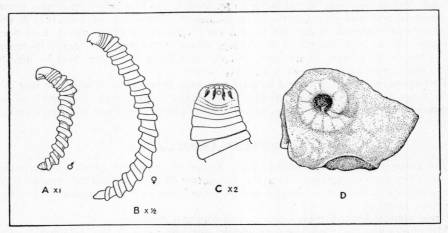

Fig. 261.—*Porocephalus armillatus*

A, male; *B,* female; *C,* anterior end, ventral view; *D,* nymph in liver (*A, B* and *D* redrawn from Sambon, 1910; *C* redrawn from Sambon, 1912).

ORDER *ACARINA*

The order ACARINA, ticks and mites, includes many parasites and vectors of diseases of man and lower animals.

Morphology.—Ticks and mites are small arachnids in which the head, thorax and abdomen are fused in an unsegmented body. A portion of the head region including the mouth parts and their base, the capitulum, is attached to the anterior end of the body by a movable hinge. One or more pairs of simple eyes, if present, are on the anterior part of the body. The integument may be membranous or thickened into plates or shields on the dorsal and ventral surfaces. The four pairs of six-jointed legs are covered with regularly-distributed hairs or bristles. The sexes are separate and the genital pore is on the anterior part of the ventral surface. In some mites spiracles are present on the cephalothoracic portion of the body, while in the ticks a pair is found near the base of the third or fourth pair of legs. The internal anatomy, differing somewhat from that of insects, is described in Chapter XLVIII.

Life Cycle.—The females are fertilized by the introduction of spermatozoa in the form of spermatophores into the genital opening by the capitulum of the male. The egg hatches into a larva with three pairs of legs; the larva molts into an eight-legged nymph and the nymph in turn into a sexually-differentiated adult.

Habits.—Mites are terrestrial and aquatic and certain species are ecto- and endo-parasitic on animals and plants. Ticks are terrestrial and parasitic on animals. These arachnids feed on decaying organic matter or on living animals and plants.

Classification.—Table 44 lists some of the common parasites of man or vectors of human disease arranged by superfamily, family, genus and species.

TABLE 44
SOME IMPORTANT SPECIES OF ACARINA

Superfamily	Family	Genus	Species
IXODOIDEA	ARGASIDÆ	Argas	A. persicus
		Ornithodorus	O. erraticus O. moubata O. rostratus O. savignyi O. talaje O. turicata O. venezuelensis
	IXODIDÆ	Amblyomma	A. americanum A. cajennense A. hebræum A. maculatum A. variegatum
		Boophilus	B. annulatus
		Dermacentor	D. andersoni D. occidentalis D. reticulatus D. variabilis
		Hæmaphysalis	H. leporis-palustris
		Hyalomma	H. ægyptium
		Ixodes	I. holocyclus I. pilosus I. ricinus
		Rhipicephalus	R. sanguineus
DEMODICOIDEA	DEMODICIDÆ	Demodex	D. folliculorum
PARASITOIDEA	DERMANYSSIDÆ	Dermanyssus	D. gallinæ
		Liponyssus	L. bacoti
SARCOPTOIDEA	SARCOPTIDÆ	Sarcoptes	S. scabiei
TARSONEMOIDEA	PEDICULOIDIDÆ	Pediculoides	P. ventricosus
TROMBIDOIDEA	TROMBIDIIDÆ	Trombicula	T. akamushi T. alfreddugèsi
TYROGLYPHOIDEA	TYROGLYPHIDÆ	Glyciphagus	G. domesticus
		Tyroglyphus	T. farinæ T. longior

REFERENCES

BALL, C. R.   Scorpion Stings, Science, 1938, 88:427.

BASU, U. P.   Observations of Scorpion-sting and Snake-bite, Am. J. Trop. Med., 1939, 19:385.

BLAIR, A. W.   Spider Poisoning, Experimental Study of the Effects of the Bite of the Female *Latrodectus mactans* in Man, Arch. Int. Med., 1934, 54:831.

——— Life History of *Latrodectus mactans*, Arch. Int. Med., 1934, 54:884.

BOGEN, E.   Poisonous Spider Bites, Ann. Int. Med., 1932, 6:375.

D'AMOUR, F. E., BECKER, F. E. and VAN RIPER, W.   The Black Widow Spider, Quart. Rev. Biol., 1936, 11:123.

GINSBERG, H. M.   Black Widow Spider Bite; Report of Forty-four Cases, California and West. Med., 1937, 46:381.

GOWANLOCK, J. N. and LEEPER, B. F.   Report on the Black Widow Spider, Louisiana Cons. Rev., 1935, 4:13.

KASTON, B. J.   The Black Widow Spider in New England, Bull. N. E. Mus. Nat. Hist., 1937, 84:3.

SAMBON, L. W.   Porocephaliasis in Man, J. Trop. Med., 1910, 13:212.

STALINKE, H. L.   The Venomous Effect of Some Arizona Scorpions, Science, 1938, 88:166.

Chapter XLVIII

THE SUPERFAMILY IXODOIDEA (TICKS)

The ticks differ from the mites in their larger size, leathery skin, armed hypostome, and the presence of a pair of spiracles behind the coxæ of the third or fourth pair of legs. About 300 species are bloodsucking ectoparasites of mammals, birds, reptiles and amphibians, and nearly all are capable of biting man. Certain species are vectors of important avian and mammalian diseases and a few transmit human diseases.

MORPHOLOGY

The sexes are separate. The cephalothorax and abdomen are fused into an oval or elliptical body, flattened dorsoventrally and slightly convex dorsally, bearing four pairs of six-jointed legs and a false head or capitulum (Fig. 262).

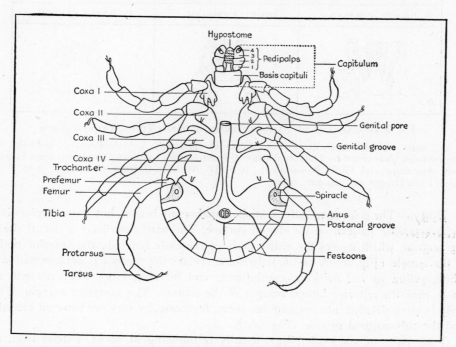

Fig. 262.—Ventral View of Male *Dermacentor andersoni* Showing Anatomical Structures

(Redrawn from Hegner, Root, Augustine and Huff, *Parasitology,* 1938, D. Appleton-Century Company).

737

Capitulum.—In the hard ticks the capitulum projects from the anterior end of the body, while in the soft ticks it extends from beneath the anterior end. In the former it consists of a basal plate, the **basis capituli,** the shape of which is of taxonomic value and the mouth parts (**hypostome, cheliceræ** and **pedipalps**) (Fig. 263). The median, elongated, bisymmetrical hypostome, covered with transverse rows of recurrent, file-like teeth of variable pattern, anchors.the parasite to the host. The lateral paired cheliceræ are long, cylindrical, chitinous shafts, enclosed in finely-denticulate, mandibular sheaths. Each chelicera terminates in a retractile, chitinous digit of two movable toothed parts. They act as cutting organs to permit the insertion of the hypostome. The paired, four-jointed, flap-like, hirsute pedipalps of variable shape and length do not penetrate the tissues but serve as supports. In most genera they lie in close apposition to the other mouth parts but in *Hæmaphysalis* they have a lateral spread (Fig. 263).

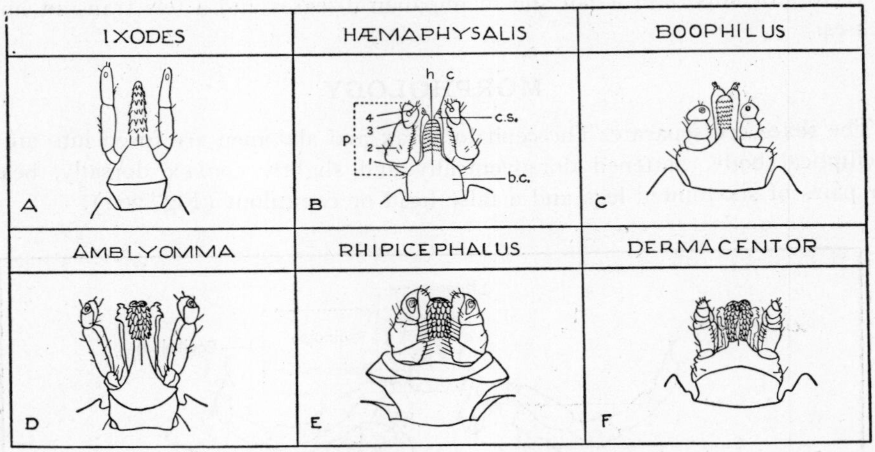

FIG. 263.—CAPITULA OF VARIOUS GENERA OF HARD TICKS, VENTRAL VIEW

b.c., basis capituli; *c,* chelicera; *c.s.,* sheath of chelicera; *h,* haustellum; *p,* pedipalps (*A* adapted from photograph by Hamilton, 1940; *B* from various sources; *C,* redrawn from Hegner, Root, Augustine and Huff, *Parasitology,* 1938, D. Appleton-Century Company; *D* to *F* redrawn from Hunter and Hooker, 1907).

Body.—The color is usually reddish or mahogany brown, but some species show a characteristic pattern on the dorsal surface. The hard ticks have a dorsal shield, the scutum, which covers the entire body of the male but only the anterior region of the female (Fig. 270A and C). In some species the scutum is ornamented with white, yellow or red markings, sculpturing and furrows. Eyes, when present, are on or near the anterior lateral margin of the scutum. The posterior margin of the body is often divided into rectangular areas, **festoons,** by furrows between the edge and the submarginal groove (Fig. 262).

Four pairs of six-jointed legs, usually terminating in hooks, extend from the shield-like plates of the basal coxæ on the ventral surface (Fig. 262). Coxal glands between coxæ I and II secrete a tenacious fluid during feeding and copulation. An olfactory organ (Haller's organ) is situated on the tarsi of the first pair of legs. The spiracles are located on chitinized plates in front of or behind the fourth coxæ. The anus is at the posterior end, but the genital opening lies well forward in the midline. The genital grooves run from the sides of the genital opening to the posterior margin of the body. A single anal groove may connect the genital grooves and is usually situated behind the anus, except in the genus *Ixodes* where it forms an arch in front of the anus and extends to the posterior margin without contact with the genital grooves. In some genera of hard ticks ventral plates are present. The size of the fourth coxæ, the position of the anal groove, the form of the spiracles, the ventral plates, and the structure of the capitulum are aids in distinguishing genera and species (Fig. 268).

Internal Structures.—The capacious digestive system is divided into foregut, midgut and hindgut (Fig. 264). The foregut includes the tubular buccal cavity, the pump-like chitinous muscular pharynx, the thin-walled S-shaped esophagus, and the accessory paired salivary glands. The midgut consists of a large, four-lobed, thin-walled stomach that serves for food storage. The hindgut is made up of a narrow rectum and a large vesicular rectal sac which receives the two long, convoluted malpighian tubules.

The vascular system consists of a heart dorsal to the stomach, a cephalic aorta running forward to the periganglionic sinus, and four arteries leading from this sinus to the legs. Contraction of the dorsoventral muscles causes the blood to return to the heart through the lacunar spaces. A highly-developed tracheal respiratory system connects the spiracles with the organs. The nervous system consists of a large, anterior, midline ganglion with numerous nerve trunks.

The female genital organs include a duplex ovary, coiled oviducts, uterus, vagina, accessory vaginal glands, and Gené's organ which supplies secretions during oviposition. The male has a duplex testis, a pair of vasa deferentia, a seminal vesicle, where spermatophores are formed, an ejaculatory duct, and accessory glands.

HABITS

Habitat.—During their larval, nymphal and adult stages most ticks are intermittent parasites of mammals, spending the main part of their existence on ground covered with small bushes and shrubs. Some species, however (*Boophilus, Hæmaphysalis*) pass most of their life on animals (Fig. 266). Favorable environmental conditions include numerous small and large mammals for hosts, abundant vegetation, and moisture.

Resistance.—Ticks are susceptible to sunlight, desiccation and excessive rainfall, while hot, dry weather lessens their activity. The hard ticks are resistant to cold, nymphs and adults hibernating in protected places during the winter in cold climates. Low temperatures, however, retard breeding.

Longevity.—Ticks are long lived; specimens of *Ornithodorus turicata* have been kept under observation for seven years.[1] The life cycle of *Dermacentor andersoni* is about 20 months but may last 3 years.

---

[1] Francis, E., 1938.

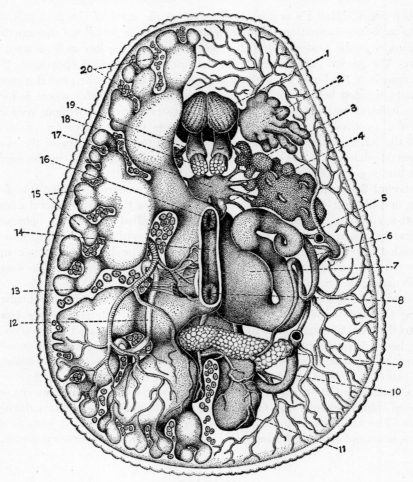

FIG. 264.—INTERNAL ANATOMY OF TICK

1, Gené's organ; 2, glandular portion, Gené's organ; 3, salivary gland; 4, accessory genital gland; 5, trachea; 6, oviduct; 7, uterus; 8, rectum; 9, ovary; 10, malpighian tubule; 11, rectal sac; 12, malpighian tubule; 13, heart; 14, stomach; 15, alimentary ceca; 16, esophagus; 17, brain; 18, muscles of chelicera; 19, chelicera; 20, dorso-ventral body muscles (Redrawn from Robinson and Davidson by Esther Bohlman, in Hegner, Root, Augustine and Huff, *Parasitology*, 1938, D. Appleton-Century Company).

Feeding.—The larvæ and nymphs feed on small and the adult ticks on large mammals. They attach themselves to animals that come in contact with infested vegetation. Both sexes are bloodsuckers and require a feeding period of four to six days before copulation. After engorgement the adult female *Ixodes holocyclus* increases three to four times its original length and from 1 to 450 mg. in weight (Fig. 265).[2] The male tick does not increase greatly in size. The time of engorgement of *Dermacentor variabilis,* prolonged by cold weather, is 3 to 12 days for

[2] Hamilton, D. G., 1940.

larvæ, 3 to 10 days for nymphs and 5 to 13 days for adults.[3] The adult female *Dermacentor andersoni* completes her blood meal in 8 to 14 days after copulation.[4] Ticks can undergo long periods of starvation; larvæ (*D. variabilis*) 90 days; nymphs (*D. andersoni*) 300 days and adults (*D. andersoni*) 413 days. Unfed specimens of *Ornithodorus turicata* have survived five years.[1]

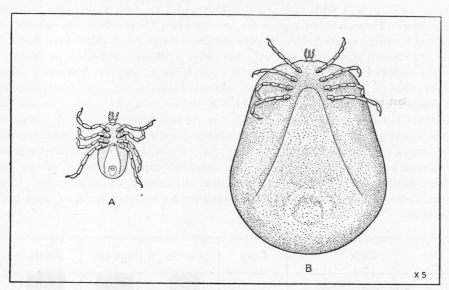

FIG. 265.—*Ixodes holocyclus*

A, unengorged female; *B*, engorged female (Adapted from photographs by Hamilton, 1940).

Copulation.—Copulation takes place after preliminary feeding upon the mammalian host. During copulation the male tick lies beneath the female, with their ventral surfaces in apposition. The spermatophores are introduced into the vagina by the capitulum. In *Ornithodorus moubata* the neck of the flask-shaped spermatophore, adherent to the hypostome, is introduced into the dilated female orifice and its contents expressed.[5] The males usually die after copulation.

Oviposition.—Upon completing her final blood meal the engorged female hard tick drops off the host, and deposits 2,000 to 8,000 eggs in masses on the ground after a variable preovipositional period depending upon temperature (3 to 24 days for *Dermacentor variabilis*). The time of oviposition is 14 to 32 days for *Dermacentor variabilis* and 30 to 41 days for *D. andersoni*. The female *D. variabilis* dies in 3 to 36 days after oviposition. The soft ticks lay fewer eggs, 100 to 200, in several batches following successive blood meals.

---

[3] Bishopp, F. C. and Smith, C. N., 1938.   [5] Nuttall, G. H. F. and Merriman, G., 1911.
[4] Hunter, W. D. and Bishopp, F. C., 1911.

LIFE CYCLE

The life cycle embraces egg, larva, nymph and adult. The larvæ (Fig. 269D) have three pairs of legs and no tracheal system. These active creatures attach themselves to small mammals to obtain a blood meal, then drop off and molt into nymphs (Fig. 269E) with four pairs of legs and a tracheal system but without a genital pore. These in turn molt after one or more blood meals into adults. The female is fertilized either before or after she becomes attached to the final host. The same or different species of mammals may serve as hosts for the several stages.

This complicated life cycle permits but few larvæ to survive. Various modifications of the cycle, such as change of host, length of time on the host, number of molts and frequency of ovipositions, occur in different species (Fig. 266). In the hard ticks there is but a single nymphal stage; in the soft ticks several may follow successive blood meals. In the genus *Boophilus* and some species of *Dermacentor* the three stages are passed on a single host; in *Rhipicephalus evertsi, R. bursa* and *Hyalomma ægyptium* both the larval and nymphal stages are passed on one host. In the soft ticks the female indulges in several blood meals and ovipositions. In one species, *Ornithodorus megnini,* the adult requires no preliminary blood meal before oviposition.

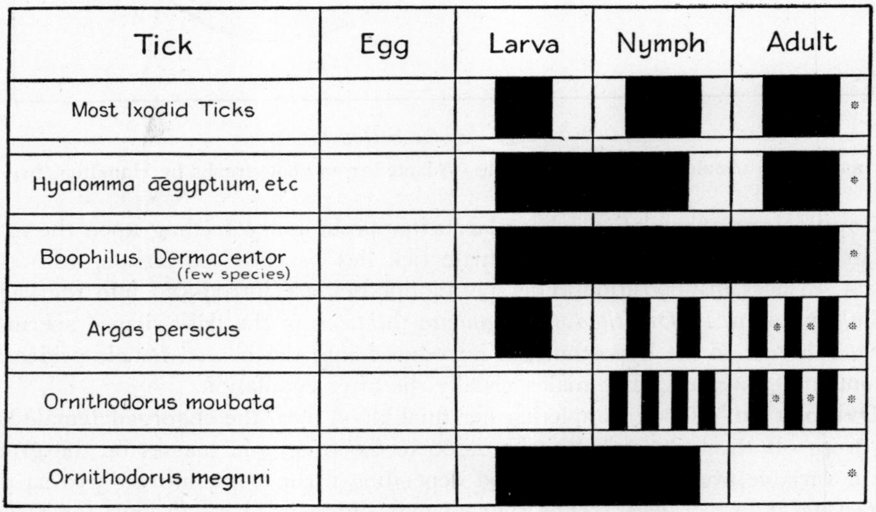

Tick	Egg	Larva	Nymph	Adult
Most Ixodid Ticks		■	■	■ (*)
Hyalomma aegyptium, etc		■	■	■ (*)
Boophilus, Dermacentor (few species)		■	■	■ (*)
Argas persicus		■	‖‖	‖ ‖ (* * *)
Ornithodorus moubata			‖‖‖‖	‖ ‖ (* * *)
Ornithodorus megnini		■	■	(*)

Fig. 266.—Graphic Representation of Host-Attachment (Black) and Oviposition (*) in the Life Cycles of Various Ticks

(Adapted from diagram in Hegner, Root, Augustine and Huff, *Parasitology,* 1938, D. Appleton-Century Company).

CLASSIFICATION

Ticks are divided into two large families, the ARGASIDÆ or soft ticks with two genera, and the IXODIDÆ or hard ticks with several. The argasid ticks are more primitive, are less constantly parasitic, produce less progeny and infest the habitat of the host. The ixodid ticks are more specialized and more highly parasitic, produce more progeny and infest the migratory host itself.

THE FAMILY *ARGASIDÆ* (SOFT TICKS)

The soft ticks are primarily ectoparasitic on birds, less commonly on bats, other small mammals and man.

Geographical Distribution.—Cosmopolitan. Species of ARGASIDÆ are found in temperate climates, but are more numerous in warm countries.

Morphology.—Sexes are similar; there is no hard dorsal plate; the capitulum is situated ventral to the anterior extremity; the spiracles lie in front of the third pair of coxæ; the coxæ are unspurred; and the tarsi bear no pads or pulvilli.

Habits.—The soft ticks are nocturnal feeders and seldom travel far from their local habitat. Species of *Ornithodorus* resemble bedbugs in their frequent blood meals and in their habit of hiding by day in cracks and crevices. They can withstand prolonged fasts.

Life Cycle.—The adult female deposits in small batches with intervening blood meals from 100 to 200 oval yellowish eggs, 0.9 mm. in length, usually in the nests or lairs of birds and mammals or in crevices of human habitations. The larval stage is absent in *Ornithodorus moubata;* the nymph emerges directly from the egg in from 15 to 23 days and indulges in several blood meals before attaining the adult stage (Fig. 266).

Classification.—The family ARGASIDÆ contains but two genera, *Argas* and *Ornithodorus*. Ticks of the genus *Argas* have a thin, flat body, with a sharp-edged margin distinct even in engorged ticks, and a minutely-wrinkled integument adorned with numerous oval or rounded disks. Those of the genus *Ornithodorus* have a thick body with a poorly-defined, rounded margin and a mammillated integument that is usually without disks.

SPECIES OF *ARGASIDÆ* INJURIOUS TO MAN

Argas persicus.—A natural parasite of fowls, *Argas persicus* occasionally bites man. It is a relatively large, brownish-red, oval tick, the female measuring 7 to 10 mm., and the male 4 to 5 mm. It is found in many tropical and subtropical countries and abounds in Persia, the Sudan and South Africa, where it has proved a veritable scourge. It oviposits and the young undergo metamorphosis in the crevices of chicken houses and dwellings. It bites man preferably at night, producing painful wounds that are subject to secondary infection. Foreigners are more susceptible than natives. It is the vector of fowl spirochætosis (*Spironema gallinarum*) and other avian diseases, and it is a suspected but unproved vector of a form of human relapsing fever that is prevalent throughout Persia.

Ornithodorus moubata.—The African tick, *Ornithodorus moubata*, known by the natives as bibo, tampan and mabata, has an oval, yellowish-brown, tuberculated, leathery body (Fig. 267). The female usually measures from 8 to 9 mm. in length but may reach 12 mm. Though primarily infesting birds and small mammals, it has become a parasite of man and domestic animals. It inhabits cracks in the floors of native huts and rest houses, whence it attacks its victims at night. It is not migratory, but may be transported in the bundles of porters. The bites of both nymphs and adults produce hard red wheals that remain painful for 24 hours. It is the important vector of the tropical African or endemic type of relapsing fever (*Borrelia duttoni*).

Several species of *Ornithodorus* are vectors of local types of relapsing fever throughout the world. *O. moubata* in Africa and *O. rostratus* in Brazil have been shown experimentally to be vectors of yellow fever. *O. megnini*, the spinose ear tick of cattle and horses, rarely if ever attacks man and is of interest only because of its aberrant life cycle in which the adult does not feed. The bite of *O. coriaceus*, the pajaroello of Mexico and California, causes severe pain and inflammation.

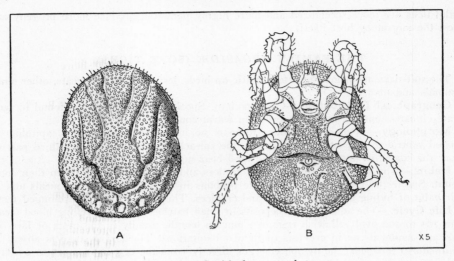

FIG. 267.—*Ornithodorus moubata*

A, dorsal view, female; *B,* ventral view, female (Redrawn from Nuttall, 1916).

THE FAMILY *IXODIDÆ* (HARD TICKS)

Hard ticks are so called because of a horny shield (scutum) that in the female partially and in the male entirely covers the dorsal surface.

Geographical Distribution.—Cosmopolitan.

Morphology.—Sexes are usually dissimilar; there is a hard dorsal scutum; the capitulum extends forward from its articulation with the anterior end of the body; the spiracles lie behind the third pair of coxæ; the coxæ are spurred; and the tarsi bear pulvilli.

Habits.—Both sexes are bloodsuckers. They remain attached to the host for a considerable time, take only one blood meal in each of the larval, nymphal and adult stages and the adult female oviposits after her blood meal (Fig. 266). While absent from the host the ticks infest ground covered with small bushes or shrubs. Although resistant to cold, they are susceptible to desiccation and require a moist environment. The larvæ can survive an eight to twelve-month fast and adults a much longer period.

Life Cycle.—The female deposits on or near the ground a large mass of small, oval, brownish eggs, ranging in number from 2,000 to 8,000. The size of the egg varies in different species, usually ranging from 0.55 to 0.75 mm. The eggs of *Dermacentor variabilis* hatch in from 2 to 7 weeks into hexapod larvæ or "seed" ticks about 0.6 mm. in length (Fig. 269D). These pale-yellow larvæ with brick-red markings on the sides of the shield first remain in masses on the soil and then scatter over low-growing vegetation, where they await a passing host. The larvæ are usually five days old before they become attached to a suitable host. After a blood meal of 3 to 12 days and a resting period of 6 to 87 days depending upon the temperature they molt into yellow-brown octopod nymphs, 1.5 mm. in length, with the hind border of the shield dark, and the sides brick red (Fig. 269E). Four-day-old nymphs are able to attach themselves to hosts and after a blood meal of 3 to 10 days and a resting period of from 17 to 109 days, molt into adults. The life cycle usually requires three hosts, preferably animals of varied size for larva, nymph and adult, although some species pass all three stages on the same mammal. If this complicated life cycle is interrupted, the tick can survive for long periods, even hibernating through the winter. In fact, the life cycle, though usually completed in a single year, may be extended for two or three years.

Classification.—The family IXODIDÆ comprises several genera and many species. The males may be classified by the ventral plates, but the females, lacking these plates, are difficult to identify especially when engorged. The following characteristics differentiate the more important genera (Figs. 263 and 268).

Preanal groove in female, male chitinous ventral plates, eyes absent, pedipalps spatulate —*Ixodes.*

Anal grooves behind anus or absent in female.

No adanal plates in male

Eyes absent

Anal groove plainly visible, festoons usually present not much longer than wide, second joint of pedipalps extends beyond edges of the basis capituli, mouth parts about as long as basis capituli—*Hæmaphysalis.*

Ornate, mouth parts much longer than basis capituli, second joint of pedipalps much longer than wide—*Aponomma.*

Eyes present

Eyes marginal, males without ventral plate—*Amblyomma.*

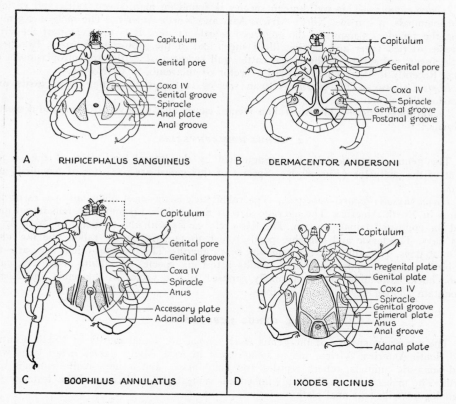

FIG. 268.—VENTRAL VIEW OF VARIOUS SPECIES OF MALE IXODID TICKS, SHOWING GENITAL AND ANAL GROOVES, COXÆ AND PLATES

Differential characteristics are indicated by heavy lines and dotted areas (*A* adapted from Patton and Cragg, 1913; *B* to *D* redrawn from Hegner, Root, Augustine and Huff, *Parasitology,* 1938, D. Appleton-Century Company).

Fourth coxa much larger than others, basis capituli rectangular in dorsal view, scutum usually ornate—*Dermacentor.*

Basis capituli hexagonal in dorsal view, scutum usually not ornate.—*Rhipicentor.*

One or two pairs adanal plates in male

Eyes present

Eyes submarginal—*Hyalomma.*

Fourth coxa not much larger than others—*Rhipicephalus.*

Joints of fourth pair of legs normal, male with paired adanal and accessory plates—*Boophilus.*

SPECIES OF *IXODIDÆ* INJURIOUS TO MAN

1. GENUS *IXODES*

The genus *Ixodes* is characterized by a preanal groove, spatulate pedipalps and chitinous ventral plates in the male (Fig. 268). It is the only genus in which there is sexual differentiation in the hypostome. Three different mammals are required as hosts for its larval, nymphal and adult stages. Males are rarely found on the host.

Ixodes ricinus.—This well-known species is found on man, sheep, cattle and various wild mammals in Europe, North Africa, Asia and North America. The male is 2.5 mm. long, the female 3.5 mm. and the engorged female 11 mm. It is the vector of the viral diseases of tick fever and louping ill of sheep and of the protozoan diseases, European cattle fever, red water of sheep and cattle, gall sickness of cattle, and piroplasmosis of dogs. Recently it has been considered a vector of tularemia in California.

Ixodes pilosus.—This South African species is found on cattle, sheep, goats and occasionally on man.

Ixodes holocyclus.—This Australian species causes tick paralysis of man and domestic animals.[2]

2. GENUS *HÆMAPHYSALIS*

The genus *Hæmaphysalis* is distinguished by the lateral projection of the second joint of the pedipalps (Fig. 263B). Species of this genus are parasites of mammals and birds.

Hæmaphysalis leporis-palustris.—The rabbit tick is the most abundant species of the genus in North America. The average size of the male is 1.9 mm., the female 3.9 mm. and the engorged female 10 mm. The life cycle varies with the temperature from 87 to 405 days. The larvæ and nymphs spend from 6 to 11 days on the rabbit and the adult 19 to 26 days. The adults have a longevity of 13 months. The immature ticks are parasites of birds and pine squirrels, and the adults infest six species of rabbits and hares, cats, woodchuck, chipmunks and occasionally grouse.[6] It is a vector of tularemia and Rocky Mountain spotted fever among animals.

3. GENUS *AMBLYOMMA*

The numerous species of the genus *Amblyomma* are found mostly in North, Central and South America, Africa, and to some extent in Asia. Many species infest large wild and domestic animals, others reptiles and amphibians, and a few small mammals and birds. The males have small, deeply-imbedded, ventral plates in front of the festoons not homologous with true anal plates.

Amblyomma americanum.—The lone-star tick, characterized by a silvery spot and fine punctations on the scutum of the female, infests cattle in the Southern and Eastern United States and South America. It is an experimental vector of Rocky Mountain spotted fever. *A. maculatum,* the Gulf Coast tick of the United States, also attacks cattle.

---

[6] Hearle, E., 1938.

Amblyomma cajennense.—In Central and South America and in Texas and New Mexico *A. cajennense* is a parasite of cattle, horses, dogs and man. It is the vector of São Paulo fever and yellow fever (experimentally).

Amblyomma hebræum.—The bout tick of South Africa is a scourge to domestic cattle. It also attacks antelopes, other wild mammals and occasionally man. It is the vector of heartwater fever of sheep, goats and cattle, and of African tick typhus of men. *A. variegatum* is a vector of heartwater fever and also transmits Nairobi sheep disease.

4. GENUS *DERMACENTOR*

The genus *Dermacentor* is characterized by the large size of the fourth coxæ (Fig. 268), the ornate scutum and the rectangular basis capituli (Fig. 263F). The morphology of the stigmal plates has been recommended for differentiating species.[7]

Dermacentor andersoni.—The wood tick, sometimes called *D. venustus,* is the most important North American species from a medical standpoint, since it produces tick paralysis and transmits Rocky Mountain spotted fever and tularemia. It is found in the Rocky Mountain region northward from New Mexico through southern British Columbia and western Alberta. The male tick has a large scutum decorated with characteristic black and white markings (Fig. 270A). The female has a small white shield on the anterior dorsal surface with a wrinkled, dark, reddish-brown, elastic posterior portion (Fig. 270C). The unengorged male rarely exceeds 4 mm. in length, while the female ranges from 4 to 6 mm. and, when engorged, from 12 to 15 mm. Its life cycle is that of the typical ixodid tick.

The chief hosts for the larval and nymphal ticks are the Columbian ground squirrel, yellow-bellied chipmunk, and squirrel, but the large chipmunk, woodchuck, snowshoe rabbit, rock squirrel, wood rat, meadow mouse and white-footed mouse may also be infested.[4] The adult tick attacks principally cattle, sheep and horses, but may also infest man, dogs, cats, hogs, mules, mountain goats, brown bears, coyotes, wildcats, badgers, snowshoe and jack rabbits, and woodchucks.[3]

Dermacentor variabilis.—The American dog tick is widely distributed throughout the United States of America east of the Rocky Mountains. It is also found in California, Oregon, Alaska, Labrador, Mexico and the Canadian provinces of Manitoba, Ontario and Nova Scotia.[3] It is most abundant on the Atlantic coast from Massachusetts to Florida, inhabiting fields covered with low shrubs and areas of beach grass. The male (Fig. 269F), 4 to 5 mm. in length and slightly smaller than the female, has an oval body narrower at the anterior end. It is light-chestnut to chocolate-brown and its ornate scutum bears white markings, depressions and tactile hairs. The female (Fig. 269G), a darker chestnut-brown with a yellowish tinge to the dorsal surface, has a small, white, anterior, dorsal scutum with two brown lateral lines, large and small brown dots, ridges and tactile hairs.[8]

The dog is the principal host of the adult tick, although man, cattle, hogs, horses, sheep and practically all large fur-bearing mammals may be attacked. The hosts of the immature forms are small rodents, principally the field mouse (*Microtus pennsylvanicus*) and less frequently the pine, white-footed and house mouse; but rats, rabbits, shrews and moles, and occasionally larger mammals may be infested.[3]

The life cycle is that of a typical ixodid tick. Adults are most prevalent in the spring and early summer and disappear early in August, but in the Southern United States they are found throughout the year. Both immature and adult ticks hibernate and molt in the spring; thus nymphs and adults are abundant at that time while larvæ are relatively scarce. It is a pest to dogs and man and transmits the eastern form of Rocky Mountain spotted fever and tularemia to man. Its bite has also produced tick paralysis.[9]

---

[7] Stiles, C. W., 1910.
[8] Zebrowski, G., 1926.

[9] Robinow, M. and Carrol, T. B., 1938.

Dermacentor occidentalis.—The Pacific tick of western California and southwest Oregon also attacks man, and has been implicated in the transmission of Rocky Mountain spotted fever.

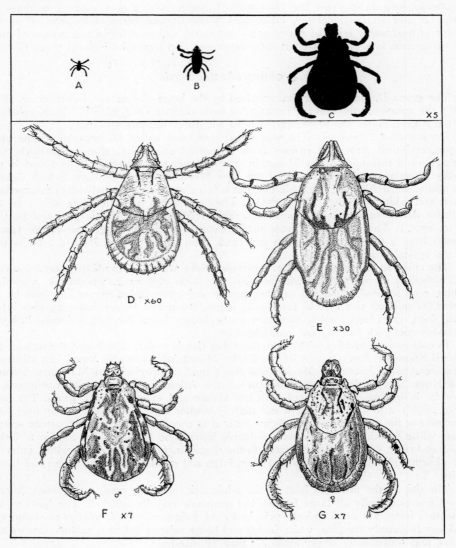

FIG. 269.—*Dermacentor variabilis*

A to *C* relative sizes of larva, nymph and adult; *D*, larva; *E*, nymph; *F*, adult male; *G*, adult female (*D* to *G* redrawn from Bishopp and Smith, 1938).

Dermacentor reticulatus.—Many large mammals in Europe, Asia and Africa are attacked by *D. reticulatus*.

Dermacentor nitens.—The ears of horses in tropical America are often infested with *D. nitens*.

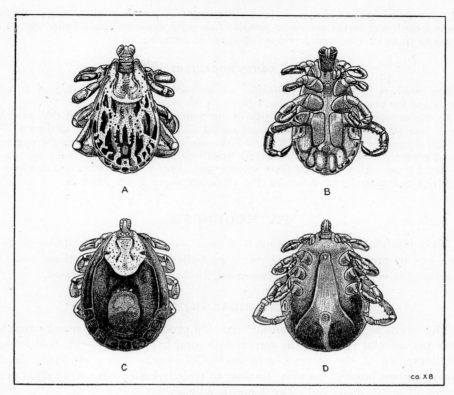

Fig. 270.—*Dermacentor andersoni*

A, male, dorsal view; *B*, male, ventral view; *C*, female, dorsal view; *D*, female, ventral view (Redrawn from colored plate by Stiles, 1910).

5. GENUS *HYALOMMA*

Hyalomma ægyptium.—Of the relatively few species of this genus *Hyalomma ægyptium* is the most important. The male has a brown scutum with numerous unequal punctations, rectangular adanal plates, and two chitinous tipped protrusions from the posterior end of the abdomen. In Africa, Asia and southern Europe it infests cattle, other large domestic and wild mammals, and occasionally man. Experimentally it transmits African tick typhus of man, and the Rhodesian fever of animals. *H. lusitanicum* is a vector of anaplasmosis of cattle.

6. GENUS *RHIPICEPHALUS*

The numerous species of the genus *Rhipicephalus* have triangular adanal plates in the male (Fig. 268), a vase-shaped basis capituli (Fig. 263E), elongated spiracles and flat eyes.

Rhipicephalus sanguineus. The brown European dog tick is found in Africa, southern Europe, southern United States, and other warm regions. The other species of this genus are largely confined to Africa. Its principal host is the dog, but it has been found on the fox, jackal, cat, lion, hare, horse, camel and man. It requires three distinct hosts in its life cycle, not necessarily of the same species. The male, 3.3 mm., has a large brown scutum, and the female, 3 to 11 mm., an oval shield. It is the vector of boutonneuse fever and African tick typhus of man. It is also the vector of piroplasmosis of dogs, anaplasmosis of cattle and of the protozoan parasite *Leucocytogregarina canis*. Other species of the genus transmit viral and protozoan diseases of animals.

7. GENUS *BOOPHILUS*

The members of the genus *Boophilus* are characterized by the absence of an anal groove and the presence of four adanal plates in the male (Fig. 268).

Boophilus annulatus.—The cattle tick of the Southern United States is the vector of Texas fever, a scourge which causes an annual loss of $40,000,000 to cattlemen. The etiological agent of Texas fever, *Babesia bigemina,* is transmitted through the egg to a second generation of ticks. This relatively small tick remains attached to the host from the larval stage until the female becomes pregnant. Among the varieties are *decoloratus* of Africa and *australis* of Australia, the Philippines and South America.

PATHOGENESIS

Ticks injure man and lower animals in three ways: (1) by the irritation of their bites, (2) by producing tick paralysis through their poisonous secretions, and (3) by serving as vectors of bacterial, rickettsial, viral and protozoan diseases.

MECHANICAL INJURY

The insertion of the capitulum into the skin produces an inflammatory reaction of the perivascular tissues of the corium with local hyperemia, edema, hemorrhage, and thickening of the stratum corneum.[10] Occasionally ticks, especially *Ixodes ricinus,* burrow beneath the skin. Because of their irritating bites ticks are a great scourge to cattle, sheep and other domestic animals.

A certain resistance to attacks of ticks is acquired by animals through previous infestation or inoculations with extracts of ticks.[11] A two-weeks infestation with *Dermacentor variablis* produced in guinea pigs an acquired immunity of three months' duration, which prevented subsequent batches of larvæ from engorging. The immune animals showed an intense local inflammatory reaction and a thickening of the epithelium that walled off the tick from the blood supply. Partial immunity was also produced by intracutaneous injections of extracts of ticks. Evidence of cross-immunity, the transfer of passive immunity and the presence of alexinfixative antibodies were demonstrated.

TICK PARALYSIS

Tick paralysis occurs in northwestern United States, southwestern Canada, South Africa, Australia and Crete. Sheep are commonly affected, cattle and dogs less frequently and man and cats occasionally. The disease is usually associated with *Dermacentor andersoni* in North America, *Ixodes holocyclus* in Australia and *Ixodes pilosus* in South Africa, though other species, including *Ixodes ricinus,* *Rhipicephalus simus* and *Dermacentor variabilis,* have been implicated.

The probable cause of the paralysis is a toxic substance secreted by the salivary

---

[10] Hoeppli, R. and Feng, L. C., 1933.   [11] Trager, W., 1939.

glands of the tick rather than a neurotropic virus, since the onset of symptoms, 9 to 16 days after attachment, corresponds to the time of engorgement, and the removal of the ticks permits recovery after paralysis has started. The toxic substance is possibly elaborated by the ovaries. Eggs of the brown tick injected in animals produce similar symptoms, and the female tick loses her toxicity after oviposition.[12] Ticks vary in their toxin-producing ability.

Children are usually affected, adults rarely except occasionally aged individuals. Age immunity apparently depends on the size of the host in relation to the amount of toxic secretion; children under two years of age succumb rapidly. One attack does not confer immunity in dogs.[13] The intoxication is more pronounced when the ticks are attached to the neck or along the spinal column.

The disease is a progressive, ascending, flaccid, motor paralysis. The early symptoms are malaise, lack of appetite, irritability, incoördination, and paralysis of the lower extremities, at times with loss of reflexes. There may be diarrhea, convulsions, and a slight fever or even a subnormal temperature. The paralysis ascends to the muscles of the thorax, deglutition and speech, and also involves the involuntary muscles of the anal and vesicle sphincters. Death results from respiratory paralysis, although most affected persons recover.

The toxin chiefly affects the lower motor neurones of the spinal cord and cranial nerves.[2] No gross changes are observed other than congestion and punctate hemorrhages in the adventitial sheath and around the nerve cells. Microscopically there is extensive destruction of the myelin sheath, an excess of mononuclear cells and some perivascular infiltration.[13]

Treatment of man involves the complete removal of ticks and their capitula by hand. Chloroform or ether applied to the head of the tick facilitates removal. Their removal before the onset of respiratory paralysis ensures recovery.

VECTORS OF DISEASE

Ticks have been recognized as vectors of disease in man and lower animals since 1893, when Smith and Kilbourne discovered that *Boophilus annulatus* transmitted Texas fever in cattle. In many species the causative organisms not only are carried through the metamorphic stages in the tick, but are also transmitted through the eggs to succeeding generations. Diseases transmitted by ticks among domestic animals cause immense financial loss. An incomplete list of the diseases transmitted by ticks to man and lower animals and their vectors is given below.

I. HUMAN DISEASES TRANSMITTED BY TICKS

A. Rickettsial Diseases
   1. Rocky Mountain spotted fever (*R. rickettsi*)
      Dermacentor andersoni, D. occidentalis, D. variabilis (eastern type), and experimentally *D. marginatus* and *Amblyomma americanum*, the United States of America.
   2. Boutonneuse fever
      Rhipicephalus sanguineus, Mediterranean countries.
   3. African tick typhus
      Rhipicephalus sanguineus, R. appendiculatus, Amblyomma hebræum, Boophilus annulatus var. *decoloratus,* and *Hyalomma ægyptium* (experimentally).

---

[12] Regendanz, P. and Reichenow, E., 1931.   [13] Ross, I. C., 1926.

    4. Russian tropical typhus
      Dermacentor nuttalli

    5. São Paulo fever (*R. braziliensis*)
      Amblyomma cajennense, A. striatum and *Rhipicephalus sanguineus,* Brazil.

    6. Montana "Q" fever (*R. diaporica*)
      Dermacentor andersoni, the United States of America

B. Viral Diseases

    1. Equine encephalitis (western strain)
      Dermacentor andersoni (experimentally), the United States of America.

    2. Yellow fever
      Experimentally *Ornithodorus moubata,* Africa and *O. rostratus* and *Amblyomma cajennense,* Brazil.

    3. Spring and summer encephalitis
      Ixodes persulcatus, Dermacentor silvarum and *Hæmaphysalis concinna,* Russia.

    4. Lymphocytic choriomeningitis
      Dermacentor andersoni (experimentally), the United States of America.

    5. Colorado tick fever
      Dermacentor andersoni (suspected), the United States of America.

C. Bacterial and Spirochætal Diseases

    1. Tularemia
      Dermacentor andersoni; D. variabilis, Ixodes ricinus, and *Ornithodorus turicata* and *O. parkeri* (experimentally), the United States of America; species of *Ixodes,* Russia; *Hyalomma ægyptium* (experimentally), Greece.

    2. Relapsing fever (*Borrelia duttoni,* etc.)
      Ornithodorus moubata, southeastern Africa; *O. erraticus,* northern Africa; *O. marocanus,* Spain and Morocco; *O. papillipes,* central and eastern Asia; *O. savignyi,* eastern Asia; *O. venezuelensis* and *O. talaje,* South and Central America and Mexico; *O. turicata,* Mexico and the United States of America; *O. hermsi* and *O. parkeri,* the United States of America; and *Rhipicephalus sanguineus,* Africa.

D. Protozoan Diseases

    1. American trypanosomiasis (*Trypanosoma cruzi*)
      Experimentally *Amblyomma cajennense, Rhipicephalus sanguineus,* and *Ornithodorus moubata* and other species of *Ornithodorus.*

II. DISEASES OF LOWER ANIMALS TRANSMITTED BY TICKS

A. Rickettsial Diseases

    1. Rocky Mountain spotted fever
      Dermacentor andersoni and *Hæmaphysalis leporis-palustris,* the United States of America.

    2. Heartwater disease of sheep, goats and cattle
      Amblyomma hebræum and *A. variegatum,* South Africa.

B. Viral Diseases

    1. Equine encephalitis (western strain)
      Dermacentor andersoni (experimentally), United States of America.

    2. Nairobi sheep disease
      Rhipicephalus appendiculatus and *Amblyomma variegatum,* Africa.

    3. Tick fever of sheep
      Ixodes ricinus

    4. Louping ill of sheep
      Ixodes ricinus and *Rhipicephalus appendiculatus*

    5. Lymphocytic choriomeningitis of rodents
      Dermacentor andersoni (experimentally).

C. Bacterial Diseases

    1. Tularemia
      Hæmaphysalis leporis-palustris, Dermacentor andersoni. D. variabilis and species of *Rhipicephalus* and *Amblyomma* in the United States of America, and species of *Ixodes* in Russia

    2. Spirochætosis of cattle
      Boophilus annulatus var. *decoloratus,* South Africa

3. Spirochætosis of fowls
   Argas persicus
4. Bacterial disease of moose
   Dermacentor albipictus, North America

D. Protozoan Diseases
1. Texas fever of cattle
   Boophilus annulatus, North and South America and Africa; *Rhipicephalus capensis,* South Africa; *R. appendiculatus,* Europe and *Hæmaphysalis punctata* (experimentally), Europe
2. European cattle fever
   Ixodes ricinus and *I. hexagonius,* Europe
3. Piroplasmosis of dogs
   Hæmaphysalis leachi, South Africa; *Rhipicephalus sanguineus,* Asia, Europe, North Africa; *Ixodes ricinus,* Europe, *Dermacentor reticulatus,* Europe; and *Dermacentor andersoni* (experimentally), United States of America
4. Piroplasmosis of jackals and dogs
   Hæmaphysalis bispinosum, India
5. Biliary fever of horses, mules and donkeys
   Rhipicephalus evertsi, Africa and *Dermacentor reticulatus,* Russia
6. Red water fever of sheep
   Rhipicephalus bursa, Ixodes ricinus and *Hæmaphysalis punctata,* Europe
7. Hemoglobinuric fever of sheep and goats
   Rhipicephalus bursa
8. Rhodesian fever
   Rhipicephalus simus, R. capensis, R. evertsi, R. appendiculatus, Dermacentor reticulatus, D. nitens, Hyalomma ægyptium, Africa
9. European hemoglobinuric fever of horses
   Dermacentor reticulatus
10. African hemoglobinuric fever of horses
    Rhipicephalus evertsi, South Africa, and *Rhipicephalus bursa,* Italy
11. Gallsickness of cattle
    Boophilus annulatus var. *decoloratus, Rhipicephalus bursa, R. simus, R. sanguineus, Dermacentor andersoni, D. variabilis, D. occidentalis, D. albipictus, Ixodes ricinus* and *Hyalomma lusitanicum*
12. Anaplasmosis of sheep
    Dermacentor silvarum
13. *Leucocytogregarina canis* of dogs
    Rhipicephalus sanguineus
14. *Eperythrozoon wenyoni* of cattle
    Species of *Hyalomma.*

Relapsing Fever.—Several forms of relapsing fever, a disease of man characterized by recurrent febrile paroxysms, have been described in various parts of the world. They differ in minor features of pathology, serology and transmission, but have closely allied varieties of the spirochæte *Borrelia recurrentis* as etiological agents, present in the blood during the pyrexial stages. Some of these diseases are transmitted by ticks and others by lice. Among the best known agents of tick-borne relapsing fever are *Borrelia duttoni, B. turicata* and *B. venezuelensis.* In man tick-borne relapsing fever develops as a sudden acute illness with high fever that lasts from three to ten days, severe frontal headache, muscular aching, digestive upset, respiratory involvement, leukocytosis and enlarged spleen. Three or four febrile attacks recur at intervals of about a week until immunity is established. The fatality is about 4 per cent.

The spirochætes, when ingested by the tick with the blood meal, pass from the digestive tract and multiply in the tissues. Ticks remain infective for life, *Ornithodorus turicata* transmitting the disease after five years.[1] The spirochætes are discharged from the coxal and salivary glands.[14] Infection usually takes place by contamination of the wound or skin by the coxal secretions. The coxal glands are the chief reservoir for the spirochætes.[15]

Rocky Mountain Spotted Fever.—Rocky Mountain spotted fever is an acute febrile disease of wild rodents transmissible to man and laboratory animals. The two forms of the disease, the western and the eastern, are caused by *Rickettsia rickettsi*. The former, the more severe, occurs chiefly in Montana and Idaho, although it has been found throughout the Western United States. The latter is widely distributed throughout the Eastern United States, but is most prevalent in the Allegheny Mountains. The western type is characterized by an incubational period of five to ten days, an abrupt onset, chill, rapid rise in temperature with morning remissions, and rash over face and trunk. The rash appears on the third or fourth day after the onset, not only on the skin but also on the mucous membranes of the mouth and pharynx. The pathological lesions suggest typhus fever but the vascular changes are more pronounced. The mortality rate is about 10 per cent, but shows wide variations, reaching 90 per cent in certain parts of Montana. One attack confers a moderate degree of immunity. Prophylactic immunization with vaccines confers a high degree of immunity for a limited time.

The western type is transmitted by *Dermacentor andersoni* and the eastern type by *D. variabilis*. *D. marginatus* and *Amblyomma americanum* have been shown to transmit the disease experimentally and *D. occidentalis* has also been implicated. It is spread from animal to animal by *D. andersoni* and *Hæmaphysalis leporis-palustris*. Both male and female adult ticks may infect man. They usually acquire the infection in the larval or nymphal stages. The causative organism lives intracellularly in the tick, and may be transmitted to subsequent generations through the eggs. Only a small percentage of ticks are infected in nature and the number of infected humans, except in certain districts, is small. In these localities the prevention of the disease depends on tick control, protection against tick bites and vaccination.

Other forms of tick-borne rickettsial infections include a number of closely related diseases variously known as exanthematous typhus or São Paulo fever of Brazil, Montana "Q" fever, boutonneuse fever of the Mediterranean littoral, South African tick typhus, Marseilles spotted fever and Russian tropical typhus.

Tularemia.—Tularemia, a disease of lower animals and man, is caused by a plague-like bacterium, *Pasteurella tularensis*. The disease in man is characterized typically by the rapid onset of typhoidal symptoms and the coördinate development of an ulcerating lesion with local adenitis at the site of the infection. The mortality rate is about 5 per cent. In the United States of America 2,200 cases with approximately 150 deaths were reported in 1939. The disease has been observed in a variety of animals, including wild rodents, other wild mammals, domestic animals and game birds.

Most human infections are acquired in handling diseased animals, chiefly rabbits, the organisms entering the body through wounds, superficial abrasions or

---

[14] Feng, L. and Chung, H., 1938.   [15] Bone, G., 1939.

conjunctiva. The organism may also be transmitted from animals to man by the bite of the tick. *Ornithodorus turicata* harbors the organism for 618 days and *O. parkeri* for 509 days.[16] *Dermacentor andersoni* has caused 53 human cases in Montana and surrounding states and *Dermacentor variabilis* 73, principally in the Southern United States. In Russia species of the genus *Ixodes* are the chief vectors. The larvæ and nymphs acquire the infection by feeding on diseased rodents. The organisms persist in the adult tick and may even be transmitted to subsequent generations. Thus larvæ and nymphs may transmit the disease to small mammals and adults to large. The rabbit tick, *Hæmaphysalis leporis-palustris,* is the chief vector in the transmission of the disease from rabbit to rabbit and less frequently to other rodents and birds. Ticks of the genera *Ixodes, Rhipicephalus* and *Amblyomma* are also reported to transmit the disease from rodent to rodent.

PREVENTION

ARGASIDÆ.—Soft ticks are best combated by destroying their nests and lairs. Native huts infested with ticks of the genus *Ornithodorus* should be burned, since these ticks can survive long periods without feeding. If this is not advisable, the walls and floors should be plastered with mud to eliminate crevices, and the floors, walls, ceilings and furniture cleaned and treated with kerosene, crude oil or cresol. Kerosene containing 5 per cent cresol and 5 per cent turpentine has proved effective. The huts may also be fumigated with sulphur. Inmates should avoid sleeping on the floor. The application of hot coal tar to the walls of chicken houses is a common method of controlling *Argas persicus.*

IXODIDÆ.—Hard ticks are most readily limited by controlling their hosts. In areas where small and large animals abound this is almost impossible. Destruction of rodents by trapping, poisoning, shooting, or rendering their habitats unsuitable is sometimes effective, particularly with the meadow mouse, the principal host of the immature *Dermacentor variabilis.* Cutting down or burning bushes and grasses on wild land, cultivation of arable land, and expansion of pasturage reduce the rodent population near human habitations. Sheep grazing is especially effective in destroying vegetation that affords shelter and food for wild rodents. Infested pastures have been freed from the Texas fever tick (*Boophilus annulatus*) by introducing pasture rotation, the ticks dying of starvation within eight months.

The method of control for such ticks as *Dermacentor andersoni* is their destruction on domestic animals. Often the infestational season is relatively short, thus reducing the labor of removal but lessening the effectiveness of this method of control. Ticks may be removed by the application of chemicals by hand or by dipping. Sheep and cattle are usually treated in vats with an arsenical solution (arsenic trioxide 8 lbs., sodium carbonate 24 lbs., pure tar 2 gal. and water 500 gal.). Sprays of kerosene or crude petroleum are also used. Dogs may best be freed from *Dermacentor variabilis* by applying powdered or liquid derris root or some commercial preparation containing its active principal, rotenone, which destroys adherent ticks and for a short time prevents reinfection. The powder is easier to apply but is less

---

[16] Davis, G. E., 1940.

effective than the wash (soap 1 oz., derris powder 2 to 4 oz., water 1 gal.). The powder should be applied at intervals of two to three days and the wash every five to six days. Coal-tar creosote and the standard arsenical dip, used for cattle, may be used for dogs but is less effective than derris powder.

Men traversing tick-infested areas should use tick-proof clothing and afterward should search carefully for and remove attached ticks. In removing ticks care should be taken not to squeeze the parasite or tear off the imbedded capitulum.

The natural enemies of ticks are a small, parasitic, hymenopteric insect, *Ixodiphagus caucurtei* that deposits its eggs on the nymph of *Dermacentor andersoni*, *Hunterellus hcokeri* that likewise develops in the nymphs of *Dermacentor variabilis*, and the chalis fly, birds and mice, which devour engorged ticks.

REFERENCES

BARNETT, E. J. Wood Tick Paralysis in Children, J. Am. M. Ass., 1937, 109:846.

BISHOPP, F. C. and SMITH, C. N. The American Dog Tick, Eastern Carrier of Rocky Mountain Spotted Fever, U. S. Dept. Agric., 1938, Circ. 478, 25 pp.

BRUMPT, E., MAZZOTTI, L. and BRUMPT, L. C. Étude epidemologique de la fiévre récurrente endémique des hauts plateaux mexicains, Ann. de parasitol., 1939, 17:275.

HAMILTON, D. G. Tick Paralysis; a Dangerous Disease in Children, M. J. Australia, 1940, 1:759.

HUNTER, W. D. and BISHOPP, F. C. The Rocky Mountain Spotted Fever Tick, U. S. Dept. Agric. Bur. Ent., 1911, Bull. No. 105.

NUTTALL, G. H. F., WARBURTON, C., COOPER, W. F. and ROBINSON, L. E. Ticks, a Monograph of the Ixodoidea, 1908. Part I. Argasidæ, pp. 1-104, 1911. Part II. Classification of the Genus Ixodes, pp. 105-348, 1915. Part III. The Genus Hæmaphysalis, pp. 349-550, 1926. Part IV. The Genus Amblyomma, pp. 1-302, Cambridge, England.

STILES, C. W. The Taxonomic Value of the Microscopic Structure of the Stigmal Plates in the Tick Genus *Dermacentor*, U. S. Hyg. Lab., 1910, Bull. No. 62, 72 pp.

TRAGER, W. Acquired Immunity to Ticks, J. Parasitol., 1939, 25:57.

——— Further Observations on Acquired Immunity to the Tick *Dermacentor variabilis* Say., J. Parasitol., 1939, 25:137.

ZEBROWSKI, G. A Preliminary Report on the Morphology of the American Dog Tick, Tr. Am. Ent. Soc., 1926, 51:331.

Chapter XLIX

THE PARASITIC MITES

The term, mite, is usually applied to members of the order ACARINA other than the IXODOIDEA or ticks. Most of these minute free-living or parasitic arthropods lead a varied terrestrial or aquatic existence, particularly those of the temperate zones. The parasitic species infest numerous forms of plant and animal life and manifest all types of parasitism. Some cause direct injury to man and others transmit human diseases. Although certain species are localized, their distribution in general is worldwide.

MORPHOLOGY

The many species, though differing greatly in size and morphology, have certain common characteristics. Their structure in general resembles that of the ticks. The head region or capitulum is hinged to the body as a movable base for the mouth parts, which comprise two mandibles, two jointed pedipalps and a median hypostome. Two or more simple eyes may be present but never on the capitulum. The four pairs of legs, usually six-jointed, are attached to the ventral surface of the fused cephalothorax.

The digestive tract comprises a foregut, a large thin-walled stomach or midgut with a bifurcated diverticulum, and a hindgut. The foregut is subdivided into a buccal cavity, a pharynx or pumping organ and an esophagus. The hindgut terminates in a sacculate rectum, which receives the malpighian tubules. There are paired salivary glands, a nervous system, a single-chambered heart, and two external spiracles. The female genitalia include a single ovary with ducts, uterus, vagina and Gené's organ, the secretions of which are supposed to prevent premature drying of eggs. The male genitalia comprise a single testis, seminal vesicle and ejaculatory duct. There is no penial organ; the spermatozoa in the form of spermatophores are introduced into the vagina by the male capitulum.

HABITS

Mites are most numerous in the temperate zones, from 300 to 500 species being present in some localities. Some species are destructive to plant life. A special migratory stage has developed in the life cycle of the TYROGLYPHIDÆ and PARASITIDÆ. The most primitive species are found in caves. Most species are free-living but some are parasitic. The parasitic habit appears to have developed independently in those families which have both free-living and parasitic species. The free-living forms that inhabited the nests of small animals and fed on the decaying organic matter, gradually acquired the habit of feeding on the animal itself. Some species use insects as a means of transportation and a source of food. General rather than specific host-specificity seems to be the rule. Mites are most frequently ectoparasites of the skin, mucous membranes and feathers, but a few are tissue parasites.

LIFE CYCLE

During metamorphosis mites usually pass through four stages: egg, larva, nymph and adult. The larval form has three pairs of legs, the nymph four and the adult four and also sexual organs. The eggs are deposited in soil or on the skin of the host. The larval forms feed upon blood or plant juices. Some become parasitic upon birds and animals.

CLASSIFICATION

The following superfamilies contain mites that are either directly injurious to man or serve as vectors of human disease: (1) TROMBIDOIDEA, (2) PARASITOIDEA, (3) TARSONEMOIDEA, (4) TYROGLYPHOIDEA, (5) SARCOPTOIDEA, and (6) DEMODICOIDEA.

SUPERFAMILY *TROMBIDOIDEA*

The family TROMBIDIIDÆ alone contains species of medical interest. Members of the genus *Trombicula,* variously known as harvest mites, red bugs or chiggers, are annoying pests. They are usually bright red but may be ornamented with red, orange or black spots. The body, thickly covered with minute hairs, is divided by a constriction into two distinct parts, the cephalothorax with the mouth parts and the two anterior pairs of legs, and the longer abdomen with the two posterior pairs. The palps have an accessory finger-like appendage. Though usually minute, some species attain a length of 1.25 mm.

The adults are mainly predaceous, feeding upon other arthropods or decaying vegetable matter, but the six-legged larvæ are bloodsucking parasites of animals. Their hosts are rodents, turtles, snakes, and less frequently larger mammals including man. The larvæ emerge from small brown eggs laid on the ground, crawl on the animal hosts for their blood meal, and then drop to the ground, where after one or two molts they become nymphs and finally adults. Three species are of medical significance: (1) *Trombicula alfreddugèsi* (*irritans*), (2) *T. autumnalis* and (3) *T. akamushi.*

Trombicula alfreddugèsi.—The North American chigger or red bug commonly infests grasses and bushes, particularly blackberry, whence it attacks animals and man. The adult form, known as *Trombicula cinnabaris* (Fig. 271C) is a scavenger living on the feces of insects and decaying woody substances.[1] It is an orange-red mite, about the size of the head of a pin, which lives for about ten months, requires abundant moisture and probably has one generation per year. The larva, a six-legged red mite about one-fifth the size of the adult, attacks man. It frequents regions of wild brush or blackberries, where it lives on the ground. It is found from New Jersey south on the Atlantic coast and in the central, northern and western parts of the United States of America.

The larvæ like ticks attach themselves to the skin by the capitulum and after their blood meal drop off in three to five days. They select the thin, tender wrinkled cutaneous surfaces, such as the popliteal region and waist, passing actively up the legs but seldom going above the waist. Women and children are more susceptible than men. Attachment takes place a few hours after exposure.

---

[1] Ewing, H. E., 1925.

Itching, increasing in intensity to a maximum on the second day, begins the latter part of the first 24 hours. During the second day the swelling subsides and a light pinkish color, which gradually turns to a deep red by the third day, surrounds the puncture point. Vesicles frequently occur. The discoloration disappears about the seventh day. Severe infestations may produce fever and nervous symptoms. The patient suffers extreme discomfort and torture with attendant loss of sleep. Treatment includes bathing the

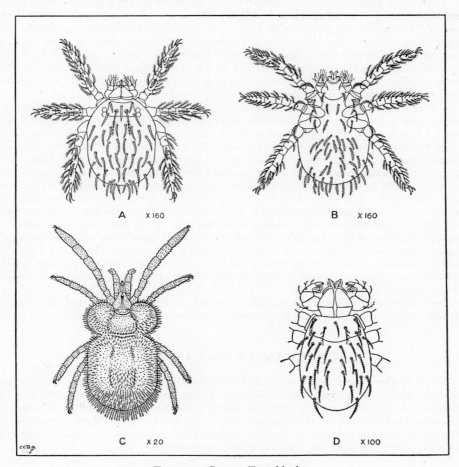

FIG. 271.—GENUS *Trombicula*

A, Trombicula akamushi larva, dorsal view; *B, T. akamushi* larva, ventral view; *C, T. alfreddugèsi* (North American chigger) adult; *D, T. alfreddugèsi* larva, dorsal view (legs omitted) (*A* and *B* redrawn from Nagayo *et al.*, 1921; *C* redrawn from Ewing, 1925; *D* redrawn from Ewing, 1921).

affected parts with alcohol, or applying a thick lather of soap or sulphur ointment. Ammonia, baking soda, weak alcoholic solution of iodine, camphor, or a saturated solution of salicylic acid in alcohol with a little sweet oil have been used as palliatives. The mite may be removed with a needle.

Protection against chiggers requires closely-woven clothing with tight-fitting edges to prevent entry of the mite. High shoes, boots or puttees afford protection. Repellents, such as powdered sulphur dusted on the legs, are also useful.[2] Breeding grounds may be destroyed by clearing underbrush to reduce moisture, by cultivation and by sheep grazing.

Trombicula autumnalis.—The harvest mite of Europe at times has been a serious annoyance to harvesters of certain crops. Allied species have caused similar trouble in various parts of the world. This pest probably represents the larvæ of several species.

Trombicula akamushi.—The Kedani mite of Japan (Fig. 271A and B) is an orange-red, hairy, larval mite about 400 μ in length. The adults, about 1 mm. in length, live in the soil. The larvæ are parasites of field mice, particularly *Microtus montebelli.* They infest these rodents, especially about the ears, suck blood for three or four days, and then fall to the ground where they undergo metamorphosis into nymphs and finally non-parasitic adults. Species of *Trombicula* are prevalent in Japan, Malaya, Formosa, China, the East Indies, Samoa and South Australia. Man is an accidental host, the larva attaching itself to the axillary or inguinal regions of field laborers.

Of the five Japanese species *T. akamushi* alone attacks man and is a proved vector of tsutsugamushi disease or Japanese river fever, an acute exanthematous disease that resembles typhus.[3] The disease, caused by *Rickettsia nipponica,* occurs in the river valleys, where its natural reservoir is the field mouse. The larvæ become infected by feeding on diseased mice. The organisms can pass from one generation of mites to the next, so that larvæ of the second generation are still capable of infecting man. The bite of an infected larva is marked by a painless ulcer with an accompanying enlargement of the neighboring lymph glands, followed within two weeks by sudden fever, chills and headache. The disease is characterized by a remittent fever, generalized lymphadenitis, splenomegaly, and a bright red eruption that spreads from the face to the chest and extremities, and usually disappears within ten days. Mortality is high, ranging from 15 to 60 per cent in Japan, though much lower in the Malay Archipelago. No specific treatment has so far been discovered. *T. akamushi* and other species of *Trombicula* that are parasites of mice and rats are believed to be the vectors of this or similar diseases in Formosa, Sumatra, China, Malaya and Samoa.

Preventive measures involve the extermination of the rodent host and the protection of field workers by high leather boots. Both, unfortunately, are economically impractical.

SUPERFAMILY *PARASITOIDEA*

Small, leathery mites, often with coriaceous shields and sternal plates; venter without furrows; eyes absent; hypostome small without recurrent teeth or absent; usually stylate cheliceræ; five-jointed palps; spiracles on lateral chitinous plates; parasites of vertebrates and invertebrates. Among the families are: UROPODIDÆ, free-living and parasites of arthropods; PARASITIDÆ, free-living and parasites of vertebrates and invertebrates; and DERMANYSSIDÆ, parasites of reptiles, birds and mammals.

FAMILY *DERMANYSSIDÆ*

The members of the family DERMANYSSIDÆ have edentate often stylate or needle-like cheliceræ and weakly chitinous plates. Species of the genera *Dermanyssus* and *Liponyssus* are injurious to man.

The chicken mite, *Dermanyssus gallinæ,* a serious pest of poultry, sometimes attacks man. It hides in crevices of chicken houses during the day and at night sucks the blood of fowls. Its bite causes an itching dermatitis in poultrymen, usually on the backs of the hands and forearms. Petrolatum containing 1 per cent phenolized camphor allays the

---

[2] Ewing, H. E., 1921.

[3] Nagayo, M., Miyagawa, Y., Mitamura, T., Tamiya, T. and Tenjin, S., 1921.

itching. Powdered sulphur or sulphur fumigation effectively controls these pests in chicken houses. Painting roosts with crude petroleum is also effective.

The rat mite, *Liponyssus bacoti* (Fig. 272), is prevalent in warm countries, including the Southern United States. It requires four blood meals to complete its life cycle. Its bites produce a vesicular dermatitis with urticaria in workers in stores, factories, warehouses and stockyards. Subsequent scratching, particularly in children, may cause secondary infection. Local treatment is the same as for *D. gallinæ*. It serves as a vector for the transmission of endemic typhus from rat to rat.[4] The rickettsial organisms are passed from one generation to the next through the eggs. Other species of *Liponyssus* are parasites of fowls and rats. *L. nagayoi*, a parasite of rats and man in the Far East, is a potential vector of bubonic plague.

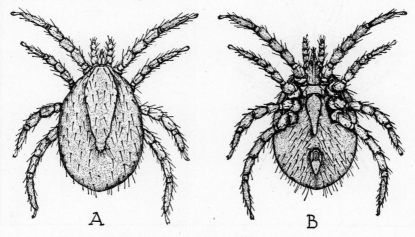

Fig. 272.—*Liponyssus bacoti*, THE TROPICAL RAT MITE

A, female, dorsal view; *B*, female, ventral view (×50) (After Dove and Shelmire, 1932, from Hegner, Root, Augustine and Huff, *Parasitology*, 1938, D. Appleton-Century Company).

SUPERFAMILY *TARSONEMOIDEA*

Soft-bodied mites with needle-like chelicerae and minute palpi; body divided into cephalothorax and abdomen; ventral suckers absent; spiracles on ventral surface; two posterior pairs of short legs near end of body; anterior tarsi terminate in a single claw, other tarsi often in two claws and a sucker; abdomen in a few species slightly segmented; anus terminal; a few simple hairs on body and legs; small elongate genital opening between fourth coxæ. Many species are destructive parasites of plants and insects. The two most important families are the TARSONEMIDÆ, chiefly parasites of plants and the PEDICULOIDIDÆ, parasites of insects and plants.

FAMILY *PEDICULOIDIDÆ*

The hind legs of the female end in two claws and a sucker, the stout hind legs of the male are shorter than the third pair, and the female is usually ovoviviparous, whereas in the TARSONEMIDÆ the hind legs of the female terminate in two long hairs, those of the male are as long as the third pair, and the female is usually oviparous. Species of the genus *Pediculoides* produce dermatitis among workers in the grain-producing countries of Europe, Asia, Africa and North America.

---

[4] Dove, W. E. and Shelmire, B., 1932.

Pediculoides ventricosus.—The North American "grain itch" mite, feeds upon the larvæ of insects that infest wheat, barley, rye, other grains and straw. The short, oval male (Fig. 273B), 125 μ in length, has an abbreviated abdomen that terminates in an angulate sucker. The unfertilized female (Fig. 273A), 250 μ in length, is elliptiform with a long abdomen. The female is viviparous, and from 200 to 300 young develop to sexual maturity within the abdomen, which expands like an inflated balloon until the enlarged mite, 1.5 mm. in size, resembles a white, spherical grain.[5]

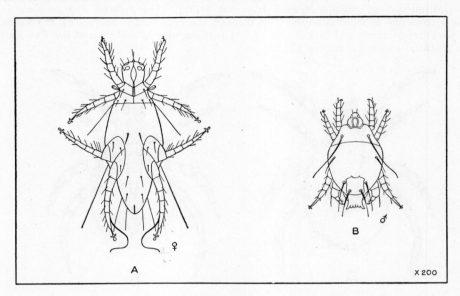

FIG. 273.—*Pediculoides ventricosus*

A, unfertilized female, ventral view; *B,* male, dorsal view (Redrawn from Banks, 1904).

The mites, frequently in large numbers, attack the entire surface of the human body. Threshers, grain-handlers and persons sleeping on straw mattresses are subject to infestation. The mites burrow superficially in the skin, producing local petechiæ and erythema followed by wheals, vesicles and pustules. Unlike the SARCOPTIDÆ, they soon leave the skin. They cause an annoying pruritus, sometimes accompanied in severe cases by sweating and fever. Local applications of warm water and mild antiseptics relieve irritation and prevent secondary infection. Preventive measures include: (1) the avoidance of infested grain and straw, (2) the burning of infested straw mattresses and stubble, and (3) the immediate threshing of grain after harvesting.

SUPERFAMILY *TYROGLYPHOIDEA*

Small, pale-colored, soft-bodied, stout mites devoid of tracheæ and usually without eyes; prominent chelceræ and small palpi; cephalothorax and abdomen usually differentiated; abdomen without true segmentation; few, mostly long hairs on the dorsum; tarsi ending in a claw and often a sucker; anus subterminal; a clavate hair near base of the tarsi of first two pairs of legs; elongate genital aperture between hind coxæ with the two U-shaped marks on each side; small copulatory aperture behind anus.

[5] Banks, N., 1915.

Of the several genera *Glyciphagus* (Fig. 274C) and *Tyroglyphus* (Fig. 274A and B) are of medical interest. The genus *Glyciphagus* has a finely-granular dorsal integument, small weak claws, feathered body hairs, large ventral aperture, no ventral suckers in the male and a copulatory bursa in the female situated at the tip of the abdomen. The genus *Tyroglyphus* has a nongranular dorsal integument, distinct claws, no prominent feathered hairs and a small ventral aperture.

The life cycle is somewhat involved. In certain species the nymph enters a hypopal or migratory stage. The **hypopus** (Fig. 274D) is a distinct creature with a hard chitinous body, no mouth orifice, short legs, and usually a ventral plate of sucking disks for attachment or less often a longitudinal groove for clinging to the hairs of small mammals. The sucking disks permit attachment to insects or small mammals and thus enable the hypopus to invade new breeding grounds where it molts into an octopod nymph.[6]

The cheese mites feed on such dried vegetable food products as cheese, sugar, flour, cereals, dried fruits, seeds and hay; a few on hair, feathers and insects. Other species live in the nests of mice and ants; in decaying bark, vegetable matter and roots; and are destructive to cultivated flowers and plants. They are rapid breeders, infest masses of stored food, and are most abundant in warm climates. Species of the genus *Tyroglyphagus* are the most numerous.

A few species occasionally infest man. Although not bloodsuckers, they produce a temporary pruritus by penetrating under the superficial scales of the epidermis. *Glyciphagus domestica* of Europe and other species of this genus that infest sugar, *Tyroglyphus siro* of cheese, *T. longior* of cheese and cereals, and *T. farinæ* of flour, grains, cheese and stored foods are considered responsible for "grocers' itch." *T. siro* or similar species cause "vanillism" in workers handling vanilla pods; a species resembling *T. longior* "copra itch" in those handling copra;[7] and *Rhizoglyphus parasiticus* "coolie itch," an affliction of the feet among coolies in the tea plantations of India. Bathing the affected parts with a kerosene-soapsuds mixture is recommended. Cheese mites are frequently swallowed and both the mites and their eggs are found in human feces. It is doubtful if they cause intestinal trouble, though a transient diarrhea from *T. longior* has been reported.[8]

Tyroglyphids are difficult to destroy. Since they have no trachea prolonged fumigation is required. Destruction of infested material is often the only effective method. The predaceous mites *Cheyletus* and *Parasitus* are their natural enemies.

SUPERFAMILY *SARCOPTOIDEA*

The superfamily SARCOPTOIDEA contains five families parasitic on animals: (1) LISTROPHORIDÆ, the hair-clasping mites of small mammals, (2) ANALGESIDÆ, the feather mites of birds, (3) CYTOLEICHIDÆ, parasites of the tissues of birds, (4) CANESTRINIIDÆ parasites of insects, and (5) SARCOPTIDÆ, the itch and mange mites of man, other mammals and birds.

FAMILY *SARCOPTIDÆ*

The itch and mange mites are of medical and veterinary importance. These minute, globular, white mites have a finely-striated integument adorned with bristles; two widely separated groups of legs; tarsi usually ending in a stout pair of claws, often in a terminal sucker or hair; and a prominent capitulum with three-jointed palpi and two-jointed serrated cheliceræ. Most of the ten genera are nonburrowing mites that produce a many-layered scab by irritation. The genus *Sarcoptes,* however, causes itch or mange by burrowing into the skin of man and other mammals, while the genus *Notædres* produces similar lesions in cats and rodents.

---

[6] Banks, N., 1904.
[7] Hirst, S., 1912.

[8] Hinman, E. H. and Kampmeier, R. H., 1934.

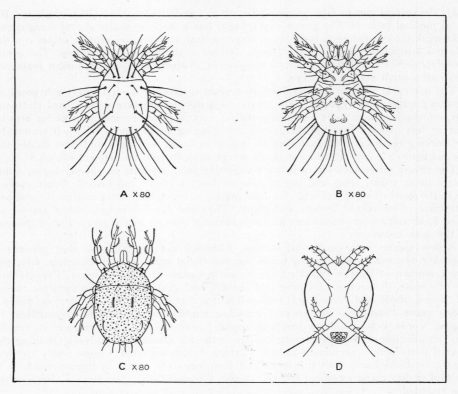

FIG. 274.—GENERA *Tyroglyphus* AND *Glyciphagus*

A, Tyroglyphus longior, dorsal view; *B, T. longior,* ventral view; *C, Glyciphagus obesus* (nonpathogenic); *D,* hypopus of *Tyroglyphus,* ventral view (*A* and *B* redrawn from Hirst, 1912; *C* and *D* redrawn from Banks, 1904).

GENUS *SARCOPTES*

Soft-bodied, oviparous mites; anus terminal; long unjointed ambulacra on the two anterior pairs of legs in the female and also on the last posterior pair in the male; mouth parts free; vulva transverse. The numerous parasitic species of animals occasionally infest man, but *Sarcoptes scabiei* is responsible for human scabies.

SARCOPTES SCABIEI

Scabies was described as early as the sixteenth century, and the cause of the disease was definitely established by 1835. Since that time numerous additions to our knowledge of the causative parasite, *Sarcoptes scabiei,* have been made.

Geographical Distribution.—Cosmopolitan. The parasite is especially prevalent in the poorer urban populations.

Morphology.—*Sarcoptes scabiei* Latreille, 1806, is a small, oval, dorsally convex, ventrally flattened, translucent, dirty white, eyeless mite. The male, 200 to 250 μ, is smaller than the female, 330 to 450 μ. The body is divided into an anterior **notothorax** bearing the first two pairs of legs and a posterior **notogaster** bearing the second two pairs. The finely-striated integument is ornamented dorsally with cones, spines, acorn-shaped scales and bristles of taxonomic importance except a clear rectangular space or **plastron** on the notothorax and small areas on the noto-gaster of the male (Fig. 275A and C). On the ventral surface supporting chitinous bars, **epimeres,** differing in arrangement in the sexes, extend inward from the legs (Fig. 275B and D). The larger first two pairs of chitinous legs bear two terminal claws and one trochanteric claw, and terminate in long tubular processes with a bell-shaped sucker, **ambulacra.** The smaller second two pairs of legs of the female terminate in long bristles, but the last pair in the male bear ambulacra. The mouth parts consist of toothed cheliceræ, three-jointed conical pedipalps and labial palps fused to the hypostome. A transverse slit, the **tocostome** or egg-bearing aperture of the female, lies posterior to the end of the sternal bar formed by the epimeres of the first legs (Fig. 275D). The male genital aperture, between the fourth pair of legs, is guarded by a chitinous inverted Y-shaped structure (Fig. 275B).

Habits.—Copulation occurs on the surface of the skin. The male usually dies soon afterward, but may survive for several weeks in the tunnels excavated by the female. The fertilized female immediately starts excavating a sinuous inward-sloping burrow in the epidermis, completely burying herself in two and one half minutes.[9] Burrowing proceeds at the rate of 2 to 3 mm. per day, usually at night when the parasite is activated by warmth. The burrow (Fig. 275E) which may extend to 3 cm. in length, is confined to the corneous layer of the skin. At intervals there may be holes for air or for the egress of larvæ and nymphs. The female continues to lay eggs during her life span of four or five weeks, depositing two to four at a time as she excavates her burrow. She may lay from 40 to 50 eggs, though rarely more than 20 are found in the burrow. The male excavates lateral branches or pockets in the burrows.

Life Cycle.—The transparent, oval eggs, 150 by 100 μ, are laid in various stages of development. Incubation may require ten days, but usually is from 64 to 76 hours.[10] The life cycle from egg to adult is from 8 to 15 days. The female differs from the male in having two nymphal stages. The six-legged larvæ live in the burrow, bore into its floor or emerge to burrow in the outside skin. The larva (Fig. 275F), 110 to 140 μ in length, has indistinct dorsal scales and posterior legs ending in bristles. The first nymph, 160 μ in length, has a fourth pair of legs shorter than the third. The second nymph, 220 to 250 μ in length, resembles the adult female except for the tocostome. It excavates burrows smaller than those of the adult.

Pathogenesis.—The preferential sites are between the fingers and toes, the flexor surfaces of the forearm, shoulder blades, small of back, the inguinal region and the genitalia. The lesions appear as slightly reddish elevated tracts on the surface of the skin. Minute, translucent, vesicular swellings, possibly produced by the irritating fecal deposits or excretions, form beneath the gallery a short distance behind the mite. The intense itching, aggravated by warmth and perspiration, causes scratching, which spreads the parasite, irritates the lesions, and induces secondary bacterial infection. As a result multiple papular, vesicular and pustular

---

[9] Munro, J. W., 1919.   [10] Warburton, C., 1920.

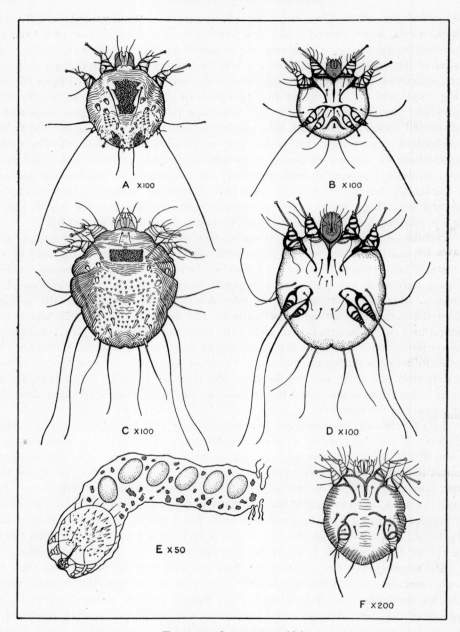

FIG. 275.—*Sarcoptes scabiei*

A, male, dorsal view; *B*, male, ventral view; *C*, female, dorsal view; *D*, female, ventral view; *E*, female with eggs in burrow; *F*, hexapod larva, ventral view (*A* to *D* redrawn from Munro, 1919; *E*, redrawn from Banks, 1904; *F*, redrawn from Blanchard, 1890).

lesions may be produced. Unless treated, a chronic condition may ensue, and severe infestations may prove a serious health hazard.

Diagnosis.—The type and distribution of the lesions are characteristic. Conclusive evidence is obtained by removing the mite from its burrow with a needle.

Treatment.—The standard treatment of scabies is the application of some form of sulphur ointment. After a preliminary scrubbing with tincture of green soap and prolonged soaking of the body in warm water to open the tunnels, a 5 per cent sulphur ointment or the Danish ointment (Section **VII**, XIII, 35) is thoroughly rubbed on the skin and allowed to remain overnight. The patient after a bath puts on clean clothing, and all soiled garments and bed linen are boiled. Since the eggs are not killed, treatment should be repeated in six to ten days, occasionally as many as six times, in order to kill the newly hatched larvæ.

Prevention.—Infection usually occurs from intimate personal contact especially persons sleeping together, less frequently from towels, clothing and bed linen. Except for the form of scabies known as the Norwegian itch, infectivity is relatively low, since transmission from slightly-infected individuals is infrequent and, if successful, tends to run a limited course in healthy individuals of cleanly habits. The itch mite thrives amid filth, where personal hygiene is neglected. It is common, therefore, in slum sections, jails and armies. Prevention requires the treatment of infected individuals, the sterilization of garments and bedding, and personal cleanliness.

SUPERFAMILY *DEMODICOIDEA*

The superfamily DEMODICOIDEA contains but one family, DEMODICIDÆ, and one genus, *Demodex,* species of which are parasites of the sebaceous glands and hair follicles of mammals. They produce mange in dogs and tubercules in the skin of hogs and cattle.

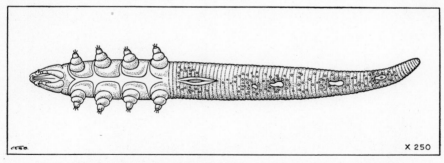

FIG. 276.—SCHEMATIC REPRESENTATION OF FEMALE *Demodex folliculorum*

DEMODEX FOLLICULORUM

Demodex folliculorum, a parasite of the hair follicles and sebaceous glands of man has a cosmopolitan distribution.

Morphology.—It is an elongate cylindrical mite with four pairs of short three-jointed legs, a short median sucking capitulum, and a long tapering transversely striated abdomen with rounded tip (Fig. 276). The female, 400 by 40 μ, has a long vulva at the base of the abdominal venter. The male rarely exceeds 300 μ in length and is correspondingly slender.

Habits.—The adult mites burrow head downward in the hair follicles and the sebaceous glands, where they may group themselves in clusters, sometimes numbering 200 or more.

Life Cycle.—The fusiform eggs hatch into hexapod larvæ that molt into octopod nymphs, which after two molts become adults.

Pathogenesis.—The parasites rarely cause discomfort. Occasionally they manifest their presence in "black heads" and when unusually numerous may cause a dry chronic erythema with burning irritation and scaling of the epidermis.[11] An ointment, consisting of beta-naphthol 4 gm., sublimated sulphur 8 gm., balsam of Peru 30 ml., and petrolatum 30 gm., is recommended.

REFERENCES

BANKS, N. The Acarina or Mites, U. S. Dept. Agric. Bur. Ent. Rep. No. 108, 1915, 153 pp.

DOVE, W. E. and SHELMIRE, B. Some Observations on the Tropical Rat Mites and Endemic Typhus, J. Parasitol., 1932, 18:159.

EWING, H. E. Studies on the Biology and Control of Chiggers, U. S. Dept. Agric. Bur. Ent., Bull. No. 986, 1921, 19 pp.

MUNRO, J. W. Report of Scabies Investigation, J. Roy. Army M. Corps, 1919, 33:1.

NAGAYO, M., MIYAGAWA, Y., MITAMURA, T., TAMIYA, T. and TENJIN, S. Five Species of Tsutsugamushi (the Carrier of Japanese River Fever) and Their Relation to the Tsutsugamushi Disease, Am. J. Hyg., 1921, 1:569.

WARBURTON, C. Sarcoptic Scabies in Man and Animals, Parasitology, 1920, 12:265.

[11] Ayres, S. and Anderson, N. P., 1932.

TECHNICAL METHODS FOR THE DIAGNOSIS AND TREATMENT OF PARASITIC INFECTIONS

In the following pages the ordinary technical methods employed in the diagnosis and treatment of parasitic infections have been grouped into 13 sections for ready reference by laboratory workers and physicians.

I. EQUIPMENT FOR THE STUDY OF PARASITES

The microscopical study of parasites, both in the living state and in stained preparations, and the proper preparation of such material for examination are requisite for the identification of parasites.

APPARATUS

Certain pieces of apparatus are essential, and others increase the accuracy and ease of examination. The following equipment will usually suffice for the diagnosis of the common parasitic infections:

Microscope equipped with 5 and 10 oculars; 32, 16, 4 and 1.8 mm. objectives; mechanical stage; day-light lamp; dark-field substage condenser; and stage and ocular micrometers.

Apparatus:

Slides, 3 x 1 inch	Hand lens	Hæmocytometer
Cover-glasses No. 1	Dissecting needles	Alcohol lamp
Watch glasses	Platinum loop	Centrifuge
Test tubes	Wide-mouth bottles, 1 oz.	Capillary pipettes

Chemicals:

Alcohol	Sodium chloride	Basic fuchsin
Carbolic acid	Sodium hydroxide	Gentian violet
Formalin	Xylene	Methylene blue
Glycerol	Iodine	Wright's or Giemsa's stain

Slides and Cover-glasses.—Slides for microscopical work should be made of plain, clear, noncorrosive, colorless glass. The cover-glasses should not exceed 0.2 mm. in thickness. Fresh material may be examined on a slide with or without a cover-glass. In order to remove oily material the slides and cover-glasses are placed in a cleaning fluid composed of potassium bichromate one part, water four parts, and concentrated sulphuric acid six parts. They are then rinsed thoroughly in water, dipped in alcohol, and wiped dry with a cloth free from lint.

MICROSCOPY

It is assumed that the reader is familiar with the construction and use of the compound microscope and with the principles of ordinary microscopical technic. If not, he may obtain this information from any of several textbooks on microscopy or from the excellent pamphlets supplied by manufacturers of these instruments. The lower objectives (32 and 16 mm.) permit rapid examination of the material, while the 4 mm. lens is used to give greater detail. The student should accustom himself to using the hand lens or dissecting microscope for examining adult parasites. The oil immersion lens (1.8 mm.) is used principally for examining smears of blood, fluids or tissues. The warm stage is an advantage in examining the vegetative forms of Protozoa.

DARK FIELD

The dark field microscope is a valuable aid, though infrequently used, in the study of Protozoa. Light is introduced into the microscopical field at an angle, instead of directly, by means of a special substage condenser that permits only the marginal rays from the mirror to reach the object. The parasite stands out as a white or brilliant object on a dark background. The source of light must be powerful, either an arc lamp, preferably with a mechanical feed, or an incandescent nitrogen-filled lamp of at least 100 watts. If the oil immersion objective is used, a special stop is inserted in the objective to avoid excessive diffusion of light.

In using the dark field microscope all equipment must be scrupulously clean and the cover-glasses and slides thin and clear. The preparation should be thinly spread, free from bubbles and covered with a cover-glass. The dark-field condenser is centered under low power so that the ring etched on its upper surface is concentric with the circumference of the microscopical field. If the oil immersion objective is used, cedar oil must be placed between the condenser and the under surface of the slide and between the lens and the cover-glass before the object can be brought into proper focus. Bubbles in the drops of oil interfere with clear definition.

MEASUREMENTS

The unit of measurement for microscopical objects is the micron, which is one-thousandth of a millimeter. The simplest device for measuring in this unit is the ocular micrometer, a scale etched on a glass disk which fits into the ocular of the microscope. The scale consists of a number of equal linear divisions or sometimes of a large square subdivided into smaller squares. The ocular micrometer is standardized by means of the stage micrometer, which consists of an etched scale accurately divided into tenths and hundredths of a millimeter mounted on a slide. By superimposing the ocular scale on the true scale of the stage micrometer the exact value of each subdivision of the ocular micrometer may be determined for the several objectives at the standard length of the draw tube of the microscope. If the operator desires, he may vary the length of the draw tube, thus changing the magnification, so that even numbers represent each division of the ocular micrometer, but he must be sure to keep the draw tube always at the corrected length when making measurements. Special filar screw micrometers, which have movable and fixed wires regulated by a graduated drum, record more accurate readings.

Measurements may be made with the aid of the camera lucida, which is used for drawing purposes, the image of the object being projected upon a scale previously made by projecting the divisions of the stage micrometer. For very accurate work a micro-projection apparatus is necessary. A strong light, preferably that of an arc lamp, is passed through the microscope in such a manner that the image of the specimen under examination is projected upon a screen at a definite magnification or upon a scale previously made by projecting the divisions of the stage micrometer.

It should be kept in mind that Protozoa, protozoan cysts, and helminthic ova and larvæ of the individual species vary considerably in size, and cannot always be differentiated by size alone. It is well to know the approximate dimensions, but it should be remembered that the living animal may show great variation in different strains and in different stages, and that in fixed preparations the shape and size may be modified.

PSEUDOPARASITES IN HUMAN FECES

Coprozoic Protozoa.—Free-living Protozoa that live in fecal material are known as coprozoic species. They either reach the feces already passed from the human body or are swallowed as cysts and pass unchanged through the alimentary tract to hatch after leaving the body. They may be confused with parasitic Protozoa. A safe rule to follow is that motile trophozoites in old feces or in specimens kept warm and moist belong to coprozoic species.

Miscellaneous Objects.—Various objects in the feces may be mistaken for intestinal Protozoa and helminthic ova. Figure 277 shows some of the animal and plant cells and artifacts that may confuse the inexperienced observer. The intestinal yeasts and fungi furnish perhaps the greatest source of confusion. The ovoid yeast cell, from 2 to 8 μ in size, may assume various shapes during budding. It has a thick capsular outline, a large vacuole in the protoplasm, and a nucleus. Species of *Monilia* have elongate forms with vacuoles and chromatin. *Blastocystis hominis,* a harmless intestinal parasite, ranging from 2 to 35 μ but usually from 9 to 16 μ, is the form most frequently mistaken for protozoan cysts. It has a small spherical central mass, a relatively thick outer protoplasm and a thin cell membrane. It multiplies by binary fission and by exogenous and endogenous budding.

Vegetable cells from food are of all shapes and sizes and may resemble cysts. Their thick cellulose walls and striations aid in their identification. Pollen grains may be recognized by their capsular markings, micropyles, and coloring.

Epithelial and squamous cells, leukocytes, and particularly large endothelial macrophages with ingested erythrocytes may be mistaken for Protozoa. The macrophage has a large prominent eccentric nucleus and vacuolated cytoplasm. Squamous cells are flat, have a central nucleus, and small bright granules in the protoplasm.

Extraneous materials, even air bubbles and oil globules, have been mistaken for cysts. Starch granules are of various forms but usually are marked by concentric rings. Mucus may assume all manner of shapes, but lacks a smooth even contour. Partially saponified fat globules may be misleading.

II. DIRECT EXAMINATION OF PROTOZOA FROM THE GASTRO-INTESTINAL TRACT

The laboratory worker should be familiar with the proper methods of obtaining, preparing and examining material for the diagnosis of protozoan infections. Whenever practical, material should be examined in the fresh state and in as natural a medium as possible. Fixed material is more convenient to transport, does not deteriorate, and can be examined at leisure; but the immediate examination of fresh material is often essential in field work. Because of the prevalence of pseudoparasitic forms and similarity between species, the successful identification of the parasitic Protozoa requires experience on the part of the laboratory worker. (See Section **VII,** I.)

Species.—The Protozoa that may be present in the digestive tract of man include six species of SARCODINA (*Dientamœba fragilis, Endamœba coli, Endamœba gingivalis, Endamœba histolytica, Endolimax nana,* and *Iodamœba bütschlii*); two species of INFUSORIA (*Balantidium coli* and *Nyctotherus faba*); six species of MASTIGOPHORA (*Chilomastix mesnili, Embadomonas intestinalis, Enteromonas hominis, Giardia lamblia, Trichomonas elongata,* and *Trichomonas hominis*); and one species of SPOROZOA (*Isospora hominis*). Of these *Endamœba histolytica* and *Balantidium coli* are of considerable pathogenic importance, *Trichomonas hominis* and *Giardia lamblia* of minor importance, and the others commensals. Therefore, it is important to differentiate the pathogenic from the nonpathogenic species and to recognize other cells or extraneous material that may simulate Protozoa. Except for the oral species, *Endamœba gingivalis* and *Trichomonas elongata,* the parasites appear in the feces as trophozoites or more frequently as

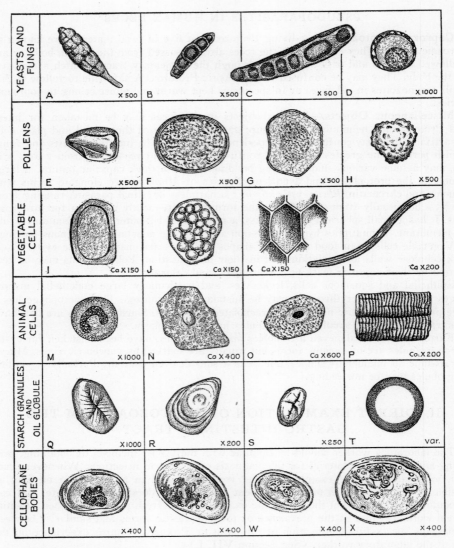

FIG. 277.—OBJECTS IN FECES SOMETIMES MISTAKEN FOR PROTOZOAN CYSTS AND HELMINTHIC OVA

A, Alternaria spore; *B, Acrothecium* spore; *C, Helminthosporium* spore; *D, Blastocystis hominis*; *E,* hemp pollen; *F,* orchard grass pollen; *G,* timothy pollen; *H,* ragweed pollen; *I to L,* vegetable cells; *M,* leukocyte; *N,* squamous epithelial cell; *O,* epithelial cell; *P,* muscle fiber; *Q,* corn starch; *R,* potato starch; *S,* rice starch; *T,* oil globule; *U to X,* cellophane bodies (*U to X* redrawn from Reardon, 1938).

cysts. *Endamœba gingivalis, Dientamœba fragilis, Trichomonas hominis,* and *T. elongata* apparently form no cysts. (See Chapter V for Identification Keys and Sources of Material.)

COLLECTION OF MATERIAL

1. **Mouth.**—Scrapings are made from the teeth and gums, especially from gingival cavities and accumulations of tartar. *Endamœba gingivalis* is found frequently and *Trichomonas elongata* less frequently about the teeth, particularly when they are carious or coated with tartar.

2. **Gastric and Duodenal Drainage.**—Under normal conditions no Protozoa, except *Endamœba gingivalis* and *Trichomonas elongata,* are obtained from the mouth, esophagus or stomach. Under abnormal conditions of reverse peristalsis *Giardia lamblia* and *Trichomonas intestinalis* may be found in the stomach contents.

Biliary drainage, the best method of diagnosing giardiasis, may yield large numbers of *Giardia lamblia* and *Trichomonas intestinalis,* and occasionally *Endamœba histolytica.* In the aspirated fluid trophozoites of *Giardia lamblia,* either actively motile or inactivated by magnesium sulphate, are often found attached to ribbons of duodenal cells. Duodenal drainage is effected by siphonage through a small flexible rubber tube with perforated tip, which is introduced through the stomach. The flow of bile is stimulated by the injection of magnesium sulphate or other cholagogical agent. The detailed technic is given in Lyon's *Non-Surgical Drainage of the Gall Tract,* Lea and Febiger, Phila., 1923, or in Kolmer and Boerner's *Approved Laboratory Technic,* Third Edition, 1941, D. Appleton-Century Company, New York.

3. **Feces.**—Most of the Protozoa inhabiting the gastro-intestinal tract are found in the feces. Feces should be collected in a clean, dry container and should not be mixed with urine. Feces from patients to whom barium, bismuth or oil has been administered are unsatisfactory for the identification of amœbæ.

When the patient is diarrheic, the feces should be examined immediately because trophozoites of the amœbæ succumb rapidly outside the body. When the specimen cannot be obtained at the laboratory, the feces should be passed into a warm glass container, placed in another container holding water at body temperature, and rushed to the laboratory. Thermos bottles make ideal containers. The specimen should be kept warm during examination. Nondiarrheic stools may be sent through the mail, since cysts in semiformed and formed feces can be identified up to 3 or 4 days. Entire specimens may be packed in cartons; or samples may be taken from various parts of the specimen and placed in pill boxes, which are enclosed in cylindrical mailing cases. Specimens should arrive at the laboratory in a moist condition. It is generally believed that specimens should be kept near body temperature, but de Rivas (1935) states that the cysts survive longer when packed in ice.

Protozoa are found more frequently after purging than in normal stools. If the examination of formed stools is negative a saline cathartic may be administered and the first or second movement thereafter examined. If purgation is contraindicated, a high enema of tepid physiological sodium chloride solution may be substituted. The best material for determining the presence of *Endamœba histolytica* is bits of mucus and necrotic mucosa obtained directly from ulcerated areas through the use of the sigmoidoscope.

PREPARATION OF FRESH MATERIAL FOR EXAMINATION

Whenever possible, the examination for intestinal Protozoa should be made from fresh material. Fixed, stained preparations are made for permanent mounts and special study.

4. **Selection of Material.**—Certain parts of the fecal specimen are more likely to contain parasites. When the feces are fluid, examine the bloody mucus or tiny specks of tissue; when semifluid, select bloody mucus if present or any other portion; and when

formed, scrape material from the surface. In every case examine not only the selected portions but several samples from different parts of the stool and, if necessary, resort to concentration methods.

5. **Cover-glass Preparations.**—A small portion of the selected material is placed on a warm slide with a toothpick or platinum wire, thoroughly emulsified in two or more drops of warm physiological sodium chloride solution, and covered with a cover-glass. The emulsion should show a moderate opacity when held toward a window. Examine first with the low-power 16 mm. objective, and then study suspicious objects or selected fields with the high-power 4 mm. objective, using reduced light. Cysts and motile trophozoites appear in their natural shapes and colors in fresh, warm material. Hakansson (1940) suggests that tap or distilled water, which causes the disintegration of *Blastocystis hominis* and trophozoites but leaves the cysts intact, be used in making cover-glass preparations. This procedure facilitates examination under low magnification and shortens the time involved.

It is advantageous, although not essential, in examining material containing motile Protozoa to use either a water-warmed or electrically-heated stage or a microscope placed in an incubator box. A convenient method of keeping a slide warm is to place a heated cent on one end.

6. **Iodine Preparations.**—A drop of iodine solution may be added to the fecal emulsion. The chromatin material of the amœbic cysts stands out in light relief against the yellow-brown cytoplasm, the nuclear structures are differentiated, and the glycogen masses stain a mahogany brown. The iodine mount, which may be made on the same slide as the plain mount, is useful for the examination of cysts, but the trophozoites are killed. The use of neutral red or eosin, 1 :10,000, has been recommended, since these dyes stain the débris but not the cysts and do not kill the trophozoites. Iodine solutions of various strengths have been used, three of which are given here.

A. **Iodine Solution:**

>   Potassium iodide .... 4 gm.
>   Iodine .... 2 gm.
>   Distilled water .... 100 ml.

The protoplasm of the cyst is lemon yellow and the glycogen dark brown, while the nuclear membrane and karyosome are bright and refractile.

B. **D'Antoni's Standardized Iodine Solution (1937):**

This preparation is made from a standardized potassium iodide solution, which is adjusted by the specific gravity method to an exact 10 per cent strength. To 100 ml. of a 1% solution 1.5 gm. of powdered iodine crystals are added and, after standing four days, this stock solution is ready for use. It may be kept for long periods, if tightly stoppered to prevent volatilization. For immediate use a small portion is filtered into a dropping bottle. The filtered solution should be discarded after ten days. Sealed tubes of potassium iodide (10.0434 gm.) and glass-stoppered bottles of iodine (15 gm.) to make 1,000 ml. of stock solution may be purchased.

The cysts have the same appearance as in **A.**

C. **Donaldson's Iodine-eosin Solution:**

>   Eosin (saturated solution in physiological saline)......................... 2 ml.
>   Iodine solution .... 1 ml.
>   Physiological saline .... 100 ml.
>   Potassium iodide .... 5 gm.
>   Iodine to saturation ....
>   Physiological saline .... 2 ml.

The cysts assume a yellow or brown color, the nucleus is clearly defined, and bacteria, yeast and fecal particles stain pink. Glycogen bodies in the cysts are stained brown.

PREPARATION OF PERMANENT MOUNTS

Permanent mounts permit species-determination through detailed study of structures and insure material for demonstration or reference. This method requires fixation and staining.

7. **Fixation.**—Wet-fixation is the method of choice since it causes less distortion of the parasites than dry-fixation. It is accomplished by making a thin, moist smear on a slide or cover-glass with a toothpick or platinum loop and quickly immersing the slide in the fixing fluid or subjecting it to a fixing vapor. Material which contains no albuminous matter should be mixed with serum or smeared upon a slide coated with egg albumin in order to make it adhere. Schaudinn's sublimate solution is a satisfactory general fixative. For flagellated and ciliated Protozoa, the wet-film may be exposed to osmic acid fumes in a closed container for 30 seconds, then dried and treated with methyl or absolute alcohol.

Schaudinn's Fixative Method:

Saturated aqueous solution of mercuric chloride .... 200 ml.
Alcohol (96%) .... 100 ml.

Add 1 ml. glacial acetic acid to each 20 ml. of the above mixture immediately before using.

(a) Immerse undried smears face downward in the solution, warmed to 60° C., for 10 to 20 minutes (10 minutes for trophozoites, 20 minutes for cysts).

(b) Wash in 50% alcohol for 5 minutes.

(c) Transfer for 10 minutes to 70% alcohol, which has been brought to a deep port wine color by adding a few drops of alcoholic iodine solution (to remove mercuric chloride).

(d) Dehydrate further by hardening in 96% alcohol for at least an hour or until convenient for staining.

(e) Prior to staining place film successively in 70, 50 and 30% alcohol and distilled water for 5 minutes each.

8. **Staining.**—There are many methods of staining fecal smears. Heidenhain's iron hematoxylin and Mann's stain, the two standard methods that produce the best results, are the longest and most complicated. It is important to prevent drying of the film at any stage in the staining process.

A. **Heidenhain's Iron-hematoxylin Method.**—This method is excellent for the preservation and accurate differentiation of structures and species of intestinal Protozoa, but several slides should be stained at a time, since only a few will give good results.

Composition of mordant:

> Ferric ammonium sulphate (iron alum).................... 4 gm.
> Distilled water .... 100 ml.

Composition of stain:

> Hematoxylin (any standard hematoxylin)................ 0.5 gm.
> Distilled water .... 100.0 ml.

Dissolve the hemotoxylin in about 5 ml. of 95% alcohol. Dilute to 100 ml. with distilled water. Let ripen for at least two days before using.

Method:

(1) Fix in Schaudinn's solution.

(2) Cover with mordant for 15 minutes in incubator at 37° C. *Note:* Overnight is better but, if pressed for time, *steam* gently for 15 minutes.

(3) Drain off mordant and wash in several changes of tap water for 5 to 10 minutes.

(4) Drain and place in 0.5% aqueous solution of hematoxylin for the same period as used in the mordant stage.

(5) Differentiate in fresh 2% aqueous solution of ferric ammonium sulphate.

Note: This is the critical step. Remove the slide from the hematoxylin with forceps, dip it into the differentiating solution, and quickly rinse in a beaker of tap water. Examine carefully under the 4 mm. objective of the microscope to see if sufficient differentiation has been accomplished. If not, then repeat the process until the nucleus stands out as blue-black and the cytoplasm and débris assume a gray or bluish-gray shade.

(6) Wash in running tap water for 20 to 30 minutes.

(7) Dehydrate in graded alcohols: 30, 50, 70, 70 with iodine, 85, 95%, and absolute alcohol.

(8) Clear in xylene 5 minutes.

(9) Mount in balsam.

B. **Heidenhain's Rapid Iron-hematoxylin Method.**—This method may be applied to tissues embedded in paraffin as well as to fecal smears.

Composition of Stain:

Hematoxylin	0.5 gm.
Absolute alcohol	10.0 ml.
Distilled water	90.0 ml.

Dissolve hematoxylin in alcohol, add distilled water, and ripen for 2 or 3 months in sunlight. Process may be hastened by adding 5 to 10 ml. of 0.25% $KMnO_3$.

(1) Fix in methyl alcohol for about 5 minutes and dry in the air.

(2) Wash in tap water.

(3) Leave in 4% aqueous iron-alum solution for 3 hours, in incubator. (In preparing this solution select pure violet crystals of ferric ammonium sulphate.)

(4) Wash in tap water.

(5) Stain in 0.5% ripened hematoxylin for 30 minutes.

(6) Wash thoroughly in tap water.

(7) Differentiate in 4% iron-alum until nuclei are well defined. Observe differentiation under microscope, rinsing smears in tap water before each examination.

(8) Wash thoroughly in tap water and dry in air.

(9) Mount in balsam.

C. **Mann's Method of Staining.**—This permanent stain, properly used, is excellent for revealing minute details of the structures of amœbæ or of the intestinal flagellates.

Composition of Stain:

Aqueous solution of methyl blue (1%)	35 ml.
Aqueous solution of eosin (1%)	45 ml.
Distilled water	100 ml.

Method:

(1) Fix in Schaudinn's solution.

(2) Immerse in graded alcohols, 10 minutes each: 50, 70, 70 with iodine, 80 and 90%.

(3) Immerse in distilled water 10 minutes.

(4) Immerse in stain and leave for 4 to 10 hours as determined by trial.

(5) Wash thoroughly in distilled water.

(6) Differentiate, observing the usual precautions, in 70% alcohol to which a little Orange G. has been added (a few drops of a saturated solution of Orange G. in 100 ml. of 70% alcohol).

(7) Wash in distilled water.

(8) Dehydrate in graded alcohols, 5 minutes in each: 30, 50, 70 and 90% and in absolute alcohol for 10 to 15 minutes.

(9) Place for 5 minutes in equal parts of absolute alcohol and xylene.

(10) Clear with xylene.

(11) Mount in xylene-balsam.

CONCENTRATIVE AND QUANTITATIVE METHODS

When direct examination for cysts is negative, it is well to resort to methods of concentration. The methods for concentrating helminthic ova (Section VII, VII) are also useful for cysts (Faust *et al.,* 1938).

9. Craig's Method for Concentration of Cysts:

(a) Emulsify a portion of stool about the size of a pea in 10 ml. of water or 0.85% sodium chloride solution.

(b) Strain the emulsion into a centrifuge tube through two layers of cheesecloth. Add sufficient of the salt solution to fill the tube. Mix thoroughly.

(c) Centrifuge at moderate speed for 5 minutes.

(d) With a wide-mouthed pipette secure the sediment.

(e) Make stained and unstained preparations and examine for cysts.

10. Knowles and Cole's Method of Counting Protozoan Cysts in Feces (1917):

(a) Emulsify 1 gm. of feces in 10 ml. of iodine solution.

(b) Transfer the emulsion with a capillary pipette to a blood counting chamber and count the cysts in 3 or 4 samples, each count representing 0.1 cmm.

III. DIRECT EXAMINATION OF PROTOZOA FROM BLOOD AND TISSUES

Species.—The Protozoa that may be present in the blood and tissues of man include one species of SARCODINA (*Endamœba histolytica*); one species of INFUSORIA (*Balantidium coli*); seven species of MASTIGOPHORA (*Leishmania braziliensis, L. donovani, L. tropica, Trichomonas vaginalis, Trypanosoma cruzi, T. gambiense, T. rhodesiense*); and five sporozoa (*Plasmodium falciparum, P. malariæ, P. ovale, P. vivax, Sarcocystis lindemanni*). All these species are of pathogenic importance. *Endamœba histolytica* and *Balantidium coli* are primarily parasites of the intestinal tract and the technics for their identification have been considered in Section VII, II. The flagellate, *Trichomonas vaginalis,* primarily a superficial parasite of the atria of the body, causes only a low-grade inflammation.

Blood.—Changes in the corpuscles and chemical composition of the blood, and serological reactions may aid in the diagnosis of parasitic infections and in evaluating the general condition of the patient. The various technical methods employed in hemoglobin determinations, blood counts, hemolysis, coagulation, blood chemistry, and blood grouping are given in standard textbooks on hematology and blood chemistry. The study of the blood as an aid in the detection of parasitic infections presupposes a knowledge of the technic required and of normal and abnormal blood morphology. The most common changes in the blood morphology are a reduction in hemoglobin and number of erythrocytes and an increase in eosinophils. Color charts, dilution methods, the spectroscope and photo-electric colorimeter are used to determine the amount of hemoglobin or its compounds.

Hemolysis, the diffusion of hemoglobin from the red blood cell, occurs both within and without the body. The red cells of certain individuals are particularly susceptible to hemolysis. Their fragility may be tested with graded hypotonic sodium chloride solutions. In specimens of blood, hemolysis is often produced by wet syringes and containers or by mechanical agitation. The clotting of blood specimens may be prevented by the addition of anti-coagulants such as potassium oxalate, sodium citrate and heparin, or by defibrinating the blood by shaking with glass beads.

COLLECTION OF BLOOD

The small amount of blood ordinarily required for the detection of parasitic Protozoa or for blood counts may be obtained from the finger or ear. When larger amounts are desired, venipuncture is used. It is not advisable to take blood within one hour after a meal. Sterile containers are preferable although not essential.

1. **Finger Puncture.**—(a) Make sure that the patient's hand is warm with good circulation. If it is cold and clammy, have patient hold hand in hot water for a few minutes and rub briskly with a towel.

(b) Cleanse tip of finger with alcohol; let dry.

(c) Puncture across the lines at tip of finger with a blood lancet, half a pen nib, a three-cornered surgical needle or a cataract knife. Cleanse the instrument with alcohol before use.

(d) Massage blood into small test tube or make smears directly on slides.

2. **Ear Puncture.**—Blood may be obtained from the lobe of the ear by a procedure similar to that for finger puncture. The puncture should be made on the anterior edge of the dependent portion of the lobe. Gentle massage of the ear before cleansing with alcohol facilitates the flow of blood.

3. **Venipuncture.**—The most convenient method of obtaining large quantities of blood from adults is by venipuncture.

(a) Adjust tourniquet about arm above elbow, but not so tightly as to shut off arterial circulation; request patient to open and close his hand vigorously. Select a suitable vein, usually the basilic, which may be seen or felt on the flexor surface of the elbow.

(b) Cleanse skin over vein with alcohol or tincture of iodine.

(c) Remove 5 to 10 ml. of blood with a sterilized Luer's syringe fitted with a #20 to #22 needle. Transfer blood to sterile container.

(d) Release tourniquet and *then* withdraw needle. Dressings are unnecessary unless several punctures have been made.

4. **Collection from Infants and Children.**—Blood may be obtained at birth from the umbilical cord. A few milliliters of blood may be obtained from infants by puncturing the large toe after the manner of a finger puncture. From infants under one year blood may be obtained from the longitudinal sinus through the open anterior fontanel. The method of choice in infants and young children is venipuncture of the external jugular. Also, children over one year of age may have blood taken from the fingers, and after four years of age by venipuncture in the arm or leg. Blood from the jugular vein is obtained as follows:

(a) Place infant on its side so that the head hangs over the edge of a table or bed. During crying the jugular vein is easily seen and felt.

(b) Have an assistant press with a finger in the supraclavicular fossa to distend the vein.

(c) Steady the vein below the angle of the jaw and enter the vein with the needle pointed toward the assistant's finger.

(d) Remove 3 to 5 ml. of blood with sterile syringe and transfer blood to a sterile container.

5. **Mailing Blood Samples.**—Containers should be filled almost to the rubber or cork stopper to avoid undue agitation and consequent hemolysis. Pack the labeled container with cotton in a mailing case. Wherever feasible ship specimens at once by air mail or special delivery.

PREPARATION OF BLOOD FOR EXAMINATION

Good blood preparations are important in the identification of Protozoa. In fresh blood protozoan parasites may be detected by their movements or by the agitation of the erythrocytes. Thin stained films permit more careful differentiation of species; thick stained films yield a higher concentration and are therefore extremely useful when thin films have proved negative. Films from centrifuged blood also yield high concentrations of parasites. In general, it is good practice to make one or two fresh films, three or four thin smears, and at least one thick film for each examination.

Extraneous Material.—The stained blood film may contain objects that may be mistaken for Protozoa, particularly the malarial parasites. Blood platelets with their irregular crenated outline, purplish coloring, and occasional filamentous projections may be mistaken for flagellated Protozoa and not infrequently, when lying on red cells, for plasmodia. The films may contain extraneous material from dirty slides, skin of the patient, precipitated stain, insects, and from dust containing bacteria, fungi and pollens. Precipitated stain, granules from degenerated leukocytes, platelets and distorted corpuscles may be confused with malarial parasites.

6. **Fresh Wet Film.**—The fresh film is useful for the detection of trypanosomes and malarial parasites and for microfilariæ and other helminthic larvæ. For immediate examination fresh blood is prepared as follows:

(a) Place a drop of blood the size of a pinhead on the center of a clean cover-glass. If the drop is taken directly from the patient, the cover-glass should not touch the skin.

(b) Carefully lower the inverted cover-glass on a clean slide with a needle. The center of the film should be so thin that it is almost colorless.

(c) Examine first with the low-power 16 mm., then with the 4 mm., and, if necessary, with the 1.8 mm. objective.

If it is desirable to observe fresh films for a period of several days, they may be sealed by coating the edges of the cover-glass with melted vaseline before placing it on the drop of blood.

7. **Thin Dry Film.**—The thin film, when stained, permits the study of the morphology of the blood and of the protozoan parasite. Diagnosis of such diseases as leishmaniasis, trypanosomiasis and malaria may thus be based upon the study of the morphology of the parasite and its relation to the blood cells. The method of making thin smears is the same as in hematological technic.

A. **Slide Method:**

(1) Touch one end of a clean slide to a small drop of blood from the finger or ear, taking care not to let the slide come in contact with the skin.

(2) Place the slide on a flat surface and steady with the index finger and thumb of the left hand.

(3) Choose as a spreader a slide with a sharp smooth edge on one end. Place the edge of the spreader against the part of the drop nearest the middle of the first slide.

(4) Hold the spreader at an angle of 45° to the first slide slanting away from its center. Wait until the blood has spread along the entire edge of the spreader.

(5) With a firm rapid motion push the spreader along the first slide maintaining the 45° angle. In this way the blood is drawn after the spreader in a thin smear which, if the original drop is small enough, ends in a drawn-out tail well before reaching the end of the first slide.

(6) Let slide dry in air protected from dust. The parasites and leukocytes are usually more abundant at the thin end of the smear.

B. **Cover-glass Method:**

(1) Place a small drop of blood on the first cover-glass. Hold with thumb and forefinger of left hand.

(2) Lower a second cover-glass evenly onto the first with the same fingers of the right hand so that an eight-pointed star results. Wait until the blood spreads between the two cover-glasses.

(3) Draw apart smoothly in a plane parallel to the surfaces of the cover-glasses. The result is two thin smears.

8. **Thick Dry Film.**—The thick film, a modified concentration method, is useful when parasites are few and thin films are negative. It is of particular value for the detection of plasmodia in malarial surveys and in patients with chronic infections or under quinine treatment. It is also of value for detecting trypanosomes, leishmanian parasites and microfilariæ.

(a) Place four medium-sized drops of blood on a clean slide at the corners of a one-half inch square.

(b) Draw the drops into a pool with a needle so that a thick moist layer one-half inch square is formed.

(c) Allow the film to dry for one and one-half hours in an incubator at 37° C. or overnight at room temperature, protected from dust by an inverted Petri dish. The smears should be dried only long enough to make them adhere, since too much drying will prevent satisfactory staining of the parasites.

(d) Flood the film with a mixture of four parts of a 2.5% aqueous solution of glacial acetic acid and one part of an aqueous solution of 2% tartaric acid until a grayish-white color denotes the completion of dehemoglobinization. Treatment with distilled water or weak acids will also produce dehemoglobinization.

(e) Fix smear by covering with methyl alcohol for 3 to 4 minutes.

(f) Wash thoroughly in distilled water to remove traces of acid.

Preliminary dehemoglobinization and fixation are not used in the method of Barber and Komp (1927), in which the films are treated directly with Giemsa's stain.

9. **Concentration Methods.**—It may be advisable at times to use concentration methods for the detection of trypanosomes and plasmodia.

A. **Method for Trypanosomes:**

(1) Collect blood in a 1% sodium citrate physiological sodium chloride solution to prevent coagulation.

(2) Filter into a centrifuge tube through cheesecloth to remove clots, fibrin, etc.

(3) Centrifuge for 20 minutes to sediment the corpuscles and trypanosomes. Remove the supernate.

(4) Hemolyze by adding distilled water or 2% acetic acid.

(5) Centrifuge for 30 minutes and remove supernate.

(6) Make smears of sediment containing parasites and stroma of hemolyzed erythrocytes.

B. **Bass and Johns' Method for Plasmodia (1912):**

(1) Draw 10 ml. of blood from a vein and mix with 0.2 ml. of the following: sodium citrate, 5 gm.; dextrose, 5 gm.; water (distilled), 10 ml.

(2) Divide the blood between two centrifuge tubes and centrifuge at high speed (2,500 revolutions per minute) for about five minutes.

(3) With a capillary pipette remove the supernatant plasma. Then carefully skim off the grayish layer of leukocytes and parasites and place in a tube about 12 cm. long with an inside diameter of about 0.5 cm. Add an equal volume of plasma.

(4) Mix and centrifuge as before.

(5) With a capillary pipette draw off the "cream." Mix by forcing in and out upon a slide. Then draw into the pipette and seal the tip in a flame. Nick with a file and break off above the blood column.

(6) Place this slender tube in the centrifuge and spin again as above.

(7) The parasites will be most numerous in the grayish layer of leukocytes upon the surface of the sediment and in the upper portion of the erythrocytic layer.

(8) Nick with a file and break off the capillary tube at a point 1 to 2 mm. below the bottom of the leukocytic layer.

(9) With a capillary pipette, the stem of which will pass inside the capillary tube, remove the small amount of red cells and leukocytes together with a little plasma.

(10) Mix well and prepare smears on slides for staining with Wright's stain.

(11) Best results are obtained with æstivo-autumnal crescents and adult tertian and quartan parasites.

METHODS OF STAINING BLOOD FILMS

Of the several methods for staining blood, Wright's and Giemsa's have been selected as the most satisfactory for general use. Careful preparation of films on clean slides is essential for accurate results. These modified Romanowsky stains may be purchased from reputable supply houses in liquid form. Powdered Wright's stain may be obtained and prepared with methyl alcohol as needed. As a routine, Wright's stain is more convenient, but Giemsa's stain, which gives a deeper and more lasting color to the parasites, is preferable for permanent mounts and special morphological characteristics. The objections to Giemsa's stain are the length of time required for staining, the tendency to overstain, and the relatively high cost.

10. **Wright's Method of Staining Thin Films:**

(a) Cover film with 8 drops of Wright's stain and allow to remain for 2 minutes to fix the film.

(b) Add an equal amount of distilled water and allow the diluted stain to remain for 2 minutes or more, depending upon the particular lot of stain and the species of Protozoa. A metallic sheen should appear on the diluted stain. A buffer solution is sometimes used instead of distilled water.

(c) Wash thoroughly with tap water, drain and dry in air. Washing is important since it rids the film of precipitated stain and aids in differentiating the cytoplasm and nucleus of Protozoa.

(d) If cover-glass preparations are used, mount on slides in balsam or gum dammar.

11. **Giemsa's Method of Staining Thin Films:**

(a) Dilute 1 ml. of Giemsa's stain in 10 ml. of neutral or very slightly alkaline distilled water. If 1:1,000 potassium carbonate solution is used instead of water, the stain will be deeper.

(b) Fix the film in methyl alcohol for 2 to 5 minutes.

(c) Submerge in the diluted Giemsa's stain for 25 to 30 minutes. The stain should be used immediately after diluting.

(d) Wash thoroughly with distilled water, drain and dry.

12. **Barber and Komp's Method of Staining Thick Films with Giemsa's Stain:**

The thick films are prepared without dehemoglobinization or fixation, but the dehemoglobinized films may be stained in the same way.

(a) After the film has dried enough to make it adhere to the slide, dilute 1 part of Giemsa's stain with 6 parts of neutral or slightly alkaline distilled water.

(b) Place slide in the diluted staining solution for about 30 minutes.

(c) Place slide in distilled water for about 5 minutes for partial decolorization. Examine under the microscope. If the smear shows a deep blue background and the leukocytes are almost black, it is overstained and probably useless, although longer washing in distilled water may decolorize it somewhat. The time required for staining depends upon the dilution of the stain, the volume used, and the thickness of the smear:

(d) Drain and allow to dry in air.

Wright's stain may be employed in staining thick blood films, using a 1 to 30 dilution of the stock solution with distilled water, but is not as satisfactory as Giemsa's stain.

Giemsa's stain may be diluted with 20 parts of a buffer solution of pH 7.2 (Pampana, 1938).

QUANTITATIVE METHODS FOR PROTOZOA IN THE BLOOD

Quantitative methods have been employed to ascertain the abundance of trypanosomes and malarial parasites in the blood.

13. Kolmer's Method of Counting Trypanosomes (1915):

(a) The diluting fluid consists of 2 ml. formalin, 2 ml. glacial acetic acid, 96 ml. distilled water, and 2 ml. Ziehl-Neelson's carbolfuchsin. It dehemoglobinizes the red cells and kills, fixes and stains the trypanosomes.

(b) The blood is diluted in a hæmatocytometer pipette either 1:20 or 1:200, depending upon the number of organisms. Other dilutions may be necessary.

(c) Place in the blood counting chamber and take the average of three counts of the trypanosomes in the entire 0.1 cmm.

14. Christophers' Method of Enumerating Malaria Parasites (1924):

(a) Obtain 10 cmm. of blood from the patient in a graduated capillary tube.

(b) Spread it evenly in a thick film over a rectangular area 2 x 1 cm. on a slide.

(c) Dehemoglobinize and stain by Wright's or Giemsa's method.

(d) Adjust square of the ocular micrometer to cover 0.01 sq. mm.

(e) Count malarial parasites in 200 fields across the middle of the film.

(f) Multiply actual count by 10 to give total count in 1 cmm. of blood.

COLLECTION OF PROTOZOA FROM TISSUES, SECRETIONS AND EXUDATES

Protozoan parasites may be found in the various organs and tissues of the body as well as in the blood. Special methods of collecting material for examinations have been devised.

15. **Spleen Puncture.**—In order to obtain material for the diagnosis of leishmanian infection, splenic puncture is performed. Reported fatalities have caused this procedure to be held in some disrepute; but statistics from India indicate that when a careful technic is followed and patients with leukemia and hemorrhagic tendencies are eliminated, the mortality rate is extremely low. Nevertheless, it should be resorted to only after other methods have failed. The following technic is recommended:

(a) Have patient flat on his back with hands folded beneath head. Children may be given a general anæsthetic. Prolonged coagulation time is a contra-indication.

(b) Sterilize area of puncture with tincture of iodine.

(c) Have assistant hold spleen firmly against the diaphragm and costal region.

(d) Using a 15-gauge needle and a dry syringe, puncture the spleen with a direct firm thrust, while the patient holds his breath.

(e) Without delay make forcible aspiration and then immediately withdraw the needle sharply in one motion.

(f) Have patient remain recumbent for 1½ to 2 hours, and check his pulse rate at intervals for signs of hemorrhage. An abdominal binder may be advisable.

(g) Eject 2 drops of the aspirated material onto slides and spread in the same manner as thin blood films.

(h) Draw a few drops of sterile citrated saline into the syringe to facilitate the inoculation of culture media.

16. **Liver Puncture.**—Since liver puncture requires less skill and is accompanied by less danger, it is preferred to splenic puncture even though leishmanian parasites may be less abundant in the liver.

(a) Exclude patients with leukemia, hemorrhagic disease, malaria, and hydatid cyst.

(b) Administer a local anæsthetic.

(c) Sterilize region to be punctured with tincture of iodine.

(d) Insert a dry sterile needle, not more than $3\frac{1}{2}$ inches long, into the eighth inter-costal space in the anterior axillary line 1 to $1\frac{1}{2}$ inches from the costal margin, direct-ing it inward, upward and backward. Several punctures may be made in different parts of the liver through the same aperture.

(e) Aspirate material and withdraw needle.

(f) Prepare material for examination and culture in same manner as in splenic puncture.

17. **Lymph Gland Puncture.**—Lymph glands may be examined for trypanosomes and leishmania when the peripheral blood is negative.

(a) Use a large needle and a dry syringe or one containing a few drops of sodium chloride solution, which may be injected into the gland before aspiration.

(b) Hold gland firmly in position and thrust the needle sharply into its substance.

(c) Aspirate and remove needle.

(d) Use aspirated material for smear or culture.

18. **Spinal Puncture.**—The examination of spinal fluid is useful in the late stages of trypanosomiasis. The spinal fluid is removed by lumbar puncture or more rarely by cistern puncture. The horizontal position is preferred. Local anesthesia may be used. The point of entry is between the fourth and fifth lumbar vertebræ, on a line connecting the iliac crests. A three and one-half inch 19-gauge needle is inserted under sterile precautions. About 5 ml. of the fluid should be removed and the patient should be kept in bed for about 18 hours in order to avoid postoperative headache. For a full de-scription of the technic, see Kolmer and Boerner, *Approved Laboratory Technique,* D. Appleton-Century Co., Inc., 1941, Third Edition, pp. 296-299.

19. **Body Fluids.**—Hydrocele, pericardial, peritoneal and joint fluids may be col-lected by aspiration with a large needle under rigid aseptic conditions. In most instances the technic of obtaining these fluids requires skilled surgical training.

20. **Sputum.**—Sputum may be collected in wide-mouthed bottles, Petri dishes or paper cups. A preliminary rinsing of the mouth and throat with a solution of baking soda will decrease the amount of mouth contamination. The sputum should come from the bronchi. Bronchial secretions may be aspirated with the Jackson bronchoscope. The sputum is of no practical importance in the diagnosis of protozoan infections, but is of value in such helminthic infections as paragonimiasis.

21. **Urine.**—The urine may be passed into clean containers or may be obtained by catheterization. It is of relatively limited importance in protozoan infections, since only *Trichomonas vaginalis* is encountered; but it provides an important means of diagnosis in bilharziasis.

22. **Skin and Mucous Membranes.**—Leishmanian lesions are superficially cleaned with alcohol and allowed to dry. If possible, the serous exudate from a lesion is obtained by puncturing the indurated margin with a sterile capillary pipette or hypodermic needle. Another method is to scrape the surface of the lesion with a scalpel until it bleeds. The blood is removed after the hemorrhage has ceased and the serous exudate which collects is then taken for examination. Ordinarily the removal of material by scraping with a scalpel is sufficient. Biopsy specimens may be taken.

23. **Tissues.**—Specimens of tissue containing parasites may be obtained by biopsy from accessible locations, from bone marrow by sternal puncture, or at autopsy.

PREPARATION AND STAINING OF PROTOZOA IN TISSUES, SECRETIONS AND EXUDATES

24. **Liver, Lymph Gland, Spleen and Skin.**—Material aspirated from the liver, lymph glands and spleen or collected from lesions of the skin is emulsified in physio-

logical sodium chloride solution and either spread like blood smears or examined in cover-glass preparations. The methods of staining are similar to those used for blood films. Dark-field examination may be employed.

25. **Body Fluids.**—The direct identification of parasites in the spinal, pleural, pericardial, peritoneal, hydrocele and joint fluids, and urine is usually confined to the microscopical examination of the centrifuged sediment in wet cover-glass preparations or in stained films. The physical character of the fluids may modify the procedure, which usually is carried out in the following manner:

(a) Centrifuge for 20 minutes.

(b) Ordinarily the sediment may be examined directly but, if it contains an excess of cells, wash in physiological sodium chloride solution and recentrifuge. An excess of red blood cells may require dehemoglobinization.

(c) Prepare wet and dry stained films in the same manner as blood films.

26. **Tissues.**—Films from solid tissues may be made by lightly smearing a piece of tissue across the surface of a slide or by making an impression of the freshly-cut surface. The smear is stained like blood films. Tissues may be imbedded and sectioned, using the ordinary technic for pathological specimens including fixation, dehydration, imbedding and sectioning. The hematoxylin-eosin and eosin-methylene-blue methods of staining ordinarily used in histopathological work are often sufficient. Special methods of staining to bring out certain morphological details in the parasites occasionally are used.

IV. CULTURAL METHODS FOR PROTOZOA

Cultural methods have greatly increased our knowledge of the life histories and transmission of Protozoa. To a lesser extent they have been adapted to the helminths. Various media, most of them satisfactory, have been devised for the cultivation of Protozoa. In general, the pathogenic species are more difficult to cultivate than the free-living. Certain useful media have been selected for presentation here. Also, laboratory animals have been employed for perpetuating certain species.

INTESTINAL PROTOZOA

Successful cultivation of the intestinal amœbæ and flagellates depends upon careful technical methods rather than upon the exact medium used, since familiarity and experience with a single satisfactory medium is preferable to the casual use of several media. Cultivation requires fresh material and as far as possible the reduction of bacterial contamination. The usual procedure is to obtain an appreciable amount of well-sampled material, such as a small piece of solid or 0.5 ml. of semi-fluid feces, which is mixed with the liquid medium or with the water of condensation on the surface of the solid medium. Incubation is carried out at 37° C. for 24 to 48 hours. An appreciable amount, at least 0.1 ml. of the sediment, should be removed from the culture with a wide-mouthed pipette and examined under a warm cover-glass preparation. Growth is slow and the numbers are often small, particularly in the case of intestinal amœbæ which are most numerous in the bottom sediment of liquid media or in the sediment at the junction of the liquid and the solid media in slant cultures. Several preparations should be examined before a negative report is made.

In keeping stock cultures, subcultures should be made every 24 hours by transferring an appreciable amount of the sediment of the original culture to the fresh medium with a large-bore capillary pipette. *Endamœba histolytica* is readily maintained in cultures containing bacteria, although different strains present growth-idiosyncrasies. The various species of intestinal flagellates also vary in their adaptability to cultivation.

1. **Boeck and Drbohlav's Locke-egg-serum Medium (1925).**—This solid medium, which consists of eggs and Locke's solution, is one of the earliest and most generally used media for the cultivation of parasitic amœbæ. The medium, warmed to body temperature, is inoculated by emulsifying the feces in the fluid portion by rubbing the specimen against the sides of the test tube with a sterile applicator or inoculating needle.

Locke's Solution

Sodium chloride	9.0 gm.
Calcium chloride	0.2 gm.
Potassium chloride	0.4 gm.
Sodium bicarbonate	0.2 gm.
Glucose	2.5 gm.
Distilled water	1,000 ml.

Wash 4 eggs with tap water, brush with alcohol, and carefully break into a sterile flask containing glass beads. Add 50 ml. of Locke's solution (filtered and autoclaved at 121° C. for 15 minutes) and shake until the eggs are thoroughly broken up. The hydrogen-ion concentration is usually between pH 7.2 and 7.8, the favorable range for amœbæ, but adjustment may be required. Pour into test tubes a sufficient quantity to produce a slant 1 to 1½ inches in length. Slant the tubes in an inspissator and heat at 70° C. until the mixture is solidified. Autoclave at 121° C. for 20 minutes or by fractional sterilization in the Arnold sterilizer. The temperature of the autoclave must be raised and lowered slowly. Cover the media in the tubes to a depth of 1 cm. with a sterile mixture of equal parts of Locke's solution and inactivated human blood serum.

2. **Craig's Locke-serum Medium (1926).**—This fluid medium consists of a mixture of Locke's solution (without glucose) and animal blood serum, not over 48 hours old, inactivated at 56° C. for 30 minutes. To 7 parts of sterile Locke's solution 1 part of inactivated blood serum is added. The mixture is passed through a Berkefeld filter until the solution is clear. It is tubed, 10 ml. per tube, and incubated for sterility. The reaction does not need adjusting. The addition of a minute amount of rice flour or starch just before inoculation adds to the efficiency of the medium.

3. **Cleveland and Collier's Medium (1930).**—This medium is preferred by many workers for the cultivation of *Endamœba histolytica*.

Liver infusion agar (Difco dehydrated)	30 gm.
Disodium phosphate	2 gm.
Distilled water	1,000 ml.

The medium is placed in tubes, autoclaved, and slanted. The slants are covered with a 1 to 6 dilution of sterile fresh horse serum in physiological sodium chloride solution. A 5 mm. loop of sterile rice flour or powdered unpolished rice is added to each tube. In making subcultures remove 2 or 3 drops of the rice flour débris from the bottom of the tube with a sterile wide-mouthed pipette.

4. **Hogue's Ovomucoid Medium (1921).**—Although the media of Boeck and Drbohlav and of Craig are suitable for the cultivation of intestinal flagellates, special media have been devised for their cultivation.

In preparing Hogue's medium the whites of 6 eggs, aseptically obtained, are thoroughly shaken with glass beads in a sterile flask and 600 ml. of sterile 0.7 per cent sodium chloride solution is added. The mixture is heated for 20 to 30 minutes over a boiling water bath, being constantly agitated while cooking. It is filtered through cheesecloth and cotton using a suction pump. Culture tubes containing 5 ml. of the opalescent filtrate are plugged with cotton and autoclaved at 120° C. for 20 minutes.

A bit of fecal material, about 4 x 2 mm., is collected on a sterile toothpick, which is dropped into the medium in the culture tube. After incubation at 37° C. for 24 hours the medium is examined for flagellates which are most numerous at the surface on the third day after inoculation.

5. **Loeffler's Blood Serum and Ringer's Fluid.**—Bland, Goldstein, Wenrich and Weiner (1932) had the best success in cultivating *Trichomonas vaginalis* with a modified Ringer's fluid, containing 0.25 per cent Loeffler's dried blood serum, superimposed upon a slant of nutrient agar. Transfers were made every 3 or 4 days and occasionally a change of medium was beneficial.

Sodium chloride	6.0 gm.
Potassium chloride	0.1 gm.
Sodium bicarbonate	0.1 gm.
Calcium chloride	0.1 gm.
Distilled water	1,000 ml.
Loeffler's dried blood serum, per 100 ml. of solution...	0.25 gm.

6. **Media for *Balantidium coli*.**—Barrett and Yarbrough's Medium (1921) consists of 1 part of inactivated human blood serum and 16 parts of 0.5 per cent sodium chloride solution. The blood serum is inactivated at 56° C. for 30 minutes before it is added to the sterile sodium chloride solution. The mixture is sterilized by filtering through a Berkefeld filter. It is added in 8 ml. lots to tubes, 150 x 10 mm., giving the medium a depth of about 100 mm.

About 0.1 ml. of undiluted mucoid feces is inserted with a capillary pipette down to the bottom of the tube in order to insure reduced oxygen tension, which favors the growth of *Balantidium coli*. Incubation is carried out at 37° C. and subcultures are made every second day. The organisms are present only in the lower portion of the tube.

Schumaker (1931) cultivated *Balantidium coli* on a medium consisting of 9 parts of Ringer's solution and 1 part of sterile horse serum, to each 10 ml. of which 0.007 gm. of rice starch was added. He also used a Ringer's solution containing 3% horse serum and 0.1% asparagin.

Atchley (1935) employed a medium consisting of 4 parts of Ringer's solution and 1 part of feces. After standing 24 hours the mixture was filtered through gauze, centrifuged, passed through filter paper and infusorial earth, and finally sterilized by passage through a Seitz filter.

BLOOD AND TISSUE PROTOZOA

The protozoan parasites from the blood and tissues include the genera *Trypanosoma*, *Leishmania* and *Plasmodium*. The most useful medium for the cultivation of the first two is Novy, MacNeal and Nicolle's medium (N. N. N.) and for the plasmodia various modifications of Bass and Johns' method. Strict asepsis is important.

7. **Novy, MacNeal and Nicolle's Medium (1903).**—This medium, commonly known as N. N. N. medium, contains the following ingredients:

Agar	14 gm.
Sodium chloride	6 gm.
Distilled water	900 ml.

Culture tubes containing 6 ml. of the medium are sterilized in the autoclave and stored in the refrigerator. To prepare for use the tubed medium is melted and cooled to 48° C. Sterile defibrinated rabbit blood, 2 ml. per tube, is added and thoroughly mixed by rotating the tube. The tube is then slanted and allowed to cool rapidly on ice to insure abundant water of condensation, in which the organisms develop best. The tube is incubated at 37° C. for 24 hours to insure sterility before use. A rubber cap prevents loss of the water of condensation. No adjustment of pH is necessary, the pH being about 7.6.

Tissue obtained by lymph gland, splenic or hepatic puncture or from cutaneous lesions is inoculated directly. About 10 ml. of blood from the basilic vein is placed in a flask containing 50 to 75 ml. of Locke's solution. It is then centrifuged in 50 ml. tubes at low speed until the red cells are lightly packed. For *Trypanosoma*, inoculate from the buffy layer that appears above the packed cells. For the less numerous *Leishmania*, decant the cloudy supernatant liquid which is then centrifuged at high speed. Inoculate sediment in water of condensation and incubate at 22° to 25° C. for 10 days. Another method recommended for leishmanian infections is to place 0.5 ml. of blood in 20 ml. of 1.5 per cent sodium citrate in physiological sodium chloride solution. Shake gently and place in icebox overnight. Centrifuge, decant supernatant fluid, and transfer the corpuscles with a sterile pipette to the water of condensation of the medium.

In examining for growth scrape the surface of the agar beneath and just above the water of condensation. Neither *Trypanosoma gambiense* nor *T. rhodesiense* can be cultivated indefinitely but they will remain alive and multiply slightly. *Leishmania* will appear as flagellated forms in 10 to 12 days. Cultural methods are of little use in the diagnosis of trypanosomiasis. *Leishmania* and *T. cruzi* may be maintained in cultures.

8. **Bass and Johns' Method of Cultivating Plasmodia (1912).**—This method is successful in cultivating three or four generations of the malarial parasites. Its chief use has been in the control of treatment, since positive cultures may be obtained when blood films are negative.

Draw 10 ml. of blood from the patient's vein and place in a tube containing 0.1 ml. of a 50% sterile glucose solution. The blood is defibrinated with a sterile wire or glass rod. The defibrinated blood is transferred to several narrow test tubes to a depth of at least 2.5 cm. and is centrifuged until there is about 1.2 cm. of serum above the cells. When incubated at 37° to 39° C. the parasites develop in the thin upper layer of cells just below the clear plasma. The parasites in the deeper lying red cells die. To observe development, red cells from the upper layer are drawn up with a capillary pipette. Should more than one generation be desired the buffy layer of leukocytes must be carefully removed and the erythrocytes placed in fresh serum. Only the parasites in the red blood cells escape phagocytosis. Sinton (1922), following the same general method, has developed a more refined but more complicated technic, using sealed capillary pipettes incubated at 35° to 38° C.

Chorine (1932) adds the defibrinated blood and glucose to a height of 2.5 cm. in small test tubes, adjusts the pH between 6.9 and 7.3 with carbonic or hydrochloric acid, warms the upper part of the test tube to dispel the air, closes it hermetically with a rubber stopper, and incubates at 37° C. The plasma, leukocytes and erythrocytes form three layers. Material for examination is taken from the upper part of the erythrocytic layer with a capillary pipette. The cultivated parasites are recognized by their dark pigment.

V. EXAMINATION OF HELMINTHIC OVA AND LARVÆ FROM INTESTINAL TRACT

Species.—Many helminthic infections may be diagnosed by identifying the ova or larvæ in the feces or in the intestinal tract. In addition, ova may be recovered from the perianal region and the respiratory tract. Some of the important helminths so identified are: *Ascaris lumbricoides, Trichuris trichiura, Enterobius vermicularis, Necator americanus, Ancylostoma duodenale, Strongyloides stercoralis, Clonorchis sinensis, Fasciola hepatica, Fasciolopsis buski, Schistosoma mansoni, S. japonicum, Tænia saginata, T. solium, Diphyllobothrium latum, Hymenolepis nana, H. diminuta, Dipylidium caninum, Opisthorchis felineus* and *Paragonimus westermani.*

COLLECTION OF MATERIAL

1. **Feces.**—Stools are collected in clean, dry containers. Most helminthic ova are identifiable for several days after passage, and usually a small, representative sample of feces is sufficient. Specimens obtained by enemata will often be positive for ova or segments of tapeworms when the ordinary stool is negative. In stools secured by purging, the whole or fragments of the adult worm and ova may be readily obtained.

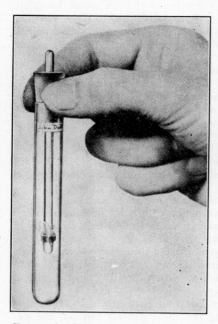

FIG. 278.—NATIONAL INSTITUTE OF HEALTH CELLOPHANE SWAB FOR COLLECTING *Enterobius* OVA

(From Sandground, *Physician's Bulletin,* March-April, 1941, Eli Lilly and Company).

If vermifuges have been employed, all the stools for at least 24 and preferably for 48 hours should be saved for examination as a check on anthelmintic treatment. Small amounts of the soft or liquid stool are successively examined in a large Petri dish to facilitate careful search for the scolices of tapeworms and small nematodes. As a rule the feces are examined at intervals after treatment for ova and larvæ. Such examinations may need to be continued for a long period in strongyloidiasis and clonorchiasis.

2. **Perianal Region.**—Enterobiasis is best diagnosed from scrapings of the anal and perianal regions. Although many varieties of blunt curettes and anal swabs have been used, the most efficient is the NIH cellophane swab (Hall, 1937). A small square of cellophane is wrapped about the tip of a glass rod and held in place by a rather wide rubber band (Fig. 278). The prepared swab is inserted in a perforated stopper and placed in a test tube to prevent loss of material after collection and to protect the handler from infection. The swab is used with a firm stroking motion, directed outward from the anal opening, parallel to and entering the folds of skin of the entire perianal region. The best time for swabbing is early morning before defecation and bathing. Eggs of helminths and sometimes the entire worm are picked up by the swab. For examination, the rubber band is cut, the cellophane with the adherent material is spread on a glass slide in a few drops of sodium hydroxide, covered with another slide and pressed together. The low power of the microscope is used for examination. At least seven swabs procured on different days should be examined before a negative diagnosis is warranted, although most infections will be detected by the first examination. This method is four to five times as effective as stool examinations (Sawitz *et al.,* 1939).

The ova of *Enterobius* are also found frequently in the nose and under the finger nails of young children. The nose is swabbed with cotton, and the dirt is removed from under the nails with forceps holding pieces of cotton soaked in 0.5 to 1% sodium hydroxide. The swab or pieces of cotton are shaken in a small amount of sodium hydroxide and the liquid centrifuged. The sediment is examined microscopically. The method is not reliable, since the finding of ova in these two places is dependent upon the habits of the patient.

3. **Stomach and Duodenum.**—At times the duodenal contents will reveal parasites, when ova or larvæ have not been detected in the feces, but the method of obtaining material for examination is so unpleasant for the patient that it is not often used. In cases with definite clinical evidence and negative feces, it is possible that duodenal or

intraintestinal lavage (de Rivas, 1926) with warm magnesium sulphate or sodium chloride solution will dislodge helminths or their ova, which may subsequently be found in the feces.

MICROSCOPICAL EXAMINATION OF FECES

4. **Thin Film.**—Thoroughly emulsify a representative bit of feces or mucus in a few drops of sodium chloride solution on a clean slide. Spread thinly and evenly and cover with a cover-glass. A satisfactory film is slightly opaque and allows newsprint to be read through it. Examine the film systematically in meander lines. At least three films should be examined before a negative diagnosis is made; even one ovum or larva constitutes a positive diagnosis. In schistosomiasis the ova are more often found in flecks of blood or mucus. Usually the surface of the feces will yield the most ova. The thin film is diagnostically accurate in hookworm infection only when 500 or more ova are present in each gram of feces (Hausheer and Herrick, 1926). Concentrative methods (Section **VII**, VII) may be used in light infections with negative thin films or in field work where numbers of specimens are examined.

5. **Thick Film.**—This technic, which is not often used, yields varying results. The thick, dry fecal smears, cleared with cedar, wintergreen or paraffin oil, are about ten times as concentrated as the thin film. Faust (1939) states the method is excellent for the ova of *Ascaris, Tænia, Trichuris* and *Hymenolepis*. The eggs of *Clonorchis, Opisthorchis* and *Metagonimus* are readily found but their differential characters are not clearly visible. The thin-shelled ova of *Ancylostoma, Trichostrongylus* and *Diphyllobothrium* are often overlooked because of their transparency, while those of *Fasciola, Fasciolopsis* and *Schistosoma* are unidentifiable because of shrinkage.

VI. EXAMINATION OF HELMINTHIC OVA AND LARVÆ IN BLOOD, BODY FLUIDS AND TISSUES

In addition to the methods described in Section **VII**, V, special technics are available for recovering the ova and larvæ of helminths from the blood, sputum, urine, exudates, transudates and tissues.

1. **Larvæ from the Blood.**—The larvæ of the following helminths may at times be demonstrated in the blood: *Wuchereria bancrofti, Loa loa, Acanthocheilonema perstans, Mansonella ozzardi,* other filariæ, and more rarely *Trichinella spiralis.*

Microfilariæ are rarely found in thin films of peripheral blood, but thick films will often show them. Blood should be withdrawn at the optimal time: between 10 P.M. and 4 A.M. for *Wuchereria bancrofti;* about noon for *Loa loa;* and at any hour of the day for *Acanthocheilonema perstans* and *Mansonella ozzardi*. Thick films are prepared as described in Section **VII**, III, 8. The smear may be examined under low power while still wet. The microfilariæ appear as readily distinguishable glistening objects. The smear may then be stained with Giemsa's or Wright's stain (Section **VII**, III, 10 and 11), or it may be stained with Delafield's hematoxylin for five minutes, washed in water, differentiated in acid water, washed in tap water until blue, dehydrated in absolute alcohol, cleared, and mounted in balsam. Knott (1939) states that results comparable to the standard thick film examination of nocturnal blood for *Wuchereria bancrofti* microfilariæ may be obtained by laking with 2% formalin and concentrating 1 ml. of venous blood taken during the day. This method is more convenient for surveys among children.

The larvæ of *Trichinella spiralis* may be recovered from the blood during their migration from the intestine to the muscles. About 5 to 10 ml. of venous blood are withdrawn, placed in citrate solution, and centrifuged for a minute or more at about 1,000 r.p.m. The larvæ are found in the bottom of the tube. Initial dehemoglobinization will permit easier recognition of the larvæ.

2. **Ova and Larvæ from Urine and Lymph.**—The ova of *Schistosoma hæmatobium* are ordinarily found in the urine, which is allowed to settle in a urinalysis glass or is centrifuged. Barlow (1931) recommends staining the sediment by adding a drop of aqueous solution of methylene blue. The sediment is smeared, allowed to dry and examined. If examined at once, the eggs are pale amber on a blue background. If the smears are left for some days the film should be moistened before examination; the eggshells then have a blue color. The background may be decolorized by careful washing in water, which leaves the ova stained blue. The ova tend to lie on their sides with the spines in view. The microfilariæ of *Wuchereria bancrofti* occur at times in the lymph or, when chyluria is present, in the urine. They are easily separated from the urine and lymph by centrifuging. *Ascaris* larvæ have been found in the urine in heavy experimental infections.

3. **Ova and Larvæ from Sputum.**—The ova of *Paragonimus westermani* are commonly found in the sputum of infected persons. Occasionally the larvæ of *Strongyloides stercoralis* and more rarely those of *Ascaris lumbricoides* and the hookworms may be coughed up during their migration from the bronchioles to the glottis. The mouth is thoroughly rinsed with hydrogen peroxide, and sputum from the deeper respiratory passages is passed into a clean sputum jar. In *Paragonimus* infection the sputum is flecked with brownish spots, the ova of the parasite. A small amount of sputum is transferred to a slide with a toothpick and examined under a cover-glass. The sputum may be preserved temporarily with 1 per cent phenol.

4. **Ova and Larvæ from Exudates and Transudates.**—The ova and larvæ of various helminths occasionally are found in exudates and transudates. The sediment is examined after centrifuging.

5. **Identification of Larvæ in Tissues.**—Specimens of tissues may be obtained by biopsy or at autopsy. The microfilariæ of *Onchocerca volvulus* may be demonstrated by teasing thin slices of skin in a drop of water or by sectioning the nodules. *Trichinella spiralis* is the helminth that is commonly diagnosed by biopsy of muscle tissue, although cysticerci and spargana may at times be removed from the tissues. A small piece of muscle is taken by biopsy from the deltoid, biceps, gastrocnemius or pectoralis major, usually near their tendinous attachments, and is divided into two parts. The first may be crushed in a trichina press or between two slides and examined under the low power of the microscope for precystic or encysted larvæ. As an alternative the crushed muscle may be impregnated with a 0.1, 0.5 or 2.0% solution of iodine in potassium iodide for 10 minutes; washed, differentiated and decolorized in 2.5% sodium thiosulphate; treated with a 10% solution of ammoniated silver nitrate to impregnate the iodized portions with silver; and the preparation is finally washed and cleared in 5% sodium thiosulphate. The *Trichinella* larvæ are well differentiated by this method (Kalwaryjski, 1936).

A second strip of muscle may be run through the usual histological technic for sections and stained with hematoxylin and eosin; or it may be digested for several hours in an artificial digestive juice at 37° C. and the larvæ concentrated by centrifuging. The latter procedure is a more accurate diagnostic method than the direct examination of the crushed muscle.

6. **Roentgen-ray Diagnosis.**—The Roentgen ray is not an important means of diagnosis in helminthic infections except in echinococcosis, in which the hydatid cysts, particularly of the bones, are often diagnosed roentgenologically. Filariæ, the cysticerci of *Tænia solium,* and larvæ of *Trichinella spiralis* are sometimes demonstrable by x-ray if sufficiently calcified.

7. **Staining of Larvæ.**—Blood films prepared for the study of *Trichinella* larvæ or microfilariæ may be stained with any of the Romanowsky stains although Giemsa's is preferable. Staining for one-half hour or longer in diluted Giemsa's stain, about 1 drop of stock to 1 ml. of neutral distilled water or buffer solution, usually furnishes the

most clear-cut definition. The body of the microfilaria stains azure, the excretory and anal pores deep red, and the sheath a pale pink.

Bohmer's hematoxylin is recommended for staining the sheath more deeply. Solution A, 1 gm. hematoxylin crystals and 12 ml. absolute alcohol; Solution B, alum 1 gm. and distilled water 240 ml. Mix 2 or 3 drops of A with 10 or 15 ml. of B. Blood films are dehemoglobinized in distilled water, dried, covered with mixed stain, steamed, rinsed with distilled water, differentiated in acid alcohol (2% HCl in 70% alcohol), rinsed in 1:10,000 ammonia water, run up rapidly through alcohols to xylene, and mounted in dammar, Canada balsam or euparol.

8. **Vital Staining of Larvæ.**—There has been little work done on vital staining of larval forms. Faust and Meleney and others have reported success in staining free-swimming trematode miracidia with dilute solutions of neutral red and cresyl blue. Methylene blue, 1:5,000 in physiological sodium chloride solution, may be used to stain and differentiate microfilariæ of *Loa loa, Wuchereria bancrofti, Onchocerca volvulus* and *Acanthocheilonema perstans*. Sharp (1927) states that the microfilariæ of *W. bancrofti* are practically inert to the action of the dye, but that the microfilariæ of *Loa loa* and *O. volvulus* absorb it readily, and *A. perstans* very readily.

VII. CONCENTRATIVE AND QUANTITATIVE METHODS FOR OVA AND LARVÆ OF HELMINTHS

If thin or thick films of feces are negative (Section **VII**, V, 4 and 5) or if a count of the number of ova is desired in order to estimate the intensity of infection, some concentrative method must be applied. The following methods are among the most satisfactory of the many that have been reported:

SEDIMENTATION

1. **Simple Sedimentation:**

Value.—No distortion of ova. Satisfactory for most helminth ova, especially for *Schistosoma japonicum* and *S. mansoni*.

Disadvantage.—Time consuming. Not adapted to quantitative studies.

Technic.—Thoroughly emulsify the whole fecal specimen in 10 to 20 times its volume of tap water and let settle for an hour or two. (Cone-shaped graduates of a pint to quart capacity are advisable but not obligatory.) Carefully pour or siphon off the top two-thirds with its débris. Nearly fill container with water, thoroughly mix, and let settle. Repeat until supernatant fluid is nearly clear. Pour off water, remove small amount of sediment to slide with pipette, and examine for ova.

Several authorities recommend an amplification of this fundamental method for miracidia. After washing and sedimentation, the sediment is diluted with water, placed preferably in an Erlenmeyer flask and left as long as 24 hours. The miracidia will have hatched and with a hand lens may be observed swimming in the upper layers of water in the neck of the flask. Care must be taken not to confuse the free-living infusorians of stale water with the miracidia. This modification is valuable in checking treatment of schistosomiasis, as it will detect very small numbers of ova.

2. **Straining:**

Value.—Useful for all helminth ova or larvæ. Removes bulky matter and concentrates ova.

Disadvantage.—Slowness. Danger of contamination from incomplete removal of ova from previously used screen.

Technic.—Emulsify a piece of feces about the size of a pecan in a small amount of water. Pour through bolting cloth (5 meshes to the millimeter) supported in a funnel, or through a bronzed wire screen (30 to 120 meshes per inch). Coarser particles are retained, the ova are collected in a tube or beaker. Loopfuls of the filtrate are examined on slides.

3. **Centrifuging:**

Value.—Best general method for fecal examination in clinical laboratory, since both ova and cysts are concentrated. An effective method for the operculated ova of *Diphyllobothrium, Fasciola, Fasciolopsis, Clonorchis, Opisthorchis, Metagonimus,* and *Heterophyes.* Also of value for *Ascaris* and hookworm ova and *Strongyloides* larvæ in light infections.

Disadvantage.—Not quantitative, effective concentration not great.

Technic.—Thoroughly comminute 1 to 10 gm. of feces in 10 to 20 times its volume of water. Strain through dampened cheesecloth or wire basket (about 40 meshes to inch) into centrifuge tubes preferably with rounded bottoms. Centrifuge 1 to 2 minutes at about 2,500 r.p.m. Repeat, stirring between runs, until supernatant fluid is fairly clear. Pour off fluid. Ova and larvæ are concentrated in sediment.

4. **De Rivas' Acid-ether Technic (1928):**

Value.—Concentration and clarification of ova.

Disadvantage.—Cysts of Protozoa shrunken and not recognizable. Ether expensive.

Technic.—Mix thoroughly by shaking 1 to 2 gm. of feces and 10 ml. of 5% acetic acid in a small centrifuge tube. Let stand ½ to 1 minute to allow heavy particles to settle. Strain supernatant liquid through 2 layers of cheesecloth into a second centrifuge tube. Add an equal volume of ether, stopper tube, and shake thoroughly for 30 seconds. Centrifuge tube 2 to 5 minutes. Four layers are differentiated in the tube: (a) top layer of ether; (b) plug of débris; (c) acid layer; and (d) small amount of sediment in the bottom. Rim the plug with a wire or wooden applicator and pour off all but the sediment. Remove sediment to a slide with a capillary pipette and examine. The top layer of ethereal extract may be pipetted off and the benzidine test for occult blood applied to it.

FLOTATION

The principle on which all flotation technics for concentration are based is that of differences in specific gravity of the salt solutions and of the ova and larvæ. The latter float to the surface in the heavier solution while fecal material sinks gradually to the bottom. For all except operculated ova and those of *Schistosoma,* which shrink beyond recognition in salt solution, flotation methods are superior to centrifuging. The larger operculated ova of *Diphyllobothrium, Fasciola* and *Fasciolopsis* open up or shrivel and sink in the salt solution, while the greater density of the smaller, thick-shelled ova of *Metagonimus, Clonorchis* and *Dicrocœlium* cause them to settle.

In the following technics, unless otherwise noted, the brine solution is a saturated one made from crude salt which usually has a somewhat greater density than refined salt. After filtration it is kept in a stoppered bottle. The specific gravity of the solution will range from 1.120 to 1.210. The optimal time to examine specimens from brine flotation is 5 to 20 minutes, and in light infections 5 to 10 minutes.

5. **Kofoid-Barber Brine Flotation-loop Technic (1919):**

Value.—Rapid but less satisfactory than several other methods.

Disadvantage.—Looping does not remove many of the ova in film. Method not quantitative.

Technic.—Comminute fecal specimen in original paraffined containers with 2 to 3 times its volume of brine. Force coarse roughage to bottom with disk of steel or glass wool. Let stand 1 hour. Transfer entire surface film to slide with a large wire loop.

6. **Willis-Malloy Technic (1921):**

Value.—Rapid concentration of ova. Good both for diagnosis and for field work.

Disadvantage.—Not accurate for ova-counting.

Technic.—Dilute and thoroughly emulsify 0.5 to 1 gm. of feces with 10 to 20 volumes of brine in a glass cylinder about 2.5 cm. in diameter. Use enough brine to form a meniscus. Carefully place a clean fecal slide (75 x 37 mm.) on the meniscus and allow to remain for 10 to 60 minutes. Remove slide, invert and examine.

Hausheer and Herrick (1926) emphasize the need of thorough mixing of the specimen and its thorough comminution in brine, and recommend that the feces should remain in the salt solution no longer than half an hour before examination to avoid disintegration of the ova. They believe that if these details are properly handled, the method is as accurate as Lane's D. C. F. Method (Section VII, VII, 8).

7. Faust's Zinc Sulphate Centrifugal Flotation Technic (1938 and 1939):

Value.—Detects light infections of both ova and larvæ and also protozoan cysts. (Recommended by Department of Tropical Medicine, Tulane University, New Orleans, La.)

Disadvantage.—Not quantitative.

Technic.—(a) Make suspension by using one part of specimen (about size of a pecan) with about 10 parts of lukewarm tap water.

(b) Strain about 10 ml. of suspension through one layer of *wet* cheesecloth in a small funnel into a test tube.

(c) Centrifuge 45 to 60 seconds at top speed. Pour off supernatant fluid, add 2 or 3 ml. of water, break up sediment by shaking or tapping, and add more water to fill tube. Repeat (usually 3 or 4 times) until supernatant fluid is clear.

(d) Pour off last supernatant fluid, add 3 to 4 ml. of zinc sulphate solution of specific gravity of 1.180 (33 per cent solution), break up packed sediment and add more zinc sulphate solution to within about one-half inch of the rim.

(e) Centrifuge for 45 to 60 seconds at top speed.

(f) With a bacteriological loop remove several loopfuls of material floating in the surface film to a clean slide, add one drop of D'Antoni's iodine stain, and agitate the preparation manually to insure uniform staining. Mount with a cover-glass.

METHODS OF COUNTING OVA

In surveys of infected populations it is sometimes desirable to determine the intensity of infection. One method of doing this is to employ a technic that is both diagnostic and quantitative, the number of ova measuring more or less accurately the degree of infection. The reliability of the ova-count from only one fecal specimen is questionable, since the effect of such factors as consistency of the stool, diet, faulty digestion, drugs, etc., is still unknown. In field surveys and in public health laboratories it is not always practical to perform a series of ova-counts. Although the exact correlation between ova-counts and the number of worms harbored has not yet been established, the ova-count will give the field worker and physician an idea of the relative intensity of the infection.

Since the daily output of feces varies rather widely, Faust and Khaw (1926) recommend that ova-counts should be made on a series of specimens over a period of 10 to 14 days in order to obtain the average daily output. The number per day is more dependable than that of the ova per gram of feces because of fluctuations in fecal consistency; also, the ova output per worm even in the same species may vary widely in different hosts.

Various investigators have determined the egg-laying capacity of several species of worms per unit of time or per unit of formed fecal material: e.g., *Necator americanus* 8,830 ova per day (Stoll, 1923). If the average daily output of ova in a patient is divided by these figures, the number of ova-producing worms may be estimated. In hermaphroditic species the result of the division indicates the number of worms; whereas, in bisexual species the figure is the estimated number of females, and the total number of worms is roughly twice the estimated number of females, since the sexes are present in almost equal numbers.

Several workers have found that the differences in ova-counts on stools of various consistencies may be somewhat lessened by converting all specimens to a formed-stool basis with the following ratios: formed 1, mush-formed 1.5, mushy 2, mushy diarrheic 3, and diarrheic 4. More recently, however, Scott and Headlee (1938) have concluded that this reduction to a formed-stool basis is unnecessary.

8. Lane's Direct Centrifugal Flotation (D. C. F. Method) (1923):

Value.—Precise and suited for a central diagnostic laboratory. It is a sufficiently accurate means of estimating the number of adult hookworms, *Ascaris* or *Trichuris* by counting the ova.

Disadvantage.—Requires competent technical assistance. Too complicated for field work. Difficult to count a large number of ova in hanging drop.

Technic.—Measure 1 ml. of specimen and place in special ground-top centrifuge tube. Fill with tap water to within 1 inch of top. Stopper and shake until thoroughly comminuted. Spin for 1 minute at 1,000 r.p.m. Pour off supernatant fluid. Nearly fill tube with sodium chloride solution (specific gravity 1.200). Cork and gently agitate laterally until the suspension is homogeneous. Return tube to centrifuge, fill to the brim with more brine, and cover with a thick cover-glass which is secured by the four horns of a special holder. Centrifuge 1 minute at 1,000 r.p.m. Pick off cover-glass, place it film side down on cone-shaped plasticine supports, and examine as a hanging drop. As many as 95% of all ova present in the feces appear on the cover-glass.

If the technic is to be used for ova-counts Lane (1924) stipulates that three additional cover-glasses be obtained by adding a few drops of brine to the tube between spins. Soper (1926) reports that between-spin stirring of the tube is necessary to secure complete egg counts. A negligible number of ova appear on the fourth cover-glass. The first pour-off is centrifuged, treated with brine, and spun with a cover-glass. In the second pour-off care is taken to lose no precipitate. The number of ova found on the cover-glass of the pour-offs added to the count of the four original covers is the minimal ova-count of the specimen per milliliter of feces.

9. Hamburg Cover-glass Technic (1926 and 1927):

Value.—Accurate and rapid.

Disadvantage.—Three separate cover-glass preparations must be counted and special cylinders are required.

Technic.—Place 1 gm. of feces in the bottom depression of a special glass or metal cylinder about 5 cm. in diameter and 3.5 cm. high. Fill the container with brine solution and thoroughly mix specimen and diluent. Place three 18 mm. square cover-glasses on surface and leave for 10 minutes. Remove with forceps and place on slides, film down. Count all ova under each cover-glass and average counts. Compute total number of ova in a specimen as follows: if average is 20-40, multiply by 7; if 40-70, by 7.5; if 70-90, by 8.5; and if 90 or more by 9.5.

10. Stoll Egg-count (1923).—The technic, a dilution rather than a concentration method, was designed for the accurate counting of helminthic ova.

Value.—More rapid than Lane's D. C. F. method. Suitable for field work. Stoll (1923) and Stoll and Hausheer (1926) claim the method is accurate to within 10 per cent and believe it superior to Lane's D. C. F. counting method. Detects light infections where more than 50 ova occur per gram of feces if two slides are examined (Hausheer and Herrick, 1926). The small-drop modification does not always identify infections having fewer than 200 ova per gram of feces.

Disadvantage.—Light infections may be missed.

Technic.—Weigh 3 gm. feces into large test tube or centrifuge tube graduated to 45 ml. Add N/10 sodium hydroxide to 45 ml. mark. Add 10 small glass beads, insert rubber stopper, and shake vigorously for about 1 minute to secure *complete* homogeneity. (Compact feces may be left in the hydroxide overnight if necessary.) With a graduated pipette withdraw 0.15 ml. of the suspension from about the middle of the tube, transfer to the center of a large slide (2 by 3 inches), and cover with a 22 by 40 mm. cover-glass. Count ova under the low power of the microscope. The total ova counted multiplied by

100 is the number of ova per gram of feces. Multiplying the count per gram of feces by the total daily fecal production gives the total daily output of ova.

Stoll and Hausheer (1926) suggest the following simplification: in a pyrex Erlenmeyer flask ("hookworm flask"), graduated at 56 and 60 ml. levels, place 56 ml. of N/10 sodium hydroxide and 4 ml. of feces. After complete comminution by shaking with glass beads, withdraw either 0.075 or 0.15 ml. with a special pipette and place on a fecal slide. For the smaller amount the factor for converting the count into ova per gram of feces is 200, for the larger amount 100. The smaller amount will not ordinarily reveal infections of fewer than 100 ova per gram of feces. The authors recommend that the results be expressed as ova per milliliter rather than per gram of feces when this displacement method is used.

11. **Caldwell and Caldwell's Ova-counting Technic (1926).**—This method, a combination of dilution and flotation principles, was designed for counting hookworm ova in field surveys, but it is applicable to other species. Caldwell and Caldwell believe that it adequately replaces both the Willis' flotation technic for diagnosis and the Stoll method of ova-counting in field work.

Value.—Rapid. Sugar film maintains position on slide and does not dry or crystallize as rapidly as sodium hydroxide solution. May be used for ova in soil.

Disadvantage.—Not diagnostic or enumerative in light infections under 100 ova per gram, unless a large sample of the suspension is examined.

Technic.—In a tube or flask calibrated at 40 ml. place 4 gm. (approximately 4 ml.) of the stirred fecal specimen, add 4 ml. 30% antiformin, and thoroughly mix with a glass stirring rod. Leaving the rod in the tube, allow suspension to stand at room temperature or in incubator for one hour or more. Add 32 ml. sugar solution of 1.230 sp. gr. (750 gm. of sugar in 1,000 ml. of tap water) and stir thoroughly. Insert a serological pipette to the bottom of tube and bubble air through suspension. Withdraw 0.1 ml. of suspension from the middle of the tube immediately after bubbling. Place sample on slide and spread with a pointed instrument into a small, flat square or rectangular film. No cover-glass is needed. Count ova and multiply by 100 to obtain ova per gram of feces.

The use of a 0.2 ml. specimen will register the presence of 50 ova per gram and sometimes fewer than that number. In this case the factor is 50. As a diagnostic alternative when the films are negative, the rest of the fecal suspension is placed in a wider container and the ova are allowed to rise for at least 20 minutes. The surface film of ova is then removed with the open end of a test tube or vial.

RECOVERY OF OVA AND LARVÆ FROM SOIL

When epidemiological surveys are being made, it is often desirable to determine the extent of the pollution of the soil by helminthic ova and larvæ. Headlee's method (1936) is a modification of earlier methods devised by Caldwell and Caldwell (1928) and Spindler (1929). The Baermann apparatus may be used to isolate larvæ from the soil. The larvæ most frequently isolated from soil are those of hookworm, *Ascaris, Strongyloides* and *Trichuris.*

12. **Headlee's Method for Ova.**—A pint or more of the thin surface layer of the soil is collected in jars, sent to the laboratory, and examined promptly. The soil is first crushed and mixed. Then representative 5 to 10 gm. portions are placed in 50 ml. centrifuge tubes and treated for an hour with 10 ml. of 30 per cent antiformin. Stir the suspensions frequently and thoroughly to free ova from dirt particles. Fill tubes with sodium dichromate (sp. gr. 1.35), shake vigorously and centrifuge at 1,000 r.p.m. for one to two minutes. Loop ova from surface film into 15 ml. centrifuge tube, add water nearly to top, and centrifuge for one minute at 1,000 r.p.m. Pipette off the supernatant fluid. Spread the sediment evenly in a rectangle over one or more broad fecal slides, depending on the amount of débris. No cover-glass is needed if the films are carefully prepared.

The ova may be classified according to their stages of development, using the nomenclature and divisions of Looss (1911) as defined by Brown (1927). These stages are: *degenerate eggs* (showing annulation, vacuolation or clearing); *one-cell; early morula* (1-15 cells); *late morula* (16 cells to complete morula); *tadpole;* and *motile embryo.*

13. **Maplestone and Mukerjii's Method (1936).**—The authors found through examining soil samples experimentally infected with *Ascaris* ova that from 2 to 51% of the ova were recovered with their technic. The soil is mixed with 10 ml. of a 2.13% caustic soda solution and allowed to stand for 2 hours. Freshly prepared chlorine is bubbled through the mixture for ten minutes. After centrifuging, the supernatant fluid is drawn off, saturated sodium chloride solution added, and the tubes again spun.

METHODS OF CULTIVATING LARVÆ FROM FECES AND SOIL

The use of cultural methods for helminthic larvæ is confined usually to experimental work, although occasionally fecal cultures may be warranted in clinical studies. For rhabditoid species, in which ova develop rapidly in the feces or soil, a simple method suffices.

14. **Simple Culture.**—The sample of feces or soil, thoroughly mixed with an equal amount of sterile sand or powdered animal charcoal is placed on filter paper cut to fit a Petri dish or Stender jar. Within a few hours or days, depending on the species, the larvæ are found in the water of condensation on the under side of the cover. Thence they are removed to a slide for microscopical examination. If the original mixture of feces and charcoal is placed in the Baermann apparatus, almost all the larvæ in the sample may be collected. If the culture is kept in contact with 2% formalin, development is accelerated. The formalin must be completely removed by washing before experimental use of the embryonated larvæ (Faust, 1939).

Shallow water cultures at 20° to 30° C. give good results with fully embryonated ova of *Diphyllobothrium, Paragonimus, Fasciola* and *Fasciolopsis.* The ova of many cestodes and some trematodes, although fully embryonated when recovered from the feces, do not ordinarily hatch outside their intermediate host.

15. **The Baermann Apparatus (1917).**—Although the Baermann apparatus is most valuable for isolating hookworm larvæ from soil, it is also well adapted for removing other nematode larvæ from the soil and feces. It may be used as a substitute for Stoll's ova-counting or Lane's D. C. F. method in estimating the number of hookworms in a fecal sample, but considerable time is required for all the larvæ to hatch. The effectiveness of the apparatus depends on the fact that nematode larvæ will migrate from soil downward to water of a warmer temperature, if the two are in contact.

The apparatus consists of a glass funnel fitted with rubber tubing and a clamp and almost filled with water about 10° F. warmer than the specimen. After comminution the soil, feces or fecal culture is put in a small sieve (1 mm. mesh) so placed in the funnel that the water level is just above the lower surface of the sample in the sieve. Cort et al. (1922) state that most of the larvæ come out of the soil within six hours, but that an appreciable number may be collected after that time. Faust (1939) recommends placing a piece of ice on top of the specimen to expedite the movement of the larvæ into the water thus permitting the maximal number of the larvæ to be collected within an hour. About 50 ml. of fluid are withdrawn from the funnel into a centrifuge tube, centrifuged, the supernatant fluid pipetted off, and the sediment examined on a fecal slide. It is sometimes advisable to repeat the separation stage to obtain the maximal yield of larvæ, or, if too much soil is present in the run-off, a smaller Baermann apparatus may be used for a better separation of larvæ and soil.

16. **Beach's Semisolid Medium (1936).**—For cultivating the larvæ of *Strongyloides simiæ,* Beach used a semisolid medium composed of 2 gm. of dehydrated meat extract agar, 25 ml. of filtered aqueous extract of monkey feces, and 75 ml. of distilled water. The fecal extract was prepared by comminuting feces in distilled water, straining through

cheesecloth, and filtering through paper and a Seitz filter. He also employed half strength Locke's solution with less satisfactory results. Transplanting from the original cultures to fresh medium was generally unsuccessful.

17. **Nutrient Agar Medium.**—McCoy (1930) found that the larvæ of the dog hookworm grew readily on half strength nutrient agar inoculated with bacteria, which served as food. The ova, which were added to 24-hour cultures of bacteria in flasks, were obtained by preliminary straining, centrifuging and flotation. They were sterilized by a 5% antiformin solution in 10% formalin for 30 minutes and washed several times in sterile water. The ova hatched at room temperature in about 36 hours and more rapidly at 25° to 30° C. About 50 ml. of warm (40° to 45° C.) water were placed in the flasks, shaken gently to wash the larvæ from the surface of the agar and samples of the suspension withdrawn for microscopical examination.

18. **Sterilized Feces.**—Augustine (1940) used sterilized feces for culturing *Strongyloides* larvæ from monkeys and dogs. A dab of sterilized feces was placed in the center of small Petri dishes, several of which were put into a larger one with moistened filter paper inserted in the cover. The cultures were incubated at room temperature, more rapid development occurring in the warmer months.

METHODS OF STAINING LARVÆ FROM FECES AND SOIL

19. **Svensson and Kessel's Method (1926).**—This staining technic for larvæ is a modification of the methods of Cobb (1890) and of Magath (1916). The technic was first used to differentiate the larvæ of *Necator* and *Ancylostoma* but it is applicable to other larval worms. The larvæ may be extracted from the soil by the Baermann apparatus (Section **VII**, VII, 15). If only a few larvæ are required, 1 or 2 gm. of top soil are placed in a small linen bag on a large slide, enough warm water is poured over the bag to moisten the soil and leave a medium-sized drop on the slide, and within a few minutes the larvæ will pass from the bag into the water on the slide. It is advisable to "clear" the larvæ of food particles, which obscure anatomical details, by having them migrate one or more times through a column of moist sterile sand.

(a) Larvæ are allowed to sink to the bottom of a test tube, the excess water is pipetted off, and sufficient 50% alcohol at 70° C. is added to kill them.

(b) A small round piece of linen or silk of fine texture is equipped with one thread through the center and another thread stitched in and around the edge but with free ends (Fig. 279, 1). With the aid of the central thread the cloth is inserted into a little glass funnel (Fig. 279, 2). The larvæ suspended in alcohol are strained through the funnel, using a wide-mouthed pipette for their transfer. The cloth is tied into a bag by using the peripheral thread as a drawstring and inserted into the object holder (Fig. 279, 3), a piece of glass tubing, 4 x 1 cm., using the central thread as a leader.

(c) The object holder is placed for 2 hours in a test tube containing fixing fluid composed of equal parts of acetic acid, 95% alcohol and saturated aqueous corrosive sublimate.

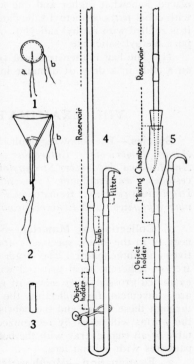

Fig. 279.—Apparatus for Staining Nematode Larvæ

(From Svenson and Kessel, 1926).

(d) The staining apparatus (Fig. 279, 4) consists of a reservoir and filter with an adjustable flow. The reservoir and filter are first filled with 35% alcohol containing enough tincture of iodine to give a dark amber color. Then the object holder, filled with alcohol of the same strength, is attached and a cotton plug inserted. The flow is regulated by a clamp so that 30 ml. of the iodine-alcohol may pass through the apparatus in 12 hours.

(e) Distilled water is passed through the apparatus for about an hour.

(f) The apparatus is filled with Delafield's hematoxylin (1:25 dilution) and left for 24 hours.

(g) Water is passed through for 20 minutes.

(h) Acetic acid (5%) is passed through for 5 minutes, followed immediately by distilled water.

(i) Ammonia (5%) is passed through for 5 minutes and then distilled water.

(j) The object holder is transferred to Magath's differentiator having a mixing chamber (Fig. 279, 5). The reservoir is filled successively with 35, 50, 70 and 85% alcohol. When it has nearly emptied itself, 20 ml. of 95% alcohol is added and then absolute alcohol until 50 ml. of the latter have been used. When only absolute alcohol remains in the reservoir, a glass tube like the object holder containing CaO and plugged with cotton in both ends is attached to the upper end of the reservoir to prevent the absorption of moisture by the absolute alcohol. The flow is then regulated so as to allow 24 hours for the dehydration process.

(k) The object holder is then transferred from the differentiator to a Stender dish filled with absolute alcohol, which is connected by wick syphons to two other Stenders, one placed somewhat higher and one a little lower than the first. The highest dish is filled with equal parts of methyl salicylate and absolute alcohol. When the top dish has drained, it is refilled with methyl salicylate. About 36 hours are needed to bring the specimens into pure methyl salicylate.

(l) The bag is then removed from the object holder and the specimens are mounted on a slide in a drop of dammar in methyl salicylate.

VIII. EXAMINATION OF ADULT HELMINTHS

Species.—The following adult helminths may be recovered from the feces: nematodes, *Ascaris lumbricoides, Enterobius vermicularis, Trichuris trichiura, Necator americanus, Ancylostoma duodenale, Strongyloides stercoralis,* and very rarely *Trichinella spiralis;* cestodes, *Tænia saginata, Tænia solium, Diphyllobothrium latum, Hymenolepis nana,* and *Dipylidium caninum;* trematodes, *Fasciolopsis buski, Heterophyes heterophyes, Metagonimus yokogawai,* and *Echinochasmus perfoliatus.*

1. **Collection of Material.**—Since these adult worms only rarely appear spontaneously in the feces, specimens are usually obtained after the administration of purgatives and anthelmintics. The larger species are easily "fished" from the specimen, washed free of adherent fecal material with warm physiological sodium chloride solution, and examined grossly. Wire sieves of graduated sizes (6, 12, 24 and 40 meshes to the inch) are convenient for collecting the smaller helminths. The fecal specimen is strained through these sieves and the débris rinsed with warm sodium chloride solution. Usually the worms will be easily recognized on one of the four sieves. A Petri dish on a black table or an enamel tray with the bottom painted black facilitates the examination of these parasites with a hand lens.

2. **Examination.**—Mouth parts are sometimes diagnostic as in differentiating *Necator americanus* and *Ancylostoma duodenale.* Examination of the tail may indicate the sex of nematodes, the male being often distinguished by the curvature, spicules or caudal bursa. Proglottides of tapeworms may be cleared by immersing in carbol-xylene (75% carbolic

acid, 25% xylene). This method, which reveals the branches of the gravid uterus, is of value in differentiating *Tænia solium* from *T. saginata*.

The scolex with its characteristic suckers and armed or unarmed rostellum makes identification of the species of tapeworm easy, but it is difficult to find in fecal specimens. All intestinal discharges for a period of two or three days following anthelmintic treatment should be carefully examined. This involves the tedious job of hunting for a scolex little larger than a pinhead. The task is made somewhat easier if only the small immature segments, about as thick as heavy sewing thread near the neck, are examined. Since treatment must be repeated unless the scolex has been recovered, the necessity for a careful search is obvious.

Trematode parasites may be flattened between glass slides so that their characteristics may be examined more easily.

3. **Recovery from Tissues.**—For the diagnosis of *Onchocerca volvulus* infections an excised nodule may be sectioned grossly in order to demonstrate the thread-like worms in the matrix. In patients without palpable nodules a biopsied specimen of skin or of bulbar conjunctiva is placed in a drop of physiological sodium chloride solution on a slide, and the microfilariæ are teased out of the tissues for microscopical examination. Adult *Loa loa* worms may be recovered from their migratory tracts, often from about the head and eyeball. Other adult helminths may be obtained in a similar manner from the tissues. Reference to the Keys for the Identification of Adult Helminths of Man (Chapter V) will facilitate recognition.

4. **Maintenance of Helminths *in Vitro.*—**Some attempts have been made to keep adult helminths viable *in vitro*. Lee and Chu (1935) were able to maintain adult schistosomes for 2½ months in horse, sheep or rabbit serum, or in human ascitic fluid at 37° C. using aseptic methods and changing the medium at 1 to 2 weeks. Schistosomes, obtained aseptically from the portal vein of experimental animals, were first placed in sterile Locke's or sodium chloride solution and subsequently transferred to small, modified tissue flasks in which had been placed 2 ml. of the sterile culture fluid protected from desiccation and contamination by a tight-fitting rubber cap. No more than 5 worms were allotted to a flask. The worms soon died in flasks contaminated by bacteria. Chu (1938), by using weekly changes of diluted sera, maintained males of *Schistosoma japonicum* for 5 months and females for 2 months. *Clonorchis sinensis* survived for 5 months. Egg-laying was stimulated at first but later inhibited.

5. **Fixation and Preservation.**—Small nematodes may be conveniently killed in hot 70% alcohol containing 5% glycerol, or in steaming 70% alcohol with a few drops of glacial acetic acid. For large nematodes 10% formalin with a small amount of glycerol makes a good preservative. Specimens may be left in formalin, or washed with water and transferred through 35, 50 and 70% alcohol in which they may be stored permanently. Nematodes killed in formalin or alcohol can be cleared for immediate study in a solution of 4 parts of carbolic acid to 1 part of absolute alcohol. Carbol-lactic acid has been used as a preservative for some helminths.

Because the small nematodes are sensitive to changes in osmotic pressure, they are difficult to fix and stain. Fresh specimens may be relaxed in chloroform-water and then killed by heat. Faust (1939) recommends placing specimens for 10 to 24 hours in a steaming mixture of a saturated solution of mercuric chloride in physiological sodium chloride solution plus a few drops of glacial acetic acid. Specimens are thoroughly washed in water and run up through 35, 50 and 70% alcohol. Alcoholic iodine solution is then added a drop at a time to remove the remaining corrosive sublimate, until the alcohol remains a sherry color. After 24 hours in this solution the specimen is transferred to 70% alcohol.

Both *in toto* mounts and serial sections of parasites are often useful for study and demonstration. Larval forms can usually be mounted whole. In large tapeworms it is often advisable to fix and stain proglottides from several regions. The uteri of gravid segments may be injected with India ink with a hypodermic syringe before fixation.

Ristroph's (1934) method of fixing, staining and mounting of tapeworms gives excellent results.

Fixing Solution:

Commercial formalin	100 ml.
95% alcohol	250 ml.
Glacial acetic acid	50 ml.
Glycerol	100 ml.
Distilled water	500 ml.

For killing and fixing, a shallow pan or tray is lined with heavy filter paper well moistened with fixative. The scolex of each worm is first removed and fixed separately to avoid its loss and to prevent distortion.

Beginning with the anterior end flatten each specimen upon the damp paper in a normal extended position. If the animal is not fully extended there is a transverse wrinkling of the cuticle, but overstretching should be avoided, since it results in longitudinal wrinkling. After the tray has been filled, the tapeworms are covered with another sheet of absorbent paper moistened with fixative and allowed to stand for about 30 minutes, with just enough fixative added to cover the specimens. A second or even third layer of worms may be placed upon the first with equally good results. After twelve hours, the tapeworms are removed from the tray and placed for 4 hours in 35, 50 and 70% alcohol. They may be stored in 70% alcohol. Avoid crowding during dehydration to prevent tangling and curling.

Mayer's Hydrochloric Acid Carmine:

Carmine	4 gm.
Water	15 ml.
Hydrochloric acid	20 drops

Boil until carmine is dissolved; add 95 ml. of 85% alcohol, filter, and neutralize with ammonia almost to precipitation point. Refilter.

A dilution of 10% of the above mixture in very slightly acidified alcohol is used for staining the tapeworms. Overstain and then destain in acid alcohol until the proper differentiation is obtained. Grossly the worms are now a light rose in color. Dehydrate successively through 85%, 95% and absolute alcohol and clear slowly in oil of wintergreen.

For mounting place in a mixture of equal parts of thick balsam and oil of wintergreen. Thick balsam, which shortens the drying period, may be handled easily if kept warm by some such device as a substage lamp. Place warm balsam upon a warm slide and spread into the general shape of the cover-glass. Remove each segment from the balsam-wintergreen mixture, drain on filter paper, place in position in the warm balsam, and gently cover with a warm cover-glass.

Worms may also be stained with Delafield's or other hematoxylins. Delafield's stain is prepared by dissolving 1 gm. of hematoxylin crystals in 6 ml. of 95% alcohol and adding 100 ml. of saturated aqueous solution of ammonium alum. It is exposed to bright light for a week to "ripen," then 25 ml. of glycerol and 25 ml. of methyl alcohol are added and it is filtered after 2 days. The stain should be filtered whenever sediment has formed. This stock solution should be diluted 10 to 15 times with water.

Overstaining is practiced with subsequent destaining in 0.5% HCl in 70% alcohol until the material is a light red-brown color. After thorough washing in water the specimen may be immersed in a weakly alkaline solution, or better, differentiated in 1% lithium carbonate to bring out the violet shades.

Serial sections of helminthic worms may be made either by the paraffin or celloidin methods. Since the integument of the parasites shrinks easily, the worms must be run slowly through the alcohols and clearing solutions.

IX. SEROLOGICAL AND CHEMICAL METHODS OF DIAGNOSIS

Agglutinative, precipitative and alexin-fixative tests are used for the serological diagnosis of parasitic infections and for the identification of parasites. Their success depends upon the efficacy of the antigens, the technic employed, and the presence of detectable antibodies in the host. Nonspecific flocculation and chemical tests are also of diagnostic value.

PREPARATION OF ANTIGENS

Antigens for serological and cutaneous tests are prepared in various ways from adult and larval parasites and their products. The exact method of preparation depends upon the parasite, the serological procedure, and the ideas of the investigator. In general, antigens consist of suspensions of living or dead parasites, extracts of parasites, products of parasites, or extracts of tissues or secretions containing parasites.

For precipitative, alexin-fixative and cutaneous tests two types of antigens have been used: (1) aqueous extracts and (2) alcoholic extracts. Aqueous extracts are prepared from the fresh or dried parasite using physiological sodium chloride solution with or without formalin, phenol, toluol, glycerol or other preservatives; acid or alkalis that are subsequently neutralized; or Coca's fluid (sodium chloride 0.5 per cent, sodium bicarbonate 0.275 per cent, and phenol 0.4 per cent). Alcoholic extracts are made by direct extraction or after preliminary treatment with ether and acetone. These extracts are used unaltered or are evaporated to dryness and redissolved in an aqueous solution. The source of the material and the method of preparing the antigen vary with the parasite. Opinions differ as to the relative antigenic efficacy of aqueous and alcoholic extracts.

The preparation of antigens for helminthic parasites presents considerable difficulty, since the immunological importance of the lipoids and polysaccharides is unknown. No standard methods have evolved from the various published technics that have been adapted for individual parasites. Antigens are prepared from (1) adult worms or (2) their larvæ. In the former, aqueous and alcoholic extracts are made of fresh worms, dried powdered worms, parts of worms or special organs, or after the worms have been treated with chemicals to obtain fractionated antigens. In the latter, the extracts are made from fresh or dried larvæ, from tissues containing larvæ, or from the cystic fluids secreted by the larvæ.

PROTOZOA

1. **Flagellated Protozoa for Agglutinative Tests.**—The leishmanian and trypanosomal flagellates are the only parasites suitable for agglutinative tests. The necessary suspensions of living or dead organisms are best obtained from cultures, although trypanosomes may be concentrated from the blood of heavily infected animals. Suspensions of organisms, killed by heat or by chemicals, are preferred for the macroscopical agglutinative test.

In preparing a trypanosomal antigen, organisms from 10 to 12 cultures are washed free of extraneous material by centrifuging, suspended in physiological sodium chloride solution, and preserved in 0.5% phenol. When no cultures are available, trypanosomes may be concentrated from the blood of susceptible laboratory animals by hemolyzing the blood, and separating the trypanosomes from the stroma by centrifuging. Wagener and Koch (1926) prepared leishmanian antigens by suspending washed flagellates grown for 12 days on N. N. N. medium in physiological sodium chloride solution to which a drop of toluol had been added. Noguchi (1924) used living leishmanian flagellates.

Endamœba.—Wagener (1924) extracted the ulcerated intestines of infected cats with Coca's fluid to obtain an *Endamœba histolytica* antigen for precipitative tests. Craig (1927 and 1928), Weiss and Arnold (1934) and Tsuchiya (1934) prepared alcoholic extracts for alexin-fixation from cultures of *Endamœba histolytica*.

2. Antigen from Cultures.

Craig (1927) prepared an antigen for alexin-fixation by adding 7 to 8 volumes of absolute alcohol to the sediment of a 48-hour culture of *Endamœba histolytica*, extracting for 15 days at 37° C. with daily shaking, and using the filtrate as an antigen.

Leishmania.—Antigens are prepared from infected spleens or from cultures.

3. Antigen from Tissues.

Hindle, Hou and Patton (1926) triturated the spleen of a hamster heavily infected with *L. donovani* in 5 ml. of physiological sodium chloride solution, strained the extract through muslin, and preserved it by adding 1% glycerol and 0.5% phenol.

4. Antigen from Cultures.

Antigens free from extraneous tissue-products may be prepared from 10- to 12-day cultures by suspending the flagellates in physiological sodium chloride solution. Alcoholic extracts may be prepared in the same manner as those of *Endamœba histolytica*.

Trypanosoma.—Aqueous and alcoholic extracts of macerated infected spleens or trypanosomes concentrated from the blood of infected animals and of cultured trypanosomes have been prepared.

5. Antigen from Tissues.

Villela and Bicalho (1923) prepared an aqueous phenolized antigen of *T. cruzi* that was potent for 4 months, by freeing the spleen of an infected dog of blood clots by washing in saline, cutting it in small pieces, and triturating in a mortar (1 part spleen, 2 parts 0.5 per cent phenol in distilled water, and 1 part glycerol); straining through gauze after 48 hours at 22° C.; allowing the sediment to separate in the icebox; and storing the filtrate to be used as antigen in the icebox.

6. Antigen from Blood.

Aqueous and alcoholic antigens may be prepared from trypanosomes concentrated from the blood of animals infected with *T. equiperdum* and other trypanosomes. Watson's (1920) method of concentration is as follows: the blood of heavily infected rats is mixed with an equal amount of citrated physiological sodium chloride solution and is strained to remove clots. The mixture is centrifuged in 10 ml. centrifuge tubes at 1,500 r.p.m., and the trypanosomes in the supernatant layer are washed and centrifuged until a sediment of pure trypanosomes is obtained. This method may be modified by hemolyzing the red blood cells.

Dahmen (1922) prepared an aqueous antigen of *T. equiperdum* by extracting the concentrated trypanosomes with 0.5% phenolized physiological sodium chloride solution for two days with shaking, allowing the mixture to stand in the icebox for one day, and removing the supernate for the antigen.

Dahmen (1922) also prepared an alcoholic extract by drying the concentrated trypanosomes at 50° C.; pulverizing them in a mortar; extracting with 10 parts of ether for an hour with shaking and filtering; drying the filtered residue at 37° C.; extracting the residue with absolute alcohol for two days at 37° C.; and using the supernate as an antigen.

7. Antigen from Cultures.

Antigens free from extraneous products may be prepared from 10- to 12-day cultures by washing and centrifuging the trypanosomes. Aqueous and alcoholic extracts are made in the same manner as with trypanosomes concentrated from the blood of infected animals. Kelser (1936) made a glycerolated antigen from *T. cruzi* cultures.

Plasmodium.—Aqueous extracts of the malarial plasmodia have been prepared from the blood and heavily infected organs such as the placenta.

8. Antigen from Blood.

Thomson (1919), in preparing an antigen for alexin-fixation, cultured infected red blood cells to increase the number of parasites, hemolyzed the erythrocytes with distilled water, dissolved the sedimented parasites and cellular débris in N/1 sodium hydroxide, neutralized with N/1 hydrochloric acid, and diluted with physiological sodium chloride solution.

Eaton and Coggeshall (1939) used monkey erythrocytes parasitized with *Plasmodium knowlesi,* which were concentrated, washed, frozen, dried and preserved in sealed tubes. A 1:10 suspension in physiological sodium chloride was then frozen and thawed four times, centrifuged and the supernatant fluid used as antigen.

9. Antigen from Placenta.

Taliaferro and Taliaferro (1928) concentrated *P. falciparum* schizonts in a heavily infected placenta by centrifuging, digested the dried material in 0.05% HCl in physiological sodium chloride solution for 10 to 20 hours, and used the supernate, after adjusting the reaction from *p*H 7.6 to 7.8, as an antigen for precipitative tests.

TREMATODA

Considerable attention has been devoted to the preparation and study of antigens in the schistosomes. Since the same methods of preparing antigens apply equally well to all trematodes, the technics employed with the genus *Schistosoma* are given as examples.

The serological reactions of the mammalian schistosomes represent a group response, indicating similarity in the antigenic constitution of the several species. Advantage of this fact is taken in preparing antigens from the more available animal species for use in the serological diagnosis of human schistosomiasis. Two sources of material are utilized: (1) the adult worm from animal hosts, and (2) the livers of snails infected with cercariæ. Both aqueous and alcoholic extracts prepared in various ways are employed.

Adult Schistosomes.—Antigens have been prepared from animal schistosomes or human species in reservoir hosts: from *S. bovis* by Khalil and Hassan (1932) and Salam (1935), and from *S. japonicum* by Yoshimoto (1910) and Miyaji and Muto (1928).

10. Aqueous Antigen.

Aqueous antigens are prepared by mixing 1 part of finely triturated flukes with 20 parts of physiological sodium chloride solution, extracting for two days at 22° C., centrifuging, and storing the clear supernate in the ice chest for use as an antigen. It is also possible to make aqueous antigens from dried powdered worms or from the insoluble portion after treatment with alcohol and ether.

11. Alcoholic Antigen.

Alcoholic antigens are prepared by extracting the dried powdered worms with 20 parts of absolute alcohol for 24 hours with frequent shaking, centrifuging until clear, and storing the supernate in ampules in the ice chest. The alcoholic extract is diluted for use with physiological sodium chloride solution. It may be evaporated and an aqueous solution made from the residue.

Larval Schistosomes.—Antigens from the livers of snails infected with cercariæ of human and animal schistosomes have been prepared by several investigators. Among these may be cited the production of antigens from *S. hæmatobium* by Fairley (1919); *S. mansoni* by Taliaferro, Hoffman and Cook (1928); *S. japonicum* by Andrews (1935); *S. bovis* by Khalil and Hassan (1932); and *S. spindale* by Fairley (1926), Fairley and Williams (1927), and Fairley and Jasudasan (1930).

12. Aqueous Antigen.

The method of Fairley and Williams (1927) for preparing aqueous antigens for intracutaneous tests is as follows:

(a) Dry freshly dissected livers of a snail, *Planorbis exustus,* infected with cercariæ of *S. spindale,* a cattle schistosome, in a desiccator with calcium chloride under reduced pressure. Grind to a fine powder and store in ampules in the icebox. Approximately 106 gm. of powdered liver is obtained from 180 snails.

(b) Triturate 0.25 gm. of the dried powder in a mortar with 50 ml. of physiological sodium chloride solution and shake the resulting mixture.

(c) Incubate for one hour at 37° C. with frequent shakings.

(d) Centrifuge and remove supernate.

(e) Filter supernate through No. 3 Seitz filter.

(f) Store in ice chest in sealed ampules containing 0.5 ml.

13. **Alcoholic Antigen.**

The method of Fairley and Williams (1927) for preparing alcoholic antigens is as follows:

(a) Add 10 ml. absolute alcohol to 0.1 gm. of dried powdered liver prepared as above, and shake for 20 minutes.

(b) Incubate for 24 hours at 37° C. and shake again for 20 minutes or shake for three periods of 20 minutes during incubation.

(c) Centrifuge and remove supernate.

(d) Use filtered supernate as antigen for the alexin-fixative test by diluting 1:20 with physiological sodium chloride solution, after testing antigenic properties against sera of immunized animals.

(f) If an aqueous antigen is desired, evaporate alcoholic extract at 45° C. by means of an exhaust pump. Dissolve 0.05 gm. dried residue in 20 ml. physiological sodium chloride solution with or without 0.5% phenol.

14. **Alcoholic Antigen for Alexin-fixation.**

Fairley (1926) used the following modified method of preparing an alcoholic antigen for alexin-fixation:

(a) Tease wet snail livers directly into absolute alcohol (1 ml. per liver) and shake for 20 minutes.

(b) Extract at 37° C. for 24 hours with shaking.

(c) Concentrate filtrate in water bath at 45° C. by bubbling air through the solution until turbid.

(d) Dilute with absolute alcohol sufficient to clarify solution.

(e) Store in 1 ml. ampules in ice chest.

(f) Dilute for use with 39 parts of physiological sodium chloride solution.

15. **Alcoholic Antigen for Precipitative Test.**

Taliaferro, Hoffman and Cook (1928) prepared antigens for the precipitative test from the livers of the snail, *Planorbis guadeloupensis,* infected with *Schistosoma mansoni.* Because of pseudopositive reactions with syphilitic sera and instability of the ordinary alcoholic antigen they prepared their antigens by first extracting dried liver powder in a Soxhlet apparatus with ether, absolute alcohol or both, then extracting the lipoid-free residue with Coca's solution, and using the clear supernate adjusted to pH 7.4 as an antigen. They consider that this method increases the rapidity of preparing the antigen, eliminates cloudiness and spontaneous precipitation, and gives high antigenic properties, but that it does not eliminate pseudopositive reactions in syphilitic sera. In order to avoid such reactions they recommend separating the larval schistosomes from the macerated liver tissue by centrifuging and then preparing aqueous extracts of the powdered concentrated larvæ.

CESTOIDEA

The methods of preparing antigens from the adult cestodes are similar to those used for the trematodes. *Tænia solium, T. saginata* and *Diphyllobothrium latum* may be obtained from man and *Dipylidium caninum* from dogs.

Antigens are prepared from the fluid or from the scolices of the larval cysticerci for precipitative, alexin-fixative and intracutaneous tests. Both aqueous and alcoholic antigens have been used. Most antigens are prepared from hydatid cysts (*Echinococcus granulosus*) and less frequently from the cysticerci of *Tænia solium* and *T. saginata* in animals.

16. **Aqueous Hydatid Antigens.**

Fluid is obtained aseptically from hydatid cysts in infected cattle, sheep, hogs or man. Fluid from degenerating cysts or that contaminated with blood or serum is discarded. Several samples are pooled. The fluid is filtered through a Seitz filter, incubated to determine sterility, sealed in ampules, and stored in the icebox. It may or may not be preserved with 0.5% phenol. It retains its antigenic properties for several months. It should be tested against normal persons for pseudopositive reactions due to animal proteins and against persons with known *Echinococcus* infection for antigenic properties.

A better antigen may be obtained by grinding the moist scolices with fine sand in a mortar, adding 9 volumes of the hydatid fluid or physiological sodium chloride solution, preserving in 0.25% phenol, incubating for 4 days at $37°$ C., and storing the filtrate in the icebox. Senelje (1941) has prepared an efficient polysaccharide scolex antigen.

17. **Alcoholic Hydatid Antigens.**

Fairley prepared an alcoholic extract by grinding the scolices with fine sand, adding 9 volumes of absolute alcohol, incubating at $37°$ C. for 2 days, and using the filtrate as an antigen.

Dennis (1937) added crystalline trichloracetic acid, to a concentration of 5%, to chilled, fresh, sterile hydatid cyst fluid, obtained from sheep and cattle. The mixture was held at $4°$ C. overnight. The precipitate was collected, washed and treated with dilute NaOH until the protein was in solution. The protein was reprecipitated with N/1 glacial acetic acid, washed, dried at $37°$ C., ground to a powder, and stored in desiccator in the dark. About 0.1 gm. of purified antigen is obtained from each liter of hydatid fluid. Stock antigen solutions are made up to 1 to 1,000 in slightly alkalinized physiological sodium chloride solution. It is sterilized by filtering through a Seitz filter and by adding 0.5% chloroform. Dennis considers that the antigen is about 10 times as potent as ordinary hydatid fluid. For alexin-fixation the antigen is used in a 1:1,000 dilution and higher.

NEMATODA

The methods of preparing antigens from the adult nematodes are the same as with the trematodes. The serological and cutaneous reactions are often group-specific and antigens for the diagnosis of human infections may be prepared from the parasites of animals (*Dirofilaria immitis* of dogs for filarial infections). The use of the blister fluid of *Dracunculus medinensis* as an antigen is one of the few departures from the custom of making antigenic extracts directly from the adult worm.

Larval nematodes are infrequently used for antigens. The outstanding exception is *Trichinella spiralis,* in which an especially effective antigen for precipitative and intracutaneous tests is obtained from the encysted larvæ.

18. **Trichinella Antigen.**

Sawitz (1937) has modified Bachman's (1928) technic in preparing *Trichinella* antigen.

(a) Digest 80 gm. of muscle from an infected rat in 1,500 ml. of 0.6% pepsin in 0.3% HCl solution at $37°$ C. for 5 to 12 hours, shaking from time to time.

(b) Strain through 6 layers of cheesecloth.

(c) Dilute with an equal amount of water and allow to stand for 2 hours in a sedimentation glass.

(d) Siphon off upper third of liquid and replace with tap water; repeat 6 to 8 times until supernatant fluid is clear.

(e) Leave purified material in sedimentation glass overnight; then place in a Petri dish and allow to dry.

(f) Transfer to a beaker and treat with ether for 24 hours.

(g) Remove ether and dry residue *in vacuo* over sulphuric acid for 48 hours.

(h) Pulverize dried residue in a mortar and store in sterile ampules.

(i) Dissolve in Coca's solution, 1 gm. to 100 ml. to make stock solution.

(j) Store in icebox. Dilute for intracutaneous tests 1 :50 to give a strength of 1 :5,000.

SPECIFIC SEROLOGICAL TESTS

19. **Agglutination.**—Agglutinative tests are only suitable for flagellated Protozoa. The technic is similar to that used for bacteria. Microscopical agglutinative tests are best done in hanging-drop preparations. This method may be used advantageously when only a small amount of serum is available or when living flagellates are tested with immune serum. Live trypanosomes manifest agglutination by orientation in masses with their posterior ends at the center, whereas dead trypanosomes collect in disorderly clumps.

The macroscopical test, which requires larger amounts of reagents, is usually done in a series of small test tubes containing graded dilutions of serum in order to give quantitative readings. Suspensions of killed flagellates are ordinarily employed. A suspension of flagellates is added to the several dilutions of serum, incubated for 6 to 12 hours at 37° C. or for 2 hours at 56° C., and read after standing at room temperature or in the icebox for 12 to 24 hours. Cross-agglutination and agglutinin adsorption may be used to exclude natural and group agglutinins.

The adhesion reaction has been used in the diagnosis of trypanosomiasis and leishmaniasis. The red blood cells of humans or primates are mixed *in vitro* with the parasite, alexin and serum of the suspected patient. If the adhesin body is present, the red blood cells adhere to the parasite.

20. **Precipitation.**—The reaction in precipitative tests is fundamentally the same as in agglutinative tests, but the antigen consists of an extract derived from the parasites and the interaction of the antigen and immune serum results in the appearance of a precipitate instead of in the clumping of the organisms. Two methods of detecting precipitins in the blood serum have been employed: (1) general mixing of the antigen and serum with the formation in positive reactions of a fine, hazy precipitate, and (2) the "ring" test. The latter is the method of choice and is performed as follows:

The test is done in small or dwarf test tubes, 0.2 ml. of the serum to be tested being placed in each of five tubes. Five dilutions of antigen, one for each tube, are carefully layered over the serum. Control tubes of a known positive serum and a known negative serum also receive the antigen, while a third tube containing the unknown serum receives the diluent but no antigen. The test may be read in 30 minutes at room temperature or the tubes may be incubated in a water bath at 37° C. The formation of a white, cloudy disk at the zone of contact is indicative of a positive reaction. The contents of the tube may then be thoroughly mixed and allowed to stand overnight in the icebox before a final reading is made. Prezoning may be observed in the latter method.

21. **Alexin-fixation.**—The alexin-fixative test requires for its operation: (1) an antigen consisting of extracts of the parasite or its products capable of combining with specific antibodies in the serum of the infected animal and by this union fixing or binding alexin (complement); (2) a measured amount of alexin; and (3) a hemolytic system comprising red blood cells (usually sheep) sensitized by a specific antierythrocytic lysin (amboceptor). The reaction is based on the use of sensitized cells as an indicator to detect antibody-antigen combinations which do not manifest themselves in a visible reaction. Thus, when an antibody comes in contact with its specific antigen in the presence of alexin, the alexin will be "fixed" by the union of the antibody and antigen. If the amounts of the various reagents are correctly chosen, the alexin present in the mixture will be bound to the antibody-antigen complex. If the serum contains no alexin-fixing antibodies, the presence of unbound alexin may be detected by the lysis

of the sensitized erythrocytes at the completion of the primary reaction. By means of this test the presence of antibodies even in high dilution may be demonstrated.

There are many modifications in the technic of this test, but good results may be obtained with most procedures if they are carefully controlled. Theoretically, antibodies against all species of parasites should be demonstrated by this test and conversely antigens identified by the use of known immune sera, but from a practical standpoint it is of limited value in diagnosing most parasitic infections. Its success depends largely upon the preparation of specific antigens, which necessitates obtaining satisfactory extracts uncontaminated by extraneous material from infected tissues. Since tissue-extracts are used as antigens in the Wassermann test, the possibility of pseudopositive reactions in syphilitic patients should be kept in mind when using alcoholic extracts of infected organs.

22. Preparation of Immune Sera.—Specific immune sera are used for the identification of unknown or morphologically similar parasites. Diagnostic sera may be prepared by immunizing laboratory animals with injections of small gradually increasing doses of antigens prepared from the parasites or their products. Rabbits and guinea pigs are most frequently used, but larger animals such as monkeys, sheep, goats, horses and calves are sometimes employed for the production of diagnostic and therapeutic sera. The intravenous route is usually preferred, but the antigen may be injected intraäbdominally, intramuscularly or subcutaneously. A series of five injections of increasing strength is given at intervals of three to seven days. The serum is collected by bleeding the animal five days after the last injection.

NONSPECIFIC FLOCCULATIVE AND CHEMICAL TESTS

Several nonspecific flocculative tests based upon the disequilibrium of the serum proteins have been used in the diagnosis of protozoan infections. Although these tests have no specific relation to the causative organisms, they have a practical diagnostic value since other diseases do not commonly produce sufficient changes in the serum proteins to produce positive reactions.

23. Henry's Melano-flocculative Test for Malaria (1934).—Henry's test for malaria was originally based on the assumption that malarial pigment gave rise to the production of antibodies that produced flocculation in the presence of melanin. Later investigators have demonstrated that no antibodies are produced by melanin and that the melano-flocculation results from changes in the serum proteins, particularly by an increase in euglobulin. The test gives a high percentage of positive reactions in malarial patients, but at times is positive in syphilis and other diseases.

The "antigen" is a suspension of melanin, derived from the choroidal melanin of the ox-eye, in distilled water containing 0.005% formaldehyde. Its opacity is so adjusted that a 1:10 dilution will correspond to an optical density of 48 to 49 photometric degrees. One part of the serum is mixed with 4 parts of the melanin suspension in stoppered tubes and incubated at 37° C. for 3 hours. The reaction is read after the tubes have stood at room temperature for 30 minutes. Distinct flocculation of the melanin indicates a positive reaction, provided the serum and "antigen" controls are clear. Because of the difficulty of reading weakly positive reactions the use of the photometer for evaluating the optical density is advocated. Henry's photometric indices for the test are: 1 to 12 degrees negative, 13 to 18 doubtful, 19 to 100 positive for malaria.

24. Protein Tyrosin Test for Malaria.—To avoid the use of Henry's photometer, Proske and Watson (1938) have devised a colorimetric test to measure the euglobulin. It is based on the fact that proteins possess a chromogenic property which can be measured quantitatively against the color produced by pure tyrosin in the presence of a phenol agent.

(a) A 14% sodium sulphate solution is made by dissolving 70 gm. of c.p. anhydrous sodium sulphate in 300 ml. of freshly distilled water and diluting to 500 ml. at a temperature of 37° C. This solution keeps indefinitely when stored in an incubator at 37° C.

(b) A N/5 sodium hydroxide solution is prepared by diluting saturated, carbonate-free sodium hydroxide solution to a 20% strength.

(c) Tyrosin standard solution. Dissolve 200 mg. of pure tyrosin (Pfanstiehl) in 1,000 ml. of approximately N/10 HCl; 5 ml. of the solution contains 1 mg. tyrosin.

(d) Phenol reagent of Folin and Ciocalteu. Into a 1,500 ml. Florence flask introduce 100 gm. of sodium tungstate ($Na_2WO_4.2H_2O$), 25 gm. of sodium molybdate ($Na_2MoO_4.H_2O$), 700 ml. water, 50 ml. 85% phosphoric acid, and 100 ml. concentrated hydrochloric acid. Reflux gently for 10 hours. Add 150 gm. lithium sulphate, 50 ml. water, and a few drops of bromine. Boil the mixture for 15 minutes without condenser to remove the excess of bromine. Cool, dilute to 1,000 ml., and filter. The reagent should have no greenish tint.

(e) Measure 3.0 ml. of 14% sodium sulphate solution into a small test tube, 75 x 10 mm.; from an accurately calibrated pipette add 0.1 ml. of unheated, clear, nonhemolyzed, nonchylous serum; mix by inverting a dozen times, avoiding air bubbles; stopper the tube and place in the incubator at 37° C. for 3 hours. Centrifuge at 1,500 r.p.m. for 10 minutes; completely pipette off the supernatant fluid; and wash the precipitate twice with fresh sodium sulphate solution by centrifugation. (This step is necessary in order to remove traces of albumin and pseudoglobulin that may have been caught in the precipitate or may adhere to the walls of the tube, and which will also react with the phenol reagent, giving too high a reading.) Dissolve the washed precipitate in 1.75 ml. of distilled water and add 0.1 ml. of N/5 sodium hydroxide.

(f) At this point prepare the stock standard by introducing into a test tube, graduated at 20 ml., 2 ml. of the tyrosin solution, 5 ml. of water, and 1 ml. of N/5 sodium hydroxide. Heat the unknown and the standard in boiling water for 10 minutes, and allow to cool. Now add to the unknown 0.15 ml. and to the stock standard 1.5 ml. of the phenol reagent and make up the standard to the 20 ml. mark with distilled water.

(g) While the color is developing, set up a series of small test tubes, 75 x 10 ml., and mark the tubes with a wax pencil 100, 90, 80, 70, 60, 50, 40, 30, 20, and 10. Prepare the substandards in these tubes according to the following scheme:

Substandards, per cent	Stock standard, ml.	Water, ml.
100	2.0	0
90	1.8	0.2
80	1.6	0.4
70	1.4	0.6
60	1.2	0.8
50	1.0	1.0
40	0.8	1.2
30	0.6	1.4
20	0.4	1.6
10	0.2	1.8

Compare the color intensity of the unknown with these standards. For example, if the unknown falls between 60 and 50, then the reading is 55.

The following precautions should be observed: All glassware must be chemically clean, but sterility is unnecessary. The serum pipettes should have fine tips, because small droplets of serum adhering to blunt tips may cause a considerable error. Sera should be clear. Hemolyzed sera give too high tyrosin values owing to their globin content; chylous sera give too low values owing to the fact that chyle interferes with the protein precipitation.

From the examination of 2,941 consecutive sera the following tyrosin indices (TI) for serum euglobulin have been determined:

TI— 50 to 80....Normal persons.
TI— 80 to 100....Doubtful for malaria. In this range fall new malaria cases which have experienced only one paroxysm, treated cases, and a few cases of syphilis.
TI—105 and over..Presumptively positive for malaria.

25. **Napier's Aldehyde Test for Leishmaniasis (1922).**—The aldehyde or formol-gel test of Napier has proved of diagnostic value in kala-azar, from 82 to 85 per cent of patients with active infection of 4 months' duration giving a positive reaction. This test is not specific since somewhat similar reactions may also occur in tuberculosis, leprosy, trypanosomiasis, malaria, and schistosomiasis.

(a) Place 1 ml. of patient's serum in a small test tube.

(b) Add one drop of commercial formalin (36% formaldehyde), mix thoroughly, and allow to stand at room temperature.

(c) In positive cases the serum immediately becomes opaque and will assume a stiff white jelly-like consistency, resembling the coagulated white of egg, in from 3 to 30 minutes.

(d) If negative no reaction should occur in 24 hours.

Another method of performing the test is to deposit a drop of clear serum on a slide which is inverted over a watch glass containing a few drops of formalin. Kala-azar serum will form a stiff opaque jelly adhering to the slide, while negative serum will remain fluid and will run off the slide.

26. **Chopra's Antimony Test for Leishmaniasis (1936).**—This test is said to be more sensitive than Napier's aldehyde test in early kala-azar but gives more false re-actions with other diseases.

(a) Place 0.2 ml. of whole serum and serum diluted 1:10 with distilled water in two miniature test tubes (65 x 4 mm.).

(b) Carefully overlay with a 4% solution of urea-stibamine in distilled water, letting the antimony solution run slowly along the side of the tubes.

(c) If positive a thick flocculent disk will form at the junction of the two fluids within 10 to 15 minutes. Reaction may rarely be delayed for 1 to 2 hours.

Chopra also uses a quick method of performing this test. A drop of blood from the cleaned finger is received into a small test tube (50 x 9 mm.) containing 0.25 ml. of 2% potassium oxalate. The corpuscles are allowed to settle and the test is performed with the supernatant fluid. A 4% solution of urea-stibamine is added as in the serum test. A flocculant precipitate from 5 to 10 minutes after mixing indicates a positive reaction.

27. **Sia's Precipitative Test for Leishmaniasis (1921).**—In this test 20 cmm. of blood are added to 0.6 ml. of distilled water by a hemoglobin pipette and the mixture is gently agitated until thoroughly mixed. Observations are made at 15-minute intervals up to an hour. Sedimentation of a flocculent precipitate within 15 minutes denotes a 4-plus reaction, within 30 minutes a 3-plus reaction, within 45 minutes a 2-plus reaction, and within an hour or longer a 1-plus reaction.

X. CUTANEOUS TESTS

Supersensitiveness is a state of exaggerated response to the injection of, or other contact with, an antigen. Thus, an antigen that may produce no apparent change in the normal individual, may produce severe general or local reactions in the supersensitive individual. Persons infected with animal parasites may develop a supersensitiveness against the proteins and other products of these organisms. The demonstration of super-sensitiveness by cutaneous tests provides a means of diagnosing parasitic infections.

Several methods of testing with parasitic extracts, such as conjunctival instillation, inhalation, ingestion and cutaneous scratches, have been used, but the intracutaneous method provides the most delicate means of demonstrating supersensitiveness and also, if extracts of known concentration are used, gives quasiquantitative determinations.

Attempts to develop specific diagnostic tests for various parasitic infections have been made with cutaneous and intracutaneous inoculations of antigens in the form of powders, suspensions or extracts of the parasites. The success attending these efforts has depended upon the production of specific antigens uncontaminated by extraneous proteins and upon freedom from group- and cross-reactions. As a result cutaneous diagnostic tests have proved satisfactory in certain parasitic diseases, unsatisfactory in others, and in some, although specific, of little practical value because of other more efficient methods of diagnosis.

Antigens.—The preparation of antigens from animal parasites for cutaneous tests is essentially the same as for serological work (Section **VII**, IX, 1 to 18). For intracutaneous tests aqueous solutions of the dried antigen must be made if the original material has been extracted with alcohol. When the parasites cannot be isolated, tissues heavily infected with parasites are used in spite of the inclusion of extraneous tissue-proteins.

1. **Technic.**—The cutaneous scratch method has been used by many investigators; a scratch about 0.5 cm. in length is made, and a small amount of the dried substance of the parasite is placed on the scratch and moistened with dilute sodium hydroxide.

In the intracutaneous test a small amount, usually 0.02 to 0.05 ml., is injected intracutaneously on the volar surface of the forearm after cleansing the skin with alcohol. A tuberculin syringe with 26 gauge needle is used as in the Schick test. Measures for guarding against pseudoreactions should include the determination of abnormal skin sensitiveness and dermographism by the stroke test with a blunt metal probe and control injections for extraneous foreign proteins or other substances in the antigen. Two types of positive reaction are observed, (1) the immediate and (2) the delayed.

A. **Immediate Reaction.**—In supersensitive individuals the intracutaneous introduction of the antigenic extract is followed by the formation of a wheal of varying size showing pseudopodia and surrounded by an area of erythema. The reaction reaches its maximum in from 10 to 20 minutes and disappears usually within 60 minutes. Occasionally smaller wheals suddenly appear a short distance from the primary wheal and later merge with it. Measurements of the length and breadth of the wheal including pseudopodia are helpful in determining positive and excluding negative reactions, but the use of measurements depends upon the experience of the observer. The variations in the results of investigators may be due to different linear standards in judging positive reactions.

B. **Delayed Reaction.**—After from 8 to 24 hours an intense local inflammation occurs at the site of the injection. The capillaries are dilated and engorged, and an intense infiltration of large mononuclear, polynuclear, and eosinophilic leukocytes occurs. There is an increase in intercellular and intracellular fluid causing edema. Superficially there is an area of erythema with subjacent induration due to the edematous infiltration. The area should be at least 4 cm. in diameter for a positive response. The erythema may fade within 12 hours. The indurated areas often have a definite edge similar to that observed in erysipelas. Intense reactions with vesiculation may simulate erysipelas or cellulitis. Intense local itching is a frequent complaint.

2. **Passive Transfer of Sensitivity.**—About 0.1 ml. of serum from the supersensitive patient is introduced intracutaneously into the skin of a normal individual. After a latent period of 24 to 48 hours to allow the immediate irritative reaction to subside and to allow fixation of the circulating reagin from the allergic patient in the tissues of the recipient, the site of passive transfer is tested by the intracutaneous injection of the antigen, a control test being made on a corresponding area of normal unsensitized skin. The formation of the characteristic wheal in the sensitized area with no

reaction in the normal skin is proof of the presence of specific reagin in the serum of the donor. Sensitiveness that manifests itself in the delayed reaction cannot be thus transferred. The test is useful when abnormal conditions of the skin render intra-cutaneous tests unreliable.

XI. EXAMINATION OF INTERMEDIATE AND RESERVOIR HOSTS

Examination of intermediate and reservoir hosts is important in the studying of the life cycle of parasites and in determining the epidemiology of parasitic infections.

ARTHROPODA

The technical methods of dissecting the smaller intermediate arthropod hosts for parasites are given in Section **VII**, XII, 8. The larger DECOPODA, which include the fresh-water crabs and crayfishes serving as intermediate hosts for *Paragonimus wester-mani*, are examined by removing the carapace and dissecting the gills, liver and muscles that contain the encysted parasites. The determination of species depends upon the morphological characteristics of the larva and it is often necessary to resort to feeding experiments for absolute identification. Table 9 lists the protozoan and helminthic para-sites that may be found in arthropod hosts.

MOLLUSCA

The larval stages of the digenetic trematodes are found in both pulmonate and non-pulmonate fresh-water gastropods and rarely in lamellibranchiate mollusks. The identi-fication of species and even of genera of these mollusks is beyond the capabilities of most parasitologists and requires the services of skilled malacologists. It is advisable, therefore, to submit suspected snails to authorities on mollusks to insure proper identification. Snails are the intermediate hosts of numerous species of trematodes parasitic in lower animals. Consequently it is difficult to distinguish the species belonging to man, although not infrequently the larval forms may be identified by certain distinguishing morpho-logical characteristics.

Preservation.—The snails should be kept cool and moist. Pulmonate gastropods perish rapidly and should be kept in moist containers, but operculated nonpulmonate snails, if properly packed in dry moss, may be held for a considerable length of time.

Dissection.—The liver, which occupies the apical part of the snail, is the most frequent site of infection. The larval trematodes are usually found in the interhepatic lymph spaces and in the region between the liver and the reproductive organs. After the removal of the shell, the soft tissues are teased with a needle and either examined directly with a dissecting microscope for the presence of larvæ or transferred to a cover-glass mount for more detailed examination.

Experimental Investigations.—The method of ascertaining whether or not a given species of mollusks is an intermediate host is to infect experimentally a susceptible un-infected mammal with the cercariæ from the snail and determine the species of the adult worm. Another method is to infect the snail with the miracidia of a known parasite. The latter method is open to the objection that, unless the snails have been reared artificially in uncontaminated water, there is always the possibility that the snail may have been previously infected with other cercariæ.

Methods of Control.—Effective control of intermediate gastropod hosts is important in preventing human diseases produced by trematodes. A knowledge of the habits of the particular species of snail is necessary for the institution of worthwhile control meas-ures. The two principal methods are desiccation and the use of chemical poisons, but other less effective measures are also employed.

(a) **Desiccation.**—Efficient measures for the control of nonoperculate snails, such as species of LYMNÆIDÆ and PLANORBIDÆ which seldom leave the water, are draining the waters that serve as their habitat, clearing the bottoms of mud, and burning the rushes and grasses. However, certain species under favorable conditions can withstand drying for 10 days or more, and the operculate snails can stand desiccation for several months.

(b) **Chemicals.**—Chemical poisons are most effective in shallow and stagnant water and are most successful against the nonoperculate snails. The species *Blanfordia* and *Hemibia,* which are found on the banks as well as in the water, are the most difficult to eradicate by chemical agents.

Copper sulphate and unslaked lime have been most frequently used because they are cheap and effective, but unfortunately they destroy other aquatic fauna and flora. Copper sulphate may be dusted or sprayed over the water, or towed in a bag. The lethal concentration for snails is variously estimated from 0.2 to 2.0 p.p.m., but the usual strength is 0.5 p.p.m. The proper dilution may be calculated from the volume of the water to be treated. Unslaked lime, CaO, in a concentration of 0.1%, may be spread thickly on the banks and added to slowly running water. Ammonium sulphate and calcium cyanamid (CaNCN) have also been used. Copper carbonate has been recommended.

(c) **Collection.**—Where labor is cheap and where desiccation and chemical measures are not practicable, the collection of the snails by hand may be employed.

(d) **Predaceous Animals.**—Ducks and many species of fishes feed on snails. Their introduction into infested waters may prove useful.

(e) **Parasites.**—The possibility of destroying snails by introducing parasitic beetles has been suggested, since the larva of the flyworm, *Luciola picticollis,* infests snails in Japan. These parasites, however, attack only terrestrial or semiaquatic snails.

FISHES

The metacercariæ of trematodes, the plerocercoid larvæ of cestodes, and the larval nematodes of genera *Dioctophyme*(?) and *Gnathostoma* are found in fishes. The larvæ are present on the underside of the scales, on the gills, and in the subcutaneous and muscular tissues. The scales are readily removed for examination, and the tissues may be teased upon a slide, compressed in a "trichina" press, or prepared as histological sections. The spargana of the cestodes are small, white, flat, elongated bodies that may be dissected out of the tissues. The metacercariæ are small, round or oval, encapsulated forms. Differentiation between the larvæ of the parasitic species of man and those of lower animals often requires feeding experiments. The spargana of the DIPHYLLO-BOTHRIIDÆ and occasionally the larvæ of *Gnathostoma* are also found in the muscles and subcutaneous tissues of frogs and snakes.

Fishes that serve as second intermediate hosts are all fresh-water species except the brackish-water hosts of the HETEROPHYIDÆ. They become infected with larval cestodes by the ingestion of infected copepods and with larval trematodes by the attachment and penetration of cercariæ. Practically all species of fresh-water teleosts are potential hosts. Species of the salmon, perch and pike families are predominantly the intermediate hosts of the DIPHYLLOBOTHRIIDÆ, the family CYPRINIDÆ of the OPISTHORCHIDÆ, and the brackish-water mullets of the HETEROPHYIDÆ.

MAMMALS

Mammals serve as both definitive and intermediate hosts of the parasites of man. The sparganal stage of the DIPHYLLOBOTHRIIDÆ, the cysticercal stage of the TÆNIIDÆ, and the larvæ of *Trichinella spiralis* are found in mammals. The adult and larval parasites are obtained and examined in the same way as those from man. The larval parasites in the muscles and other tissues may be detected by the naked eye, with a hand lens, or with a compound microscope. Projection methods are sometimes employed for the detection of *Trichinella* larvæ.

PLANTS

Semiaquatic and aquatic plants and grasses serve for the encystment of the metacercariæ of trematodes of the families FASCIOLIDÆ and DICROCŒLIIDÆ. The cysts, small whitish objects near the surface of the plants, may be scraped onto a slide and examined microscopically.

ANIMAL EXPERIMENTATION

Certain species of Protozoa and helminths may be carried from generation to generation in susceptible animals. This method of perpetuating parasites is often easier than culturing on artificial media and may be used when culturing is impossible. Animal inoculations are also of value in diagnosis. The virulence of a given organism for a particular animal and the nature of the lesions produced are sometimes characteristic. Isolation of parasites may be facilitated by the inoculation and subsequent recovery of the organism from the animal. Care should be taken that the animals are not already infected with a similar species that may be confused with the inoculated species. It is best, therefore, to use young animals reared under supervised conditions.

Laboratory animals are a source of immune sera and provide facilities for testing the chemotherapeutic action of drugs (*Trypanosoma*) and for evaluating anthelmintic treatment. Antigens for intracutaneous and serological diagnosis may be prepared from allied species of parasites in animals (*Dirofilaria immitis* for filarial infections) and from the same species in reservoir hosts (*Trichinella*). Animals have proved useful as definitive or intermediate hosts in working out the life cycle of parasites, and the study of mammalian parasites, allied or similar to those infecting man, has thrown light upon the life histories of the species of man.

Animals may be infected through the gastro-intestinal tract and by inoculations. Parasites are introduced into the gastro-intestinal tract orally and rectally. Dogs, cats and other laboratory animals may be infected with helminthic parasites by feeding infective larvæ, e.g., *Clonorchis sinensis, Echinococcus granulosus,* and *Trichinella spiralis.* Dogs and kittens may be inoculated with *Endamœba histolytica* by colonic injections, a method which provides a source of material for study.

Trypanosomes may be injected into rats, mice and guinea pigs. Usually two animals are inoculated at a time to prevent the loss of a virulent strain by the sudden death of the animal, and the organism is transplanted to new animals at regular intervals. The inoculations may be made by subcutaneous, intramuscular, intraäbdominal or intravenous injections using the accepted technical methods. Insect hosts may be infected for experimental purposes or for maintaining infective material.

XII. METHODS OF COLLECTING, PREPARING AND EXAMINING PARASITIC ARTHROPODA

EQUIPMENT

For the collection and preservation of arthropods the following equipment is required: (1) insect net; (2) killing bottle; (3) collecting bottles; (4) variously sized entomological pins; (5) air-tight mounting boxes; (6) 70% alcohol and special preserving fluids; (7) preserving jars; (8) dehydrating agents such as alcohol, xylene and cedar oil; (9) stains; and (10) occasionally equipment for histological preparations.

A compound microscope, a dissecting microscope (binocular if possible), and a good hand lens are used in dissecting insects. Dissection is accomplished with fine, absolutely smooth needles, fine scissors, and forceps. One or two lancet-shaped needles, ground into a sharp blade on one side only, are also essential. Dissection is carried out either upon a glass slide or upon a small dissecting trough partially filled with paraffin darkened with lamp black. A tile, half black and half white, is a useful base for the dissecting slide since various structures show to advantage against different backgrounds. Physiological sodium chloride solution is used to keep the dissection material moist.

COLLECTION OF PARASITIC ARTHROPODS

From the standpoint of the collector, parasitic arthropods fall into three groups: (1) the blood-sucking adult DIPTERA; (2) the parasitic dipterous larvæ; and (3) the ectoparasitic insects and arachnids. If the intermediate arthropod hosts of helminthic parasites are desired, the CRUSTACEA must also be included.

Source.—The females of the blood-sucking DIPTERA may be captured when feeding on their hosts and the males may be obtained by hatching the larvæ. The adult muscid flies may be collected from garbage, manure, decaying meat, or in the vicinity of animals; but better specimens are obtained by rearing the adults from eggs or larvæ. The ectoparasitic insects and arachnids, such as fleas, lice and ticks, may be collected from their hosts.

Method of Collection.—The smaller blood-sucking DIPTERA such as mosquitoes, sandflies, and midges may be captured by inverting a wide-mouthed bottle over the feeding or resting insects. Eggs, pupæ and larvæ may be obtained from their aquatic breeding grounds. Filth flies may be attracted with bait or hatched from eggs and larvæ deposited on body lesions and excreta. Fleas from dogs, cats and rats may be obtained with a camel's hair brush moistened with xylene or with a fine-toothed comb. Mites and lice may be obtained directly from man or animals, and bedbugs and flea larvæ from dwelling houses. It is unnecessary to obtain the adult forms of readily identifiable larvæ.

MOUNTING, PRESERVATION AND PREPARATION FOR EXAMINATION

Methods of preparation for microscopic examination vary with the genus of the arthropod, the type of examination, the condition of the specimen when it reaches the laboratory, and the type of preservation desired. Insects may reach the laboratory alive, freshly killed, dried, or in preserving fluid.

1. **Dry Mounts.**—The larger insects and those with hard exoskeletons may be taken to the laboratory in dry containers, after killing with cyanide or chloroform. They should be mounted as soon as possible, since certain genera shrink badly on drying. The following method is suitable for mosquitoes and insects of slightly larger size:

(a) Place the freshly killed insect on its back on a piece of white paper.

(b) Use a mounting stage consisting of a piece of celluloid, 1.5 x 1.0 cm., pierced by two pins, a fine insect pin (minutin pin) pointing upward, and a mounting pin (No. 5) pointing downward.

(c) Insert the minutin pin into the middle of the ventral surface of the thorax. Press the dorsal surface of the thorax against the thumb-nail to insure the point of the pin just piercing this surface.

(d) Straighten the wings with a needle so that they project outward and forward.

(e) Draw the fine pin through the celluloid stage so as to lower the insect until its legs touch the stage. Arrange the legs with a needle so that they have a symmetrical spread and lower the insect so that its ventral surface is a short distance above the surface of the stage.

(f) After being labeled the insect is ready for examination or for demonstration. In permanent collections the insect is pinned in a cork-lined box to protect against dust, breakage, molds and insect pests. The boxes should be tight and should contain para-dichlorobenzene crystals in a small tea bag to prevent the destruction of the specimens by the larvæ of dermestid beetles.

Another method of mounting small insects is to "point" them, that is to fix them with a tiny drop of shellac to the tips of wedge-shaped bits of cardboard previously pierced by mounting pins.

The larger insects may be coated with thin shellac. Large flies may be transfixed dorsally with No. 3 pins and pinned directly. If the specimens have dried before mounting, they should be placed in a watch glass, set on a piece of water-saturated cotton, and covered with a small bell jar. After remaining overnight the legs and body will be sufficiently pliable to permit arrangement and mounting.

Careful labelling is important. The label should bear the place and date of collection, the name of the host (if parasitic), the name of the specimen, and the name of the collection. The label is transfixed by the pin.

2. **Fluid Mounts.**—Insects may be preserved in 70% alcohol in small vials, containing paper labels written in India ink. Formalin should not be used, since it disintegrates the exoskeleton. Permanent mounts of small insects may be made in balsam on a concave slide without preliminary preparation.

To demonstrate fine points of anatomy in the larger or dark-colored insects or to aid in the study of special organs remove the specimens from the preservative and heat in hot water, not boiling, for 10 minutes; then transfer to 10% sodium hydroxide for 12 hours or overnight. Before removal from the sodium hydroxide heat the solution without boiling for 10 minutes. Transfer to distilled water and boil gently for 5 minutes. If rapid examination is essential, the insects may be punctured with needles, heated immediately in sodium hydroxide, washed, dehydrated, and mounted. The sodium hydroxide destroys the soft parts and leaves the chitinous integument. The slower, cold process usually yields better results, since there is less danger of damaging the chitinous parts. The insect now is ready for mounting.

The insect may be mounted without clearing.

(a) The insect is placed on its back in the concavity of the slide and the wings and legs properly spread.

(b) Fill the concavity with absolute methyl alcohol, flooding beneath the insect with a capillary pipette, and allow it to evaporate.

(c) Repeat process and dry thoroughly, removing all traces of fluid with filter paper.

(d) Place drop of balsam over center of specimen. After 12 hours add another drop or two and let stand until nearly dry.

(e) Fill concavity with balsam and seal with cover-glass. Dry and label.

The lateral surfaces of the specimen are not visible by this method.

If the specimens have been in a preservative, transfer to absolute methyl alcohol. If in borax-formalin medium (see larvae) first wash in distilled water for one hour.

(a) Let stand in absolute methyl alcohol for one hour or more.

(b) Transfer to fresh absolute methyl alcohol for 10 minutes.

(c) Remove alcohol, clear in cedarwood oil for 2 to 3 hours or overnight, or in xylene for 15 minutes. (Carbol-xylene, carbolic crystals 1 part—xylene 3 parts, is preferred by many workers.)

(d) Place drop of balsam on concave slide.

(e) Place insect in drop of balsam dorsal surface up.

(f) Fill concavity with balsam and place over it a cover-glass, on the underside of which a drop of balsam has been placed.

(g) Remove surplus balsam at edge of cover-glass with xylene.

Fluid Mounts for Insect Larvae.—The entire larva or parts of the larva may be mounted in balsam or borax-formalin. It is frequently unnecessary to mount the entire dipterous larva since the stigmal plates are the chief means of identification. The posterior segments are cut off with a sharp razor blade and mounted. If the anterior end is to be mounted, it is first treated with 10% sodium hydroxide.

3. **Mounting Larvae in Balsam.**

(a) Place larva or portion of larva in absolute methyl alcohol for 10 minutes.

(b) Transfer to fresh methyl alcohol for 5 to 10 minutes. Pour off alcohol and add xylene or carbo-xylene for 10 to 15 minutes.

(c) Transfer to concave slide. If portion of larva, place anterior end dorsum down and posterior end on the lateral side.

(d) Fill concavity with balsam and seal with cover-glass, to the under surface of which a drop of balsam has been added. (Some larvæ tend to collapse when passed directly from xylene to balsam and it is necessary to pass them through cedar oil before the balsam.)

4. **Macgregor's Borax-formalin Method of Mounting Larvæ.**—The borax-formalin medium is a suitable mount for the entire mosquito larva. The modified Macgregor's method is as follows:

Borax-formalin:

Borax, 4% in water	12.5	ml.
Formaldehyde, 36%	10.0	ml.
Glycerol, pure	0.25	ml.
Distilled water	77.25	ml.

(a) Kill live larva with water heated to about 60° C.

(b) Remove water and add borax-formalin medium. Specimens may be mounted immediately or held until ready to mount.

(c) Transfer larva and solution to concave slide, placing larva dorsal side up with extended lateral thoracic and abdominal tufts.

(d) Seal with cover-glass.

(e) Remove excess medium around edge of cover-glass with filter paper and let specimen stand for a few minutes.

(f) With thin brush carefully seal edges of cover-glass with a narrow coat of moderately thin balsam. For permanent mounts after thorough drying (18 hours) apply a second coat and after that dries, a third.

5. **Histological Sections.**—For histological sections the fresh material is placed in an alcohol-formalin-acetic acid fixative (formalin 7 parts, 70% alcohol 90 parts, glacial acetic acid 3 parts). The usual histological technic of dehydration, imbedding, sectioning and staining is followed. The whole arthropod or special organs may be sectioned.

6. **Staining.**—Small insects, after treatment with sodium hydroxide and thorough washing, may be stained with acid fuchsin and magenta red before mounting.

7. **Transportation.**—For transportation unmounted dried specimens of small insects should be placed between layers of lens paper in pill-boxes packed with cotton so as to avoid movement. These pill-boxes may be kept in cans with tight-fitting covers where they may be fumigated at intervals with a few drops of carbon disulphide.

DISSECTION OF ARTHROPODS

8. **Examination of Arthropods for Parasites.**—Arthropods act as intermediate hosts for many parasites of man. The organs most commonly infected are the intestinal tract, salivary glands and connective tissues. The special methods used for the detection and study of protozoan and helminthic parasites that infect the insect host depend upon the parasite and the particular organs affected. The suspected parts of fresh specimens may be examined in cover-glass preparations. Free the parasites by teasing the tissues with a sharp needle in as small an amount of physiological sodium chloride solution as possible. If protozoan parasites are extracellular, they may be fixed by osmic acid vapor and then smeared on a slide, dried in air, placed in alcohol for 15 minutes, and then stained. If intracellular, they must be teased out of the tissues or both the tissues and parasites may be fixed and stained. Parasites may also be demonstrated in histological sections.

9. **General Dissection.**—Successful dissection of arthropods depends more upon actual experience than upon written descriptions. Certain general observations may prove helpful.

(a) Complete the dissection rapidly because the living cells die quickly out of their natural environment and become unrecognizable.

(b) Before dissecting pull off, rather than cut, the legs and wings of the insect close to the thorax. Brush off other loose structures such as scales.

(c) Rest the dissecting slide on a half black and half white tile. Begin work on the white area, but when internal structures are handled, push the slide onto the black area.

(d) Small insects are usually held on one side and dissected on a glass slide to which just enough physiological saline has been added to keep the tissues moist. Large insects are usually pinned on their backs with small entomological pins to the paraffin surface of a small dissecting trough which is then flooded with the saline.

(e) When a system is freed from its attachments to the integument and surrounding tissues, it may be drawn out of the opened body cavity. Certain organs, especially in small insects, are difficult to extract and require careful dissection under magnification with good illumination. In withdrawing the organs hold the arthropod firmly with needles and apply gentle traction.

(f) When muscle tissue is ruptured, or if an organ is broken, flood the slide with saline to wash away the milky fluid. Remove the saline with a fine pipette and add a fresh supply.

(g) Keep the working area clear of all structures no longer required and transfer all organs to be examined to fresh saline on a clean slide.

Mites.—Small insects, such as mites, are best examined in the fresh state by making a cover-glass mount in physiological sodium chloride solution. Dissection is difficult and is best done under the microscope. By nicking the integument with a fine needle it is possible to remove most of the organs.

Larvæ.—The dissection of the alimentary tract of larvæ is most readily accomplished by severing the integument of the last segment, cutting off the head, and drawing the gut through the posterior opening by traction on the posterior segment.

The methods of obtaining the intestinal tract, salivary glands, proboscis, and reproductive organs are described below with comments upon the modifications necessary for the different classes of arthropods.

10. **Digestive System.**—The digestive system consisting of pharynx, esophagus, proventriculus, midgut, and hindgut runs almost the entire length of the body.

(a) Place the trimmed insect on its back in physiological sodium chloride solution.

(b) Detach last segment by cutting the intersegmental membrane, but do not sever the intestine.

(c) Remove head.

(d) Firmly supporting the thorax with a needle, apply traction to the last segment with a second needle. As the digestive tract comes into view reduce tension by severing the adherent silvery-white tracheæ. Free from reproductive organs.

(e) Place digestive tract in the saline on a clean slide.

(f) If the midgut, filled with blood, is desired, remove the head and last abdominal segment, slit the chitin at the ventral junction of the head and thorax, enlarge the opening and pull the midgut out of the body cavity; or open the abdominal wall and remove without undue pressure on gut.

Small DIPTERA.—The gut of small flies of the size of mosquitoes may be removed by the above method or with equal ease by the anterior route, severing the last abdominal segment and pulling on the head.

TABANIDÆ.—A similar procedure is followed with the TABANIDÆ except that it is useful to slit the abdominal integument of the larger insects with fine scissors so as to remove the dorsal wall.

Muscid Flies.—Coiling of the gut in the muscid flies makes its removal difficult. In the male it may be removed in the ordinary manner, but in the female, because of the large reproductive organs, the body must be pulled apart between the fifth and sixth abdominal segments near the base of the ovipositor, so that the ovipositor and the posterior attachment of the gut may be drawn out.

Tsetse Flies.—Incise the thorax longitudinally in the middorsal line and cut laterally along several transverse grooves of the thorax almost to the bases of the legs. Sever the longitudinal muscles and free the tracheæ. Traction with needles at each end of the longitudinal incision will cause the thorax to break apart and the intestinal tract to rupture between the pharynx and the proventriculus. The pharynx is removed anteriorly with the head, and the intestines are removed posteriorly as in the small flies.

Fleas.—The tough hard-surfaced integument requires sharp needles. The removal of the midgut and coiled hindgut requires separate procedures. For the midgut insert one needle between head and prothorax. Separate by traction the first abdominal segment from the thorax. Cut the last abdominal segment and insert another needle in it. Pull until the proventriculus and midgut pass anteriorly from the abdomen. To obtain the coiled hindgut cut across the anterior portion of the abdomen, severing the midgut. Remove the ovaries and fat bodies by pressure or by opening the abdomen. Insert one needle between the dorsal margins of the eighth and ninth segments and another near the anterior end of the abdomen. Pull posteriorly until the last segment with the adherent rectum and hindgut is torn loose.

Lice.—The integument is so tough and the exoskeleton so closely knit that ordinary methods of incision are not practical. Cut off both lateral margins internal to the stigmata. Make a transverse incision of the ventral integument. Strip back the flaps by severing the attached tracheæ. Remove the digestive tract by cutting the esophagus and the posterior end of the gut, and dissecting forward and backward.

HEMIPTERA.—The method of dissecting depends upon the individual species. With *Triatoma* the lateral margins are cut with scissors and the ventral abdominal wall is removed. With the bedbug, *Cimex,* the last segment is separated from the body and the hindgut is pulled out with it. The esophagus and midgut may be removed with the salivary glands.

Ticks.—With fine scissors cut the posterior edge of the integument starting around posteriorly from the level of the fourth leg. Pin down the ventral integument and reflect the dorsal integument anteriorly, extending the operation by lateral cuts and detaching adherent structures. Hook up and unravel the intestinal diverticula with a bent needle. Remove the exposed esophagus, midgut and hindgut starting at the esophagus.

11. **Salivary Glands.**—The salivary glands, which usually lie in the anterior and ventral part of the thorax below the main body of muscles, are withdrawn from the thorax by pulling off the head, provided that they do not extend back into the abdomen and are not bound down firmly by the tracheæ or other adherent tissues. The steps in the procedure are as follows:

(a) Place the insect stripped of appendages on its side with proboscis facing worker.

(b) Open thorax and free salivary glands if necessary.

(c) Hold thorax firmly with needle and draw head slowly forward with second needle.

(d) The intestinal tract will usually rupture at the juncture of the pharynx and esophagus, or it may be severed as the salivary glands are pulled out of the thorax, and freed from the adhering tracheæ.

(e) The salivary glands are then placed on a clean slide in physiological sodium chloride solution and freed from adhering tissue.

The different classes of arthropods require considerable modification of this general technic.

Small DIPTERA.—In the small flies the head is merely pulled forward; the gut ruptures at the esophagus and retracts into the thorax; and the intact salivary duct with the attached glands is freed from the cervical tracheæ and is pulled out. The glistening glands may be examined with or without separation from the adherent tissues. By severing the last abdominal segment and using traction on the head, the salivary glands and intestinal tract may be removed together.

Barber and Rice (1936) have evolved a technic for examining the salivary glands and stomach of mosquitoes. The insect, with legs and head removed, is placed in a drop of dissecting fluid on a slide. A cover-glass is sloped on the thorax and pressed gently down with forceps, while the torso is withdrawn to one side, thus forcing out the salivary glands under the cover-glass. After the glands are removed the thorax is held with a needle, the tip of the abdomen is grasped with the forceps, and the stomach is slowly drawn out. Permanent preparations may be made by wet fixation and Giemsa's stain without removing the cover-glass.

TABANIDÆ.—Slit the thorax along the middorsal line, separate the surrounding muscle fibers from the salivary glands, and detach the tracheæ. Break through the chitinous arch at the thoracic inlet, and pull the head slightly away from the thorax. Sever the esophagus above the proventriculus and cut the cervical tracheæ and the nerve cord. Gentle forward traction of the head will pull the salivary glands out of the thorax.

Muscid Flies.—Slit the thorax and abdomen in the middorsal line. Spread body open in physiological sodium chloride solution, remove the fat bodies, and free the intestine and glands from each other and the surrounding muscles. Sever the pharynx. Draw the head gently forward with a needle passed through the basal part of the proboscis and the salivary glands will appear attached to the hypopharynx.

Tsetse Flies.—Dissect fly as in obtaining the intestinal tract. The salivary glands are drawn out with the head from the thorax and abdomen and disengaged from the head and thorax.

Fleas.—Transfix the head firmly with a needle and insert another needle bent like a retractor in the interspace between thorax and abdomen. Pull the thorax and abdomen apart by steady traction and the salivary glands will appear.

Lice.—Make same incisions as in obtaining digestive tract. Remove the ventral wall of thorax with its attached muscles. Free the kidney-shaped glands from adherent fat and cells.

HEMIPTERA.—Cut through the junction of the pro- and mesothorax and pull out the esophagus and midgut with the attached glands. The ovoid salivary glands lie free and the cardiac glands are on each side of the anterior end of the midgut.

Ticks.—Uncover internal organs as in dissecting the digestive tract. After removal of the digestive tract, the lobulate white salivary glands and ducts form the lateral sides of a triangle with its apex at the chitinous mouth.

12. **Proboscis.**—The proboscis may be dissected after its removal with the entire salivary glands, or it may be removed with their anterior portion.

(a) Hold the thorax firmly transfixed and draw off the head with a needle.

(b) Separate proboscis from head. The proximal portion of the salivary glands will remain attached to the proboscis.

(c) Place the point of the needle in the base of the labium and draw it away from the labium and bulb.

(d) If the hypopharynx is still within the labium, draw it out with one needle while pressing on the bulb with another.

13. **Reproductive Organs.**—The reproductive organs are obtained in the same manner as the digestive system. As they are pulled out of the posterior part of the body, the oviducts or vasa are cut. If the ova are fully matured, they may be expelled by gentle pressure from the thorax backward. If the whole ovary is desired, enlarge the posterior opening. The reproductive organs are then freed from adhesions to the digestive tract.

Small DIPTERA.—Proceed as above. In larger insects slit abdominal integument and remove wall.

Muscid Flies.—In males proceed as above. In females pull abdomen apart between fifth and sixth segment at base of ovipositor and draw out the attached reproductive organs.

Tsetse Flies.—The reproductive organs are removed in the same manner as the digestive tract, but in the female the posterior opening may need to be enlarged.

Fleas.—Slit open the abdominal wall and remove organs after cutting away the tergites and sternites. The mature ova may be obtained by pressure on the body.

Lice.—Make incisions as in obtaining digestive tract. The reproductive organs can be removed before the digestive tract. The male or female genitalia must be carefully dissected from the other tissues. Mature ova may be removed with a pipette.

HEMIPTERA.—Cut the lateral borders of the abdominal segments and remove ventral integument. Free the genitalia from adherent tissues.

Ticks.—Uncover the internal organs as in the dissection of the digestive tract. The testis or ovary lies above the posterior diverticula and rectum and can be removed after the digestive tract has been taken out.

EXPERIMENTAL INVESTIGATIONS

In experimental inoculations of arthropods, only laboratory bred individuals free from natural infection should be used. If "wild" specimens are inoculated, results often are worthless because of the likelihood of previous infection. Since arthropods such as ticks may transmit infections to their progeny, specimens for breeding must be tested for freedom from disease by being allowed to bite uninfected animals.

The technics required for the successful breeding, handling and using of arthropods for experimental purposes are so specialized that they should be undertaken only by experienced investigators. The handling of venomous arthropods or those transmitting dangerous diseases demands a technical knowledge sufficient to insure safety to the worker.

Specialized technics are required in breeding arthropods even among closely related species. While a single metamorphosis may be observed readily and adults procured from collected ova or larvæ, continued breeding of most species demands technical skill and special equipment that most laboratories cannot supply. For detailed discussions of breeding of parasitic arthropods the reader is referred to Galstoff, Lutz, Welch and Needham (1937); for lice to Wolbach, Todd and Palfrey (1922); and for fleas to Bacot (1914).

XIII. DRUGS USEFUL IN THE TREATMENT OF PARASITIC DISEASES

The search for specific drugs for the cure of parasitic diseases began early in medical history. The crude drugs of ancient times have been replaced by semirefined or refined drugs or by chemicals developed by pharmacological research. These drugs are of two types: (1) those having a parasiticidal action on the adult or larval parasites invading the tissues, and (2) those acting upon the parasites of the intestinal tract. The majority of the anthelmintic drugs are in the latter class. They are termed **vermicides** when they kill the worms and **vermifuges** when they simply cause the evacuation of the worms from the intestine.

Successful chemotherapy depends on the pathological activities of the parasite, on the condition of the patient, and on the pharmacological action of the selected drug. Before treatment of the patient the parasite should be identified, its location in the host determined, the intensity of the infection (number of parasites) estimated, and the amount of damage approximated. The general physical condition, the impairment of vital organs by other diseases, and the hygienic habits of the patient may contraindicate the use of certain drugs. The physician should be familiar with the parasiticidal action and toxic properties of the common drugs in order to select the appropriate and most useful drug for a specific case.

Toxicity.—Most drugs in concentrations capable of destroying parasites are more or less toxic to the patient, and in some instances there is only a narrow range between the therapeutic and toxic dose. The administration of drugs requires thorough supervision, since patients vary as to age, physical condition and individual idiosyncrasies. Chemotherapy is often contraindicated in patients with anemia; febrile conditions; acute cardiac, renal, pulmonary and hepatic disease; alcoholism; and pregnancy.

Administration.—Drugs are administered orally, intravenously and intramuscularly, depending upon the nature of the drug and the condition of the patient. Some may also be used in enemata or applied directly to local lesions. When enemata are given, the rectum should first be cleansed with an enema of warm water and the drug administered in a concentration that will not produce unnecessary irritation.

Dosage.—The doses for the listed drugs are those ordinarily administered to adults of average size. It is impossible to state the exact dosage for any drug. The dose of a drug varies with the method of administration, because of rapidity of absorption. The rate of administration governs its excretion and destruction, so that a dose otherwise innocuous, when given rapidly may provoke serious symptoms.

The dose refers to the amount per day, although the drug is usually given in divided doses, so that the daily dose is three or four times the single dose. In general, dosage is based upon the weight of the patient, a factor rarely necessary for adults but extremely useful for calculating doses for children. Women, because of lower weight and functional peculiarities, usually require one-half to four-fifths the dosage for men. For persons above 60 years the dose is reduced to four-fifths or two-thirds, and in extreme old age to one-half. Individuals suffering from debilitating conditions or faulty nutrition should receive less than the standard dosage.

The dosage for children may be calculated in proportion to the weight of the child or by certain empirical rules, although children are comparatively tolerant to cathartics and can stand proportionately greater amounts of certain drugs than adults. Cowling's rule is to multiply the adult dose by the age of the child at its next birthday and divide by the adult age, which is taken as 24, but the results are somewhat low below four years and above fifteen years. Clark's rule is to multiply the average adult dose by the weight of the child in pounds and divide by 150. Fried's rule for infants is to divide the age in months by 150 and multiply by the adult dose.

Anthelmintic Treatment.—The administration of anthelmintic drugs usually requires preliminary preparation of the patient and purgation. The patient should either refrain from eating or partake only of a light evening meal on the day previous to treatment. Certain drugs require a preliminary fat-free diet for several days. Breakfast is omitted.

Adequate purgation is an important part of the routine. Magnesium sulphate is given before and after the anthelmintic drug and often on the previous evening. The preliminary purge is designed to remove from the intestinal tract excess food, which will interfere with the action of the drug on the parasite. In constipated patients purges and enemata should be given on the day before treatment. A purge is administered after the drug to decrease absorption, hasten elimination, distribute the drug along the intestinal tract, and to remove the worms. The purge should be given in doses of sufficient size to produce results, not in divided doses. The usual dose of magnesium sulphate, 30 gm. for an adult and 2 gm. for each 10 pounds of weight in children, is dissolved in a glass of water. Sodium sulphate is preferred by some physicians because the sodium ion is less toxic than that of magnesium and this salt is more efficient in removing mucus from the intestinal mucosa. Its disagreeable taste is a disadvantage with children. If the purge does not take effect within a few hours or if signs of vermicidal toxicity occur, it may be repeated and enemata may also be used.

Contraindications to severe purgation are intestinal obstruction, debilitation and pregnancy.

The more important drugs used in the treatment of parasitic diseases are briefly described below. Some have been adopted from empirical usage and others have been proved by pharmacological and biological methods. They are arranged according to their chemical nature.

ARSENICAL COMPOUNDS

The arsenicals are used chiefly in protozoan infections and are rarely of value in helminthic diseases.

1. ARSPHENAMINES

Other Names.	Salvarsan, 606, arsenobenzol. Arsphenamine derivatives include neoarsphenamine, sulfarsphenamine, and silver arsphenamine.
Composition.	Dihydrochloride of Diaminodihydroxyarsenobenzene. Arsenic content 30%. The addition of sodium hydroxide forms the mono- and disodium salts.
Use.	Has been used without much success in amœbiasis, trypanosomiasis, filariasis, clonorchiasis.
Administration.	Intravenous injections of 0.4% solution in sterile freshly distilled water with the addition of a specified amount of alkali. Neoarsphenamine and sulfarsphenamine dissolve directly in water and may be given intramuscularly.
Dosage.	A course of treatment consists of 6 to 8 injections once or twice weekly, starting with 0.2 gm. and increasing to 0.5 gm.
Toxicity.	The toxic manifestations include immediate anaphylactoid collapse; early febrile, kidney and skin reactions; delayed (after 24 hours) febrile and arsenic reactions; late arsenic intoxications (after 3 days) in the form of hemorrhagic encephalitis, jaundice, exfoliative dermatitis and paresthesia.

2. ATOXYL

Other Names.	Sodium arsanilate, soamin.
Composition.	Sodium p-Aminophenylarsonate. $NH_2C_6H_4.AsO(OH)ONa.4H_2O$. Arsenic content 31.4%.
Use.	Trypanosomiasis.
Administration.	Intramuscular injection of a 10% solution in sterile distilled water,
Dosage.	0.02 to 0.2 gm. every other day until 6.5 gm. have been given. In trypanosomiasis 0.5 gm. once a week until trypanosomes have left the blood and then at longer intervals.
Toxicity.	High toxicity limits use. Acute symptoms of arsenic poisoning when dosage exceeds 0.5 gm. Chronic poisoning similar to chronic arsenic intoxication. Toxic symptoms include: nausea, vomiting, colic, vertigo, general weakness and somnolence, neuritis, pain in limbs, deafness, retention of urine, sometimes nephritis, iritis, and not uncommonly optic atrophy. The eye symptoms begin with scintillation, cloudiness, diminished vision, and contraction of the visual field.

3. TRYPARSAMIDE

Other Names. French preparations Fourneau 270 or Orsanine. Belgian preparation trypanarsyl meurice.

Composition. Pentavalent arsenic derivative. Sodium N-Phenylglycinamide-p-arsonate. $C_8H_{10}O_4N_2AsNa.\frac{1}{2}H_2O$. Arsenic content 25.3%.

Use. Gambesian trypanosomiasis. Specific in early stage, 17 to 50% recoveries after invasion of central nervous system. Little value in Rhodesian trypanosomiasis in early stage, worthless when central nervous system invaded.

Administration. Intravenous injections of a 10% freshly prepared, filtered, not boiled solution in sterile water. Intramuscular injections of a 20% solution less satisfactory.

Dosage. Injections once a week. Initial dose 1 gm. increasing to 3 gm. (not to exceed 0.04 gm. per kilogram of body weight) for 8 to 15 injections. Total dosage of 20 to 80 gm. may be necessary to eliminate *Trypanosoma gambiense*. Rest period of one month between courses. Chopra (1936) recommends 10 weekly injections of 0.04 gm. per kilogram of body weight and Manson-Bahr (1936) states that the average amount per course is 24 gm. If trypanosomes reappear in blood, another course of treatment is given.

Toxicity. Acute toxicity low, but drug may cause visual impairment, jaundice, nephritis, and other symptoms of arsenic poisoning. Not cumulative. The eyes should be carefully checked during treatment, since optic neuritis preceded by pain, photophobia and lacrimation follow its administration in some patients. Any eye symptoms call for discontinuing the drug.

4. STOVARSOL

Other Names. Acetarsone, spirocide, orarsan.

Composition. Pentavalent arsenical. Acetylamino-hydroxyphenylarsonic acid. $C_8H_{10}O_5NAs$. Arsenic content 27.2%.

Use. Amœbiasis, balantidiasis.

Administration. Oral.

Dosage. 0.25 gm. 2 or 3 times per day for seven days. Second course of treatment after a week's rest.

Toxicity. Highly toxic.

5. CARBARSONE

Other Names. None.

Composition. p-Carbamylamino-phenylarsonic acid. $C_7H_9O_4N_2As$. Pentavalent arsenical compound. Arsenic content 28.85%.

Use. It is useful in the treatment of carriers of *Endamœba histolytica*, especially if other drugs have proved ineffective.

Administration. Oral, in gelatin capsules.

Dosage. A course of treatment in amœbiasis comprises the administration of one capsule, 0.25 gm., twice a day for ten days. A second course may be given after an interval of ten days. May be given as a retention enema, 1% carbarsone in 2% sodium bicarbonate solution.

Toxicity.   The toxicity of this drug, though slight, is that of arsenic and its administration requires the same precautions as other arsenic preparations.

ANTIMONY

The action of antimony resembles that of arsenic, but it produces greater local irritation, is absorbed less readily, and is excreted more rapidly. Trivalent compounds are more toxic than pentavalent. Excessive doses produce symptoms resembling acute and subacute arsenic poisoning. The symptoms of chronic antimony poisoning are: headache, somnolence, mental depression, vertigo, muscular weakness, loss of appetite, diarrhea, general malaise, dimness of vision, lowered blood pressure, a weak arrhythmic pulse, and at times jaundice and albuminuria.

6. POTASSIUM ANTIMONY TARTRATE

Other Names.   Tartar emetic, antimonyl potassium tartrate.

Composition. $K(SbO)C_4H_4O_6 \cdot \frac{1}{2}H_2O$. Cheapest and most stable of antimony compounds.

Use.   Leishmaniasis, schistosomiasis, clonorchiasis, opisthorchiasis, paragonimiasis.

Administration.   Intravenously in a freshly prepared 2% solution in freshly distilled water sterilized at 120°C. for 15 minutes. The patient should remain recumbent for at least one hour after treatment to avoid respiratory symptoms. Inflammation and even sloughing may result from the escape of the solution into the perivascular tissues.

Dosage.   In leishmaniasis the initial dose is 2 ml. (0.04 gm.) increased by 1 ml. (0.02 gm.) to a maximum of 5 ml. (0.1 gm.). Injections are repeated every second day until a total of 2 gm. has been given (about 6 weeks). The initial dose is reduced one-half for weak or debilitated patients and increased gradually. The dosage in children is proportional to size but the total amount administered is the same as for adults. In schistosomiasis the initial dose is 0.06 gm. increased to a maximum of 0.12 gm. by the third dose and continued every other day for a period of 4 or more weeks until a total of 1.3 to 1.8 gm. has been given.

Toxicity.   One of the most toxic of the antimony compounds. About 0.1% of patients die under treatment. Bronchitis, nausea, vomiting, diarrhea, abdominal colic, dizziness, fainting, bradycardia, edema, prostration and collapse may occur. Bronchitis and pneumonia are common complications. The most common symptom is coughing as the result of bronchial irritation. Tartar emetic is contraindicated in febrile, cardiac, respiratory, renal, hepatic and central nervous system diseases. Toxic reactions call for temporary cessation of treatment or greater intervals between reduced doses.

7. SODIUM ANTIMONY TARTRATE

Other Names.   None.

Composition.   Unstable.

Use.   Schistosomiasis. Preferred in *Schistosoma japonicum* infections.

Administration.   Intravenous injection of a 1 to 2% solution.

Dosage.	Similar to that of potassium antimony tartrate.
Toxicity.	Toxicity similar to but slightly less than that of potassium antimony tartrate.

8. STIBOSAN

Other Names.	Von Heyden 471.
Composition.	A pentavalent antimony compound. Metachlor-para-acetylamino-phenylstibiate of sodium.
Use.	Leishmaniasis.
Administration.	Intravenous, in 1 to 5% solution in freshly distilled water.
Dosage.	Initial dose 0.2 gm. followed by doses of 0.3 gm. injected on alternate days. The average curative amount is 3 to 4 gm. (11 to 15 injections).
Toxicity.	Less toxic than tartar emetic, but some symptoms occur in susceptible patients or with overdosing. Vomiting, coughing and anaphylactoid symptoms call for cessation or reduction of treatment.

9. NEOSTIBOSAN

Other Names.	Von Heyden 693, Bayer 693 B.
Composition.	Pentavalent antimony compound. Antimony content 40%. p-Aminophenylstibiate of diethylamine.
Use.	Leishmaniasis.
Administration.	Intravenous and intramuscular, in 25% isotonic solution.
Dosage.	Initial dose 0.1 gm., increased by 0.1 gm. to a maximum of 0.3 gm. continued daily for 10 days or until symptoms disappear. Average curative amount 2.4 to 3.0 gm.
Toxicity.	Toxic manifestation rare. Neostibosan is the least toxic of the pentavalent antimony compounds and the most efficient in *Leishmania donovani* infections.

10. UREA STIBAMINE

Other Names.	Stiburea, stiburamin, ureastibol.
Composition.	Pentavalent antimony compound. Exact chemical structure unknown. Unstable and variable in its antimony content; therefore, not wholly satisfactory.
Use.	Leishmaniasis.
Administration.	Intravenous, in freshly prepared 5 or 10% solution in distilled water. Solution should *not* be boiled.
Dosage.	Initial dose 0.10 gm. increased by 0.05 gm. until a maximal dose of 0.25 gm. is reached. The total curative amount is 2.5 gm. or approximately 10 injections at weekly intervals.
Toxicity.	Toxic manifestations are rare and vary with the composition of the drug. Occasionally diarrhea and pulmonary symptoms develop.

11. FUADIN

Other Names.	Neoantimosan.
Composition.	Trivalent antimony compound. Antimony-pyrocatechol-sodium di-sulphonate. $C_{12}H_4O_{16}SbS_4Na_5.7H_2O$. Antimony content 13.6%.
Use.	The drug of choice in *L. tropica* and *L. braziliensis* infections. Also used in kala-azar and schistosomiasis.
Administration.	Intramuscular, in 7% solution.
Dosage.	For schistosomiasis: first day 1.5 ml. (0.105 gm.), second day 3.5 ml. (0.245 gm.), third day 5.0 ml. (0.35 gm.) and every other day for a total of 10 injections over 17 days, in which a total of 3.15 gm. will have been given. If necessary, 15 injections may be given. Infants under 1 year should receive ½ and older children ⅔ to ¾ of the dosage for adults.
Toxicity.	Toxicity low. Safer than the intravenously administered antimony preparations. It causes no local irritation or necrosis and no nausea, bronchial irritation, or significant liver damage.

IODINE COMPOUNDS

The curative properties of iodine compounds depend upon the iodine content. Iodine combines with the proteins of the cells and has an irritant and antiseptic action. In large doses it produces iodism. It is convertible into thyroxin and thus affects metabolism. It increases the secretions and is excreted mainly in the urine. Organic iodine compounds are decomposed in the body and act like inorganic iodides. The symptoms of iodine toxicity are gastro-intestinal uneasiness, metallic taste, abdominal pain, diarrhea, and circulatory failure. In severe cases hemorrhagic nephritis may develop.

12. CHINIOFON

Other Names.	Anayodin, yatren, quinoxyl, loretin.
Composition.	7-iodo-8-hydroxyquinoline-5-sulphonic acid ($C_9H_6NIO_4S$) 80% and sodium bicarbonate 20%. Iodine content 26.5 to 28.9%.
Use.	In amœbiasis for the treatment of carriers and patients with chronic dysentery and in combination with emetine.
Administration.	Oral, in enteric coated pills containing 0.25 gm. and by enemata.
Dosage.	A course of treatment consists of 3 to 4 pills daily (maximum 1 gm. in divided doses) for 10 days. Repeat after one week. Retention enemata, 250 ml. of a 2½% solution, may be given daily for 10 days in combination with oral emetine bismuth iodide.
Toxicity.	Nontoxic, but excess doses may cause diarrhea. Contraindicated in patients with thyroid disease and liver damage.

13. VIOFORM

Other Names.	Nioform.
Composition.	7-iodo-5-chlor-8-hydroxyquinoline (C_9H_5NOICl). Iodine content 41.56%.

Use.

In amœbiasis particularly if chiniofon has proved ineffective.

Administration.

Oral, in gelatin capsules of 0.25 gm.

Dosage.

Three or four capsules (maximum 1.0 gm. per day in divided doses) for 10 days constitutes a course of treatment. A second course may be given after 10 days.

Toxicity.

Toxicity low. In rare cases abdominal discomfort and diarrhea have been observed. Contraindications, thyroid disease and liver damage.

ALKALOIDS

Alkaloids are organic compounds of alkaline reaction, composed of carbon, hydrogen, nitrogen and sometimes other elements. Pure alkaloids are not soluble in water, but their salts readily dissolve. They occur mostly in the higher plants, although some may be prepared artificially.

14. EMETINE

Other Names.

None.

Composition.

An alkaloid of ipecacuanha. Supplied as emetine hydrochloride. $C_{29}H_{40}O_4N_2.2HCl$.

Use.

Acute amœbiasis for the control of diarrhea and in secondary amœbic infections of the liver and other organs. Ineffective against cysts and unsatisfactory in the treatment of chronic and subacute amœbiasis. It has also been used in fascioliasis and paragonimiasis and locally for oriental sore.

Administration.

Subcutaneous or intramuscular. Patient should remain in bed during and several days after treatment.

Dosage.

Daily dosage not to exceed 0.065 gm. (single injection or divided in two parts given morning and evening) for a course of not more than 12 injections. At least two and preferably three weeks should intervene between courses.

Toxicity.

Protoplasmic poison with marked toxic effect on muscles, producing pain, tenderness and weakness. Acute degeneration of cardiac muscle. Nausea, vomiting and diarrhea from irritation. Profound muscular depression, asthenia, and even death may occur. Contraindicated in renal or cardiac disease, pregnancy, and in young children, except in severe dysentery uncontrolled by other drugs.

15. EMETINE BISMUTH IODIDE

Other Names.

Bismuth emetine iodide.

Composition.

Emetine 17 to 23%, iodine 58%, bismuth 15 to 20%.

Use.

Amœbiasis in acute and chronic stages. Permits oral use of emetine and is amœbicidal.

Administration. Oral, preferably in gelatin enteric coated capsules. Patient should remain in bed during and several days after treatment.

Dosage. 0.2 gm. once a day for 12 days 4 hours after evening meal, patient recumbent.

Toxicity. Less vomiting than with emetine hydrochloride. Toxic symptoms include nausea, vomiting, salivation, and severe diarrhea. There may be mental depression, asthenia, and circulatory irregularities. Contraindications similar to those for emetine.

16. QUININE

Other Names. Cinchona, Peruvian bark, Jesuit's bark.

Composition. $C_{20}H_{24}N_2O_2.3H_2O$. A quinoline ring with a methoxy side chain is attached by a secondary alcohol to a quinuclidine ring with a vinyl side chain. The various salts are: the sulphate (73.5%), the bisulphate (59.1%), the hydrochloride (81.7%), the dihydrochloride (81.6%), and the tannate (33%).

Use. Malaria, enterobiasis (enemata).

Administration. Oral administration preferable because of rapid intestinal absorption. Intravenous for emergencies. Intramuscular injections painful and intravenous may cause thrombosis. Dihydrochloride and bisulphate salts are preferred for oral use because of solubility. Given in cachets, tablets, pills, capsules or in sugared solutions. The dihydrochloride or dihydrobromide is used intravenously.

Dosage. The United States National Malaria Committee in 1918 recommended 2 gm. of quinine sulphate daily, divided into three doses for 4 days or until subsidence of acute symptoms and then 0.65 gm. per day for 8 weeks. More rigorous eliminative treatment is 3 gm. in divided doses daily until the plasmodia disappear and then 1 gm. daily for 2 months. The Malaria Commission of the League of Nations recommends 1.3 gm. per day for 7 to 10 days for the control of symptoms and subsequent treatment during relapses, except in *P. falciparum* infections where there is danger of pernicious symptoms. The intravenous dose is 1 gm. of dihydrochloride in 100 ml. or less of physiological sodium chloride solution.

For prophylaxis 0.4 gm. is given daily as long as exposure continues. Nocht's intermittent method of prophylaxis, as cited by Nocht and Mayer (1937), prescribes 1.0 gm. of quinine in 5 doses of 0.2 gm. on each of two successive weekdays. During periods of exposure to intense infection and undue physical strain the daily dose may be increased to 1.0 gm. for short periods.

Action. The method of action upon the malarial parasites is unknown. Direct plasmodicidal effects *in vitro* may only be obtained in over ten times the concentration in the tissues. Nevertheless, the drug abolishes acute symptoms by inhibiting the asexual multiplication of the parasites. It affects only the schizonts and has a limited action on the sexual forms of *P. vivax* and *P. malariæ* and none on those of *P. falciparum*.

Toxicity.

Symptoms of cinchonism are ringing in the ears, deafness, slight dizziness or sense of constriction in the head, cardiac irregularity, and more rarely nausea or gastric discomfort. The drug is absorbed from the stomach and intestine, appears in the urine in fifteen to twenty minutes, and in 72 hours is completely eliminated. Two-thirds of the quinine is destroyed by the liver, kidneys and muscles, and one-third excreted by the kidney and, to a small extent, through the feces. To maintain a constant concentration, it should be administered in divided doses.

Sensitive individuals may show severe symptoms of cyanosis, cardiac palpitation, dizziness and dyspnea even with a small dose. Fatal cases show hemoglobinuria, failure of heart and respiration, coma, and convulsions. Death has resulted from 0.5 gm. and recovery from 30 gm.

17. ATABRINE

Other Names.

Atebrine, chinacrin.

Composition.

2-chloro-7-methoxy-5-α-diethylamino-δ-pentylamino-acridine (N.N.R., Council on Pharmacy and Chemistry) 2-methoxy-6-chloro-9-α-diethylamino-δ-pentylamino-acridine (American Chemical Society). $C_{23}H_{31}ON_3$.

Use.

Introduced by Mauss and Mietzsch in 1933 for the treatment of malaria. Not plasmodicidal for the sexual forms of *P. facliparum*. Most valuable specific for malaria.

Administration.

Preferably oral as dihydrochloride in tablet form, although it may be administered intramuscularly or intravenously, particularly in the pernicious type of malaria. Administration requires medical supervision.

Dosage.

One tablet of 0.1 gm. three times daily after meals for 5 successive days, or twice daily for 8 days. For children: 1 to 4 years, one-third; 4 to 8 years, two-thirds; and over 8 years, the full adult dose. In relapses the course may be repeated after an interval of a week or more and continued for 7 or even 10 consecutive days. Intravenously a total of 0.1 to 0.3 gm. may be injected daily in doses of 0.1 gm. in 10 ml. of distilled water, given slowly, the number of doses depending upon the severity of symptoms. Same dosage for intramuscular administration.

For prophylaxis a total of 0.4 gm. per week in two doses on successive or nonsuccessive days or 0.05 gm. daily. A larger dosage is given in highly endemic areas. Continue treatment for four weeks after leaving endemic area.

Toxicity.

Rapidly absorbed and excreted slowly by kidney and liver. Usually eliminated in 36 to 40 days, although traces may persist over 50 days. Its toxicity is greater than that of quinine but less than that of plasmochin. Slight disagreeable symptoms such as gastro-intestinal disturbances in the form of colic, nausea and gaseous eructation have been observed during its administration. Long-continued large doses may cause severe toxic symptoms in 0.02% of patients, in

the form of mental excitement, melancholia, mania, severe headaches, insomnia, delusions, mental confusion and convulsions. The
yellow color of the skin; produced by the deposition of drug in
about one-half the patients, is the only disadvantage in its prophylactic use.

18. PLASMOCHIN

Other Names.   Plasmoquine, aminoquin.

Composition.   N-diethylamino-isopentyl-8-amino-6-methoxyquinoline. $[(C_2H_5)_2N.$
$(CH_2)_3.CH(CH_3)NH]CH_3O.C_9H_5N.$

Use.   This quinoline derivative, introduced in the treatment of malaria in
1926, is destructive to the gametocytes and is of particular value in
eliminating the carrier state.

Administration.   Oral, as the hydrochloride salt in capsules, tablets and pills. After
meals alone or in combination with quinine.

Dose.   The daily amount is 0.06 gm. in three doses for 5 days and then for
3 days with 4-day intervals for 2 to 6 weeks. About one-half of the
patients show some toxic effect after 5 days. When combined with
quinine as chinoplasm, the dosage is reduced one-half, which is
within a safe limit, and this combination is effective in the general
treatment of malaria.

Toxicity.   Cyanosis, nausea and vomiting, sweating, abdominal pain, diarrhea,
jaundice, subnormal temperature, lowered blood pressure, methemo-
globinuria and methemoglobinemia. Contraindicated in debilitated
patients and those with cardiac, renal and hepatic diseases.

19. BERBERINE SULPHATE

Other Names   Karamchandani.

Composition.   Berberine is one of the alkaloids of hydrastis.
$(C_{20}H_{18}O_4N)_2SO_4.3H_2O.$

Use.   Oriental sore.

Administration.   Subcutaneous local injections for oriental sore.

Dosage.   0.016 gm. dissolved in 1.6 ml. distilled water (1%). Weekly injections
of 2 ml. each for 2 to 4 weeks.

Toxicity.   Large doses increase peristalsis, lower the temperature and kill by
central paralysis.

20. PELLETIERIN

Other Names.   None.

Composition.   A mixture of the several alkaloids obtained from the bark of the
root and stem of the pomegranate, *Punica granatum*. The tannate,
usually used to avoid gastric irritation, is a light yellow, amorphous,
astringent powder slightly soluble in water.

Use.	For all tapeworms except *Hymenolepis nana;* especially recommended for *Tænia solium.* Removal rate about 35%. Drug is expensive.
Administration.	Oral, on fasting stomach followed by a saline purge in one-half to two hours. An infusion of pomegranate bark, an ancient remedy, may be given in the same manner. Patient should take no alcohol for 48 hours before and 24 hours after treatment.
Dosage.	Average dose 0.25 gm., not to exceed 0.5 gm., suspended in water or a syrup. If necessary, treatment with pelletierin may be alternated with oleoresin of aspidium at intervals of not less than 10 days.
Toxicity.	The drug is extremely toxic to nervous tissue and, when given in larger than therapeutic doses, may produce mydriasis, temporary or partial blindness, prostration, ascending paralysis and convulsions. In some cases therapeutic doses may cause vertigo, headache, dimmed vision, diplopia, formication, diarrhea, intestinal colic and vomiting. Contraindicated in pregnancy. Too toxic for children and debilitated persons.

HYDROCARBONS

21. CARBON TETRACHLORIDE

Other Names.	Perchloromethane, tetrachloromethane, benzinoform.
Composition.	A clear colorless, pungent liquid related to chloroform. Chemical formula CCl_4.
Use.	Hookworm, tapeworm and *Fasciolopsis* infections. Although extensively and effectively (90 to 95%) used in hookworm disease, it is not recommended because of its toxicity. It is being replaced by tetrachlorethylene, which is as effective and is less toxic.
Administration.	Oral. Given in morning on empty stomach either emulsified in skimmed milk or in hard gelatin capsules. (Sometimes advantage to give a light meal the previous evening followed by a saline purge.) Saline purge should follow within 1 to 2 hours. The patient should remain in bed during treatment and should refrain from eating until the purge has acted. At times a second purge may be necessary. Treatment should not be repeated within 3 weeks. In tapeworm infections following the action of the purge a warm soapsuds enema is given. To prevent hepatic injury, preliminary oral or intramuscular administration of 0.5 gm. calcium lactate or gluconate for several days is recommended, especially if patient is deficient in calcium. Also a high carbohydrate low fat diet is advised. Patients should refrain from taking alcohol and fats before treatment since they increase absorption of the drug.
	In mixed infections of *Ascaris* and hookworm, combined treatment with oil of chenopodium and carbon tetrachloride (1 ml. oil of chenopodium and 2 ml. carbon tetrachloride in 30 ml. of liquid paraffin) has proved effective. A 3 to 2 mixture has been used in the mass treatment of hookworm infection.

Dosage.   3 ml. (for children 0.2 ml. for each year of age).

Toxicity.   Highly toxic. Toxicity depends upon rapidity of absorption from
the intestine especially when alcohol is taken. May cause fatty
degeneration and central necrosis of the liver even in moderate
doses, and cloudy swelling and fatty infiltration of the kidneys. In
calcium deficiency, a guanidine intoxication secondary to liver damage may result. The drug is contraindicated in alcoholism and in
cardiac, hepatic, renal or pulmonary disease.

22. TETRACHLORETHYLENE

Other Names.   Carbon dichloride, perchloroethylene, ethylene tetrachloride.

Composition.   A chlorinated aliphatic hydrocarbon, $Cl_2C:CCl_2$.

Use.   Drug of choice for hookworm infections. 90 to 95% efficient. Also
used for intestinal trematodes.

Administration.   Same as carbon tetrachloride. Repeat treatment in one week if
necessary. In treating mixed *Ascaris* and hookworm infections the
same procedure is followed, the dose being 2 ml. of tetrachlorethylene and 1.0 ml. of oil of chenopodium.

Dosage.   Adults 3 ml. (for children 0.2 ml. for each year of age).

Toxicity.   The drug is nonirritating to mucosa and absorption is negligible.
Toxic manifestations are rare except for headache and vertigo,
which disappear following the posttreatment purgation. Alcohol and
fats should not be taken for two days before treatment, since they
may increase absorption. A few intoxications have been recorded.

23. HEXYLRESORCINOL

Other Names.   Caprokol (an olive oil solution).

Composition.   1,3-Hydroxy-4-hexylbenzene.

Uses.   Crystalline hexylresorcinol is the most efficient and safest ascaricide.
It is also active against other helminths including hookworm, pin-
worm, whipworm, dwarf tapeworm and intestinal trematodes. It is
useful in children, debilitated patients, and when the more toxic
drugs are contraindicated. Reports indicate that the drug is effective
in removing 95% of *Ascaris,* 75% hookworm, 50% *Fasciolopsis,*
and 30% *Trichuris.*

Administration.   Oral in hard gelatin capsules, because of local irritation to mouth.
The intestinal tract should be free of food to permit full action of
the drug. For this reason a light evening meal should be eaten and
breakfast omitted. A saline purge after the evening meal is desirable
but not essential. One to 2 hours after the drug a saline purge is
administered. Food should not be taken for 5 hours after treatment.
Treatment may be repeated every 3 to 4 days as often as necessary.
Usually two treatments suffice.

For *Enterobius* infections the drug should be given by mouth as
above and also by enemata. On the day of treatment light noon
and evening meals are allowed and at night a warm soapsuds enema

is followed by an enema of one pint to one quart of 0.1% solution of hexylresorcinol crystals in water retained for 15 minutes. The combined treatment is followed in 3 days by enema alone. Two or more full courses of treatment may be necessary. The oral treatment is directed against the worms in the small intestine and the enemata against those in the large intestine. In the elimination of intestinal trematodes both pre- and posttreatment purgation are required.

Dosage.	For adults and children over 10 years 1 gm. Below 10 years 0.1 gm. for each year of age.
Toxicity.	The drug causes superficial erosion of the buccal mucosa but produces no untoward effects after swallowing. Its low toxicity permits treatment of ambulatory patients and allows repeated treatments every few days without danger.

24. THYMOL

Other Names.	Methyl-isopropyl-phenol.
Composition.	1-Methyl-3-hydroxy-4-isopropylbenzene. Aromatic translucent crystals with pungent somewhat caustic taste.
Use.	Hookworm and rarely other helminthic infections. Replaced by newer, less toxic drugs.
Administration.	Oral as a powder with lactose or sodium bicarbonate and followed by a saline purge within two hours. Fats, oils and alcohols prohibited.
Dosage.	For adults 3 gm. in divided doses.
Toxicity.	Irritant to gastro-intestinal tract. Stimulates and later depresses the nervous system causing headache, vomiting, tinnitus and vertigo. Excessive doses cause renal irritation, depress circulation, and may produce subnormal temperature and collapse. Contraindicated in gastritis, nephritis and cardiac disease.

25. SANTONIN

Other Names.	None.
Composition.	Inner anhydride of santoninic acid from Levant wormseed and related species of *Artemisia*. $C_{15}H_{18}O_3$.
Use.	*Ascaris* and *Enterobius* infections. Formerly a favorite drug for ascariasis.
Administration.	Oral. Santonin is combined with an equal amount of calomel. Given either in one dose not over 0.2 gm. in the evening 5 hours after a light meal followed in the morning by a saline purge or in doses of 0.06 to 0.12 gm. after a meal for 3 consecutive days. May be repeated after 2 weeks.
Dosage.	For adults 0.2 gm. maximum.
Toxicity.	The toxic effects are ocular disturbances (yellow vision), vomiting, diarrhea, headache, vertigo, mental confusion, hallucinations, hematuria, albuminuria, convulsions, prostration and coma.

26. BETANAPHTHOL

Other Names. Isonaphthol.

Composition. β-Hydroxynaphthalene. $C_{10}H_8O$. Yellowish white crystalline powder.

Use. Hookworm, tapeworm and *Fasciolopsis* infections. Toxicity precludes its general use. Other less dangerous drugs more effective.

Administration. Oral. Same as thymol.

Dosage. For adults ordinary maximal dose 1 gm., but doses of 1 to 4 gm. have been reported.

Toxicity. Highly toxic. Large doses produce nephritis, gastric disturbances, cataract and circulatory changes.

27. GENTIAN VIOLET (MEDICINAL)

Other Names. Methylrosaniline.

Composition. A mixture of penta- and hexa-methyl-*p*-rosanilin chlorides.

Use. Strongyloidiasis, clonorchiasis, enterobiasis.

Administration. Oral in enteric coated tablets before meals. In refractory cases of intestinal strongyloidiasis, where the worms are too high in the intestine or too deeply imbedded to be affected by the slowly dissolving enteric coated tablets, a single transduodenal intubation of 25 ml. of 1% solution is efficient. For bronchial strongyloidiasis intravenous injection of 25 ml. of a sterile 0.5% aqueous solution may be given every third day for as many as 8 injections. For enterobiasis oral treatment is given for 8 days and repeated after an interval of a week.

Dosage. For adults, 0.195 gm. in three divided doses daily before meals until a total of 3.3 gm. (50 doses) has been given. For children the daily dosage is 0.01 gm. for each year of age.

Toxicity. The dye irritates the gastric but not the intestinal mucosa. Symptoms occur in about 15% of patients and include headache, vertigo, lassitude, nausea, vomiting and diarrhea. Intravenous injection may cause a transient violet coloration of the skin. Contraindicated in moderate or severe cardiac, hepatic, renal and gastro-intestinal disease.

28. BAYER 205

Other Names. Germanin, Formeau 309, Moranyl, Naganol.

Composition. Urea of acid dimeta-aminobenzoyl-meta-aminoparamethyl-benzoyl-1-naphylamino-4-6-8-trisulphonate of sodium. $C_{51}H_{34}O_{23}\ N_6S_6Na_6$.

Use. Less effective than tryparsamide in early stages of *Trypanosoma gambiense* infection. More effective than tryparsamide in early acute febrile infection with *T. rhodesiense*.

Administration. Intravenously or intramuscularly as a sterile 10% solution in freshly distilled water. Initial dose of 0.5 gm. increased according to patient's tolerance to a maximum of 1 gm.

Dosage.

For adults the average dose is 1 gm. repeated at intervals of 3 days to 1 week. 5 to 10 gm. of the drug is usually curative.

Toxicity.

Low, but drug is eliminated slowly and is cumulative. It is a kidney irritant. Chief symptoms are albuminuria, toxic dermatitis and gastro-intestinal disturbances. Contraindicated in kidney disease.

SEMIREFINED PLANT PRODUCTS

29. OLEORESIN OF ASPIDIUM

Other Names.

Male fern, Filix-mas.

Composition.

The oleoresin or the extract of rhizone and stipes of *Dryopteris filix-mas*. Active constituents are acids, of which filicic acid is the most prominent.

Use.

It is the drug of choice in tæniasis, hymenolepiasis and diphyllobothriasis, but is ineffective against nematodes and trematodes.

Administration.

Alcohol and absorbable fats are prohibited for 2 days prior to treatment. The patient is allowed black coffee, tea and water, but neither luncheon nor supper, the day before treatment. A saline purge (15 to 30 gm. magnesium sulphate) is given at 6:00 P.M. and another at 6:00 A.M. the next day. The patient remains in bed, receives no breakfast and, after the bowels have moved, is given 30 ml. of the following emulsion: oleoresin of aspidium, 6 ml.; powdered acacia, 8 gm.; distilled water sufficient to make 60 ml. One hour later a second 30 ml. is given and 2 hours after this second dose 30 gm. of magnesium sulphate. Two hours later a large soapsuds enema is administered. Stools should be examined for segments and scolex of tapeworm. Oleoresin of aspidium may be administered in a single transduodenal intubation, a saline purge having been given the night before treatment.

Dosage.

For adults the dosage is 4 to 8 ml., usually 6 ml., of the fresh oleoresin of aspidium.

Toxicity.

Variations in absorption and susceptibility produce unexpected toxic effects. The drug is irritating to the intestinal mucosa and may affect the liver, kidneys, the smooth muscles and the nervous system. Toxic effects are reduced by complete rest in bed for several hours before and after treatment. The most common symptoms are headache, vertigo, nausea, vomiting, diarrhea and hyperactive reflexes. In severe poisoning bilirubinemia, jaundice, albuminuria, dyspnea, convulsions, visual disturbances, optic neuritis, and respiratory and cardiac failure may result. The drug is contraindicated in pregnancy, in profound anemia, in renal, hepatic and cardiac diseases, in debilitated individuals, in infants and in aged persons.

30. OIL OF CHENOPODIUM

Other Names.

Oil of American wormseed.

Composition.

An extract of *Chenopodium ambrosioides* var. *anthelminticum*. Active contituent ascaridol (60 to 70%), an organic peroxide.

Use.

Hookworm, *Ascaris* and *Enterobius* infections, especially in combined infections of *Ascaris* and hookworm. A single treatment removes from 70 to 99% of ascarids and 60 to 70% of hookworms. Also for dwarf tapeworm infection and less frequently for intestinal trematodes. Because of its toxicity, it is not recommended for use except in combination with carbon tetrachloride or tetrachlorethylene.

Administration.

Oral. Alcohol and absorbable fats are prohibited for several days before treatment. A saline purge is given the night before treatment following a light evening meal. In the morning the patient takes no solid food and, resting in bed, receives three equally divided doses of the drug in hard gelatin capsules at intervals of one hour. A saline purge is given in from one to two hours after the last dose. For children the drug is sometimes given as a single dose combined with castor oil.

In combination with carbon tetrachloride or tetrachlorethylene for simultaneous *Ascaris* and hookworm infections, the adult dose is 1 ml. of chenopodium and 2 ml. of either of the other two drugs. The method of administration is the same as above, the drugs either being combined in a gelatin capsule or given in liquid paraffin or in a teaspoon with sugar.

Dosage.

Total dose for adults 1.5 to 3.0 ml., but 1.5 ml. is ordinarily used.

Toxicity.

Relatively safe, but full doses are sometimes toxic. Many disturbances and even deaths have been reported. Toxic manifestations include gastro-intestinal irritation with nausea, headache, blurred vision, vertigo, paresthesia and tinnitus. In profound systemic intoxication lowered blood pressure, depressed respiration, stupor, prostration, collapse and death may occur. Albuminuria, hematuria and icterus may follow renal and hepatic damage. Contraindicated in nephritis, cardiac disease, hepatic dysfunction, intestinal ulceration and pregnancy.

31. LECHE DE HIGUÉRON

Other Names.

None.

Composition.

The crude sap of the bastard fig tree, *Ficus laurifolia,* containing the proteolytic enzyme, ficin, is used extensively in South America. Ferments rapidly and becomes unpalatable unless preserved in the icebox or with 1% sodium benzoate.

Use.

Trichuris and *Enterobius* infections. A single treatment will remove 85% of trichurid worms.

Administration.

Oral. Saline purgation is given the evening before treatment. The drug is administered in a single dose the next morning on a fasting stomach and is followed by a saline purge within two to four hours.

Dosage.

30 to 60 ml. No reduction for children.

Toxicity.

No toxic effects following therapeutic doses have been noted.

32. PUMPKIN SEED

Other Names.   Pepo.

Composition.   The effective principle is possibly heat-resistant fraction of the aqueous extract of crushed pumpkin or melon seeds.

Use.   Tæniasis, but not an efficient tæniafuge. An ancient household remedy.

Administration.   Oral. The seeds crushed in syrup or extracted with 2 volumes of boiling water, are given on a fasting stomach. A posttreatment saline purge is required.

Dosage.   30 to 120 gm. of crushed fresh or dried seeds prepared as above.

Toxicity.   Therapeutic dose nontoxic.

33. QUASSIA

Other Names.   Bitter wood, bitter ash.

Composition.   Infusion of the powdered wood of the Jamaican *Picrasma excelsa* or the Surinam *Quassia amara*. Bitter principles (0.1 to 0.2%) are picrasmin, quassin and neoquassin.

Use.   Tæniasis. Rarely expels the head. Enterobiasis (enemata).

Administration.   An infusion is made by covering 30 gm. of the powdered wood with 500 ml. of boiling water and allowing it to stand for 12 hours. This infusion is given orally on three successive mornings and is followed by a saline purge. In enterobiasis a 1 to 20 aqueous infusion may be given as an enema.

Dosage.   150 ml. of the infusion.

Toxicity.   Large doses may produce nausea and vomiting.

34. ARECA

Other Names.   Betel nut, Piuang.

Composition.   Nuts (seeds) of *Areca catechu*. Effective principle an alkaloid, arecoline.

Use.   Tæniasis; has been recommended when other tæniafuges have proved unsuccessful. Used in veterinary medicine.

Administration.   Oral. Decoction of 30 gm. of powdered nuts in 200 ml. distilled water, boiled for 30 minutes.

Dosage.   Decoction of 30 gm. of powdered nuts.

Toxicity.   Therapeutic dose nontoxic.

35. DANISH OINTMENT FOR SCABIES

Composition. 1 kg. of sublimed sulphur is dissolved at a gentle heat in 2 kg. of a 50 per cent solution of potassium hydroxide, making a clear yellow solution; 225 gm. of petrolatum and 225 gm. of anhydrous lanolin are carefully mixed without heating; to this mixture 375 gm. of the described sulphur solution are added; fresh zinc hydroxide is prepared by mixing 28 gm. zinc sulphate and 40 gm. of 20 per cent sodium hydroxide, and this is added to the ointment. Liquid petrolatum is then added to obtain a total weight of 1,000 gm., and finally 5 gm. of benzaldehyde to counteract the odor of sulphuretted hydrogen.

Administration. An ordinary cleansing bath is taken, the ointment is rubbed gently over the entire body (except the head) and allowed to remain for twenty-four hours, after which time another bath is taken and fresh underclothing put on.

36. PYRETHRUM INSECTICIDAL SPRAYS

Other Names. Powdered flower of Pyrethrum species—Persian Powder, and of *Chrysanthemum cinerariæfolium*—Dalmatian Powder.

Composition. Many insecticides depend for their toxicity on pyrethrum or its derivatives (neuromuscular poisons) dissolved in a mineral oil base with or without carbon tetrachloride. A common insecticide is: (1) pyrethrum extract 1 part, (2) mineral oil (low flash point) 16 parts, and (3) carbon tetrachloride 68 parts.

For airplane disinfection the spray should be noninflammable and innocuous to passengers. Two preparations have proved satisfactory: (1) Standard pyrethrum extract (2% pyrethrin) 1 part and refined mineral oil (high flash point) 4 parts (Welch, 1939) and (2) "Deskito," an aqueous base pyrethrum insecticide.

Administration. Atomizer sprayers are used in houses. Various types of atomizer sprayers, such as the Phantomyst nebulizer, at 30 to 40 pounds pressure are effective in airplanes (Mackie and Crabtree, 1938). Interior of airplane may be sprayed one half hour before landing or at any time during flight. Ventilators should remain closed for 10 minutes after spraying.

Dosage. For airplanes 5 to 10 ml. of the oil spray or 150 ml. of 1:30 "Deskito" to 1,000 cubic feet of air space.

37. CYANIDE FUMIGATION

Hydrocyanic acid gas is highly toxic to animal life. The danger to human life lies in entering a room after completion of fumigation before the gas has been thoroughly removed. Cyanide fumigation should be employed only by experienced workers and in vacated houses. Its advantage lies in its effectiveness and in the fact that it is not injurious to textiles or metals.

(a) Remove all foodsuffs.

(b) Be sure that the building is vacated. If parts of an occupied building permit this type of fumigation, make certain that there are no crevices for leakage from the fumigated to the occupied rooms.

(c) All exit crevices should be sealed tightly.

(d) A temperature of 70° F. gives optimal results. Cold detracts.

(e) The amount of sodium cyanide, depending upon the species of insects, varies from ½ to 10 ounces per 1,000 cubic feet and the time of exposure from ½ to 2 hours. The maximal amount per 100 cubic feet is:

Sodium cyanide .... 1 oz.
Sulphuric acid (66° Baume).......... 1 fl. oz.
Water .... 3 fl. oz.

(f) The sulphuric acid and water are put in a 2- to 3-gallon earthenware jug, placed on thick paper because of spattering. The sodium cyanide in a paper bag is dropped into the fluid, the operator leaving the room immediately.

(g) After five hours the windows are opened from the outside and the room allowed to air until the "peach kernel" odor has disappeared.

38. SULPHUR DIOXIDE FUMIGATION

Sulphur dioxide (SO_2) is poisonous to mammalian and insect life and therefore is of value as a fumigant. Its disadvantages are: bleaching coloring matter of vegetable origin, weakening linen and cotton fabrics and discoloring metals.

(a) Prepare rooms as for hydrocyanic gas fumigation.

(b) Remove all metallic objects and fine, vegetable-dyed fabrics. Metallic objects may be coated with vaseline.

(c) Place powdered sulphur in a large, shallow, iron pot. The latter is placed in a tub of water, which is elevated on a table or box. From 2 to 4 pounds of sulphur per 1,000 cubic feet should be used, depending upon the species of insects.

(d) Make a little crater of the sulphur, soak freely with wood or grain alcohol, and ignite.

(e) Continue fumigation up to six hours; then air room thoroughly.

REFERENCES

ANDREWS, M. N. Complement fixation reaction in *Schistosoma japonicum* with cercarial antigen prepared from *Oncomelania hupensis*, J. Helminthol., 1935, 13:25.

ATCHLEY, F. O. Effects of environmental changes on growth and multiplication in populations of *Balantidium*, Am. J. Hyg., 1935, 21:151.

AUGUSTINE, D. L. Experimental studies on the validity of species in the genus *Strongyloides*, Am. J. Hyg., 1940, 32, Sec. D:24.

BACHMAN, G. W. An intradermal reaction in experimental trichinosis, J. Prev. Med., 1929, 2:513.

BACOT, A. W. A study of the bionomics of the common rat fleas and other species associated with human habitations, etc., J. Hyg., 1914, 13:447. Plague Supp. III.

BAERMANN, G. Eine einfache Methode zur Auffindung von Ankylostomum (Nematoden) Larven in Erdproben, Geneesk. Laborat. Weltevreden, Feestbundel, 1917, p. 41.

BARBER, M. A., KOMP, W. H. W. and HAYNE, T. B. Methods of estimating amount of malaria in regions of low endemicity, South M. J., 1927, 20:471.

—— and RICE, J. B. Methods of dissecting and making permanent preparations of the salivary glands and stomachs of *Anopheles*, Am. J. Hyg., 1936, 24:32.

BARLOW, C. H. A new method for examining urine for helminth eggs, Am. J. Hyg., 1931, 14:212.

BARRETT, H. P., and YARBROUGH, N. A method for the cultivation of *Balantidium coli*, Am. J. Trop. Med., 1921, 1:161.

BASS, C. C. and JOHNS, F. M. The cultivation of malarial plasmodia (*Plasmodium vivax* and *Plasmodium falciparum*) in vitro, J. Exper. Med., 1912, 16:567.

BEACH, T. D. Experimental studies on human and primate species of *Strongyloides*, Am. J. Hyg., 1936, 23:243.

BLAND, P. B., GOLDSTEIN, L., WENRICH, D. H. and WEINER, E. Studies on the biology of *Trichomonas vaginalis*, Am. J. Hyg., 1932, 16:492.

BOECK, W. C. and DRBOHLAV, J. The cultivation of *Endamœba histolytica*, Am. J. Hyg., 1925, 5:371.

BROWN, H. W. A study on the rate of development and viability of the eggs of *Ascaris lumbricoides* and *Trichuris trichiura* under field conditions, J. Parasitol., 1927, 14:1.

CALDWELL, F. C. and CALDWELL, E. L. A dilution-flotation technic for counting hookworm ova in field surveys, Am. J. Hyg., 1926 (supp.), 6:146.

—— A Preliminary report on the development of ova of pig and human *Ascaris* under natural conditions and studies of factors influencing development, J. Parasitol., 1928, 14:254.

CHOPRA, R. N. The antimony test in the diagnosis of kala-azar, Indian M. Gaz., 1927, 62:688.

—— A Manual of Tropical Therapeutics, Calcutta, 1936, 1748 pp.

CHORINE, V. Essais de culture de *Plasmodium falciparum*; action de l'acide carbonique, Bull. Soc., path. exot., 1932, 25:953.

CHRISTOPHERS, S. R. The mechanism of immunity against malaria in communities living under hyper-endemic conditions, Indian J. M. Res., 1924, 112:273.

CHU, H. V. Certain behavior reactions of *S. japonicum* and *C. sinensis in vitro*, Chinese M. J. (supp.), 1938, 2:411.

CLEVELAND, L. R. and COLLIER, J. Various improvements in the cultivation of *Entamœba histolytica*, Am. J. Hyg., 1930, 20:606.

COBB, N. A. Two new instruments for biologists, Proc. Linn. Soc., N. S. Wales, 1890, 5:157.

CORT, W. W., ACKERT, J. E., AUGUSTINE, D. L. and PAYNE, F. K. The description of an apparatus for isolating infective hookworm larvæ from soil, Am. J. Hyg., 1922, 2:1.

CRAIG, C. F. A simplified method for the cultivation of *Endamœba histolytica*, Am. J. Trop. Med., 1926, 6:333.

—— Hemolytic cytolytic and complement-binding properties of extracts of *Endamœba histolytica*, Am. J. Trop. Med., 1927, 7:225.

—— Complement fixation in diagnosis of infections with *Endamœba histolytica*, Am. J. Trop. Med., 1928, 8:29.

—— Laboratory diagnosis of protozoan diseases, Philadelphia, 1942, 349 pp.

DAHMEN, H. Die Serodiagnostik der Beschälseuche, Arch. f. wissen. u. prakt. Tierheilk., 1922, 47:319.

D'ANTONI, J. S. Standardization of the iodine stain for method of preparation of intestinal protozoa, Am. J. Trop. Med., 1937, 17:79.

DENNIS, E. W. A stable concentrated purified antigen for the immunological study of hydatid disease, J. Parasitol., 1937, 23:62.

EATON, M. D. and COGGESHALL, L. T. Complement fixation in human malaria with antigen prepared from monkey parasite *Plasmodium knowlesi*, J. Exper. Med., 1939, 69:379.

FAIRLEY, K. D. and WILLIAMS, F. E. A preliminary report on an intradermal reaction in schistosomiasis, M. J. Australia, 1927, 2:811.

FAIRLEY, N. H. The discovery of a specific complement-fixation test for bilharziasis, J. Roy. Army M. Corps, 1919, 32:449.

—— The serological diagnosis of *Schistosomum spindalis*, Arch. f. Schiffs-u.Tropen-Hyg., 1926, 30:372.

FAIRLEY, N. H. and JASUDASAN, F. Studies in *Schistosoma spindale:* complement fixation reaction with cercarial antigen—study in experimental serology, Indian J. M. Res., (Memoir No. 17), 1930, 180 pp.

FAUST, E. C. Human Helminthology, Lea and Febiger, Philadelphia, 1939, 2nd ed., 780 pp.

——, D'ANTONI, J. S., ODOM, V., MILLER, M. J., PERES, C., SAWITZ, W., THOMEN, L. F., TOBIE, J. and WALKER, J. H. A critical study of clinical laboratory technics for the diagnosis of protozoan cysts and helminth eggs in feces, Am. J. Trop. Med., 1938, 18:169.

—— and KHAW, O. K. The egg-laying capacity of *Clonorchis sinensis,* Proc. Soc. Exper. Biol. & Med., 1926, 23:606.

——, SAWITZ, W., TOBIE, J., ODOM, V., PERES, C. and LINCICOME, D. R. Comparative efficiency of various technics for diagnosis of protozoa and helminths in feces, J. Parasitol., 1939, 25:241.

FÜLLEBORN, F. Zur Hamburger "Deckglasauszählung" für Hakenwurmeier, Arch. f. Schiffs-u. Tropen-Hyg., 1927, 31:232.

GALTSOFF, P. S., LUTZ, F. E., WELCH, P. S. and NEEDHAM, J. G. Culture methods for invertebrate animals, 1937. Ithaca, N. Y., 622 pp.

HAKANSSON, E. G. A method of destroying the blastocysts (*Blastocystis hominis*) in fecal wet smears in order to facilitate the examination of *Endamœba histolytica,* J. Lab. & Clin. Med., 1940, 25:546.

HALL, M. C. Types of anal swabs and scrapers with a description of an improved type of swab, Am. J. Trop. Med., 1937, 17:445.

HAUSHEER, W. C., HERRICK, C. A. and PEARSE, A. S. Evaluation of the methods of Stoll and Lane in light hookworm infections and accuracy in diagnosis of the Willis flotation method, Am. J. Hyg., 1926 (supp.), 6:118.

—— and HERRICK, C. A. The place of the smear in hookworm diagnosis, Am. J. Hyg., 1926 (supp.), 6:136.

HENRY, A. F. X. A propos de la densité optique dans les techniques sérologiques, photométriques et en particulier dans la malaria floculation, Compt. rend. Soc. de biol., 1934, 115:1606.

HINDLE, E., HOU, P. C. and PATTON, W. S. Serological studies on Chinese kala-azar, Proc. Roy. Soc., London, S. B. 1926, 100:368.

HOGUE, M. J. The cultivation of *Trichomonas hominis,* Am. J. Trop. Med., 1921, 1:211.

KALWARYJSKI, B. E. Studien über die Trichinellen. 2. Über Todsilberimprägnation der Muskeltrichinellen, Zentralbl. f. Bakt. (Abt. 1), 1936, 137:303.

KELSER, R. A. Complement-fixation test for Chagas' disease, Am. J. Trop. Med., 1936, 16:405.

KESSEL, J. F. and SVENSSON, R. M. Morphological differences between *Necator* and *Ancylostoma* larvæ, J. Parasitol., 1926, 13:146.

KHALIL, M. and HASSAN, A. Preliminary note on new skin reaction in human schistosomiasis, J. Egyptian M. A., 1932, 15:129.

—— Serum globulin in human schistosomiasis, Bull. Soc. path. exot., 1932, 25:149. Also J. Egyptian M. A., 1932, 15:211.

KNOTT, J. Method for making microfilarial surveys on day blood. Trans. Roy. Soc. Trop. Med. & Hyg., 1939, 33:191.

KNOWLES, R. and COLE, A. F. Study of entamœbic cysts in stools, Indian J. M. Res., 1917, 4:498.

KOFOID, C. A. and BARBER, M. A. Rapid method for detection of ova of intestinal parasites in human stools, Calif. State Board of Health, Parasitology Reprint Ser., 1919, 1, 16 pp.

KOLMER, J. A. A method of transmitting known numbers of trypanosomes with a note on the numeric relation of trypanosomes to infection, J. Infect. Dis., 1915, 17:79.

LANE, C. The mass diagnosis of *Ankylostoma* infestation, I-XIV, Tr. Roy. Soc. Trop. Med. & Hyg., 1923-1925, vols. 16-19.

LEE, C. U. and CHU, H. V. A simple technique for studying schistosome worms *in vitro,* Proc. Soc. Exper. Biol. & Med., 1935, 32:1397.

LOOSS, A. The anatomy and life history of *Agchylostoma duodenale* Dub., Records Egyptian Gov. School of Med., 1911, 4:163.

MACKIE, F. P. and CRABTREE, H. S. The destruction of mosquitoes in aircraft, Lancet, 1938, 2:447.

MAGATH, T. B. Nematode technique. Tr. Am. Micro. Soc., 1916, 35:245.

MAPLESTONE, P. A. and MUKERJII, P. K. An improved technique for the isolation of *Ascaris* eggs from soil, Indian J. M. Res., 1936, 23.

MANSON-BAHR, P. H. Manson's Tropical Diseases, Baillière, Tindall and Cox, London, 1936, 1003 pp.

McCoy, O. R. The suitability of various bacteria as food for hookworm larvæ, Am. J. Hyg., 1930, 10:140.

MIYAJI, S. and IMAI, B. Serologische Studien bei *Schistosomiasis japonica,* Centralbl. f. Bakt., 1928, (Abt. 1), 106:237.

NAPIER, L. E. A new serum test for kala-azar, Indian J. M. Res., 1922, 9:830.

NOGUCHI, H. Action of certain biological, chemical and physical agents upon cultures of *Leishmania;* some observations on plant and insect herpetomonads, Proc. Internat. Conf. Health Prob. in Trop. Am., United Fruit Co., Boston, 1924, p. 455.

NOVY, F. G., and MACNEAL, W. J. On the cultivation of *T. lewisi,* Contrib. to Med. Res. Dedicated to V. C. Vaughn, 1903, p. 549.

PAMPANA, E. J. Staining thick drop preparations and laking with isotonic solutions, Riv. di malariol., 1938, 17:300.

PAYNE, F. K. Field experiments on vertical migration of hookworm larvæ, Am. J. Hyg., 1923, 3:46.

PROSKE, H. O. and WATSON, R. B. The protein tyrosin reaction. A biochemical diagnostic test for malaria, U. S. Pub. Health Rep., 1939, 54:158.

RISTROPH. C. A. "Turtox News." General Biological Supply House, Inc., Chicago, 1934, 12, No. 1.

DE RIVAS, D. The effect of temperature on protozoan and metazoan parasites, and the application of intra-intestinal thermal therapy in parasitic and other affections of the intestine, Am. J. Trop. Med., 1926, 6:47.

—— An efficient and rapid method of concentration for the detection of ova and cysts of intestinal parasites, Am. J. Trop. Med., 1928, 8:63.

—— and DE RIVAS, C. T., Clinical Parasitology and Tropical Medicine, Philadelphia, 1935.

SALAM, A. A. New antigen for diagnosis of bilharziasis by complement fixation test, J. Egyptian M. A., 1935, 18:353.

SAWITZ, W. Serodiagnostic technic in trichinosis. Personal communication, p. 609, Faust, Human Helminthology, Philadelphia, 1939.

——, ODOM, V. L. and LINCICOME, D. R. The diagnosis of oxyuriasis: comparative efficiency of the NIH swab examination and stool examination by brine and zinc sulfate floatation for *Enterobius vermicularis* infection, U. S. Pub. Health Rep., 1939, 54:1148.

SCHUMAKER, E. The cultivation of *Balantidium coli,* Am. J. Hyg., 1931, 13:281.

SCOTT, J. A. and HEADLEE, W. H. Studies in Egypt on the correction of helminth egg count data for the size and consistency of stool, Am. J. Hyg., 1938, 27:176.

SHARP, N. A. D. *Filaria bancrofti* and *Loa loa.* A note on some methods of differentiation of their embryos. Tr. Roy. Soc. Trop. Med., 1927, 17:177.

SIA, R. H. P. Ray's "hemolytic" test in kala-azar, Chinese M. J., 1921, 35:397.

SINTON, J. A. A simplified method for the cultivation of *Plasmodium falciparum in vitro,* Indian J. M. Res., 1922, 10:203.

SOPER, F. L. Comparison of Stoll and Lane egg-count methods for the estimation of hookworm infestation, Am. J. Hyg., 1926, 2:62.

SPINDLER, L. A. On the use of a method for the isolation of *Ascaris* eggs from soil, Am. J. Hyg., 1929, 10:157.

STOLL, N. R. Investigations on the control of hookworm disease. XV. An effective method of counting hookworm eggs in feces, Am. J. Hyg., 1923, 3:59.

—— and HAUSHEER, W. C. Concerning two options in dilution egg counting: small drop and displacement, Am. J. Hyg., 1926 (supp.), 6:134.

TALIAFERRO, W. H. A precipitin test in malaria (2nd rept.), J. Prev. Med., 1928, 2:147.

——, HOFFMAN, W. A. and COOK, D. H. Precipitin test in intestinal schistosomiasis (*S. mansoni*), J. Prev. Med., 1928, 2:395.

THOMSON, J. G. Experiments on complement fixation in malaria with antigens prepared from cultures of malarial parasites, Proc. Roy. Soc. Med. (sect. Med.), April, May 1919, 12.

TSUCHIYA, H. Further studies on cultivation of *Endamœba histolytica* and complement fixation test for amebiasis, J. Lab. & Clin. Med., 1934, 19:495.

VILLELA, E. and BICALHO, C. As pesquisas de laboratorio no diagnostico da moléstia de Chagas, Mem. Inst. Oswaldo Cruz, 1923, 16:13, Eng. transl.: 31.

WAGENER, E. H. A precipitin test in experimental amebic dysentery in cats, Univ. California Publ. Zoöl., 1924, 26:15.

WAGENER, E. H. and KOCH, D. A. The biological relationships of *Leishmania* and certain herpetomonads, Univ. California Publ. Zoöl., 1926, 28:365.

WATSON, E. A. Dourine in Canada, 1904-1920: history, research and suppression, Canada, Dept. Agric. Health of Animals Branch, 1920, 43 pp.

WEISS, E. and ARNOLD, L. Specificity of complement fixation test for amebiasis, Am. J. Digest. Dis., 1934, 1:548.

WILLIS, H. H. A simple levitation method for the detection of hookworm ova, M. J. Australia, 1921, 2:375.

WOLBACH, S. B., TODD, J. L. and PALFREY, F. W. The etiology and pathology of typhus, 1922, Cambridge, Mass., 222 pp.

YOSHIMOTO, M. Über die Komplementbindungsreaktion bei der Schistosomumkrankheit in Japan, Ztschr. f. Immunitätsforsch. u. exper. Therap., 1910, 5:438.

WELCH, E. V. Insects found on aircraft at Miami, Florida in 1938. U. S. Pub. Health Rep. 1939, 54:561.

BIBLIOGRAPHY

BOOKS

ALCOCK, A. 1920. Entomology for Medical Officers. 380 pp. London.

AUSTEN, E. E. 1911. A Handbook of the Tsetse-flies. 110 pp. London.

BAYLIS, H. A. 1929. A Manual of Helminthology. 303 pp. London.

BERLESE, A. Vol. I, 1909. Vol. II, 1925. Gli insetti. 1004, 992 pp. Milano.

BLACKLOCK, D. B. and SOUTHWELL, T. 1931. A Guide to Human Parasitology. 271 pp. London.

BOYD, M. F. 1930. An Introduction to Malariology. 437 pp. Cambridge, Mass.

BRAUN, M. and SEIFERT, O. 1925. Die Tierischen Parasiten des Menschen. 6th ed. 608 pp. Leipzig.

BRONN, H. G. Klassen und Ordnungen des Tierreichs. Bd. 1, 4 and 5. 1879-1940. Leipzig.

BRUMPT, E. 1936. Précis de Parasitologie. 5th ed. 2139 pp. Paris.

BYAM, W. and ARCHIBALD, R. G. 1921. The Practice of Medicine in the Tropics. Vol. I, 855 pp. London.

CALKINS, G. N. 1933. The Biology of the Protozoa. 2nd ed. 607 pp. Philadelphia.

CASTELLANI, A. and CHALMERS, A. J. 1919. A Manual of Tropical Medicine. 3d ed. 2436 pp. London.

CHANDLER. A. C. 1936. Introduction to Human Parasitology. 5th ed. 661 pp. New York and London.

CHITWOOD, B. G. and CHITWOOD, M. B. An introduction to Nematology. Sec. I, Part I, 1937, Washington, D. C. Sec. I, Parts II and III, Sec. II, Part 1, 1938, Babylon, N. Y.

COMSTOCK, J. H. 1924. An Introduction to Entomology. 1044 pp. Ithaca, N. Y.

CRAIG, C. F. 1926. Parasitic Protozoa of Man. 569 pp. Philadelphia and London.

CRAIG, C. F. 1934. Amebiasis and Amebic Dysentery. 315 pp. Springfield, Ill.

CRAIG, C. F. and FAUST, E. C. 1940. Clinical Parasitology. 2nd ed. 772 pp. Philadelphia.

CULBERTSON, J. T. 1941. Immunity Against Animal Parasites. 274 pp. New York.

DOBELL, C. 1919. The Amœbæ Living in Man. 150 pp. London and New York.

DOBELL, C. and O'CONNOR, F. W. 1921. The Intestinal Protozoa of Man. 211 pp. London and New York.

DYAR, H. G. 1928. The Mosquitoes of the Americas. Carnegie Inst. Publications, No. 387. 616 pp. Washington.

EDWARDS, F. W., OLDROYD, H. and SMART, J. 1936. British Blood-sucking Flies. 156 pp. London.

EWING, H. E. 1929. A Manual of External Parasites. 225 pp. Springfield, Ill.

FANTHAM, H. B., STEPHENS, J. W. W. and THEOBALD, F. V. 1916. The Animal Parasites of Man. 900 pp. London and New York.

FAUST, E. C. 1939. Human Helminthology. 2nd ed. 780 pp. Philadelphia.

FOX, C. 1925. Insects and Diseases of Man. 349 pp. Philadelphia.

GALTSOFF, P. S., LUTZ, F. E., WELCH, P. S. and NEEDHAM, J. G. 1937. Culture Methods for Invertebrate Animals, 590 pp. Ithaca, N. Y.

GAY, F. P. and Associates 1935. Agents of Disease and Host Resistance. 1581 pp. Springfield, Ill.

HACKETT, L. W. 1937. Malaria in Europe, an Ecological Study. 336 pp. London.

HALL, M. C. 1936. Control of Animal Parasites. 162 pp. Evanston, Ill.

HEGNER, R. 1927. Host-Parasite Relations between Man and his Intestinal Protozoa. 231 pp. New York.

HEGNER, R.. ROOT, F. M., AUGUSTINE, D. L. and HUFF, C. G. 1938. Parasitology. 731 pp. New York and London.

HERMS, W. B. 1939. Medical Entomology. 3rd ed. 582 pp. New York.

HUTYRA, F. and MAREK, J. 1926. Special Pathology and Therapeutics of the Diseases of Animals. 3 vols. Chicago.

IMMS, A. D. 1925. A General Textbook of Entomology. 698 pp. London.

KNOWLES, R. 1928. Introduction to Medical Protozoology. 887 pp. Calcutta.

LEPAGE, G. 1937. Nematodes Parasitic in Animals. 163 pp. London.

LEUCKART, R. 1879-1901. Die Parsiten des Menschen und die von ihnen herrührenden Krankheiten. 1753 pp. Leipzig.

LEUCKART, R. 1886. The Parasites of Man. 771 pp. Edinburgh.

MANSON-BAHR, P. 1936. Manson's Tropical Diseases. 10th ed. 1003 pp. Baltimore.

MARSHALL, J. F. 1938. The British Mosquitoes. 282 pp. London.

MATHESON, R. 1932. Medical Entomology. 489 pp. Springfield, Ill.

MÖNNIG, H. O. 1934. Veterinary Helminthology and Entomology. 402 pp. Baltimore.

NEVEU-LEMAIRE, M. 1936. Traité d'helminthologie médicale et vétérinaire. 1514 pp. Paris.

NEWSTEAD, R. 1924. Guide to the Study of Tsetse-flies. Liverpool School of Trop. Med. Memoir (new series) No. 1. 294 pp. Liverpool.

PATTON, W. S. and CRAGG, F. W. 1913. A Textbook of Medical Entomology. 768 pp. London.

PATTON, W. S. and EVANS, A. E. 1929, 1931. Insects, Ticks, Mites and Venomous Animals of Medical and Veterinary Importance. Part I, 1929 Medical, 785 pp. Part II, 1931 Public Health, 740 pp. Croydon, England.

RILEY, W. A. and JOHANNSEN, O. A. 1932. Medical Entomology. 476 pp. New York and London.

ROGERS, L. and MEGAW, J. W. D. 1935. Tropical Medicine. 2nd ed. 547 pp. London.

STILES, C. W. (1905) 1926. The International Code of Zoological Nomenclature as Applied to Medicine. Hyg. Lab. Bull. 24. Revised and reprinted in Proc. Biol. Soc. (Washington), 1926, 39:75-104.

STILES, C. W. and HASSALL, A. 1926. Key-catalogue of the Worms Reported for Man. Hyg. Lab. Bull., No. 142. Washington.

STILES, C. W. and HASSALL, A. Index-catalogue of Medical and Veterinary Zoology. Washington.

   1. Trematodes and Trematode Diseases. Hyg. Lab. Bull. No. 37, 1908.
   2. Cestoda and Cestodaria. Hyg. Lab. Bull. No. 85, 1912.
   3. Roundworms. Hyg. Lab. Bull. No. 114, 1920.

STITT, E. R., CLOUGH, P. W. and CLOUGH, M. C. 1938. Practical Bacteriology, Haematology and Animal Parasitology. 9th ed. 961 pp. Philadelphia.

TALIAFERRO, W. H. 1929. The Immunology of Parasitic Infections. 414 pp. New York and London.

THOMSON, J. G. and ROBERTSON, A. 1929. Protozoology. 376 pp. London and New York.

WARD, H. B. and WHIPPLE, G. C. 1918. Fresh-Water Biology. 1111 pp. New York.

WENYON, C. M. 1926. Protozoology. 2 vols. 1563 pp. London.

YORKE, W. and MAPLESTONE, P. A. 1926. The Nematode Parasites of Vertebrates. 536 pp. Philadelphia.

JOURNALS

Acta pathologica et microbiologica Scandinavica. Copenhagen. Vol. 1, 1924.

American Journal of Tropical Medicine. Baltimore. Vol. 1, 1921.

Annales de l'Institut Pasteur. Paris. Vol. 1, 1887.

Annales de la Société belge de médecine tropicale. Brussels. Vol. 1, 1920.

Annales de parasitologie humaine et comparée. Paris. Vol. 1, 1923.

Annals of Tropical Medicine and Parasitology. Liverpool. Vol. 1, 1907.

Archiv für Protistenkunde. Jena. Vol. 1, 1902.

Archiv für Schiffs- und Tropen-Hygiene. Leipzig. Vol. 1, 1897.

Archives de l'Institut Pasteur de Tunis. Tunis. Vol. 1, 1906.

Archives of Pathology. Chicago. Vol. 1, 1926.

Australian Journal of Experimental Biology and Medical Science. Adelaide. Vol. 1, 1924.

Biological Bulletin. Woods Hole, Mass. Vol. 1, 1906.

Bulletin of Entomological Research. London. Vol. 1, 1910.

Bulletin of Hygiene. London. Vol. 1, 1926.

Bulletin de la Société de pathologie exotique. Paris. Vol. 1, 1908.

Bulletin de l'Institut Pasteur. Paris. Vol. 1, 1903.
Bulletins of the Bureau of Animal Industry. Washington. Vol. 1. 1890.
Bulletins of the Hygienic Laboratory. Washington. Vol. 1, 1900.
China Medical Journal. Shanghai. Vol. 1, 1887. (cont. as Chinese Medical Journal. Peiping, 1932).
Comptes rendus hebdomadaires des séances de l'académie des sciences. Paris. Vol. 1, 1835.
Comptes rendus des séances de la société de biologie. Paris. Vol. 1, 1849.
Entomological News. Philadelphia. Vol. 1, 1890.
Helminthological Abstracts. St. Albans, Eng. Vol. 1, 1931.
Illinois Biological Monographs. Urbana. Vol. 1, 1914.
Indian Journal of Medical Research. Calcutta. Vol. 1, 1913.
Indian Medical Gazette. Calcutta. Vol. 1, 1866.
Japan Medical World. Tokyo. Vol. 1, 1921.
Journal of Agricultural Research. Washington. Vol. 1, 1913.
Journal of the American Veterinary Medical Association. Chicago. Vol. 1, 1877.
Journal of Economic Entomology. Geneva, N. Y. Vol. 1, 1908.
Journal of Experimental Medicine. New York. Vol. 1, 1896.
Journal of Experimental Zoology. Baltimore. Vol. 1, 1904.
Journal of Helminthology. St. Albans, Eng. Vol. 1, 1923.
Journal of Hygiene. Cambridge, Eng. Vol. 1, 1901.
Journal of Immunology. Baltimore. Vol. 1, 1916.
Journal of the London School of Tropical Medicine. London. Vol. 1, 1911. Vol. 2, 1913.
Journal of the Medical Association of Formosa (Taiwan Igakkwai Zassi) Taihoku (Formosa).
    (In Japanese with English or German summaries).
Journal of Parasitology. Princeton, N. J. Vol. 1, 1914.
Journal of the Royal Army Medical Corps. London. Vol. 1, 1903.
Journal of Tropical Medicine and Hygiene. London. Vol. 1, 1898.
Kitasato Archives of Experimental Medicine. Tokyo. Vol. 1, 1909.
League of Nations, Health Organization. Quarterly Bulletin. Geneva. Vol. 1, 1932.
League of Nations, Health Section. Epidemiological Intelligence. Geneva. Vol. 1, 1921.
Memorias do Instituto Oswaldo Cruz. Rio de Janeiro. Vol. 1, 1909.
Monographs of the Rockefeller Institute for Medical Research. New York. No. 1, 1910.
Onderstepoort Journal of Veterinary Science and Animal Industry. Onderstepoort. Vol. 1, 1933.
Parasitology. Cambridge. Vol. 1, 1908.
Philippine Journal of Science. Manila. Vol. 1, 1905.
Proceedings of the Society for Experimental Biology and Medicine. New York. Vol. 1, 1903.
Puerto Rico Journal of Public Health and Tropical Medicine. San Juan. Vol. 1, 1925.
Quarterly Journal of Microscopical Science. London. Vol. 1, 1853. n.s. Vol. 1, 1861.
Research Memoirs of the London School of Tropical Medicine. London. No. 1, 1912.
Review of Applied Entomology. Ser. B. Medical and Veterinary. Vol. 1, 1912.
Revista de Medicina Tropical y Parasitologia Bacteriologia, Clinica y Laboratorio. Havana. Vol. 1, 1935.
Revue Suisse de Zoologie. Geneva. Vol. 1, 1893.
Revue de Zoologie et de Botanique Africaines. Brussels. Vol. 1, 1911.
Rivista di Malariologia. Rome. Vol. 1. 1922.
Rivista di Parasitologia. Rome. Vol. 1, 1937.
Transactions of the American Microscopical Society. Urbana, Ill. Vol. 1. 1892.
Transactions of the Far Eastern Association of Tropical Medicine. Vol. 1, 1911.
Transactions of the Royal Society of Tropical Medicine and Hygiene. London. Vol. 1, 1907.
Tropical Diseases Bulletin. London. Vol. 1, 1912.
Tropical Veterinary Bulletin. London. Vol. 1, 1912.
University of California Publications in Zoölogy. Berkeley. Vol. 1, 1902.
Zeitschrift für Infektionskrankheiten. Berlin. Vol. 1, 1906.
Zentralblatt für Bakteriologie, Parasitenkunde und Infektionskrankheiten. Jena. Vol. 1, 1887.

INDEX OF AUTHORS

INDEX OF SUBJECTS

All numbers refer to pages. Words in *italics* are names of genera or species; divisions higher than genera rank are indicated by SMALL CAPITALS. When a series of pages is listed, the numbers in **bold face type** indicate the important sections.

Parasites—*Continued*
  types, 2
Parasitic diseases, diagnosis, 40-64
  clinical, 40-46
  intermediate hosts, 61-64
  keys, diagnostic, 47-53
  laboratory, 44, 46-62
  serological, 53-61
  immunity, 22-29
  pathology, 15-21
  prevention, 68-70
  transmission, 30-39
  treatment, 65-68
PARASITIDÆ, 757, 760
Parasitism, 1
PARASITOIDEA, 735, 758, **760**
Parasitology, 1, 2
Parasitus, 763
Parathelphusa, 63
  sinensis, 480, 529, 591, 605
Paregoric, 65
Paris green, 659
Parorchis acanthus, 481
Paryphostomum sufrartyfex, 456, 540, 541, **543**
Passalurus ambiguus, 307
Pasteurella pestis, 591, 592, 714
  tularensis, 594, 595, 597, 653, 673, 754
Patagiamyia, 644
PECTINIBRANCHIATA, 466, 472, 474
PEDICULIDÆ, 591, 698
Pediculoides, 761
  ventricosus, 735, **762**
PEDICULOIDIDÆ, 735, **761**
Pediculosis, 698
Pediculus humanus, 591
    var. *capitis*, 698, 701, 702, 703
    var. *corporis*, 698, 699, 700, 701, 703
    maculatus, 698
Pelletierin, 66, 437, **830**
PENTASTOMIDA, 732
Pentatrichomonas ardin delteili, 133, 136, 138
Pepo, 837
Perchloroethylene, 832
Perchloromethane, 831
PERCIDÆ, 62
Peripetus, 589, 600
Periplaneta americana, 592, 615, 616
  australasiæ, 615
PERITRICHIDA, 112
Persian powder, 838
Peruvian bark, 828
Peyer's patches, 171
Phanæus splendidulus, 613
PHASMIDIA, 226, 228
Phenol, 684
Philæmatomyia, **675,** 687
PHILÆMATOMYINÆ, 675
Phinotas oil, 669
Phlebotomus, 12, 625, **665-666**
  argentipes, 168, 171, 594, 667
  chinensis, 171, 174, 594, 667
  longipalpis, 171, 667
  longipennis, 594
  intermedius, 171, 179, 180, 594, 667
  major, 171, 594, 666
  migonei, 179, 594, 667
  minutus, 593, 666

Phlebotomus—Continued
  noguchii, 594, 667
  papatasii, 171, 175, 178, 593, 594, 629, 665, 666
  perniciosus, 171, 593, 594, 666, 667
  sergenti, 175, 178, 594, 666
  squamiventris, 179, 594, 667
  verrucarum, 594, 667
PHORIDÆ, 684
Phormia, 683, 687, **693**
  regina, 629, 685, 686, 693
Photophormia, 687
Phthirus pubis, 698, 700, 701, 702, 703
Phyllophaga fervens, 613
  rugosa, 613
  vehemens, 613
Physa ancillaria parkeri, 586
Physaloptera caucasica, 227, **330**
  clausa, 236
  mordens, 330
PHYSALOPTERIDÆ, 227, **330**
Physella magnalacustris, 586
  parkeri, 586
Physopsis, 466, 471, 472, 559
  africana, 476, 478, 488, 584
  globosa, 476
  nasuta, 476
Phytomonas, 143
Pian bois, 178
Pila luzonica, 474, 480, 547
Pinworm infection (see *Enterobius vermicularis*)
Piophila casei, 684
Pironella, 466
  conica, 474, 518
Piroplasma donovani, 168
PIROPLASMIDÆ, 189
Piroplasmosis, 746, 750, 753
Pistia, 369, 650
  stratiotes, 370, 661
Piuang, 837
Plagiotoma coli, 112
Plague, 2, 591, 592, 682, 706, 707, 714, 721
Planaria, 471
  latiuscula, 483
PLANORBIDÆ, 472, 475
Planorbis, 466, 471, 472, 473, 475, 553, 559
  adowensis 475
  alexandrinus, 475
  antiguensis, 475
  boissyi, 475, 478
  centimetralis, 475
  cænosus, 475, 491
  dufourii, 475
  guadeloupensis, 471, 475, 804
  herbeni, 475
  olivaceus, 475
  pfeifferi, 475
  sudanicus, 475
Plants, examination of, 813
Plasmochin, 66, 213, **830**
PLASMODIDÆ, 72, 189
Plasmodium, 72, 189, **190-222**
  antigens, 802, 803
  blood, effect on, 203
  clinical differentiation, 208
  concentration methods, 780
  counting methods, 782

(4)